ENGINEERING MATHEMATICS – III

(With Large Number of MCQ's & Solved Problems)

FOR

S.E. : SECOND YEAR DEGREE COURSE IN MECHANICAL ENGINEERING

MECHANICAL SANDWICH, PRODUCTION, PRODUCTION SANDWITCH
INDUSTRIAL AND AUTOMOBILE ENGINEERING

ACCORDING TO NEW REVISED CREDIT SYSTEM SYLLABUS
OF SAVITRIBAI PHULE PUNE UNIVERSITY
(EFFECTIVE FROM ACADEMIC YEAR – JUNE 2016)

Dr. M. Y. GOKHALE

M. Sc. (Pure Maths.), M. Sc. (App. Maths.)
Ph. D. (I. I. T., Mumbai)
Professor and Head, Deptt. of Mathematics,
Maharashtra Institute of Technology,
Kothrud, PUNE.

Dr. N. S. MUJUMDAR

M. Sc., M. Phil., Ph. D. (Maths.)
Professor in Mathematics,
JSPM's Rajarshi Shahu
College of Engineering,
Tathawade, PUNE.

S. S. KULKARNI

M. Sc. (Maths.) (I. I. T. Mumbai)
Associate Professor,
Formerly Deptt. of Mathematics, SRTTC,
Faculty of Engineering, Kamshet, PUNE

A. N. SINGH

M. A. (Mathematics Gold Medalist)
Formerly, Head of Mathematics Deptt.
D. Y. Patil College of Engineering,
Pimpri, PUNE.

K. R. ATAL

M. Sc. (Mathematics)
Lecturer (Selection Grade) Deptt. of Applied Sciences,
Pune Institute of Computer Technology,
Dhankawdi, PUNE

N3531

ENGINEERING MATHEMATICS-III (Mechanical Engg. Group)　　ISBN 978-93-86084-05-7

Second Edition : June 2017

© : **Authors**

Published By :　　　　　　　　　　**Polyplate**

NIRALI PRAKASHAN

Abhyudaya Pragati, 1312, Shivaji Nagar,
Off J.M. Road, PUNE – 411005
Tel - (020) 25512336/37/39, Fax - (020) 25511379
Email : niralipune@pragationline.com

☞ **DISTRIBUTION CENTRES**

PUNE

Nirali Prakashan : 19, Budhwar Peth, Jogeshwari Mandir Lane, Pune 411002, Maharashtra
Tel : (020) 2445 2044, 66022708, Fax : (020) 2445 1538
Email : bookorder@pragationline.com, niralilocal@pragationline.com

Nirali Prakashan : S. No. 28/27, Dhyari, Near Pari Company, Pune 411041
Tel : (020) 24690204 Fax : (020) 24690316
Email : dhyari@pragationline.com, bookorder@pragationline.com

MUMBAI

Nirali Prakashan : 385, S.V.P. Road, Rasdhara Co-op. Hsg. Society Ltd.,
Girgaum, Mumbai 400004, Maharashtra
Tel : (022) 2385 6339 / 2386 9976, Fax : (022) 2386 9976
Email : niralimumbai@pragationline.com

☞ **DISTRIBUTION BRANCHES**

JALGAON

Nirali Prakashan : 34, V. V. Golani Market, Navi Peth, Jalgaon 425001,
Maharashtra, Tel : (0257) 222 0395, Mob : 94234 91860

KOLHAPUR

Nirali Prakashan : New Mahadvar Road, Kedar Plaza, 1st Floor Opp. IDBI Bank
Kolhapur 416 012, Maharashtra. Mob : 9850046155

NAGPUR

Pratibha Book Distributors : Above Maratha Mandir, Shop No. 3, First Floor,
Rani Jhanshi Square, Sitabuldi, Nagpur 440012, Maharashtra
Tel : (0712) 254 7129

DELHI

Nirali Prakashan : 4593/21, Basement, Aggarwal Lane 15, Ansari Road, Daryaganj
Near Times of India Building, New Delhi 110002 Mob : 08505972553

BENGALURU

Pragati Book House : House No. 1, Sanjeevappa Lane, Avenue Road Cross,
Opp. Rice Church, Bengaluru – 560002.
Tel : (080) 64513344, 64513355,Mob : 9880582331, 9845021552
Email:bharatsavla@yahoo.com

CHENNAI

Pragati Books : 9/1, Montieth Road, Behind Taas Mahal, Egmore,
Chennai 600008 Tamil Nadu, Tel : (044) 6518 3535,
Mob : 94440 01782 / 98450 21552 / 98805 82331,
Email : bharatsavla@yahoo.com

niralipune@pragationline.com　|　www.pragationline.com

Also find us on 🅕 www.facebook.com/niralibooks

PREFACE TO THE SECOND EDITION

We are glad and excited to announce that the First Edition of this book received an overwhelming response from the engineering student community, compelling us to release its **Second Edition** within a very short period of time.

This thoroughly revised **Second Edition** has been updated with additional matter, many solved problems, including solutions to all University Examination Problems and Numerous Exercises for practice.

Special care has been taken to maintain high degree of accuracy in the theory and numericals throughout the book.

We take this opportunity to express our sincere thanks to Dineshbhai Furia of Nirali Prakashan, a reputed pioneer in the publication field. Our special thanks to Jignesh Furia for their effective cooperation and great care in bringing out this revised edition. We also appreciate the efforts of M. P. Munde and the entire staff of Engineering Books Deptt. of Nirali Prakashan namely Mrs. Deepali Lachake (Co-ordinator) for bringing this book to the students in a timely manner.

We sincerely hope that this "**Second Edition**" will also be warmly received by all concerned as in the past.

Valuable suggestions from our esteemed readers to improve the book are most welcome and highly appreciated.

Pune   **Authors**

PREFACE TO THE FIRST EDITION

Our text books on **Engineering Mathematics-III** have occupied place of pride among engineering student's community for more than **twenty years** now. All the teachers of this group of authors have been teaching mathematics in engineering colleges for the past several years. Difficulties of engineering students are well understood by the authors and that is reflected in the text material.

As per the policy of the University, Engineering Syllabi is revised every five years. Last revision was in the year 2012. New revision is coming little earlier, as university has introduced **online** system of examination from year 2012.

As per the new credit system, the **Insem (Online) Examinations** (Combined Phase-I and Phase-II) will be conducted based on first, second, third and fourth units. The **Online** examinations will have objective types of questions with multiple choices. End semester examination will be based on all the six units and that will be conducted in traditional way.

New text book is written, taking in to account all the new features that have been introduced. All the entrants to the engineering field will definitely find this book, complete in all respect. Students will find the subject matter presentation quite lucid. There are large number of illustrative examples and well graded exercises. **Addition of Multiple Choice Questions will be very useful to the students**, especially for **Online** examinations.

We take this opportunity to express our sincere thanks to Shri. Dineshbhai Furia of Nirali Prakashan, pioneer in all fields of education. Thanks are also due to Shri. Jignesh Furia, whose dynamic leadership is helpful to all the authors of Nirali Prakashan.

We specially appreciate the efforts of Shri. M. P. Munde and entire team of Nirali Prakashan namely Mrs. Deepali Lachake (Co-ordinator) who really have taken keen interest and untiring efforts in publishing this text.

We have no doubt that like our earlier texts, student's community will respond favourably to this new venture.

The advice and suggestions of our esteemed readers to improve the text are most welcomed, and will be highly appreciated.

Pune   **Authors**

SYLLABUS

Unit I : Linear Differential Equations (LDE) and Applications :   **(09 Hrs.)**

LED of nth order with constant coefficients, Method of variation of parameters, Cauchy's and Legendre's DE, Simultaneous and Symmetric simultaneous DE. Modeling of mass-spring systems, Free and forced damped and undamped systems.

Unit II : Transforms   **(09 Hrs.)**

Laplace Transform (L.T.) : LT of standard functions, Properties and theorems, Inverse LT, Applications of LT to solve LDE.

Fourier Transform (FT) : Fourier integral theorem, Fourier transform, Fourier sine and cosine transform, Inverse Fourier Transform.

Unit III : Statistics and Probability   **(09 Hrs.)**

Measure of central tendency, Standard deviation, Coefficient of variation, Moments, Sketwness and Kurtosis, Correlation and Regression, Probability distribution : Binomial, Poisson and Normal distributions, Population and sample, Sampling distributions, t-distribution, Chi-square distribution.

Unit IV : Vector Differential Calculus   **(09 Hrs.)**

Physical interpretation of vector differentiation, Vector differential operator, Gradient, Divergence and Curl, Directional derivative, Solenoidal, Irrotational and Conservative fields, Scalar potential, Vector identities.

Unit V : Vector Integral Calculus and Applications   **(09 Hrs.)**

Line, Surface and Volume integrals, Work-done, Green's Lemma, Gauss's Divergence theorem, Stoke's theorem. Applications to problems in Fluid Mechanics, Continuity equations, Stream lines, Equations of motion, Bernoulli's equation.

Unit VI : Applications of Partial Differential Equations (PDE)   **(09 Hrs.)**

Basic concepts, Modeling of Vibrating string, Wave equation, One and two dimensional heat flow equations, Method of separation of variables, Use of Fourier series. Solution of heat equation by Fourier transforms, Two-dimensional wave equation.

CONTENTS

•••

CHAPTER ONE

LINEAR DIFFERENTIAL EQUATIONS WITH CONSTANT COEFFICIENTS

1.1 INTRODUCTION

Differential equations are widely used in fields of Engineering and Applied Sciences. Mathematical formulations of most of the physical problems are in the forms of differential equations. Use of differential equations is most prominent in subjects like Circuit Analysis, Theory of Structures, Vibrations, Heat Transfer, Fluid Mechanics etc. Differential equations are of two types : Ordinary and Partial Differential Equations. In ordinary equations, there is one dependent variable depending for its value on one independent variable. Partial differential equations will have more than one independent variables.

In what follows, we shall discuss ordinary and partial differential equations, which are of common occurrence in engineering fields. Applications to some areas will also be dealt.

1.2 PRELIMINARIES

I.   Second Degree Polynomials and Their Factorization :

(a)

(i) $D^2 - 2D - 3 = (D + 1)(D - 3)$ (ii) $D^2 + 5D + 6 = (D + 2)(D + 3)$

(iii) $D^2 + 2D + 1 = (D + 1)^2$ (iv) $D^2 - 5D + 6 = (D - 2)(D - 3)$

(v) $D^2 + 3D + 2 = (D + 2)(D + 1)$ (vi) $D^2 - D - 2 = (D - 2)(D + 1)$

(vii) $D^2 - 4D + 4 = (D - 2)^2$ (viii) $D^2 - a^2 = (D - a)(D + a)$

(ix) $D^2 + a^2 = (D + ia)(D - ia)$

(b) The roots of $ax^2 + bx + c = 0$ are $x = \dfrac{-b \pm \sqrt{b^2 - 4ac}}{2a}$, these roots are imaginary if $b^2 - 4ac < 0$.

(i) $D^2 + 2D + 2 = 0 \Rightarrow D = \dfrac{-2 \pm \sqrt{4 - 8}}{2} = -1 \pm i$

(ii) $D^2 + D + 1 = 0 \Rightarrow D = \dfrac{-1 \pm \sqrt{1 - 4}}{2} = \dfrac{-1}{2} \pm \dfrac{\sqrt{3}}{2} i$

If $D = \dfrac{-1}{2} \pm i \dfrac{\sqrt{3}}{2} = \alpha \pm i\beta$ then $\alpha = -\dfrac{1}{2}$, $\beta = \dfrac{\sqrt{3}}{2}$, β is always positive;

α may be positive, negative or zero.

(iii) $D^2 + 1 = 0 \Rightarrow D^2 = -1$ i.e. $D = \pm i$ $\therefore$ $\alpha = 0, \beta = 1.$

(iv) $D^2 + 4 = 0 \Rightarrow D^2 = -4$ i.e. $D = \pm 2i$ $\therefore$ $\alpha = 0, \beta = 2.$

II. Third Degree Polynomials and Their Factorization :

(a) (i) $D^3 - a^3 = (D - a)(D^2 + aD + a^2)$ (iii) $D^3 + a^3 = (D + a)(D^2 - aD + a^2)$

    (ii) $D^3 + 3D^2 + 3D + 1 = (D + 1)^3$ (iv) $D^3 - 3D^2 + 3D - 1 = (D - 1)^3$

(b) Use of synthetic division :

(i) $f(D) = D^3 - 7D - 6 = 0$; for $D = -1$, $f(-1) = 0$ $\therefore$ $(D + 1)$ is one of the factors.

$$
\begin{array}{r|rrrr}
-1 & 1 & 0 & -7 & -6 \\
   &   & -1 & 1 & 6 \\
\hline
   & 1 & -1 & -6 & \underline{|0} \\
\end{array}
$$

$\therefore$ $D^3 - 7D - 6 = 0 \Rightarrow (D + 1)(D^2 - D - 6) = 0$

    $(D + 1)(D - 3)(D + 2) = 0 \Rightarrow D = -1, -2, 3.$

(ii) For $D^3 - 2D + 4 = 0$; $D = -2$ $\therefore$ $f(-2) = 0$ $\therefore$ $(D + 2)$ is one of the factors.

$$
\begin{array}{r|rrrr}
-2 & 1 & 0 & -2 & 4 \\
   &   & -2 & 4 & -4 \\
\hline
   & 1 & -2 & 2 & \underline{|0} \\
\end{array}
$$

$\therefore$ $D^3 - 2D + 4 = 0 \Rightarrow (D + 2)(D^2 - 2D + 2) = 0$

    $D = -2$ and $D = 1 \pm i$, $\alpha = 1$, $\beta = 1.$

III. Fourth Degree Polynomials and Their Factorization :

(a) $D^4 - a^4 = (D^2 - a^2)(D^2 + a^2) = (D - a)(D + a)(D + ia)(D - ia)$

(b) Making a perfect square by introducing a middle term :

(i) For $D^4 + a^4 = 0$; consider $(D^2 + a^2)^2 = D^4 + 2a^2 D^2 + a^4$

$$D^4 + a^4 = (D^4 + 2a^2 D^2 + a^4) - (2a^2 D^2) = (D^2 + a^2)^2 - \left(\sqrt{2}\, a\, D\right)^2$$

$$D^4 + a^4 = \left(D^2 - \sqrt{2}\, a\, D + a^2\right)\left(D^2 + \sqrt{2}\, a\, D + a^2\right)$$

(ii) For $\quad D^4 + 1 = D^4 + 2D^2 + 1 - 2D^2 = (D^2 + 1)^2 - \left(\sqrt{2}\, D\right)^2$

$$D^4 + 1 = \left(D^2 - \sqrt{2}\, D + 1\right)\left(D^2 + \sqrt{2}\, D + 1\right)$$

(c) $\quad D^4 + 8D^2 + 16 = (D^2 + 4)^2,\ D^4 + 2D^2 + 1 = (D^2 + 1)^2 = (D + i)^2 (D - i)^2$

$\quad\quad\quad D^4 + 10D^2 + 9 = (D^2 + 9)(D^2 + 1) = (D + 3i)(D - 3i)(D + i)(D - i)$

(d) (i) $f(D) = D^4 - 2D^3 - 3D^2 + 4D + 4 = 0$, for $D = -1$, $f(-1) = 0$

$$
\begin{array}{r|rrrrr}
-1 & 1 & -2 & -3 & 4 & 4 \\
   &   & -1 & 3 & 0 & -4 \\
\hline
-1 & 1 & -3 & 0 & 4 & \underline{|0} \\
   &   & -1 & 4 & -4 & \\
\hline
2 & 1 & -4 & 4 & \underline{|0} & \\
   &   & 2 & -4 & & \\
\hline
   & 1 & -2 & \underline{|0} & & \\
\end{array}
$$

$\therefore$ Factors are

$(D + 1)^2 (D - 2)^2 = 0.$

On a similar line,

(ii) $D^4 - D^3 - 9D^2 - 11\,D - 4 = (D+1)^3\,(D-4)$

(e) Perfect square of the type $(a + b + c)^2$

(i) $\begin{aligned}[t] D^4 + 2D^3 + 3D^2 + 2D + 1 &= (D^2)^2 + 2 \cdot D^2 \cdot D + D^2 + 2D^2 + 2D + 1\\ &= (D^2 + D)^2 + 2\,(D^2 + D) + 1\\ &= [(D^2 + D) + 1]^2 = (D^2 + D + 1)^2 \end{aligned}$

(ii) $\begin{aligned}[t] D^4 - 4D^3 + 8D^2 - 8D + 4 &= (D^2)^2 - 2D^2 \cdot 2D + (2D)^2 + 4D^2 - 8D + 4\\ &= (D^2 - 2D)^2 + 4\,(D^2 - 2D) + 4\\ &= [(D^2 - 2D) + 2]^2 = (D^2 - 2D + 2)^2 \end{aligned}$

IV. Fifth Degree Polynomials and Their Factorization :

(i) $\begin{aligned}[t] D^5 - D^4 + 2D^3 - 2D^2 + D - 1 &= D^4(D-1) + 2D^2(D-1) + 1\,(D-1)\\ &= (D^4 + 2D^2 + 1)\,(D-1) = (D-1)\,(D^2+1)^2\\ &= (D-1)\,(D+i)^2\,(D-i)^2 \end{aligned}$

1.3 THE nth ORDER LINEAR DIFFERENTIAL EQUATION WITH CONSTANT COEFFICIENTS

A differential equation which contains the differential coefficients and the dependent variable in the first degree, does not involve the product of a derivative with another derivative or with dependent variable, and in which the coefficients are constants is called a *linear differential equation with constant coefficients.*

The general form of such a differential equation of order "n" is

$$a_0\frac{d^ny}{dx^n} + a_1\frac{d^{n-1}y}{dx^{n-1}} + a_2\frac{d^{n-2}y}{dx^{n-2}} + \dots + a_{n-1}\frac{dy}{dx} + a_n\,y = f(x) \qquad \dots (1)$$

Here $a_0, a_1, a_2 \dots$ are constants. Equation (1) is a nth order linear differential equation with constant coefficients.

e.g. Put $n = 3$ in equation (1), we get $a_0\dfrac{d^3 y}{dx^3} + a_1\dfrac{d^2 y}{dx^2} + a_2\dfrac{dy}{dx} + a_3\,y = f(x)$ which is a 3rd order linear differential equation with constant coefficients.

Using the differential operator D to stand for $\dfrac{d}{dx}$ i.e. $Dy = \dfrac{dy}{dx}$; $D^2 y = \dfrac{d^2 y}{dx^2}, \dots$ $D^n y = \dfrac{d^n y}{dx}$, the equation (1) will take the form

$$a_0\,D^n y + a_1\,D^{n-1} y + a_2\,D^{n-2} y + \dots + a_{n-1}\,Dy + a_n\,y = f(x)$$

OR $\qquad (a_0\,D^n + a_1\,D^{n-1} + a_2\,D^{n-2} + \dots + a_{n-1}\,D + a_n)\,y = f(x) \qquad \dots (2)$

in which each term in the parenthesis is operating on y and the results are added.

Let $\phi(D) \equiv a_0 D^n + a_1 D^{n-1} + a_2 D^{n-2} + \ldots + a_{n-1} D + a_n$, $\phi(D)$ is called as n^{th} order polynomial in D.

$\therefore$ Equation (2) can be written as $\boxed{\phi(D) \, y \, = \, f(x)}$ ... (3)

Note : In equation (1), if $a_0, a_1, \ldots a_n$ are functions of x then it is called n^{th} order linear differential equation.

1.4 THE NATURE OF DIFFERENTIAL OPERATOR "D"

It is convenient to introduce the symbol D to represent the operation of differentiation with respect to x. i.e. $D \equiv \dfrac{d}{dx}$, so that

$$\frac{dy}{dx} \, = \, Dy; \quad \frac{d^2 y}{dx^2} \, = \, D^2 y; \quad \frac{d^3 y}{dx^3} \, = D^3 y; \, \ldots\ldots; \quad \frac{d^n y}{dx^n} \, = \, D^n y \text{ and } \frac{dy}{dx} + ay = (D + a) \, y$$

The differential operator D or (D^n) obeys the laws of Algebra.

Properties of the operator D :

If y_1 and y_2 are differentiable functions of x and "a" is a constant and m, n are positive integer then

(i) $D^m (D^n) \, y \, = \, D^n (D^m) \, y \, = \, D^{m+n} \, y$

(ii) $(D - m_1) (D - m_2) \, y \, = \, (D - m_2) (D - m_1) \, y$

(iii) $(D - m_1) (D - m_2) \, y \, = \, [D^2 - (m_1 + m_2) \, D + m_1 \, m_2] \, y$

(iv) $D \, (au) \, = \, a \cdot D(u); \quad D^n \, (au) = a \cdot D^n \, (u)$

(v) $D \, (y_1 + y_2) \, = \, D \, (y_1) + D(y_2); \quad D^n \, (y_1 + y_2) \, = \, D^n \, (y_1) + D^n \, (y_2).$

1.5 LINEAR DIFFERENTIAL EQUATION ϕ (D) y = 0

Consider $\quad \phi(D) \, y \, = \, 0$ ... (4)

where, $\phi(D) \, = \, a_0 \, D^n + a_1 \, D^{n-1} + a_2 \, D^{n-2} + a_3 \, D^{n-3} + \ldots + a_{n-1} \, D + a_n$ is n^{th} order polynomial in D and D obeys the laws of algebra, we can in general factorise $\phi(D)$ in n linear factors as $\phi(D) \, = \, (D - m_1) \, (D - m_2) \, (D - m_3) \, \ldots (D - m_n)$ where $m_1, m_2, m_3, \ldots m_n$ are the roots of the algebraic equation $\phi(D) = 0$

$\therefore$ Equation (4) can be written as

$$\phi(D) \, y \, = \, (D - m_1) \, (D - m_2) \, (D - m_3) \, \ldots \, (D - m_n) \, y = 0 \qquad \ldots (5)$$

Note : These factors can be taken in any sequence.

1.6 AUXILIARY EQUATION (A.E.)

The equation $\phi(D) = 0$ is called as an *auxiliary equation* (A.E.) for equations (3), (4).

e.g. $\quad \dfrac{d^2 y}{dx^2} - 5 \dfrac{dy}{dx} + 6y \, = \, 0$

By using operator D for $\dfrac{d}{dx}$, we have $(D^2 - 5D + 6) \, y \, = \, 0$

$\therefore \qquad \phi(D) = D^2 - 5D + 6 \, = \, 0$ is the A.E.

$\therefore (D^2 - 5D + 6) \, y = (D - 3) \, (D - 2) \, y = (D - 2) \, (D - 3) \, y.$

1.7 SOLUTION OF $\phi(D)\, y = 0$

Being n^{th} order DE, equation (4) or (5) will have exactly n arbitrary constants in its general solution.

The equation (5) will be satisfied by the solution of the equation $(D - m_n)\, y = 0$

i.e. $\dfrac{dy}{dx} - m_n\, y = 0$

On solving this 1st order 1st degree DE by separting variables, we get $y = c_n\, e^{m_n x}$, where, c_n is an arbitrary constant.

Similarly, since the factors in equation (5) can be taken in any order, the equation will be satisfied by the solution of each of the equations $(D - m_1)\, y = 0$, $(D - m_2)\, y = 0$ ... etc., that is by $y = c_1\, e^{m_1 x}$, $y = c_2\, e^{m_2 x}$ .... etc.

It can, therefore, easily be proved that the sum of these individual solutions, i.e.

$$y \;=\; c_1\, e^{m_1 x} + c_2\, e^{m_2 x} + \ldots + c_n\, e^{m_n x} \qquad\qquad \ldots (6)$$

also satisfies the equation (5) and as it contains n arbitrary constants, and the equation (4) is of the nth order, (6) constitutes the general solution of the equation (4).

$\therefore$ **The general solution of the equation $\phi(D)\, y = 0$ is**

$$y = c_1\, e^{m_1 x} + c_2\, e^{m_2 x} + \ldots + c_n\, e^{m_n x}$$

where m_1, m_2, ... m_n are the roots of the auxiliary equation $\phi(D) = 0$.

Ex. 1 : Solve $\dfrac{d^3 y}{dx^3} - 6\dfrac{d^2 y}{dx^2} + 11\dfrac{dy}{dx} - 6y = 0.$

Sol. : Let D stand for $\dfrac{d}{dx}$ and the given equation can be written as

$(D^3 - 6D^2 + 11D - 6)\, y = 0.$

Here auxiliary equation is $D^3 - 6D^2 + 11D - 6 = 0$

i.e. $(D - 1)(D - 2)(D - 3) = 0 \Rightarrow m_1 = 1, m_2 = 2, m_3 = 3$, are roots of AE.

$\therefore$ The general solution is $y = c_1\, e^x + c_2\, e^{2x} + c_3\, e^{3x}$.

2. For $(4D^2 - 8D + 1)\, y = 0$, $D = 1 \pm \dfrac{\sqrt{3}}{2} \Rightarrow y = c_1\, e^{\left(1 + \frac{\sqrt{3}}{2}\right)x} + c_2\, e^{\left(1 - \frac{\sqrt{3}}{2}\right)x}$.

1.8 DIFFERENT CASES DEPENDING UPON THE NATURE OF ROOTS OF THE AUXILIARY EQUATION $\phi(D) = 0$.

A. The Case of Real and Different Roots :

If roots of $\phi(D) = 0$ be m_1, m_2, m_3 ... m_n, all are real and different, then the solution of $\phi(D)\, y = 0$ will be

$$y \;=\; c_1\, e^{m_1 x} + c_2\, e^{m_2 x} + c_3\, e^{m_3 x} + \ldots + c_n\, e^{m_n x}$$

B. The Case of Real and Repeated Roots (The Case of Multiple Roots) :

Let $m_1 = m_2$, m_3, m_4 ... m_n be the roots of $\phi(D) = 0$, then the part of solution corresponding to m_1 and m_2 will look like

$$c_1 e^{m_1 x} + c_2 e^{m_1 x} \; (m_1 = m_2) \; = \; (c_1 + c_2)\, e^{m_1 x} \; = c' e^{m_1 x}$$

But this means that number of arbitrary constants now in the solution will be $n - 1$ instead of n. Hence it is no longer the general solution. The anomaly can be rectified as under.

Pertaining to $m_1 = m_2$, the part of the equation will be $(D - m_1)\,(D - m_1)\, y \; = \; 0$

Put $(D - m_1)\, y \; = \; z$, temporarily, then we have $(D - m_1)\, z \; = \; 0 \quad \therefore \; z = c_1 e^{m_1 x}$

Hence putting value of z in $(D - m_1)\, y \; = z$, we have

$$(D - m_1)\, y \; = \; c_1 e^{m_1 x} \quad \text{or} \quad \frac{dy}{dx} - m_1\, y \; = \; c_1 e^{m_1 x}$$

which is a linear differential equation. Its $\text{I.F.} \; = \; e^{-\int m_1 dx} \; = e^{-m_1 x}$ and hence solution is

$$y \left(e^{-m_1 x} \right) \; = \; \int c_1 e^{m_1 x} \cdot e^{-m_1 x} \; dx + c_2 \; = \; c_1 x + c_2$$

$$\therefore \qquad\qquad y \; = \; (c_1 x + c_2)\, e^{m_1 x}$$

If $m_1 = m_2$ are real, and the remaining roots m_3, m_4, m_5, ..., m_n are real and different then solution of $\phi(D)\, y \; = 0$ is

$$\boxed{y \; = \; (c_1 x + c_2)\, e^{m_1 x} + c_3 e^{m_3 x} + c_4 e^{m_4 x} + ... + c_n e^{m_n x}}$$

Similarly, when three roots are repeated. i.e. if $m_1 = m_2 = m_3$ are real, and the remaining roots m_4, m_5, ... m_n are real and different then solution of $\phi(D)\, y = 0$ is

$$\boxed{y \; = \; (c_1 x^2 + c_2 x + c_3)\, e^{m_1 x} + c_4 e^{m_4 x} + ... + c_n e^{m_n x}}$$

If $m_1 = m_2 = m_3 = ... = m_n$ i.e. n roots are real and equal then solution of $\phi(D)\, y = 0$ is

$$\boxed{y \; = \; (c_1 x^{n-1} + c_2 x^{n-2} + ... + c_{n-1} x + c_n)\, e^{m_1 x}}$$

Ex. 1. For $(D^2 - 6D + 9)\, y = 0$ A.E. $= (D - 3)^2 = 0$ and solution is $y = (c_1 x + c_2)\, e^{3x}$

    2. For $(D - 1)^3\,(D + 1)\, y = 0$, solution is $y = (c_1 x^2 + c_2 x + c_3)\, e^x + c_4 e^{-x}$

    3. For $(D - 1)^2\,(D + 1)^2\, y = 0$, solution is $y = (c_1 x + c_2)\, e^x + (c_3 x + c_4)\, e^{-x}$.

C. The Case of Imaginary (Complex) Roots

For practical problems in engineering, this case has special importance. Since the coefficients of the auxiliary equation are real, the imaginary roots (if exists) will occur in conjugate pairs. Let $\alpha \pm i\beta$ be one such pair. Therefore $m_1 = \alpha + i\beta$, $m_2 = \alpha - i\beta$

The corresponding part of the solution of the equation $\phi(D)\, y = 0$, then takes the form

$$y = A\, e^{(\alpha + i\beta)\, x} + B\, e^{(\alpha - i\beta)\, x}$$

$$= e^{\alpha x} \left[A\, e^{i\beta x} + B\, e^{-i\beta x} \right]$$

$$= e^{\alpha x} [A (\cos \beta x + i \sin \beta x) + B (\cos \beta x - i \sin \beta x)]$$

$$= e^{\alpha x} [(A + B) \cos \beta x + i (A - B) \sin \beta x]$$

$$\boxed{y = e^{\alpha x} [c_1 \cos \beta x + c_2 \sin \beta x]}$$

where, $c_1 = A + B$ and $c_2 = i (A - B)$ are arbitrary constants.

Using $c_1 = C \cos \theta$, $c_2 = - \sin \theta$, this can also be put sometimes into the form as given below (recall SHM).

$$\boxed{y = C \, e^{\alpha x} \cos (\beta x + \theta) \text{ where } C, \theta \text{ are arbitrary constants.}}$$

ILLUSTRATIONS

Ex. 1 : *Solve $(D^2 + 2D + 5) y = 0$.*

Sol. : The auxiliary equation is $D^2 + 2D + 5 = 0$ whose roots are $D = - 1 \pm 2i$ which are both imaginary. Here $\alpha = - 1$, $\beta = 2$. Hence the solution is

$$y = e^{-x} [A \cos 2x + B \sin 2x]$$

Ex. 2 : *Solve $\dfrac{d^4 y}{dx^4} - 5 \dfrac{d^2 y}{dx^2} + 12 \dfrac{dy}{dx} + 28y = 0$.*

Sol. : The auxiliary equation is $D^4 - 5D^2 + 12D + 28 = 0$ having roots $D = - 2, -2, \ 2 \pm \sqrt{3} \, i$.

(Here $\alpha = 2$, $\beta = \sqrt{3}$). Hence the solution is

$$y = (c_1 x + c_2) \, e^{-2x} + e^{2x} \left[A \cos \sqrt{3} \, x + B \sin \sqrt{3} \, x \right]$$

Ex. 3 : For $(D^2 + 4)y = 0$, $D = 0 \pm 2i$ (Here $\alpha = 0$, $\beta = 2$) $\Rightarrow$ $y = A \cos 2x + B \sin 2x$.

D. The Case of Repeated Imaginary Roots :

If the imaginary roots $m_1 = \alpha + i\beta$ and $m_2 = \alpha - i\beta$ occur twice, then the part of solution of $\phi (D) y = 0$ will be

$$y = (A x + B) \, e^{m_1 x} + (C x + D) \, e^{m_2 x} \qquad \text{... (by using case B)}$$

$$= (A x + B) \, e^{(\alpha + i\beta) x} + (C x + D) \, e^{(\alpha - i\beta) x}$$

$$= e^{\alpha x} \left[(A x + B) \, e^{i\beta x} + (C x + D) \, e^{-i\beta x} \right]$$

$$= e^{\alpha x} [(A x + B) \{\cos \beta x + i \sin \beta x\} + (C x + D) \{\cos \beta x - i \sin \beta x\}]$$

$$= e^{\alpha x} [(A x + B + C x + D) \cos \beta x + i (A x + B - C x - D) \sin \beta x]$$

$$\boxed{y = e^{\alpha x} [(c_1 x + c_2) \cos \beta x + (c_3 x + c_4) \sin \beta x]}$$

with proper changes in the constants c_1, c_2, c_3 and c_4.

ILLUSTRATIONS

Ex. 1 : *Solve* $\dfrac{d^6y}{dx^6} + 6\dfrac{d^4y}{dx^4} + 9\dfrac{d^2y}{dx^2} = 0.$

Sol. : The auxiliary equation $D^6 + 6D^4 + 9D^2 = 0$ has roots $D = 0, 0, \pm i\sqrt{3}, \pm i\sqrt{3}$ where the imaginary roots $\pm i\sqrt{3}$ are repeated. Hence the solution is

$$y = c_1 x + c_2 + (c_3 x + c_4)\cos\sqrt{3}\, x + (c_5 x + c_6)\sin\sqrt{3}\, x$$

Ex. 2 : $(D^4 + 2D^2 + 1)\, y = 0.$

Sol. : The auxiliary equation $D^4 + 2D^2 + 1 = 0$ has roots $D = \pm i, \pm i$, repeated imaginary roots. Hence the solution is

$$y = (c_1 x + c_2)\cos x + (c_3 x + c_4)\sin x$$

Now we will summarise the four cases for ready reference.

Case 1 : Real and Distinct Roots : A.E. $\Rightarrow (D - m_1)(D - m_2)(D - m_3) \dots (D - m_n) = 0$

∴ **Solution is** $y = c_1 e^{m_1 x} + c_2 e^{m_2 x} + c_3 e^{m_3 x} + \dots + c_n e^{m_n x}$

Case 2 : Repeated Real Roots :

For $m_1 = m_2 \Rightarrow$ A.E. $\Rightarrow (D - m_1)(D - m_1)(D - m_3) \dots\dots (D - m_n) = 0$

Solution is $y = (c_1 x + c_2) e^{m_1 x} + c_3 e^{m_3 x} + \dots + c_n e^{m_n x}$

For $m_1 = m_2 = m_3 \Rightarrow$ A.E. $\Rightarrow (D - m_1)(D - m_1)(D - m_1)(D - m_4) \dots (D - m_n) = 0$

Solution is $y = (c_1 x^2 + c_2 x + c_3) e^{m_1 x} + c_4 e^{m_4 x} + \dots + c_n e^{m_n x}$

Case 3 : Imaginary Roots : For $D = \alpha \pm i\beta$

Solution is $y = e^{\alpha x}[c_1\cos\beta x + c_2\sin\beta x]$

Case 4 : Repeated Imaginary Roots : For $D = \alpha \pm i\beta$ be repeated twice

Solution is $y = e^{\alpha x}[(c_1 x + c_2)\cos\beta x + (c_3 x + c_4)\sin\beta x]$

ILLUSTRATIONS

1. Solve $\dfrac{d^2 x}{dt^2} + 4x = 0$. Let D stand for $\dfrac{d}{dt}$.

∴　　　A.E. : $D^2 + 4 = 0 \Rightarrow D = 0 \pm 2i$

∴ The solution is $x = c_1\cos 2t + c_2\sin 2t$.

2. Solve $\dfrac{d^4 y}{dz^2} - 16y = 0$. Let D stand for $\dfrac{d}{dz}$.

∴　　　A.E. : $D^4 - 16 = 0,\ (D - 2)(D + 2)(D^2 + 4) = 0$.

∴ The solution is $y = c_1 e^{2z} + c_2 e^{-2z} + c_3\cos 2z + c_4\sin 2z$.

Special Case : If the two real roots of $\phi(D)\, y = 0$ be m and $-m$ [e.g. $D^2 - m^2 = 0$], then the corresponding part of the solution is

$$y = A\, e^{mx} + B\, e^{-mx}$$

OR $y = A(\cosh mx + \sinh mx) + B(\cosh mx - \sinh mx)$

OR $y = (A + B)\cosh mx + (A - B)\sinh mx$

i.e. $\boxed{y = c_1 \cosh mx + c_2 \sinh mx}$

We note here that (in some particular cases) solution of $D^2 - m^2 = 0$ can be written as

$$y = c_1 e^{mx} + c_2 e^{-mx} \quad \text{or} \quad y = c_1 \cosh mx + c_2 \sinh mx.$$

e.g.   1. $(D^2 - 1)y = 0 \Rightarrow y = c_1 \cosh x + c_2 \sinh x.$

       2. $(D^2 - 4)y = 0 \Rightarrow y = c_1 \cosh 2x + c_2 \sinh 2x.$

EXERCISE 1.1

Solve the following differential equations :

1. $\dfrac{d^2y}{dx^2} - 5\dfrac{dy}{dx} - 6y = 0.$ **Ans.** $y = c_1 e^{-x} + c_2 e^{6x}$

2. $2\dfrac{d^2y}{dx^2} - \dfrac{dy}{dx} - 10y = 0.$ **Ans.** $y = c_1 e^{-2x} + c_2 e^{(5/2)x}$

3. $\dfrac{d^3y}{dx^3} + 2\dfrac{d^2y}{dx^2} + \dfrac{dy}{dx} = 0.$ **Ans.** $y = c_1 + e^{-x}(c_2 x + c_3)$

4. $(D^4 - 2D^3 + D^2)y = 0.$ **Ans.** $y = c_1 x + c_2 + (c_3 x + c_4)e^x$

5. $(D^6 - 6D^5 + 12D^4 - 6D^3 - 9D^2 + 12D - 4)y = 0.$

     Ans. $y = (c_1 x^2 + c_2 x + c_3)e^x + (c_4 x + c_5)e^{2x} + c_6 e^{-x}$

6. $(D^3 + 6D^2 + 11D + 6)y = 0.$ **Ans.** $y = c_1 e^{-x} + c_2 e^{-2x} + c_3 e^{-3x}$

7. $4y'' - 8y' + 7y = 0.$ **Ans.** $y = e^x\left[A\cos\left(\dfrac{\sqrt{3}}{2}x\right) + B\sin\left(\dfrac{\sqrt{3}}{2}x\right)\right]$

8. $\dfrac{d^2x}{dt^2} + 2\dfrac{dx}{dt} + 5x = 0, \ x(0) = 2, \ x'(0) = 0.$ **Ans.** $x = e^{-t}(2\cos 2t + \sin 2t)$

9. $\dfrac{d^2s}{dt^2} = -16\dfrac{ds}{dt} - 64s, \ s = 0, \ \dfrac{ds}{dt} = -4$ when $t = 0.$ **Ans.** $s = -4e^{8t}t$

10. $(D^3 + D^2 - 2D + 12)y = 0.$ **Ans.** $y = c_1 e^{-3x} + e^x\left[A\cos\sqrt{3}\,x + B\sin\sqrt{3}\,x\right]$

11. $(D^2 + 1)^3(D^2 + D + 1)^2 y = 0.$

     Ans. $y = (c_1 + c_2 x + c_3 x^2)\cos x + (c_4 + c_5 x + c_6 x^2)\sin x$

$$+ e^{-x/2}\left[(c_7 + c_8 x)\cos\left(\frac{\sqrt{3}}{2}\,x\right) + (c_9 + c_{10} x)\sin\left(\frac{\sqrt{3}}{2}\,x\right)\right]$$

12. $\dfrac{d^4y}{dx^4} + m^4 y = 0.$ **Ans.** $y = e^{(mx/\sqrt{2})}\left[A\cos\left(\dfrac{mx}{\sqrt{2}}\right) + B\sin\left(\dfrac{mx}{\sqrt{2}}\right)\right]$

$$+ e^{-(mx/\sqrt{2})}\left[C\cos\left(\frac{mx}{\sqrt{2}}\right) + D\sin\left(\frac{mx}{\sqrt{2}}\right)\right]$$

13. $4\dfrac{d^2s}{dt^2} = -9s.$ **Ans.** $s = c_1 \sin\dfrac{3t}{2} + c_2 \cos\dfrac{3t}{2}$

14. The equation for the bending of a strut is $EI \dfrac{d^2y}{dx^2} + Py = 0$. If $y = 0$ when $x = 0$

and $y = a$ when $x = \dfrac{l}{2}$, find y.   **Ans.** $y = \dfrac{a \sin \sqrt{\dfrac{P}{EI}}\, x}{\sin \sqrt{\dfrac{P}{EI}} \cdot \dfrac{l}{2}}$

MULTIPLE CHOICE QUESTIONS (MCQ's)

Type I : Complementary Functions :

1. If the roots m_1, m_2, m_3, ..., m_n of auxiliary equation $\phi(D) = 0$ are real and distinct, then solution of $\phi(D)\, y = 0$ is   (1)

    (A) $c_1 e^{m_1 x} + c_2 e^{m_2 x} + \ldots + c_n e^{m_n x}$

    (B) $c_1 \cos m_1 x + c_2 \cos m_2 x + \ldots + c_n \cos m_n x$

    (C) $m_1 e^{c_1 x} + m_2 e^{c_2 x} + \ldots + m_n{}^{c_n x}$

    (D) $c_1 \sin m_1 x + c_2 \sin m_2 x + \ldots + c_n \sin m_n x$

2. The roots m_1, m_2, m_3 ..., m_n of auxiliary equation $\phi(D) = 0$ are real. If two of these roots are repeated say $m_1 = m_2$ and the remaining roots m_3, m_4, ..., m_n are distinct then solution of $\phi(D)\, y = 0$ is   (1)

    (A) $c_1 e^{m_1 x} + c_2{}^{m_2 x} + \ldots + c_n{}^{m_n x}$

    (B) $(c_1 x + c_2) \cos m_1 x + c_3 \cos m_3 x + x \ldots + c_n \cos m_n x$

    (C) $(c_1 x + c_2)\, e^{m_1 x} + c_3 e^{m_3 x} + \ldots + c_n e^{m_n x}$

    (D) $(c_1 x + c_2) \sin m_1 x + c_3 \sin m_3 x + \ldots + c_n \sin m_n x$

3. The roots m_1, m_2, m_3 ..., m_n of auxiliary equation $\phi(D) = 0$ are real. If three of these roots are repeated, say, $m_1 = m_2 = m_3$ and the remaining roots m_4, m_5, ... m_n are distinct then solution of $\phi(D)\, y = 0$ is   (1)

    (A) $c_1 e^{m_1 x} + c_2{}^{m_2 x} + \ldots + c_n\, e^{m_n x}$

    (B) $(c_1 x^2 + c_2 x + c_3)\, e^{m_1 x} + c_4 e^{m_4 x} + \ldots + c_n e^{m_n x}$

    (C) $(c_1 x^2 + c_2 x + c_3) \cos m_1 x + c_4 \cos m_4 x + \ldots + c_n \cos m_n x$

    (D) $(c_1 x^2 + c_2 x + c_3) \sin m_1 x + c_4 \sin m_4 x + \ldots + c_n \sin m_n x$

4. If $m_1 = \alpha + i\beta$ and $m_2 = \alpha - i\beta$ are two complex roots of auxiliary equation of second order DE $\phi(D)\, y = 0$ then it's solution is   (1)

    (A) $e^{\beta x} [c_1 \cos \alpha x + c_2 \sin \alpha x]$

    (B) $e^{\alpha x} [(c_1 x + c_2) \cos \beta x + (c_3 x + c_4) \sin \beta x]$

    (C) $c_1 e^{\alpha x} + c_2 e^{\beta x}$

    (D) $e^{\alpha x} [c_1 \cos \beta x + c_2 \sin \beta x]$

5. If the complex roots $m_1 = \alpha + i\beta$ and $m_2 = \alpha - i\beta$ of auxiliary equation of fourth order DE $\phi(D)\, y = 0$ are repeated twice then it's solution is   (1)

(A) $e^{\beta x}[c_1 \cos \alpha x + c_2 \sin \alpha x]$

(B) $e^{\alpha x}[(c_1 x + c_2) \cos \beta x + (c_3 x + c_4) \sin \beta x]$

(C) $(c_1 x + c_2)\, e^{\alpha x} + (c_3 x + c_4)\, e^{\beta x}$

(D) $e^{\alpha x}[c_1 \cos \beta x + c_2 \sin \beta x]$

6. The solution of differential equation $\dfrac{d^2 y}{dx^2} - 5\dfrac{dy}{dx} + 6y = 0$ is   (1)

(A) $c_1 e^{2x} + c_2 e^{-3x}$ (B) $c_1 e^{-2x} + c_2 e^{3x}$

(C) $c_1 e^{-2x} + c_2 e^{-3x}$ (D) $c_1 e^{2x} + c_2 e^{3x}$

7. The solution of differential equation $\dfrac{d^2 y}{dx^2} - 5\dfrac{dy}{dx} - 6y = 0$ is   (1)

(A) $c_1 e^{-x} + c_2 e^{6x}$ (B) $c_1 e^{-2x} + c_2 e^{-3x}$

(C) $c_1 e^{3x} + c_2 e^{2x}$ (D) $c_1 e^{-3x} + c_2 e^{-2x}$

8. The solution of differential equation $2\dfrac{d^2 y}{dx^2} - \dfrac{dy}{dx} - 10y = 0$ is   (1)

(A) $c_1 e^{2x} + c_2 e^{\frac{5}{2}x}$ (B) $c_1 e^{-2x} + c_2 e^{-\frac{5}{2}x}$

(C) $c_1 e^{-2x} + c_2 e^{\frac{5}{2}x}$ (D) $c_1 e^{-2x} + c_2 e^{\frac{3}{2}x}$

9. The solution of differential equation $\dfrac{d^2 y}{dx^2} - 4y = 0$ is   (1)

(A) $(c_1 x + c_2)\, e^{2x}$ (B) $c_1 e^{4x} + c_2 e^{-4x}$

(C) $c_1 \cos 2x + c_2 \sin 2x$ (D) $c_1 e^{2x} + c_2 e^{-2x}$

10. The solution of differential equation $\dfrac{d^2 y}{dx^2} - \dfrac{dy}{dx} - 2y = 0$ is   (1)

(A) $c_1 e^{2x} + c_2 e^{x}$ (B) $c_1 e^{2x} + c_2 e^{-x}$

(C) $c_1 e^{-2x} + c_2 e^{x}$ (D) $c_1 e^{-2x} + c_2 e^{-x}$

11. The solution of differential equation $2\dfrac{d^2 y}{dx^2} - 5\dfrac{dy}{dx} + 3y = 0$ is   (1)

(A) $c_1 e^{x} + c_2 e^{\frac{3}{2}x}$ (B) $c_1 e^{2x} + c_2 e^{-3x}$

(C) $c_1 e^{-x} + c_2 e^{\frac{3}{2}x}$ (D) $c_1 e^{\frac{x}{2}} + c_2 e^{\frac{3}{2}x}$

12. The solution of differential equation $\dfrac{d^2y}{dx^2} + 2\dfrac{dy}{dx} + y = 0$ is   (1)

(A) $c_1e^{2x} + c_2e^x$ (B) $c_1e^x + c_2e^{-x}$

(C) $(c_1x + c_2)\,e^{-x}$ (D) $(c_1x + c_2)\,e^x$

13. The solution of differential equation $4\dfrac{d^2y}{dx^2} - 4\dfrac{dy}{dx} + y = 0$ is   (1)

(A) $c_1e^{\frac{x}{2}} + c_2e^{-\frac{x}{2}}$ (B) $(c_1 + c_2x)\,e^{-2x}$

(C) $c_1 \cos 2x + c_2 \sin 2x$ (D) $(c_1 + c_2x)\,e^{\frac{x}{2}}$

14. The solution of differential equation $\dfrac{d^2y}{dx^2} - 4\dfrac{dy}{dx} + 4y = 0$ is   (1)

(A) $(c_1x + c_2)\,e^{2x}$ (B) $(c_1x + c_2)\,e^{-2x}$

(C) $c_1e^{4x} + c_2e^{-4x}$ (D) $c_1e^{2x} + c_2e^{-2x}$

15. The solution of differential equation $\dfrac{d^2y}{dx^2} + 6\dfrac{dy}{dx} + 9y = 0$ is   (1)

(A) $c_1e^{-6x} + c_2e^{-9x}$ (B) $(c_1x + c_2)\,e^{-3x}$

(C) $(c_1x + c_2)\,e^{3x}$ (D) $c_1e^{3x} + c_2e^{2x}$

16. The solution of differential equation $\dfrac{d^2y}{dx^2} + y = 0$ is   (1)

(A) $c_1e^x + c_2e^{-x}$ (B) $(c_1x + c_2)\,e^{-x}$

(C) $c_1 \cos x + c_2 \sin x$ (D) $e^x\,(c_1 \cos x + c_2 \sin x)$

17. The solution of differential equation $\dfrac{d^2y}{dx^2} + 9y = 0$ is   (1)

(A) $c_1 \cos 2x + c_2 \sin 2x$ (B) $(c_1x + c_2)\,e^{-3x}$

(C) $c_1e^{3x} + c_2e^{-3x}$ (D) $c_1 \cos 3x + c_2 \sin 3x$

18. The solution of differential equation $\dfrac{d^2y}{dx^2} + 6\dfrac{dy}{dx} + 10y = 0$ is   (1)

(A) $e^{-3x}\,(c_1 \cos x + c_2 \sin x)$ (B) $e^x\,(c_1 \cos 3x + c_2 \sin 3x)$

(C) $c_1e^{5x} + c_2e^{2x}$ (D) $e^x\,(c_1 \cos x + c_2 \sin x)$

19. The solution of differential equation $\dfrac{d^2y}{dx^2} + \dfrac{dy}{dx} + y = 0$ is   (1)

(A) $e^x\,(c_1 \cos x + c_2 \sin x)$

(B) $e^{x/2}\left[c_1 \cos\left(\dfrac{3}{2}\right)x + c_2 \sin\left(\dfrac{3}{2}\right)x\right]$

(C) $e^{-\frac{1}{2}x}\left[c_1 \cos\left(\dfrac{\sqrt{3}}{2}\right)x + c_2 \sin\left(\dfrac{\sqrt{3}}{2}\right)x\right]$

(D) $c_1e^x + c_2e^{-x}$

20. The solution of differential equation $4\dfrac{d^2y}{dx^2} + 4\dfrac{dy}{dx} + 5y = 0$ is   (1)

(A) $e^{-x}(c_1\cos 2x + c_2\sin 2x)$ (B) $e^{-x/2}[c_1\cos x + c_2\sin x]$

(C) $e^{-2x}(c_1\cos x + c_2\sin x)$ (D) $c_1 e^{-4x} + c_2 e^{-5x}$

21. The solution of differential equation $\dfrac{d^3y}{dx^3} + 6\dfrac{d^2y}{dx^2} + 11\dfrac{dy}{dx} + 6y = 0$ is   (2)

(A) $c_1 e^x + c_2 e^{2x} + c_3 e^{3x}$ (B) $c_1 e^{-x} + c_2 e^{2x} + c_3 e^{-3x}$

(C) $c_1 e^{-x} + c_2 e^{-2x} + c_3 e^{-3x}$ (D) $c_1 e^x + c_2 e^{-2x} + c_3 e^{3x}$

22. The solution of differential equation $\dfrac{d^3y}{dx^3} - 7\dfrac{dy}{dx} - 6y = 0$ is   (2)

(A) $c_1 e^x + c_2 e^{2x} + c_3 e^{3x}$ (B) $c_1 e^{-x} + c_2 e^{-2x} + c_3 3^{6x}$

(C) $c_1 e^{-x} + c_2 e^{2x} + c_3 e^{x}$ (D) $c_1 e^{-x} + c_2 e^{-2x} + c_3 e^{3x}$

23. The solution of differential equation $\dfrac{d^3y}{dx^3} + 2\dfrac{d^2y}{dx^2} + \dfrac{dy}{dx} = 0$ is   (2)

(A) $c_1 + e^x(c_2 x + c_3)$ (B) $c_1 + e^{-x}(c_2 x + c_3)$

(C) $e^{-x}(c_2 x + c_3)$ (D) $c_1 + c_2 e^x + c_3 e^{-x}$

24. The solution of differential equation $\dfrac{d^3y}{dx^3} - 5\dfrac{d^2y}{dx^2} + 8\dfrac{dy}{dx} - 4y = 0$ is   (2)

(A) $c_1 e^x + (c_2 x + c_3)\,e^{2x}$ (B) $c_1 e^x + c_2 e^{2x} + c_3 e^{3x}$

(C) $(c_2 x + c_3)\,e^{2x}$ (D) $c_1 e^{-x} + (c_2 x + c_3)\,e^{-2x}$

25. The solution of differential equation $\dfrac{d^3y}{dx^3} - 4\dfrac{dy}{dx} = 0$ is   (2)

(A) $c_1 e^{2x} + c_2 e^{-2x}$ (B) $c_1 + c_2\cos 2x + c_3\sin 2x$

(C) $c_1 e^x + c_2 e^{-2x} + c_3 e^{-3x}$ (D) $c_1 + c_2 e^{2x} + c_3 e^{-2x}$

26. The solution of differential equation $\dfrac{d^3y}{dx^3} + y = 0$ is   (2)

(A) $c_1 e^x + e^x\left(c_2\cos\dfrac{\sqrt{3}}{2}x + c_3\sin\dfrac{\sqrt{3}}{2}x\right)$ (B) $c_1 e^{-x} + e^{\frac{1}{2}x}\left(c_2\cos\dfrac{1}{2}x + c_3\sin\dfrac{1}{2}x\right)$

(C) $c_1 e^{-x} + e^{\frac{1}{2}x}\left(c_2\cos\dfrac{\sqrt{3}}{2}x + c_3\sin\dfrac{\sqrt{3}}{2}x\right)$

(D) $(c_1 + c_2 x + c_3 x^2)\,e^{-x}$

27. The solution of differential equation $\dfrac{d^3y}{dx^3} + 3\dfrac{dy}{dx} = 0$ is   (2)

(A) $c_1 + c_2\cos x + c_3\sin x$ (B) $c_1 + c_2\cos\sqrt{3}x + c_3\sin\sqrt{3}x$

(C) $c_1 + c_2 e^{\sqrt{3}x} + c_3 e^{-\sqrt{3}x}$ (D) $c_1\cos x + c_2\sin x$

28. The solution of differential equation $\dfrac{d^3y}{dx^3} + \dfrac{d^2y}{dx^2} - 2\dfrac{dy}{dx} + 12y = 0$ is   (2)

(A) $c_1 e^{-3x} + e^x \left(c_2 \cos \sqrt{3}x + c_3 \sin \sqrt{3}x\right)$

(B) $c_1 e^{-3x} + (c_2 \cos 3x + c_3 \sin 3x)$

(C) $c_1 e^{3x} + e^{-x} \left(c_2 \cos \sqrt{3}x + c_3 \sin \sqrt{3}x\right)$

(D) $c_1 e^{-x} + c_2 e^{-\sqrt{3}x} + c_3 e^{\sqrt{3}x}$

29. The solution of differential equation $(D^3 - D^2 + 3D + 5)\, y = 0$ where $D = \dfrac{d}{dx}$ is   (2)

(A) $c_1 e^{-x} + e^x (c_2 \cos 2x + c_3 \sin 2x)$ (B) $c_1 e^{-x} + (c_2 \cos 3x + c_3 \sin 3x)$

(C) $c_1 e^x + e^{-x} (c_2 \cos 2x + c_3 \sin 2x)$ (D) $c_1 e^{-x} + c_2 e^{-2x} + c_3 e^{-3x}$

30. The solution of differential equation $\dfrac{d^3y}{dx^3} - \dfrac{d^2y}{dx^2} + 4\dfrac{dy}{dx} - 4y = 0$ is   (2)

(A) $(c_1 + c_2 x)\, e^{-2x} + c_3 e^{-x}$ (B) $c_1 e^x + c_2 \cos 4x + c_3 \sin 4x$

(C) $c_1 e^x + c_2 \cos 2x + c_3 \sin 2x$ (D) $c_1 e^x + c_2 e^{2x} + c_3 e^{-2x}$

31. The solution of differential equation $\dfrac{d^4y}{dx^4} - y = 0$ is   (2)

(A) $(c_1 x + c_2)\, e^{-x} + c_3 \cos x + c_4 \sin x$ (B) $(c_1 x + c_2) \cos x + (c_3 x + c_4) \sin x$

(C) $(c_1 + c_2 x + c_3 x^2 + c_4 x^3)\, e^x$ (D) $c_1 e^x + c_2 e^{-x} + c_3 \cos x + c_4 \sin x$

32. The solution of differential equation $(D^4 + 2D^2 + 1)\, y = 0$ where $D = \dfrac{d}{dx}$ is   (2)

(A) $(c_1 x + c_2)\, e^x + (c_3 x + c_4)\, e^{-x}$ (B) $(c_1 x + c_2) \cos x + (c_3 x + c_4) \sin x$

(C) $c_1 e^x + c_2 e^{-x} + c_3 \cos x + c_4 \sin x$ (D) $(c_1 x + c_2) \cos 2x + (c_3 x + c_4) \sin 2x$

33. The solution of differential equation $(D^2 + 9)^2\, y = 0$, where $D = \dfrac{d}{dx}$ is   (2)

(A) $(c_1 x + c_2)\, e^{3x} + (c_3 x + c_4)\, e^{-3x}$ (B) $(c_1 x + c_2) \cos 3x + (c_3 x + c_4) \sin 3x$

(C) $(c_1 x + c_2) \cos 9x + (c_3 x + c_4) \sin 9x$ (D) $(c_1 x + c_2) \cos x + (c_3 x + c_4) \sin x$

34. The solution of differential equation $\dfrac{d^4y}{dx^4} + 8\dfrac{d^2y}{dx^2} + 16y = 0$ is   (2)

(A) $c_1 e^{2x} + c_2 e^{-x} + c_3 e^x + c_4 e^{-2x}$ (B) $(c_1 x + c_2)\, e^{2x} + (c_3 x + c_4)\, e^{-2x}$

(C) $(c_1 x + c_2) \cos 4x + (c_3 x + c_4) \sin 4x$ (D) $(c_1 x + c_2) \cos 2x + (c_3 x + c_4) \sin 2x$

35. The solution of differential equation $\dfrac{d^6y}{dx^6} + 6\dfrac{d^4y}{dx^4} + 9\dfrac{d^2y}{dx^2} = 0$ is   (2)

(A) $c_1 x + c_2 + (c_3 x + c_4) \cos \sqrt{3}x + (c_3 x + c_6) \sin \sqrt{3}x$

(B) $c_1 x + c_2 + (c_3 x + c_4) \cos 3x + (c_5 x + c_6) \sin 3x$

(C) $(c_1 x + c_2) \cos \sqrt{3}x + (c_3 x + c_4) \sin \sqrt{3}x$

(D) $c_1 x + c_2 + (c_3 x + c_4)\, e^{\sqrt{3}x}.$

Answers

1. (A)	2. (C)	3. (B)	4. (D)	5. (B)	6. (D)	7. (A)	8. (C)
9. (D)	10. (B)	11. (A)	12. (C)	13. (D)	14. (A)	15. (B)	16. (C)
17. (D)	18. (A)	19. (C)	20. (B)	21. (C)	22. (D)	23. (B)	24. (A)
25. (D)	26. (C)	27. (B)	28. (A)	29. (A)	30. (C)	31. (D)	32. (B)
33. (B)	34. (D)	35. (A)					

1.9 THE GENERAL SOLUTION OF THE LINEAR DIFFERENTIAL EQUATION $\phi(D) y = f(x)$

The general solution of the equation $\phi(D)y = f(x)$ can be written as $\boxed{y = y_c + y_p}$ where,

1. y_c is the solution of the given equation with $f(x) = 0$, that is of equation $\phi(D) y = 0$ (which is known as Associated equation or Reduced equation) and is called the *complimentary function* (C.F.). It involves n arbitrary constants and is denoted by C.F. then $\boxed{\phi(D) y_c = 0}$.

2. y_p is any function of x, which satisfies the equation $\phi(D) y = f(x)$, so that

$$\boxed{\phi(D) y_p = f(x)}$$

y_p is called the particular integral and is denoted by P.I. It does not contain any arbitrary constant.

Thus, on substituting $y = y_c + y_p$ in $\phi(D) y$,

$$\phi(D) [y_c + y_p] = \phi(D) y_c + \phi(D) y_p = 0 + f(x) = f(x)$$

$\therefore$ $y = y_c + y_p$ satisfies the equation $\phi(D) y = f(x)$ and as it contains exactly n arbitrary constants, is the general (or complete) solution of the equation.

Note : 1. The complete solution of $\phi(D) y = f(x)$ is $y = $ C.F. + P.I. $= y_c + y_p$.

2. The general solution of $\phi(D) y = f(x)$ has *arbitrary constants equal in number to the order of the differential equation.*

1.10 THE INVERSE OPERATOR $\dfrac{1}{\phi(D)}$ AND THE SYMBOLIC EXPRESSION FOR THE PARTICULAR INTEGRAL

We define $\dfrac{1}{\phi(D)} f(x)$ as that function of x which when acted upon by the differential operator $\phi(D)$ gives $f(x)$.

Thus by this definition, $\phi(D) \left\{ \dfrac{1}{\phi(D)} f(x) \right\} = f(x)$ and so $\left\{ \dfrac{1}{\phi(D)} f(x) \right\}$ satisfies the equation $\phi(D)\, y = f(x)$ and so is the P.I. of the equation $\phi(D)\, y = f(x)$.

Thus the P.I. of the equation $\phi(D)\, y = f(x)$ is symbolically given by

$$\boxed{\text{P.I.} = y_p = \dfrac{1}{\phi(D)} f(x)}$$

e.g.   1. $(D^2 - 1)\, y = x^2$ $\therefore$ $y_p = \dfrac{1}{D^2 - 1}\, x^2$

   2. $(D^2 - 3D + 2)\, y = \sin e^x$ $\therefore$ $y_p = \dfrac{1}{D^2 - 3D + 2} \sin e^x.$

1.11 METHODS OF OBTAINING PARTICULAR INTEGRAL

There are three methods to evaluate the particular integral $y_p = \dfrac{1}{\phi(D)} f(x)$.

(A) General method

(B) Short-cut methods

(C) Method of variation of parameters.

Now we will discuss these methods in detail.

(A) General Method :

This method is useful when the short-cut methods given in (B) are not applicable. This method involves integration.

(i) $\dfrac{1}{D - m}\, f(x)$: By definition of the P.I., $\dfrac{1}{D - m}\, f(x)$ will be the P.I. of the equation $(D - m)\, y = f(x)$ i.e. the part in the solution of this equation which does not contain the arbitrary constant. We have, $\dfrac{dy}{dx} - my = f(x)$ (linear)

$$\text{I.F.} = e^{-mx} \text{ and the general solution is}$$

$$y\, e^{-mx} = \int f(x) \cdot e^{-mx}\, dx + c_1$$

$\therefore \qquad y = (c_1\, e^{mx}) + \left(e^{mx} \int e^{-mx} f(x) \cdot dx \right)$

i.e. $y = y_c + y_p$

Here $c_1\, e^{mx}$ is the C.F. and $e^{mx} \int e^{-mx} f(x)\, dx$ must be the P.I.

$\therefore$
$$\boxed{y_p = \text{P.I.} = \dfrac{1}{D - m} f(x) = e^{mx} \int e^{-mx} f(x)\, dx}$$

Similarly,
$$\boxed{y_p = \text{P.I.} = \dfrac{1}{D + m} f(x) = e^{-mx} \int e^{mx} f(x)\, dx}$$

Put m = 0

$$\boxed{y_p \;=\; \frac{1}{D}\, f(x) \;=\; \int f(x)\, dx}$$

Also,

$$y_p \;=\; \frac{1}{D^2}\, f(x) \;=\; \frac{1}{D}\left[\frac{1}{D}\, f(x)\right]$$

$$=\; \frac{1}{D}\left[\int f(x)\, dx\right] \;=\; \int \left[\int f(x)\, dx\right] dx$$

$\therefore$

$$\boxed{y_p \;=\; \frac{1}{D^2}\, f(x) \;=\; \int \left[\int f(x)\, dx\right] dx}$$

Similarly,

$$\boxed{y_p \;=\; \frac{1}{D^3}\, f(x) \;=\; \int \left\{\int \left[\int f(x)\, dx\right] dx\right\} dx} \quad \text{... and so on.}$$

(ii) $\dfrac{1}{(D - m_1)\,(D - m_2)}\, f(x)$:

$$y_p \;=\; \frac{1}{(D - m_1)\,(D - m_2)}\, f(x) \;=\; \frac{1}{(D - m_1)}\, e^{m_2 x} \int e^{-m_2 x}\, f(x)\, dx$$

$$y_p \;=\; e^{m_1 x} \int e^{-m_1 x}\left[e^{m_2 x} \int e^{-m_2 x}\, f(x)\, dx\right] dx$$

(iii) Use of Partial Fraction :

$$y_p \;=\; \frac{1}{(D - m_1)\,(D - m_2)}\, f(x)$$

$$=\; \frac{1}{(m_1 - m_2)}\left[\frac{1}{D - m_1} - \frac{1}{D - m_2}\right] f(x)$$

$$=\; \frac{1}{m_1 - m_2}\left\{\frac{1}{D - m_1}\, f(x) - \frac{1}{D - m_2}\, f(x)\right\}$$

$$y_p \;=\; \frac{1}{m_1 - m_2}\left\{e^{m_1 x} \int e^{-m_1 x}\, f(x)\, dx - e^{m_2 x} \int e^{-m_2 x}\, f(x)\, dx\right\}$$

ILLUSTRATIONS ON GENERAL METHOD

Ex. 1 : *Solve* $\dfrac{d^2 y}{dx^2} + 3\dfrac{dy}{dx} + 2y = e e^{x}$ **(May 2007, May 2009, Dec. 2011)**

Sol. : For C.F., A.E. is $D^2 + 3D + 2 = 0 \Rightarrow (D + 2)\,(D + 1) = 0$
Hence $D = -1, -2$ and C.F. $= c_1 e^{-x} + c_2 e^{-2x}$

Here

$$\text{P.I.} = y_p \;=\; \frac{1}{(D + 2)\,(D + 1)}\, (e e^{x})$$

$$=\; \frac{1}{D + 2}\left[\frac{1}{D + 1}\, e e^{x}\right]$$

$$= \frac{1}{D+2} \left[e^{-x} \int e^x \, e^{e^x} \, dx \right] \qquad [\text{put } e^x = t \quad \therefore \ e^x \, dx = dt]$$

$$= \frac{1}{D+2} \left[e^{-x} \int e^t \, dt \right]$$

$$= \frac{1}{D+2} \left[e^{-x} \, e^{e^x} \right]$$

$$= e^{-2x} \int e^{2x} \, e^{-x} \, e^{e^x} \, dx$$

$$\text{P.I.} = e^{-2x} \int e^x \, e^{e^x} \, dx = e^{-2x} \, e^{e^x}$$

Hence the complete solution will be

$$y = c_1 e^{-x} + c_2 e^{-2x} + e^{-2x} \, e^{e^x}$$

Ex. 2 : *Solve* $\dfrac{d^2y}{dx^2} + \dfrac{dy}{dx} = \dfrac{1}{1+e^x}$. $\qquad\qquad$ **(May 2006, Dec. 2007)**

Sol. : We have $(D^2 + D)\, y = \dfrac{1}{1+e^x}$, here $D \equiv \dfrac{d}{dx}$

$\therefore \qquad$ AE $\Rightarrow D\,(D+1) = 0 \quad \therefore \quad D = 0, -1.$

$\therefore \qquad\qquad\quad$ C.F. $= y_c = c_1 + c_2 e^{-x}$

$$\text{P.I.} = \frac{1}{D\,(D+1)} \left(\frac{1}{1+e^x} \right)$$

$$= \left(\frac{1}{D} - \frac{1}{D+1} \right) \left(\frac{1}{1+e^x} \right) \qquad \text{by partial fraction}$$

$$= \frac{1}{D} \left(\frac{1}{1+e^x} \right) - \frac{1}{D+1} \left(\frac{1}{1+e^x} \right)$$

$$= \int \frac{1}{1+e^x} \, dx - e^{-x} \int e^x \frac{dx}{1+e^x}$$

$$= \int \frac{e^x \, dx}{e^x \,(1+e^x)} - e^{-x} \int e^x \frac{dx}{1+e^x} \qquad \begin{bmatrix} \text{put } 1+e^x = t \\ e^x \, dx = dt \end{bmatrix}$$

$$= \int \frac{dt}{t\,(t-1)} - e^{-x} \int \frac{dt}{t}$$

$$= \int \left(\frac{1}{t-1} - \frac{1}{t} \right) dt - e^{-x} \log\,(e^x + 1)$$

$$= \log\,(t-1) - \log t - e^{-x} \log\,(e^x + 1)$$

$$= \log\,(e^x) - \log\,(1 + e^x) - e^{-x} \log\,(e^x + 1)$$

$$= x - \log\,(1 + e^x) - e^{-x} \log\,(e^x + 1)$$

Hence the complete solution is

$$y = c_1 + c_2 e^{-x} + x - \log\,(1 + e^x) - e^{-x} \log\,(1 + e^x)$$

Ex. 3 : *Solve $(D^2 + 5D + 6)\, y = e^{-2x}\sec^2 x\,(1 + 2\tan x)$*   **(Dec. 2004, 2008, 2014)**

Sol. : $D^2 + 5D + 6 = 0$ gives $(D + 2)(D + 3) = 0 \Rightarrow D = -2, -3$

$$\text{C.F.} = c_1 e^{-2x} + c_2 e^{-3x}$$

$$\text{P.I.} = \frac{1}{(D + 3)(D + 2)}\,[e^{-2x}\sec^2 x\,(1 + 2\tan x)]$$

$$= \frac{1}{D + 3}\left[e^{-2x}\int e^{2x}\cdot e^{-2x}\sec^2 x\,(1 + 2\tan x)\,dx\right]$$

$$= \frac{1}{D + 3}\left[e^{-2x}\int \sec^2 x\,(1 + 2\tan x)\,dx\right] \quad \text{put } \tan x = t,\ \sec^2 x\,dx = dt$$

$$= \frac{1}{D + 3}\left[e^{-2x}\int (1 + 2t)\,dt\right]$$

$$= \frac{1}{D + 3}\,[e^{-2x}\,(t + t^2)]$$

$$= \frac{1}{D + 3}\,[e^{-2x}\,(\tan x + \tan^2 x)]$$

$$= e^{-3x}\int e^{3x}\cdot e^{-2x}\,[(\tan x - 1) + \sec^2 x]\,dx$$

$$= e^{-3x}\int e^x\,[(\tan x - 1) + \sec^2 x]\,dx$$

$$= e^{-3x}\,[e^x\,(\tan x - 1)] \qquad\qquad \because \int e^x\,[f(x) + f'(x)]\,dx = e^x f(x)$$

$$= e^{-2x}\,(\tan x - 1)$$

Hence the complete solution is

$$y = c_2 e^{-3x} + e^{-2x}\,[c_1 + \tan x - 1]$$

$$= c_2 e^{-3x} + e^{-2x}\,[c_3 + \tan x]$$

Ex. 4 : *Solve $\dfrac{d^2 y}{dx^2} + 9y = \sec 3x$*

Sol. : A.E. is $D^2 + 9 = 0$, or $D = \pm 3i$

$$\text{C.F.} = c_1 \cos 3x + c_2 \sin 3x \ \text{ and}$$

$$\text{P.I.} = \frac{1}{D^2 + 9}\,(\sec 3x) = \frac{1}{(D + 3i)(D - 3i)}\,\sec 3x$$

$$= \frac{1}{6i}\left[\frac{1}{D - 3i} - \frac{1}{D + 3i}\right]\sec 3x$$

$$= \frac{1}{6i}\,\frac{1}{D - 3i}\,\sec 3x - \frac{1}{6i}\,\frac{1}{D + 3i}\,\sec 3x \qquad\qquad \dots (1)$$

Now, $\dfrac{1}{D - 3i}\,\sec 3x = e^{3ix}\int e^{-3ix}\,\sec 3x\,dx$

$$= e^{3ix}\int \frac{\cos 3x - i \sin 3x}{\cos 3x}\,dx$$

$$= e^{3ix} \int [1 - i \tan 3x] \, dx$$

$$= e^{3ix} \left[x + \frac{i}{3} \log (\cos 3x) \right]$$

Changing i to $-i$ in this, we have

$$\frac{1}{D + 3i} (\sec 3x) = e^{-3ix} \left[x - \frac{i}{3} \log (\cos 3x) \right]$$

Putting values in (1), we have

$$\text{P.I.} = \frac{1}{6i} \left[e^{3ix} \left\{ x + \frac{i}{3} \log (\cos 3x) \right\} - e^{-3ix} \left\{ x - \frac{i}{3} \log (\cos 3x) \right\} \right]$$

$$= \frac{x}{6i} \cdot e^{3ix} + \frac{e^{3ix} \log (\cos 3x)}{18} - \frac{x \, e^{-3ix}}{6i} + \frac{e^{-3ix} \log (\cos 3x)}{18}$$

Combining the like terms, we get

$$= \frac{x}{3} \left[\frac{e^{3ix} - e^{-3ix}}{2i} \right] + \frac{1}{9} \left[\frac{e^{3ix} + e^{-3ix}}{2} \right] \log (\cos 3x)$$

$$\text{P.I.} = \frac{x}{3} \sin 3x + \frac{1}{9} \cos 3x \log (\cos 3x)$$

Hence the general solution will be

$$y = c_1 \cos 3x + c_2 \sin 3x + \frac{x}{3} \sin 3x + \frac{1}{9} \cos 3x \cdot \log (\cos 3x)$$

Ex. 5 : *Solve* $\dfrac{d^2 y}{dx^2} - \dfrac{dy}{dx} - 2y = 2 \log x + \dfrac{1}{x} + \dfrac{1}{x^2}$

Sol. : $(D^2 - D - 2) \, y = 2 \log x + \dfrac{1}{x} + \dfrac{1}{x^2}$

$$\text{A.E.} : \quad D^2 - D - 2 = 0 \qquad \therefore \quad (D - 2) (D + 1) = 0$$

$$\therefore \qquad y_c = c_1 e^{2x} + c_2 e^{-x}$$

$$y_p = \frac{1}{(D - 2) (D + 1)} \left(2 \log x + \frac{1}{x} + \frac{1}{x^2} \right)$$

$$= \frac{1}{D - 2} \left[e^{-x} \int e^x \left(2 \log x + \frac{1}{x} + \frac{1}{x^2} \right) dx \right]$$

$$= \frac{1}{D - 2} \left[e^{-x} \int e^x \left\{ 2 \log x + \frac{2}{x} - \frac{1}{x} + \frac{1}{x^2} \right\} dx \right]$$

$$= \frac{1}{D-2} \left\{ e^{-x} \int e^x \left[\left(2 \log x - \frac{1}{x} \right) + \left(\frac{2}{x} + \frac{1}{x^2} \right) \right] dx \right\}$$

$$= \frac{1}{D-2} \, e^{-x} \cdot e^x \left(2 \log x - \frac{1}{x} \right) = \frac{1}{D-2} \left(2 \log x - \frac{1}{x} \right)$$

$$= e^{2x} \int e^{-2x} \left(2 \log x - \frac{1}{x} \right) dx$$

$$= e^{2x} \left\{ \int 2 \log x \cdot e^{-2x} dx - \int e^{-2x} \frac{1}{x} dx \right\}$$

$$= e^{2x} \left\{ 2 \log x \left(\frac{e^{-2x}}{-2} \right) - \int \frac{2}{x} \cdot \left(\frac{e^{-2x}}{-2} \right) dx - \int e^{-2x} \cdot \frac{1}{x} \, dx \right\}$$

$$= e^{2x} \left\{ - \log x \cdot e^{-2x} + \int e^{-2x} \frac{1}{x} \, dx - \int e^{-2x} \frac{1}{x} dx \right\}$$

$$= e^{2x} \left\{ - \log x \, e^{-2x} \right\} = - \log x$$

$$\therefore \qquad y = \text{C.F.} + \text{P.I.} = y_c + y_p$$

$$y = c_1 e^{2x} + c_2 e^{-x} - \log x$$

Ex. 6 : *Solve $(D^2 - 1) y = e^{-x} \sin e^{-x} + \cos e^{-x}$.* **(Dec. 2006, 2007)**

Sol. : AE : $D^2 - 1 = 0$ or $(D - 1)(D + 1) = 0 \Rightarrow D = -1, +1$ $\therefore y_c = c_1 e^x + c_2 e^{-x}$

$$y_p = \frac{1}{(D-1)(D+1)} \left(e^{-x} \sin e^{-x} + \cos e^{-x} \right)$$

$$= \frac{1}{D-1} \left\{ e^{-x} \int e^x \left(\cos e^{-x} + e^{-x} \sin e^{-x} \right) dx \right\} \left\{ \text{Use } \int e^x [f + f'] \, dx = e^x \cdot f \right\}$$

$$= \frac{1}{D-1} \left\{ e^{-x} \cdot e^x \cos e^{-x} \right\} = \frac{1}{D-1} \cdot \cos e^{-x}$$

$$= e^x \int e^{-x} \cos e^{-x} dx = e^x \int \cos e^{-x} \left(- e^{-x} dx \right) \qquad \left\{ \text{Use } e^{-x} = t \right\}$$

$$= - e^x \sin e^{-x}$$

$$\therefore \qquad y = c_1 e^x + c_2 e^{-x} - e^x \sin e^{-x} .$$

Ex. 7 : *Solve $(D^2 - 1) y = (1 + e^{-x})^{-2}$.* **(Dec. 2010)**

Sol. : A.E. : $D^2 - 1 = 0$

$$\text{C.F.} = c_1 e^x + c_2 e^{-x}$$

$$\text{P.I.} = \frac{1}{(D+1)(D-1)} \, (1 + e^{-x})^{-2}$$

$$= \frac{1}{D+1} \, e^x \int e^{-x} (1 + e^{-x})^{-2} dx$$

$$= \frac{1}{D+1} \, (-e^x) \int (1 + e^{-x})^{-2} (- e^{-x} dx)$$

$$= \frac{-1}{D+1} \left[-e^x (1 + e^{-x})^{-1} \right]$$

$$= e^{-x} \int \frac{e^x \cdot e^x}{1 + e^{-x}} \, dx$$

$$= e^{-x} \int \frac{e^{2x} \cdot (e^x \, dx)}{1 + e^x} \quad (1 + e^x = t)$$

$$= e^{-x} \int \frac{(t-1)^2}{t} \, dt$$

$$= e^{-x} \left[\frac{t^2}{2} - 2t + \log t \right]$$

$$= e^{-x} \left[\frac{(1 + e^x)^2}{2} - 2(1 + e^x) + \log(1 + e^x) \right]$$

$$\therefore \qquad y = c_1 e^x + c_2 e^{-x} + \frac{e^{-x}}{2} (1 + e^x)^2 + e^{-x} \log(1 + e^x) - 2e^{-x} - 2$$

or
$$y = A e^x + B e^{-x} + e^{-x} \left[\frac{(1 + e^x)^2}{2} + \log(1 + e^x) \right] - 2$$

Ex. 8 : *Solve $(D^2 + 3D + 2) y = e^{e^x} + \cos e^x$.*   **(Dec. 2008)**

Sol. :   A.E. : $D^2 + 3D + 2 = (D + 2)(D + 1) = 0$

C.F. $= c_1 e^{-2x} + c_2 e^{-x}$

$$\text{P.I.} = \frac{1}{(D+2)(D+1)} (e^{e^x} + \cos e^x)$$

$$= \frac{1}{D+2} \, e^{-x} \int e^x (e^{e^x} + \cos e^x) \, dx$$

$$= \frac{1}{D+2} \, e^{-x} (e^{e^x} + \sin e^x)$$

$$= e^{-2x} \int e^{2x} \, e^{-x} (e^{e^x} + \sin e^x) \, dx$$

$$= e^{-2x} \int e^x (e^{e^x} + \sin e^x) \, dx$$

$$= e^{-2x} (e^{e^x} - \cos e^x)$$

$$\therefore \qquad y = c_1 e^{-2x} + c_2 e^{-x} + e^{-2x} (e^{e^x} - \cos e^x)$$

Ex. 9 : *Solve $(D^2 + 3D + 2) y = \sin e^x$.*   **(May 2005, Dec. 2009)**

Sol. : A.E. : $D^2 + 3D + 2 = (D + 2)(D + 1) = 0 \Rightarrow D = -2, -1.$

C.F. $= c_1 e^{-2x} + c_2 e^{-x}$

$$\text{P.I.} = \frac{1}{(D+2)(D+1)} \sin e^x = \frac{1}{D+2} e^{-x} \int e^x \sin e^x \, dx$$

$$= \frac{1}{D+2} e^{-x} (-\cos e^x) = -e^{-2x} \int e^x \cos e^x \, dx$$

$$= -e^{-2x} \sin e^x$$

$$\therefore \quad y = c_1 e^{-2x} + c_2 e^{-x} - e^{-2x} \sin e^x$$

Ex. 10 : *Solve* $\dfrac{d^2 y}{dx^2} + y = cosec\, x.$ **(Dec. 2006)**

Sol. : A.E. : $D^2 + 1 = (D + i)(D - i) = 0 \Rightarrow D = \pm i.$

C.F. $= c_1 \cos x + c_2 \sin x$

$$\text{P.I.} = \frac{1}{D^2 + 1} cosec\, x = \frac{1}{2i}\left(\frac{1}{D-i} - \frac{1}{D+i}\right) cosec\, x$$

$$= \frac{1}{2i}\left[\frac{1}{D-i} cosec\, x - \frac{1}{D+i} cosec\, x\right]$$

$$= \frac{1}{2i}\left[e^{ix} \int e^{-ix} cosec\, x \, dx - e^{-ix} \int e^{ix} cosec\, x \, dx\right]$$

$$= \frac{1}{2i}\left[e^{ix} \int (\cos x - i \sin x)\, cosec\, x \, dx - e^{-ix} \int (\cos x + i \sin x)\, cosec\, x \, dx\right]$$

$$= \frac{1}{2i}\left[e^{ix} \int (\cot x - i)\, dx - e^{-ix} \int (\cot x + i)\, dx\right]$$

$$= \frac{1}{2i}\, [e^{ix}(\log \sin x - ix) - e^{-ix}(\log \sin x + ix)]$$

$$= \frac{1}{2i}\, [\log \sin x)(e^{ix} - e^{-ix}) - ix\,(e^{ix} + e^{-ix})]$$

$$= \sin x \log \sin x - x \cos x$$

$$\therefore \quad y = c_1 \cos x + c_2 \sin x + \sin x \log \sin x - x \cos x$$

(B) Short-cut Methods for Finding P.I. in Certain Standard Cases

Although the general method (A) discussed in the previous article will always work in the theory, it many a times leads to laborious and difficult integration. To avoid this, short methods of finding P.I. without actual integration are developed depending upon the particular form of function f(x).

Case I : P.I. when f(x) $= e^{ax}$, a is any constant.

To obtain $y_p = \dfrac{1}{\phi(D)} e^{ax}$, we have $D\, e^{ax} = a\, e^{ax}, \quad D^2 e^{ax} = a^2 e^{ax} \; \ldots\ldots \; D^n\, e^{an} = a^n\, e^{ax}$

$$\therefore \quad (a_0 D^n + a_1 D^{n-1} + \ldots\ldots + a_n)\, e^{ax} = (a_0\, a^n + a_1\, a^{n-1} + \ldots\ldots + a_n)\, e^{ax}$$

or $\qquad \phi(D)\, e^{ax} = \phi(a)\, e^{ax}$

Operating on both sides by $\dfrac{1}{\phi(D)}$, we have

$$\frac{1}{\phi(D)}\,[\phi(D)\,e^{ax}] = \frac{1}{\phi(D)}\,[\phi(a)\,e^{ax}]$$

or $\qquad\qquad e^{ax} = \phi(a)\,\dfrac{1}{\phi(D)}\,(e^{ax}),\qquad\qquad \left(\because \dfrac{1}{\phi(D)} \text{ is a linear operator}\right)$

Dividing by $\phi(a)$, we have the formula

$$\boxed{\frac{1}{\phi(D)}\,e^{ax} = \frac{1}{\phi(a)}\,e^{ax} \text{ provided } \phi(a) \neq 0}\qquad\qquad \text{... (A)}$$

Case of failure : If $\phi(a) = 0$, above rule fails and we proceed as under.

Since $\phi(a) = 0$, $D - a$ must be a factor of $\phi(D)$ (by Factor Theorem).

Let $\qquad\qquad \phi(D) = (D - a)\,\psi(D)$ where, $\psi(a) \neq 0$. Then

$$\frac{1}{\phi(D)}\,(e^{ax}) = \frac{1}{D-a}\,\frac{1}{\psi(D)}\,e^{ax}$$

$$= \frac{1}{D-a}\,\frac{e^{ax}}{\psi(a)}\qquad\qquad\qquad \text{... from (A)}$$

$$= \frac{1}{\psi(a)}\,\frac{1}{D-a}\,e^{ax}$$

$$= \frac{1}{\psi(a)}\,e^{ax}\int e^{-ax}\,e^{ax}\,dx\qquad\qquad \text{... (refer 1.11-A (i))}$$

$$= \frac{1}{\psi(a)}\,e^{ax}\int dx$$

$$= x\cdot\frac{1}{\psi(a)}\,e^{ax},\ \text{ where } \psi(a) = \phi'(a) \neq 0.$$

i.e. $\qquad\qquad \boxed{\dfrac{1}{\phi(D)}\,e^{ax} = x\cdot\dfrac{1}{\phi'(a)}\,e^{ax} \text{ provided } \phi'(a) \neq 0}\qquad\qquad \text{... (B)}$

If $\phi'(a) = 0$ then we shall apply (B) again to get

$$\boxed{\frac{1}{\phi(D)}\,(e^{ax}) = x^2\,\frac{1}{\phi''(a)}\,e^{ax},\ \text{ provided } \phi''(a) \neq 0}\ ,\ \text{ and so on.}$$

Remark 1 : Since $\quad \phi(D) = (D-a)\,\psi(D)$

$$\phi'(D) = (D-a)\,\psi'(D) + \psi(D)$$

$\therefore \qquad\qquad \phi'(a) = 0 + \psi(a)$

or $\qquad\qquad \phi'(a) = \psi(a)$

Remark 2 : It can also be established that

$$\frac{1}{(D-a)^r\, \psi(D)}\, e^{ax} \;=\; \frac{1}{\psi(a)}\, \frac{x^r}{r!}\, e^{ax} \text{, provided } \psi(a) \neq 0.$$

Remark 3 : Any constant k can be expressed as $k = k \cdot e^{0x}$

$$\therefore \qquad y_p \;=\; \frac{1}{\phi(D)}\, (k) \;=\; \frac{1}{\phi(D)}\, k \cdot e^{0x} = k \cdot \frac{1}{\phi(D)}\, e^{0x}$$

$$= k \cdot \frac{1}{\phi(0)}, \;\; \phi(0) \neq 0$$

Remark 4 : If $f(x) = a^x$ then we use $a^x = e^{x \log a}$

$$\therefore \qquad y_p \;=\; \frac{1}{\phi(D)}\, a^x = \frac{1}{\phi(D)}\, e^{x \log a}$$

$$= \frac{1}{\phi(\log a)}\, a^x \qquad\qquad \text{Replace D with } \log a.$$

If $f(x) = a^{-x}$ then we use $a^{-x} = e^{x \log 1/a} = e^{x\,(-\log a)}$

$$\therefore \qquad y_p \;=\; \frac{1}{\phi(D)}\, a^{-x} = \frac{1}{\phi(D)}\, e^{x\,(-\log a)}$$

$$= \frac{1}{\phi(-\log a)}\, a^{-x}. \qquad\qquad \text{Replace D with } -\log a.$$

Formulae for Ready Reference :

1. $\dfrac{1}{D-a}\, e^{ax} = x \cdot e^{ax}$ 2. $\dfrac{1}{(D-a)^2}\, e^{ax} = \dfrac{x^2}{2!}\, e^{ax}$ 3. $\dfrac{1}{(D-a)^3}\, e^{ax} = \dfrac{x^3}{3!}\, e^{ax}$

4. $\dfrac{1}{(D-a)^r}\, e^{ax} = \dfrac{x^r}{r!}\, e^{ax}$

5. $\dfrac{1}{(D-a)^r\, \psi(D)}\, e^{ax} = \dfrac{1}{\psi(a)}\, \dfrac{1}{(D-a)^r}\, e^{ax} = \dfrac{1}{\psi(a)}\, \dfrac{x^r}{r!}\, e^{ax}, \;\; \psi(a) \neq 0$

ILLUSTRATIONS

Ex. 1 : *Find the Particular Integral of $(D^2 - 5D + 6)\, y = 3\, e^{5x}$.*

Sol. :
$$\text{P.I.} \;=\; \frac{3}{D^2 - 5D + 6}\, (e^{5x})$$

$$= \frac{3\, e^{5x}}{5^2 - 5.5 + 6} = \frac{e^{5x}}{2}$$

Ex. 2 : *Find the Particular Integral of $\dfrac{d^2y}{dx^2} + 4\dfrac{dy}{dx} + 3y = e^{-3x}$*

Sol. : Here
$$\text{P.I.} \;=\; \frac{1}{D^2 + 4D + 3}\, (e^{-3x}), \qquad \phi(D) = D^2 + 4D + 3$$

But $\qquad \phi(-3) = 9 - 12 + 3 = 0$ hence $\quad \phi(-3) = 0$ and case I fails.

$$\therefore \qquad \text{P.I.} \ = \ \frac{x\,e^{-3x}}{\phi'(a)} \ = \ x \cdot \frac{1}{2D+4} \cdot e^{-3x}, \ \ D \to a = -3$$

$$= \ \frac{x\,e^{-3x}}{2(-3)+4} \ = \ \frac{x\,e^{-3x}}{-2}$$

Ex. 3 : *Find the Particular Integral of* $(D-1)^3\,y = e^x + 2^x - \dfrac{3}{2}.$

Sol. : $\qquad y_p \ = \ \dfrac{1}{(D-1)^3}\,e^x + \dfrac{1}{(D-1)^3}\,2^x - \dfrac{3}{2}\,\dfrac{1}{(D-1)^3}\,e^{0x}$

$$= \ \frac{x^3}{3!}\,e^x + \frac{1}{(\log 2 - 1)^3}\,2^x - \frac{3}{2}\,\frac{1}{(0-1)^3}$$

$$= \ \frac{x^3}{6}\,e^x + \frac{1}{(\log 2 - 1)^3}\,2x + \frac{3}{2}$$

Ex. 4 : *Find the Particular Integral of* $(D-2)^2(D+1)\,y = e^{2x} + 2^{-x}$

Sol. : $\qquad y_p \ = \ \dfrac{1}{(D-2)^2(D+1)}\,e^{2x} + \dfrac{1}{(D-2)^2(D+1)}\,2^{-x}$

$$= \ \frac{1}{(D-2)^2} \cdot \frac{1}{(2+1)}\,e^{2x} + \frac{2^{-x}}{(-\log 2 - 2)^2(-\log 2 + 1)}$$

$$= \ \frac{1}{3} \cdot \frac{x^2}{2!}\,e^{2x} + \frac{2^{-x}}{(-\log 2 - 2)^2(-\log 2 + 1)}$$

Case II :   P.I. when $f(x) = \sin(ax+b)$ or $\cos(ax+b)$.

To obtain $y_p = \dfrac{1}{\phi(D^2)}\sin(ax+b)$ or $\dfrac{1}{\phi(D^2)}\cos(ax+b)$, we have

$$\begin{aligned}
D\,\sin(ax+b) \ &= \ a\cos(ax+b)\\
D^2\,\sin(ax+b) \ &= \ -a^2\sin(ax+b)\\
D^3\,\sin(ax+b) \ &= \ -a^3\cos(ax+b)\\
D^4\,\sin(ax+b) \ &= \ a^4\sin(ax+b)
\end{aligned}$$

or $\qquad\qquad (D^2)^2\,\sin(ax+b) \ = \ (-a^2)^2\sin(ax+b)$

Similarly $\qquad (D^2)^p\,\sin(ax+b) \ = \ (-a^2)^p\sin(ax+b)$

and we may generalise that

$$\phi(D^2)\,\sin(ax+b) \ = \ \phi(-a^2)\,\sin(ax+b)$$

Operating on both sides by $\dfrac{1}{\phi(D^2)}$, we have

$$\frac{1}{\phi(D^2)}\,[\phi(D^2)\,\sin(ax+b)] \ = \ \frac{1}{\phi(D^2)}\,[\phi(-a^2)\,\sin(ax+b)]$$

$$\sin(ax+b) \ = \ \phi(-a^2)\,\frac{1}{\phi(D^2)}\,\sin(ax+b)$$

Dividing now by $\phi\,(-a^2)$, we have

$$\boxed{\frac{1}{\phi\,(D^2)}\,\sin\,(ax+b)\ =\ \frac{1}{\phi\,(-a^2)}\,\sin\,(ax+b),\ \text{provided } \phi\,(-a^2)\neq 0}$$

Case of failure : But if $\phi\,(-a^2)=0$, above rule fails and we proceed as under :

We know by Euler's Theorem that $\cos\,(ax+b)+i\,\sin\,(ax+b)\ =\ e^{i\,(ax+b)}$ hence

$$\frac{1}{\phi\,(D^2)}\,\sin\,(ax+b)\ =\ \text{Imag. Part of}\ \frac{1}{\phi\,(D^2)}\,e^{i\,(ax+b)}$$

$$=\ \text{I.P. of}\ \frac{1}{\phi\,(D^2)}\,e^{i\,(ax+b)}$$

$$=\ \text{I.P. of}\ x\,\frac{1}{\phi(D^2)}\,e^{i\,(ax+b)},\ (D^2=-a^2)$$

Hence $$\boxed{\frac{1}{\phi\,(D^2)}\,\sin\,(ax+b)\ =\ x\,\frac{1}{\phi'\,(-a^2)}\,\sin\,(ax+b)\ \text{provided } \phi'\,(-a^2)\neq 0}$$

Add if $\phi'\,(-a^2)\neq 0$, we have

$$\boxed{\frac{1}{\phi(D^2)}\,\sin\,(ax+b)\ =\ x^2\,\frac{1}{\phi''(-a^2)}\,\sin\,(ax+b),\ \text{provided } \phi''(-a^2)\neq 0}$$

Similarly formulae for $\cos\,(ax+b)$ viz.

$$\boxed{\frac{1}{\phi\,(D^2)}\,\cos\,(ax+b)\ =\ \frac{1}{\phi\,(-a^2)}\,\cos\,(ax+b),\ \text{provided } \phi\,(-a^2)\neq 0}$$

But if $\phi\,(-a^2)=0$, we have

$$\boxed{\frac{1}{\phi\,(D^2)}\,\cos\,(ax+b)\ =\ x\,\frac{1}{\phi'\,(-a^2)}\,\cos\,(ax+b),\ \text{provided } \phi'\,(-a^2)\neq 0}$$

And if $\phi'\,(-a^2)=0$, we have

$$\boxed{\frac{1}{\phi\,(D^2)}\,\cos\,(ax+b)\ =\ x^2\,\frac{1}{\phi''\,(-a^2)}\,\cos\,(ax+b),\ \text{provided } \phi''\,(-a^2)\neq 0}$$

and so on and so forth.

Additional Results :

$$\frac{1}{\phi(D^2)}\,\sin\,ax\ =\ \frac{1}{\phi(-a^2)}\,\sin\,ax\ ,\ \ \phi(-a^2)\neq 0\ \ (\text{Replace } D^2 \text{ with } -a^2)$$

$$\frac{1}{\phi(D^2)}\,\cos\,ax\ =\ \frac{1}{\phi(-a^2)}\,\cos\,ax\ ,\ \ \phi(-a^2)\neq 0,\ (\text{Replace } D^2 \text{ with } -a^2)$$

For the case of failure, it can also be established that

$$\boxed{\frac{1}{D^2+a^2}\,\sin\,(ax+b)\ =\ -\frac{x}{2a}\,\cos\,(ax+b)}$$

$$\boxed{\frac{1}{D^2 + a^2} \cos(ax + b) = \frac{x}{2a} \sin(ax + b)}$$

$$\boxed{\frac{1}{(D^2 + a^2)^r} \sin(ax + b) = \left(\frac{-x}{2a}\right)^r \frac{1}{r!} \sin\left(ax + b + \frac{r\pi}{2}\right)}$$

$$\boxed{\frac{1}{(D^2 + a^2)^r} \cos(ax + b) = \left(\frac{-x}{2a}\right)^r \frac{1}{r!} \cos\left(ax + b + \frac{r\pi}{2}\right)}$$

Useful Formulae :

$$\sin^2 x = \frac{1 - \cos 2x}{2} = \frac{e^{0x}}{2} - \frac{\cos 2x}{2}$$

$$\cos^2 x = \frac{1 + \cos 2x}{2} = \frac{e^{0x}}{2} + \frac{\cos 2x}{2}$$

$$\sin A \sin B = \frac{1}{2}[\cos(A - B) - \cos(A + B)]$$

$$\sin A \cos B = \frac{1}{2}[\sin(A + B) + \sin(A - B)]$$

$$\cos A \cos B = \frac{1}{2}[\cos(A + B) + \cos(A - B)]$$

$$\sin x = 2 \sin \frac{x}{2} \cos \frac{x}{2}; \ \sin 2x = 2 \sin x \cos x.$$

Note : Write $D^3 = D^2 \cdot D$; $D^4 = (D^2)^2$; $D^5 = (D^2)^2 \cdot D$. Always replace D^2 by $- a^2$ and *keep D as it is.* To get D^2 in the denominator, rationalise the denominator and then replace D^2 by $- a^2$. Now numerator will contain an operator in D, therefore open the bracket.

ILLUSTRATIONS

Ex. 1 : *Solve $(D^2 + 2D + 1) y = 4 \sin 2x$.*

Sol. : A.E. is $D^2 + 2D + 1 = 0 \Rightarrow D = - 1, - 1.$

$$\text{C.F.} = (c_1 x + c_2) e^{-x}$$

$$\text{P.I.} = \frac{1}{D^2 + 2D + 1}(4 \sin 2x)$$

$$= \frac{1}{- 4 + 2D + 1}(4 \sin 2x) \qquad \text{(putting } D^2 = - 2^2 = - 4)$$

$$= \frac{4}{2D - 3}(\sin 2x)$$

$$= \frac{4(2D + 3)}{4D^2 - 9}(\sin 2x)$$

$$\qquad\qquad [\text{(Multiply numerator and denominator by } (2D + 3)]$$

$$= \frac{4(2D + 3)}{4(-4) - 9}(\sin 2x) \qquad \text{(replace } D^2 \text{ with } - 4)$$

$$= -\frac{4}{25} (2D + 3) (\sin 2x)$$

$$= -\frac{4}{25} [4 \cos 2x + 3 \sin 2x]$$

$\therefore$ General solution is

$$y = (c_1 x + c_2) e^{-x} - \frac{4}{25} [4 \cos 2x + 3 \sin 2x]$$

Ex. 2 : *Solve* $\dfrac{d^3y}{dx^3} + 4 \dfrac{dy}{dx} = \sin 2x.$

Sol. : A.E. will be $D^3 + 4D = 0 \Rightarrow D (D^2 + 4) = 0$

Hence $D = 0$ and $D = \pm 2 i.$

    C.F. = Complementary Function $= c_1 + c_2 \cos 2x + c_3 \sin 2x$

$$\text{P.I.} = \frac{1}{D (D^2 + 4)} (\sin 2x) \qquad\qquad [\because D^2 + 4 = 0, \text{ for } D^2 = -2^2 = -4\,]$$

$$= x \frac{1}{3 D^2 + 4} (\sin 2x), \left[\frac{d}{dD} (D^3 + 4D) = 3D^2 + 4, \text{ then put } D^2 = -4\right]$$

$$= x \cdot \frac{1}{3 (-4) + 4} (\sin 2x)$$

$$= -\frac{x}{8} \sin 2x.$$

Hence the solution is

$$y = c_1 + c_2 \cos 2x + c_3 \sin 2x - \frac{x \sin 2x}{8}$$

Ex. 3 : *Solve* $(D^2 + 1) y = \sin x \sin 2x.$

Sol. : A.E. is $D^2 + 1 = 0 \Rightarrow D = \pm i$

$\therefore$ C.F. $= c_1 \cos x + c_2 \sin x$

We have   P.I. $= \dfrac{1}{D^2 + 1} (\sin x \sin 2x)$

$$= \frac{1}{D^2 + 1} \left[\frac{1}{2} (\cos x - \cos 3x)\right]$$

$$= \frac{1}{2} \frac{1}{D^2 + 1} \cos x - \frac{1}{2} \frac{1}{D^2 + 1} \cos 3x$$

$$(D^2 \to -9 \text{ in } 2^{nd} \text{ term, case fails for } 1^{st} \text{ term})$$

$$= \frac{1}{2} x \cdot \frac{1}{2D} \cos x - \frac{1}{2} \frac{1}{-9 + 1} \cos 3x$$

$$= x \cdot \frac{1}{4} \frac{D}{D^2} \cos x + \frac{1}{16} \cos 3x, \quad (D^2 \to -1)$$

$$= \frac{1}{4} x \cdot \frac{D(\cos x)}{-1} + \frac{1}{16} \cos 3x$$

$$= \frac{1}{4} x \sin x + \frac{1}{16} \cos 3x$$

Hence the solution is

$$y = c_1 \cos x + c_2 \sin x + \frac{1}{4} x \sin x + \frac{1}{16} \cos 3x$$

Case III : P.I when $f(x) = \cosh (ax + b)$ or $\sinh (ax + b)$.

To find $y_p = \dfrac{1}{\phi(D^2)} \cosh (ax + b)$ or $\dfrac{1}{\phi(D^2)} \sinh (ax + b)$

As earlier on the similar line, we can prove that

$$\frac{1}{\phi(D^2)} \cosh (ax + b) = \frac{1}{\phi(a^2)} \cosh (ax + b), \ \phi(a^2) \neq 0$$

$$\text{and} \quad \frac{1}{\phi(D^2)} \sinh (ax + b) = \frac{1}{\phi(a^2)} \sinh (ax + b), \ \phi(a^2) \neq 0$$

ILLUSTRATION

Ex. 1 : *Solve* $\dfrac{d^3y}{dx^3} - 4 \dfrac{dy}{dx} = 2 \cosh 2x$

Sol. : A.E. is $D^3 - 4D = 0 \Rightarrow D(D^2 - 4) = 0, \ D = 0, \ \pm 2$

Hence   C.F. $= c_1 + c_2 e^{2x} + c_3 e^{-2x}$

$$\text{P.I.} = \frac{1}{(D^2 - 4)} \left[\frac{1}{D} (2 \cosh 2x) \right]$$

$$= \frac{1}{D^2 - 4} \int 2 \cosh 2x \, dx$$

$$= \frac{2}{D^2 - 4} \left(\frac{\sinh 2x}{2} \right)$$

$$= \frac{1}{D^2 - 4} (\sinh 2x) \qquad [\text{case of failure, hence differentiate } \phi(D)]$$

$$= \frac{x(\sinh 2x)}{2D} = \frac{x \, D(\sinh 2x)}{2D^2}$$

$$= \frac{x}{2} \frac{D(\sinh 2x)}{(4)} = \frac{x}{8} D(\sinh 2x)$$

$$= \frac{x}{4} \cosh 2x$$

$\therefore$ Solution is $y = c_1 + c_2 e^{2x} + c_3 e^{-2x} + \dfrac{x}{4} \cosh 2x$

Case IV : P.I. when f(x) = x^m

To find $y_p = \dfrac{1}{f(D)} x^m$, we write $\dfrac{1}{\phi(D)} (x^m) = [\phi(D)]^{-1} x^m$.

We shall now expand $[\phi(D)]^{-1}$ in ascending powers of D as far as the term in D^m and operate on x^m term by term. Since $(m+1)^{th}$ and higher derivatives of x^m will be zero, we need not consider terms beyond D^m.

Important Formulae :

$$\frac{1}{1+x} = (1+x)^{-1} = 1 - x + x^2 - x^3 + \ldots\ldots$$

$$\frac{1}{1-x} = (1-x)^{-1} = 1 + x + x^2 + x^3 + \ldots\ldots$$

$$(1+x)^n = 1 + nx + \frac{n(n-1)}{2!} x^2 + \ldots\ldots\ldots$$

Also note that $D^n (x^n) = n!$ and $D^{n+1} (x^n) = 0$.

Note : To find $y_p = \dfrac{1}{\phi(D)} x^m$

(i) we always take constant term common from the denominator and use the formulae $(1+x)^{-1}, (1-x)^{-1}, (1+x)^n, (1-x)^n$.

(ii) if constant term is absent in the denominator then the minimum power of D is taken common from the denominator.

e.g. $$\frac{1}{D^2 - 3D - 2} x^m = \frac{1}{-2\left[1 - \left(\dfrac{D^2 - 3D}{2}\right)\right]} x^m$$

$$\frac{1}{D^2 - 3D + 3} x^m = \frac{1}{3\left[1 + \left(\dfrac{D^2 - 3D}{3}\right)\right]} x^m$$

$$\frac{1}{D^3 - 3D^2 + 2D} x^m = \frac{1}{2D\left[1 + \left(\dfrac{D^2 - 3D}{2}\right)\right]} x^m$$

ILLUSTRATION

Ex. 1 : *Find the particular solution of* $\dfrac{d^2y}{dx^2} - \dfrac{dy}{dx} + y = x^3 - 3x^2 + 1.$

Sol. : It can be put as $(D^2 - D + 1) y = x^3 - 3x^2 + 1.$

$$\begin{aligned}
\text{P.I.} &= \frac{1}{(1 - D + D^2)} (x^3 - 3x^2 + 1) \\
&= [1 - (D - D^2)]^{-1} (x^3 - 3x^2 + 1)
\end{aligned}$$

Expanding by Binomial theorem upto D^3 terms

$$\begin{aligned}
&= [1 + (D - D^2) + (D - D^2)^2 + (D - D^2)^3 + \ldots] (x^3 - 3x^2 + 1) \\
&= [1 + D - D^2 + D^2 - 2D^3 + \ldots + D^3 + \ldots] (x^3 - 3x^2 + 1)
\end{aligned}$$

$$= (1 + D - D^3)(x^3 - 3x^2 + 1)$$

$$= x^3 - 6x - 5$$

Hence   P.I. $= x^3 - 6x - 5$.

Case V : P.I. when $f(x) = e^{ax} V$, where V is any function of x.

To find $y_p = \dfrac{1}{f(D)} e^{ax} V$, we have

$$D(e^{ax} V) = e^{ax} DV + a e^{ax} V = e^{ax}(D + a) V$$

and

$$D^2(e^{ax} V) = e^{ax} D^2 V + 2a\, e^{ax} DV + a^2\, e^{ax} V$$

$$= e^{ax}(D + a)^2 V$$

and proceeding similarly, we may have in general

$$D^n(e^{ax} V) = e^{ax}(D + a)^n V$$

Hence $\phi(D)(e^{ax} V) = e^{ax} \phi(D + a) V$ ... (I)

Now, let $\phi(D + a) V = V_1 \Rightarrow V = \dfrac{1}{\phi(D + a)} V_1$

If we put value of V in (I), we have

$$\phi(D)\left[e^{ax} \frac{1}{\phi(D + a)} V_1 \right] = e^{ax} V_1$$

Operating on both sides by $\dfrac{1}{\phi(D)}$ now, we get

$$e^{ax} \frac{1}{\phi(D + a)} V_1 = \frac{1}{\phi(D)}(e^{ax} V_1)$$

Here V_1 is any function of x, and hence, we have the formula

$$\boxed{\dfrac{1}{\phi(D)}(e^{ax} V) = e^{ax} \dfrac{1}{\phi(D + a)}(V)}$$

ILLUSTRATION

Ex. 1 : *Solve $(D^2 - 4D + 3) y = x^3 e^{2x}$.*   **(Dec. 2005)**

Sol. :   A.E. $= D^2 - 4D + 3 = (D - 1)(D - 3) \Rightarrow D = 1, 3.$

Hence   C.F. $= c_1 e^x + c_2 e^{3x}$

$$\text{P.I.} = \frac{1}{D^2 - 4D + 3}(x^3 e^{2x})$$

$$= e^{2x} \frac{1}{(D + 2)^2 - 4(D + 2) + 3}(x^3) \qquad \dots (D \to D + 2)$$

$$= e^{2x} \frac{1}{D^2 + 4D + 4 - 4D - 8 + 3}(x^3)$$

$$= e^{2x} \frac{1}{D^2 - 1}(x^3) = -e^{2x}(1 - D^2)^{-1}(x^3) \qquad \text{(by case IV)}$$

$$= -e^{2x}[1 + D^2 + D^4 + \dots\dots](x^3) = -e^{2x}[x^3 + 6x]$$

Hence solution is $y = c_1 e^x + c_2 e^{3x} - e^{2x}(x^3 + 6x)$

Case VI : P.I. when $f(x) = x^m \sin ax$, or $x^m \cos ax$.

To find $y_p = \dfrac{1}{f(D)} x^m \sin ax$ or $\dfrac{1}{f(D)} x^m \cos ax$, we have

$$\frac{1}{\phi(D)} x^m [\cos ax + i \sin ax] = \frac{1}{\phi(D)} x^m e^{iax}$$

$$= e^{iax} \frac{1}{\phi(D + ia)} x^m$$

Now $\dfrac{1}{\phi(D + ia)} x^m$, can be evaluated by method of case IV and equating the Real and Imaginary parts, we get the required results.

ILLUSTRATION

Ex. 1 : *Solve $(D^4 + 2D^2 + 1)\, y = x^2 \cos x$.*

Sol. : A.E. is $(D^2 + 1)^2 = 0 \Rightarrow D = \pm i, \pm i$.

$\therefore$ C.F. $= (c_1 x + c_2) \cos x + (c_3 x + c_4) \sin x$

For Particular Integral, we have

$$\frac{1}{(D^2 + 1)^2} [x^2 (\cos x + i \sin x)] = \frac{1}{(D^2 + 1)^2} x^2 \cdot e^{ix}$$

$$= e^{ix} \frac{1}{[(D + i)^2 + 1]^2} (x^2) = e^{ix} \frac{1}{(D^2 + 2iD)^2} (x^2)$$

$$= e^{ix} \frac{1}{-4D^2 \left(1 - \dfrac{iD}{2}\right)^2} (x^2) \qquad \left(\because \frac{1}{i} = -i\right)$$

$$= -\frac{e^{ix}}{4} \frac{1}{D^2} \left(1 - \frac{iD}{2}\right)^{-2} (x^2)$$

$$= -\frac{e^{ix}}{4} \frac{1}{D^2} \left(1 + iD - \frac{3}{4} D^2 + \dots \right)(x^2)$$

$$= -\frac{e^{ix}}{4} \frac{1}{D^2} \left[x^2 + 2ix - \frac{3}{2}\right]$$

$$= -\frac{e^{ix}}{4} \left[\frac{x^4}{12} + \frac{ix^3}{3} - \frac{3}{4} x^2\right] \text{ Integrating twice}$$

$$= -\frac{1}{4} [\cos x + i \sin x] \left[\frac{x^4}{12} + \frac{ix^3}{3} - \frac{3}{4} x^2\right]$$

Equating the real parts on both sides,

$$\frac{1}{(D^2 + 1)^2} (x^2 \cos x) = -\frac{1}{4} \left(\frac{x^4}{12} - \frac{3}{4} x^2\right) \cos x + \frac{1}{12} x^3 \sin x$$

Hence the general solution is

$$y = (c_1 x + c_2) \cos x + (c_3 x + c_4) \sin x + \frac{x^3 \sin x}{12} - \frac{(x^4 - 9x^2)}{48} \cos x$$

Case VII : P.I. when $f(x) = x\,V$, V being any function of x.

To find $\dfrac{1}{f(D)}\,xV$ we have by successive differentiations

$$
\begin{aligned}
D\,(xV) &= x\,DV + V \\
D^2\,(xV) &= x\,D^2V + 2DV \\
D^3\,(xV) &= x\,D^3V + 3D^2V
\end{aligned}
$$

and so on, we may have

$$D^n\,(xV) = x\,D^n\,V + n\,D^{n-1}\,(V)$$

Or
$$D^n\,(xV) = x\,D^n\,V + \frac{d}{dD}\,(D^n)\,V \qquad\qquad \dots (A)$$

Since $\phi(D)$ is a polynomial in D, we may write in general from (A) using

$$\phi'(D) = \frac{d}{dD}\,\phi(D)$$

$$\phi(D)\,(xV) = x\,\phi(D)\,V + \phi'(D)\,V \qquad\qquad \dots (B)$$

Now, put $\phi(D)\,V = V_1$ so that $V = \dfrac{1}{\phi(D)}\,V_1$ in equation (B), we have

$$\phi(D)\left[x\,\frac{1}{\phi(D)}\,V_1\right] = x\,V_1 + \phi'(D)\,\frac{1}{\phi(D)}\,V_1$$

Operating on both sides by $\dfrac{1}{\phi(D)}$, we get

$$x\cdot\frac{1}{\phi(D)}\,V_1 = \frac{1}{\phi(D)}\,[xV_1] + \frac{1}{\phi(D)}\,\phi'(D)\,\frac{1}{\phi(D)}\,V_1$$

and if we adjust the terms on both sides, we get

$$\frac{1}{\phi(D)}\,[xV_1] = \left[x - \frac{1}{\phi(D)}\,\phi'(D)\right]\frac{1}{\phi(D)}\,V_1$$

But here V_1 is any function of x, hence we have the formula

$$\boxed{\;\frac{1}{\phi(D)}\,[xV] = \left[x - \frac{1}{\phi(D)}\,\phi'(D)\right]\frac{1}{\phi(D)}\,V\;}$$

Remark : 1. The rule xV is applied if

(i) power of x is one

(ii) $\dfrac{1}{\phi(D)}\,V$ is not a case of failure.

2. If power of x is one and $\dfrac{1}{\phi(D)}\,V$ is a case of failure then do not apply xV rule. In this case, apply rule given by case (VI).

e.g. $\qquad\qquad\qquad y_p = \dfrac{1}{D^2+1}\,x\sin x$

Here $\dfrac{1}{D^2+1}\,\sin x$ is a case of failure. Therefore use case (VI) method.

ILLUSTRATIONS

Ex. 1 : *Solve* $\dfrac{d^2y}{dx^2} + 4y = x \sin x.$

Sol. :   A.E. : $D^2 + 4 = 0 \Rightarrow D = \pm 2i$

$\therefore$ C.F. $= c_1 \cos 2x + c_2 \sin 2x,$

and   P.I. $= \dfrac{1}{D^2 + 4} (x \sin x)$

$$= \left[x - \dfrac{2D}{D^2 + 4} \right] \dfrac{1}{D^2 + 4} (\sin x) \qquad \text{[by case (VII)]}$$

$$= \left[x - \dfrac{2D}{D^2 + 4} \right] \dfrac{1}{-1 + 4} (\sin x)$$

$$= \dfrac{1}{3} \left[x - \dfrac{2D}{D^2 + 4} \right] \sin x = \dfrac{1}{3} \left[x \sin x - \dfrac{2D}{D^2 + 4} \sin x \right]$$

$$= \dfrac{1}{3} \left[x \sin x - \dfrac{2D (\sin x)}{-1 + 4} \right] = \dfrac{1}{3} \left[x \sin x - \dfrac{2}{3} (\cos x) \right]$$

$$= \dfrac{1}{3} x \sin x - \dfrac{2}{9} \cos x.$$

Hence the complete solution is

$$y = c_1 \cos 2x + c_2 \sin 2x + \dfrac{x \sin x}{3} - \dfrac{2}{9} \cos x$$

Ex. 2 : *Solve* $(D^2 - 2D + 1) y = x \, e^x \sin x$ **(May 2005)**

Sol. :   A.E. : $D^2 - 2D + 1 = 0$

$$\Rightarrow (D - 1)^2 = 0, \ D = 1, 1.$$

Hence   C.F. $= (c_1 x + c_2) e^x$

$$\text{P.I.} = \dfrac{1}{(D - 1)^2} [x \, e^x \sin x]$$

$$= e^x \dfrac{1}{(D + 1 - 1)^2} (x \sin x) \qquad \text{(by case V)}$$

$$= e^x \dfrac{1}{D^2} (x \sin x)$$

$$= e^x \left[x - \dfrac{2D}{D^2} \right] \dfrac{1}{D^2} (\sin x) \qquad \text{(by case VII)}$$

$$= e^x \left[x - \dfrac{2}{D} \right] (-\sin x) = - e^x \left[x \sin x - \dfrac{2}{D} \sin x \right]$$

$$= - e^x [x \sin x + 2 \cos x]$$

Hence the complete solution is

$$y = (c_1 x + c_2) e^x - e^x [x \sin x + 2 \cos x]$$

Now, we will summarise the short-cut methods of P.I. and the corresponding formulae :

Case I : $\dfrac{1}{\phi(D)}\, e^{ax} = \dfrac{e^{ax}}{\phi(a)}, \quad \phi(a) \neq 0$

Case of failure : If $\phi(a) = 0$, $\dfrac{1}{\phi(D)}\, e^{ax} = x \cdot \dfrac{1}{\phi'(a)}\, e^{ax}, \phi'(a) \neq 0$

$$\dfrac{1}{(D-a)^r}\, e^{ax} = \dfrac{x^r}{r!}\, e^{ax}; \quad \dfrac{1}{\phi(D)}\,(k) = k \cdot \dfrac{1}{\phi(0)}, \quad \phi(0) \neq 0$$

$$\dfrac{1}{\phi(D)}\, a^x = \dfrac{a^x}{\phi(\log a)}$$

Case II : $\dfrac{1}{\phi(D^2)}\, \sin(ax+b) = \dfrac{1}{\phi(-a^2)}\, \sin(ax+b), \; \phi(-a^2) \neq 0$

$$\dfrac{1}{\phi(D^2)}\, \cos(ax+b) = \dfrac{1}{\phi(-a^2)}\, \cos(ax+b), \; \phi(-a^2) \neq 0$$

Case of failure : If $\phi(a^2) = 0$, $\dfrac{1}{\phi(D^2)}\, \sin(ax+b) = x \cdot \dfrac{1}{\phi'(-a)^2}\, \sin(ax+b), \phi'(-a)^2 \neq 0$

If $\phi(a^2) = 0$, $\dfrac{1}{\phi(D^2)}\, \cos(ax+b) = x \cdot \dfrac{1}{\phi'(-a^2)}\, \cos(ax+b), \; \phi'(-a^2) \neq 0$

Case of failure formulae :

$$\dfrac{1}{D^2+a^2}\, \sin ax = -\dfrac{x}{2a}\, \cos ax; \quad \dfrac{1}{D^2+a^2}\, \cos ax = \dfrac{x}{2a}\, \sin ax$$

$$\dfrac{1}{(D^2+a^2)^r}\, \sin(ax+b) = \left(-\dfrac{x}{2a}\right)^r \dfrac{1}{r!}\, \sin\left(ax+b+r\dfrac{\pi}{2}\right) \text{ and}$$

$$\dfrac{1}{(D^2+a^2)^r}\, \cos(ax+b) = \left(-\dfrac{x}{2a}\right)^r \dfrac{1}{r!}\, \cos\left(ax+b+r\dfrac{\pi}{2}\right)$$

Case III : $\dfrac{1}{\phi(D^2)}\, \sinh ax = \dfrac{1}{\phi(a^2)}\, \sinh ax, \; \phi(a^2) \neq 0$ and

$$\dfrac{1}{\phi(D^2)}\, \cosh ax = \dfrac{1}{\phi(a^2)}\, \cosh ax, \; \phi(a^2) \neq 0$$

Case IV : $\dfrac{1}{\phi(D)}\, x^m = [\phi(D)]^{-1}\, x^m$, expand by using Binomial theorem.

Case V : $\dfrac{1}{\phi(D)}\, e^{ax} V = e^{ax}\, \boxed{\dfrac{1}{\phi(D+a)}}\, V$

Case VI : $\dfrac{1}{\phi(D)}\, x^m \sin ax = \text{I.P. of } \dfrac{1}{\phi(D)}\, x^m\, e^{iax} = \text{I.P. of } e^{iax}\, \dfrac{1}{\phi(D+ia)}\, x^m$

$$\dfrac{1}{\phi(D)}\, x^m \cos ax = \text{R.P. of } \dfrac{1}{\phi(D)}\, x^m\, e^{iax} = \text{R.P. of } e^{iax}\, \dfrac{1}{\phi(D+ia)}\, x^m$$

Case VII : $\dfrac{1}{\phi(D)}\, xV = \left[x - \dfrac{\phi'(D)}{\phi(D)}\right] \dfrac{1}{\phi(D)}\, V$

ILLUSTRATIONS ON SHORT-CUT METHODS

Ex. 1 : *Solve $(D^2 + 2D + 1) y = 2 \cos x + 3x + 2 + 3e^x$.*

Sol. : Here AE is $(D + 1)^2 = 0 \Rightarrow D = -1, -1$

$\therefore \quad$ C.F. $= (c_1 x + c_2) e^{-x}$

and $\quad$ P.I. $= 2 \dfrac{1}{D^2 + 2D + 1} \cos x + \dfrac{1}{[1 + (2D + D^2)]} (3x + 2) + 3 \dfrac{1}{(D + 1)^2} e^x$

$$= \dfrac{1}{-1 + 2D + 1} 2 \cos x + [1 + (2D + D^2)]^{-1} (3x + 2) + \dfrac{3e^x}{4}$$

$$= \int \cos x \, dx + [1 - 2D - D^2 + \ldots] (3x + 2) + \dfrac{3}{4} e^x$$

$$= \sin x + 3x + 2 - 6 + \dfrac{3e^x}{4}$$

$$= \dfrac{3e^x}{4} + \sin x + 3x - 4$$

Hence the complete solution is

$$y = (c_1 x + c_2) e^{-x} + \dfrac{3e^x}{4} + \sin x + 3x - 4$$

Ex. 2 : *Solve $\dfrac{d^2 y}{dx^2} + a^2 y = \dfrac{a^2 R}{p} (l - x)$ where a, R, p and l are constants, subject to the conditions $y = 0$, $\dfrac{dy}{dx} = 0$ at $x = 0$.* **(May 2007)**

Sol. : Given equation is

$$(D^2 + a^2) y = \dfrac{a^2 R}{p} (l - x)$$

$$\text{A.E.} = D^2 + a^2 = 0 \quad \text{or} \quad D = \pm ia$$

$$\text{C.F.} = c_1 \cos ax + c_2 \sin ax$$

$$\text{P.I.} = \dfrac{1}{D^2 + a^2} \dfrac{a^2 R}{p} (l - x) = \dfrac{a^2 R}{p} \cdot \dfrac{1}{a^2} \dfrac{1}{\left(1 + \dfrac{D^2}{a^2}\right)} (l - x)$$

$$= \dfrac{R}{p} \left(1 + \dfrac{D^2}{a^2}\right)^{-1} (l - x) = \dfrac{R}{p} \left[1 - \dfrac{D^2}{a^2}\right] (l - x) = \dfrac{R}{p} (l - x)$$

Hence the general solution is

$$y = c_1 \cos ax + c_2 \sin ax + \dfrac{R}{p} (l - x) \qquad \ldots (1)$$

For initial conditions, now put $y = 0$ when $x = 0$ in (1), we get

$$0 = c_1 + \dfrac{R}{p} l \Rightarrow c_1 = \dfrac{-Rl}{p}$$

If we differentiate equation (1),

$$\frac{dy}{dx} = -ac_1 \sin ax + ac_2 \cos ax - \frac{R}{p}$$

Putting $x = 0$　and　$\frac{dy}{dx} = 0$ in this, we get

$$0 = ac_2 - \frac{R}{p}, \quad \text{hence } c_2 = \frac{R}{ap}$$

Now put values of c_1 and c_2 in A, then the required particular solution is

$$y = \frac{R}{p}\left[\frac{\sin ax}{a} - l \cos ax + l - x\right]$$

Ex. 3 : *Solve $(D^3 - 1)\, y = (1 + e^x)^2$.*

Sol. : A.E. : $D^3 - 1 = 0$ or $(D - 1)(D^2 + D + 1) = 0$ $\therefore D = 1, -\frac{1}{2} \pm i\frac{\sqrt{3}}{2}$

$$y_c = c_1 e^x + e^{(-1/2)x}\,[c_2 \cos (\sqrt{3}/2)\,x + c_3 \sin (\sqrt{3}/2)\,x]$$

$$y_p = \frac{1}{D^3 - 1}(1 + e^x)^2 = \frac{1}{D^3 - 1}(1 + 2e^x + e^{2x})$$

$$= \frac{1}{D^3 - 1}e^{0x} + 2\frac{1}{D^3 - 1}e^x + \frac{1}{D^3 - 1}e^{2x}$$

$$= -1 + \frac{2}{3}xe^x + \frac{1}{7}e^{2x}$$

$\therefore \qquad y = c_1 e^x + e^{(-1/2)x}\,[c_2 \cos (\sqrt{3}/2)\,x + c_3 \sin (\sqrt{3}/2)\,x] - 1 + \frac{2}{3}xe^x + \frac{1}{7}e^{2x}$

Ex. 4 : *Solve $(D - 1)^2 (D^2 + 1)^2\, y = \sin^2 \frac{x}{2}$.*

Sol. : A.E. : $(D - 1)^2 (D^2 + 1)^2 = 0$, $D = 1, 1, \pm i, \pm i$.

$$y_c = (c_1 x + c_2)\,e^x + (c_3 x + c_4)\cos x + (c_5 x + c_6)\sin x.$$

$$y_p = \frac{1}{(D - 1)^2 (D^2 + 1)^2}\sin^2 \frac{x}{2} = \frac{1}{(D - 1)^2 (D^2 + 1)^2}\left(\frac{1 - \cos x}{2}\right)$$

$$= \frac{1}{2}\left[\frac{1}{(D - 1)^2 (D^2 + 1)^2}e^{0x} - \frac{1}{(D - 1)^2 (D^2 + 1)^2}\cos x\right]$$

$$= \frac{1}{2}\left[1 - \frac{1}{(D^2 + 1)^2 (-1 - 2D + 1)}\cos x\right]$$

$$= \frac{1}{2}\left[1 + \frac{1}{2}\frac{1}{(D^2 + 1)^2}\sin x\right]$$

$$= \frac{1}{2}\left[1 + \frac{1}{2}x^2 \frac{1}{-8}\sin x\right]$$

$$\left\{\frac{d^2}{dD^2}(D^2+1)^2 = \frac{d}{dD}2(D^2+1)2D = 4(3D^2+1),\text{ then put }D^2 = -1\right\}$$

$$= \frac{1}{2} - \frac{1}{32}x^2 \sin x$$

$$y = (c_1 x + c_2)e^x + (c_3 x + c_4)\cos x + (c_5 x + c_6)\sin x + \frac{1}{2} - \frac{1}{32}x^2 \sin x$$

Ex. 5 : *Solve $(D^4 - 2D^3 - 3D^2 + 4D + 4)\, y = x^2 e^x$.*

Sol. :　　A.E. :　$(D-2)^2(D+1)^2 = 0$

$$y_c = (c_1 x + c_2)e^{2x} + (c_3 x + c_4)e^{-x}$$

$$y_p = \frac{1}{(D^2 - D - 2)^2}e^x \cdot x^2 = e^x \frac{1}{[(D+1)^2 - (D+1) - 2]^2}x^2$$

$$= e^x \frac{1}{(D^2 + D - 2)^2}x^2 = \frac{e^x}{4}\frac{1}{\left[1 - \left(\dfrac{D^2 + D}{2}\right)\right]^2}x^2$$

$$= \frac{e^x}{4}\left[1 + (D^2 + D) + \frac{3}{4}(D^2 + D)^2 + \dots\right]x^2$$

$$= \frac{e^x}{4}\left[1 + D + \frac{7}{4}D^2 + \dots\right]x^2 = \frac{e^x}{4}\left[x^2 + 2x + \frac{7}{2}\right]$$

$\therefore$　　$$y = (c_1 x + c_2)e^{2x} + (c_3 x + c_4)e^{-x} + \frac{e^x}{4}\left(x^2 + 2x + \frac{7}{2}\right).$$

Ex. 6 : *Solve $(D^4 - 1)\, y = \cos x \cosh x$*　　　　　　　**(Dec. 2008, May 2009)**

Sol. :　　A.E. :　$(D-1)(D+1)(D+i)(D-i) = 0$

$$y_c = c_1 e^x + c_2 e^{-x} + c_3 \cos x + c_4 \sin x.$$

$$y_p = \frac{1}{D^4 - 1}\cos x\left(\frac{e^x + e^{-x}}{2}\right)$$

$$= \frac{1}{2}\frac{1}{D^4 - 1}e^x \cos x + \frac{1}{2}\cdot\frac{1}{D^4 - 1}e^{-x}\cos x$$

$$= \frac{e^x}{2}\frac{1}{(D+1)^4 - 1}\cos x + \frac{e^{-x}}{2}\frac{1}{(D-1)^4 - 1}\cos x$$

$$= \frac{e^x}{2}\cdot\frac{1}{D^4 + 4D^3 + 6D^2 + 4D + 1 - 1}\cos x +$$

$$\frac{e^{-x}}{2}\frac{1}{D^4 - 4D^3 + 6D^2 - 4D + 1 - 1}\cos x$$

$$= \frac{e^x}{2} \frac{1}{1 - 4D - 6 + 4D} \cos x + \frac{e^{-x}}{2} \frac{1}{1 + 4D - 6 - 4D}$$

$$= \frac{e^x}{2} \cdot \frac{\cos x}{-5} + \frac{e^{-x}}{2} \frac{\cos x}{-5} = \frac{\cos x}{-5} \cosh x$$

$$\therefore \quad y = c_1 e^x + c_2 e^{-x} + c_3 \cos x + c_4 \sin x - \frac{\cos x \cosh x}{5}$$

Ex. 7 : *Solve $(D^4 + 1) y = 2 \sinh x \sin x$.*

Sol. : A.E. : $D^4 + 1 = 0 \qquad \therefore \quad D^4 + 2D^2 + 1 - 2D^2 = 0$

or $(D^2 + 1)^2 - (\sqrt{2} D)^2 = 0 \qquad$ or $\quad (D^2 - \sqrt{2} D + 1)(D^2 + \sqrt{2} D + 1) = 0$

$$\therefore \quad D = \frac{1}{\sqrt{2}} \pm \frac{1}{\sqrt{2}} i, \qquad\qquad D = \frac{-1}{\sqrt{2}} \pm \frac{1}{\sqrt{2}} i$$

$$y_c = e^{x/\sqrt{2}} \left[c_1 \cos \frac{x}{\sqrt{2}} + c_2 \sin \frac{x}{\sqrt{2}} \right] + e^{-x/\sqrt{2}} \left[c_3 \cos \frac{x}{\sqrt{2}} + c_4 \sin \frac{x}{\sqrt{2}} \right]$$

$$y_p = \frac{1}{D^4 + 1} \, 2 \sinh x \sin x$$

$$= \frac{1}{D^4 + 1} \, (e^x - e^{-x}) \sin x$$

$$= \frac{1}{D^4 + 1} \, e^x \sin x - \frac{1}{D^4 + 1} \, e^{-x} \sin x$$

$$= e^x \frac{1}{(D + 1)^4 + 1} \sin x - e^{-x} \frac{1}{(D - 1)^4 + 1} \sin x$$

$$= e^x \cdot \frac{1}{D^4 + 4D^3 + 6D^2 + 4D + 2} \sin x - e^{-x} \frac{1}{D^4 - 4D^3 + 6D^2 - 4D + 2} \sin x$$

$$= e^x \frac{1}{(-1)^2 + 4D(-1) + 6(-1) + 4D + 2} \sin x$$

$$- e^{-x} \frac{1}{(-1)^2 - 4D(-1) + 6(-1) - 4D + 2} \sin x$$

$$= e^x \left(\frac{\sin x}{-3} \right) - e^{-x} \left(\frac{\sin x}{-3} \right)$$

$$= \frac{-2}{3} \sin x \cdot \left(\frac{e^x - e^{-x}}{2} \right) = -\frac{2}{3} \sin x \sinh x$$

$$\therefore \quad y = \text{C.F.} + \text{P.I.}$$

$$y = e^{x/\sqrt{2}} \left[c_1 \cos \frac{x}{\sqrt{2}} + c_2 \sin \frac{x}{\sqrt{2}} \right] + e^{-x/\sqrt{2}} \left[c_3 \cos \frac{x}{\sqrt{2}} + c_4 \sin \frac{x}{\sqrt{2}} \right] - \frac{2}{3} \sin x \sinh x$$

Ex. 8 : *Solve* $\dfrac{d^3y}{dx^3} - 7\dfrac{dy}{dx} - 6y = e^{2x}(1+x)$.   **(Nov. 13, Nov. 16)**

Sol. : Given D.E. is written as

$$(D^3 - 7D - 6)\,y = e^{2x}(1+x) \quad \text{where } D \equiv \frac{d}{dx}$$

A.E. : $D^3 - 7D - 6 = 0 \quad \therefore \quad (D+1)(D+2)(D-3) = 0$

$\therefore \qquad\qquad\quad$ C.F. $= c_1 e^{-x} + c_2 e^{-2x} + c_3 e^{3x}$

$$\text{P.I.} = \frac{1}{D^3 - 7D - 6}\, e^{2x}\,(1+x)$$

$$= e^{2x}\,\frac{1}{(D+2)^3 - 7(D+2) - 6}\,(1+x), \qquad \text{by } D \to D + 2$$

$$= e^{2x}\,\frac{1}{D^3 + 6D^2 + 5D - 12}\,(1+x)$$

$$= \frac{-e^{2x}}{12}\left[1 - \frac{D^3 + 6D^2 + 5D}{12}\right]^{-1}(1+x)$$

$$= \frac{-e^{2x}}{12}\left[1 + \frac{5D}{12} + \dots\right](1+x)$$

$$= \frac{-e^{2x}}{12}\left(1 + x + \frac{5}{12}\right) = \frac{-e^{2x}}{12}\left(x + \frac{17}{12}\right)$$

$\therefore \qquad\qquad$ $y = $ C.F. $+$ P.I. $= c_1 e^{-x} + c_2 e^{-2x} + c_3 e^{3x} - \dfrac{e^{2x}}{12}\left(x + \dfrac{17}{12}\right)$

Ex. 9 : *Solve $(D^2 - 1)\,y = x \sin x + (1 + x^2)\,e^x$.*   **(Dec. 2009)**

Sol. : $\qquad\qquad$ A.E. : $D^2 - 1 = 0$

$(D-1)(D+1) = 0 \qquad \therefore \quad$ C.F. $= c_1 e^x + c_2 e^{-x}$

$$\text{P.I.} = \frac{1}{D^2 - 1}\, x \sin x + \frac{1}{D^2 - 1}\, e^x (1 + x^2)$$

$$= x\,\frac{1}{D^2 - 1}\, \sin x - \frac{2D}{(D^2 - 1)^2}\, \sin x + e^x\,\frac{1}{(D+1)^2 - 1}\,(1 + x^2)$$

$$= \frac{x \sin x}{-2} - \frac{2D}{4}\, \sin x + e^x\,\frac{1}{D^2 + 2D}\,(1 + x^2)$$

$$= -\frac{x}{2}\sin x - \frac{\cos x}{2} + e^x\,\frac{1}{2D}\left(1 - \frac{D}{2} + \frac{D^2}{4} + \dots\right)(1 + x^2)$$

$$= -\frac{x}{2}\sin x - \frac{\cos x}{2} + \frac{e^x}{2}\,\frac{1}{D}\left(1 + x^2 - x + \frac{1}{2}\right)$$

$$= -\frac{x}{2}\sin x - \frac{\cos x}{2} + \frac{e^x}{2}\left(\frac{x^3}{3} - \frac{x^2}{2} + \frac{3x}{2}\right)$$

$$y = c_1 e^x + c_2 e^{-x} - \frac{1}{2}(x \sin x + \cos x) + \frac{e^x}{12}(2x^3 - 3x^2 + 9x)$$

Ex. 10 : $(D^2 - 4D + 4)\, y = e^x \cos^2 x.$ **(May 2013, Dec. 2014)**

Sol. : A.E. is $D^2 - 4D + 4 = 0$ $\therefore$ $D = 2, 2$

$$y_c = (c_1 x + c_2)\, e^{2x}$$

$$y_p = \frac{1}{(D - 2)^2}\, e^x \cos^2 x = e^x \frac{1}{(D - 1)^2} \cos^2 x$$

$$= e^x \frac{1}{(D - 1)^2} \left(\frac{1 + \cos 2x}{2}\right) = 0$$

$$= \frac{e^x}{2}\left[\frac{1}{(D - 1)^2}\, e^{0x} + \frac{1}{D^2 - 2D + 1}\cos 2x\right]$$

$$= \frac{e^x}{2}\left[1 - \frac{1}{(2D + 3)}\cos 2x\right] = \frac{e^x}{2}\left[1 - \frac{(2D - 3)}{4D^2 - 9}\cos 2x\right]$$

$$= \frac{e^x}{2}\left[1 + \frac{1}{25}(2D - 3)\cos 2x\right] = \frac{e^x}{2}\left[1 - \frac{1}{25}(4\sin 2x + 3\cos 2x)\right]$$

$$y = (c_1 x + c_2)\, e^{2x} + \frac{e^x}{2}\left[1 - \frac{1}{25}(4\sin 2x + 3\cos 2x)\right]$$

Ex. 11 : *Solve* $(D^2 + 1)\, y = x^2 \sin 2x.$ **(Dec. 2005)**

Sol. : A.E. is $D^2 + 1 = 0$ $\therefore$ $D = \pm i.$

$$y_c = c_1 \cos x + c_2 \sin x$$

$$y_p = \frac{1}{D^2 + 1} x^2 \sin 2x = \text{I.P. of } \frac{1}{D^2 + 1} e^{i2x} x^2$$

$$= \text{I.P. of } e^{i2x} \frac{1}{(D + 2i)^2 + 1} x^2 = \text{I.P. of } e^{i2x} \frac{1}{D^2 + 4iD - 4 + 1} x^2$$

$$= \text{I.P. of } \frac{e^{i2x}}{(-3)} \frac{1}{\left[1 - \frac{1}{3}(4iD + D^2)\right]} x^2 = \text{I.P. of } \frac{e^{i2x}}{(-3)}\left[1 - \frac{1}{3}(4iD + D^2)\right]^{-1} x^2$$

$$= \text{I.P. of } \frac{e^{i2x}}{(-3)}\left[1 + \frac{1}{3}(4iD + D^2) + \frac{1}{9}(-16D^2 + 8iD^3 + D^4) + \ldots\right] x^2$$

$$= \text{I.P. of } \frac{e^{i2x}}{(-3)}\left[1 + \frac{4}{3}iD - \frac{13}{9}D^2 + \ldots\right] x^2$$

$$= \text{I.P. of } \frac{(\cos 2x + i\sin 2x)}{(-3)}\left[\left(x^2 - \frac{26}{9}\right) + i\frac{8}{3}x\right]$$

$$= -\frac{1}{3}\left(x^2 - \frac{26}{9}\right)\sin 2x - \frac{8}{9}x \cos 2x$$

$$\therefore \quad y = c_1 \cos x + c_2 \sin x - \frac{1}{3}\left(x^2 - \frac{26}{9}\right)\sin 2x - \frac{8}{9}x \cos 2x$$

Ex. 12 : $(D^2 + D + 1)\, y \ = x\, \sin x.$	**(May 2014)**

Sol. : A.E. is $D^2 + D + 1 = 0$ $\therefore$ $D = -\dfrac{1}{2} \pm i\,\dfrac{\sqrt{3}}{2}$.

$$y_c \ = \ e^{(-1/2)\,x}\,[c_1 \cos (\sqrt{3}/2)\,x + c_2 \sin (\sqrt{3}/2)\,x]$$

$$y_p \ = \ \frac{1}{D^2 + D + 1}\,x\,\sin x = \left[x - \frac{2D + 1}{D^2 + D + 1}\right]\frac{1}{D^2 + D + 1}\,\sin x$$

$$= \left[x - \frac{2D + 1}{D^2 + D + 1}\right]\frac{1}{D}\,\sin x = \left[x - \frac{2D + 1}{D^2 + D + 1}\right](-\cos x)$$

$$= \ -x \cos x + (2D + 1)\frac{1}{D}\cos x$$

$$= \ -x \cos x + (2D + 1)\sin x$$

$$= \ -x \cos x + 2 \cos x + \sin x$$

$\therefore$ $\quad y \ = \ e^{(-1/2)\,x}\,[c_1 \cos (\sqrt{3}/2)\,x + c_2 \sin (\sqrt{3}/2)\,x] - x \cos x + 2 \cos x + \sin x$

Ex. 13 : $(D^2 + 2D + 1)\, y \ = \ x\, e^{-x} \cos x.$

Sol. : A.E. is $D^2 + 2D + 1 = 0$ $\quad \therefore$ $D = -1, 1.$

$$y_c \ = \ (c_1 x + c_2)\, e^{-x}$$

$$y_p \ = \ \frac{1}{(D + 1)^2}\,e^{-x}\,x \cos x \ = e^{-x}\,\frac{1}{D^2}\,x \cos x$$

$$= \ e^{-x}\left[x - \frac{2D}{D^2}\right]\frac{1}{D^2}\cos x \ = \ e^{-x}\left[x - \frac{2}{D}\right](-\cos x)$$

$$= \ e^{-x}\,(-x \cos x + 2 \sin x)$$

$$y \ = \ (c_1 x + c_2)\, e^{-x} + e^{-x}\,(-x \cos x + 2 \sin x)$$

Ex. 14 : *Solve* $(D^2 + 4)\, y \ = x \sin 2x.$	**(Dec. 2008, May 2015)**

Sol. : $\quad$ A.E. : $\ D^2 + 4 = 0$ $\quad \therefore$ $D = \pm\, 2i$

$$y_c \ = \ c_1 \cos 2x + c_2 \sin 2x$$

$$y_p \ = \ \frac{1}{D^2 + 4}\,x \cdot \left(\frac{1 - \cos 2x}{2}\right) = \frac{1}{2} \cdot \frac{1}{D^2 + 4}\,x - \frac{1}{2}\,\frac{1}{D^2 + 4}\,x \cos 2x.$$

$$= \ y_{p_1} + y_{p_2}$$

$$y_{p_1} \ = \ \frac{1}{2} \cdot \frac{1}{D^2 + 4}\,x = \frac{1}{8}\,\frac{1}{1 + \dfrac{D^2}{4}}\,x = \frac{1}{8}\left(1 - \frac{D^2}{4} + \ldots\ldots\right) x = \frac{x}{8}$$

$$y_{p_2} \ = \ -\frac{1}{2} \cdot \frac{1}{D^2 + 4}\,x \cos 2x.$$

Here we can not apply "xV" rule (case VII) because $\dfrac{1}{D^2 + 4}\,\cos 2x$ is a case of failure.

$$\therefore \qquad \frac{1}{D^2+4} \, x \, e^{i2x} = e^{i2x} \, \frac{1}{(D+2i)^2 + 4} \, x$$

$$= e^{i2x} \, \frac{1}{D^2+4\,i\,D} \, x = \frac{e^{i2x}}{4\,i\,D} \left(\frac{1}{1-\dfrac{Di}{4}} \right) x$$

$$= -\frac{e^{i2x}\,i}{4D} \left(1 + \frac{iD}{4} \right) x = \frac{-\,e^{i2x}\,i}{4D} \left(x + \frac{i}{4} \right)$$

$$= -\frac{e^{i2x}\,i}{4} \left(\frac{x^2}{2} + \frac{ix}{4} \right)$$

$$= -\frac{1}{16} \, (\cos 2x + i \sin 2x)(-x + i\,2x^2)$$

Taking real parts on both sides,

$$\frac{1}{D^2+4} \, x \cos 2x = -\frac{1}{16} \, (-x \cos 2x - 2x^2 \sin 2x)$$

$$\therefore \qquad y_{p_2} = -\frac{1}{2} \left[\frac{1}{16} (x \cos 2x + 2x^2 \sin 2x) \right]$$

$$y_p = \frac{x}{8} - \frac{1}{32} \, (x \cos 2x + 2x^2 \sin 2x)$$

$$y = c_1 \cos 2x + c_2 \sin 2x + \frac{x}{8} - \frac{1}{32} \, (x \cos 2x + 2x^2 \sin 2x)$$

EXERCISE 1.2

Solve the following differential equations :

(A) On General Method :

1. $(D^2 + 5D + 6)\, y = e^{e^x}$.   **Ans.** $y = c_1 e^{-2x} + c_2 e^{-3x} + (e^{-2x} - 2e^{-3x})\, e^{e^x}$.

2. $\dfrac{d^2y}{dx^2} + a^2 y = \tan ax$ **Ans.** $y = c_1 \cos ax + c_2 \sin ax - \dfrac{1}{a^2} \cos ax \log [\sec ax + \tan ax]$

3. $(D^2 - 3D + 2)\, y = \dfrac{1}{e^{e^{-x}}} + \cos \left(\dfrac{1}{e^x} \right)$ **Ans.** $y = c_1 e^{2x} + c_2 e^x + e^{2x} \left[e^{-e^{-x}} - \cos (e^{-x}) \right]$

(Dec. 2006, 2008)

4. $(D^2 - 9D + 18)\, y = e^{e^{-3x}}$ **Ans.** $y = c_1 e^{6x} + c_2 e^{3x} + \dfrac{e^{6x}}{9} \, e^{e^{-3x}}$

5. $(D^2 - 2D - 3)\, y = 3e^{-3x} \sin (e^{-3x}) + \cos (e^{-3x})$ **Ans.** $y = c_1 e^{3x} + c_2 e^{-x} - \dfrac{e^{3x}}{3} \, \sin e^{-3x}$

(B) On Short Methods :

1. $\dfrac{d^2y}{dx^2} - 7\dfrac{dy}{dx} + 6y = e^{2x}$ **Ans.** $y = c_1 e^{6x} + c_2 e^x - \dfrac{e^{2x}}{4}$

2. $\dfrac{d^2y}{dx^2} - 4y = (1 + e^x)^2 + 3$ **Ans.** $y = c_1 e^{2x} + c_2 e^{-2x} - 1 - \dfrac{2}{3} \, e^x + \dfrac{xe^{2x}}{4}$

3. $(D^3 - 5D^2 + 8D - 4)\, y = e^{2x} + 2e^x + 3e^{-x} + 2$

$$\textbf{Ans. } y = c_1 e^x + (c_2 + c_3 x)\, e^{2x} + \frac{e^{2x}\, x^2}{2} + 2x e^x - \frac{e^{-x}}{6} - \frac{1}{2}$$

4. $(D^4 - 4D^3 + 6D^2 - 4D + 1)\, y = e^x + 2^x + \frac{1}{3}.$

$$\textbf{Ans. } y = (c_1 x^3 + c_2 x^2 + c_3 x + c_4)\, e^x + \frac{x^4}{24}\, e^x + \frac{1}{(\log 2 - 1)^4}\, 2^x + \frac{1}{3}$$

5. $\dfrac{d^2 y}{dx^2} + 4y = \cos x \cdot \cos 2x \cdot \cos 3x$

$$\textbf{Ans. } y = A \cos 2x + B \sin 2x + \frac{1}{16} + \frac{x \sin 2x}{16} - \frac{1}{48} \cos 4x - \frac{1}{128} \cos 6x$$

6. $(D^5 - D^4 + 2D^3 - 2D^2 + D - 1)\, y = \cos x$

$$\textbf{Ans. } y = c_1 e^x + (c_2 x + c_3) \cos x + (c_4 x + c_5) \sin x + \frac{1}{16}\, [(x^2 + 2x) \cos x - x^2 \sin x]$$

7. $(D^4 - m^4)\, y = \sin mx$

$$\textbf{Ans. } y = c_1 e^{mx} + c_2 e^{-mx} + c_3 \cos mx + c_4 \sin mx + \frac{x}{4m^3} \cos mx$$

8. $(D^3 + D)\, y = \cos x$ **(Dec. 08, May 2016) Ans.** $c_1 + c_2 \cos x + c_3 \sin x - \dfrac{x \cos x}{2}$

9. $\operatorname{cosec} x \, \dfrac{d^4 y}{dx^4} + y \operatorname{cosec} x = \sin 2x$

$$\textbf{Ans. } y = e^{\frac{x}{\sqrt{2}}} \left[c_1 \cos \frac{x}{\sqrt{2}} + c_2 \sin \frac{x}{\sqrt{2}} \right] + e^{-\frac{x}{\sqrt{2}}} \left[c_3 \cos \frac{x}{\sqrt{2}} + c_4 \sin \frac{x}{\sqrt{2}} \right] + \frac{1}{2} \left(\frac{\cos x}{2} - \frac{\cos 3x}{82} \right)$$

10. $\dfrac{d^2 x}{dt^2} + 9x = 4 \cos \left(\dfrac{\pi}{3} + t \right)$, given that $x = 0$ at $t = 0$ and $x = 2$ at $t = \dfrac{\pi}{6}$.

$$\textbf{Ans. } x = \frac{1}{4} \cos 3t + 2 \sin 3t + \frac{1}{2} \cos \left(\frac{\pi}{3} + t \right)$$

11. $\dfrac{d^2 y}{dt^2} + 2 \dfrac{dy}{dt} + 5y = \sin^2 t$

$$\textbf{Ans. } y = e^{-t} [A \cos 2t + b \sin 2t] + \frac{1}{10} - \frac{1}{34}\, [4 \sin 2t + \cos 2t]$$

12. $\dfrac{d^2 y}{dx^2} + 2 \dfrac{dy}{dx} + 2y = \sin 2x - 2 \cos 2x$, given that $y = 0$ and $\dfrac{dy}{dx} = 0$ when $x = 0$.

$$\textbf{Ans. } y = e^{-x} \sin x - \frac{1}{2}\, \sin 2x$$

13. $\dfrac{d^2 y}{dx^2} + n^2 y = h \sin px$, where h, p and n are constants satisfying the condition $y = 0$,

$\dfrac{dy}{dx} = b$ for $x = 0$. $\textbf{Ans. } y = a \cos nx + \left[\dfrac{b}{n} - \dfrac{ph}{n\,(n^2 - p^2)} \right] \sin nx + \dfrac{h \sin px}{(n^2 - p^2)}$

14. $(D^3 + 1) y = \cos (2x - 1) - \cos^2 \dfrac{x}{2}$

Ans. $y = c_1 e^{-x} + e^{x/2} \left[c_2 \cos \dfrac{\sqrt{3}}{2} x + c_3 \sin \dfrac{\sqrt{3}}{2} x \right]$

$+ \dfrac{1}{65} [\cos (2x - 1) - 8 \sin (2x - 1)] - \dfrac{1}{2} - \dfrac{1}{4} (\cos x - \sin x)$

15. $\dfrac{d^2 y}{dx^2} - 2 \dfrac{dy}{dx} + 5y = 10 \sin x.$ **(Dec. 2011)**

Ans. $y = e^x (A \cos x + B \sin x) + 2 \sin x + \cos x$

16. $(D^4 + 10D^2 + 9) y = 96 \sin 2x \cos x$

Given that at $x = 0$, $y = 0$, $y' = -2$, $y'' = -8$, $y''' = -18$.

Ans. $y = \cos 3x - \cos x + x (\cos 3x - 3 \cos x)$

17. $(D^4 + 6D^2 + 8) y = \sin^2 x \cos 2x$

Ans. $y = c_1 \cos 2x + c_2 \sin 2x + c_3 \cos \sqrt{2}\ x + c_4 \sin \sqrt{2}\ x - \dfrac{x \sin 2x}{16} - \dfrac{1}{32} - \dfrac{\cos 4x}{672}$

18. $(D^3 + 3D) y = \cosh 2x \sinh 3x.$

Ans. $y = c_1 + \left(c_2 \cos \sqrt{3}\ x + c_3 \sin \sqrt{3}\ x \right) + \dfrac{\cosh 5x}{280} + \dfrac{\cosh x}{8}$

19. $(D^3 - 25D) y = \cosh 2x \sinh 3x.$

Ans. $y = c_1 + c_2 e^{5x} + c_3 e^{-5x} + \dfrac{x}{100} \sinh 5x - \dfrac{1}{48} \cosh x$

20. $(D^4 - 1) y = \cosh x \sinh x$ **Ans.** $y = c_1 e^x + c_2 e^{-x} + c_3 \cos x + c_4 \sin x + \dfrac{1}{30} \sinh 2x$

21. $(D^2 + 13D + 36) y = e^{-4x} + \sinh x.$ **(May 17)**

Ans. $y = c_1 e^{-9x} + c_2 e^{-4x} + \dfrac{x}{5} e^{-4x} - \dfrac{1}{1200} (13 \cosh x - 37 \sinh x)$

22. $(D^3 + 1) y = \sin (2x + 3) + e^{-x} + 2^x.$

Ans. $y = c_1 e^{-x} + e^{(1/2) x} [c_2 \cos (\sqrt{3}/2) x + c_3 \sin (\sqrt{3}/2) x]$

$+ \dfrac{1}{65} [\sin (2x + 3) + 8 \cos (2x + 3)] + \dfrac{x}{3} e^{-x} + \dfrac{2^x}{(\log 2)^3 + 1}$

23. $\dfrac{d^2 y}{dx^2} + 6 \dfrac{dy}{dx} + 10y = 50 x$ with $y = 0$, $\dfrac{dy}{dx} = 1$ at $x = 0$

Ans. $y = 5x - 3 + e^{-3x} (3 \cos x + 5 \sin x)$

24. $(D^2 - 2D + 5) y = 25x^2.$ **Ans.** $y = e^x [c_1 \cos 2x + c_2 \sin 2x] + 5x^2 + 4x - \dfrac{2}{5}$

25. $(D^4 + D^2 + 1) y = 53x^2 + 17$

Ans. $y = e^{-x/2} \left[c_1 \cos \dfrac{\sqrt{3}}{2} x + c_2 \sin \dfrac{\sqrt{3}}{2} x \right] + e^{x/2} \left[c_3 \cos \dfrac{\sqrt{3}}{2} x + c_4 \sin \dfrac{\sqrt{3}}{2} x \right] + 53x^2 - 89$

26. $(D^2 + 5D + 4) y = x^2 + 7x + 9.$ **Ans.** $y = c_1 e^{-4x} + c_2 e^{-x} + \dfrac{1}{4} \left(x^2 + \dfrac{9x}{2} + \dfrac{23}{8} \right)$

27. $(D^4 + 6D^2 + 25)\, y = x^4 + x^2 + 1.$ **(Dec. 2005)**

Ans. $y = e^x [c_1 \cos 2x + c_2 \sin 2x] + e^{-x} [c_3 \cos 2x + c_4 \sin 2x] + \dfrac{1}{25} \left[x^4 - \dfrac{47}{25} x^2 + \dfrac{589}{625} \right]$

28. $(D^2 - D + 1)\, y = x^3 - 3x^2 + 1$

$$\textbf{Ans. } y = e^{x/2} \left[c_1 \cos \frac{\sqrt{3}}{2} x + c_2 \sin \frac{\sqrt{3}}{2} x \right] + x^3 - 6x - 5$$

29. $(D^3 - 3D^2 + 3D - 1)\, y = 2x^3 - 3x^2 + 1.$

$$\textbf{Ans. } y = (c_1 x^2 + c_2 x + c_3)\, e^x - (2x^3 + 15x^2 + 54x + 85)$$

30. $(D^3 - 2D + 4)\, y = 3x^2 - 5x + 2.$

$$\textbf{Ans. } c_1 e^{-2x} + e^x (c_2 \cos x + c_3 \sin x) + \frac{1}{4} (3x^2 - 2x + 1)$$

31. $\dfrac{d^3 y}{dx^3} + 8y = x^4 + 2x + 1.$

$$\textbf{Ans. } y = c_1 e^{-2x} + e^x \left[A \cos \sqrt{3}\, x + B \sin \sqrt{3}\, x \right] + \frac{1}{8} (x^4 - x + 1)$$

32. $(D^2 - 3D + 2)\, y = x^2 + \sin x.$ **(Nov. 2013)**

$$\textbf{Ans. } y = c_1 e^x + c_2 e^{2x} + \frac{1}{2} \left(x^2 + 3x + \frac{7}{2} \right) + \frac{1}{10} \sin x + \frac{3}{10} \cos x$$

33. $(D^3 + 3D^2 - 4)\, y = 6e^{-2x} + 4x^2.$ **Ans.** $y = c_1 e^x + (c_2 x + c_3)\, e^{-2x} - x^2 e^{-2x} - x^2 - \dfrac{3}{2}$

34. $(D^3 + 6D^2 + 12D + 8)\, y = e^{-2x} + x^2 + 3^x + \cos 2x.$

$$\textbf{Ans. } y = (c_1 x + c_2 x + c_3)\, e^{-2x} + \frac{x^3}{6} e^{-2x} + \frac{1}{8} (x^2 - 3x + 3)$$

$$+ \frac{1}{(\log 3 + 2)^3} 3^x + \frac{1}{32} (\sin 2x - \cos 2x)$$

35. $(D^2 - 4D + 4)\, y = 8 (e^{2x} + \sin 2x + x^2).$

$$\textbf{Ans. } y = (c_1 x + c_2)\, e^{2x} + 4x^2 e^{2x} + \cos 2x + 2 \left(x^2 + 2x + \frac{3}{2} \right)$$

36. $(D^5 - D)\, y = 12\, e^x + 8 \sin x - 2x$

$$\textbf{Ans. } y = c_1 + c_2 e^{-x} + c_3 e^x + A \cos x + B \sin x + 3x\, e^x + 2x \sin x + x^2$$

37. $(D^2 - 1)\, y = e^x + x^3.$ **Ans.** $y = c_1 e^x + c_2 e^{-x} + \dfrac{1}{2} x e^x - x^3 - 6x$

38. $(D^2 - 4D + 4)\, y = e^{2x} + x^3 + \cos 2x$

$$\textbf{Ans. } y = (c_1 + c_2 x)\, e^{2x} + \frac{1}{2} x^2 e^{2x} - \frac{1}{8} \sin 2x + \frac{1}{8} [2x^3 + 6x^2 + 9x + 6]$$

39. $(D^5 - D)\, y = 12e^x + 85mx + 2^x$

$$\textbf{Ans. } y = c_1 + c_2 e^x + c_3 e^{-x} + c_4 \cos x + c_5 \sin x + 3x\, e^x - 35\, m\, \frac{x^2}{2} + \frac{2^x}{(\log 2)^5 - \log 2}$$

40. $(D^2 - 4)\, y = e^{3x}\, x^2.$ **Ans.** $y = c_1 e^{2x} + c_2 e^{-2x} + \dfrac{e^{3x}}{125} (125x^2 - 60x + 62)$

41. $\dfrac{d^3y}{dx^3} - 7\dfrac{dy}{dx} - 6y = e^{2x}(1 + x^2)$ **Ans.** $y = c_1 e^{-x} + c_2 e^{-2x} + c_3 e^{3x} - \dfrac{e^{2x}}{12}\left[\dfrac{169}{72} + x^2 + \dfrac{5x}{6}\right]$

$$\textbf{(Dec. 2005, 2008)}$$

42. $(D^3 - 3D^2 + 3D - 1)y = \sqrt{x}\, e^x.$ **Ans.** $y = (c_1 x^2 + c_2 x + c_3)\, e^x + \dfrac{8e^x\, x^{7/2}}{105}$

43. $(D^2 - 4D + 4)y = e^{2x}\sin 3x$ **Ans.** $y = (c_1 + c_2 x)\, e^{2x} - \dfrac{1}{9}\, e^{2x}\sin 3x$

44. $(D^3 - D^2 + 3D + 5)y = e^x \cos 3x$

$$\textbf{Ans. } y = c_1 e^{-x} + e^x(c_2 \cos 2x + c_3 \sin 2x) - \dfrac{e^x}{65}(3\sin 3x + 2\cos 3x)$$

45. $(D^2 + 2D + 1)y = \dfrac{e^{-x}}{x + 2}$

$$\textbf{Ans. } y = (c_1 + c_2 x)\, e^{-x} - e^{-x}[x \log(x + 2) + 2\log(x + 2) - x]$$

46. $(D^2 + 6D + 9)y = \dfrac{1}{x^3}\, e^{-3x}$ **Ans.** $y = (c_1 x + c_2)\, e^{-3x} + \dfrac{e^{-3x}}{2x}$

47. $(D^4 - 3D^3 - 2D^2 + 4D + 4)y = x^2 e^x.$ **(Dec. 2008)**

$$\textbf{Ans. } y = (c_1 x + c_2)\, e^{-x} + (c_3 x + c_4)\, e^{2x} + \dfrac{e^x}{4}\left(x^2 + 2x + \dfrac{7}{2}\right)$$

48. $(D^3 - 3D - 2)y = 540\, x^3 e^{-x}.$

$$\textbf{Ans. } y = (c_1 x + c_2)\, e^{-x} + c_3 e^{2x} - 180e^{-x}\left(\dfrac{x^5}{20} + \dfrac{x^4}{12} + \dfrac{x^3}{9} + \dfrac{x^2}{9}\right)$$

49. $\dfrac{d^2y}{dx^2} + 2\dfrac{dy}{dx} + 2y = e^{-x}\sec^3 x$ **Ans.** $y = e^{-x}\left[c_1 \cos x + c_2 \sin x + \dfrac{\sin x}{2}\tan x\right]$

$$\textbf{(Dec. 2005)}$$

50. $(D^2 + 2D + 1)\, y = e^{-x}\log x.$ **Ans.** $y = (c_1 x + c_2)\, e^{-x} + \dfrac{e^{-x} x^2}{4}(2\log x - 3x^2)$

$$\textbf{(May 2006)}$$

51. $(D^4 + D^2 + 1)\, y = e^{-x/2}\cos\left(\dfrac{\sqrt{3}}{2}x\right)$

$$\textbf{Ans. } y = e^{x/2}\left[c_1 \cos\dfrac{\sqrt{3}}{2}x + c_2 \sin\dfrac{\sqrt{3}}{2}x\right] + e^{-x/2}\left[c_3 \cos\dfrac{\sqrt{3}}{2}x + c_4 \sin\dfrac{\sqrt{3}}{2}x\right]$$

$$+ \dfrac{1}{4\sqrt{3}}\, x\, e^{-x/2}\left[\sin x\dfrac{\sqrt{3}}{2} + \sqrt{3}\cos x\dfrac{\sqrt{3}}{2}\right]$$

52. $(D^3 - D^2 - D + 1)\, y = \cosh x \sin x.$

$$\textbf{Ans. } y = (c_1 x + c_2)\, e^x + c_3 e^{-x} + \dfrac{e^x}{10}(\cos x - 2\sin x) - \dfrac{e^{-x}}{50}(3\cos x - 4\sin x)$$

53. $\dfrac{d^2y}{dx^2} - y = \cosh x \cos x$ **Ans.** $y = c_1 e^x + c_2 e^{-x} + \dfrac{1}{5}(2\sinh x \sin x - \cosh x \cos x)$

54. $(D^2 + 40D + 8)\, y = 12e^{-2x}\sin x \sin 3x.$

$$\textbf{Ans. } y = e^{-2x}(c_1 \cos 2x + c_2 \sin 2x) + \dfrac{3}{2}x\, e^{-2x}\sin 2x + \dfrac{1}{2}e^{-2x}\cos 4x$$

55. $(D^3 - 6D^2 + 11D - 6) y = e^x x + \sin x + \cos x.$

$$\textbf{Ans. } y = c_1 e^x + c_2 e^{2x} + c_3 e^{3x} + \frac{e^x}{2}\left(\frac{x^2}{3} + \frac{3}{2}x\right) - \frac{1}{10}\cos x + \frac{1}{10}\sin x$$

56. $\dfrac{d^2y}{dx^2} + 5\dfrac{dy}{dx} + 6y = e^{-2x}\sin 2x + 4x^2 e^x$ **(May 2011)**

$$\textbf{Ans. } y = c_1 e^{-2x} + c_2 e^{-3x} - \frac{e^{-2x}}{10}(\cos 2x + 2\sin 2x) + \frac{e^x}{3}\left(x^2 - \frac{7}{6}x + \frac{37}{72}\right)$$

57. $\dfrac{d^3y}{dx^3} - \dfrac{d^2y}{dx^2} = 3x + x\, e^x.$ $\textbf{Ans. } y = c_1 + c_2 x + c_3 e^x - 2x\, e^x + \dfrac{x^2 e^x}{2} - \dfrac{x^3}{2} - \dfrac{3x^2}{2}$

58. $\dfrac{d^2y}{dx^2} - 3\dfrac{dy}{dx} + 2y = x\, e^{3x} + \sin 2x.$

$$\textbf{Ans. } y = c_2 e^x + c_1 e^{2x} + e^{3x}\left(\frac{x}{2} - \frac{3}{4}\right) + \frac{1}{20}(3\cos 2x - \sin 2x)$$

59. $(D^2 - 6D + 13) y = 8\, e^{3x}\sin 4x + 2^x$ **(Dec. 2004, May 2015)**

$$\textbf{Ans. } y = e^{3x}(A\cos 2x + B\sin 2x) - \frac{2e^{3x}\sin 4x}{3} + \frac{2^x}{(\log 2)^2 - 6\log 2 + 13}$$

60. $(D^4 + D^2 + 1) y = ax^2 + be^{-x}\sin 2x.$

$\textbf{Ans. } y = e^{(-1/2)\,x}[c_1\cos(\sqrt3/2)\,x + c_2\sin(\sqrt3/2)\,x] + e^{(1/2)\,x}[c_3\cos(\sqrt3/2)\,x$

$$+\, c_4\sin(\sqrt{3/2}\,x] + a(x^2 - 2) - \frac{b}{481}e^{-x}(20\cos 2x + 9\sin 2x)$$

61. $(D^2 - 4) y = x\sinh x$ **(May 11) Ans.** $y = c_1 e^{2x} + c_2 e^{-2x} - \dfrac{1}{3}\left[x\sinh x + \dfrac{2}{3}\cosh x\right]$

62. $(D^2 - 2D + 1) y = x^2 e^x\sin x.$ **Ans.** $y = (c_1 x + c_2) e^x - e^x[4x\cos x + (x^2 - 6)\sin x]$

63. $\dfrac{d^2y}{dx^2} - 4\dfrac{dy}{dx} + 4y = 8x^2 \cdot e^{2x}\sin 2x.$

$$\textbf{Ans. } y = e^{2x}[c_1 + c_2 x + 3\sin 2x - 2x^2\sin 2x - 4x\cos 2x]$$

64. $(D^2 + 2D + 1) y = x\cos x$ $\textbf{Ans. } y = (c_1 x + c_2) e^{-x} + \dfrac{1}{2}(x\sin x + \cos x - \sin x)$

65. $\dfrac{d^2y}{dx^2} + 3\dfrac{dy}{dx} + 2y = x\sin 2x$

$$\textbf{Ans. } y = c_1 e^{-2x} + c_2 e^{-x} + \left(\frac{7 - 30x}{200}\right)\cos 2x + \left(\frac{12 - 5x}{100}\right)\sin 2x$$

66. $(D^4 + 2D^2 + 1) y = x\cos x.$ **(Dec. 2011)**

$$\textbf{Ans. } y = (c_1 x + c_2)\cos x + (c_3 x + c_4)\sin x - \frac{x^3}{24}\cos x + \frac{x^2}{2}\sin x$$

67. $(D^2 + 1)^2 y = 24x\cos x.$

$$\textbf{Ans. } y = (c_1 x + c_2)\cos x + (c_3 x + c_4)\sin x - x^3\cos x + 3x^2\sin x$$

68. $(D^2 + 2D + 5)^2 y = x\, e^{-x}\cos 2x.$

$$\textbf{Ans. } y = e^{-x}[(c_1 x + c_2)\cos 2x + (c_3 x + c_4)\sin 2x] - \frac{e^{-x}}{32}\left[(x^3 - x^2)\cos 2x - \frac{2}{3}x^3\sin 2x\right]$$

69. $(D^2 - 2D + 4)^2 y = xe^x \cos\left[\sqrt{3}\, x + \alpha\right]$　　　　　　**(Dec. 2006; May 2007, 2008)**

$$\textbf{Ans. } y = e^x\left[(c_1 + c_2 x)\cos\sqrt{3}\, x + (c_3 + c_4 x)\sin\sqrt{3}\, x\right]$$

$$-\frac{e^x}{12}\left[\frac{x^3}{6}\cos\left(\sqrt{3}\, x + \alpha\right) + \frac{x^2}{2\sqrt{3}}\sin\left(\sqrt{3}\, x + \alpha\right)\right]$$

70. $(D^2 - 4D + 4)\, y = x\, e^{2x}\sin 2x.$　　**Ans.** $y = (c_1 x + c_2)\, e^{2x} - \dfrac{e^{2x}}{4}\,[x\sin 2x + \cos 2x]$

MULTIPLE CHOICE QUESTIONS (MCQ's)

Type : Particular Integral :

1. Particular Integral of linear differential equation with constant coefficient $\phi(D)\, y = f(x)$ is given by　　　　　(1)

(A) $\dfrac{1}{\phi(D)}\, f(x)$　　　　　　　　　　　(B) $\dfrac{1}{\phi(D)\, f(x)}$

(C) $\phi(D)\,\dfrac{1}{f(x)}$　　　　　　　　　　　(D) $\dfrac{1}{\phi(D^2)}\, f(x)$

2. $\dfrac{1}{D - m}\, f(x)$, where $D \equiv \dfrac{d}{dx}$ and m is constant, is equal to　　　　　(1)

(A) $e^{mx}\int e^{-mx}\, dx$　　　　　　　　　　(B) $\int e^{-mx}\, f(x)\, dx$

(C) $e^{mx}\int e^{-mx}\, f(x)\, dx$　　　　　　　(D) $e^{-mx}\int e^{mx}\, f(x)\, dx$

3. $\dfrac{1}{D + m}\, f(x)$, where $D \equiv \dfrac{d}{dx}$ and m is constant, is equal to　　　　　(1)

(A) $e^{-mx}\int e^{mx}\, dx$　　　　　　　　　　(B) $\int e^{mx}\, f(x)\, dx$

(C) $e^{mx}\int e^{-mx}\, f(x)\, dx$　　　　　　　(D) $e^{-mx}\int e^{mx}\, f(x)\, dx$

4. Particular Integral $\dfrac{1}{\phi(D)}\, e^{ax}$, where $D \equiv \dfrac{d}{dx}$ and $\phi(a) \neq 0$ is　　　　　(1)

(A) $\dfrac{1}{\phi(-a)}\, e^{ax}$　　　　　　　　　　(B) $x\,\dfrac{1}{\phi(a)}\, e^{ax}$

(C) $\dfrac{1}{\phi(a^2)}\, e^{ax}$　　　　　　　　　　(D) $\dfrac{1}{\phi(a)}\, e^{ax}$

5. Particular Integral $\dfrac{1}{(D - a)^r}\, e^{ax}$ where $D \equiv \dfrac{d}{dx}$ is　　　　　(1)

(A) $\dfrac{1}{r!}\, e^{ax}$　　　　　　　　　　　　(B) $\dfrac{x^r}{r}\, e^{ax}$

(C) $\dfrac{x^r}{r!}\, e^{ax}$　　　　　　　　　　　(D) $x^r\, e^{ax}$

6. Particular Integral $\dfrac{1}{\phi(D^2)} \sin(ax+b)$, where $D \equiv \dfrac{d}{dx}$ and $\phi(-a^2) \neq 0$ is   (1)

  (A) $\dfrac{1}{\phi(-a^2)} \cos(ax+b)$ (B) $\dfrac{1}{\phi(-a^2)} \sin(ax+b)$

  (C) $x\dfrac{1}{\phi(-a^2)} \sin(ax+b)$ (D) $\dfrac{1}{\phi(a^2)} \sin(ax+b)$

7. Particular Integral $\dfrac{1}{\phi(D^2)} \sin(ax+b)$, where $D \equiv \dfrac{d}{dx}$ and $\phi(-a^2) = 0$, $\phi'(-a^2) \neq 0$ is   (1)

  (A) $x\dfrac{1}{\phi'(-a^2)} \cos(ax+b)$ (B) $x\dfrac{1}{\phi'(-a^2)} \sin(ax+b)$

  (C) $\dfrac{1}{\phi(-a^2)} \sin(ax+b)$ (D) $\dfrac{1}{\phi'(-a^2)} \sin(ax+b)$

8. Particular Integral $\dfrac{1}{\phi(D^2)} \cos(ax+b)$, where $D \equiv \dfrac{d}{dx}$ and $\phi(-a^2) \neq 0$ is   (1)

  (A) $\dfrac{1}{\phi(-a^2)} \cos(ax+b)$ (B) $\dfrac{1}{\phi(-a^2)} \sin(ax+b)$

  (C) $x\dfrac{1}{\phi'(-a^2)} \cos(ax+b)$ (D) $\dfrac{1}{\phi(a^2)} \cos(ax+b)$

9. Particular Integral $\dfrac{1}{\phi(D^2)} \cos(ax+b)$, where $D \equiv \dfrac{d}{dx}$ and $\phi(-a^2) = 0$, $\phi'(-a^2) \neq 0$ is   (1)

  (A) $\dfrac{1}{\phi'(-a^2)} \cos(ax+b)$ (B) $\dfrac{1}{\phi'(-a^2)} \cos(ax+b)$

  (C) $x\dfrac{1}{\phi'(-a^2)} \sin(ax+b)$ (D) $x\dfrac{1}{\phi'(-a^2)} \cos(ax+b)$

10. Particular Integral $\dfrac{1}{\phi(D^2)} \sinh(ax+b)$, where $D \equiv \dfrac{d}{dx}$ and $\phi(a^2) \neq 0$ is   (1)

  (A) $\dfrac{1}{\phi(a^2)} \cosh(ax+b)$ (B) $x\dfrac{1}{\phi'(a^2)} \sinh(ax+b)$

  (C) $\dfrac{1}{\phi(a^2)} \sinh(ax+b)$ (D) $\dfrac{1}{\phi(-a^2)} \sinh(ax+b)$

11. Particular Integral $\dfrac{1}{\phi(D^2)} \cosh(ax+b)$, where $D \equiv \dfrac{d}{dx}$ and $\phi(a^2) \neq 0$ is   (1)

  (A) $\dfrac{1}{\phi(a^2)} \cosh(ax+b)$ (B) $x\dfrac{1}{\phi'(a^2)} \cosh(ax+b)$

  (C) $\dfrac{1}{\phi(a^2)} \sinh(ax+b)$ (D) $\dfrac{1}{\phi(-a^2)} \cosh(ax+b)$

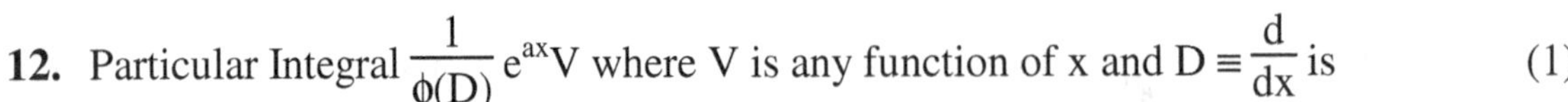

12. Particular Integral $\dfrac{1}{\phi(D)}\, e^{ax}V$ where V is any function of x and $D \equiv \dfrac{d}{dx}$ is   (1)

(A) $e^{ax}\, \dfrac{1}{\phi(D-a)}\, V$

(B) $e^{ax}\, \dfrac{1}{\phi(a)}\, V$

(C) $e^{ax}\, \dfrac{1}{\phi(D+a)}\, V$

(D) $\dfrac{1}{\phi(D+a)}\, V$

13. Particular Integral $\dfrac{1}{\phi(D)}\, xV$ where V is a function of x and $D \equiv \dfrac{d}{dx}$ is   (1)

(A) $\left[x - \dfrac{1}{\phi(D)}\right]\dfrac{1}{\phi(D)}\, V$

(B) $\left[x - \dfrac{\phi'(D)}{\phi(D)}\right]\phi(D)\, V$

(C) $\left[x + \dfrac{\phi'(D)}{\phi(D)}\right]V$

(D) $\left[x - \dfrac{\phi'(D)}{\phi(D)}\right]\dfrac{1}{\phi(D)}\, V$

14. Particular integral $\dfrac{1}{D+1}\, e^{e^{x}}$, where $D \equiv \dfrac{d}{dx}$ is   (2)

(A) $e^{-x}\, e^{e^{x}}$

(B) $e^{e^{x}}$

(C) $e^{x}\, e^{e^{x}}$

(D) $e^{-2x}\, e^{e^{x}}$

15. Particular Integral $\dfrac{1}{D+2}\, e^{-x}\, e^{e^{x}}$ where $D \equiv \dfrac{d}{dx}$ is   (2)

(A) $e^{2x}\, e^{e^{x}}$

(B) $e^{-2x}\, e^{e^{x}}$

(C) $e^{e^{x}}$

(D) $e^{-x}\, e^{e^{x}}$

16. particular Integral $\dfrac{1}{D+1}\, \sin e^{x}$, where $D \equiv \dfrac{d}{dx}$ is   (2)

(A) $-\, e^{-x} \sin e^{x}$

(B) $e^{x} \cos e^{x}$

(C) $-\, e^{-x} \cos e^{x}$

(D) $e^{-x} \cos e^{x}$

17. Particular Integral $\dfrac{1}{D+2}\, e^{-x} \cos e^{x}$, where $D \equiv \dfrac{d}{dx}$ is   (2)

(A) $e^{-x} \cos e^{x}$

(B) $e^{-x} \sin e^{x}$

(C) $e^{-2x} \cos e^{x}$

(D) $e^{-2x} \sin e^{x}$

18. Particular Integral $\dfrac{1}{D+2}\, e^{-2x} \sec^{2} x\, (1 + 2 \tan x)$, (use $\tan x = t$ and $D \equiv \dfrac{d}{dx}$) is   (2)

(A) $e^{-2x}\, (1 + 2 \tan^{2} x)$

(B) $e^{-2x}\, (\tan x + \tan^{2} x)$

(C) $e^{2x}\, (\tan x + 2 \tan^{2} x)$

(D) $e^{-2x}\, (\tan x + \sec x)$

19. Particular Integral $\dfrac{1}{D+1}\left(\dfrac{1}{1+e^x}\right)$ where $D \equiv \dfrac{d}{dx}$ is   (2)

(A) $e^x \log(1 - e^x)$ (B) $\log(1 + e^x)$

(C) $e^x \log(1 + e^x)$ (D) $e^{-x} \log(1 + e^x)$

20. Particular Integral of differential equation $\dfrac{d^2y}{dx^2} - 7\dfrac{dy}{dx} + 6y = e^{2x}$ is   (2)

(A) $-\dfrac{xe^{2x}}{3}$ (B) $-\dfrac{e^{2x}}{4}$

(C) $\dfrac{e^{2x}}{4}$ (D) $\dfrac{e^{2x}}{24}$

21. Particular Integral of differential equation $(D^2 - 5D + 6)\,y = 3e^{5x}$ is   (2)

(A) $\dfrac{e^{5x}}{2}$ (B) $\dfrac{e^{5x}}{6}$

(C) $-\dfrac{e^{5x}}{14}$ (D) $-\dfrac{e^{2x}}{2}$

22. Particular Integral of differential equation $(D^2 - 9)\,y = e^{3x} + 1$ is   (2)

(A) $\dfrac{3x}{2}e^{3x} - \dfrac{1}{9}$ (B) $x\dfrac{e^{3x}}{6} + \dfrac{3}{8}$

(C) $x\dfrac{e^{3x}}{6} - \dfrac{1}{9}$ (D) $xe^{3x} + \dfrac{1}{8}$

23. Particular Integral differential equation $(D^2 + 4D + 3)\,y = e^{-3x}$ is   (2)

(A) xe^{-3x} (B) $-\dfrac{1}{2}e^{-3x}$

(C) $-\dfrac{x}{10}e^{-3x}$ (D) $-\dfrac{x}{2}e^{-3x}$

24. Particular Integral of differential equation $(D - 2)^3\,y = e^{2x} + 3^x$ is   (2)

(A) $\dfrac{x^3}{3!}e^{2x} + \dfrac{1}{(\log 3 - 2)^3}\,3^x$ (B) $\dfrac{x^3}{3!}e^{2x} + \dfrac{1}{(e^3 - 2)^3}\,3^x$

(C) $\dfrac{x}{3!}e^{2x} + \dfrac{1}{(\log 3 - 2)^3}\,3^x$ (D) $\dfrac{x^3}{3!}e^{2x} + \dfrac{1}{(\log 3 - 2)^3}$

25. Particular Integral of differential equation $(D^5 - D)\,y = 12e^x$ is   (2)

(A) $3e^x$ (B) $\dfrac{12}{5}xe^x$

(C) $12xe^x$ (D) $3xe^x$

26. Particular Integral of differential equation $(D^2 + 1)(D - 1)\,y = e^x$ is   (2)

(A) xe^x (B) $\dfrac{1}{2}x^2 e^x$

(C) $\dfrac{1}{2}xe^x$ (D) $x^2 e^x$

27. Particular Integral of differential equation $(D^2 - 4D + 4)\,y = \sin 2x$ is   (2)

(A) $-\dfrac{\cos 2x}{8}$ (B) $\dfrac{\cos 2x}{8}$ (C) $\dfrac{\sin 2x}{8}$ (D) $x\dfrac{\cos 2x}{8}$

28. Particular Integral of differential equation $(D^3 + D)\, y = \cos x$ is   (2)

(A) $-\dfrac{x}{2}\sin x$ (B) $\dfrac{x}{4}\cos x$

(C) $-\dfrac{1}{2}\cos x$ (D) $-\dfrac{x}{2}\cos x$

29. Particular Integral of differential equation $(D^2 + 1)\, y = \sin x$ is   (2)

(A) $-\dfrac{x}{2}\cos x$ (B) $-\dfrac{x}{4}\cos x$

(C) $-\dfrac{x}{2}\sin x$ (D) $-\dfrac{1}{2}\cos x$

30. Particular Integral of differential equation $(D^3 + 9D)\, y = \sin 3x$ is   (2)

(A) $-\dfrac{x}{18}\cos 3x$ (B) $-\dfrac{x}{18}\sin 3x$

(C) $-x \sin 3x$ (D) $-\dfrac{1}{18}\sin 3x$

31. Particular integral of differential equation $(D^4 + 10D^2 + 9)\, y = \sin 2x + \cos 4x$ is   (2)

(A) $-\dfrac{1}{23}\sin 2x - \dfrac{1}{105}\cos 4x$ (B) $\dfrac{1}{15}\sin 2x + \cos 4x$

(C) $-\dfrac{1}{15}\sin 2x + \dfrac{1}{105}\cos 4x$ (D) $-\dfrac{1}{15}\sin 2x + \dfrac{1}{87}\cos 4x$

32. Particular Integral of differential equation $\dfrac{d^2y}{dx^2} - 2\dfrac{dy}{dx} + 5y = 10 \sin x$ is   (2)

(A) $\dfrac{8}{3}\sin x$ (B) $\sin x - 2\cos x$

(C) $4\sin x + 2\cos x$ (D) $2\sin x + \cos x$

33. Particular Integral of differential equation $(D^4 - m^4)\, y = \cos mx$ is   (2)

(A) $\dfrac{-x}{4m^3}\cos mx$ (B) $\dfrac{x}{m^3}\sin mx$

(C) $-x \sin mx$ (D) $\dfrac{-x}{4m^3}\sin mx$

34. Particular Integral of differential equation $\dfrac{d^3y}{dx^3} - 4\dfrac{dy}{dx} = 2 \cosh 2x$ is   (2)

(A) $\dfrac{1}{4}\cosh 2x$ (B) $\dfrac{x}{8}\cosh 2x$

(C) $\dfrac{x}{4}\cosh 2x$ (D) $\dfrac{x}{4}\sinh 2x$

35. Particular Integral of differential equation $(D^2 + 6D - 9)\, y = \sinh 3x$ is   (2)

(A) $\dfrac{1}{18}\cosh 3x$ (B) $\dfrac{1}{2}\cosh 3x$

(C) $\dfrac{1}{18}\sinh 3x$ (D) $-\dfrac{1}{18}\cosh 3x$

36. Particular Integral of differential equation $\dfrac{d^3y}{dx^3} + 8y = x^4 + 2x + 1$ is   (2)

(A) $\dfrac{1}{8}(x^4 + 5x + 1)$ (B) $\dfrac{1}{8}(x^3 - 3x^2 + 1)$

(C) $x^4 - x + 1$ (D) $\dfrac{1}{8}(x^4 - x + 1)$

37. Particular Integral of differential equation $(D^4 + D^2 + 1)\, y = 53x^2 + 17$ is   (2)
(A) $53x^2 + 17$ (B) $53x^2 - 89$
(C) $53x^2 + 113$ (D) $3x^2 - 17$

38. Particular integral of differential equation $(D^2 - D + 1)\, y = 3x^2 - 1$ is   (2)
(A) $3x^2 + 6x + 5$ (B) $x^2 - 6x + 1$
(C) $3x^2 + 6x - 1$ (D) $x^2 + 18x - 11$

39. Particular Integral of differential equation $(D^2 - 1)\, y = x^3$ is   (2)
(A) $-x^3 + 6x$ (B) $x^2 + 6$
(C) $x^3 + 6x$ (D) $-x^3 - 6x$

40. Particular Integral of differential equation $(D^3 + 3D^2 - 4)\, y = x^2$ is   (2)

(A) $-\dfrac{1}{4}\left(x^2 + \dfrac{3}{2}\right)$ (B) $\dfrac{1}{4}\left(x^2 + \dfrac{3}{2}x\right)$

(C) $\left(x^2 + \dfrac{3}{2}\right)$ (D) $-\dfrac{1}{4}\left(x^2 - \dfrac{3}{2}\right)$

41. Particular Integral of differential equation $(D^4 + 25)\, y = x^4 + x^2 + 1$ is   (2)

(A) $\left(x^4 + x^2 - \dfrac{1}{25}\right)$ (B) $\left(x^4 + x^2 + \dfrac{49}{25}\right)$

(C) $\dfrac{1}{25}(x^4 + x^2 + 24x + 1)$ (D) $\dfrac{1}{25}\left(x^4 + x^2 + \dfrac{1}{25}\right)$

42. Particular Integral of differential equation $(D^2 - 4D + 4)\, y = e^{2x} x^4$ is   (2)

(A) $\dfrac{x^6}{120}\, e^{2x}$ (B) $\dfrac{x^6}{60}\, e^{2x}$

(C) $\dfrac{x^6}{30}\, e^{2x}$ (D) $\dfrac{x^5}{20}\, e^{2x}$

43. Particular Integral of differential equation $\dfrac{d^2y}{dx^2} + 2\dfrac{dy}{dx} + y = e^{-x}\cos x$ is   (2)

(A) $e^x \cos x$ (B) $-e^{-x}\sin x$
(C) $-e^{-x}\cos x$ (D) $(c_1 x + c_2)\, e^{-x}$

44. Particular integral of differential equation $(D^2 + 6D + 9)\, y = e^{-3x} x^{-3}$ is   (2)

(A) $\dfrac{e^{-3x}}{2x}$ (B) $e^{-3x} x$

(C) $\dfrac{e^{-3x}}{12x}$ (D) $(c_1 x + c_2)\, e^{-3x}$

45. Particular Integral of differential equation $(D^2 + 2D + 1) y = e^{-x} (1 + x^2)$ is   (2)

(A) $e^{-x} \left(\dfrac{x^2}{2} - \dfrac{x^4}{12} \right)$ (B) $e^{-x} \left(x + \dfrac{x^3}{3} \right)$

(C) $e^{-x} \left(\dfrac{x^2}{2} + \dfrac{x^4}{12} \right)$ (D) $\left(\dfrac{x^2}{2} + \dfrac{x^4}{12} \right)$

46. Particular Integral of differential equation $(D - 1)^3 y = e^x \sqrt{x}$ is   (2)

(A) $\dfrac{4}{15} e^x x^{5/2}$ (B) $\dfrac{8}{105} e^x x^{7/2}$

(C) $e^x x^{7/2}$ (D) $\dfrac{3}{8} e^x x^{-5/2}$

47. Particular integral of differential equation $\dfrac{d^2y}{dx^2} - 2 \dfrac{dy}{dx} + y = xe^x \sin x$ is   (2)

(A) $- e^x (x \sin x + 2 \cos x)$ (B) $e^x (x \sin x - 2 \cos x)$
(C) $(x \sin x + 2 \cos x)$ (D) $- e^x (x \cos x + 2 \sin x)$

48. Solution of differential equation $\dfrac{d^2y}{dx^2} + \dfrac{dy}{dx} + y = e^{2x}$ is   (2)

(A) $e^x \left(c_1 \cos \dfrac{\sqrt{3}}{2} x + c_2 \sin \dfrac{\sqrt{3}}{2} x \right) - \dfrac{1}{7} e^{2x}$

(B) $e^{\frac{1}{2} x} \left(c_1 \cos \dfrac{\sqrt{3}}{2} x + c_2 \sin \dfrac{\sqrt{3}}{2} x \right) + \dfrac{1}{5} e^{2x}$

(C) $e^{-\frac{1}{2} x} \left(c_1 \cos \dfrac{1}{2} x + c_2 \sin \dfrac{1}{2} x \right) + \dfrac{1}{7} e^{x}$

(D) $e^{-\frac{1}{2} x} \left(c_1 \cos \dfrac{\sqrt{3}}{2} x + c_2 \sin \dfrac{\sqrt{3}}{2} x \right) + \dfrac{1}{7} e^{2x}$

49. Solution of differential equation $(D^2 + 1) y = x$ is   (2)

(A) $c_1 \cos x + c_2 \sin x - x$ (B) $c_1 \cos x + c_2 \sin x + x$
(C) $c_1 \cos x + c_2 \sin x + 2x$ (D) $c_1 \cos x + c_2 \sin x - 2x$

Answers

1. (A)	2. (C)	3. (D)	4. (D)	5. (C)	6. (B)	7. (B)	8. (A)
9. (D)	10. (C)	11. (A)	12. (C)	13. (D)	14. (A)	15. (B)	16. (C)
17. (D)	18. (B)	19. (D)	20. (B)	21. (A)	22. (C)	23. (D)	24. (A)
25. (D)	26. (C)	27. (B)	28. (D)	29. (A)	30.(B)	31. (C)	32. (D)
33.(D)	34. (C)	35. (A)	36. (D)	37. (B)	38. (C)	39. (D)	40. (A)
41. (D)	42. (C)	43. (C)	44. (A)	45. (C)	46. (B)	47. (A)	48. (D)
49. (B)							

(C) Method of Variation of Parameters

When the short-cut methods (Art. 1.13) fail to determine the particular integral then one has to make use of general method. But this method involves laborious integration and in such cases other methods are available. One such method is the method of variation of parameters. This method is due to a great Mathematician named Lagrange. To explain the rigours of this method, let us start with a simple differential equation

$$\frac{d^2y}{dx^2} + y = \tan x \qquad \ldots (1)$$

Here C.F. is very simple but the P.I. will be difficult to obtain even by general method because it is not of those special cases discussed before.

The complementary function is

$$A \cos x + B \sin x \qquad \ldots (2)$$

where, A and B are Arbitrary constants. Here Lagrange has shown his ingenuity by evolving the Particular Integral from this C.F. only by assuming that (temporarily) the constants A and B are some functions of x say A (x) and B (x) (of course it looks ridiculous).

Since the method assumes that the quantities A and B vary, this method is called *The Method of Variation of Parameters or Variation of Constants.*

Since two functions A (x) and B (x) are to be determined, they must satisfy two conditions. First is that the assumed solution (P.I.)

$$y = A (x) \cos x + B (x) \sin x \qquad \ldots (3)$$

must satisfy the differential equation. When determined, (3) actually will deliver to us the Particular Integral. The second condition is at our disposal and we shall choose it at proper time so as to evaluate A (x) and B (x) and thereby solving the equation.

If we differentiate equation (3), we get

$$y' = - A (x) \sin x + B (x) \cos x + A'(x) \cos x + B' (x) \sin x \ldots (4)$$

Since further differentiation will involve higher differentials of unknown functions A(x) and B(x), we apply our choice of second condition here only and that is what we assume

$$A'(x) \cos x + B'(x) \sin x = 0 \qquad \ldots (5)$$

and then (4) becomes simpler as

$$y' = - A (x) \sin x + B (x) \cos x \qquad \ldots (6)$$

One further differentiation will give

$$y'' = - A(x) \cos x - B(x) \sin x - A' (x) \sin x + B'(x) \cos x \ldots (7)$$

Substituting from (3) and (7) in the given differential equation, we find that

$$- A' (x) \sin x + B' (x) \cos x = \tan x \qquad \ldots (8)$$

Now, if we solve equations (5) and (8) simultaneously, we get

$$A'(x) = -\frac{\sin^2 x}{\cos x} \quad \text{and} \quad B' (x) = \sin x$$

and hence by integration, we get

$$A(x) = \int \frac{\cos^2 x - 1}{\cos x}\, dx = \int (\cos x - \sec x)\, dx$$

$$= \sin x - \log(\sec x + \tan x)$$

and $\qquad\qquad B(x) = -\cos x$

We are not using here constants of integration because it is P.I. part.

Now we frame our P.I. as follows :

$$y = A(x)\cos x + B(x)\sin x$$

$$\text{P.I.} = \cos x\,[\sin x - \log(\sec x + \tan x)] - \sin x \cos x$$

$$= -[\log(\sec x + \tan x)]\cos x$$

Hence the complete solution is

$$y = y_c + y_p$$

$$y = c_1 \cos x + c_2 \sin x - \cos x \log(\sec x + \tan x)$$

Note : Lagrange's method may be extended to higher order linear differential equations too, as may be seen by further exercises.

SECOND METHOD OF VARIATION OF PARAMETERS

When we have to solve equation of the type $\quad a\dfrac{d^2y}{dx^2} + b\dfrac{dy}{dx} + cy = X$

where, a, b, c are constants and X, any function of x, we also have an alternative method of variation of parameters.

Let the complementary function $= Ay_1 + By_2$ then the particular integral $= uy_1 + vy_2$

where $\qquad\qquad u = \int \dfrac{-y_2 X}{W}\, dx, \quad v = \int \dfrac{y_1 X}{W}\, dx$

where $\qquad\qquad W = \begin{vmatrix} y_1 & y_2 \\ y_1' & y_2' \end{vmatrix} = $ called "WRONSKIAN" $= (y_1 y_2' - y_1' y_2)$

ILLUSTRATIONS ON METHOD OF VARIATION OF PARAMETERS

Ex. 1 : *Solve the equation $(D^2 + 4)\, y = \sec 2x$ by the method of variation of parameters.* **(May 2006)**

Sol. : $\qquad$ C.F. $= A \cos 2x + B \sin 2x$ $\qquad\qquad$ ... (1)

Let $\qquad$ P.I. $= y = A(x)\cos 2x + B(x)\sin 2x$ $\qquad\qquad$ ... (2)

Differentiating (2), we have

$$y' = -2A(x)\sin 2x + 2B(x)\cos 2x + A'(x)\cos 2x + B'(x)\sin 2x \quad ... (3)$$

Assume here that

$$A'(x)\cos 2x + B'(x)\sin 2x = 0 \qquad\qquad ... (4)$$

Then equation (3) will become

$$y' = -2A(x)\sin 2x + 2B(x)\cos 2x \qquad\qquad ... (5)$$

If we differentiate (5) again, we get

$$y'' = -4A\cos 2x - 4B\sin 2x - 2A'\sin 2x + 2B'\cos 2x \quad \ldots (6)$$

[Briefly $A(x) = A$, $A' = A'(x)$, $B(x) = B$, $B' = B'(x)$]

Putting values of y, y' and y'' in the differential equation

$$\frac{d^2y}{dx^2} + 4y = \sec 2x, \text{ we have}$$

$$(-4A\cos 2x - 4B\sin 2x - 2A'\sin 2x + 2B'\cos 2x) + (4A\cos 2x + 4B\sin 2x) = \sec 2x$$

$$\Rightarrow \quad -2A'\sin 2x + 2B'\cos 2x = \sec 2x \qquad \ldots (7)$$

Solving (4) and (7) simultaneously, we have

$$A'\cos 2x + B'\sin 2x = 0$$

$$-A'\sin 2x + B'\cos 2x = \frac{1}{2}\sec 2x$$

$$B' = \frac{1}{2} \quad \Rightarrow \quad B = \frac{1}{2}x \text{ and}$$

$$A' = \frac{-1}{2}\tan 2x \quad \Rightarrow \quad A = \frac{1}{4}\log(\cos 2x)$$

Hence

$$\text{P.I.} = A\cos 2x + B\sin 2x$$

$$= \frac{1}{4}\cos 2x\,\log(\cos 2x) + \frac{x}{2}\sin 2x$$

Hence the complete solution is

$$y = c_1\cos 2x + c_2\sin 2x + \frac{x}{2}\sin 2x + \frac{1}{4}\cos 2x\,\log\cos 2x$$

Alternative Method :

$$(D^2 + 4)y = \sec 2x$$

$$\text{C.F.} = A\cos 2x + B\sin 2x = Ay_1 + By_2$$

Here $\quad y_1 = \cos 2x$ and $y_2 = \sin 2x$

Let $\quad$ P.I. $= u(x)\,y_1 + v(x)\,y_2$

$$W = \begin{vmatrix} y_1 & y_2 \\ y_1' & y_2' \end{vmatrix} = \begin{vmatrix} \cos 2x & \sin 2x \\ -2\sin 2x & 2\cos 2x \end{vmatrix} = 2(\cos^2 2x + \sin^2 2x) = 2$$

$$u = \int \frac{-y_2 X}{W}\,dx = \int \frac{-\sin 2x\,\sec 2x}{2} = -\frac{1}{2}\int \tan 2x\,dx$$

$$= \frac{1}{4}\log(\cos 2x)$$

$$v = \int \frac{y_1 X}{W}\,dx = \int \frac{\cos 2x\,\sec 2x}{2}\,dx = \frac{1}{2}\int dx = \frac{1}{2}x$$

$$\therefore \quad \text{P.I.} = \left\{\frac{1}{4}\log(\cos 2x)\right\}\cos 2x + \left\{\frac{1}{2}x\right\}\sin 2x$$

Hence the general solution is

$$y = A\cos 2x + B\sin 2x + \frac{1}{4}\cos 2x\,\log(\cos 2x) + \frac{1}{2}x\sin 2x$$

Ex. 2 : *Solve by method of variation of parameters* $\dfrac{d^2y}{dx^2} + y = \operatorname{cosec} x$.

(Dec. 05, 11, 14, 15)

Sol. : A.E. is $D^2 + 1 = 0$ $\therefore$ $D = \pm i$

$$\text{C.F.} = A \cos x + B \sin x$$
$$= A y_1 + B y_2$$

Here $y_1 = \cos x$ and $y_2 = \sin x$

Let

$$\text{P.I.} = u y_1 + v y_2$$

$$W = \begin{vmatrix} y_1 & y_2 \\ y_1' & y_2' \end{vmatrix} = \begin{vmatrix} \cos x & \sin x \\ -\sin x & \cos x \end{vmatrix} = 1$$

$$u = \int \frac{-y_2 X}{W}\, dx = \int \frac{-\sin x \, \operatorname{cosec} x}{1}\, dx = \int -dx$$

$$= -x$$

and

$$v = \int \frac{y_1 X}{D}\, dx = \int \frac{\cos x \, \operatorname{cosec} x}{1}\, dx = \int \cot x \, dx$$

$$= \log (\sin x)$$

$\therefore$

$$\text{P.I.} = (-x) \cos x + \{\log (\sin x)\} \sin x$$

Hence the general solution is

$$y = A \cos x + B \sin x - x \cos x + \sin x \log (\sin x)$$

Ex. 3 : *Solve by method of variation of parameters* $\dfrac{d^2y}{dx^2} - y = \dfrac{2}{1 + e^x}$. **(Dec. 2004)**

Sol. : A.E. is $D^2 - 1 = 0$ $\therefore$ $D = \pm 1$

$$\text{C.F.} = c_1 e^x + c_2 e^{-x}$$
$$= c_1 y_1 + c_2 y_2$$

Here $y_1 = e^x$ and $y_2 = e^{-x}$, then

$$W = \begin{vmatrix} y_1 & y_2 \\ y_1' & y_2' \end{vmatrix} = \begin{vmatrix} e^x & e^{-x} \\ e^x & -e^{-x} \end{vmatrix} = -2$$

$$u = \int \frac{-y_2 X}{W}\, dx = -\int \frac{y_2 X}{-2} = -\int \frac{e^{-x}}{-2} \left(\frac{2}{1 + e^x} \right) dx$$

$$= \int \frac{e^{-x}}{1 + e^x}\, dx = \int \frac{dx}{e^x (1 + e^x)} = \int \left(\frac{1}{e^x} - \frac{1}{1 + e^x} \right) dx$$

$$u = \int e^{-x}\, dx - \int \frac{e^{-x}\, dx}{e^{-x} + 1} = -e^{-x} + \log (1 + e^{-x})$$

$$v = \int \frac{y_1 X}{W} \, dx = \int \frac{e^x}{-2} \left(\frac{2}{1 + e^x} \right) dx$$

$$= - \int \frac{e^x \, dx}{1 + e^x} = - \log (1 + e^x)$$

$\therefore$ P.I. $= u\,y_1 + v\,y_2 = [- e^{-x} + \log (1 + e^{-x})]\, e^x - \{\log (1 + e^x)\}\, e^{-x}$

$$= - 1 + e^x \log (e^{-x} + 1) - e^{-x} \log (e^x + 1)$$

$\therefore$ Hence the general solution is

$$y = c_1 e^x + c_2 e^{-x} - 1 + e^x \log (e^{-x} + 1) - e^{-x} \log (e^x + 1)$$

Ex. 4 : *Solve by method of variation of parameters*

$$(D^2 - 6D + 9)\, y = \frac{e^{3x}}{x^2}. \hspace{3cm} \textbf{(May 05, 09, Nov. 15)}$$

Sol. : A.E. is $D^2 - 6D + 9 = 0$ $\therefore$ $D = 3, 3$

$$\text{C.F.} = (c_1 x + c_2)\, e^{3x}$$

$$= c_1 y_1 + c_2 y_2$$

Here $y_1 = x\, e^{3x}$ and $y_2 = e^{3x}$

Let   P.I. $= u y_1 + v y_2$

$$W = \begin{vmatrix} y_1 & y_2 \\ y_1' & y_2' \end{vmatrix} = \begin{vmatrix} x\, e^{3x} & e^{3x} \\ (3x + 1)\, e^{3x} & 3e^{3x} \end{vmatrix} = - e^{6x}$$

$$u = \int \frac{-y_2 X}{W} \, dx = \int \frac{- e^{3x}\, (e^{3x}/x^2)}{- e^{6x}} \, dx = \int \frac{1}{x^2} \, dx$$

$$= - \frac{1}{x}$$

and $$v = \int \frac{y_1 X}{W} \, dx = \int \frac{x e^{3x}\, (e^{3x}/x^2)}{- e^{6x}} \, dx = \int - \frac{1}{x} \, dx$$

$$= - \log x$$

$\therefore$ P.I. $= - \dfrac{1}{x} (x\, e^{3x}) - \log x\, (e^{3x}) = - e^{3x} (1 + \log x)$

Hence the general solution is

$$y = (c_1 x + c_2)\, e^{3x} - e^{3x} (1 + \log x)$$

Ex. 5 : *Use method of variation of parameters to solve* $(D^2 - 2D + 2)\, y = e^x \tan x.$

Sol. : A.E. is $D^2 - 2D + 2 = 0$ $\therefore$ $D = 1 \pm i.$ **(Dec. 09, May 17)**

$$\text{C.F.} = e^x (c_1 \cos x + c_2 \sin x)$$

$$= c_1 y_1 + c_2 y_2$$

Here, $y_1 = e^x \cos x$ and $y_2 = e^x \sin x$

Let $P.I. = uy_1 + vy_2$

$$W = \begin{vmatrix} y_1 & y_2 \\ y_1' & y_2' \end{vmatrix} = \begin{vmatrix} e^x \cos x & e^x \sin x \\ e^x (\cos x - \sin x) & e^x (\sin x + \cos x) \end{vmatrix} = e^{2x}$$

$$u = \int \frac{-y_2 X}{W} dx = \int \frac{-e^x \sin x \, e^x \tan x}{e^{2x}} dx$$

$$= \int \frac{-\sin^2 x}{\cos x} dx = -\int \frac{(1 - \cos^2 x)}{\cos x} dx$$

$$= -\log (\sec x + \tan x) + \sin x$$

$$v = \int \frac{y_1 X}{W} dx = \int \frac{e^x \cos x \, e^x \tan x}{e^{2x}} dx = \int \sin x \, dx = -\cos x$$

$\therefore$ $P.I. = (-\log \sec x + \tan x + \sin x) e^x \cos x + (-\cos x) e^x \sin x$

Hence the general solution is

$$y = e^x (c_1 \cos x + c_2 \sin x) - e^x \cos x \log (\sec x + \tan x)$$

Ex. 6 : *Solve by method of variation of parameters* $(D^2 + 9) y = \dfrac{1}{1 + \sin 3x}$. **(May 2015)**

Sol. : A.E. is $D^2 + 9 = 0$ $\therefore$ $D = \pm i3$.

$$C.F. = c_1 \cos 3x + c_2 \sin 3x$$

$$= c_1 y_1 + c_2 y_2$$

Here, $y_1 = \cos 3x$ and $y_2 = \sin 3x$

Let $P.I. = uy_1 + vy_2$

$$W = \begin{vmatrix} y_1 & y_2 \\ y_1' & y_2' \end{vmatrix} = \begin{vmatrix} \cos 3x & \sin 3x \\ -3 \sin 3x & 3 \cos 3x \end{vmatrix} = 3$$

$$u = \int \frac{-y_2 X}{W} dx = \int \frac{-\sin 3x \, (1/1 + \sin 3x)}{3} dx$$

$$= -\frac{1}{3} \int \frac{\sin 3x \, (1 - \sin 3x)}{(1 + \sin 3x) (1 - \sin 3x)} dx$$

$$= -\frac{1}{3} \int \frac{\sin 3x - \sin^2 3x}{\cos^2 3x} dx = -\frac{1}{3} \int (\sec 3x \tan 3x - \tan^2 3x) dx$$

$$= -\frac{1}{3} \int (\sec 3x \tan 3x - \sec^2 3x + 1) dx$$

$$= \frac{1}{3} \left(-\frac{1}{3} \sec 3x + \frac{1}{3} \tan 3x - x \right)$$

$$v = \int \frac{y_1 X}{W}\, dx = \int \frac{\cos 3x \,(1/1 + \sin 3x)}{3}\, dx = \frac{1}{3} \int \frac{\cos 3x}{1 + \sin 3x}\, dx$$

$$= \frac{1}{9} \log (1 + \sin 3x)$$

$$\therefore \quad \text{P.I.} = \left\{ \frac{1}{9}(-\sec 3x + \tan 3x - 3x) \right\} \cos 3x + \left\{ \frac{1}{9} \log (1 + \sin 3x) \right\} \sin 3x$$

Hence the general solution is

$$y = (c_1 \cos 3x + c_2 \sin 3x) + \frac{1}{9}(-1 + \sin 3x - 3x \cos 3x)$$

$$+ \frac{1}{9} \sin 3x \log (1 + \sin 3x)$$

Ex. 7 : *Solve by method of variation of parameters*

$$\frac{d^2 y}{dx^2} - y = e^{-x} \sin (e^{-x}) + \cos (e^{-x}) \qquad \ldots (1)$$

Sol. : 　　　　　　　C.F. $= A\,e^x + B\,e^{-x}$

Let 　　　　　　　P.I. $= y = A\,(x)\,e^x + B\,(x)\,e^{-x}$ 　　　　$\ldots (2)$

$A\,(x)$ and $B\,(x)$ are functions to be determined.

Differentiating (2), we have

$$y' = A\,e^x - B\,e^{-x} + A'\,e^x + B'\,e^{-x} \qquad \ldots (3)$$

Put $A'\,e^x + B'\,e^{-x} = 0,$ 　　　　　　　　　　$\ldots (4)$

then (3) will become 　　$y' = A\,e^x - B\,e^{-x}$

Differentiating again

$$y'' = A\,e^x + B\,e^{-x} + A'\,e^x - B'\,e^{-x} \qquad \ldots (5)$$

Putting values of y'' and y in (1), we have

$$A\,e^x + B\,e^{-x} + A'\,e^x - B'\,e^{-x} - A e^x - B e^{-x} = e^{-x} \sin (e^{-x}) + \cos (e^{-x})$$

$$\therefore \quad A'\,e^x - B'\,e^{-x} = e^{-x} \sin (e^{-x}) + \cos (e^{-x}) \qquad \ldots (6)$$

Solving (4) and (6) simultaneously for A', B',

$$A'\,e^x + B'\,e^{-x} = 0$$

$$A'\,e^x - B'\,e^{-x} = e^{-x} \sin (e^{-x}) + \cos (e^{-x}) \qquad \ldots (7)$$

Adding the equations in (7), we have

$$2\,A'\,e^x = e^{-x} \sin (e^{-x}) + \cos (e^{-x})$$

$$\therefore \quad A' = \frac{1}{2}\, e^{-x} [e^{-x} \sin (e^{-x}) + \cos (e^{-x})] \qquad \ldots (8)$$

and similarly, 　　　　$B' = -\frac{1}{2}\, e^{x} [e^{-x} \sin (e^{-x}) + \cos (e^{-x})] \qquad \ldots (9)$

Integrating (8)

$$A = \frac{1}{2} \int e^{-x} [e^{-x} \sin(e^{-x}) + \cos(e^{-x})] \, dx \quad [\text{put } e^{-x} = t, \ -e^{-x} \, dx = dt]$$

$$A = -\frac{1}{2} \int [t \sin t + \cos t] \, dt = -\frac{1}{2} [-t \cos t + \sin t + \sin t]$$

$$= \frac{1}{2} t \cos t - \sin t$$

Hence $\quad A(x) = \frac{1}{2} e^{-x} \cos(e^{-x}) - \sin(e^{-x})$ $\hspace{2cm}$ ... (10)

If we integrate (9),

$$B = -\frac{1}{2} \int e^{x} (e^{-x} \sin e^{-x} + \cos e^{-x}) \, dx = -\frac{1}{2} e^{x} \cdot \cos e^{-x}$$

$$B(x) = -\frac{1}{2} e^{x} \cos e^{-x}, \text{ hence P.I. will be given by}$$

$$y = e^{x} \left[\frac{1}{2} e^{-x} \cos e^{-x} - \sin e^{-x} \right] - \frac{1}{2} e^{x} \cos(e^{-x}) \cdot e^{-x}$$

$$= \frac{1}{2} \cos(e^{-x}) - e^{x} \sin(e^{-x}) - \frac{1}{2} \cos e^{-x} = -e^{x} \sin(e^{-x})$$

Hence the complete solution is

$$y = A e^{x} + B e^{-x} - e^{x} \sin(e^{-x})$$

Ex. 8 : *By the method of variation of parameters, solve* $\hspace{1cm}$ **(May 2007, 2008)**

$$(D^3 + D) y = cosec \ x \hspace{3cm} ... (I)$$

Sol. : $\hspace{2cm}$ C.F. $= A + B \cos x + C \sin x$

$\hspace{1.5cm}$ Let the $\hspace{1.5cm}$ P.I. $= y_p = A(x) + B(x) \cos x + C(x) \sin x$ $\hspace{1.5cm}$ ... (II)

where $A(x)$, $B(x)$ and $C(x)$ are the parameters to be determined. For brevity, take $A(x) = A, B(x) = B, C(x) = C$.

Hence $\hspace{2.5cm}$ P.I. $= y = A + B \cos x + C \sin x$

$\hspace{4cm} y' = A' + (B' \cos x - B \sin x) + (C' \sin x + C \cos x)$

Put $A' + B' \cos x + C' \sin x = 0$ $\hspace{4cm}$ ... (III)

So that the new value of y' becomes

$\hspace{4cm} y' = -B \sin x + C \cos x$

$\therefore \hspace{3cm} y'' = -B' \sin x - B \cos x + C' \cos x - C \sin x$

Choose B' and C' such that

$\hspace{1cm} -B' \sin x + C' \cos x = 0$ $\hspace{4cm}$ ... (IV)

hence $\hspace{3cm} y'' = -B \cos x - C \sin x$

and $\hspace{3cm} y''' = -B' \cos x + B \sin x - C' \sin x - C \cos x$

Substituting in (I) values of y, y' and y''', we get

$\hspace{1cm} -B' \cos x - C' \sin x = cosec \ x$ $\hspace{4cm}$ ...(V)

Solving simultaneously (III), (IV) and (V), we get

$\hspace{3cm} A' = cosec \ x, \ B' = -\cot x \ \text{ and } \ C' = -1$

and integration yields

$$A = \log[\csc x - \cot x]$$
$$B = -\log \sin x$$
$$C = -x$$

∴ $P.I. = \log(\csc x - \cot x) - \cos x \log \sin x - x \sin x$

Hence the complete solution is

$$y = A + B\cos x + C\sin x + \log[\csc x - \cot x] - \cos x \, \log(\sin x) - x \sin x$$

EXERCISE 1.3

Solve the following differential equations by the method of variation of parameters.

1. $\dfrac{d^2y}{dx^2} + 4y = \tan 2x$ **Ans.** $y = A\cos 2x + B\sin 2x - \dfrac{1}{4}\cos 2x \log(\sec 2x + \tan 2x)$

$\hspace{6cm}$ **(Dec. 2005, 2007, 2008; May 2008, 2009)**

2. $\dfrac{d^2y}{dx^2} + y = x\sin x.$ $\hspace{1cm}$ **Ans.** $y = A\cos x + B\sin x + \dfrac{x}{2}\sin x - \dfrac{x^2}{4}\cos x$

3. $(D^2 + 3D + 2)\,y = \sin e^x$ $\hspace{1cm}$ **Ans.** $y = c_1 e^{-x} + c_2 e^{-2x} - e^{-2x}\sin e^x$

4. $\dfrac{d^2y}{dx^2} - 2\dfrac{dy}{dx} = e^x \cdot \sin x$ $\hspace{0.5cm}$ **(May 2011) Ans.** $y = A + B\,e^{2x} - \dfrac{e^x}{2}\sin x$

5. $(D^2 + 4)\,y = 4\sec^2 2x.$

$\hspace{2.5cm}$ **Ans.** $y = A\cos 2x + B\sin 2x - 1 + \sin 2x \log(\sec 2x + \tan 2x)$

6. $(D^2 - 1)\,y = (1 + e^{-x})^{-2}$ $\hspace{0.3cm}$ **(Dec. 2008) Ans.** $y = A\,e^x + B\,e^{-x} - 1 + e^{-x}\log(1 + e^x)$

7. $\dfrac{d^2y}{dx^2} + 3\dfrac{dy}{dx} + 2y = e^{e^x}$ **(May 2006, Dec. 2006) Ans.** $y = A e^{-x} + B\,e^{-2x} + e^{-2x}e^{e^x}$

8. $(D^2 + 1)\,y = 3x - 8\cot x.$ $\hspace{4cm}$ **(Nov. 2016)**

$\hspace{2cm}$ **Ans.** $y = c_1\cos x + c_2\sin x + 3x - 8\sin x \log(\csc x - \cot x)$

9. $(D^2 - 4D + 4)\,y = e^{2x}\sec^2 x$ $\hspace{1.5cm}$ **Ans.** $y = [c_1 + c_2 x + \log(\sec x)]\,e^{2x}$

$\hspace{6cm}$ **(Dec. 2004, 2011; May 2005, 2016)**

10. $\dfrac{d^2y}{dx^2} + y = \tan x.$ $\hspace{1.5cm}$ **Ans.** $y = A\cos x + B\sin x - \cos x \log(\sec x + \tan x)$

11. $\dfrac{d^2y}{dx^2} + y = \sec x \tan x$

$\hspace{2cm}$ **Ans.** $y = A\cos x + B\sin x + x\cos x - \sin x + \sin x \log(\sec x)$

12. $y'' + y = \sec x$ $\hspace{5cm}$ **(Dec. 2006, May 2011)**

$\hspace{2.5cm}$ **Ans.** $y = A\cos x + B\sin x + x\sin x + \cos x \log\cos x$

13. $(D^2 + D)\,y = (1 + e^x)^{-1}$ $\hspace{0.5cm}$ **Ans.** $y = c_1 + c_2\,e^{-x} + x - \log(1 + e^x) - e^{-x}\log(1 + e^x)$

$\hspace{6cm}$ **(May 2007)**

14. $(D^2 + 4)\,y = \dfrac{1}{1 + \cos 2x}$

$\hspace{2.5cm}$ **Ans.** $y = c_1\cos 2x + c_2\sin 2x + \dfrac{1}{4}(\cos 2x)\log(1 + \cos 2x)$

$$+\frac{1}{2}\left(x - \frac{1}{2}\tan x\right)\sin 2x \quad \textbf{(Dec. 2007)}$$

MULTIPLE CHOICE QUESTIONS (MCQ's)

Type : Method of Variation of Parameter :

1. Complimentary function of differential equation $a_0 \dfrac{d^2y}{dx^2} + a_1 \dfrac{dy}{dx} + a_2 y = f(x)$ is $c_1 y_1 + c_2 y_2$. Then by method of variation of parameters, particular integral is $u(x, y)\, y_1 + v(x, y)\, y_2$ where u is obtained from (1)

(A) $\displaystyle \int \frac{f(x)}{y_1 y_2' + y_2 y_1'} \, dx$ (B) $\displaystyle \int \frac{y_1\, f(x)}{y_1 y_2' + y_2 y_1'} \, dx$

(C) $\displaystyle \int \frac{y_2\, f(x)}{y_1 y_2' + y_2 y_1'}$ (D) $\displaystyle \int \frac{- y_2\, f(x)}{y_1 y_2' + y_2 y_1'} \, dx$

2. Complementary function of differential equation $a_0 \dfrac{d^2y}{dx^2} + a_1 \dfrac{dy}{dx} + a_2 y = f(x)$ is $c_1 y_1 + c_2 y_2$. Then by method of variation of parameters, particular integral is $u(x, y)\, y_1 + v(x, y)\, y_2$ where v is obtained from (1)

(A) $\displaystyle \int \frac{y_1\, f(x)}{y_1 y_2' + y_2 y_1'} \, dx$ (B) $\displaystyle \int \frac{- y_1\, f(x)}{y_1 y_2' + y_2 y_1'} \, dx$

(C) $\displaystyle \int \frac{- y_2\, f(x)}{y_1 y_2' + y_2 y_1'} \, dx$ (D) $\displaystyle \int \frac{f(x)}{y_1 y_2' + y_2 y_1'} \, dx$

3. In solving differential equation $\dfrac{d^2y}{dx^2} + y = \operatorname{cosec} x$ by method of variation of parameters, complimentary function $= c_1 \cos x + c_2 \sin x$,
Particular Integral $= u \cos x + v \sin x$ then u is equal to (2)
(A) $-\log \sin x$ (B) x (C) $-x$ (D) $\log \sin x$

4. In solving differential equation $\dfrac{d^2y}{dx^2} + 4y = \sec 2x$ by method of variation of parameters, complimentary function $= c_1 \cos 2x + c_2 \sin 2x$,
Particular Integral $= u \cos 2x + v \sin 2x$ then u is equal to (2)

(A) $-\dfrac{1}{2} x$ (B) $\dfrac{1}{4} \log (\cos 2x)$

(C) $-\dfrac{1}{4} \log (\cos 2x)$ (D) $\left(\dfrac{1}{2}\right) x$

5. In solving differential equation $\dfrac{d^2y}{dx^2} - y = (1 + e^{-x})^{-2}$ by method of variation of parameters, complimentary function $= c_1 e^x + c_2 e^{-x}$, Particular Integral $= u e^x + v e^{-x}$ then u is equal to (2)

(A) $\dfrac{1}{(1 + e^{-x})}$ (B) $\dfrac{1}{2(1 + e^{-x})^2}$

(C) $\log (1 + e^x)$ (D) $\dfrac{1}{2(1 + e^{-x})}$

6. In solving differential equation $\dfrac{d^2y}{dx^2} + 3\dfrac{dy}{dx} + 2y = \sin e^x$ by method of variation of parameters, complimentary function $= c_1 e^{-x} + c_2 e^{-2x}$, Particular Integral $= ue^{-x} + ve^{-2x}$ then u is equal to (2)

   (A) $-e^x \cos(e^x) + \sin(e^x)$ (B) $-\cos(e^x)$

   (C) $\cos(e^x)$ (D) $e^x \sin(e^x) + \cos(e^x)$

7. In solving differential equation $\dfrac{d^2y}{dx^2} - 6\dfrac{dy}{dx} + 9y = \dfrac{e^{3x}}{x^2}$ by method of variation of parameters, complimentary function $= c_1 xe^{3x} + c_2 e^{3x}$, Particular Integral $= uxe^{3x} + ve^{3x}$ then u is equal to (2)

   (A) $-\dfrac{2}{x^3}$ (B) $\dfrac{1}{x}$

   (C) $-\dfrac{1}{x}$ (D) $-\log x$

8. In solving differential equation $\dfrac{d^2y}{dx^2} + y = \tan x$ by method of variation of parameters, complimentary function $= c_1 \cos x + c_2 \sin x$, Particular Integral $= u \cos x + v \sin x$ then v is equal to (2)

   (A) $-\cos x$ (B) $[\log(\sec x + \tan x)] - \sin x$

   (C) $-[\log(\sec x + \tan x)] + \sin x$ (D) $\cos x$

9. In solving differential equation $\dfrac{d^2y}{dx^2} + 9y = \dfrac{1}{1 + \sin 3x}$ by method of variation of parameters, complimentary function $= c_1 \cos 3x + c_2 \sin 3x$,

   Particular Integral $= u \cos 3x + v \sin 3x$ then v is equal to (2)

   (A) $\dfrac{1}{3}\left(-\dfrac{1}{3}\sec 3x + \dfrac{1}{3}\tan 3x - x\right)$ (B) $-\dfrac{1}{9}\log(1 + \sin 3x)$

   (C) $\dfrac{1}{9}\log(1 + \sin 3x)$ (D) $\dfrac{1}{3}\log \cos x$

10. In solving differential equation $\dfrac{d^2y}{dx^2} - y = \dfrac{2}{1 + e^x}$ by method of variation of parameters, complimentary function $= c_1 e^x + c_2 e^{-x}$, particular integral $= ue^x + ve^{-x}$ then v is equal to (2)

   (A) $e^{-x} - \log(1 + e^{-x})$ (B) $-\log(1 + e^x)$

   (C) $\log(1 + e^x)$ (D) $-e^{-x} + \log(1 + e^{-x})$

11. In solving differential equation $\dfrac{d^2y}{dx^2} + 3\dfrac{dy}{dx} + 2y = e^{e^x}$ by method of variation of parameters, complimentary function $c_1 e^{-2x} + c_2 e^{-x}$, Particular Integral $= u e^{-2x} + v e^{-x}$ then v is equal to   (2)

   (A) $- e^{e^x}$

   (B) $e^{-2x} e^{e^x}$

   (C) $e^x e^{e^x}$

   (D) e^{e^x}

12. In solving differential equation $\dfrac{d^2y}{dx^2} + 4y = 4\sec^2 2x$ by method of variation of parameters, complimentary function $= c_1 \cos 2x + c_2 \sin 2x$,
    Particular Integral $= u \cos 2x + v \sin 2x$ then v is equal to   (2)

   (A) $\log(\sec 2x + \tan 2x)$

   (B) $-\sec 2x$

   (C) $\sec 2x + \tan 2x$

   (D) $\log(\tan 2x)$

Answers

1. (D)	2. (A)	3. (C)	4. (B)	5. (D)	6. (B)	7. (C)	8. (A)
9. (C)	10. (B)	11. (D)	12. (A)				

1.12 EQUATIONS REDUCIBLE TO LINEAR WITH CONSTANT COEFFICIENTS

We shall now study two types of linear differential equations with *variable coefficients* which can be reduced to the case of linear differential equation with constant coefficients by suitable transformations of variables.

1.3 CAUCHY'S OR EULER'S HOMOGENEOUS LINEAR DIFFERENTIAL EQUATION

An equation of the type
$$(a_0 x^n D^n + a_1 x^{n-1} D^{n-1} + \dots + a_{n-1} x D + a_n) y = F(x)$$

where $a_0, a_1, a_2 \dots a_n$ are constants is called Cauchy's Homogeneous Equation. It is sometimes attributed to Euler also. It may also be written as

$$a_0 x^n \frac{d^n y}{dx^n} + a_1 x^{n-1} \frac{d^{n-1}y}{dx^{n-1}} + \dots + a_{n-1} x \frac{dy}{dx} + a_n y = F(x) \qquad \dots (1)$$

It can be reduced to linear differential equation with constant coefficients by putting
$$x = e^z \text{ or } z = \log x \qquad \dots (2)$$

Now
$$\frac{dy}{dx} = \frac{dy}{dz}\frac{dz}{dx} = \frac{1}{x}\frac{dy}{dz}$$

or
$$x\frac{dy}{dx} = \frac{dy}{dz} = Dy, \text{ here we took } D \equiv \frac{d}{dz}$$

Also,
$$\frac{d^2y}{dx^2} = \frac{d}{dx}\left(\frac{1}{x}\frac{dy}{dz}\right) = -\frac{1}{x^2}\frac{dy}{dz} + \frac{1}{x}\frac{d}{dz}\left(\frac{dy}{dz}\right)\frac{dz}{dx}$$

$$= -\frac{1}{x^2}\frac{dy}{dz} + \frac{1}{x}\left(\frac{d^2y}{dz^2}\right)\frac{1}{x}$$

$$= -\frac{1}{x^2}\frac{dy}{dz} + \frac{1}{x^2}\frac{d^2y}{dz^2}$$

Hence $\qquad x^2 \dfrac{d^2y}{dx^2} = -Dy + D^2y = D(D-1)y$

Similarly, we can show that

$$x^3 \dfrac{d^3y}{dx^3} = D(D-1)(D-2)y \text{ and so on.}$$

....

....

$$x^r \dfrac{d^ry}{dx^r} = D(D-1)(D-2)\ldots\ldots(D-r+1)y \qquad \ldots (3)$$

Making these substitutions in (1) it can be reduced to linear differential equation with constant coefficients. The following examples can clarify further.

ILLUSTRATIONS

Ex. 1 : *Solve* $x^2 \dfrac{d^2y}{dx^2} - x\dfrac{dy}{dx} + 4y = \cos(\log x) + x\sin(\log x)$ **(May 2006)**

Sol. : Given equation is Cauchy's homogeneous linear differential equation. We use substitution $z = \log x$ or $x = e^z$ and let $D \equiv \dfrac{d}{dz}$.

Then we note from article (1.18),

$$x^2\dfrac{d^2y}{dx^2} = D(D-1)y, \quad x\dfrac{dy}{dx} = Dy, \text{ where } D \equiv \dfrac{d}{dz}$$

and equation is transformed into

$$D(D-1)y - Dy + 4y = \cos(z) + e^z \sin z$$

or $\qquad (D^2 - D - D + 4)y = \cos(z) + e^z \sin z$

or $\qquad (D^2 - 2D + 4)y = \cos(z) + e^z \sin z$

which is linear with constant coefficients in y and z. Now

A.E. is $D^2 - 2D + 4 = 0 \Rightarrow D = 1 \pm i\sqrt{3}$

Hence $\qquad$ C.F. $= e^z \left[A\cos\sqrt{3}\,z + B\sin\sqrt{3}\,z\right]$

and $\qquad$ P.I. $= \dfrac{1}{D^2 - 2D + 4}\cos z + \dfrac{1}{D^2 - 2D + 4}e^z \sin z$

$$= \dfrac{1}{-1 - 2D + 4}\cos z + e^z \dfrac{1}{(D+1)^2 - 2(D+1) + 4}\sin z$$

$$= \dfrac{1}{3 - 2D}\cos z + e^z \dfrac{1}{D^2 + 3}\sin z$$

$$= -\dfrac{2D+3}{4D^2 - 9}\cos z + e^z \dfrac{1}{-1+3}(\sin z)$$

$$= -\dfrac{(2D+3)\cos z}{-4-9} + e^z \dfrac{1}{2}\sin z$$

$$= \dfrac{1}{13}[-2\sin z + 3\cos z] + \dfrac{1}{2}e^z \sin z$$

Hence the general solution in terms of y and z is

$$y = e^z \left[A \cos (\sqrt{3}\, z) + B \sin (\sqrt{3}\, z) \right] + \frac{1}{13} [3 \cos z - 2 \sin z] + \frac{1}{2} e^z \sin z$$

Changing to y and x, we have

$$y = x \left[A \cos \sqrt{3}\, (\log x) + B \sin \sqrt{3}\, (\log x) \right]$$

$$+ \frac{1}{13} [3 \cos (\log x) - 2 \sin (\log x)] + \frac{1}{2}\, x \sin (\log x)$$

Ex. 2 : *Find the equation of the curve, which satisfies the differential equation*

$4x^2 \dfrac{d^2y}{dx^2} - 4x \dfrac{dy}{dx} + y = 0$ *and crosses the x-axis at an angle of* 60° *at x = 1.*

Sol. : Given equation is Cauchy's homogeneous linear differential equation. The solution will be the equation of the curve.

Put $x = e^z \Rightarrow z = \log x$, and $\dfrac{d}{dz} \equiv D$, then the given equation is transformed into

$$[4\, D\, (D - 1) - 4\, D + 1]\ y = 0$$

A.E. is $4D^2 - 8D + 1 = 0 \therefore\ D = 1 \pm \dfrac{\sqrt{3}}{2}$

$$\text{C.F.} = c_1 e^{\left(1 + \frac{\sqrt{3}}{2}\right) z} + c_2 e^{\left(1 - \frac{\sqrt{3}}{2}\right) z} \quad \text{and solution is}$$

$$y = c_1\, x^{\left(1 + \frac{\sqrt{3}}{2}\right)} + c_2\, x^{\left(1 - \frac{\sqrt{3}}{2}\right)} \qquad \qquad \dots (1)$$

But initially when x = 1, y = 0 and $\dfrac{dy}{dx} = \sqrt{3}$

$$\therefore\quad 0 = c_1 + c_2 \Rightarrow c_1 = - c_2 \qquad \qquad \dots (2)$$

Differentiating (1) w.r.t. x

$$\frac{dy}{dx} = \left(1 + \frac{\sqrt{3}}{2}\right) c_1\, x^{\frac{\sqrt{3}}{2}} + \left(1 - \frac{\sqrt{3}}{2}\right) c_2\, x^{-\frac{\sqrt{3}}{2}}$$

Put $x = 1$ and $\dfrac{dy}{dx} = \sqrt{3}$ in this

$$\sqrt{3} = \left(1 + \frac{\sqrt{3}}{2}\right) c_1 + \left(1 - \frac{\sqrt{3}}{2}\right) c_2$$

Solving with (2), we get $c_1 = 1$, $c_2 = - 1$

$\therefore$ Solution or the equation of the curve will be

$$y = x^{\left(1 + \frac{\sqrt{3}}{2}\right)} - x^{\left(1 - \frac{\sqrt{3}}{2}\right)}$$

Ex. 3 : *Solve $x^3 \cdot \dfrac{d^3y}{dx^3} + 2x^2 \cdot \dfrac{d^2y}{dx^2} + 2y = 10 \left(x + \dfrac{1}{x}\right)$*   **(May 2009, Dec. 2011)**

Sol. : The given equation is Cauchy's homogeneous linear differential equation.

Put $x = e^z$, $\Rightarrow z = \log x$ and $\dfrac{d}{dz} \equiv D$ then equation is transformed into

$[D (D - 1) (D - 2) + 2 D (D - 1) + 2] \, y = 10 \, (e^z + e^{-z})$

A.E. is $D^3 - D^2 + 2 = 0$ $\therefore$ $D = -1, \ 1 \pm i$

$$\text{C.F.} = c_1 e^{-z} + e^z \, [c_2 \cos z + c_3 \sin z]$$

$$= \frac{c_1}{x} + x \, [c_2 \cos (\log x) + c_3 \sin (\log x)]$$

$$\text{P.I.} = 10 \, \frac{1}{D^3 - D^2 + 2} \, (e^z + e^{-z})$$

$$= 10 \left[\frac{1}{D^3 - D^2 + 2} \, e^z + \frac{1}{D^3 - D^2 + 2} \, e^{-z} \right]$$

$$= 10 \left[\frac{1}{1 - 1 + 2} \, e^z + z \, \frac{1}{3D^2 - 2D} \, e^{-z} \right] = 10 \left[\frac{e^z}{2} + \frac{1}{5} \, z \, e^{-z} \right]$$

$$= 5 \, e^z + 2 \, z \, e^{-z} = 5x + \frac{2}{x} \, \log x$$

Hence the general solution will be

$$y = \frac{c_1}{x} + x \, [c_2 \cos (\log x) + c_3 \sin (\log x)] + 5x + \frac{2}{x} \, \log x$$

Ex. 4 : *Solve* $x^2 \dfrac{d^2 y}{dx^2} - 3x \dfrac{dy}{dx} + 5y = x^2 \sin (\log x)$.

Sol. : Given equation is Cauchy's homogeneous linear differential equation.

Put $z = \log x$ or $x = e^z$ and $\dfrac{d}{dz} \equiv D$, then equation is transformed into

$[D (D - 1) - 3D + 5] \, y = e^{2z} \sin z$

$(D^2 - 4D + 5) \, y = e^{2z} \sin z$

A.E. is $D^2 - 4D + 5 = 0$ $\therefore$ $D = 2 \pm i$.

$$\text{C.F.} = e^{2z} \, (c_1 \cos z + c_2 \sin z)$$

$$\text{P.I.} = \frac{1}{D^2 - 4D + 5} \, e^{2z} \sin z = e^{2z} \, \frac{1}{(D + 2)^2 - 4 (D + 2) + 5} \sin z$$

$$= e^{2z} \, \frac{1}{D^2 + 1} \, \sin z = -e^{2z} \frac{z}{2} \cos z$$

$$= -\frac{1}{2} \, e^{2z} \, z \cos z$$

General solution in terms of y and z is

$$y = e^{2z} \, (c_1 \cos z + c_2 \sin z) - \frac{1}{2} \, e^{2z} \, z \cos z$$

General solution in terms of y and x is

$$y = x^2 \, [c_1 \cos (\log x) + c_2 \sin (\log x)] - \frac{1}{2} x^2 \, (\log x) \cos (\log x)$$

Ex. 5 : *Solve* $u = r\dfrac{d}{dr}\left(r\dfrac{du}{dr}\right) + r^3.$ **(May 2007)**

Sol. : Given equation is $u = r\left\{r\dfrac{d^2u}{dr^2} + \dfrac{du}{dr}\right\} + r^3$ or $r^2\dfrac{d^2u}{dr^2} + r\dfrac{du}{dr} - u = -r^3$

which is a homogeneous equation.

Put $z = \log r$ or $r = e^z$ and using D for $\dfrac{d}{dz}$, equation is transformed into

$$[D(D-1) + D - 1]\, u = -e^{3z} \quad \text{or} \quad (D^2 - 1)\, u = -e^{3z}.$$

A.E. is $D^2 - 1 = 0$ $\therefore$ $D = \pm 1$

$$\text{C.F.} = c_1 e^z + c_2 e^{-z}$$

$$\text{P.I.} = \dfrac{1}{D^2 - 1}(-e^{3z}) = -\dfrac{1}{8}\, e^{3z}$$

$\therefore$ $\qquad u = c_1 e^z + c_2 e^{-z} - \dfrac{1}{8}\, e^{3z}$

The general solution in u and r is

$$u = c_1 r + \dfrac{c_2}{r} - \dfrac{r^3}{8}$$

1.14 LEGENDRE'S LINEAR EQUATION

An equation of the type

$$a_0 (ax+b)^n \dfrac{d^n y}{dx^n} + a_1 (ax+b)^{n-1}\dfrac{d^{n-1} y}{dx^{n-1}} + \ldots + a_n y = F(x)$$

where, $a_0, a_1, a_2 \ldots \ldots a_n$ are constants is called *Legendre's Linear Equation.*

In case of such equations, we put $ax + b = e^z$ to reduce it to linear with constant coefficients.

If we put $\quad ax + b = e^z \Rightarrow z = \log(ax+b)$

then $\qquad \dfrac{dy}{dx} = \dfrac{dy}{dz} \cdot \dfrac{dz}{dx} = \left(\dfrac{a}{ax+b}\right)\dfrac{dy}{dz}$

$\Rightarrow \qquad (ax+b)\dfrac{dy}{dx} = a\dfrac{dy}{dx} = a\,Dy \qquad\qquad \left[\because \dfrac{d}{dz} = D\right]$

$$\dfrac{d^2 y}{dx^2} = \dfrac{d}{dx}\left(\dfrac{a}{ax+b} \cdot \dfrac{dy}{dz}\right)$$

$$= \dfrac{-a^2}{(ax+b)^2}\dfrac{dy}{dz} + \dfrac{a}{ax+b}\dfrac{d}{dz}\left(\dfrac{dy}{dz}\right)\dfrac{dz}{dx}$$

$$= -\dfrac{a^2}{(ax+b)^2}\dfrac{dy}{dz} + \dfrac{a^2}{(ax+b)^2}\dfrac{d^2 y}{dz^2}$$

$$= \dfrac{a^2}{(ax+b)^2}\left[\dfrac{d^2 y}{dz^2} - \dfrac{dy}{dz}\right]$$

$$\Rightarrow \quad (ax+b)^2 \frac{d^2y}{dx^2} = a^2[D^2 - D]\,y = a^2 D(D-1)\,y$$

Similarly, we shall get

$$(ax+b)^3 \frac{d^3y}{dx^3} = a^3 D(D-1)(D-2)\,y \text{ and so on.}$$

If we make these substitutions in the differential equation (Legendre's), we shall see that it has been transformed into one with constant coefficients.

ILLUSTRATIONS

Ex. 6 : *Solve* $(2x+1)^2 \dfrac{d^2y}{dx^2} - 2(2x+1)\dfrac{dy}{dx} - 12y = 6x$ **(May 09, Nov. 16)**

Sol. : Put $2x+1 = e^z \Rightarrow z = \log(2x+1)$, $\dfrac{dz}{dx} = \dfrac{2}{2x+1}$, $\dfrac{d}{dz} \equiv D$.

Then we shall have

$$(2x+1)^2 \frac{d^2y}{dx^2} = 4 \cdot D(D-1)\,y, \quad (2x+1)\frac{dy}{dx} = 2\,Dy$$

and the equation is transformed into

$$4D(D-1)\,y - 4(Dy) - 12y = 6\left(\frac{e^z - 1}{2}\right)$$

$$\Rightarrow \qquad [4(D^2 - D) - 4D - 12]\,y = 3e^z - 3$$
$$\Rightarrow \qquad (4D^2 - 8D - 12)\,y = 3e^z - 3$$
$$\Rightarrow \qquad (D^2 - 2D - 3)\,y = \frac{3}{4}(e^z - 1)$$

which is now linear with constant coefficient in y, z.

$$\text{A.E.} \ : \ D^2 - 2D - 3 = 0 \ \Rightarrow \ D = 3, -1$$
$$\text{C.F.} = c_1 e^{3z} + c_2 e^{-z}$$
$$\text{P.I.} = \frac{1}{D^2 - 2D - 3}\,\frac{3}{4}(e^z - e^{0z})$$
$$\text{P.I.} = \frac{3}{4}\left[\frac{1}{D^2 - 2D - 3}e^z - \frac{1}{D^2 - 2D - 3}e^{0z}\right]$$
$$= \frac{3}{4}\left[\frac{e^z}{1 - 2 - 3} - \frac{e^{0z}}{0 - 0 - 3}\right] = \frac{3}{4}\left[\frac{e^z}{-4} + \frac{1}{3}\right]$$
$$= \frac{3e^z}{-16} + \frac{1}{4}$$

Hence the complete solution in terms of y and z is

$$y = c_1 e^{3z} + c_2 e^{-z} - 3\frac{e^z}{16} + \frac{1}{4}$$

Changing back to y and x, we have

$$y = c_1(2x+1)^3 + c_2(2x+1)^{-1} - \frac{3}{16}(2x+1) + \frac{1}{4}$$

Ex. 7 : *Solve* $(1 + x)^2 \dfrac{d^2y}{dx^2} + (1 + x) \dfrac{dy}{dx} + y = 2 \sin [\log (1 + x)]$

(Dec. 2005, 2009, May 2008, 2016)

Sol. : Put $(1 + x) = e^z \Rightarrow z = \log (1 + x)$, $\dfrac{d}{dz} \equiv D$

Then the equation will become

$$D (D - 1) y + Dy + y = 2 \sin z$$

$$\Rightarrow \qquad (D^2 + 1) y = 2 \sin z$$

Here   A.E. : $D^2 + 1 = 0$, $D = \pm i$, hence

$$\text{C.F.} = A \cos z + B \sin z$$

$$\text{P.I.} = \frac{2 \sin z}{D^2 + 1} = \frac{2 \sin z}{-1 + 1} \quad \text{(case of failure)}$$

$$\therefore \qquad \text{P.I.} = z \frac{1}{2D} 2 \sin z = z \int \sin z \, dz = - z \cos z$$

General solution in terms of y and z is

$$y = A \cos z + B \sin z - z \cos z$$

$$\therefore \qquad y = A \cos [\log (1 + x)] + B \sin [\log (1 + x)] - \log (1 + x) \cos [\log (1 + x)]$$

Ex. 8 : *Solve* $(3x + 2)^2 \dfrac{d^2y}{dx^2} + 3 (3x + 2) \dfrac{dy}{dx} - 36y = 3x^2 + 4x + 1.$ **(May 2014)**

Sol. : Given equation is Legendre's linear differential equation.

Put $z = \log (3x + 2)$ or $(3x + 2) = e^z$ and let $\dfrac{d}{dz} \equiv D$ then the equation is transformed

into $[9D (D - 1) + 3.3D - 36] y = \dfrac{1}{3} (e^{2z} - 1)$ or $(D^2 - 4) y = \dfrac{1}{27} (e^{2z} - 1)$

A.E. is $D^2 - 4 = 0 \quad \therefore \quad D = \pm 2.$

$$\text{C.F.} = c_1 e^{2z} + c_2 e^{-2z}$$

$$\text{P.I.} = \frac{1}{27} \frac{1}{D^2 - 4} (e^{2z} - 1) = \frac{1}{27} \left[\frac{1}{D^2 - 4} e^{2z} - \frac{1}{D^2 - 4} e^{0z} \right]$$

$$= \frac{1}{27} \left[\frac{z \, e^{2z}}{4} + \frac{1}{4} \right] = \frac{1}{108} [ze^{2z} + 1]$$

The general solution in y and z is

$$y = c_1 e^{2z} + c_2 e^{-2z} + \frac{1}{108} [ze^{2z} + 1]$$

The general solution in y and x is

$$y = c_1 (3x + 2)^2 + c_2 (3x + 2)^{-2} + \frac{1}{108} [(3x + 2)^2 \log (3x + 2) + 1]$$

EXERCISE 1.4

Solve following differential equations with variable coefficients.

1. $x^2 \dfrac{d^2y}{dx^2} - 4x \dfrac{dy}{dx} + 6y = x^5$ **(Dec. 08, May 17)**

> **Ans.** $y = c_1 x^2 + c_2 x^3 + \dfrac{x^5}{6}$

2. $x^2 \dfrac{d^2y}{dx^2} - 2x \dfrac{dy}{dx} - 4y = x^2 + 2 \log x$

> **Ans.** $y = c_1 x^4 + \dfrac{c_2}{x} - \dfrac{x^2}{6} - \dfrac{1}{2} \log x + \dfrac{3}{8}$

3. $x^2 \dfrac{d^3y}{dx^3} + 3x \dfrac{d^2y}{dx^2} + \dfrac{dy}{dx} + \dfrac{y}{x} = \log x$

> **Ans.** $y = \dfrac{c_1}{x} + \sqrt{x}\left[c_2 \cos\left(\sqrt{3}/2\right) \log x + c_3 \sin\left(\sqrt{3}/2\right) \log x\right] + \dfrac{x}{2}\left(\log x - \dfrac{3}{2}\right)$

4. $x^3 \dfrac{d^3y}{dx^3} + x^2 \dfrac{d^2y}{dx^2} - 2y = x^2 + x^{-3}$.

> **Ans.** $y = c_1 x^2 + c_2 \cos(\log x) + c_3 \sin(\log x) + \dfrac{x^2}{5} \log x - \dfrac{1}{50} x^{-3}$

5. $(x^3 D^3 + x^2 D^2 - 2) y = x + x^{-3}$

> **Ans.** $y = c_1 x^2 + c_2 \cos(\log x) + c_3 \sin(\log x) - \dfrac{x}{2} - \dfrac{1}{50} x^{-3}$

6. $\dfrac{d^2y}{dx^2} + \dfrac{1}{x} \dfrac{dy}{dx} = A + B \log x$ **(Nov. 2013)**

> **Ans.** $y = (c_1 + c_2 \log x) + \dfrac{A}{4} x^2 + \dfrac{B}{4} x^2 (\log x - 1)$

7. $\left(\dfrac{d^2}{dx^2} - \dfrac{2}{x^2}\right)^2 y = 0$ **(May 2008)**

> **Ans.** $y = c_1 x^4 + c_2 x^2 + c_3 x + \dfrac{c_4}{x}$

8. $\left(\dfrac{d^2}{dx^2} - \dfrac{2}{x^2}\right)^2 y = x^2$ **(May 2006)**

> **Ans.** $y = c_3 x^2 + \dfrac{c_4}{x} + c_5 x^4 + c_6 x + \dfrac{x^6}{280}$

9. $(x^2 D^2 - xD + 1) y = x \log x$ **(Nov. 2015)**

Ans. $y = x \, [A \log x + B] + \dfrac{x}{6} \, (\log x)^3$

10. $x^2 \dfrac{d^2y}{dx^2} - 3x \dfrac{dy}{dx} + 5y = x^2 \log x.$ **(Dec. 2009)**

Ans. $y = x^2 \, [c_1 \cos (\log x) + c_2 \sin (\log x)] + x^2 \log x$

11. $x^3 \dfrac{d^2y}{dx^2} + 3x^2 \dfrac{dy}{dx} + xy = \sin (\log x)$ **(Dec. 2004, 2007)**

Ans. $y = \dfrac{1}{x} \, \{ c_1 + c_2 \log x - \sin (\log x) \}$

12.   The radial displacement 'u' in a rotating disc at a distance 'r' from axis is given by

$$\dfrac{d^2u}{dr^2} + \dfrac{1}{r} \dfrac{du}{dr} - \dfrac{u}{r^2} + kr = 0$$

Find the displacement if u = 0 for r = 0, r = a

Ans. $u = \dfrac{kr}{8} \, (a^2 - r^2)$

13. $x^2 \dfrac{d^2y}{dx^2} + x \dfrac{dy}{dx} - y = \dfrac{x^3}{1 + x^2}$

Ans. $y = Ax + \dfrac{B}{x} + \dfrac{x}{4} \, \log (1 + x^2) - \dfrac{x}{4} + \dfrac{1}{4x} \log (x^2 + 1)$

14. $u = r \dfrac{d}{dr} \left[r \dfrac{du}{dr} \right] + ar^3$

Ans. $u = Ar + \dfrac{B}{r} - \dfrac{a}{8} \, r^3$

15. $x \dfrac{d^2y}{dx^2} + \dfrac{dy}{dx} + x = 0$

[**Hint :** Multiply by x]   **Ans.** $y = A + B \log x - \dfrac{x^2}{4}$

16. $(x^3 D^3 + 2 x^2 D^2 + 3 x D - 3) y = x^2 + x$

Ans. $y = c_1 x + c_2 \cos (\log x) + c_3 \sin (\log x) + \dfrac{x}{7} + \dfrac{x}{4} \log x$

17. $x^2 \dfrac{d^2y}{dx^2} + 3x \dfrac{dy}{dx} + y = \dfrac{1}{(1 - x)^2}$

Ans. $y = \dfrac{1}{x} \left[c_1 \log x + c_2 + \log \left(\dfrac{x}{x - 1} \right) \right]$

18. $x^2 \dfrac{d^2y}{dx^2} + x \dfrac{dy}{dx} + y = \sin(\log x^2)$

Ans. $y = c_1 \cos(\log x) + c_2 \sin(\log x) - \dfrac{1}{3} \sin(\log x^2)$

19. $x^3 \dfrac{d^3y}{dx^3} + 3x^2 \dfrac{d^2y}{dx^2} + x \dfrac{dy}{dx} + 8y = 65 \cos(\log x).$

Ans. $y = c_1 x^{-2} + x\,(c_2 \cos \sqrt{(3)} \log x + c_3 \sin(\sqrt{3}) \log x)$

$- \sin(\log x) + 8 \cos(\log x)$

20. $(x^2 D^2 + 5xD + 3)\, y = \left(1 + \dfrac{1}{x}\right)^2 \log x$

21. $(x^2 D^2 - 3xD + 1)\, y = \log x \left[\dfrac{\sin(\log x) + 1}{x} \right]$

22. $\left(D^3 - \dfrac{4}{x} D^2 + \dfrac{5}{x^2} D - \dfrac{2}{x^3} \right) y = 1$

Ans. $y = c_1 x^2 + c_2\, x^{\left(\frac{5 - \sqrt{21}}{2} \right)} + c_3\, x^{\left(\frac{5 - \sqrt{21}}{2} \right)} - \dfrac{x^3}{5}$

23. $(x^2 D^2 - 4xD + 6)\, y = -x^4 \sin x$ **(May 2005)**

Ans. $y = c_1 x^2 + c_2 x^3 + x^2 \sin x$

24. $(2x + 3)^2 \dfrac{d^2y}{dx^2} - 2\,(2x + 3) \dfrac{dy}{dx} - 12y = 6x$ **(Dec. 2005, 2008)**

Ans. $y = c_1\,(2x + 3)^3 + c_2\,(2x + 3)^{-1} - \dfrac{3}{16}\,(2x + 3) + \dfrac{3}{4}$

25. $(x + a)^2 \dfrac{d^2y}{dx^2} - 4\,(x + a) \dfrac{dy}{dx} + 6y = x$

Ans. $y = A\,(x + a)^3 + B\,(x + a)^2 + \dfrac{3x + 2a}{6}$

26. $7\,(2 + x)^2 \dfrac{d^2y}{dx^2} + 8\,(2 + x) \dfrac{dy}{dx} + y = 4 \cos[\log(2 + x)]$

27. $(1 + x)^2 \dfrac{d^2y}{dx^2} + (1 + x) \dfrac{dy}{dx} + y = 4 \cos[\log(1 + x)]$ **(May 2011)**

Ans. $y = c_1 \cos[\log(x + 1)] + c_2 \sin[\log(1 + x)]$

28. $(x + 2)^2 \dfrac{d^2y}{dx^2} - (x + 2) \dfrac{dy}{dx} + y = 3x + 4$

Ans. $y = (x + 2)[c_1 + c_2 \log(x + 2)] + \dfrac{3}{2}\,(x + 2)[\log(x + 2)]^2 - 2$

29. $(x + 2)^2 \dfrac{d^2y}{dx^2} + 3 (x + 2) \dfrac{dy}{dx} + y = 4 \sin [\log (x + 2)]$

$\qquad\qquad$ **Ans.** $y = [\{c_1 + c_2 \log (x + 2)\} (x + 2)^{-1} - 2 \cos [\log (x + 2)]$

30. $(2x + 1)^2 \dfrac{d^2y}{dx^2} - 6 (2x + 1) \dfrac{dy}{dx} + 16y = 8 (2x + 1)^2.$

$\qquad\qquad$ **Ans.** $y = [c_1 + c_2 \log (2x + 1)] (2x + 1)^2 + (2x + 1)^2 [\log (2x + 1)]^2$

31. $(x + 1)^2 \dfrac{d^2y}{dx^2} + (x + 1) \dfrac{dy}{dx} = (2x + 3) (2x + 4).$ $\qquad\qquad$ **(Dec. 2010)**

$\qquad\qquad$ **Ans.** $y = c_1 + c_2 \log (x + 1) + (x + 1)^2 + 6 (x + 1) + [\log (x + 1)]^2$

32. $(4x + 1)^2 \dfrac{d^2y}{dx^2} + 2 (4x + 1) \dfrac{dy}{dx} + y = 2x + 1.$

$\qquad\qquad$ **Ans.** $y = [c_1 + c_2 \log (4x + 1)] (4x + 1)^{1/4} + \dfrac{1}{18} (4x + 1) + \dfrac{1}{2}$

33. $(x + 1)^2 \dfrac{d^2y}{dx^2} + (x + 1) \dfrac{dy}{dx} - y = 2 \log (x + 1) + x - 1.$

$\qquad\qquad$ **Ans.** $y = c_1 (x + 1) + c_2 (x + 1)^{-1} - 2 \log (x + 1) + \dfrac{1}{2} (x + 1) \log (x + 1) + 2$

34. $(x - 1)^3 \dfrac{d^3y}{dx^3} + 2 (x - 1)^2 \dfrac{d^2y}{dx^2} - 4 (x - 1) \dfrac{dy}{dx} + 4y = 4 \log (x - 1)$

$\qquad\qquad$ **Ans.** $y = c_1 + c_2 (x - 1)^2 + c_3 (x - 1)^{-2} - \dfrac{4}{3} (x - 1) \log (x - 1)$

MULTIPLE CHOICE QUESTIONS (MCQ's)

Type : Cauchy's and Legendre's Linear Differential Equations :

1. The general form of Cauchy's linear differential equation is $\qquad\qquad$ (1)

(A) $a_0 \dfrac{d^ny}{dx^n} + a_1 \dfrac{d^{n-1}y}{dx^{n-1}} + a_2 \dfrac{d^{n-2}y}{dx^{n-2}} + \ldots + a_n y = f(x)$, where $a_0, \; a_1, \; a_2, \; \ldots, \; a_n$ are constants.

(B) $\dfrac{dx}{P} = \dfrac{dy}{Q} = \dfrac{dz}{R}$, where P, Q, R are functions of x, y, z.

(C) $a_0 x^n \dfrac{d^ny}{dx^n} + a_1 x^{n-1} \dfrac{d^{n-1}y}{dx^{n-1}} + a_2 x^{n-2} \dfrac{d^{n-2}}{dx^{n-2}} + \ldots + a_n y = f(x)$, where $a_0, a_1, a_2 \ldots a_n$ are constants

(D) $a_0 (ax + b)^n \dfrac{d^ny}{dx^n} + a_1 (ax + b)^{n-1} \dfrac{d^{n-1}y}{dx^{n-1}} + a_2 (ax + b)^{n-2} \dfrac{d^{n-2}y}{dx^{n-2}} + \ldots + a_n y = f(x)$, where $a_0, a_1, a_2 \ldots, a_n$ are constant.

2. Cauchy's linear differential equation $a_0 x^n \dfrac{d^n y}{dx^n} + a_1 x^{n-1} \dfrac{d^{n-1}y}{dx^{n-1}} + a_2 x^{n-2} \dfrac{d^{n-2}y}{dx^{n-2}} + \ldots + a_n y$

   $= f(x)$ can be reduced to linear differential equation with constant coefficients by using substitution   (1)

   (A) $x = e^z$ (B) $y = e^z$

   (C) $x = \log z$ (D) $x = e^{z^2}$

3. The general form of Legendre's linear differential equation is   (1)

   (A) $a_0 \dfrac{d^n y}{dx^n} + a_1 \dfrac{d^{n-1}y}{dx^{n-1}} + a_2 \dfrac{d^{n-2}y}{dx^{n-2}} + \ldots + a_n\, y = f(x)$, where $a_0, a_1, a_2 \ldots, a_n$ are constant.

   (B) $\dfrac{dx}{P} = \dfrac{dy}{Q} = \dfrac{dz}{R}$, where P, Q, R are functions of x, y, z.

   (C) $a_0 x^n \dfrac{d^n y}{dx^n} + a_1 x^{n-1} \dfrac{d^{n-1}y}{dx^{n-1}} + a_2 x^{n-2} \dfrac{d^{n-2}}{dx^{n-2}} + \ldots + a_n y = f(x)$, where $a_0, a_1, a_2 \ldots, a_n$ are

       constant

   (D) $a_0\,(ax + b)^n \dfrac{d^n y}{dx^n} + a_1\,(ax + b)^{n-1} \dfrac{d^{n-1}y}{dx^{n-1}} + a_2\,(ax + b)^{n-2} \dfrac{d^{n-2}y}{dx^{n-2}} + \ldots + a_n y = f(x)$,

       where $a_0, a_1, a_2, \ldots, a_n$ are constant.

4. Legendre's linear differential equation $a_0\,(ax + b)^n \dfrac{d^n y}{dx^n} + a_1\,(ax + b)^{n-1} \dfrac{d^{n-1}y}{dx^{n-1}} +$

   $a_2\,(ax + b)^{n-2} \dfrac{d^{n-2}y}{dx^{n-2}} + \ldots + a_n y = f(x)$ can be reduced to linear differential equation

   with constant coefficients by using substitution   (1)

   (A) $x = e^z$ (B) $ax + b = e^z$

   (C) $ax + b = \log z$ (D) $ax + b = e^{z^2}$

5. To reduce the differential equation $x^2 \dfrac{d^2 y}{dx^2} - 4x \dfrac{dy}{dx} + 6y = x^4$ to linear differential

   equation with constant coefficients, substitutions is   (1)

   (A) $x = z^2 + 1$ (B) $x = e^z$

   (C) $x = \log z$ (D) $x^2 = \log z$

6. To reduce the differential equation $(x + 2)^2 \dfrac{d^2 y}{dx^2} - (x + 2) \dfrac{dy}{dx} + y = 4x + 7$ to linear

   differential equation with constant coefficients, substitution is   (1)

   (A) $x + 2 = e^{-z}$ (B) $x = z + 1$

   (C) $x + 2 = e^z$ (D) $x + 2 = \log z$

7. To reduce the differential equation $(3x + 2)^2 \dfrac{d^2y}{dx^2} + 3\,(3x + 2)\dfrac{dy}{dx} - 36y = x^2 + 3x + 1$ to linear differential equation with constant coefficients, substitution is   (1)

(A) $3x + 2 = e^z$

(B) $3x + 2 = z$

(C) $x = e^z$

(D) $3x + 2 = \log z$

8. On putting $x = e^z$ and using $D \equiv \dfrac{d}{dz}$ the differential equation $x^2 \dfrac{d^2y}{dx^2} + x\dfrac{dy}{dx} + y = x$ is transformed into   (1)

(A) $(D^2 - 1)\, y = e^z$

(B) $(D^2 + 1)\, y = e^z$

(C) $(D^2 + 1)\, y = x$

(D) $(D^2 + D + 1)\, y = e^z$

9. The differential equation $x^2 \dfrac{d^2y}{dx^2} - x\dfrac{dy}{dx} + 4y = \cos\,(\log x) + x \sin\,(\log x)$, on putting $x = e^z$ and using $D \equiv \dfrac{d}{dz}$ is transformed into   (1)

(A) $(D^2 - D + 4)\, y = \sin z + e^z \cos z$

(B) $(D^2 - 2D + 4)\, y = \cos\,(\log x) + x \sin\,(\log x)$

(C) $(D^2 + 2D + 4)\, y = \cos z + e^{-z} \sin z$

(D) $(D^2 - 2D + 4)\, y = \cos z + e^z \sin z$

10. On putting $x = e^z$ the transformed differential equation of

$x^2 \dfrac{d^2y}{dx^2} - 3x\dfrac{dy}{dx} + 5y = x^2 \sin\,(\log x)$ using $D \equiv \dfrac{d}{dz}$ is   (1)

(A) $(D^2 - 4D + 5)\, y = e^{2z} \sin z$

(B) $(D^2 - 4D + 5)\, y = x^2 \sin\,(\log x)$

(C) $(D^2 - 4D - 4)\, y = e^z \sin z$

(D) $(D^2 - 3D + 5)\, y = e^{z^2} \sin z$

11. The differential equation $x^2 \dfrac{d^2y}{dx^2} + x\dfrac{dy}{dx} - y = \dfrac{x^3}{1 + x^2}$, on putting $x = e^z$ and using $D \equiv \dfrac{d}{dz}$ is transformed into   (1)

(A) $(D^2 - 1)\, y = \dfrac{x^3}{1 + x^2}$

(B) $(D^2 - 2D - 1)\, y = \dfrac{e^{3z}}{1 + e^{2z}}$

(C) $(D^2 - 1)\, y = \dfrac{e^{3z}}{1 + e^{2z}}$

(D) $(D^2 - 1)\, y = \dfrac{e^{z^3}}{1 + e^{z^2}}$

12. The differential equation $x^2 \dfrac{d^2y}{dx^2} - 5x \dfrac{dy}{dx} + 5y = x^2 \log x$, on putting $x = e^z$ and using

$D \equiv \dfrac{d}{dz}$ is transformed into   (1)

(A) $(D^2 - 5D + 5)\, y = z\, e^{z^2}$ (B) $(D^2 - 5D - 5)\, y = e^{2z}\, z$

(C) $(D^2 - 6D + 5)\, y = x^2 \log x$ (D) $(D^2 - 6D + 5)\, y = z\, e^{2z}$

13. The differential equation $(2x + 1)^2 \dfrac{d^2y}{dx^2} - 2(2x + 1)\dfrac{dy}{dx} - 12y = 6x$, on putting

$2x + 1 = e^z$ and putting $D \equiv \dfrac{d}{dz}$ is transformed into   (1)

(A) $(D^2 - 2D - 3)\, y = \dfrac{3}{4}(e^z - 1)$ (B) $(D^2 + 2D + 3)\, y = 3(e^z - 1)$

(C) $(D^2 + 2D - 12)\, y = \dfrac{3}{4}(e^z - 1)$ (D) $(D^2 - 2D - 3)\, y = 6x$

14. The differential equation $(3x + 2)^2 \dfrac{d^2y}{dx^2} + 3(3x + 2)\dfrac{dy}{dx} - 36y = \dfrac{1}{3}\left[(3x + 2)^2 - 1\right]$. On

putting $3x + 2 = e^z$ and using $D \equiv \dfrac{d}{dz}$ is transformed into   (1)

(A) $(D^2 + 3D - 36)\, y = \dfrac{1}{27}(e^{2z} - 1)$ (B) $(D^2 + 4)\, y = \dfrac{1}{9}(e^{2z} - 1)$

(C) $(D^2 - 4)\, y = \dfrac{1}{27}(e^{2z} - 1)$ (D) $(D^2 - 9)\, y = (e^{2z} - 1)$

15. The differential equation $(1 + x)^2 \dfrac{d^2y}{dx^2} + 3(1 + x)\dfrac{dy}{dx} - 36y = 4 \cos[\log(1 + x)]$ on

putting $1 + x = e^z$ and using $D \equiv \dfrac{d}{dz}$ is transformed into   (1)

(A) $(D^2 + 2D - 36)\, y = 4 \cos[\log(1+ x)]$ (B) $(D^2 + 2D - 36)\, y = 4 \cos z$

(C) $(D^2 + 3D - 36)\, y = 4 \cos z$ (D) $(D^2 - 2D - 36)\, y = 4 \cos(\log z)$

16. The differential equation $(4x + 1)^2 \dfrac{d^2y}{dx^2} + 2(4x + 1)\dfrac{dy}{dx} + 2y = 2x + 1$ on putting

$4x + 1 = e^z$ and using $D \equiv \dfrac{d}{dz}$ is transformed into   (1)

(A) $(D^2 + D + 2)\, y = \dfrac{1}{2}(e^z + 1)$ (B) $(16D^2 + 8D + 2)\, y = (e^z + 1)$

(C) $(16D^2 - 8D + 2)\, y = \dfrac{1}{2}(e^z + 1)$ (D) $(D^2 + 2D + 2)\, y = (e^z - 1)$

17. The differential equation $(x + 2)^2 \dfrac{d^2y}{dx^2} + 3(x + 2) \dfrac{dy}{dx} + y = 4 \sin [\log (x + 2)]$ on

putting $x + 2 = e^z$ and using $D \equiv \dfrac{d}{dz}$ is transformed into   (1)

(A) $(D^2 + 3D + 1) y = 4 \sin (\log z)$ (B) $(D^2 + 1) y = 4 \sin z$

(C) $(D^2 + 2D + 1) y = 4 \sin [\log (x + 2)]$ (D) $(D^2 + 2D + 1) y = 4 \sin z$

18. For the differential equation $x^2 \dfrac{d^2y}{dx^2} + x \dfrac{dy}{dx} + y = x^2 + x^{-2}$, complimentary function is

given by   (2)

(A) $c_1 x + c_2$ (B) $c_1 \log x + c_2$

(C) $c_1 \cos x + c_2 \sin x$ (D) $c_1 \cos (\log x) + c_2 \sin (\log x)$

19. For the differential equation $\dfrac{d^2y}{dx^2} + \dfrac{1}{x} \dfrac{dy}{dx} = A + B \log x$, complimentary function is

given by   (2)

(A) $c_1 x + c_2$ (B) $c_1 x^2 + c_2$

(C) $c_1 \log x + c_2$ (D) $\dfrac{c_1}{x} + c_2$

20. For the differential equation $x^2 \dfrac{d^2y}{dx^2} - 4x \dfrac{dy}{dx} + 6y = x^5$, complimentary function is

given by   (2)

(A) $c_1 x^2 + c_2 x^3$ (B) $c_1 x^2 + c_2 x$

(C) $c_1 x^{-2} + c_2 x^{-3}$ (D) $c_1 x^5 + c_2 x$

21. For the differential equation $x^2 \dfrac{d^2y}{dx^2} - x \dfrac{dy}{dx} + 4y = \cos (\log x) + x \sin (\log x)$,

complimentary function is given by   (2)

(A) $\left[c_1 \cos \sqrt{3} (\log x) + c_2 \sin \sqrt{3} (\log x)\right]$
(B) $x \left[c_1 \cos \sqrt{2} (\log x) + c_2 \sin \sqrt{2} (\log x)\right]$
(C) $x \left[c_1 \cos (\log x) + c_2 \sin (\log x)\right]$
(D) $x \left[c_1 \cos \sqrt{3} (\log x) + c_2 \sin \sqrt{3} (\log x)\right]$

22. For the differential equation $r^2 \dfrac{d^2u}{dr^2} + r \dfrac{du}{dr} - u = -kr^3$, complimentary function is

given by

(A) $(c_1 \log r + c_2) r$ (B) $c_1 r + \dfrac{c_2}{r}$

(C) $[c_1 \cos (\log r) + c_2 \sin (\log r)]$ (D) $c_1 r^2 + \dfrac{c_2}{r^2}$

23. For the differential equation $x^2 \dfrac{d^2y}{dx^2} + x \dfrac{dy}{dx} + y = x$, particular integral is given by (2)

(A) x

(B) $\dfrac{x}{2}$

(C) $\dfrac{x}{3}$

(D) $2x$

24. For the differential equation $x^2 \dfrac{d^2y}{dx^2} - 4x \dfrac{dy}{dx} + 6y = x^5$, particular integral is given by (2)

(A) $\dfrac{x^5}{6}$

(B) $\dfrac{x^5}{56}$

(C) $\dfrac{x^4}{6}$

(D) $-\dfrac{x^5}{44}$

25. Solution of differential equation $x \dfrac{d^2y}{dx^2} + \dfrac{dy}{dx} = x$ is (2)

(A) $(c_1 x + c_2) - \dfrac{x^2}{4}$

(B) $(c_1 x^2 + c_2) + \dfrac{x^2}{4}$

(C) $(c_1 \log x + c_2) - \dfrac{x^2}{4}$

(D) $(c_1 \log x + c_2) + \dfrac{x^2}{4}$

26. Solution of differential equation $x^2 \dfrac{d^2y}{dx^2} + 2x \dfrac{dy}{dx} = \dfrac{1}{x^2}$ is (2)

(A) $(c_1 x + c_2) - \dfrac{x^2}{4}$

(B) $(c_1 x^2 + c_2) + \dfrac{x^2}{4}$

(C) $c_1 + c_2 \dfrac{1}{x} + \dfrac{1}{2x^2}$

(D) $(c_1 \log x + c_2) + \dfrac{x^2}{4}$

27. For the differential equation $(x + 1)^2 \dfrac{d^2y}{dx^2} + (x + 1) \dfrac{dy}{dx} + y = 2 \sin [\log (x + 1)]$, complimentary function is given by (2)

(A) $c_1 (x + 1) + c_2 (x + 1)^{-1}$

(B) $c_1 \cos [\log (x + 1)] + c_2 \sin [\log (x + 1)]$

(C) $[c_1 \log (x + 1) + c_2] (x + 1)$

(D) $c_1 \cos (\log x) + c_2 \sin (\log x)$

28. For the differential equation $(2x + 3)^2 \dfrac{d^2y}{dx^2} - 2 (2x + 3) \dfrac{dy}{dx} - 12y = 6x$, complimentary function is given by (2)

(A) $c_1 (2x + 3)^3 + c_2 (2x + 3)^{-1}$

(B) $c_1 (2x + 3)^{-3} + c_2 (2x + 3)$

(C) $c_1 (2x + 3)^3 + c_2 (2x + 3)^2$

(D) $c_1 (2x - 3)^2 + c_2 (2x - 3)^{-1}$

29. For the differential equation $(3x + 2)^2 \dfrac{d^2y}{dx^2} + 3(3x + 2)\dfrac{dy}{dx} - 36y = (3x + 2)^2$, complimentary function is given by　　　　(2)

(A) $c_1(3x + 2)^3 + c_2(3x + 2)^{-3}$

(B) $[c_1 \log(3x + 2) + c_2](3x + 2)^{-2}$

(C) $c_1(3x + 2)^2 + c_2(3x + 2)^{-2}$

(D) $c_1(3x - 2)^2 + c_2(3x - 2)^{-2}$

30. For the differential equation $(x + 2)^2 \dfrac{d^2y}{dx^2} - (x + 2)\dfrac{dy}{dx} + y = (3x + 6)$, complimentary function is given by　　　　(2)

(A) $c_1(x + 2) + c_2(x + 2)^{-1}$

(B) $c_1 \log(x + 2) + c_2$

(C) $c_1(x - 2) + c_2(x - 2)^{-1}$

(D) $[c_1 \log(x + 2) + c_2](x + 2)$

Answers

1. (C)	2. (A)	3. (D)	4. (B)	5. (B)	6. (C)	7. (A)	8. (B)
9. (D)	10. (A)	11. (C)	12. (D)	13. (A)	14. (C)	15. (B)	16. (C)
17. (D)	18. (D)	19. (C)	20. (A)	21. (D)	22. (B)	23. (B)	24. (A)
25. (D)	26. (C)	27. (B)	28. (A)	29. (C)	30. (D)		

CHAPTER TWO

SIMULTANEOUS LINEAR DIFFERENTIAL EQUATIONS

2.1 INTRODUCTION

Sometimes in applications we come across equations, containing one independent but two or more dependent variables. For example :

$$\frac{dx}{dt} + 3 \frac{dy}{dt} + y = t$$

$$\frac{dy}{dt} - x - y = t^2$$

Here t is single independent and x and y are the two dependent variables. Such equations are called *Simultaneous Linear Differential Equations*. The number of equations is the same as the number of dependent variables.

2.2 METHOD OF SOLUTION

Method of solution is analogous to that of solving two linear simultaneous equations in algebra; either by Elimination or by Substitution. The equations of the system are so combined as to get a simple equation containing only one of the dependent variables and its derivatives. Then by integration, a relation between this dependent and the independent variable is found. Then either in a similar way or by substitution, a relation between the second dependent variable and the independent variable can be easily obtained. Examples will explain more.

2.3 ILLUSTRATIONS ON SIMULTANEOUS LINEAR DIFFERENTIAL EQUATIONS

Ex. 1 : *Solve*

$$\frac{dx}{dt} + 2x - 3y = t$$

$$\frac{dy}{dt} - 3x + 2y = e^{2t}$$

(May 2009, Dec. 2011)

Sol. : Writing in terms of operator $D = \frac{d}{dt}$, we have

$$Dx + 2x - 3y = t \quad \text{or} \quad (D + 2)\,x - 3y = t \qquad \dots (1)$$

$$Dy - 3x + 2y = e^{2t} \quad \text{or} \quad (D + 2)\,y - 3x = e^{2t} \qquad \dots (2)$$

Solving for x (i.e. eliminating y) :

Operating (1) by (D + 2), we have

$$(D + 2)^2\,x - 3\,(D + 2)\,y = (D + 2)\,t$$

$$\text{or} \quad (D + 2)^2\,x - 3\,(D + 2)\,y = 1 + 2t \qquad \dots (3)$$

Multiplying (2) by 3, we have

$$3\,(D+2)\,y - 9x \; = \; 3e^{2t} \qquad \qquad \text{... (4)}$$

Adding (3) and (4), we have

$$(D^2 + 4D - 5)\,x \; = \; 1 + 2t + 3e^{2t} \qquad \qquad \text{... (5)}$$

This is a linear differential equation with constant coefficients.

$$\text{AE} : D^2 + 4D - 5 = 0 \;\; \text{gives}\; D = -5,\,1$$

$$\text{C.F.} \; = \; c_1\,e^{-5t} + c_2\,e^t$$

$$\text{P.I.} \; = \; \frac{1}{D^2 + 4D - 5}\,(1+2t) + \frac{3e^{2t}}{D^2 + 4D - 5}$$

$$= \; -\frac{1}{5}\left[1 - \frac{4D + D^2}{5}\right]^{-1}(1+2t) + \frac{3e^{2t}}{4 + 8 - 5}$$

$$= \; -\frac{1}{5}\left(1 + \frac{4D}{5}\right)(1+2t) + \frac{3}{7}\,e^{2t}$$

$$= \; -\frac{1}{5}\left(\frac{13}{5} + 2t\right) + \frac{3e^{2t}}{7}$$

Hence the general solution for x is

$$x \; = \; c_1\,e^{-5t} + c_2\,e^t - \frac{13}{25} - \frac{2t}{5} + \frac{3e^{2t}}{7} \qquad \qquad \text{... (6)}$$

Next, the general solution for y :

Differentiating (6) with respect to t,

$$\frac{dx}{dt} \; = \; -5\,c_1\,e^{-5t} + c_2\,e^t - \frac{2}{5} + \frac{6}{7}e^{2t}$$

Putting values of x and $\dfrac{dx}{dt}$ in equation (1), we have

$$y \; = \; \frac{1}{3}\left[\frac{dx}{dt} + 2x - t\right]$$

$$= \; \frac{1}{3}\left[-5\,c_1\,e^{-5t} + c_2\,e^t - \frac{2}{5} + \frac{6}{7}\,e^{2t} + 2\,c_1\,e^{-5t} + 2\,c_2\,e^t - \frac{26}{25} - \frac{4t}{5} + \frac{6e^{2t}}{7} - t\right]$$

Simplifying, we get

$$y \; = \; -c_1\,e^{-5t} + c_2\,e^t - \frac{12}{25} - \frac{3t}{5} + \frac{4e^{2t}}{7} \qquad \qquad \text{... (7)}$$

Hence (6) and (7) together constitute the general solution.

Ex. 2 : *Solve the simultaneous linear differential equations with given conditions.*

$$\frac{du}{dx} + v \; = \; \sin x$$

$$\frac{dv}{dx} + u \; = \; \cos x$$

Given that when x = 0, then u = 1 and v = 0.

Sol. : In terms of operator $D \equiv \dfrac{d}{dx}$, the equations become :

$$Du + v = \sin x \qquad \qquad \dots (1)$$

$$Dv + u = \cos x \qquad \qquad \dots (2)$$

On differentiating (1), we get

$$D^2 u + Dv = \cos x \qquad \qquad \dots (3)$$

Now subtracting (2) from (3), we get

$$D^2 u - u = 0 \Rightarrow (D^2 - 1) u = 0,$$

whose solution is $\quad u = c_1 e^x + c_2 e^{-x} \qquad \qquad \dots (4)$

and $\qquad \qquad \dfrac{du}{dx} = c_1 e^x - c_2 e^{-x} \qquad \qquad \dots (5)$

Now if we put value of $\dfrac{du}{dx}$ from (5) in (1), we get v, as

$$v = \sin x - c_1 e^x + c_2 e^{-x} \qquad \qquad \dots (6)$$

Hence (4) and (6) together constitute the general solution.

To find c_1, c_2, we apply initial condition at $x = 0$, $u = 1$ and $v = 0$, hence

$$c_1 + c_2 = 1 \quad \text{and} \quad c_2 - c_1 = 0$$

Solving for c_1 and c_2, we obtain $c_1 = c_2 = \dfrac{1}{2}$

Hence $\qquad \qquad u = \dfrac{1}{2} (e^x + e^{-x}) \text{ and } v = \sin x - \dfrac{1}{2} (e^x - e^{-x}) \qquad \dots (7)$

or $\qquad \qquad u = \cosh x \quad \text{and} \quad v = \sin x - \sinh x \qquad \dots (8)$

Hence the solution of equations are given by equation (7) and (8).

Ex. 3 : *Solve simultaneously*

$$\dfrac{dx}{dt} - 3x - 6y = t^2 \qquad \qquad \dots (1)$$

$$\dfrac{dy}{dt} + \dfrac{dx}{dt} - 3y = e^t \qquad \qquad \textbf{(Dec. 2008)} \ \dots (2)$$

Sol. : Using $D \equiv \dfrac{d}{dx}$, equations (1) and (2) can be written as

$$(D - 3) x - 6y = t^2 \qquad \qquad \dots (3)$$

$$Dx + (D - 3) y = e^t \qquad \qquad \dots (4)$$

To eliminate x from (3) and (4), operating (3) by D and (4) by (D – 3), we get

$$D (D - 3) x - 6Dy = 2t \qquad \qquad \dots (5)$$

$$D (D - 3) x + (D - 3)^2 y = (D - 3) e^t = e^t - 3e^t = -2e^t \qquad \qquad \dots (6)$$

Subtracting (5) from (6), we have

$$(D^2 + 9)\, y = -2e^t - 2t$$

whose general solution is

$$y = c_1 \cos 3t + c_2 \sin 3t - \frac{e^t}{5} - \frac{2t}{9} \qquad \text{... (7)}$$

To eliminate y from (3) and (4), operate (3) by $(D - 3)$ and multiply (4) by 6 and subtract, we obtain

$$(D^2 + 9)\, x = 6e^t - 3t^2 + 2t$$

whose general solution is

$$x = c_3 \cos 3t + c_4 \sin 3t + \frac{3e^t}{5} - \frac{t^2}{3} + \frac{2t}{9} + \frac{2}{27} \qquad \text{... (8)}$$

We have too many constants. To deal with this problem (i.e. to obtain relation between c_1, c_2 and c_3, c_4), we put values of x and y in (3) to find

$$(\sin 3t)\,(-3c_3 - 3c_4 - 6c_2) + \cos 3t\,(3c_4 - 3c_3 - 6c_1) + t^2 = t^2$$

This must be identity, hence

$$-3c_3 - 3c_4 - 6c_2 = 0 \qquad \text{and} \qquad 3c_4 - 3c_3 - 6c_1 = 0$$

Solving and simplifying these, we get

$$c_1 = \frac{c_4}{2} - \frac{c_3}{2} \qquad \text{and} \qquad c_2 = -\frac{c_3}{2} - \frac{c_4}{2}$$

Hence on substituting c_1, c_2 in (8) the required solutions are

$$x = c_3 \cos 3t + c_4 \sin 3t + \frac{3}{5} e^t - \frac{1}{3} t^2 + \frac{2t}{9} + \frac{2}{27}$$

and
$$y = \left(\frac{c_4}{2} - \frac{c_3}{2}\right) \cos 3t + \left(-\frac{c_3}{2} - \frac{c_4}{2}\right) \sin 3t - \frac{e^t}{5} - \frac{2t}{9}$$

Remark : Alternatively, we note that in equation (1), coefficient of y is constant. Hence, we can solve the system for x first and then using this solution we can obtain y. Thus we can avoid obtaining a relation between constants c_1, c_2 and c_3, c_4 in the solutions for x and y.

Ex. 4 : *The currents x and y in the coupled circuits are given by*

$$L\,\frac{dx}{dt} + Rx + R\,(x - y) = E$$

$$L\frac{dy}{dt} + Ry - R\,(x - y) = 0$$

Find x and y in terms of t, given that $x = y = 0$ at $t = 0$.   **(Dec. 2005)**

Sol. : In terms of operator $D \equiv \dfrac{d}{dt}$, the equations are :

$$(LD + 2R)\ x - Ry = E \qquad\qquad \dots (1)$$

$$(LD + 2R)\, y - Rx = 0 \qquad\qquad \dots (2)$$

To eliminate y, operating (1) by (LD + 2R), we have

$$(LD + 2R)^2\, x - R\,(LD + 2R)\, y = (LD + 2R)\, E = 0 + 2\, RE$$

or $\qquad (LD + 2R)^2\, x - R\,(Rx) = 2RE$ (since from (2), we have $(LD + 2R)\, y = Rx$)

or $\qquad\quad (LD + 2R)^2\, x - R^2 x = 2RE$

i.e. $\quad L^2\,\dfrac{d^2 x}{dt^2} + 4RL\,\dfrac{dx}{dt} + 3R^2 x = 2RE$

A.E. is $\quad L^2\, D^2 + 4RLD + 3R^2 = 0$ or $(LD + 3R)\,(LD + R) = 0$

$$\therefore \qquad\qquad\qquad D = -\frac{3R}{L},\, -\frac{R}{L}$$

$$\text{C.F.} = c_1\, e^{-(Rt/L)} + c_2\, e^{-(3Rt/L)}$$

$$\text{P.I.} = 2RE\, \frac{1}{L^2\, D^2 + 4RLD + 3R^2}\, e^{ot}$$

$$= 2RE\, \frac{1}{0 + 0 + 3R^2}\, e^{ot} = \frac{2E}{3R}$$

Hence the general solution for x is

$$x = c_1\, e^{-(Rt/L)} + c_2\, e^{-(3Rt/L)} + \frac{2E}{3R} \qquad\qquad \dots(3)$$

To find y, from (1), we have $y = \dfrac{1}{R}\,[(LD + 2R)\, x - E] \qquad\qquad \dots (4)$

Now, $\quad (LD + 2R)\, x = L \cdot \dfrac{dx}{dt} + 2\, Rx$

$$= L\left[-\frac{c_1 R}{L}\, e^{-(Rt/L)} - \frac{3R}{L}\, c_2\, e^{-(3Rt/L)}\right]$$

$$+ 2R\left[c_1\, e^{-(Rt/L)} + c_2\, e^{-(3Rt/L)} + \frac{2E}{3R}\right]$$

$$= -c_1 R\, e^{-(Rt/L)} - 3R\, c_2\, e^{-(3Rt/L)} + 2R\, c_1\, e^{-(Rt/L)} + 2R\, c_2\, e^{-(3Rt/L)} + \frac{4E}{3}$$

$$\therefore \qquad (LD + 2R)\, x = c_1 R e^{-(Rt/L)} - c_2\, R\, e^{-(3Rt/L)} + \frac{4E}{3} \qquad\qquad \dots (5)$$

Putting value of $(LD + 2R) x$ from (5) in (4), we obtain

$$y = \frac{1}{R}\left[c_1 Re^{-(Rt/L)} - c_2 Re^{-(3Rt/L)} + \frac{4E}{3} - E \right]$$

$$\therefore \qquad y = c_1 e^{-(Rt/L)} - c_2 e^{-(3Rt/L)} + \frac{E}{3R} \qquad \dots (6)$$

Initially, at $t = 0$, $x = 0$ and $y = 0$, hence

$$0 = c_1 + c_2 + \frac{2E}{3R} \qquad \text{and} \quad 0 = c_1 - c_2 + \frac{E}{3R}$$

Solving for c_1 and c_2, we get

$$c_1 = -\frac{E}{2R} \quad \text{and} \ \ c_2 = -\frac{E}{6R}$$

Putting these values of c_1 and c_2 in (3) and (6) for x and y,

$$x = \frac{E}{R}\left[\frac{2}{3} - \frac{1}{2} e^{-(Rt/L)} - \frac{1}{6} e^{-(3Rt/L)} \right]$$

$$y = \frac{E}{R}\left[\frac{1}{3} - \frac{1}{2} e^{-(Rt/L)} + \frac{1}{6} e^{-(3Rt/L)} \right]$$

Ex. 5 : *The equations of motion of an electron under certain conditions are :*

$$m\frac{d^2x}{dt^2} + eH\frac{dy}{dt} = e E$$

$$m\frac{d^2y}{dt^2} - eH\frac{dx}{dt} = 0 \qquad \dots (I)$$

with condition $x = \dfrac{dx}{dt} = y = \dfrac{dy}{dt} = 0$ when $t = 0$, find the path of the electron.

Sol. : Multiply the second equation of (I) by an arbitrary constant k and add to the first of equation (I).

$$m\frac{d^2}{dt^2}(x + ky) + eH\frac{d}{dt}(y - kx) = e E$$

$$\text{or} \quad m\frac{d^2}{dt^2}(x + ky) - eHk\frac{d}{dt}\left(x - \frac{1}{k}y \right) = e E \qquad \dots (II)$$

Herein choose k such that :

$$x - \frac{1}{k}y = x + ky \implies k = -\frac{1}{k}$$

$$\text{or} \qquad k^2 + 1 = 0, \text{ hence } k = \pm\ i \qquad \dots (III)$$

Now put $x + ky = u$, then from (II),

$$m \frac{d^2u}{dt^2} - eHk \frac{du}{dt} = eE$$

$$\Rightarrow \quad \frac{d^2u}{dt^2} - wk \frac{du}{dt} = \frac{eE}{m} \qquad \text{where,} \quad w = \frac{eH}{m} \qquad \qquad \dots \text{(IV)}$$

If we solve equation (IV) as linear with constant coefficients, we get

$$u = x + ky = A + B\,e^{wkt} - \frac{Et}{Hk} \qquad \qquad \dots \text{(V)}$$

Also, $$\frac{du}{dt} = -\frac{E}{Hk}\,Bwk\,e^{wkt} \qquad \qquad \dots \text{(VI)}$$

$$= Bwk\,e^{wkt}$$

But initially $x = y = \dfrac{dx}{dt} = \dfrac{dy}{dt} = 0$ at $t = 0$ and $x + ky = u$, we can easily get

$$u = \frac{du}{dt} = 0 \text{ at } t = 0 \text{ and from (V) and (VI), we have at } t = 0$$

$$A + B = 0 \quad \text{and} \quad wkB = \frac{E}{Hk}$$

Solving these two, we get

$$A = -\frac{E}{Hwk^2} \quad \text{and} \quad B = \frac{E}{Hwk^2}$$

Putting for A and B in (V),

$$u = x + ky = -\frac{E}{Hwk^2} + \frac{E}{Hwk^2} \cdot e^{wkt} - \frac{Et}{Hk} \qquad \qquad \dots \text{(VII)}$$

But $k = i$ and $-i$.

when $(k = i)$, $\quad x + iy = \dfrac{E}{Hw} - \dfrac{E}{Hw}\,e^{iwt} + \dfrac{iEt}{H} \qquad \qquad \dots \text{(VIII)}$

and $(k = -i)$, $\quad x - iy = \dfrac{E}{Hw} - \dfrac{E}{Hw}\,e^{-iwt} - \dfrac{iEt}{H} \qquad \qquad \dots \text{(IX)}$

If we add and subtract (VIII) and (IX), we can easily get

$$x = \frac{E}{Hw}\,(1 - \cos wt) \qquad \qquad \left[w = \frac{eH}{m}\right]$$

$$y = \frac{E}{Hw}\,(wt - \sin wt)$$

Alternative Method :

System (I) can also be written as

$$\frac{d^2x}{dt^2} + a\frac{dy}{dt} = b \qquad \qquad \dots \text{(1)}$$

$$\frac{d^2y}{dt^2} - a\frac{dx}{dt} = 0 \quad \text{where } a = \frac{eH}{m} \text{ and } b = \frac{eE}{m} \qquad \qquad \dots \text{(2)}$$

Integrating (2) with respect to t, we get

$$\frac{dy}{dt} - ax = c_1$$

Initially, $x = \frac{dy}{dt} = 0$ at $t = 0$ $\therefore$ $c_1 = 0$

$$\therefore \quad \frac{dy}{dt} - ax = 0 \qquad \qquad \dots (3)$$

Next, integrating (1) with respect to t, we get

$$\frac{dx}{dt} + ay = bt + c_2$$

Initially, $\frac{dx}{dt} = y = 0$ at $t = 0$ $\therefore$ $c_2 = 0$

$$\therefore \quad \frac{dx}{dt} + ay = bt \qquad \qquad \dots (4)$$

From (3), substituting $x = \frac{1}{a}\frac{dy}{dt}$ in (4), we get

$$\frac{1}{a}\frac{d^2y}{dt^2} + ay = bt$$

or $\quad \dfrac{d^2y}{dt^2} + a^2y = abt \qquad \qquad \dots (5)$

which is a linear differential equation.

A.E. is $D^2 + a^2 = 0$ $\therefore$ $D = \pm ia$

$$\text{C.F.} = c_1 \cos at + c_2 \sin at$$

$$\text{P.I.} = \frac{1}{D^2 + a^2}\, abt = \frac{ab}{a^2}\left[1 + \frac{D^2}{a^2}\right]^{-1} t = \frac{b}{a}\left(1 - \frac{D^2}{a^2}\right)t = \frac{b}{a}t$$

$$\therefore \qquad \qquad y = c_3 \cos at + c_4 \sin at + \frac{b}{a}t \qquad \qquad \dots (6)$$

Again initially, $y = 0$, $t = 0$ $\therefore$ $c_3 = 0$

$$\therefore \qquad \qquad y = c_4 \sin at + \frac{b}{a}t$$

and $\qquad \qquad \dfrac{dy}{dt} = a\,c_4 \cos at + \dfrac{b}{a}$

Also, given $\dfrac{dy}{dt} = 0$, $t = 0$ $\therefore$ $c_4 = -\dfrac{b}{a^2}$

$$\therefore \qquad \qquad y = -\frac{b}{a^2}\sin at + \frac{b}{a}t = \frac{b}{a^2}(at - \sin at) \qquad \qquad \dots (7)$$

From (3), $\qquad x = \dfrac{1}{a}\dfrac{dy}{dt}$

$$x = \frac{1}{a}\left[\frac{b}{a^2}(a - a\cos at)\right] = \frac{b}{a^2}(1 - \cos at) \qquad \ldots (8)$$

where $\quad a = \dfrac{eH}{m}, \quad b = \dfrac{eE}{m}$

Hence, (7) and (8) constitute the solution.

Ex. 6 : *Solve* $\qquad t\,dx = (t - 2x)\,dt$

$$t\,dy = (tx + ty + 2x - t)\,dt \qquad \ldots (I)$$

Sol. : From first of equation (I), we have

$$\frac{dx}{dt} + \frac{2}{t}x = 1 \quad \text{which is linear in x.}$$

its solution is $\qquad x = \dfrac{t}{3} + \dfrac{c_1}{t^2} \qquad \ldots (II)$

If we add the two equations in (I), we get,

$$t\,(dx + dy) = [t - 2x + tx + ty + 2x - t]\,dt = t\,(x + y)\,dt$$

or $\qquad \dfrac{dx + dy}{x + y} = dt$

Integrating, $\displaystyle\int \dfrac{dx + dy}{x + y} = \int dt$

we get, $\quad \log(x + y) = t + c_2{'}$

or $\qquad x + y = c_2\,e^t \qquad\qquad\qquad (c_2{'} = \log c_2)$

$\therefore \qquad y = c_2\,e^t - x$

or $\qquad y = c_2\,e^t - \dfrac{t}{3} - \dfrac{c_1}{t^2}$

Hence the general solution is

$$x = \frac{t}{3} + \frac{c_1}{t^2}$$

$$y = c_2\,e^t - \frac{t}{3} - \frac{c_1}{t^2} \qquad \ldots \textbf{Ans.}$$

EXERCISE 2.1

Solve the following simultaneous equations :

1. $\qquad \dfrac{dx}{dt} + y = e^t$

   $\qquad \dfrac{dy}{dt} + x = e^{-t}$

   Ans. $x = c_1 \cos t + c_2 \sin t + \dfrac{1}{2}(e^t - e^{-t})$

   $y = c_1 \sin t - c_2 \cos t + \dfrac{1}{2}(e^t - e^{-t})$

2. $(D + 2)\,x + (D + 1)\,y = t$

$5x + (D + 3)\,y = t^2$

Ans. $x = \left(\dfrac{c_1 - 3c_2}{5}\right)\sin t - \left(\dfrac{3c_1 + c_2}{5}\right)\cos t - t^2 + t + 3$

$y = c_1 \cos t + c_2 \sin t + 2\,t^2 - 3\,t - 4$

3. $\dfrac{dx}{dt} + 5x - 2y = t$

$\dfrac{dy}{dt} + 2x + y = 0$

having been given that $x = y = 0$ at $t = 0$.

Ans. $x = -\dfrac{1}{27}\,(1 + 6t)\,e^{-3t} + \dfrac{1}{27}\,(1 + 3t)$

$y = -\dfrac{2}{27}\,(2 + 3t)\,e^{-3t} + \dfrac{2}{27}\,(2 - 3t)$

4. If $\dfrac{dx}{dt} - wy = a \cos pt$ **(May 2006, 2008)**

and $\dfrac{dy}{dt} + wx = a \sin pt$

Show that $x = A \cos wt + B \sin wt + \dfrac{a \sin pt}{p + w}$

$y = B \cos wt - A \sin wt - \dfrac{a \cos pt}{p + w}$

5. In a heat exchange, the temperatures u and v of two liquids, satisfy the equations

$4\dfrac{du}{dx} = v - u = 2\dfrac{dv}{dx}$ **(Dec. 2004, 2007, 2010)**

Solve the equations for u and v, given that   **Ans.** $u = -60 + 80\ e^{x/4}$

u = 20 and v = 100 when x = 0. $v = -60 + 160\ e^{x/4}$

6. The equations of motion of a particle are given by   **(Dec. 2006)**

$\dfrac{dx}{dt} + wy = 0,\ \dfrac{dy}{dt} - wx = 0$ **Ans.** $x = A \cos\ wt + B \sin\ wt$

Find the path of the particle. $y = A \sin\ wt - B \cos\ wt$

7. Solve the simultaneous equations for r and θ.   **(May 2005, 2007)**

$\dfrac{dr}{dt} - 2r - \theta = 0$

$\dfrac{d\theta}{dt} + r - 4\theta = 0$ **Ans.** $r = 3\ (e^{3t} - te^{3t})$

given that $\theta\,(0) = 0$ and $r'\,(0) = 6$ $\theta = -3t\ e^{3t}$

8. Solve the simultaneous equations

$$2\frac{dx}{dt} - x + 3y = \sin t, \quad \text{and obtain x and y if } x = \frac{1}{4} \text{ and } y = -\frac{1}{20} \text{ at } t = 0.$$

$$2\frac{dy}{dt} + 3x - y = \cos t$$

Ans. $x = \frac{1}{10}\left[e^{2t} + e^{-t}\right] + \frac{1}{20}\left[\cos t + 2\sin t\right]$

$$y = -\frac{1}{10}e^{2t} + \frac{1}{10}e^{-t} + \frac{2}{5}\sin t - \frac{1}{20}\cos t$$

9. Solve $(D + 5)x + (D + 7)y = 2$

$(2D + 1)x + (3D + 1)y = \sin t$

Ans. $x = -\frac{4}{3}e^t + \frac{4}{3}e^{-2t} - 1 + \cos t + 2\sin t$

under conditions $x = y = 0$, when $t = 0$ $y = -e^t + \frac{4}{5}e^{-2t} + 1 - \frac{4}{5}\cos t - \frac{7}{5}\sin t$

10. $(D - 2)x + (D - 1)y = e^t$ **Ans.** $x = c_1\cos t + c_2\sin t - \frac{1}{2}e^t$

$(D + 3)x + y = 0$ $y = (c_1 - 3c_2)\sin t - (3c_1 + c_2)\cos t + 2e^t$

11. $(D - 1)x + Dy = t$ **Ans.** $x = -2c_1 e^{2t} - \frac{2}{3}c_2 e^{-2t} - \frac{1}{4} - \frac{1}{2}t$

$3x + (D + 4)y = t^2$ $y = c_1 e^{2t} + c_2 e^{-2t} + \frac{1}{4}t + \frac{1}{4}t^2 + \frac{1}{8}$

12. $(5D + 4)y - (2D + 1)z = e^x$ **Ans.** $y = c_1 e^x + c_2 e^{-2x} - \frac{1}{2}x e^x + \frac{5}{4}e^{-x}$

$(D + 8)y - 3z = 5e^{-x}$ $z = 3c_1 e^x + 2c_2 e^{-2x} - \frac{1}{6}e^x - \frac{3}{2}xe^x + \frac{5}{4}e^{-x}$

13. $\frac{dx}{dt} + x - y = te^t$

$2y - \frac{dx}{dt} + \frac{dy}{dt} = e^t$ **Ans.** $x = (A\cos t + B\sin t)e^{-t} + \frac{1}{25}(15t - 2)e^t$

given that $x = y = 0$ when $t = 0$. $y = (B\cos t - A\sin t)e^{-t} + \frac{1}{25}(5t + 11)e^t$

14. $4\frac{dx}{dt} + 9\frac{dy}{dt} + 44x + 49y = t$ **Ans.** $x = Ae^{-t} + Be^{-6t} + \frac{19}{3}t - \frac{56}{9} - \frac{29}{7}e^t$

$3\frac{dx}{dt} + 7\frac{dy}{dt} + 34x + 38y = e^t$ $y = -Ae^{-t} + 4Be^{-6t} - \frac{17}{3}t + \frac{55}{9} + \frac{24}{7}e^t$

15. $\frac{d^2x}{dt^2} + 4x + 5y = t^2$

$\frac{d^2y}{dt^2} + 5x + 4y = t + 1$

Ans. $x = c_1 e^t + c_2 e^{-t} + c_3\cos 3t + c_4\sin 3t - \frac{1}{9}\left(4t^2 - 5t + \frac{37}{9}\right)$

$y = -c_1 e^t - c_2 e^{-t} + c_3\cos 3t + c_4\sin 3t + \frac{1}{9}\left(5t^2 - 4t + \frac{44}{9}\right)$

16. A mechanical system with two degrees of freedom satisfies the equations

$$2\frac{d^2x}{dt^2} + 3\frac{dy}{dt} = 4$$

$$2\frac{d^2y}{dt^2} - 3\frac{dx}{dt} = 0 \qquad \text{(May 2011)}$$

Obtain the expressions for x and y in terms of t, given x, y, $\frac{dx}{dt}$, $\frac{dy}{dt}$ all vanish at

t = 0.   **Ans.** $x = \frac{8}{9}\left(1 - \cos\frac{3t}{2}\right)$, $y = \frac{t}{3} - \frac{8}{9}\sin\frac{3t}{2}$

17. $\frac{d^2x}{dt^2} - y = 0$ **Ans.** $x = c_1 e^x + c_2 e^{-x} + c_3 \cos x + c_4 \sin x - 1$

$\frac{d^2y}{dt^2} - x - 1 = 0$ $y = c_1 e^x + c_2 e^{-x} - c_3 \cos x - c_4 \sin x$

18. The small oscillations of a certain system with two degrees of freedom are given by two simultaneous equations

$$D^2x + 3x - 2y = 0$$
$$D^2x + D^2y - 3x + 5y = 0$$

If $x = 0 = y$ and $Dx = 3$, $Dy = 2$ **Ans.** $x = \frac{11}{4}\sin\frac{1}{2} + \frac{1}{12}\sin\frac{3}{2}$

when t = 0, find x and y when $t = \frac{1}{2}$. $y = \frac{11}{4}\sin\frac{1}{2} - \frac{1}{4}\sin\frac{3}{2}$

19. The acceleration components of a particle moving in a plane are given by

$$\frac{d^2x}{dt^2} = b\frac{dy}{dt}$$

and $\qquad \frac{d^2y}{dt^2} = a - b\frac{dx}{dt}$

where, a and b are constants, if the particle is initially at rest at the origin then show that the path of the particle is the cycloid.

$$b^2x = a\,(bt - \sin bt)$$
$$b^2y = a\,(1 - \cos bt)$$

MULTIPLE CHOICE QUESTIONS (MCQ's)

Type : Simultaneous Linear Differential Equations :

1. For the simultaneous linear differential equations

$\frac{dx}{dt} + 2x - 3y = t$, $\frac{dy}{dx} - 3x + 2y = e^{2t}$ solution of x using $D \equiv \frac{d}{dt}$ is obtain from   (2)

(A) $(D^2 + 4D - 5)\,x = 1 + 2t + 3e^{2t}$ (B) $(D^2 - 4D - 5)\,x = 1 + 2t - 3e^{2t}$

(C) $(D^2 + 4D - 5)\,x = 3t + 3e^{2t}$ (D) $(D^2 + 4D - 5)\,y = 3t + 4e^{2t}$

2. For the system of linear differential equations $\dfrac{dx}{dt} + 2x - 3y = t$, $\dfrac{dy}{dt} - 3x + 2y = e^{2t}$

elimination of x results in $\left(\text{use } D \equiv \dfrac{d}{dt}\right)$ (2)

(A) $(D^2 + 4D - 5)\, x = 1 + 2t + 3e^{2t}$ (B) $(D^2 - 4D - 5)\, y = t - 4e^{2t}$

(C) $(D^2 - 4D + 5)\, y = 3t - 2e^{2t}$ (D) $(D^2 + 4D - 5)\, y = 3t + 4e^{2t}$

3. For the simultaneous Linear DE $\dfrac{du}{dx} + v = \sin x$, $\dfrac{dv}{dx} + u = \cos x$ solution of u using

$D \equiv \dfrac{d}{dx}$ is obtain from (2)

(A) $(D^2 + 1)\, u = 2 \cos x$ (B) $(D^2 - 1)\, u = 0$

(C) $(D^2 - 1)\, u = \sin x - \cos x$ (D) $(D^2 - 1)\, v = -2 \sin x$

4. For the simultaneous Linear DE $\dfrac{du}{dx} + v = \sin x$, $\dfrac{dv}{dx} + u = \cos x$ eliminating u results

in $\left(\text{use } D \equiv \dfrac{d}{dx}\right)$ (2)

(A) $(D^2 + 1)\, v = 0$ (B) $(D^2 - 1)\, u = 0$

(C) $(D^2 - 1)\, v = -2 \sin x$ (D) $(D^2 + 1)\, v = \sin x + \cos x$

5. For the simultaneous Linear DE $\dfrac{dx}{dt} - 3x - 6y = t^2$, $\dfrac{dy}{dt} + \dfrac{dx}{dt} - 3y = e^t$ solution of x

using $D \equiv \dfrac{d}{dt}$ is obtain from (2)

(A) $(D^2 + 9)\, x = 6e^t - 3t^2 + 2t$ (B) $(D^2 + 9)\, y = -2e^t - 2t$

(C) $(D^2 - 9)\, x = 6e^t - 3t^2$ (D) $(D^2 + 12D + 9)\, x = 6e^t + 3t^2 + 2t$

6. For the simultaneous Linear DE $L\dfrac{dx}{dt} + Rx + R(x - y) = E$, $L\dfrac{dy}{dt} + Ry - R(x - y) = 0$

where L, R and E are constants, solution of x using $D \equiv \dfrac{d}{dt}$ is obtain from (2)

(A) $(L^2D^2 + 4RLD + 5R^2)\, x = 2RE + 2R$

(B) $(L^2D^2 + 4RLD + 3R^2)\, y = RE$

(C) $(L^2D^2 + 4RLD + 3R^2)\, x = 2RE$

(D) $(L^2D^2 + 2RLD + 5R^2)\, x = 2RE$

7. For the simultaneous Liner DE $L\dfrac{dx}{dt} + Rx + R(x - y) = E$, $L\dfrac{dy}{dt} + Ry - R(x - y) = 0$

where L, R and E are constants, solution of y using $D \equiv \dfrac{d}{dt}$ is obtain from (2)

(A) $(L^2D^2 + 4RLD + 5R^2)\, y = RE + 2R$ (B) $(L^2D^2 + 4RLD + 3R^2)\, y = RE$

(C) $(L^2D^2 + 4RLD + 3R^2)\, x = 2RE$ (D) $(L^2D^2 + 2RLD + 5R^2)\, y = 2RE$

8. For the simultaneous Linear DE $\dfrac{dx}{dt} + y = e^t, \dfrac{dy}{dt} + x = e^{-t}$ solution of x using $D = \dfrac{d}{dt}$ is obtain from   (2)

    (A) $(D^2 - 1) x = 2e^t$ (B) $(D^2 - 1) y = - e^t - e^{-t}$

    (C) $(D^2 + 1) x = e^{-t} + e^t$ (D) $(D^2 - 1) x = e^t - e^{-t}$

9. From the simultaneous Linear DE $\dfrac{dx}{dt} + y = e^t, \dfrac{dy}{dt} + x = e^{-t}$, solution of y using $D \equiv \dfrac{d}{dt}$ is obtain from   (2)

    (A) $(D^2 - 1) y = 2e^t$ (B) $(D^2 - 1) y = -e^t - e^{-t}$

    (C) $(D^2 + 1) y = e^{-t} + e^t$ (D) $(D^2 - 1) x = e^t - e^{-t}$

10. For the simultaneous Linear DE $\dfrac{dx}{dt} + 5x - 2y = t, \dfrac{dy}{dt} + 2x + y = 0$, solution of x using $D \equiv \dfrac{d}{dt}$ is obtain from   (2)

    (A) $(D^2 + 6D + 9) x = 1 + t$ (B) $(D^2 - 6D + 9) x = 2t$

    (C) $(D^2 + 6D + 1) x = t$ (D) $(D^2 + 6D + 9) y = 2t$

11. For the simultaneous Linear DE $\dfrac{dx}{dt} + 5x - 2y = t, \dfrac{dy}{dt} + 2x + y = 0$, solution of y using $D \equiv \dfrac{d}{dt}$ is obtain from   (2)

    (A) $(D^2 - 6D - 9) y = 2t$ (B) $(D^2 + 6D + 9) x = 1 + t$

    (C) $(D^2 + 6D + 1) y = t$ (D) $(D^2 + 6D + 9) y = - 2t$

Answers

1. (A)	2. (D)	3. (B)	4. (C)	5. (A)	6. (C)	7. (B)	8. (D)
9. (B)	10. (A)	11. (D)					

2.4 SYMMETRICAL SIMULTANEOUS DIFFERENTIAL EQUATIONS

Definition : Equations of the type : $\dfrac{dx}{P} = \dfrac{dy}{Q} = \dfrac{dz}{R}$ …(1)

where P, Q, R are the functions of x, y and z, are said to be *symmetrical simultaneous differential equations.*

There are mainly two methods of solving such equations. The solutions of such a system consist of two independent relations of the type :

$$F_1 (x, y, z) = c_1 \text{ and } F_2 (x, y, z) = c_2$$

(A) METHOD OF COMBINATION OR GROUPING

If we can observe that z is missing from first group $\dfrac{dx}{P} = \dfrac{dy}{Q}$ or, may be cancelled from this equation, then it becomes a differential equation in x and y only. Solution of this will give one relation in the solution of simultaneous equations. Then we consider the second group $\dfrac{dy}{Q} = \dfrac{dz}{R}$. If it does not contain x, it is most ideal otherwise we cancel x (if possible) and if not try to eliminate x by the help of first relation just reached. It will then be a differential equation in y and z only and after integration yields the second relation in the solution of the system of simultaneous equations. Following examples will illustrate this method.

ILLUSTRATIONS ON SYMMETRICAL SIMULTANEOUS DIFFERENTIAL EQUATIONS

Ex. 1 : *Solve* $\qquad \dfrac{dx}{y^2} = \dfrac{dy}{x^2} = \dfrac{dz}{x^2\,y^2\,z^2}$ $\qquad\qquad$ **(Dec. 2011)**

Sol. : Consider $\qquad \dfrac{dx}{y^2} = \dfrac{dy}{x^2}$

or $\qquad\qquad x^2\,dx = y^2\,dy$

On integration $\qquad x^3 = y^3 + c_1$

$\Rightarrow \qquad\qquad x^3 - y^3 = c_1$ $\qquad\qquad\qquad$ ... (1)

which is the first solution.

Now consider $\qquad \dfrac{dy}{x^2} = \dfrac{dz}{x^2\,y^2\,z^2}$

Cancelling the common factors, we have

$$\frac{dy}{1} = \frac{dz}{y^2\,z^2} \Rightarrow y^2\,dy = \frac{dz}{z^2}$$

On integration $\qquad \dfrac{1}{3}\,y^3 = -\dfrac{1}{z} + c'_2 \quad$ or $\quad y^3 = -\dfrac{3}{z} + c_2$

$\Rightarrow \qquad\qquad y^3 + \dfrac{3}{z} = c_2$ $\qquad\qquad\qquad$ ... (2)

Equations (1) and (2) taken together constitute the answer.

Note : Here in this question, we could have considered $\dfrac{dx}{y^2} = \dfrac{dz}{x^2 y^2 z^2}$ either and after cancelling y^2, got the equation $\dfrac{dx}{1} = \dfrac{dz}{x^2 z^2}$ which would have yielded the solution

$x^3 + \dfrac{3}{z} = c_2$ $\qquad\qquad\qquad\qquad\qquad\qquad\qquad\qquad$ ... (3)

But (2) and (3) are actually the same in the light of solution (1).

Ex. 2 : *Solve* $\dfrac{dx}{y^2} = \dfrac{dy}{-xy} = \dfrac{dz}{x\,(z-2y)}$.

Sol. : Consider first two terms,

$$\frac{dx}{y^2} = \frac{dy}{-xy} \quad \text{or} \quad x\,dx + y\,dy = 0$$

On integrating, $x^2 + y^2 = c_1$ ... (1)

Next, consider second and third terms,

$$\frac{dy}{-xy} = \frac{dz}{x\,(z-2y)} \quad \text{or} \quad z\,dy + y\,dz - 2y\,dy = 0$$

On integrating, $yz - y^2 = c_2$ ... (2)

Hence, (1) and (2) together constitute the solution.

Ex. 3 : *Solve* $\dfrac{dx}{2x} = \dfrac{dy}{-y} = \dfrac{dz}{4xy^2 - 2z}$.

Sol. : Consider first two terms together.

$$\frac{dx}{2x} = \frac{dy}{-y} \quad \text{or} \quad \frac{dx}{x} + 2\,\frac{dy}{y} = 0$$

On integrating,

$$\log x + 2 \log y = \log c_1$$
$$xy^2 = c_1 \qquad \qquad \text{... (1)}$$

Next, consider first and last terms together.

$$\frac{dx}{2x} = \frac{dz}{4xy^2 - 2z}$$

Using the solution (1), we remove y from this equation and obtain

$$\frac{dx}{2x} = \frac{dz}{4c_1 - 2z} \quad \text{or} \quad \frac{dx}{x} - \frac{dz}{2c_1 - z} = 0$$

On integrating,

$$\log x + \log (2c_1 - z) = \log c_2$$
$$x\,(2c_1 - z) = c_2$$

Putting back the expression for $c_1 = xy^2$, we have

$$x\,(2xy^2 - z) = c_2 \qquad \qquad \text{... (2)}$$

Hence, (1) and (2) constitute the solution of given symmetrical equations.

Ex. 4 : *Solve* $\qquad \dfrac{dx}{x} = \dfrac{dy}{y} = \dfrac{dz}{z - a\sqrt{x^2 + y^2 + z^2}}$

Sol. : First group of equations gives :

$$\frac{dx}{x} = \frac{dy}{y}$$

$\Rightarrow \qquad\qquad \log x = \log y + \log c_1$

$\Rightarrow \qquad\qquad \log\left(\dfrac{x}{y}\right) = \log c_1 \Rightarrow x = c_1 y \Rightarrow y = c_2 x$

We shall put value of y in third ratio and eliminate it from 1st and 3rd ratios, to yield

$$\frac{dx}{x} = \frac{dz}{z - a\sqrt{x^2 + z^2 + c_2^2\, x^2}}$$

$$\Rightarrow \qquad \frac{dz}{dx} = \frac{z - a\sqrt{x^2\left(1 + c_2^2\right) + z^2}}{x}$$

which is homogeneous, we now put $z = vx$ and $\dfrac{dz}{dx} = v + x\,\dfrac{dv}{dx}$

$$\Rightarrow \qquad v + x\,\frac{dv}{dx} = \frac{vx - a\sqrt{x^2\left(1 + c_2^2\right) + v^2 x^2}}{x}$$

$$= v - a\,\sqrt{v^2 + \left(1 + c_2^2\right)}$$

$$\Rightarrow \qquad x\,\frac{dv}{dx} = -a\sqrt{v^2 + \left(1 + c_2^2\right)}$$

$$\Rightarrow \qquad \int \frac{dv}{\sqrt{\left(1 + c_2^2 + v^2\right)}} = -a\int \frac{dx}{x} \quad \text{(variable separable)}$$

$$\Rightarrow \log\left[v + \sqrt{1 + c_2^2 + v^2}\right] + a\log x = \log c_3$$

$$\Rightarrow \qquad \left(v + \sqrt{1 + v^2 + c_2^2}\right)(x^a) = c_3$$

Now, put $v = \dfrac{z}{x}$ and $c_2 = \dfrac{y}{x}$

$$\Rightarrow \qquad z + \sqrt{x^2 + y^2 + z^2} = c_3\, x^{1-a}$$

Hence the required solution is given by :

$$y = c_2\, x \quad \text{and} \quad z + \sqrt{x^2 + y^2 + z^2} - c_3\, x^{1-a} = 0$$

(B) METHOD OF MULTIPLIERS

Sometimes we select one or two sets of multipliers say l, m, n or l', m', n', not necessarily constants to find a fourth ratio by which we come to solutions viz. if the equation is

$$\frac{dx}{P} = \frac{dy}{Q} = \frac{dz}{R}$$

then choose multipliers l, m, n such that

$$\frac{dx}{P} = \frac{dy}{Q} = \frac{dz}{R} = \frac{l\,dx + m\,dy + n\,dz}{lP + mQ + nR} \qquad \text{... (1)}$$

Now, suppose the choice of l, m, n such that

$lP + mQ + nR = 0$ then $l\,dx + m\,dy + n\,dz = 0$

and if it is exact we may find its integral as

$$F_1 (x, y, z) = c_1 \qquad \qquad \dots (2)$$

which is the first solution of the system.

If it is further possible to find the other set of multipliers say l', m', n' such that :

$$\frac{dx}{P} = \frac{dy}{Q} = \frac{dz}{R} = \frac{l'dx + m'dy + n'dz}{l'P + m'Q + n'R}$$

and also if $\quad l'P + m'Q + n'R = 0$, then $l'dx + m'dy + n'dz = 0$

and solving we get another solution like

$$F_2 (x, y, z) = c_2 \qquad \qquad \dots (3)$$

Thus (2) and (3) constitute the solution of the given set of symmetrical equations.

ILLUSTRATIONS

Ex. 5 : *Solve* $\quad \dfrac{dx}{y - z} = \dfrac{dy}{z - x} = \dfrac{dz}{x - y}$

Sol. : If we take the first set of multipliers as 1, 1, 1 we have

$$\frac{dx}{y - z} = \frac{dy}{z - x} = \frac{dz}{x - y} = \frac{dx + dy + dz}{1\,(y - z) + 1\,(z - x) + 1\,(x - y)}$$

$$= \frac{dx + dy + dz}{0}$$

$$dx + dy + dz = 0$$

and by integration we get

$$x + y + z = c_1 \qquad \qquad \dots (1)$$

as first solution.

Next the question itself suggests that even x, y, z may be a set of multipliers, then

$$\frac{dx}{y - z} = \frac{dy}{z - x} = \frac{dz}{x - y} = \frac{x\,dx + y\,dy + z\,dz}{x\,(y - z) + y\,(z - x) + z\,(x - y)}$$

$$\Rightarrow \quad x\,dx + y\,dy + z\,dz = 0$$

On integration, it yields

$$x^2 + y^2 + z^2 = c_3 \qquad \qquad \dots (2)$$

Thus the equations (1) and (2) together constitute the required solutions of the set.

Ex. 6 : *Solve* $\dfrac{dx}{mz - ny} = \dfrac{dy}{nx - lz} = \dfrac{dz}{ly - mx}$

Sol. : The equation suggests that (x, y, z) may be the first set of multipliers, hence

$$\frac{dx}{mz - ny} = \frac{dy}{nx - lz} = \frac{dz}{ly - mx}$$

$$= \frac{x\,dx + y\,dy + z\,dz}{x\,(mz - ny) + y\,(nx - lz) + z\,(ly - mx)}$$

$$= \frac{x\,dx + y\,dy + z\,dz}{0}$$

$$\Rightarrow \quad x\,dx + y\,dy + z\,dz = 0$$

On integrating,

$$x^2 + y^2 + z^2 = c_1 \qquad \qquad \dots (1)$$

Let l, m, n be second set of multipliers, then each ratio equals

$$= \frac{l\,dx + m\,dy + n\,dz}{l\,(mz - ny) + m\,(nx - lz) + n\,(ly - mx)}$$

$$= \frac{l\,dx + m\,dy + n\,dz}{0}$$

$$\Rightarrow \quad l\,dx + m\,dy + n\,dz = 0$$

On integration, it gives

$$lx + my + nz = c_2 \qquad \qquad \dots (2)$$

Equations (1) and (2) together constitute the solution.

Note : In some cases, the 4th term $\dfrac{l\,dx + m\,dy + n\,dz}{lP + mQ + nR}$ turns out to be a more convenient ratio than the previous three ratios and in such a case numerator often turns out to be differential of the denominator. By this fact and by opting one or two given ratios, we are able to solve the system. Examples will strengthen this method further.

Ex. 7 : *Solve* $\quad \dfrac{dx}{3z - 4y} = \dfrac{dy}{4x - 2z} = \dfrac{dz}{2y - 3x}$ **(Dec. 2006, Dec. 2009)**

Sol. : Let us choose multipliers x, y, z then each ratio equals $\dfrac{x\,dx + y\,dy + z\,dz}{0}$

$$\Rightarrow \qquad x\,dx + y\,dy + z\,dz = 0, \text{ on integration, we get}$$

$$x^2 + y^2 + z^2 = c_1 \qquad \qquad \dots (1)$$

Second set of multipliers may be conveniently chosen as 2, 3, 4 and then each ratio equals $\dfrac{2\,dx + 3\,dy + 4\,dz}{0}$, from where

$$2\,dx + 3\,dy + 4\,dz = 0$$

$$\Rightarrow \qquad 2x + 3y + 4z = c_2 \qquad \qquad \dots (2)$$

Equations (1) and (2) constitute the answer.

Ex. 8 : *Solve* $\dfrac{dx}{x\,(2y^4 - z^4)} = \dfrac{dy}{y\,(z^4 - 2x^4)} = \dfrac{dz}{z\,(x^4 - y^4)}$

Sol. : First set of multipliers may be x^3, y^3, z^3 which will equal each ratio to

$$\frac{x^3\,dx + y^3\,dy + z^3\,dz}{0}$$

$$\Rightarrow \qquad x^3\,dx + y^3\,dy + z^3\,dz = 0$$

On integration, this yields

$$x^4 + y^4 + z^4 = c_1 \qquad \ldots (1)$$

If we choose conveniently the second set of multipliers as $\dfrac{1}{x}, \dfrac{1}{y}, \dfrac{2}{z}$, then each ratio will be equal to

$$\frac{\dfrac{dx}{x} + \dfrac{dy}{y} + \dfrac{2 \cdot dz}{z}}{0}$$

$$\Rightarrow \qquad \frac{dx}{x} + \frac{dy}{y} + \frac{2 \cdot dz}{z} = 0$$

On integration, we have

$$\log x + \log y + 2 \log z = \log c_2$$

$$\Rightarrow \qquad x \, y \, z^2 = c_2 \qquad \ldots (2)$$

Here equations (1) and (2) constitute the answer.

Ex. 9 : *Solve* $\dfrac{a \, dx}{(b-c) \, yz} = \dfrac{b \, dy}{(c-a) \, xz} = \dfrac{c \, dz}{(a-b) \, xy}$

Sol. : Use multipliers x, y, z, then each ratio equals

$$\frac{ax \, dx + by \, dy + cz \, dz}{0} \Rightarrow ax \, dx + by \, dy + cz \, dz = 0$$

Integration yields, $\qquad ax^2 + by^2 + cz^2 = c_1 \qquad \ldots (1)$

Next we shall use multipliers ax, by, cz then each ratio equals

$$\frac{a^2x \, dx + b^2y \, dy + c^2z \, dz}{0} \Rightarrow a^2x \, dx + b^2y \, dy + c^2z \, dz = 0$$

Integration will yield,

$$a^2 \, x^2 + b^2 \, y^2 + c^2 \, z^2 = c_2 \qquad \ldots (2)$$

Equations (1) and (2) constitute the answer.

Ex. 10 : *Solve* $\dfrac{dx}{y + zx} = \dfrac{dy}{-x - yz} = \dfrac{dz}{x^2 - y^2}.$

Sol. : Using the first set of multipliers y, x, 1,

$$\text{each term} = \frac{y \, dx + x \, dy + dz}{0}$$

$$\therefore \qquad y \, dx + x \, dy + dz = 0$$

On integration, $\qquad xy + z = c_1 \qquad \ldots (1)$

Again using second set of multipliers $x, y, -z,$

$$\text{each term} = \frac{x\,dx + y\,dy - z\,dz}{0}$$

$\therefore \qquad x\,dx + y\,dy - z\,dz = 0$

On integration, $x^2 + y^2 - z^2 = c^2$ $\hspace{2cm}$ … (2)

Thus (1) and (2) are solutions of the given equations.

Ex. 11 : *Solve* $\quad \dfrac{dx}{1} = \dfrac{dy}{1} = \dfrac{dz}{(1 + 2xy + 3x^2\,y^2)\,(x + y)\,z}$

Sol. : From the first two ratios, we have

$$\frac{dx}{1} = \frac{dy}{1}$$

On integration, $\qquad x - y = c_1$ $\hspace{3cm}$ … (1)

Also, $\qquad$ each ratio $= \dfrac{y\,dx + x\,dy}{y + x}$ and hence

$$\frac{y\,dx + x\,dy}{y + x} = \frac{dz}{(1 + 2xy + 3x^2\,y^2)\,(x + y)\,z}$$

$\Rightarrow \qquad \dfrac{y\,dx + x\,dy}{1} = \dfrac{dz}{(1 + 2xy + 3x^2\,y^2)\,z}$

$\Rightarrow \qquad \dfrac{d\,(xy)}{1} = \dfrac{dz}{(1 + 2xy + 3x^2\,y^2)\,z}$

$\Rightarrow \quad (1 + 2xy + 3x^2\,y^2)\,d\,(xy) = \dfrac{dz}{z}$

For convenience, put $\qquad xy = v$

$\Rightarrow \qquad x\,dy + y\,dx = dv$

$\Rightarrow \qquad d\,(xy) = dv$

$\Rightarrow \qquad (1 + 2v + 3v^2)\,dv = \dfrac{dz}{z}$ (from where variables are separable)

$\Rightarrow \qquad v + v^2 + v^3 = \log z + c_2$

$\Rightarrow \quad xy + (xy)^2 + (xy)^3 - \log z = c_2$ $\hspace{2cm}$ … (2)

Hence equations (1) and (2) together represent the solution set of the system.

Ex. 12 : *Solve* $\dfrac{dx}{1} = \dfrac{dy}{1} = \dfrac{dz}{(x + y)\,[e^{xy} + \sin xy + x^2\,y^2]}$

Sol. : Consider the first group $\dfrac{dx}{1} = \dfrac{dy}{1}$, which yields

$\Rightarrow \qquad x - y = c_1$ $\hspace{3cm}$ … (1)

Now each ratio equals $\dfrac{y\,dx + x\,dy}{y + x}$, hence

$$\frac{y\,dx + x\,dy}{y + x} = \frac{dz}{(x + y)\,[e^{xy} + \sin xy + (xy)^2]}$$

$$\Rightarrow \quad [e^{xy} + \sin xy + (xy)^2]\,(y\,dx + x\,dy) = dz$$

Put $xy = v$, then $x\,dy + y\,dx = dv$

$$\Rightarrow \quad (e^v + \sin v + v^2)\,dv = dz$$

On integration, we get $\quad e^v - \cos v + \dfrac{v^3}{3} = z + c_2$

$$\Rightarrow \quad 3e^v - 3\cos v + v^3 = 3z + c_3$$

$$\Rightarrow \quad 3e^{xy} - 3\cos(xy) + (xy)^3 - 3z = c_3 \qquad \ldots (2)$$

Equations (1) and (2) constitute the answer.

Ex. 13 : *Solve* $\quad \dfrac{dx}{x^2 - yz} = \dfrac{dy}{y^2 - zx} = \dfrac{dz}{z^2 - xy}$ $\qquad \ldots (1)$ **(Dec. 2005, 2008)**

Sol. : Each ratio equals

$$\frac{dx - dy}{(x + y + z)\,(x - y)} = \frac{dy - dz}{(x + y + z)\,(y - z)} = \frac{dz - dx}{(x + y + z)\,(z - x)}$$

$$\Rightarrow \quad \frac{dx - dy}{x - y} = \frac{dy - dz}{y - z} = \frac{dz - dx}{z - x} \qquad \ldots (2)$$

Consider the first two ratios in (2)

$$\frac{dx - dy}{x - y} = \frac{dy - dz}{y - z}$$

Each being exact, we may integrate to get

$$\log (x - y) = \log (y - z) + \log c_1$$

$$\Rightarrow \quad \frac{x - y}{y - z} = c_1 \qquad \ldots (3)$$

Next we shall select two sets of multipliers say x, y, z and (1, 1, 1) and obtain by their help the second relation. Each ratio in (1) equals

$$\frac{x\,dx + y\,dy + z\,dz}{x^3 + y^3 + z^3 - 3xyz} \text{ as well as } \frac{dx + dy + dz}{x^2 + y^2 + z^2 - yz - zx - xy}$$

Equating these two, we have

$$\frac{x\,dx + y\,dy + z\,dz}{(x + y + z)\,(x^2 + y^2 + z^2 - xy - yz - zx)} = \frac{dx + dy + dz}{x^2 + y^2 + z^2 - yz - zx - xy}$$

Cancelling factor $x^2 + y^2 + z^2 - xy - yz - zx$, we get

$$\frac{x\,dx + y\,dy + z\,dz}{x + y + z} = \frac{dx + dy + dz}{1}$$

$$\Rightarrow \quad x\,dx + y\,dy + z\,dz = (x + y + z)\,(dx + dy + dz)$$

Integration yields

$$x^2 + y^2 + z^2 = (x + y + z)^2 + c_2 \qquad \ldots (4)$$

$\therefore$ Equations (3) and (4) constitute the solution of the system.

Ex. 14 : *Solve* $\dfrac{dx}{x^2 - y^2 - z^2} = \dfrac{dy}{2xy} = \dfrac{dz}{2\,xz}$ ... (1) **(May 2005, 2009)**

Sol. : Here it is convenient to consider the later two ratios to yield $\dfrac{dy}{y} = \dfrac{dz}{z}$ which on integration gives $\log y = \log z + \log c_1$.

$$\Rightarrow \qquad \frac{y}{z} = c_1 \Rightarrow y = c_1 z \qquad\qquad ... (2)$$

Next we shall use multipliers x, y, z then each ratio in (1) equals

$$\frac{x\,dx + y\,dy + z\,dz}{x\,(x^2 - y^2 - z^2) + 2xy^2 + 2xz^2} = \frac{x\,dx + y\,dy + z\,dz}{x^3 + xy^2 + xz^2} = \frac{x\,dx + y\,dy + z\,dz}{x\,[x^2 + y^2 + z^2]}$$

If we consider this with the second ratio in (1)

$$\frac{dy}{2\,xy} = \frac{x\,dx + y\,dy + z\,dz}{x\,(x^2 + y^2 + z^2)}$$

$$\Rightarrow \qquad \frac{dy}{y} = \frac{2\,(x\,dx + y\,dy + z\,dz)}{x^2 + y^2 + z^2}$$

Hence its integration yields

$$\log y = \log (x^2 + y^2 + z^2) + \log c_2$$

$$\Rightarrow \qquad \frac{y}{x^2 + y^2 + z^2} = c_2 \qquad\qquad ... (3)$$

Equations (2) and (3) constitute the answer.

EXERCISE 2.2

Solve the following system of symmetrical simultaneous equations :

1. $\dfrac{dx}{y^2 z} = \dfrac{dy}{x^2 z} = \dfrac{dz}{y^2 x}$ **Ans.** $x^3 - y^3 = c_1$ and $x^2 - z^2 = c_2$

2. $\dfrac{x\,dx}{y^3 z} = \dfrac{dy}{x^2 z} = \dfrac{dz}{y^3}$ **Ans.** $x^4 - y^4 = c_1$, $x^2 - z^2 = c_2$

3. $\dfrac{dx}{y} = \dfrac{dy}{-x} = \dfrac{dz}{x\,e^{x^2 + y^2}}$ **(Dec. 04)**   **Ans.** $x^2 + y^2 = c_1$, $y\,e^{x^2 + y^2} + z = c_2$

4. $\dfrac{dx}{x\,(z - 2y^2)} = \dfrac{dy}{y\,(z - y^2 - 2x^3)} = \dfrac{dz}{z\,(z - y^2 - 2x^3)}$

     Ans. $\dfrac{y}{z} = c_1$, $\dfrac{z}{x} - \dfrac{y^2}{x} + x^2 = c_2$

Hint : Use solution $y_1 = c_1 z$ to find second solution.

5. $\dfrac{dx}{x} = \dfrac{dy}{y} = \dfrac{dz}{-(x + z)}.$ **Ans.** $x = c_1 y$, $\dfrac{1}{2} xy + yz = c_2$

Hint : Use solution $x = c_1 y$ to find second solution.

6. $\dfrac{dx}{1} = \dfrac{dy}{3} = \dfrac{dz}{5z + \tan (y - 3x)}.$ **Ans.** $y - 3x = c_1$,

$$5x = \log [5z + \tan (y - 3x)] + c_2$$

7. $\dfrac{dx}{x\,(y^2 + z)} = \dfrac{dy}{-\,y\,(x^2 + z)} = \dfrac{dz}{z\,(x^2 - y^2)}$ **Ans.** $xyz = c_1,\ x^2 + y^2 - 2z = c_2$

    Hint : Use the multipliers $1/x,\ 1/y,\ 1/z$ and $x,\ y,\ -1$.

8. $\dfrac{dx}{x^2\,(y - z)} = \dfrac{dy}{y^2\,(z - x)} = \dfrac{dz}{z^2\,(x - y)}.$ **Ans.** $\dfrac{1}{x} + \dfrac{1}{y} + \dfrac{1}{z} = c_1,\ xyz = c_2$

    Hint : Use the multipliers $1/x^2,\ 1/y^2,\ 1/z^2$ and $1/x,\ 1/y,\ 1/z$.

9. $\dfrac{dx}{y} = \dfrac{dy}{-\,x} = \dfrac{dz}{2x - 3y}$ **Ans.** $x^2 + y^2 = c_1,\ 3x + 2y + z = c_2$

    Hint : Use the multipliers $3, 2, 1$.

10. $\dfrac{dx}{z\,(x + y)} = \dfrac{dy}{z\,(x - y)} = \dfrac{dz}{x^2 + y^2}$ **Ans.** $x^2 - y^2 - 2xy = c_1,\ x^2 - y^2 - z^2 = c_2$

11. $\dfrac{dx}{y^3 x - 2x^4} = \dfrac{dy}{2y^4 - x^3 y} = \dfrac{dz}{9z\,(x^3 - y^3)}$ **Ans.** $x^3 y^3 z = c_1,\ (x^3 + y^3)\,z^2 = c_2$

    Hint : Use the multipliers $1/x,\ 1/y,\ 1/3z$ and then $x^2,\ y^2$ for the first two terms.

12. $\dfrac{x\,dx}{z^2 - 2yz - y^2} = \dfrac{dy}{y + z} = \dfrac{dz}{y - z}$ (**Dec. 10**) **Ans.** $x^2 + y^2 + z^2 = c_1,\ y^2 - 2yz - z^2 = c_2$

    Hint : Use the multipliers $1,\ y,\ z$ and then consider last two terms.   **(May 2008)**

13. $\dfrac{dx}{x\,(y^2 - z^2)} = \dfrac{dy}{-\,y\,(z^2 + x^2)} = \dfrac{dz}{z\,(x^2 + y^2)}$ **Ans.** $\dfrac{yz}{x} = c_2,\ x^2 + y^2 + z^2 = c_1$

14. $\dfrac{x^2\,dx}{y^3} = \dfrac{y^2\,dy}{x^3} = \dfrac{dz}{z}$ **Hint :** each ratio $= \dfrac{x^2\,dx + y^2\,dy}{y^3 + x^3}$ etc.

    Ans. $x^6 - y^6 = c_1,\ x^3 + y^3 = c_2\,z^3$

15. $\dfrac{dx}{1} = \dfrac{dy}{1} = \dfrac{dx}{(x + y)\,e^{xy} + \sin xy + x^2 y^2}$

    Ans. $x - y = c_1,\ 3e^{xy} - 3\cos xy + (xy)^3 - 3z = c_2$

16. $\dfrac{dx}{x^2 + y^2} = \dfrac{dy}{2xy} = \dfrac{dz}{(x + y)^3\,z}$ **Ans.** $(x + y)^2 - 2\log z = c_1,\ c_2 y = x^2 - y^2$

    Hint : $\dfrac{dx + dy}{(x + y)^2} = \dfrac{dz}{(x + y)^3\,z}$ and $\dfrac{dx + dy}{(x + y)^2} = \dfrac{dx - dy}{(x - y)^2}$

17. $\dfrac{dx}{y + z} = \dfrac{dy}{z + x} = \dfrac{dz}{x + y}$ **Ans.** $\dfrac{x - y}{y - z} = c_1,\ (x - y)^2\,(x + y + z) = c_2$

    Hint : $\dfrac{dx - dy}{x - y} = \dfrac{dy - dz}{y - z}$ and $\dfrac{dx - dy}{x - y} = \dfrac{dx + dy + dz}{2\,(x + y + z)}$

18. $dx + dy + (x + y)\,dz = 0,$

    $z\,(dx + dy) + (x + y)\,dz = 0$ **Ans.** $x + y = c_1\,e^{-z},\ x + y = c_2/z$

19. $(x - z)\,dx + 2\,(x + z)\,dy + (z - x)\,dz = 0$

    $x\,(z - x)\,dx + 4y\,(x + z)\,dy - z\,(z - x)\,dz = 0$

    Ans. $x + z = c_1\,(2y + z) = c_2\,(x - 2y)$

MULTIPLE CHOICE QUESTIONS (MCQ's)

Type : Symmetrical Simultaneous Differential Equations :

1. The general form of symmetric simultaneous DE is   (1)

(A) $a_0 \dfrac{d^n y}{dx^n} + a_1 \dfrac{d^{n-1} y}{dx^{n-1}} + a_2 \dfrac{d^{n-2} y}{dx^{n-2}} + \ldots + a_n y = f(x)$, where $a_0, a_1, a_2 \ldots, a_n$ are constant

(B) $\dfrac{dx}{P} = \dfrac{dy}{Q} = \dfrac{dz}{R}$, where P, Q, R are function of x, y, z

(C) $a_0 x^n \dfrac{d^n y}{dx^n} + a_1 x^{n-1} \dfrac{d^{n-1} y}{dx^{n-1}} + a_2 x^{n-2} \dfrac{d^{n-2} y}{dx^{n-2}} + \ldots + a_n y = f(x)$, where $a_0, a_1, a_2 \ldots, a_n$ are constant

(D) $a_0 (ax + b)^n \dfrac{d^n y}{dx^n} + a_1 (ax + b)^{n-1} \dfrac{d^{n-1} y}{dx^{n-1}} + a_2 (ax + b)^{n-2} \dfrac{d^{n-2} y}{dx^{n-2}} + \ldots + a_n y = f(x)$, where $a_0, a_1, a_2 \ldots, a_n$ are constant

2. Solution of symmetric simultaneous DE $\dfrac{dx}{1} = \dfrac{dy}{1} = \dfrac{dz}{1}$ is   (1)

(A) $x + y = 0, y + z = 0$ (B) $xy = c_1, yz = c_2$

(C) $x + y = c_1, y - z = c_2$ (D) $x - z = c_1, y - z = c_2$

3. Solution of symmetric simultaneous DE $\dfrac{dx}{x} = \dfrac{dy}{y} = \dfrac{dz}{z}$ is   (1)

(A) $x = c_1 y, y = c_2 z$ (B) $x - y = c_1 z, y - z = c_2 x$

(C) $x + y = c_1, y + z = c_2$ (D) $x + y = c_1, y - z = c_2$

4. Considering the first two ratio of the symmetrical simultaneous DE $\dfrac{dx}{y^2} = \dfrac{dy}{x^2} = \dfrac{dz}{x^2 y^2 z^2}$, one of the relation in the solution is DE is   (1)

(A) $\dfrac{1}{x} - \dfrac{1}{y} = c$ (B) $x - y = c$

(C) $x^2 - y^2 = c$ (D) $x^3 - y^3 = c$

5. Considering the first two ratio of the symmetrical simultaneous DE $\dfrac{dx}{y^2} = \dfrac{dy}{-xy} = \dfrac{dz}{x(z - 2y)}$, one of the relation in the solution of DE is   (2)

(A) $x^2 + y^2 = c$ (B) $x^3 + y^3 = c$

(C) $-\dfrac{x^2}{2} = \dfrac{y^3}{3} + c$ (D) $x^2 - y^2 = c$

6. Considering the first two ratio of the symmetrical simultaneous DE $\dfrac{dx}{y^2 z} = \dfrac{dy}{x^2 z} = \dfrac{dz}{y^2 x}$, one of the relation in the solution of DE is   (2)

(A) $x^2 - y^2 = c$ (B) $x - y = c$

(C) $x^3 - y^3 = c$ (D) $x^3 + y^3 = c$

7. Considering the first and third ratio of the symmetrical simultaneous DE $\dfrac{xdx}{y^3z} = \dfrac{dy}{x^2z} = \dfrac{dz}{y^3}$, one of the relation in the solution of DE is (2)

(A) $x^2 - z^2 = c$
(B) $x^4 - y^4 = c$
(C) $x^3 - z^3 = c$
(D) $x - z = c$

8. Considering the second and third ratio of the symmetrical simultaneous DE $\dfrac{dx}{x^2 - y^2 - z^2} = \dfrac{dy}{2xy} = \dfrac{dz}{2xz}$, one of the relation in the solution of DE is (2)

(A) $\dfrac{1}{y^2} - \dfrac{1}{z^2} = c$
(B) $y^2 - z^2 = c$
(C) $y = cz$
(D) $x - z = c$

9. Using a set of multiplier as 1, 1, 1 the solution of DE $\dfrac{dx}{y - z} = \dfrac{dy}{z - x} = \dfrac{dz}{x - y}$ is (2)

(A) $x^2 + y^2 + z^2 = c$
(B) $x - y - z = c$
(C) $x + y + z = c$
(D) $-x + y - z = c$

10. Using a set of multiplier as x, y, z the solution of DE $\dfrac{dx}{3z - 4y} = \dfrac{dy}{4x - 2z} = \dfrac{dz}{2y - 3x}$ is (2)

(A) $x^3 + y^3 + z^3 = c$
(B) $\dfrac{1}{x} + \dfrac{1}{y} + \dfrac{1}{z} = c$
(C) $x + y + z = c$
(D) $x^2 + y^2 + z^2 = c$

11. Using a set of multiplier as x^3, y^3, z^3 the solution of DE $\dfrac{dx}{x(2y^4 - z^4)} = \dfrac{dy}{y(z^4 - 2x^4)} = \dfrac{dz}{z(x^4 - y^4)}$ is (2)

(A) $x^3 + y^3 + z^3 = c$
(B) $x^4 + y^4 + z^4 = c$
(C) $x + y + z = c$
(D) $xyz = c$

12. Using a set of multiplier as 3, 2, 1 the solution of DE $\dfrac{dx}{y} = \dfrac{dy}{-x} = \dfrac{dz}{2x - 3y}$ is (2)

(A) $3x^2 + 2y^2 + z^2 = c$
(B) $\dfrac{3}{x} + \dfrac{2}{y} + \dfrac{1}{z} = c$
(C) $3x - 2y - z = c$
(D) $3x + 2y + z = c$

13. Using a set of multiplier as 1, y, z the solution of DE $\dfrac{dx}{z^2 - 2yz - y^2} = \dfrac{dy}{y + z} = \dfrac{dz}{y - z}$ is (2)

(A) $x^2 + y^2 + z^2 = c$
(B) $x + \dfrac{y^2}{2} + \dfrac{z^2}{2} = c$
(C) $x + y + z = c$
(D) $x + y^2 + z^2 = c$

Answers

1. (B)	2. (D)	3. (A)	4. (D)	5. (A)	6. (C)	7. (A)	8. (C)
9. (C)	10. (D)	11. (B)	12. (D)	13. (B)			

❏❏❏

CHAPTER THREE

APPLICATIONS OF DIFFERENTIAL EQUATIONS

3.1 MASS-SPRING SYSTEM (VIBRATION OF SPRINGS)

LDE with constant coefficients play very important role in representing vibrating mechanical systems. In this section we discuss the motions of a basic mechanical system, a mass attached to elastic spring (Fig. 3.1). Modelling of Mass-Spring System includes setting up its mathematical equation, solving it and discussing the nature of motion.

3.2 MODEL OF MASS-SPRING SYSTEM (FREE OSCILLATIONS)

Let an ordinary spring (which resists compression as well as extension) be suspended vertically from a fixed support. At the lower end of the spring we attach a body of mass 'm'. When the body is in rest, we describe this position as the equilibrium position. If we pull the body down a certain distance and then release it, it undergoes a motion. We shall determine the motion of mechanical system.

(a) Assumptions : (i) We assume that the body moves strictly vertically.

(ii) We choose the downward direction as the positive direction, thus we consider downward forces as positive and upward forces as negative.

(b) The mass 'm' is subjected to the following forces :

(i) **A gravitational force :** W = mg of the body acting downward (we note here that $g = 980 \text{ cm/sec}^2 = 9.80 \text{ m/sec}^2$).

(ii) **Spring restoring force :** It has tendency to restore the system to its equilibrium position. It is governed by Hooke's law which states that "the force exerted by a spring, to restore the weight W to its equilibrium position, is proportional to the distance of W from the equilibrium position (briefly restoring force is proportional to stretch). Thus if F is restoring force and x denote the position of W measured from the equilibrium position then

$$F \propto x \quad \text{or} \quad F = -kx$$

Here k (> 0) is the constant of proportionality, depends upon the stiffness of spring and is called spring constant and minus sign appears because force F points upward. We note here that a stiff spring has a large k; small stretch s_0.

Model Equation : Consider Fig. 3.1, initially, the spring is unstretched (Fig. 3.1 (a)). When we attach the body of mass 'm' it stretches the spring by amount s_0. This causes an upward force F_0 in the spring. By Hooke's law this force F_0 is proportional to the stretch s_0, thus

$$F_0 = -k s_0 \qquad \qquad \dots (1)$$

(3.1)

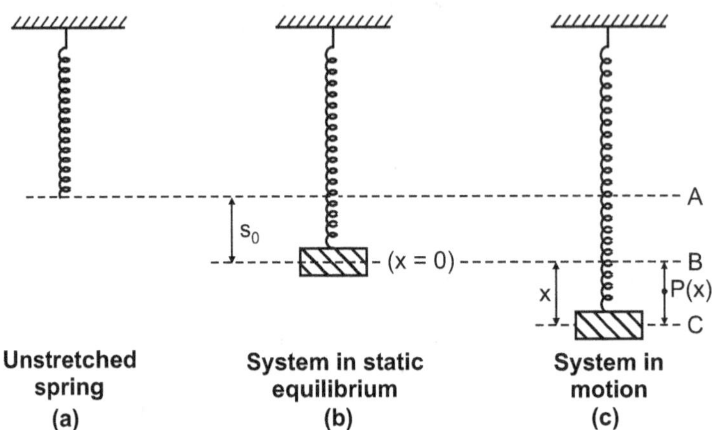

Fig. 3.1 : Mass-Spring System

The extension s_0 is such that F_0 balances the weight W of the body. Consequently,

$$F_0 + W = -k\, s_0 + mg = 0 \qquad \qquad \text{... (2)}$$

These forces will not affect the motion and the spring and the body again at rest. This is called the *static equilibrium of the system* (Refer Fig. 3.1 (b)). We take this position of the body as origin (i.e. $x = 0$) and is used to measure the displacement $x(t)$ of the body. From this position $x = 0$, we pull the body downwards which further stretches the spring by some amount $x > 0$ (the distance we pull down) (Fig. 3.1 (c)). This causes an additional upward restoring force F_1 in the spring. By Hooke's law this force F_1 is proportional to stretch x. Thus,

$$F_1 = -kx \qquad \qquad \text{... (3)}$$

Hence, F_1 is the only force causing motion for our mechanical system. This motion is governed by Newton's second law of motion, if $x(t)$ is the displacement of the body and t is the time, then

$$m \times \frac{d^2x}{dt^2} = \text{Resultant force.} \qquad \qquad \text{... (4)}$$

Remark 1 : From (2), we note that in static equilibrium $mg = ks_0$ (i.e. $F_0 = -W$).

Remark 2 : Resultant force in positive direction can also be calculated as given below.

(i) When the body of mass 'm' is attached to the spring, it stretches a distance s_0 downward, then the tension (force) $T_0 = ks_0 = W$.

(ii) When the body is pulled further by distance $x > 0$ downwards and released, then the tension (force) $T_1 = k\,(s_0 + x)$.

From (i) and (ii), net force is given by

$$T_0 - T_1 = ks_0 - k\,(s_0 + x) = -kx.$$

It follows that resultant force in the positive direction turns out to be same as given in (3).

3.3 UNDAMPED SYSTEM (FREE, UNDAMPED OSCILLATION)

Every system has damping otherwise it would keep moving forever. But here we consider those mechanical system with very ideal spring where effect of damping may often be negligible (e.g. the external forces such as air resistance and other forces) and oscillation did not decrease. For instance, the motion of an iron ball on a spring during few minutes. Then F_1 is the only force acting in (4), causing motion. Hence from (3) and (4),

$$m \frac{d^2x}{dt^2} + kx = 0 \quad \text{or} \quad \frac{d^2x}{dt^2} + \frac{k}{m} x = 0 \qquad \ldots (5)$$

Putting $\omega^2 = \dfrac{k}{m}$, the equation (5) takes the form

$$\frac{d^2x}{dt^2} + \omega^2 x = 0$$

whose general solution is sinusoidal given by

$$x(t) = c_1 \cos \omega t + c_2 \sin \omega t \qquad \ldots (6)$$

Introducing $c_1 = A \cos \phi$ and $c_2 = -A \sin \phi$, solution (6) can be rewritten as

$$x(t) = A \cos \phi \cos \omega t - A \sin \phi \sin \omega t$$

$$\text{or} \qquad x(t) = A \cos (\omega t + \phi) \qquad \ldots (7)$$

where, $A = \sqrt{c_1^2 + c_2^2}$, $\tan \phi = -\dfrac{c_2}{c_1}$. The constant A is called the *amplitude* of the motion and gives the maximum (positive) displacement of the mass from its equilibrium position. Thus the free, undamped motion of the mass is a *simple harmonic motion*, which is periodic. The period of the motion is the time interval between two successive maxima and is given by

$$T = \frac{2\pi}{\omega} = 2\pi \sqrt{\frac{m}{k}} \qquad \ldots (8)$$

The *natural frequency* (or simply frequency) of the motion (or harmonic oscillation) is the reciprocal of the period, which gives the number of oscillations/second. Thus natural frequency is the undamped frequency i.e. frequency of the system without damping.

ILLUSTRATIONS

Ex. 1 : *It is found experimentally that a weight W = 3 N stretches a spring to 15 cm. If the weight is pulled down 10 cm below the equilibrium position and then released*

(i)   find the amplitude, period and frequency of motion,

(ii) determine the position, velocity and acceleration of the weight 1/2 second after it has been released   **(Dec. 2005, 2009, 2014)**

Sol. : Since a weight $W = 3$ N stretches a spring 15 cm $\left(= \dfrac{15}{100} \text{ m} = 0.15 \text{ m}\right)$ downward, by Hooke's law, we have

$$F_0 = ks_0 \Rightarrow 3 = k \times 0.15 \quad \therefore \ k = \frac{3}{0.15} = 20 \text{ N/m (or kg/s}^2)$$

By Newton's second law, the equation of motion of the body is

$$m\frac{d^2x}{dt^2} = -kx \quad \text{or} \quad \frac{W}{g}\frac{d^2x}{dt^2} = -kx$$

$$\therefore \qquad \frac{3}{9.8}\frac{d^2x}{dt^2} = -20\,x \quad \text{or} \quad \frac{d^2x}{dt^2} + \frac{196}{3}\,x = 0 \qquad\qquad \left(\because \ m = \frac{W}{g}\right)$$

which is a linear differential equation with constant coefficients.

$$\text{A.E. is } D^2 + \frac{196}{3} = 0 \quad \therefore \ D = \pm\frac{14}{\sqrt{3}}\,i$$

$$\text{G.S. is } x = c_1 \cos\frac{14}{\sqrt{3}}t + c_2 \sin\frac{14}{\sqrt{3}}t \qquad\qquad \dots (1)$$

Differentiating (1), with respect to t, we get

$$\frac{dx}{dt} = -c_1\frac{14}{\sqrt{3}}\sin\frac{14}{\sqrt{3}}t + c_2\frac{14}{\sqrt{3}}\cos\frac{14}{\sqrt{3}}t \qquad\qquad \dots (2)$$

The initial conditions are $t = 0$, $x = 10$ cm $= 0.1$ m and since the weight is released, $t = 0$, $\dfrac{dx}{dt} = 0$. Using these conditions, we obtain

$$0.1 = c_1\,(1) + c_2\,(0) \ \Rightarrow \ c_1 = 0.1$$

$$0 = 0 + c_2\frac{14}{\sqrt{3}}\,(1) \ \Rightarrow \ c_2 = 0$$

Thus, we note that :

(1) $x(t) = (0.1)\cos\dfrac{14}{\sqrt{3}}t$
$\qquad\qquad$ (2) $v = \dfrac{dx}{dt} = -(0.1)\dfrac{14}{\sqrt{3}}\sin\dfrac{14}{\sqrt{3}}t$

(3) $a = \dfrac{d^2x}{dt^2} = -(0.1)\dfrac{196}{3}\cos\dfrac{14}{\sqrt{3}}t$
$\qquad$ (4) Amp. $= 0.1$ m

(5) Periodic time $T = \dfrac{2\pi}{\omega} = \dfrac{\sqrt{3}\,\pi}{7}$ sec.

(6) Frequency $= f = \dfrac{1}{T} = \dfrac{\omega}{2\pi} = \dfrac{7}{\sqrt{3}\,\pi}$ cycles/sec.

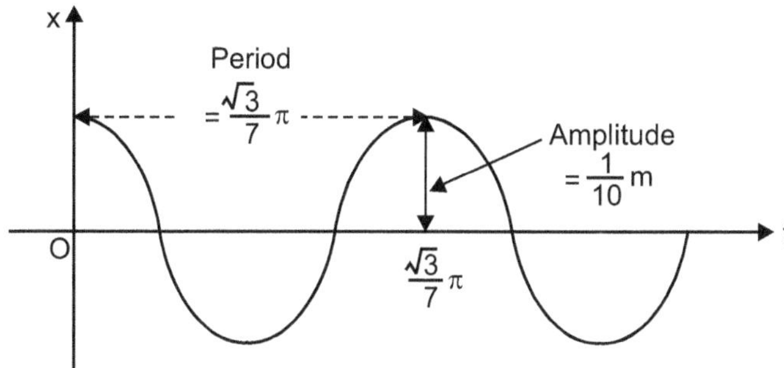

Fig. 3.2

Also, the position, velocity and acceleration of the weight 1/2 second after it has been released is obtained by putting t = 1/2 and using the fact that

$$\frac{7}{\sqrt{3}} \text{ radian} = \frac{7}{\sqrt{3}} \frac{180}{\pi} = 231.56° \text{ approximately.}$$

(1) $x(t)|_{t=1/2} = (0.1) \cos \dfrac{14}{\sqrt{3}} t = -0.0622$

(2) $v|_{t=1/2} = \left. \dfrac{dx}{dt} \right|_{t=1/2} = -(0.1) \dfrac{14}{\sqrt{3}} \sin \dfrac{14}{\sqrt{3}} t = 0.633$ m/sec

(3) $a|_{t=1/2} = \left. \dfrac{d^2x}{dt^2} \right|_{t=1/2} = -(0.1) \dfrac{196}{3} \cos \dfrac{14}{\sqrt{3}} t = 4.064$ m/sec^2.

Remark : We note here that 1/2 seconds after the weight has been released, it is 0.0622 m above equilibrium position, is travelling downward with velocity 0.633 m/sec and has acceleration downward of 4.064 m/sec^2.

Ex. 2 : *In example 1 suppose the weight is pulled 10 cm below equilibrium position and is then given a downward velocity 60 cm/sec instead of being released from rest. Find the amplitude, period and frequency of motion.* **(May 2009)**

OR

A body of weight W = 3 N stretches a spring to 15 cm. If the weight is pulled down 10 cm below the equilibrium position and then given a downward velocity 60 cm/sec, determine the amplitude, period and frequency of motion.

Sol. : Differential equation is same as in the example 1.

$$\frac{d^2x}{dt^2} + \frac{196}{3} x = 0$$

A.E. is $D^2 + \dfrac{196}{3} = 0$ $\therefore$ $D = \pm \dfrac{14}{\sqrt{3}} i$

G.S. is $x = c_1 \cos \dfrac{14}{\sqrt{3}} t + c_2 \sin \dfrac{14}{\sqrt{3}} t$ ... (1)

Differentiating (1) with respect to t, we get

$$\frac{dx}{dt} = -c_1 \frac{14}{\sqrt{3}} \sin \frac{14}{\sqrt{3}} t + c_2 \frac{14}{\sqrt{3}} \cos \frac{14}{\sqrt{3}} t \qquad \ldots(2)$$

The initial conditions are $t = 0$, $x = 10$ cm $= 0.1$ m and the since the weight is given downward velocity 60 cm/sec $= 0.6$ m/sec, $t = 0$, $\frac{dx}{dt} = 0$. Using these conditions, we obtain

$$0.1 = c_1 (1) + c_2 (0) \Rightarrow c_1 = 0.1$$

$$0.6 = 0 + c_2 \frac{14}{\sqrt{3}} (1) \Rightarrow c_2 = \frac{3\sqrt{3}}{70}$$

Hence, $$x = 0.1 \cos \frac{14}{\sqrt{3}} t + \frac{3\sqrt{3}}{70} \sin \frac{14}{\sqrt{3}} t$$

or $$x = 0.125 \sin \left(\frac{14}{\sqrt{3}} t + \phi \right), \qquad \phi = 53° 24' = 0.9337$$

(1) Amplitude $= 0.125$ m.

(2) Periodic time, $T = \dfrac{2\pi}{\omega} = \dfrac{\sqrt{3}\,\pi}{7}$ sec.

(3) Frequency $= f = \dfrac{1}{T} = \dfrac{\omega}{2\pi} = \dfrac{7}{\sqrt{3}\,\pi}$ cycles/sec.

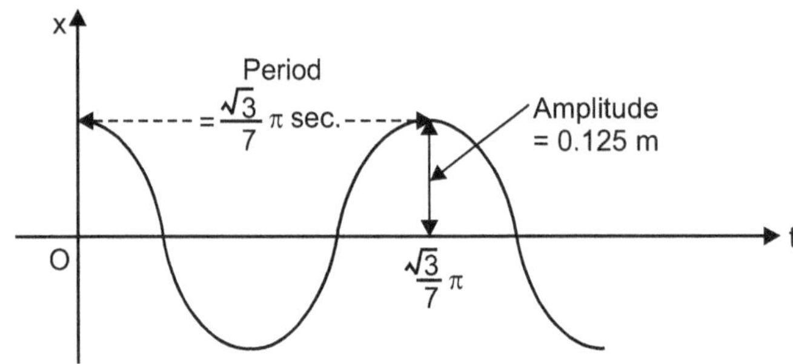

Fig. 3.3

Ex. 3 : *A body of weight W = 1 N is suspended from a spring stretches it 4 cm. If the weight is pulled down 8 cm below the equilibrium position and then released,*

(i)   Set-up a differential equation.

(ii) Find the position and velocity as function of time.

(iii) Find the amplitude, period and frequency of motion.   **(Dec. 2007, 2011)**

Sol. : Since a weight $W = 1$ N stretches a spring 4 cm $= 0.04$ m, by Hooke's law,

$$F_0 = k\, s_0 \Rightarrow 1 = k \times 0.04 \quad \therefore \ k = 25 \text{ N/m (or kg/s}^2)$$

By Newton's second law, the equation of motion of the body is

$$m \frac{d^2x}{dt^2} = -kx \quad \text{or} \quad \frac{W}{g} \frac{d^2x}{dt^2} = -kx$$

$$\therefore \quad \frac{1}{9.8} \frac{d^2x}{dt^2} = -25x \quad \text{or} \quad \frac{d^2x}{dt^2} + 245x = 0$$

which is a linear differential equation with constant coefficients.

$$\text{A.E. is } D^2 + 245 = 0 \quad \therefore \quad D = \pm i\sqrt{245}$$

$$\text{G.S. is } x = c_1 \cos \sqrt{245}\, t + c_2 \sin \sqrt{245}\, t \qquad \dots (1)$$

Differentiating (1) with respect to t, we get

$$\frac{dx}{dt} = -c_1 \sqrt{245} \sin \sqrt{245}\, t + c_2 \sqrt{245} \cos \sqrt{245}\, t \qquad \dots (2)$$

Using $x = 0.08$ at $t = 0$: $\quad 0.08 = c_1(0) + c_2(0) \Rightarrow c_1 = 0.08$

Using $\frac{dx}{dt} = 0$ at $t = 0$: $\quad 0 = 0 + c_2 \sqrt{245} \quad \Rightarrow c_2 = 0$

Thus, we note that :

(1) $\ x(t) = (0.08) \cos \sqrt{245}\, t$ $\qquad$ (2) $\ v = \frac{dx}{dt} = -(0.08) \sqrt{245} \sin \sqrt{245}\, t$

(3) $\ \text{Amplitude} = 0.08$ m $\qquad$ (4) $\ \text{Periodic time } T = \frac{2\pi}{\omega} = \frac{2\pi}{\sqrt{245}}$ sec

(5) $\ \text{Frequency} = f = \frac{1}{T} = \frac{\omega}{2\pi} = \frac{\sqrt{245}}{2\pi}$ cycles/sec.

Note : For $(D^2 + \omega^2)\, x = 0$, roots are : $D = \pm i\omega$ and G.S. $= x = c_1 \cos \omega t + c_2 \sin \omega t$.

Ex. 4 : *A body weighing W = 20 N is hung from a spring. A pull of 40 N will stretch the spring to 10 cm. The body is pulled down to 20 cm below the static equilibrium position and then released. Find the displacement of the body from its equilibrium position in time t seconds, the maximum velocity and period of oscillation.*

(Dec. 2010, May 14, 15, Nov. 16)

Sol. : Since a pull of $W = 40$ N weight stretches a spring 10 cm $= 0.1$ m, by Hooke's law,

$$F_0 = k\, s_0 \Rightarrow 40 = k \times 0.1 \quad \therefore \quad k = 400 \text{ N/m}$$

By Newton's second law, the equation of motion of the body is

$$m \frac{d^2x}{dt^2} = -kx \quad \text{or} \quad \frac{W}{g} \frac{d^2x}{dt^2} = -kx$$

$$\therefore \quad \frac{20}{9.8} \frac{d^2x}{dt^2} = -400x \quad \text{or} \quad \frac{d^2x}{dt^2} + 196x = 0 \qquad (\because m = \frac{W}{g})$$

which is a linear differential equation with constant coefficients.

$$\text{A.E. is } D^2 + 196 = 0 \quad \therefore \quad D = \pm 14i$$

$$\text{G.S. is } x = c_1 \cos 14t + c_2 \sin 14t \qquad \dots (1)$$

Differentiating (1) with respect to t, we get

$$\frac{dx}{dt} = -c_1\, 14 \sin 14\,t + c_2\, 14 \cos 14\,t \qquad \ldots (2)$$

The initial conditions are $t = 0$, $x = 20$ cm $= 0.2$ m and since the weight is released $t = 0$, $\frac{dx}{dt} = 0$. Using these conditions, we obtain

$$0.2 = c_1(1) + c_2(0) \;\Rightarrow\; c_1 = 0.2$$
$$0 = 0 + c_2\, 14 \qquad \Rightarrow\; c_2 = 0$$

Thus, we note that :

(1) $x(t) = (0.2) \cos 14t$

(2) $v = \dfrac{dx}{dt} = -(0.2)\, 14 \sin 14t$

(3)   Amplitude $= 0.2$ m

(4)   Periodic time $T = \dfrac{2\pi}{\omega} = \dfrac{2\pi}{14} = \dfrac{\pi}{7}$ sec.

(5)   Frequency $= f = \dfrac{1}{T} = \dfrac{\omega}{2\pi} = \dfrac{7}{\pi}$ cycles/sec.

Ex. 5 : *A body weighing 4.9 N is hung from a spring. A pull of 10 N will stretch the spring to 5 cm. The body is pulled down 6 cm below the static equilibrium position and then released. Find the displacement of the body from its equilibrium position in time t seconds, the maximum velocity and period of oscillation.*

Sol. : Since a pull of $W = 10$ N weight stretches a spring 5 cm $= 0.05$ m, by Hooke's law

$$F_0 = k\, s_0 \;\Rightarrow\; 10 = k \times 0.05 \quad \therefore\; k = 200 \text{ N/m}$$

By Newton's second law, the equation of motion of the body is

$$m\frac{d^2x}{dt^2} = -kx \quad \text{or} \quad \frac{W}{g}\frac{d^2x}{dt^2} = -kx \qquad (\because W = mg)$$

$$\therefore \qquad \frac{4.9}{9.8}\frac{d^2x}{dt^2} = -200x \quad \text{or} \quad \frac{d^2x}{dt^2} + 400x = 0$$

which is a linear differential equation with constant coefficients.

$$\text{A.E. is } D^2 + 200 = 0 \quad \therefore\; D = \pm 20i$$
$$\text{G.S. is } x = c_1 \cos 20t + c_2 \sin 20t \qquad \ldots (1)$$

Differentiating (1) with respect to t, we get

$$\frac{dx}{dt} = -c_1\, 20 \sin 20t + c_2\, 20 \cos 20t \qquad \ldots (2)$$

The initial conditions are $t = 0$, $x = 6$ cm $= 0.06$ m and since the weight is released $t = 0$, $\frac{dx}{dt} = 0$. Using these conditions, we obtain

$$0.06 = c_1(1) + c_2(0) \;\Rightarrow\; c_1 = 0.06$$
$$0 = 0 + c_2\, 20(1) \;\Rightarrow\; c_2 = 0$$

Thus, we note that :

(1) $x(t) = (0.06) \cos 20t$

(2) $v = \dfrac{dx}{dt} = -(0.06)\, 20 \sin 20t$ m/sec

(3) Amplitude $= 0.06$ m

(4) Periodic time, $T = \dfrac{2\pi}{\omega} = \dfrac{2\pi}{20} = \dfrac{\pi}{10}$ sec.

(5) Frequency $= f = \dfrac{1}{T} = \dfrac{\omega}{2\pi} = \dfrac{10}{\pi}$ cycles/sec.

3.4 DAMPED SYSTEM (FREE, DAMPED OSCILLATION)

If the motion of the mass m be subjected to an additional force of resistance (damping or frictional forces of medium), the oscillations are said to be damped.

If we connect the dashpot (See Fig. 3.4), we have to take corresponding viscous damping into account. The corresponding damping force has direction opposite to the instantaneous motion. We assume that it is proportional to the velocity $\dfrac{dx}{dt}$ of the body. (For small velocities this is a good approximation.) Thus the damping is of the form

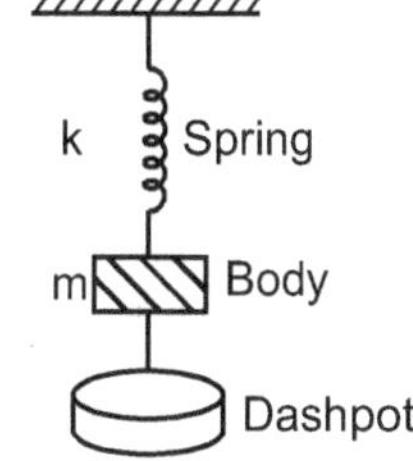

Fig. 3.4 : Damped System

$$F_2 = -c\,\frac{dx}{dt}$$

$c\ (> 0)$, constant of proportionality, is called the damping constant.

The resultant force acting on the body is now

$$F_1 + F_2 = -kx - c\,\frac{dx}{dt}$$

Hence, by Newton's second law, motion of the mass with damping force is

$$m\frac{d^2x}{dt^2} + c\frac{dx}{dt} + kx = 0 \quad \text{or} \quad \frac{d^2x}{dt^2} + \frac{c}{m}\frac{dx}{dt} + \frac{k}{m}x = 0$$

Remark : Using short notations $2b = c/m$ and $\omega^2 = k/m$ above equation can be written as

$$\frac{d^2x}{dt^2} + 2b\frac{dx}{dt} + \omega^2 x = 0 \qquad \qquad \dots (9)$$

This shows that the motion of the damped mechanical system is governed by the linear differential equation with constant coefficients. The auxiliary equation of (9) is

$$\lambda^2 + 2b\lambda + \omega^2 = 0$$

The roots are $\lambda_{1,2} = -b \pm \sqrt{b^2 - \omega^2}$ $\qquad \qquad \dots (10)$

The motion of the mass depends on the damping through the nature of discriminant $b^2 - \omega^2$. We note the following three cases :

Case I : $b^2 - \omega^2 > 0$ i.e. $c^2 > 4mk$ Distinct real roots   (Overdamping)

Case II : $b^2 - \omega^2 = 0$ i.e. $c^2 > 4mk$ Repeated real roots   (Critical damping)

Case III : $b^2 - \omega^2 < 0$ i.e. $c^2 > 4mk$ Complex conjugate roots   (Underdamping)

ILLUSTRATION

Ex. 6 : *If a damping force given in N by c = 1.5 kg/s times the velocity in meter per second acts on the weight in the solved example 1 of Article 3.3.*

(i)   Set-up the differential equation and the associated conditions.

(ii) Find the position x of the weight as a function of time.

Sol. : Considering the damping force $-1.5\,\dfrac{dx}{dt}$ in example 1, we write the equation

of motion : $\dfrac{3}{9.8}\dfrac{d^2x}{dt^2} = -20x - 1.5\dfrac{dx}{dt}$

$\Rightarrow$ $\dfrac{d^2x}{dt^2} + 4.9\dfrac{dx}{dt} + \dfrac{196}{3} = 0$ ... (1)

The initial conditions are same as in Ex. 1.

i.e. at $t = 0,$ $x = \dfrac{1}{10}$ m and $\dfrac{dx}{dt} = 0$ ... (2)

A.E. is $D^2 + 4.9\,D + \dfrac{196}{3} = 0$ $\Rightarrow$ $D = -2.45 \pm i\,7.7$

Hence the general solution of equation (1) will be,

$$x = e^{-(2.45)\,t}\,[A \cos(7.7)\,t + B \sin(7.7)\,t]$$ ... (3)

If we apply conditions (2) to this solution, then we have

$$x = e^{-(2.45)\,t}\,[(0.1)\cos(7.7)\,t + (0.032)\sin(7.7)\,t]$$ ... (4)

as the complete solution. Which can be written in the form :

$$x = (0.105)\,e^{-(2.45)\,t}\sin[(7.7)\,t + 1.261]$$ ... (5)

The graph of equation (5) shown in Fig. 3.5 lies between the graphs of

$$x = +0.105\,e^{-(2.45)\,t} \quad \text{and} \quad x = -0.105\,e^{-(2.45)\,t}$$

[Shown dashed in Fig. 3.5] since sine function varies between -1 and $+1$.

The constant difference in times between successive maxima (or minima) i.e. $\dfrac{2\pi}{7.7}$ is

called the *Quasi period* (i.e. between the points 0 and T on the t axis).

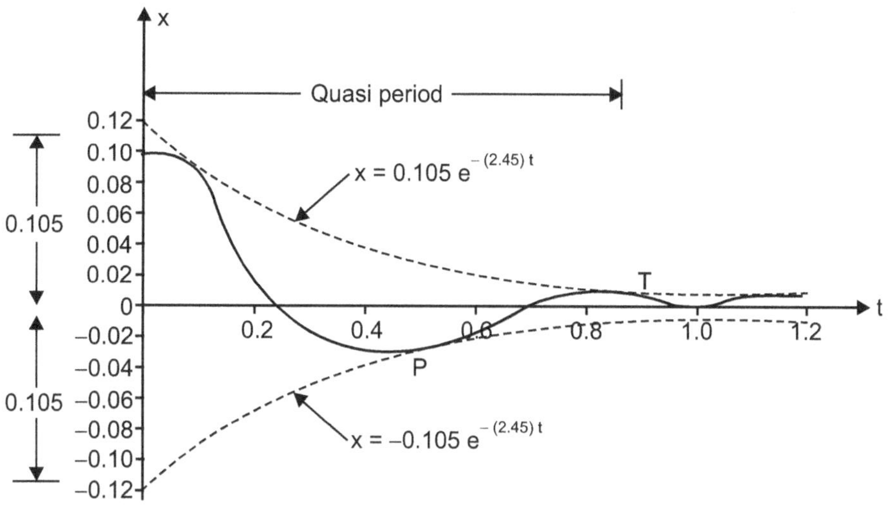

Fig. 3.5

SUMMARY : The motion described in this example is called *Damped oscillatory* or *Damped vibratory* motion. Here equation (5) has the form

$$x = A(t) \sin(\omega t + \phi) \qquad \qquad \dots (6)$$

where $\qquad A(t) = 0.105 \, e^{-(2.45)t}, \ \omega = 7.7 \ \text{and} \ \phi = 1.261$

The *quasi period* is given by

$$\frac{2\pi}{\omega} = \frac{2\pi}{7.7}$$

By analogy with the undamped case, $A(t)$ is called *Amplitude* or more exactly *Time-varying amplitude*. It is seen that the amplitude decreases with time, thus agreeing with our experience. Also frequency with damping is less than that without damping. This is possible because one would expect opposition to motion to increase the time for a complete cycle. The undamped frequency i.e. with $\beta = 0$ is often called the *Natural frequency*. It is of great importance in connection with the phenomenon of *Resonance* to be discussed later.

Note : Sometimes the damping force may be too great compared to the restoring force to permit oscillatory motion. This type of motion is called as *Overdamped motion*.

When damping is such that any decrease in it produces oscillations, the motion is called *Critically damped.*

3.5 MASS-SPRING SYSTEM (FORCED OSCILLATIONS)

Earlier we have discussed the problems of spring where only restoring and damping forces were working inspite of the weight W. We now consider cases where other external forces which depend on time may also act. Such forces may occur, for example, when the support holding the spring is moved-up and down in a prescribed manner such as in periodic motion or when the weight is given a little push everytime it reaches the lowest position. If we denote the external force by F(t), the differential equation of motion is,

$$\frac{W}{g}\frac{d^2x}{dt^2} = -kx - c\frac{dx}{dt} + F(t)$$

or $$\frac{W}{g}\frac{d^2x}{dt^2} + c\frac{dx}{dt} + kx = F(t) \qquad (W = mg)$$

This equation is called the *equation of forced vibrations*. In what follows, we shall now discuss the behaviour of mechanical system for two cases :

(i) damped forced oscillations (c > 0) and (ii) undamped forced oscillations (resonance, c = 0).

Remark : Using short notations, above equation can be written as

$$\frac{d^2x}{dt^2} + 2b\frac{dx}{dt} + \omega^2 x = F_1(t)$$

$$2b = \frac{cg}{W} = \frac{c}{m}, \qquad \omega^2 = \frac{kg}{W} = \frac{k}{m} \qquad \text{and} \qquad F_1(t) = \frac{g}{W}F(t)$$

ILLUSTRATION

Ex. 7 : *In the previous solved example 6, assume that a periodic external force given by* $F(t) = 24\cos\dfrac{14}{\sqrt{3}}t$ *is acting. Find x in terms of t, using conditions given there.*

Sol. : The differential equation will be

$$\frac{3}{9.8}\frac{d^2x}{dt^2} = -20x - 1.5\frac{dx}{dt} + 24\cos\frac{14}{\sqrt{3}}t$$

or $$\frac{d^2x}{dt^2} + 4.9\frac{dx}{dt} + \frac{196}{3}x = 78.4\cos\frac{14}{\sqrt{3}}t \qquad \qquad \ldots (1)$$

with the initial conditions $x = \dfrac{1}{10}, \quad \dfrac{dx}{dt} = 0 \quad$ at $t = 0 \qquad \qquad \ldots (2)$

If we solve equation (1), the complementary function is given by,
$$\text{C.F.} = x_c = e^{-(2.45)t}[A\cos(7.7)t + B\sin(7.7)t]$$

and particular integral is

$$\text{P.I.} = x_p = \frac{1}{D^2 + 4.9D + \dfrac{196}{3}}78.4\cos\frac{14}{\sqrt{3}}t = 1.979\sin\frac{14}{\sqrt{3}}t$$

Hence the general solution of equation (1) is

$$x = x_c + x_p = e^{-(2.45)t}[A\cos(7.7)t + B\sin(7.7)t] + 1.979\sin\frac{14}{\sqrt{3}}t \ldots (3)$$

and using the initial conditions (2), we have

$$A = \frac{1}{10}, \quad B = -2.046$$

and hence $$x = e^{-(2.45)t}[1\cos(7.7)t - (2.046)\sin(7.7)t] + 1.979\sin\frac{14}{\sqrt{3}}t \ldots (4)$$

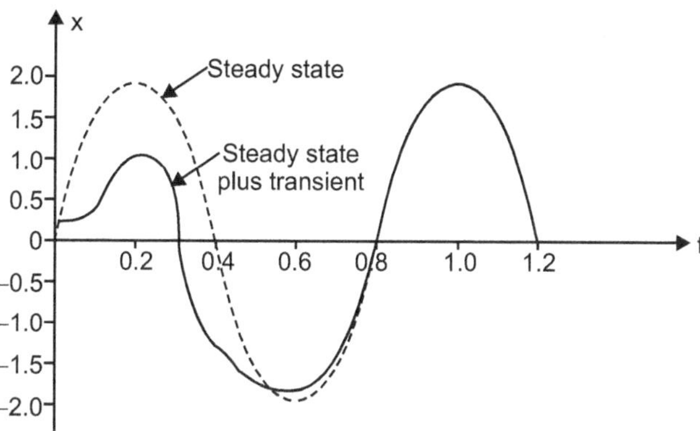

Fig. 3.6

The graph of equation (3) is given in Fig. 3.6. It will be seen that the terms in equation (4) involving $e^{-(2.45)t}$, become negligible (die down) when t is large. These terms are called *Transient terms* and are of value only when t is near zero, and these terms in the solution, when they are significant are called *Transient solution*. But when the transient terms are negligible, the term 1.979 $\sin \dfrac{14}{\sqrt{3}}$ t remains. This is called the *Steady state solution* since it indicates the behaviour of the system when things have become steady. It is seen that steady state solution (shown dashed curve in Fig. 3.6) is periodic, having same period as that of applied external force.

3.6 MECHANICAL FORCE

When the frequency of a periodic external force, applied to a mechanical system is *related to the natural frequency* of the system, *Mechanical resonance* may occur, which builds-up the oscillations to such tremendous magnitudes that the system itself may fall apart. A company of soldiers marching in step across a bridge may in this manner cause the bridge to collapse even though it would have been strong enough to carry many more soldiers had they marched out of step. Similarly, it may be possible for a musical note of proper characteristic frequency to shatter a glass. Hence mechanical resonance in general should be avoided by engineers designing structure of vibrating mechanism. The example below will indicate what may be the consequence of resonance.

ILLUSTRATIONS

Ex. 8 : *Suppose an external force given by 6 $\cos \dfrac{14}{\sqrt{3}}$ t is applied to the spring of the solved example 1 of Art. 3.3. Describe the motion which ensures if it is assumed that initially the weight is at the equilibrium position (x = 0) and that its initial velocity is zero.*

Sol. : The differential equation will be

$$\frac{3}{9.8} \frac{d^2x}{dt^2} = -20\,x + 6\cos\frac{14}{\sqrt{3}}\,t$$

or $\qquad \dfrac{d^2x}{dt^2} + \dfrac{196}{3}\,x = 19.6\cos\dfrac{14}{\sqrt{3}}\,t$ $\qquad\qquad\qquad$ ... (1)

and the initial conditions are

$$x = 0, \qquad \frac{dx}{dt} = 0 \quad \text{at } t = 0 \qquad \qquad \dots (2)$$

The solution will be (general solution),

$$x = A \cos \frac{14}{\sqrt{3}} t + B \sin \frac{14}{\sqrt{3}} t + 1.212\, t \sin \frac{14}{\sqrt{3}} t \qquad \dots (3)$$

and using initial condition, it will be (A = 0 = B)

$$x = 1.212\, t \sin \frac{14}{\sqrt{3}} t \qquad \qquad \dots (4)$$

Graph of equation (4) will lie between the graphs of x = 1.212 t and x = – 1.212 t as shown in Fig. 3.7.

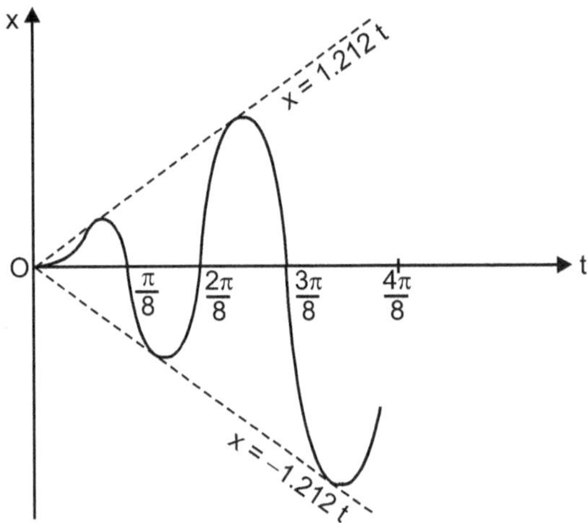

Fig. 3.7

It is seen from the graph that oscillations build-up without limit. Naturally the spring is bound to break within a short time.

It should be noted here that damping was neglected and *Resonance* occurred because the *frequency of the applied external force was equal to the Natural frequency of the undamped system.* This is a general principle. In the case where damping occurs, the oscillations do not build-up without limit but may sometimes become large.

Ex. 9 : *A spring stretches 1 cm under the tension of 2 N and has a negligible weight. It is fixed at one end and is attached to a weight W Newton at the other. It is found that resonance occurs when an axial periodic force 2 cos 2t N acts on the weight. Show that when the free vibrations have died out, the forced vibrations are given by x = ct sin 2t and find the values of W and c.* **(Dec. 2006)**

Sol. : A weight of 2 N stretches the spring by $\frac{1}{100}$ m

$$\therefore \quad 2 = T = k \cdot \frac{1}{100} \Rightarrow k = 200 \text{ N/m}$$

Let B be the equilibrium position of the weight W attached to A, then

$$W = T_B = k \cdot AB = 200 \, AB$$

$$\Rightarrow \qquad AB = \frac{W}{200} \, m$$

At any time t, let the weight be at P where BP = x. Then the tension T at P

$$= k \cdot AP = 200 \left(\frac{W}{200} + x \right) = W + 200 \, x$$

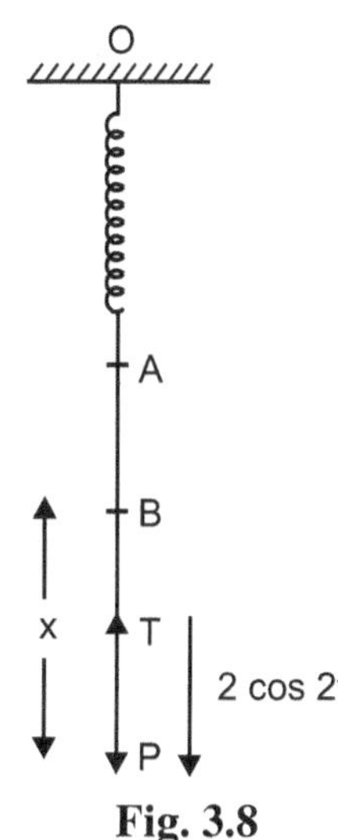

Fig. 3.8

$\therefore$ Equation of motion is,

$$\frac{W}{g} \frac{d^2x}{dt^2} = -T + W + 2 \cos 2t$$

$$\Rightarrow \qquad \frac{W}{g} \frac{d^2x}{dt^2} = -W - 200 \, x + W + 2 \cos 2t$$

Or $\qquad \dfrac{d^2x}{dt^2} + 200 \dfrac{gx}{W} = \dfrac{2g}{W} \cos 2t \qquad\qquad \ldots (1)$

The phenomenon of resonance will occur when the frequency of free oscillations is equal to the frequency of forced oscillations or (the period of free oscillations is equal to the period of forced oscillations).

If we write equation (1) as $\dfrac{d^2x}{dt^2} + \omega^2 x = \dfrac{2g}{W} \cos 2t$ where, $\omega^2 = \dfrac{200 \, g}{W}$, the period of free oscillations is found to be $\dfrac{2\pi}{\omega}$ and the period of the forced oscillations is $2\pi/2 = \pi$.

Hence $\qquad \dfrac{2\pi}{\omega} = \pi \Rightarrow \omega = 2$ or $\dfrac{200 \, g}{W} = \omega^2 = 4$

hence $\qquad\qquad W = 50 \, g$

Taking this value of W in equation (1), we have

$$\frac{d^2x}{dt^2} + 4x = \frac{1}{25}\cos 2t \qquad \ldots (2)$$

Now free oscillations are given by C.F. and forced oscillations by the P.I. Hence when the free oscillations have died out, the forced oscillations are given by the P.I. of (2).

$$\text{Now P.I. of equation (2)} = \frac{1}{25}\frac{1}{D^2+4}\cos 2t = \frac{1}{25}\, t\, \frac{1}{2D} \cdot \cos 2t$$

$$= \frac{1}{100}\, t\sin 2t = ct\sin 2t$$

$$\text{Hence } c = \frac{1}{100}$$

Ex. 10 : *A body of weight 9.8 N is suspended from a spring having constant 4 N/m. Prove that the motion is one of resonance if a force 16 sin 2t is applied and damping force is negligible. Assume that initially the weight is at rest in the equilibrium position.* **(May 17)**

Sol. : The differential equation describing phenomenon is

$$m\frac{d^2x}{dt^2} + kx = F(t)$$

$$\frac{9.8}{9.8}\frac{d^2x}{dt^2} + 4x = 16\sin 2t$$

or

$$\frac{d^2x}{dt^2} + 4x = 16\sin 2t$$

A.E. is $D^2 + 4 = 0$, Roots are $D = \pm\, 2i$

C.F. $= c_1\cos 2t + c_2\sin 2t$

$$\text{P.I.} = 16\frac{1}{D^2+4}\sin 2t = -\,4t\cos 2t$$

G.S. $= x(t) = c_1\cos 2t + c_2\sin 2t - 4t\cos 2t$

Using $x = 0$ at $t = 0$,

$$0 = c_1\,(1) + c_2\,(0) - 0 \quad \therefore\ c_1 = 0$$

$\therefore$
$$x(t) = c_2\sin 2t - 4t\cos 2t.$$

Differentiating $x(t)$ with respect to t,

$$\frac{dx}{dt} = 2c_2\cos 2t - 4\cos 2t + 8t\sin 2t$$

Using $\dfrac{dx}{dt} = 0$ at $t = 0$,

$$0 = 2c_2\,(1) - 4(1) + 8(0) \quad \therefore\ c_2 = 2$$

The position of weight at any time is

$$x(t) = 2 \sin 2t - 4t \cos 2t$$

and its velocity is

$$\frac{dx}{dt} = 4 \cos 2t - 4 \cos 2t + 8t \sin 2t$$

We note that frequency external force is $\frac{2}{2\pi} = \frac{1}{\pi}$ cycles/sec. Natural frequency of the free undamped system is $\frac{\omega}{2\pi} = \frac{2}{2\pi} = \frac{1}{\pi}$ cycles/sec. Therefore, resonance occurs in the system because the frequency of the external force equals to natural frequency of the system.

Ex. 11 : *A spring which stretches by an amount e under a force mk^2e is suspended from a support P and has a mass 'm' at its lower end. At time t = 0, the mass is at rest in its equilibrium position at a point A below P. A vertical oscillation is now given to the support P such that at any time its displacement below its initial position is 'a sin nt'. Show that the displacement x of the mass below A is*

$$\frac{d^2x}{dt^2} + k^2x = k^2 \, a \, \sin nt$$

Hence show that if $n \neq k$, the displacement is given by

$$x = \frac{ka}{k^2 - n^2} (k \sin nt - n \sin kt) \tag{May 2005}$$

Sol. : A spring under the action of force mk^2e stretches by an amount e. By Hooke's law,

$$mk^2e = \lambda e \Rightarrow \lambda = mk^2$$

Also, given external periodic force (vertical oscillation) is λ (a sin nt). Therefore, by Newton's second law, the equation of motion is

$$m\frac{d^2x}{dt^2} + \lambda x = \lambda \, (a \sin nt)$$

or

$$m\frac{d^2x}{dt} + mk^2x = mk^2 \, (a \sin nt)$$

or

$$\frac{d^2x}{dt^2} + k^2x = k^2a \, \sin nt$$

$$\text{C.F.} = c_1 \cos kt + c_2 \sin kt$$

$$\text{P.I.} = k^2a \frac{1}{D^2 + k^2} \sin nt = k^2a \frac{1}{(k^2 - n^2)} \sin nt, \ k \neq n$$

$$x = c_1 \cos kt + c_2 \sin kt + ka^2 \frac{1}{(k^2 - n^2)} \sin nt$$

Differentiating with respect to t,

$$\frac{dx}{dt} = -kc_1 \sin kt + kc_2 \cos kt + ka^2 n \frac{1}{(k^2 - n^2)} \cos nt$$

Using $x = 0$ at $t = 0$,

$$0 = c_1 (1) + c_2 (0) + 0 \quad \therefore \quad c_1 = 0$$

Using $\frac{dx}{dt} = 0$ at $t = 0$,

$$0 = k\, c_1 (0) + k\, c_2 (1) + k^2 an \frac{1}{(k^2 - n^2)} (1) \quad \therefore \quad c_2 = -\frac{kan}{k^2 - n^2}$$

Hence, if $n \neq k$, the displacement is given by

$$x = -\frac{kan}{k^2 - n^2} \sin kt + \frac{k^2 a}{k^2 - n^2} \sin nt$$

or $\qquad x = \frac{ka}{k^2 - n^2} (k \sin nt - n \sin kt)$ when $k \neq n$.

3.7 COUPLED MASSES

In coupled masses, we get a good application of simultaneous equations, an example will explain better.

ILLUSTRATION

Ex. 12 : *Two particles, each of mass m gram are suspended from two springs of same stiffness k as shown in Fig. 3.9. After the system comes to rest, the lower mass is pulled l cm, downward and released. Discuss their motion.*

Sol. : Let x and y be the displacements of the upper and lower masses, at time t from their respective positions of equilibrium.

Then the stretch of the upper spring is x and that of the lower spring is $y - x$.

$\therefore$ Restoring force acting on the upper mass $= -kx + k (y - x) = k (y - 2x)$ and that on the lower mass $= -k (y - x)$

Hence their equations of motion are :

$$m \frac{d^2x}{dt^2} = k (y - 2x) \text{ and}$$

$$m \frac{d^2y}{dt^2} = -k (y - x)$$

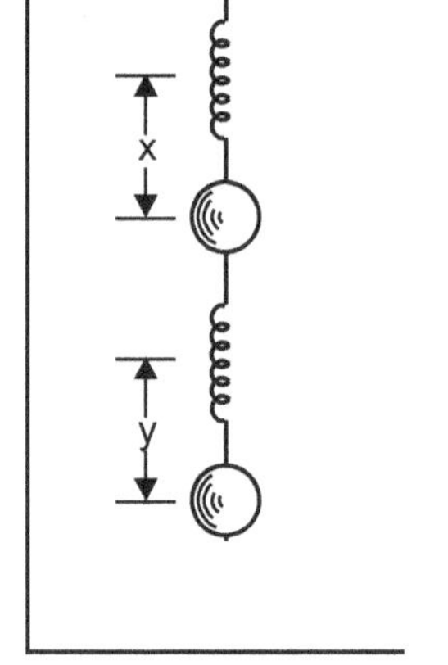

Fig. 3.9

or $\qquad (mD^2 + 2k) x - ky = 0$ $\qquad\qquad\qquad$ ... (1)

and $\qquad (mD^2 + k) y - kx = 0$ $\qquad\qquad\qquad$ ... (2)

which are the linear simultaneous equations. Operating (1) by $(mD^2 + k)$ and adding to k times (2), we get

$$[(mD^2 + k) (mD^2 + 2k) - k^2] x = 0$$

or $\qquad (D^4 + 3\lambda D^2 + \lambda^2)\, x = 0, \quad$ where $\lambda = \dfrac{k}{m}$.

Its auxiliary equation is $\quad D^4 + 3\lambda D^2 + \lambda^2 = 0$

which gives $\qquad D^2 = \dfrac{-3\lambda \pm \sqrt{9\lambda^2 - 4\lambda^2}}{2} = -2.62\,\lambda \ \text{ or } -0.38\,\lambda$

$$= -\alpha^2,\ -\beta^2 \ (\text{say})$$

So that $\qquad D = \pm\, i\alpha,\ \pm\, i\beta.$

Hence $\qquad x = C_1 \cos \alpha t + C_2 \sin \alpha t + C_3 \cos \beta t + C_4 \sin \beta t \qquad \ldots (3)$

Also from equation (1), $\ y = \left(\dfrac{D^2}{\lambda} + 2\right) x$

$\therefore \quad y = \left(2 - \dfrac{\alpha^2}{\lambda}\right) (C_1 \cos \alpha t + C_2 \sin \alpha t) + \left(2 - \dfrac{\beta^2}{\lambda}\right)(C_3 \cos \beta t + C_4 \sin \beta t) \ \ldots (4)$

But initially when $t = 0,\ x = y = l,\ \dfrac{dx}{dt} = 0 = \dfrac{dy}{dt}$

Hence from (3), $C_1 + C_3 = l \ $ and $C_2\,\alpha + C_4\,\beta = 0$

and from (4), $\qquad l = \left(2 - \dfrac{\alpha^2}{\lambda}\right) C_1 + \left(2 - \dfrac{\beta^2}{\lambda}\right) C_3$

$$0 = \left(2 - \dfrac{\alpha^2}{\lambda}\right) \alpha\,C_2 + \left(2 - \dfrac{\beta^2}{\lambda}\right) \beta C_4$$

when $\qquad C_1 = \dfrac{l\,(\lambda - \beta^2)}{\alpha^2 - \beta^2}, \quad C_3 = \dfrac{l\,(\lambda - \alpha^2)}{\beta^2 - \alpha^2},\ C_2 = C_4 = 0$

Substituting these values of the constants in (3) and (4), we get x and y which show that the motion of the string is a combination of two simple harmonic motions of periods $\dfrac{2\pi}{\alpha}$ and $\dfrac{2\pi}{\beta}$.

EXERCISE 3.1

1. A 1 N weight suspended from a spring stretches it 4 cm. If the weight is pulled 8 cm below the equilibrium position and released,
   (a) Set-up a differential equation and conditions describing the motion.
   (b) Find the velocity and the position of the weight as a function of time.
   (c) Find the amplitude, period and frequency of the motion.
   (d) Determine the position, velocity and acceleration $\dfrac{\pi}{64}$ sec. after the weight is released. **(May 2016)**

Ans. (b) $x = \dfrac{2}{25} \cos (15.65)\, t$, $v = -1.252 \sin (15.65)\, t$

(c) Amplitude $= \dfrac{2}{25}$ m, Period $= T = \dfrac{\pi}{7.825}$ sec.

Frequency $= f = \dfrac{7.825}{\pi}$ cycles/sec.

2. A 1.5 N weight on a spring stretches it 15 cm. When equilibrium is reached the weight is struck so as to give it a downward velocity of 60 cm/sec. Find :

(a) The velocity and position of the weight at time t sec. after the impact.

(b) The amplitude, period and frequency of the motion.

(c) The velocity and acceleration when the weight is 2.5 cm from the equilibrium position and moving upward.

Ans. (a) $x = (0.074) \sin (8.08)\, t$, $v = (0.598) \cos (8.08)\, t$ (ft/sec.)

(b) Amplitude $= 0.074$ m,, $T = 0.4$ sec., $f = \dfrac{4.04}{\pi}$ cycles/sec.

(c) 0.562 met/sec., 1.632 met/sec².

3. A weight W Newton is suspended from a vertical spring and produces a stretch of magnitude and when the weight is in equilibrium it is acted upon by a force which imparts to it a velocity V_0 downward. Show that the weight travels a distance $V_0 \sqrt{\dfrac{a}{g}}$ for a time $\left(\dfrac{\pi}{2}\right) \sqrt{\dfrac{a}{g}}$ before it starts to return.

4. A 2 N weight suspended from a spring stretches it 8 cm. The weight is pulled 15 cm below the equilibrium position and released. Assume that the weight is acted upon by a damping force which in N is numerically equal to 1 V, where V is the instantaneous velocity in m/sec.

(a) Set-up a differential equation and conditions describing the motion.

(b) Determine the position of the spring at any time after the weight is released.

(c) Write the result of (b) in the form A (t) sin ($\omega t + \phi$) .

Thus determine the time-varying amplitude and quasi period.

Ans. Note : $c = 1$ kg/s (b) $e^{-(2.45)\,t} [(0.15) \cos (10.79)\, t + (0.034) \sin (10.79)\, t]$

(c) $x = (0.15)\, e^{-(2.45)\,t} [\sin (10.79)\, t + 1.3478]$

$\omega = 10.79$, $\phi = 1.3478$, quasi period $= \dfrac{2\pi}{10.79} = \dfrac{\pi}{5.39}$ sec.

5. A 1 N weight suspended from a spring stretches it 15 cm. A velocity of 150 cm/sec. upward is imparted to the weight at its equilibrium position. Assume a damping force in N is numerically equal to 0.3 V, where V is the instantaneous velocity in m/sec. (a) Find the position and velocity of the spring at any time.

(b) Write a result of (a) in the form A (t) sin (ωt + ϕ).

$$\textbf{Ans.} \quad \text{(a)} \quad x = -(0.188)\, e^{-(1.48)t} \sin (7.95)\, t$$

$$V = e^{-(1.48)t}\, [0.278 \sin (7.95)\, t - (1.49) \cos (7.95)\, t]$$

$$\text{(b)} \quad x = (0.188)\, e^{-(1.48)t} \sin (7.95\, t + \pi)$$

6. A 3 N weight stretches a certain spring 15 cm. The weight is pulled 10 cm below the equilibrium position and released. A damping force in N equals to 5.75 V, where V being instantaneous velocity in m/sec. is working on the spring. Find x as a function of time t. By drawing the graph of the solution, show that it is a case of overdamped motion.

$$\textbf{Ans.} \quad x = (0.148)\, e^{-(4.615)t} - (0.048)\, e^{-(14.65)t}.$$

7. A vertical spring having constant 2 N/m has a 8 N weight suspended from it. An external force given by F(t) = 8 sin 10t is applied. A damping force given numerically in N by 4V, where V is velocity (m/sec.), is assumed to act. Initially the weight is at rest at its equilibrium position.

(a) Determine the position of the weight at any time.

(b) Indicate the transient and steady-state solutions.

(c) Find the amplitude, period and frequency of the steady-state solution.

$$\textbf{Ans.} \quad \text{(a)} \quad x = (0.193)\, e^{-(0.57)t} - (0.138)\, e^{-(8.66)t}$$

$$- (0.055) \cos 10\, t - (0.109) \sin 10\, t$$

$$\text{(b)} \quad \text{Steady-state part} - 0.55 \cos 10\, t - 0.109 \sin 10\, t = -0.12 \sin (10\, t + \phi)$$

$$- 0.397\ \sin (10\, t + 3.87)$$

$$\text{(c)} \quad \text{Steady-state amplitude} = 0.12 \text{ m, period} = \frac{\pi}{5} \text{ sec.}$$

$$\text{Frequency} = \frac{5}{\pi} \text{ cycles/sec.}$$

8. A vertical spring having constant 4 kg/m has a 32 N weight suspended from it. A force given by F (t) = 16 cos 4t is applied. Assuming that the weight initially at the equilibrium position is given an upward velocity 3 m/sec. and that the damping force is negligible, determine the position and the velocity of the weight at any time.

$$\textbf{Ans.} \quad x = 0.928 \cos (1.106)\, t - 2.712 \sin (1.106)\, t - 0.928 \cos 4t$$

$$V = -1.026 \sin (1.106)\, t - 2.999 \cos (1.106)\, t + 3.928 \sin 4t.$$

9. A vertical spring having constant 2 kg/ft. has a 16 N weight attached to it. A force given by $F(t) = 4 \sin \dfrac{7}{\sqrt{40}} t$ is applied. Assuming that at $t = 0$, the weight is at rest at the equilibrium position and the damping force is negligible,

(a) Set-up a differential equation and conditions describing the motion.

(b) Determine the position and velocity of the weight at any time.

(c) Show that the motion is one of Resonance.

$$\textbf{Ans. (b)} \quad x = 2 \sin \frac{7}{\sqrt{40}} t - \frac{7}{\sqrt{10}} t \cos \frac{7}{\sqrt{40}} t, \quad V = \frac{49}{20} t \sin \frac{7}{\sqrt{40}} t$$

10. In example 9 above, suppose that at $t = 0$, the weight is 15 cm below the equilibrium position and is struck so as to give a velocity of 1 m/sec. upward. Determine the position and the velocity of the weight at any time.

$$\textbf{Ans.} \quad x = (0.15) \cos \frac{7}{\sqrt{40}} t + (1.01) \sin \frac{7}{\sqrt{40}} t - \frac{7}{\sqrt{10}} t \cos \frac{7}{\sqrt{40}} t$$

$$V = (0.16) \sin \frac{7}{\sqrt{40}} t + (1.11) \cos \frac{7}{\sqrt{40}} t - \frac{7}{\sqrt{10}} \cos \frac{7}{\sqrt{40}} t + \frac{49}{20} t \sin \frac{7}{\sqrt{40}} t$$

11. The equation of forced vibrations of a mass on a vertical spring is

$$m \frac{d^2x}{dt^2} + \beta \frac{dx}{dt} + kx = A \cos \omega t, \quad t > 0,$$

where x is the displacement of a mass from its position of equilibrium and m, β, k, A and ω are positive constants.

(a) Show that a steady-state oscillation is given by

$$x = \frac{A}{\sqrt{(m\omega^2 - k)^2 + \beta^2 \omega^2}} \cos (\omega t + \phi)$$

(b) Show that maximum oscillations (Resonance) will occur if ω is so chosen that :

$$\omega = \sqrt{\frac{k}{m} - \frac{\beta^2}{2m^2}} \quad \text{provided } \beta^2 < 2km$$

(c) Show that at resonance, the amplitude of oscillation varies inversely as the damping constant β.

12. A mass m suspended from the end of helical spring is subjected to a periodic force $f = F \sin pt$ in the direction of its length. The force f is measured positive vertically downward and initially the mass is at rest in its equilibrium position. If the spring stiffness is k and damping force is negligible, show that the displacement of m at time t from the commencement of the motion is given by

$$x = \frac{F}{m(\omega^2 - p^2)} \left[\sin pt - \frac{p}{\omega} \sin \omega t \right], \text{ where } \omega^2 = \frac{k}{m}. \quad \textbf{(Dec. 2004; May 2007, 2009)}$$

❏❏❏

CHAPTER FOUR

LAPLACE TRANSFORM

4.1 INTRODUCTION

The theory of Laplace transforms is a very versatile tool, which has proved to be an essential part of mathematical techniques required for engineers, physicists, mathematicians and scientists. Its importance lies in the fact that its application is considerably easier than other available techniques.

Laplace transform method is widely used for solving differential equations and general system analysis. It reduces the problem of solving a differential equation to an algebraic problem. It is also useful in problems where the (mechanical or electrical) driving forces has discontinuities, forces acting for a short time only or are periodic and not merely sine or cosine functions.

In this chapter, we start with definition of the transform and state some sufficient conditions for its existence. We then derive its general properties (and theorems) and develop a table of transforms of some functions which are usually encountered in solutions of linear differential equations.

4.2 DEFINITION

Let $f(t)$ be a function of t defined for all $t > 0$. Then the *Laplace transform* of $f(t)$, denoted by $L\,[f(t)]$, is defined by

$$\boxed{L\,[f(t)] \;=\; \int_{0}^{\infty} e^{-st}\,f(t)\,dt = F(s)} \qquad \dots (1)$$

where, s is a parameter which may be real or complex.

The Laplace transform of $f(t)$ exists if the integral in (1) exists i.e. the integral in (1) converges for some value of s.

Note :

(i)   Symbol L is called the Laplace transform operator.

(ii) Generally, the transform will exist for more than one value of the parameter s, and hence $L\,[f(t)]$ defines a function of s, when it exists, and is denoted by $F(s)$.

(iii) There is one to one correspondence between f(t) and F(s), and the relation transforms f(t), a function of t, into F(s), a function of another variable s.

(iv) The operation just described, which yields F(s) from a given function f(t) is called *Laplace transformation.*

Notation :

(i) Original functions are denoted by lower case letters such as f(t), g(t), y(t) etc. and their transforms by the same letters in capital i.e. F(s), G(s), Y(s) etc.

(ii) A Bar ($^-$) can also be used to denote the Laplace transform. For example, the Laplace transforms of f(t), ϕ(t), x(t) etc. are $\bar{f}(s)$, $\bar{\phi}(s)$, $\bar{x}(s)$ etc.

We shall be using notation **L [f(t)] = F(s)** throughout our discussion.

4.3 THEORETICAL PRELIMINARIES

1. Piecewise Continuous Function

A function f(t) is said to be *piecewise continuous* in an interval a $\leq$ t $\leq$ b, if f(t) is defined on that interval and is such that the interval can be subdivided into a finite number of subintervals, in each of which f(t) is continuous and has finite limits as t approaches either end point of the interval of subdivision from the interior.

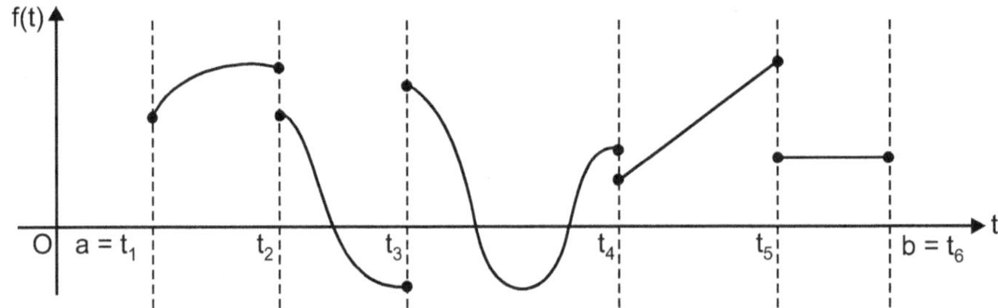

Fig. 4.1 : Example of Piecewise Continuous Function f(t)

2. Functions of Exponential Order

If there is a constant α with the property that $e^{-\alpha t} |f(t)|$ remains bounded as t $\to \infty$, then f(t) is said to be a *function of exponential order α as t $\to \infty$* or, briefly *of exponential order.* In other words, there are constants α, M, and N such that

$$e^{-\alpha t} |f(t)| < M \qquad \text{for all } t > N.$$

Remark : If a function is of exponential order α, its absolute value must not increase more rapidly than $Me^{\alpha t}$ as t increases.

Example 1 : f (t) = t^2 is of exponential order 3, since $|t^2| = t^2 < e^{3t}$ for all t.

Example 2 : f(t) = e^{t^2} is not of exponential order, because no matter how large we choose M and α, $e^{t^2} > Me^{\alpha t}$ for all t > N. In other words, $e^{t^2 - \alpha t}$ can be made larger than any given constant by increasing t.

Example 3 : Any function which is bounded in absolute value for t $\geq$ 0 such as sin ax, cos ax are of exponential order.

4.4 SUFFICIENT CONDITIONS FOR EXISTENCE OF LAPLACE TRANSFORMS

Theorem : If f(t) is piecewise continuous in every finite interval in the range $t \geq 0$ and is of exponential order α, then its Laplace transform F(s) exists for all $s > \alpha$.

Proof : Since f(t) is piecewise continuous, $e^{-st} f(t)$ is integrable over any finite interval for $t \geq 0$.

$$\therefore \quad \left| \int_0^b e^{-st} f(t)\, dt \right| \leq \int_0^b \left| e^{-st} f(t) \right| dt = \int_0^b e^{-st} \left| f(t) \right| dt$$

$$< \int_0^b e^{-st} M e^{\alpha t}\, dt = M \int_0^b e^{-(s-\alpha)t}\, dt$$

$$[\because\ f(t) \text{ is of exponential order } \alpha]$$

$$= M \left[\frac{e^{-(s-\alpha)t}}{-(s-\alpha)} \right]_0^b = \frac{M}{(s-\alpha)} [1 - e^{-(s-\alpha)b}]$$

Now if $s > \alpha$ and as $b \to \infty$, then expression on R.H.S. approaches to finite quantity $\dfrac{M}{s-\alpha}$.

$$\therefore \quad \left| L\,[f(t)] \right| = \left| \int_0^\infty e^{-st} f(t)\, dt \right| < \frac{M}{s-\alpha}, \quad s > \alpha$$

Remark : It should be noted that conditions of this theorem are sufficient to guarantee the existence of the Laplace transform. But these are not necessary conditions, which mean that even if these conditions are not satisfied, Laplace transform of functions exist.

For example, $f(t) = t^{-1/2}$ is infinite at $t = 0$ but its Laplace transform exists.

We shall consider function f(t) as piecewise continuous and of exponential order throughout our discussion.

4.5 LINEARITY PROPERTY

Theorem : If c_1 and c_2 are any constants and $f_1(t)$ and $f_2(t)$ are functions whose Laplace transforms exist, then

$$L\,[c_1 f_1(t) + c_2 f_2(t)] = c_1 L\,[f_1(t)] + c_2 L\,[f_2(t)]$$

Proof : To prove this, we have by definition

$$L\,[c_1 f_1(t) + c_2 f_2(t)] = \int_0^\infty e^{-st} [c_1 f_1(t) + c_2 f_2(t)]\, dt$$

$$= c_1 \int_0^\infty e^{-st} f_1(t)\, dt + c_2 \int_0^\infty e^{-st} f_2(t)\, dt = c_1 L\,[f_1(t)] + c_2 L\,[f_2(t)]$$

The result is easily extended to more than two functions.

Note : The property of Laplace transformation expressed in this theorem is, of course, the property of linearity. In other words, the Laplace transform is a *linear transform*.

4.6 LAPLACE TRANSFORMS OF SOME ELEMENTARY FUNCTIONS

Using the fundamental definition of Laplace transform, we can obtain a table of Laplace transform of some elementary functions.

1. $f(t) = 1$

By the definition of Laplace transform, we obtain

$$L[1] = \int_0^\infty e^{-st} \cdot 1 \, dt = \left[\frac{e^{-st}}{-s}\right]_0^\infty$$

$$= \frac{1}{s} \text{ if } s > 0$$

Hence

$$\boxed{L[1] = \frac{1}{s} \text{ if } s > 0}$$ ... (2)

2. $f(t) = e^{at}$

By the definition of Laplace transform, we obtain

$$L[e^{at}] = \int_0^\infty e^{-st} e^{at} \, dt = \int_0^\infty e^{-(s-a)t} \, dt = \left[\frac{e^{-(s-a)t}}{-(s-a)}\right]_0^\infty$$

$$= \left\{ \lim_{t \to \infty} \frac{e^{-(s-a)t}}{-(s-a)} \right\} + \frac{1}{(s-a)}$$

[The limit depends on sign of $(s-a)$. Under the restriction $s - a > 0$ i.e. $s > a$, limit will be zero.]

$$= 0 + \frac{1}{(s-a)} \text{ if } s > a = \frac{1}{(s-a)} \text{ if } s > a$$

Hence

$$\boxed{L[e^{at}] = \frac{1}{s-a} \text{ if } s > a}$$ ... (3)

Note :

(i) If in the result (3) we take $a = 0$, then we get

$$L[e^{0t}] = L[1] = \frac{1}{s} \text{ if } s > 0$$

(ii) If in the result (3) we take $-a$ in place of a, then we get

$$L[e^{-at}] = \frac{1}{s+a} \text{ if } s > -a$$

(iii) If $f(t) = c^{at}$, then we obtain

$$L[c^{at}] = L[e^{at \log c}] = \frac{1}{s - a \log c} \text{ if } s > a \log c, \ c > 0.$$

3. f(t) = sin at

By the definition of Laplace transform, we obtain

$$L\,[\sin at] \;=\; \int_{0}^{\infty} e^{-st}\,\sin at\;dt$$

$$= \left[\frac{e^{-st}}{s^2+a^2}\,(-\,s\sin at - a\cos at)\right]_{0}^{\infty}$$

$$= \left\{\lim_{t\to\infty}\frac{-\,e^{-st}}{s^2+a^2}\,(s\sin at + a\cos at)\right\} + \frac{a}{s^2+a^2}$$

[The limit depends on sign of s. Under the restriction $s > 0$, $e^{-st} \to 0$ as $t \to \infty$ while sin at and cos at remain finite (though not known) as $t \to \infty$.]

$$= 0 + \frac{a}{s^2+a^2}\ \text{if}\ s>0\ =\ \frac{a}{s^2+a^2}\ \text{if}\ s>0$$

Hence, $\boxed{\,\mathbf{L\,[\sin at]} \;=\; \dfrac{\mathbf{a}}{\mathbf{s^2+a^2}}\ \textbf{if}\ \mathbf{s}>\mathbf{0}\,}$ ... (4)

4. f(t) = cos at

By the definition of Laplace transform, we obtain

$$L\,[\cos at] \;=\; \int_{0}^{\infty} e^{-st}\,\cos at\;dt$$

$$= \left[\frac{e^{-st}}{s^2+a^2}\,(-\,s\cos at + a\sin at)\right]_{0}^{\infty}$$

$$= \left\{\lim_{t\to\infty}\frac{e^{-st}}{s^2+a^2}\,(-\,s\cos at + a\sin at)\right\} + \frac{s}{s^2+a^2}$$

$$= 0 + \frac{s}{s^2+a^2}\ \text{if}\ s>0\ =\ \frac{s}{s^2+a^2}\ \text{if}\ s>0$$

Hence $\boxed{\,\mathbf{L\,[\cos at]} \;=\; \dfrac{\mathbf{s}}{\mathbf{s^2+a^2}}\ \textbf{if}\ \mathbf{s}>\mathbf{0}\,}$ ... (5)

Another Method : Assuming that the result (3) holds for complex numbers, then we have

$$L\,[e^{iat}] \;=\; \frac{1}{s-ia} \;=\; \frac{s+ia}{(s-ia)(s+ia)} \;=\; \frac{s+ia}{s^2+a^2} \;=\; \frac{s}{s^2+a^2} + i\,\frac{a}{s^2+a^2} \quad \ldots (i)$$

But $e^{iat} = \cos at + i\sin at$, hence

$$L\,[e^{iat}] \;=\; L\,[\cos at + i\sin at] \;=\; L\,[\cos at] + iL\,[\sin at] \qquad \ldots (ii)$$

From (i) and (ii), we have on equating real and imaginary parts

$$L\,[\cos at] \;=\; \frac{s}{s^2+a^2}\ ;\quad L\,[\sin at] \;=\; \frac{a}{s^2+a^2}\ .$$

5. f(t) = sinh at

By the definition of Laplace transform, we obtain

$$L[\sinh at] = \int_0^\infty e^{-st} \sinh at\, dt = \int_0^\infty e^{-st}\left(\frac{e^{at} - e^{-at}}{2}\right)$$

$$= \frac{1}{2}\left\{\int_0^\infty e^{-st} e^{at}\, dt - \int_0^\infty e^{-st} e^{-at}\, dt\right\}$$

$$= \frac{1}{2}\left\{L[e^{at}] - L[e^{-at}]\right\}$$

$$= \frac{1}{2}\left\{\frac{1}{(s-a)} - \frac{1}{(s+a)}\right\} \text{ if } s > a \text{ and } s > -a \qquad \text{[By result (3)]}$$

$$= \frac{a}{s^2 - a^2} \text{ if } s > |a|$$

Hence $\boxed{\; L[\sinh at] = \dfrac{a}{s^2 - a^2} \text{ if } s > |a| \;}$ ... (6)

6. f(t) = cosh at

By the definition of Laplace transform, we obtain

$$L[\cosh at] = \int_0^\infty e^{-st} \cosh at\, dt = \int_0^\infty e^{-st}\left(\frac{e^{at} + e^{-at}}{2}\right) dt$$

$$= \frac{1}{2}\left\{\int_0^\infty e^{-st} e^{at}\, dt + \int_0^\infty e^{-st} e^{-at}\, dt\right\} = \frac{1}{2}\left\{L[e^{at}] + L[e^{-at}]\right\}$$

$$= \frac{1}{2}\left\{\frac{1}{s-a} - \frac{1}{s+a}\right\} \text{ if } s > a \text{ and } s > -a \qquad \text{[By result (3)]}$$

$$= \frac{s}{s^2 - a^2} \text{ if } s > |a|$$

Hence $\boxed{\; L[\cosh at] = \dfrac{s}{s^2 - a^2} \text{ if } s > |a| \;}$ ... (7)

Another Method : Using the linearity property of Laplace transformation, we have at once

$$L[\sinh at] = L\left[\frac{e^{at} - e^{-at}}{2}\right] = \frac{1}{2}\left\{L[e^{at}] - L[e^{-at}]\right\}$$

$$= \frac{1}{2}\left\{\frac{1}{(s-a)} - \frac{1}{(s+a)}\right\} = \frac{a}{s^2 - a^2}$$

$$L[\cosh at] = L\left[\frac{e^{at} + e^{-at}}{2}\right] = \frac{1}{2}\{L[e^{at}] + L[e^{-at}]\}$$

$$= \frac{1}{2}\left\{\frac{1}{(s-a)} + \frac{1}{(s+a)}\right\} = \frac{s}{s^2 - a^2}$$

7. f(t) = tⁿ

By the definition of Laplace transform, we obtain

$$L[t^n] = \int_0^\infty e^{-st} t^n \, dt \quad \text{put } st = y \quad \therefore s \, dt = dy \quad \begin{array}{|c|c|c|} \hline t & 0 & \infty \\ \hline y & 0 & \infty \\ \hline \end{array} \quad \text{and if } s > 0,$$

$$= \int_0^\infty e^{-y} \left(\frac{y}{s}\right)^n \frac{dy}{s}$$

$$= \frac{1}{s^{n+1}} \int_0^\infty e^{-y} y^n \, dy \qquad \left\{ \because \int_0^\infty e^{-y} y^{n-1} \, dy = \overline{|n} \;\; \text{if } n > 0 \right.$$

$$= \frac{\overline{|n+1}}{s^{n+1}} \quad \text{if } s > 0, \;\; n > -1$$

If n is a positive integer, $\overline{|n+1} = n!$,

then $\qquad L[t^n] = \dfrac{n!}{s^{n+1}} \quad \text{if } \;\; s > 0$

Hence $\qquad \boxed{\; \mathbf{L\,[t^n]} = \begin{cases} \dfrac{\overline{|n+1}}{s^{n+1}} \; ; & \textbf{if } \mathbf{n > -1} \\[4mm] \dfrac{n!}{s^{n+1}} \; ; & \textbf{if n is a positive integer} \end{cases} \;}$ $\qquad$ ... (8)

Note :

(i) If in the result (8) we take n = 0, then we get

$$L[t^o] = L[1] = \frac{\overline{|1}}{s} = \frac{1}{s}$$

(ii) If in the result (8) we take $n = \dfrac{-1}{2}$, then we get

$$L[t^{-1/2}] = \frac{\overline{|-1/2+1}}{s^{-1/2+1}} = \frac{\overline{|1/2}}{s^{1/2}} = \sqrt{\frac{\pi}{s}}$$

Remark : Once we know the transforms of these functions given in Table 4.1, nearly all the transforms we shall need, can be obtained with the use of some additional theorems which we consider in the subsequent sections.

The following table gives the Laplace transforms of the above elementary functions for ready reference :

Table 4.1

Table of Elementary Laplace Transforms

Sr. No.	$f(t)$	$F(s) = L[f(t)]$
1	1	$\dfrac{1}{s}$; $s > 0$
2	e^{at}	$\dfrac{1}{s-a}$; $s > a$
3	$\sin at$	$\dfrac{a}{s^2 + a^2}$; $s > 0$
4	$\cos at$	$\dfrac{s}{s^2 + a^2}$; $s > 0$
5	$\sinh at$	$\dfrac{a}{s^2 - a^2}$; $s > |a|$
6	$\cosh at$	$\dfrac{s}{s^2 - a^2}$; $s > |a|$
7	t^n if $n > -1$	$\dfrac{\lfloor n+1}{s^{n+1}}$; $s > 0$
8	t^n if n a positive integer	$\dfrac{n!}{s^{n+1}}$; $s > 0$

ILLUSTRATIONS ON LAPLACE TRANSFORM OF ELEMENTARY FUNCTIONS

Ex. 1 : *Find the Laplace transforms of the following functions :*

(i) $4e^{2t} + 5e^{-3t}$ *(ii)* $(e^{-2t} + e^{3t})^2$ *(iii)* e^{at+b} *(iv)* 4^t

Sol. : (i) $L[4e^{2t} + 5e^{-3t}] = 4\,L[e^{2t}] + 5\,L[e^{-3t}]$ (Using the linearity property)

$$= 4\,\frac{1}{s-2} + 5\,\frac{1}{s+3}$$

$$= \frac{4}{s-2} + \frac{5}{s+3} \quad \text{where} \quad s > 2$$

(ii) $L[(e^{-2t} + e^{3t})^2] = L[e^{-4t} + 2e^{t} + e^{6t}]$ (Using the linearity property)

$$= L[e^{-4t}] + 2L[e^{t}] + L[e^{6t}]$$

$$= \frac{1}{s+4} + 2\,\frac{1}{s-1} + \frac{1}{s-6}$$

$$= \frac{1}{s+4} + \frac{2}{s-1} + \frac{1}{s-6} \qquad \text{where } s > 6$$

(iii) $\qquad L\,[e^{at+b}] \;=\; L\,[e^{at}\,e^{b}] \;=\; e^{b}\,L\,[e^{at}]$

$$= e^{b}\,\frac{1}{s-a} = \frac{e^{b}}{s-a} \qquad\qquad \text{where } s>a$$

(iv) $\qquad L\,[4^{t}] \;=\; L\,[e^{t\,\log 4}] = L\,[e^{(\log 4)\,t}]$

$$= \frac{1}{s-\log 4} \qquad\qquad \text{where } s>\log 4$$

Ex. 2 : *Obtain the Laplace transform of each of the following functions :*

    (i) $at + bt^2 + ct^3$ (ii) $4t^3 + t^7 + t^{4/3}$ (iii) $(2t + 3)^3$ (iv) $5t - 7e^{-6t} + t^{5/2}$.

Sol. : (i) $L\,[at + bt^2 + ct^3] \;=\; a\,L\,[t] + b\,L\,[t^2] + c\,L\,[t^3]$ (Using the linearity property)

$$= a\,\frac{1}{s^2} + b\,\frac{2\,!}{s^3} + c\,\frac{3!}{s^4}$$

$$= \frac{a}{s^2} + \frac{2\,b}{s^3} + \frac{6\,c}{s^4} \qquad\qquad \text{where } s>0$$

(ii) $\qquad L\,[4t^3 + t^7 + t^{4/3}] \;=\; 4\,L\,[t^3] + L\,[t^7] + L\,[t^{4/3}]$

$$= 4\,\frac{3!}{s^4} + \frac{7!}{s^8} + \frac{\overline{4/3 + 1}}{s^{4/3+1}}$$

$$= \frac{24}{s^4} + \frac{5040}{s^8} + \frac{4/3 \cdot 1/3\,\overline{1/3}}{s^{7/3}}$$

(iii) $\qquad L\,[(2t+3)^3] \;=\; L\,[(2t)^3 + 3\,(2t)^2\,(3) + 3\,(2t)\,(3)^2 + (3)^3]$

$$= 8\,L\,[t^3] + 36\,L\,[t^2] + 54\,L\,[t] + 27\,L\,[1]$$

$$= 8\,\frac{3!}{s^4} + 36\,\frac{2\,!}{s^3} + 54\,\frac{1!}{s^2} + 27\,\frac{1}{s}$$

$$= \frac{48}{s^4} + \frac{72}{s^3} + \frac{54}{s^2} + \frac{27}{s} \qquad\qquad \text{where } s>0$$

(iv) $\quad L\,[5t - 7e^{-6t} + t^{5/2}] \;=\; 5\,L\,[t] - 7\,L\,[e^{-6t}] + L\,[t^{5/2}]$

$$= 5\cdot\frac{1!}{s^2} - 7\,\frac{1}{s+6} + \frac{\overline{5/2 + 1}}{s^{5/2+1}}$$

$$= \frac{5}{s^2} - \frac{7}{s+6} + \frac{\dfrac{5}{2}\cdot\dfrac{3}{2}\cdot\dfrac{1}{2}\,\overline{\dfrac{1}{2}}}{s^{7/2}}$$

$$= \frac{5}{s^2} - \frac{7}{s+6} + \frac{15}{8}\sqrt{\frac{\pi}{s^7}} \qquad\qquad \text{where } s>0$$

Ex. 3 : *Find the Laplace transform of each of the following functions :*

(i) 2 sin 4t + 5 cos 2t   (ii) sin 2t cos 3t   (iii) cos t cos 2t   (iv) cosh at – cos bt

Sol. : (i) $L [2 \sin 4t + 5 \cos 2t] = 2 L [\sin 4t] + 5 L [\cos 2t]$

$$= 2 \frac{4}{s^2 + 4^2} + 5 \frac{s}{s^2 + 2^2}$$

$$= \frac{8}{s^2 + 16} + \frac{5s}{s^2 + 4} \qquad \text{where } s > 0$$

(ii) $\qquad L [\sin 2t \cos 3t] = L \left[\frac{1}{2} (2 \cos 3t \sin 2t)\right] = L \left[\frac{1}{2} (\sin 5t - \sin t)\right]$

$$= \frac{1}{2} \{L [\sin 5t] - L [\sin t]\} = \frac{1}{2} \left\{\frac{5}{s^2 + 5^2} - \frac{1}{s^2 + 1^2}\right\}$$

$$= \frac{2 (s^2 - 5)}{(s^2 + 25) (s^2 + 1)} \qquad \text{where } s > 0$$

(iii) $\qquad L [\cos t \cos 2t] = L \left[\frac{1}{2} (2 \cos 2t \cos t)\right] = L \left[\frac{1}{2} (\cos 3t + \cos t)\right]$

$$= \frac{1}{2} \{L [\cos 3t] + L [\cos t]\} = \frac{1}{2} \left\{\frac{s}{s^2 + 3^2} + \frac{s}{s^2 + 1^2}\right\}$$

$$= \frac{s (s^2 + 5)}{(s^2 + 9) (s^2 + 1)} \qquad \text{where } s > 0$$

(iv) $\qquad L [\cosh at - \cos bt] = L [\cosh at] - L [\cos bt]$

$$= \frac{s}{s^2 - a^2} - \frac{s}{s^2 + b^2} \qquad \text{where } s > |a|$$

Ex. 4 : *Find the Laplace transforms of the following functions :*

(i) 3 cos (4t + 7) (ii) 5 sin (2t + 3) (iii) sin² 4t (iv) cos³ 2t (v) cosh³ 2t

Sol. : (i) $L [3 \cos (4t + 7)] = 3 L [\cos (4t + 7)]$

Note : (i) Here we first express $\cos (4t + 7)$ as the difference of two terms.

$\therefore \qquad 3 L [\cos (4t + 7)] = 3 L [\cos 4t \cos 7 - \sin 4t \sin 7]$

$$= 3 \{\cos 7 L [\cos 4t] - \sin 7 L [\sin 4t]\}$$

$$= 3 \left\{\cos 7 \frac{s}{s^2 + 4^2} - \sin 7 \frac{4}{s^2 + 4^2}\right\}$$

$$= \frac{3}{s^2 + 16} \{s \cos 7 - 4 \sin 7\} \qquad \text{where } s > 0$$

(ii) $\qquad L [5 \sin (2t + 3)] = 5 L [\sin (2t + 3)]$

$$= 5 L [\sin 2t \cos 3 + \cos 2t \sin 3]$$

$$= 5 \{\cos 3 \, L[\sin 2t] + \sin 3 \, L[\cos 2t]\}$$

$$= 5 \left\{\cos 3 \, \frac{2}{s^2 + 2^2} + \sin 3 \, \frac{s}{s^2 + 2^2}\right\}$$

$$= \frac{5}{s^2 + 4} \{2 \cos 3 + s \sin 3\} \qquad \text{where } s > 0$$

(iii)
$$L[\sin^2 4t] = L\left[\frac{1 - \cos 8t}{2}\right] = \frac{1}{2}\{L[1] - L[\cos 8t]\}$$

$$= \frac{1}{2}\left\{\frac{1}{s} - \frac{s}{s^2 + 8^2}\right\} = \frac{32}{s(s^2 + 64)} \qquad \text{where } s > 0$$

(iv)
$$L[\cos^3 2t] = L\left[\frac{\cos 6t + 3 \cos 2t}{4}\right] \quad \{\because \cos 3\theta = 4 \cos^3 \theta - 3 \cos \theta\}$$

$$= \frac{1}{4}\{L[\cos 6t] + 3 \, L[\cos 2t]\}$$

$$= \frac{1}{4}\left\{\frac{s}{s^2 + 6^2} + 3 \, \frac{s}{s^2 + 2^2}\right\}$$

$$= \frac{s(s^2 + 28)}{(s^2 + 4)(s^2 + 36)} \quad \text{where } s > 0$$

(v)
$$L[\cosh^3 2t] = L\left[\frac{\cosh 6t + 3 \cosh 2t}{4}\right] \quad \{\because \cosh 3\theta = 4 \cosh^3 \theta - 3 \cosh \theta\}$$

$$= \frac{1}{4}\{L[\cosh 6t] + 3 \, L[\cosh 2t]\}$$

$$= \frac{1}{4}\left\{\frac{s}{s^2 - 6^2} + 3 \, \frac{s}{s^2 - 2^2}\right\}$$

$$= \frac{s(s^2 - 28)}{(s^2 - 4)(s^2 - 36)}$$

Ex. 5 : *Obtain Laplace transforms of*

(i) $3e^{4t} + 6t^2 - 4 \sin 3t + \cos 2t$ (ii) $5e^{-t/2} + t^{-1/2} + 7 \sin \dfrac{t}{2}$.

Sol. : (i) $L[3e^{4t} + 6t^2 - 4 \sin 3t + \cos 2t]$

$$= 3 \, L[e^{4t}] + 6 \, L[t^2] - 4 \, L[\sin 3t] + L[\cos 2t]$$

$$= 3 \, \frac{1}{s - 4} + 6 \, \frac{2!}{s^3} - 4 \, \frac{3}{s^2 + 3^2} + \frac{s}{s^2 + 2^2}$$

$$= \frac{3}{s - 4} + \frac{12}{s^3} - \frac{12}{s^2 + 9} + \frac{s}{s^2 + 4} \qquad \text{where } s > 4$$

(ii) $L\left[5e^{-t/2} + t^{-1/2} + 7 \sin \dfrac{t}{2}\right] = 5\,L\,[e^{-(1/2)\,t}] + L\,[t^{-1/2}] + 7\,L\left[\sin\left(\dfrac{1}{2}\right)t\right]$

$$= 5\,\dfrac{1}{s + \dfrac{1}{2}} + \sqrt{\dfrac{\pi}{s}} + 7\,\dfrac{1/2}{s^2 + \left(\dfrac{1}{2}\right)^2}$$

$$= \dfrac{5}{s + \dfrac{1}{2}} + \sqrt{\dfrac{\pi}{s}} + \dfrac{\dfrac{7}{2}}{s^2 + \dfrac{1}{4}} \quad \text{where } s > 0$$

Ex. 6 : *Obtain Laplace transform of each of the following functions :*

(i) $f(t) = \begin{cases} t, & 0 < t < 4 \\ 5, & t > 4 \end{cases}$
(ii) $f(t) = \begin{cases} \sin 2t, & 0 < t < \pi \\ 0, & t > \pi \end{cases}$

(iii) $f(t) = \begin{cases} t/T, & 0 \le t < T \\ 1, & t > T \end{cases}$

Sol. : (i) $f(t) = \begin{cases} t, & 0 < t < 4 \\ 5, & t > 4 \end{cases}$

Note : Given function is discontinuous and we cannot get Laplace transform by using table of elementary Laplace transforms. Here we use fundamental definition (1) of Laplace transform.

Thus $\quad L\,[f(t)] = \displaystyle\int_0^\infty e^{-st}\,f(t)\,dt = \int_0^4 e^{-st}\,t\,dt + \int_4^\infty e^{-st}\,5\,dt$

$$= \left[t\left(\dfrac{e^{-st}}{-s}\right) - (1)\left(\dfrac{e^{-st}}{s^2}\right)\right]_0^4 + 5\left[\dfrac{e^{-st}}{-s}\right]_4^\infty$$

(Using the generalised rule of integration by parts)

$$= \left[\left(-\dfrac{4e^{-4s}}{s} - \dfrac{e^{-4s}}{s^2}\right) - \left(0 - \dfrac{1}{s^2}\right)\right] + 5\left[0 + \dfrac{e^{-4s}}{s}\right]$$

$$= \dfrac{1}{s^2} + e^{-4s}\left(\dfrac{1}{s} - \dfrac{1}{s^2}\right) \qquad \text{where } s > 0$$

(ii) $\qquad f(t) = \begin{cases} \sin 2t, & 0 < t < \pi \\ 0, & t > \pi \end{cases}$

$$L\,[f(t)] = \int_0^\infty e^{-st}\,f(t)\,dt = \int_0^\pi e^{-st}\,\sin 2t\,dt + \int_\pi^\infty e^{-st}\,(0)\,dt$$

$$= \left[\dfrac{e^{st}}{s^2 + 4}\,(-s \sin 2t - 2 \cos 2t)\right]_0^\pi$$

$$= \frac{1}{s^2+4} \left[e^{-s\pi}(-2) - (-2) \right]$$

$$= \frac{2}{s^2+4} (1 - e^{-s\pi}) \qquad\qquad\qquad \text{where } s > 0$$

(iii) $\qquad\qquad f(t) = \begin{cases} t/T, & 0 \le t < T \\ 1, & t > T \end{cases}$

$$L[f(t)] = \int_0^{\infty} e^{-st} f(t)\, dt = \int_0^{T} e^{-st}\left(\frac{t}{T}\right) dt + \int_{T}^{\infty} e^{-st}\, 1\, dt$$

$$= \frac{1}{T}\left[t\left(\frac{e^{-st}}{-s}\right) - (1)\left(\frac{e^{-st}}{s^2}\right) \right]_0^{T} + \left[\frac{e^{-st}}{-s}\right]_T^{\infty}$$

$$= \frac{1}{T}\left[T\left(\frac{e^{-sT}}{-s}\right) - \left(\frac{e^{-sT}}{s^2}\right) + \frac{1}{s^2} \right] + \left[0 + \frac{e^{-sT}}{s} \right]$$

$$= -\frac{e^{-sT}}{s} - \frac{(e^{-sT}-1)}{Ts^2} + \frac{e^{-sT}}{s}$$

$$= \frac{1 - e^{-sT}}{Ts^2} \qquad\qquad\qquad \text{where } s > 2$$

EXERCISE 4.1

1. Find the Laplace transform of each of the following functions :

    (i) $2e^{3t} + 3e^{-2t}$ (ii) $(e^{-at} - e^{-bt})^2$ (iii) $(2e^{3t} + 5)^2$ (iv) c^{at+b}

    Ans. (i) $\dfrac{2}{s-3} + \dfrac{3}{s+2}$ (ii) $\dfrac{1}{s+2a} + \dfrac{2}{s+(a+b)} + \dfrac{1}{s+2b}$

    (iii) $\dfrac{4}{s-6} + \dfrac{20}{s-3} + \dfrac{25}{s}$ (iv) $\dfrac{c^b}{s - a \log c}$

2. Obtain the Laplace transform of each of the following functions :

    (i) $t^2 - 3t + 5$ (ii) $t^4 + 5t^3 + t^{1/2}$ (iii) $a + \dfrac{b}{\sqrt{t}}$ (iv) $(t+2)^3 + (e^{2t}+3)^2$

    Ans. (i) $\dfrac{5s^2 - 3s + 2}{s^3}$ (ii) $\dfrac{24}{s^5} + \dfrac{30}{s^4} + \dfrac{\sqrt{\pi}}{2s^{3/2}}$ (iii) $\dfrac{a}{s} + b\sqrt{\dfrac{\pi}{s}}$

    (iv) $\dfrac{6}{s^4} + \dfrac{12}{s^3} + \dfrac{12}{s^2} + \dfrac{17}{s} + \dfrac{1}{s-4} + \dfrac{6}{s-2}$

3. Find the Laplace transform of each of the following functions :

    (i) $3\cos 2t - \sin 2t$ (ii) $\cosh 5t + \cos 5t$ (iii) $\cos 3t \cos 2t$ (iv) $\sin 2t \cos 5t$

    Ans. (i) $\dfrac{3s}{s^2+4} - \dfrac{2}{s^2+4}$ (ii) $\dfrac{s}{s^2-25} + \dfrac{s}{s^2+25}$ (iii) $\dfrac{s(s^2+13)}{(s^2+1)(s^2+25)}$ (iv) $\dfrac{2(s^2-21)}{(s^2+9)(s^2+49)}$

4. Find the Laplace transforms of the following functions :

(i) $\cos(\omega t + \alpha)$ (ii) $\sin(\omega t + \alpha)$ (iii) $\cos^2 bt$ (iv) $\sin^3 2t$ (v) $\sinh^3 2t$ (vi) $(\sin t - \cos t)^2$

Ans. (i) $\dfrac{s \cos \alpha - \omega \sin \alpha}{s^2 + \omega^2}$ (ii) $\dfrac{\omega \cos \alpha + s \sin \alpha}{s^2 + \omega^2}$ (iii) $\dfrac{s^2 + 2b^2}{s\,(s^2 + 4b^2)}$

(iv) $\dfrac{48}{(s^2 + 4)\,(s^2 + 36)}$ (v) $\dfrac{48}{(s^2 - 4)\,(s^2 - 36)}$ (vi) $\dfrac{s^2 - 2s + 4}{s\,(s^2 + 4)}$

5. Obtain Laplace transforms of

(i) $e^{2t} + 4t^3 - 2 \sin 3t + 3 \cos 3t$ (ii) $4 \cos 2t - 5t^2 + 2e^{3t}$

(iii) $3t^4 - 2t^3 + 4e^{-3t} - 2 \sin 5t + 3 \cos 2t$

Ans. (i) $\dfrac{1}{s - 2} + \dfrac{24}{s^4} - \dfrac{6}{s^2 + 9} + \dfrac{3s}{s^2 + 9}$ (ii) $\dfrac{4s}{s^2 + 4} - \dfrac{10}{s^3} + \dfrac{2}{s - 3}$

(iii) $\dfrac{72}{s^5} - \dfrac{12}{s^4} + \dfrac{4}{s + 3} - \dfrac{10}{s^2 + 25} + \dfrac{3s}{s^2 + 4}$

6. Obtain Laplace transform of each of the following functions :

(i) $f(t) = \begin{cases} a, & 0 < t < b \\ 0, & t > b \end{cases}$ (ii) $f(t) = \begin{cases} \cos t, & 0 < t < 2\pi \\ 0, & t > 2\pi \end{cases}$

(iii) $f(t) = \begin{cases} \cos t, & 0 < t < \pi \\ \sin t, & t > \pi \end{cases}$ (iv) $f(t) = \begin{cases} 0, & 0 \le t < 1 \\ t^2 - 2t + 2, & t \ge 1 \end{cases}$

(v) $f(t) = \begin{cases} 0, & 0 \le t < 1 \\ t, & 1 < t < 2 \\ 0, & t > 2 \end{cases}$

Ans. (i) $\dfrac{a}{s}\,(1 - e^{-sb})$ (ii) $\dfrac{s\,(1 - e^{-2\pi s})}{s^2 + 1}$ (iii) $\dfrac{s + (s - 1)\,e^{-\pi s}}{s^2 + 1}$

(iv) $e^{-s}\left(\dfrac{1}{s} + \dfrac{2}{s^3}\right)$ (v) $\left(\dfrac{1}{s^2} + \dfrac{1}{s}\right) e^{-s} - \left(\dfrac{1}{s^2} + \dfrac{2}{s}\right) e^{-2s}$

MULTIPLE CHOICE QUESTIONS (MCQ's)

Type : Laplace Transform of Elementary Functions :

1.   If $f(t)$, $t > 0$ then $L[f(t)]$ is   (1)

(A) $\displaystyle\int_0^\infty e^{-st} f(t)\, dt$ (B) $\displaystyle\int_0^\infty e^{st} f(t)\, dt$

(C) $\displaystyle\int_0^\infty f(t)\, dt$ (D) $\displaystyle\int_0^\infty e^{st}\, ds$

2. If $f(t) = 1$ then $L\{1\}$ is equal to   (1)

(A) $s, s > 0$

(B) $\dfrac{1}{s}, s > 0$

(C) $\dfrac{1}{s^2}, s > 0$

(D) $1, s > 0$

3. If $f(t) = e^{at}, a > 0$ then $L[e^{at}]$ is equal to   (1)

(A) $\dfrac{1}{s}, s > 0$

(B) $\dfrac{1}{s + a}, s > -a$

(C) $\dfrac{1}{s - a}, s > a$

(D) $\dfrac{a}{s^2 + a^2}, s > 0$

4. If $f(t) = e^{-at}, a > 0$ then $L[e^{-at}]$ is equal to   (1)

(A) $\dfrac{1}{s - a}, s > a$

(B) $\dfrac{a}{s^2 + a^2}, s > 0$

(C) $\dfrac{1}{s}, s > 0$

(D) $\dfrac{1}{s + a}, s > -a$

5. If $f(t) = c^{at}, a > 0$ then $L[c^{at}]$ is equal to   (1)

(A) $\dfrac{1}{s + a \log c}, s < a \log c, c > 0$

(B) $\dfrac{1}{s + a}, s > -a$

(C) $\dfrac{1}{s - a \log c}, s > a \log c, c > 0$

(D) $\dfrac{a}{s^2 + a^2}, s > 0$

6. If $f(t) = \sin at, a > 0$ then $L[\sin at]$ is equal to   (1)

(A) $\dfrac{s}{s^2 + a^2}, s > 0$

(B) $\dfrac{1}{s + a}, s > -a$

(C) $\dfrac{a}{s^2 - a^2}, s > |a|$

(D) $\dfrac{a}{s^2 + a^2}, s > 0$

7. If $f(t) = \cos at, a > 0$ then $L[\cos at]$ is equal to   (1)

(A) $\dfrac{s}{s^2 + a^2}, s > 0$

(B) $\dfrac{1}{s + a}, s > -a$

(C) $\dfrac{a}{s^2 - a^2}, s > |a|$

(D) $\dfrac{a}{s^2 + a^2}, s > 0$

8. If $f(t) = \sinh at, a > 0$ then $L[\sinh at]$ is equal to   (1)

(A) $\dfrac{s}{s^2 + a^2}, s > 0$

(B) $\dfrac{a}{s^2 - a^2}, s > |a|$

(C) $\dfrac{1}{s + a}, s > -a$

(D) $\dfrac{a}{s^2 + a^2}, s > 0$

9. If $f(t) = \cosh at$, $a > 0$ then $L[\cosh at]$ is equal to   (1)

(A) $\dfrac{s}{s^2 - a^2}$, $s > |a|$ (B) $\dfrac{1}{s + a}$, $s > -a$

(C) $\dfrac{s}{s^2 + a^2}$, $s > 0$ (D) $\dfrac{a}{s^2 + a^2}$, $s > 0$

10. If $f(t) = t^n$, $n > -1$ then $L[t^n]$ is equal to   (1)

(A) $\dfrac{1}{s^{n+1}}$, $s > 0$ (B) $\dfrac{\overline{|n + 1}}{s^{n+1}}$, $s > 0$

(C) $\dfrac{s}{s^2 + a^2}$, $s > 0$ (D) $\dfrac{\overline{|n}}{s^{n+1}}$, $s > 0$

11. If $f(t) = t^{-1/2}$ then $L[t^{-1/2}]$ is equal to   (1)

(A) $\dfrac{\overline{|n}}{s^n}$, $s > 0$ (B) $\dfrac{\overline{|n}}{s^{n+1}}$, $s > 0$

(C) $\dfrac{s}{s^2 + a^2}$, $s > 0$ (D) $\sqrt{\dfrac{\pi}{s}}$, $s > 0$

12. $L[4e^{2t} + t^2]$ is equal to   (2)

(A) $\dfrac{1}{s - 2} + \dfrac{1}{s^3}$ (B) $4\dfrac{1}{s + 2} + \dfrac{3}{s^2}$

(C) $4\dfrac{1}{s - 2} + \dfrac{2}{s^3}$ (D) $2\dfrac{1}{s - 2} + \dfrac{2}{s^3}$

13. $L[\sin^2 4t]$ is equal to   (2)

(A) $\dfrac{1}{2}\left[\dfrac{1}{s} - \dfrac{s}{s^2 + 64}\right]$ (B) $\left[\dfrac{1}{s} + \dfrac{s}{s^2 + 64}\right]$

(C) $\dfrac{1}{2}\left[1 - \dfrac{s}{s^2 + 8}\right]$ (D) $\dfrac{1}{2}\left[\dfrac{1}{s} - \dfrac{s}{s^2 - 64}\right]$

14. $L[\sin 2t \cos 3t]$ is equal to   (2)

(A) $\dfrac{5}{s^2 + 25}$ (B) $\left[\dfrac{5}{s^2 + 25} - \dfrac{1}{s^2 + 1}\right]$

(C) $\left[\dfrac{s}{s^2 + 25} - \dfrac{1}{s^2 + 1}\right]$ (D) $\dfrac{1}{2}\left[\dfrac{5}{s^2 + 25} - \dfrac{1}{s^2 + 1}\right]$

15. $L[\cosh at - \cos bt]$ is equal to   (2)

(A) $\dfrac{a}{s^2 + a^2} - \dfrac{a}{s^2 - b^2}$ (B) $\dfrac{a}{s^2 - a^2} - \dfrac{a}{s^2 - b^2}$

(C) $\dfrac{s}{s^2 - a^2} - \dfrac{s}{s^2 + b^2}$ (D) $\dfrac{s}{s^2 + a^2} - \dfrac{s}{s^2 - b^2}$

16. $L[4^t + 5]$ is equal to   (2)

(A) $\dfrac{1}{s + \log 4} + \dfrac{5}{s}$ (B) $\dfrac{1}{s - \log 4} + \dfrac{5}{s}$

(C) $\dfrac{4}{s^4} + \dfrac{5}{s}$ (D) $\dfrac{1}{s - 4} + 5$

17. $L[\sin(2t + 3)]$ is equal to   (2)

(A) $\sin 2 \left(\dfrac{s}{s^2 + 4}\right) + \cos 2 \left(\dfrac{3}{s^2 + 9}\right)$ (B) $\sin 3 \left(\dfrac{2}{s^2 + 4}\right) - \cos 3 \left(\dfrac{s}{s^2 + 9}\right)$

(C) $\cos 3 \left(\dfrac{s}{s^2 + 4}\right) + \sin 3 \left(\dfrac{2}{s^2 + 4}\right)$ (D) $\cos 3 \left(\dfrac{2}{s^2 + 4}\right) + \sin 3 \left(\dfrac{s}{s^2 + 4}\right)$

18. $L[e^{-4t} + 5t^{-1/2}]$ is equal to   (2)

(A) $\dfrac{1}{S - 4} + \dfrac{5}{2}\sqrt{\pi s}$ (B) $e^{-4t} + \dfrac{1}{2\sqrt{s}}$

(C) $\dfrac{1}{S + 4} + 5\sqrt{\dfrac{\pi}{s}}$ (D) $4\dfrac{1}{S + 4} + s^{1/2}$

19. $L[(\sin t - \cos t)^2]$ is equal to   (2)

(A) $\dfrac{s^2 - 2s + 4}{s(s^2 + 4)}$ (B) $\dfrac{s^2 + 2s - 4}{s(s^2 + 4)}$

(C) $\dfrac{s^2 - 2s - 4}{s(s^2 - 4)}$ (D) $\dfrac{2s + 4}{s(s^2 + 4)^2}$

20. If $f(t) = \begin{cases} \sin 2t , & 0 < t < \pi \\ 0 , & t > \pi \end{cases}$ then $L[f(t)]$ is equal to   (2)

(A) $\left[\dfrac{e^{-st}}{s^2 + 4}(- s \cos 2t - 2 \sin 2t)\right]_0^\pi$ (B) $\left[\dfrac{e^{-st}}{s^2 + 4}(- s \sin 2t - 2 \cos 2t)\right]_0^\pi$

(C) $\left[\dfrac{e^{-st}}{s^2 + 4}(s \sin 2t + 2 \cos 2t)\right]_0^\pi$ (D) $\left[\dfrac{e^{-st}}{s^2 + 4}(- s \sin 2t + 2 \cos 2t)\right]_0^\pi$

Answers

1. (A)	2. (B)	3. (C)	4. (D)	5. (C)	6. (D)	7. (A)	8. (B)
9. (A)	10. (B)	11. (D)	12. (C)	13. (A)	14. (D)	15. (C)	16. (B)
17. (D)	18. (C)	19. (A)	20. (B)				

4.8 GENERAL THEOREMS OF LAPLACE'S TRANSFORMS

We shall now derive a number of theorems that will be of considerable use in finding the Laplace transforms of some additional functions (not included in the Table 4.1).

(A) First Shifting Theorem

Theorem : If $L[f(t)] = F(s),$ then

$$L[e^{-at} f(t)] = F(s + a) = \{L[f(t)]\}_{s \to s + a}$$

Proof : By definition,

$$L\,[e^{-at}\,f(t)] \;=\; \int_{0}^{\infty} e^{-st}\,[e^{-at}\,f(t)]\,dt \;=\; \int_{0}^{\infty} e^{-(s+a)\,t}\,f(t)\,dt$$

$$=\; \int_{0}^{\infty} e^{-pt}\,f(t)\,dt \qquad \text{where } p = s + a$$

$$=\; F(p) \qquad\qquad\qquad\qquad \text{... by def. (1), } s \to p$$

$$=\; F(s + a)$$

Hence
$$\boxed{\;L\,[e^{-at}\,f(t)] \;=\; F(s + a) \;=\; \{L\,[f(t)]\}_{s \to s + a}\;} \qquad\qquad \text{... (9)}$$

Remark 1 : In words, this theorem states that the Laplace transform of e^{-at} times a function of t is equal to the Laplace transform of the function f(t), with s replaced by $s + a$.

Remark 2 : The first shifting theorem concerns shifting on the s-axis : the replacement of s in F(s) by $s + a$ corresponds to shifting the graph of F(s) to the left through distance a unit.

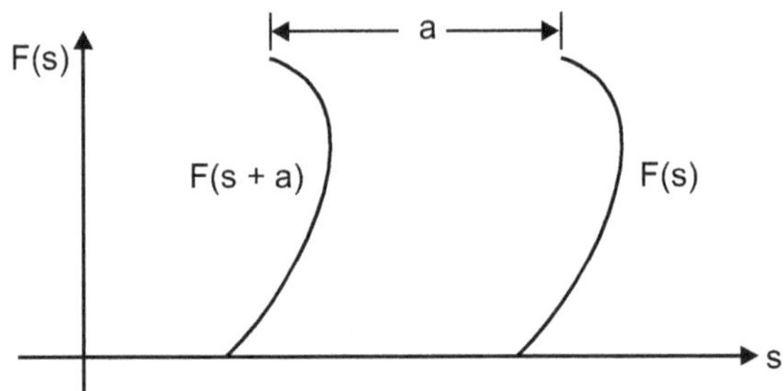

Fig. 4.2 : First Shifting Theorem, Shifting on The s-Axis

Remark 3 : In practice to obtain Laplace transform of $e^{-at}\,f(t)$, we first obtain Laplace transform of f(t) (i.e. factor e^{-at} is dropped initially) and then replace s by $s + a$ in L [f(t)] to account for the multiplying factor e^{-at}.

ILLUSTRATIONS

Ex. 1 : *Find the Laplace transform of each of the following functions :*

(i) $e^{-at} \sin bt$ *(ii)* $e^{-at} \cos bt$ *(iii)* $e^{-at} \sinh bt$ *(iv)* $e^{-at} \cosh bt$ *(v)* $e^{-at} t^n$

Sol. : (i) We have

$$L\,[\sin bt] \;=\; \frac{b}{s^2 + b^2} \qquad\qquad \text{(From Table 4.1 in sec. 4.6)}$$

$\therefore \qquad L\,[e^{-at} \sin bt] \;=\; \dfrac{b}{(s + a)^2 + b^2} \qquad\qquad$ (By the First Shifting Theorem)

(ii) We have

$$L [\cos bt] = \frac{s}{s^2 + b^2} \qquad \text{(From Table 4.1)}$$

$$\therefore \qquad L [e^{-at} \cos bt] = \frac{s + a}{(s + a)^2 + b^2} \qquad \text{(By the First Shifting Theorem)}$$

(iii) We have

$$L [\sinh bt] = \frac{b}{s^2 - b^2} \qquad \text{(From Table 4.1)}$$

$$\therefore \qquad L [e^{-at} \sinh bt] = \frac{b}{(s + a)^2 - b^2} \qquad \text{(By the First Shifting Theorem)}$$

(iv) We have

$$L [\cosh bt] = \frac{s}{s^2 - a^2} \qquad \text{(From Table 4.1)}$$

$$\therefore \qquad L [e^{-at} \cosh bt] = \frac{s + a}{(s + a)^2 - a^2} \qquad \text{(By the First Shifting Theorem)}$$

(v) We have

$$L [t^n] = \frac{\overline{\lfloor n + 1}}{s^{n+1}} \qquad \text{(From Table 4.1)}$$

$$\therefore \qquad L [e^{-at} t^n] = \frac{\overline{\lfloor n + 1}}{(s + a)^{n+1}} \qquad \text{(By the First Shifting Theorem)}$$

Ex. 2 : *Obtain the Laplace transform of each of the following functions :*

(i) $e^{4t} \cosh 5t$ (ii) $(t + 2)^2 e^{4t}$ **(May 2016)** *(iii) $e^{-2t} (3 \cos 6t - 5 \sin 6t)$ (iv) $e^{-3t} \sin^2 t$ (v) $\cosh at \sin at$*

Sol. : (i) We have

$$L [\cosh 5t] = \frac{s}{s^2 - 25}$$

$$\therefore \qquad L [e^{4t} \cosh 5t] = \left\{ \frac{s}{s^2 - 25} \right\}_{s \to s - 4} \qquad \text{(By the First Shifting Theorem)}$$

$$= \frac{s - 4}{(s - 4)^2 - 25} = \frac{s - 4}{s^2 - 8s - 9}$$

Another Method :

$$L [e^{4t} \cosh 5t] = L \left[e^{4t} \left(\frac{e^{5t} + e^{-5t}}{2} \right) \right] = \frac{1}{2} L [e^{9t} + e^{-t}]$$

$$= \frac{1}{2} \left\{ \frac{1}{s - 9} + \frac{1}{s + 1} \right\} = \frac{s - 4}{s^2 - 8s - 9} \qquad \text{(From Table 4.1)}$$

(ii) We have

$$L\,[(t+2)^2] = L\,[t^2 + 4t + 4]$$

$$= \frac{2}{s^3} + \frac{4}{s^2} + \frac{4}{s} = \frac{4s^2 + 4s + 2}{s^3}$$

$$\therefore \quad L\,[e^{4t}(t+2)^2] = \left\{\frac{4s^2 + 4s + 2}{s^3}\right\}_{s \to s-4}$$

$$= \frac{4(s-4)^2 + 4(s-4) + 2}{(s-4)^3} = \frac{4s^2 - 28s + 50}{(s-4)^3}$$

(iii) We have

$$L\,[3\cos 6t - 5\sin 6t] = 3\,L\,[\cos 6t] - 5\,L\,[\sin 6t]$$

$$= 3\,\frac{s}{s^2 + 36} - 5\,\frac{6}{s^2 + 36} = \frac{3s - 30}{s^2 + 40}$$

$$\therefore \quad L\,[e^{-2t}(3\cos 6t - 5\sin 6t)] = \left\{\frac{3s + 30}{s^2 + 36}\right\}_{s \to s+2}$$

$$= \frac{3(s+2) - 30}{(s+2)^2 + 36} = \frac{3s - 24}{s^2 + 4s + 40}$$

(iv) We have $\quad L\,[\sin^2 t] = L\left[\dfrac{1 - \cos 2t}{2}\right] = \dfrac{1}{2}\{L\,[1] - L\,[\cos 2t]\}$

$$= \frac{1}{2}\left\{\frac{1}{s} - \frac{s}{s^2 + 4}\right\} = \frac{2}{s(s^2 + 4)}$$

$$\therefore \quad L\,[e^{-3t}\sin^2 t] = \left\{\frac{2}{s(s^2 + 4)}\right\}_{s \to s+3}$$

$$= \frac{2}{(s+3)\{(s+3)^2 + 4\}} = \frac{2}{(s+3)(s^2 + 6s + 13)}$$

(v) $\quad L\,[\cosh at \sin at] = L\left[\left(\dfrac{e^{at} + e^{-at}}{2}\right)\sin at\right]$

$$= \frac{1}{2}\{L\,[e^{at}\sin at] + L\,[e^{-at}\sin at]\}$$

$$= \frac{1}{2}\left\{\frac{a}{(s-a)^2 + a^2} + \frac{a}{(s+a)^2 + a^2}\right\} \quad \left\{\because\ L\,[\sin at] = \frac{a}{s^2 + a^2}\right.$$

$$= \frac{1}{2}\left\{\frac{a}{s^2 - 2as + 2a^2} + \frac{a}{s^2 + 2as + 2a^2}\right\} = \frac{a(s^2 + 2a^2)}{s^4 + 4a^4}$$

(B) SECOND SHIFTING THEOREM

Theorem : If $\quad L\,[f(t)] = F(s)$ and $\ F(t) = \begin{cases} f(t - a), & t > a \\ 0, & t < a \end{cases}$, then

$$L\,[F(t)] = e^{-as}\,F(s)$$

Proof : By definition,

$$L[F(t)] = \int_0^\infty e^{-st} F(t)\, dt = \int_0^a e^{-st} F(t)\, dt + \int_a^\infty e^{-st} F(t)\, dt$$

$$= \int_0^a e^{-st}(0)\, dt + \int_a^\infty e^{-st} f(t-a)\, dt$$

$$= \int_a^\infty e^{-st} f(t-a)\, dt, \text{ Put } t-a = u \;\therefore\; dt = du \text{ and } \begin{array}{|c|c|c|} \hline t & a & \infty \\ \hline u & 0 & \infty \\ \hline \end{array}$$

$$= \int_0^\infty e^{-s(a+u)} f(u)\, du = e^{-as} \int_0^\infty e^{-su} f(u)\, du$$

$$= e^{-as}\, L[f(t)] = e^{-as} F(s)$$

Hence

$$\boxed{L[F(t)] = e^{-as}\, F(s), \text{ where } F(t) = \begin{cases} f(t-a) & t > a \\ 0 & t < a \end{cases}} \quad \dots (10)$$

Remark 1 : The second shifting theorem concerns shifting on t-axis : the replacement of t in f(t) by (t – a) (i.e. shifting graph of f(t) to the right through distance a, corresponds to multiplication of the transform F(s) by e^{-as}.

Remark 2 : In practice to obtain Laplace transform of F(t), we first obtain f(t) from f(t – a) and its Laplace transform F(s) and then required transform is written as $e^{-as} F(s)$.

ILLUSTRATIONS

Ex. 1 : *Find the Laplace transforms of the following functions :*

(i) $F(t) = \begin{cases} \cos(t - 2\pi/3), & t > \dfrac{2\pi}{3} \\[2mm] 0, & t < \dfrac{2\pi}{3} \end{cases}$ (ii) $F(t) = \begin{cases} (t-1)^3, & t > 1 \\ 0, & t < 1 \end{cases}$

Sol. : (i) Here $f(t-a) = \cos\left(t - \dfrac{2\pi}{3}\right)$, where $a = \dfrac{2\pi}{3}$.

$$\therefore \qquad f(t) = \cos t \quad \text{and} \quad F(s) = \frac{s}{s^2 + 1}$$

Hence by the second shifting theorem, with $a = \dfrac{2\pi}{3}$, we have

$$L[F(t)] = e^{-as} F(s) = e^{-2\pi s/3} \left(\frac{s}{s^2 + 1}\right)$$

(ii) Here $f(t-a) = (t-1)^3$, where $a = 1$.

$\therefore \qquad f(t) = t^3 \quad$ and $\quad F(s) = \dfrac{3!}{s^4} = \dfrac{6}{s^4}$

Hence by the second shifting theorem, with $a = 1$, we have

$$L[F(t)] = e^{-as} F(s) = e^{-s}\left(\dfrac{6}{s^4}\right)$$

Ex. 2 : *Obtain the Laplace transforms of the following functions :*

(i) $F(t) = \begin{cases} e^{-4(t-3)} \sin 3(t-3), & t > 3 \\ 0, & t < 3 \end{cases}$ **(Dec. 2009)** (ii) $F(t) = \begin{cases} \sin 2(t-\pi), & t > \pi \\ 0, & t < \pi \end{cases}$

Sol. : (i) Here $f(t-a) = e^{-4(t-3)} \sin 3(t-3)$ where $a = 3$.

$\therefore \qquad f(t) = e^{-4t} \sin 3t$

$\therefore \qquad F(s) = \left\{\dfrac{3}{s^2+9}\right\}_{s \to s+4} \qquad$ (By the First Shifting Theorem)

$$= \dfrac{3}{(s+4)^2+9} = \dfrac{3}{s^2+8s+25}$$

Hence by the second shifting theorem, with $a = 3$, we have

$$L[F(t)] = e^{-as} F(s) = e^{-3s}\left(\dfrac{3}{s^2+8s+25}\right)$$

(ii) Here $f(t-a) = \sin 2(t-\pi)$ where $a = \pi$

$\therefore \qquad f(t) = \sin 2t$

$\therefore \qquad F(s) = \dfrac{2}{s^2+4}$

Hence by the second shifting theorem, with $a = \pi$, we have

$$L[F(t)] = e^{-as} F(s) = e^{-\pi s}\left(\dfrac{2}{s^2+4}\right)$$

(C) CHANGE OF SCALE THEOREM

Theorem : If $L[f(t)] = F(s)$, then $L[f(at)] = \dfrac{1}{a} F\left(\dfrac{s}{a}\right)$

Proof : By definition,

$$L[f(at)] = \int_0^\infty e^{-st} f(at)\, dt \quad \text{Put } at = u \therefore a\, dt = du \quad \text{and}$$

t	0	∞
u	0	∞

$$= \int_0^\infty e^{-s(u/a)} f(u) \dfrac{du}{a} = \dfrac{1}{a} \int_0^\infty e^{-(s/a)u} f(u)\, du$$

$$= \dfrac{1}{a} F\left(\dfrac{s}{a}\right) \qquad \left(\text{by } s \to \dfrac{s}{a} \text{ in def. (1)}\right)$$

Hence $\qquad \boxed{L[f(at)] = \dfrac{1}{a} F\left(\dfrac{s}{a}\right)} \qquad \qquad \dots (11)$

ILLUSTRATIONS

Ex. 1 : *If* $L[\sin t] = \dfrac{1}{s^2 + 1}$, *find* $L[\sin at]$.

Sol. : We have given that

$$L[\sin t] = \frac{1}{s^2 + 1}$$

By the Change of Scale Theorem,

$$L[\sin at] = \frac{1}{a}\,\frac{1}{(s/a)^2 + 1} = \frac{a}{s^2 + a^2}$$

Ex. 2 : If $L\left[\dfrac{\sin t}{t}\right] = \tan^{-1}\left(\dfrac{1}{s}\right)$, find $L\left[\dfrac{\sin at}{t}\right]$.

Sol. : We have given that

$$L\left[\frac{\sin t}{t}\right] = \tan^{-1}\left(\frac{1}{s}\right)$$

By the Change of Scale Theorem,

$$L\left[\frac{\sin at}{at}\right] = \frac{1}{a}\,L\left[\frac{\sin at}{t}\right] = \frac{1}{a}\,\tan^{-1}\left\{\frac{1}{(s/a)}\right\} = \frac{1}{a}\,\tan^{-1}\left(\frac{a}{s}\right)$$

$$\therefore \qquad L\left[\frac{\sin at}{t}\right] = \tan^{-1}\left(\frac{a}{s}\right)$$

Ex. 3 : *If* $L[f(t)] = \dfrac{8 + 12s - 2s^2}{(s^2 + 4)^2}$, *find* $L[f(2t)]$.

Sol. : We have given that

$$L[f(t)] = \frac{8 + 12s - 2s^2}{(s^2 + 4)^2}$$

By the Change of Scale Theorem,

$$L[f(2t)] = \frac{1}{2}\left[\frac{8 + 12\,(s/2) - 2\,(s/2)^2}{\{(s/2)^2 + 4\}^2}\right] = \frac{4\,(16 + 12s - s^2)}{(s^2 + 16)^2}$$

(D) LAPLACE TRANSFORMS OF DERIVATIVES

To solve differential equations by Laplace transform method, we require the transforms of the derivatives. We derive below some expressions for the Laplace transforms of f'(t), f''(t) … etc. in terms of the transform of the function itself and in terms of the lower order derivatives of the function at $t = 0$ (i.e. values of the lower order derivatives as $t \to 0$ from positive values).

Theorem : If $L[f(t)] = F(s)$, then

$$L[f'(t)] = s\,L[f(t)] - f(0) = s\,F(s) - f(0) \quad \text{if } f(t) \text{ is continuous}$$

function for $t \geq 0$ and is of exponential order $\alpha\left[\text{i.e. } \lim_{b\to\infty} e^{-sb}\,f(b) = 0 \text{ for } s > \alpha\right]$.

Proof : Using integration by parts (considering e^{-st} as first function), we have

$$L\,[f\,'(t)] = \int_0^\infty e^{-st}\,f\,'(t)\,dt = \lim_{b\to\infty}\int_0^b e^{-st}\,f\,'(t)\,dt$$

$$= \lim_{b\to\infty}\left\{\left[e^{-st}\,f(t)\right]_0^b + s\int_0^b e^{-st}\,f(t)\,dt\right\}$$

$$= \lim_{b\to\infty}\left\{\left[e^{-sb}\,f(b) - f(0)\right] + s\int_0^b e^{-st}\,f(t)\,dt\right\}$$

$$= s\int_0^\infty e^{-st}\,f(t)\,dt - f(0) \quad \{\because\ f(t)\ \text{is of exponential order}\}$$

$$= s\,L\,[f(t)] - f(0)$$

$$= s\,F(s) - f(0)$$

Hence
$$\boxed{L\,[f\,'(t)] = s\,L\,[f(t)] - f(0) = s\,F(s) - f(0)}$$
$$\quad \ldots (12)$$

By applying result (12) to second order derivative $f''(t)$, we obtain

$$L\,[f\,''(t)] = L\,[\{f\,'(t)\}']$$

$$= s\,L\,[f\,'(t)] - f\,'(0)$$

$$= s\,\{s\,F(s) - f(0)\} - f\,'(0)$$

$$= s^2\,F(s) - s\,f(0) - f\,'(0)$$

Thus
$$\boxed{L\,[f\,''(t)] = s^2\,F(s) - s\,f(0) - f\,'(0)}$$
$$\quad \ldots (13)$$

Similarly, it can be proved that

$$\boxed{L\,[f\,'''(t)] = s^3\,F(s) - s^2\,f(0) - s\,f\,'(0) - f\,''(0)}$$
$$\quad \ldots (14)$$

etc. By using mathematical induction, we can obtain the following generalised result :

$$\boxed{L\,[f^n(t)] = s^n\,F(s) - s^{n-1}\,f(0) - s^{n-2}\,f\,'(0) - s^{n-3}\,f\,''(0) - \ldots s^2\,f^{n-3}\,(0) - s\,f^{n-2}\,(0) - f^{n-1}\,(0)}$$
$$\quad \ldots (15)$$

Note 1 : Following observations are quite useful in remembering the result (15) :

(a) Except first all other terms are negative.

(b) Power of s in the first term is n (i.e. the order of the derivative whose Laplace transform is required) and goes on decreasing by one in subsequent term upto zero.

(c) Multiplier of s^n is $F(s) = L[f(t)]$ and that of subsequent terms $f(0)$, $f'(0)$, $f''(0)$, ... etc.

(d) Sum of powers of s and order of the derivative of $f(0)$ in every term (except first) is $n - 1$.

Note 2 : Laplace transform of derivative of a function $f(t)$, roughly corresponds to multiplication of transform $F(s)$ by s. This permits replacing operations of calculus by simple algebraic operations on transforms.

ILLUSTRATIONS

Ex. 1 : *Obtain the Laplace transforms of (i)* $\dfrac{d^5x}{dt^5}$, *(ii)* $\dfrac{d^2y}{dt^2} - 3\dfrac{dy}{dt} + 5y$, *given that* $y(0) = 2$ *and* $y'(0) = -4$.

Sol. : (i) We have, from result (15)

$$L\left[\frac{d^5x}{dt^5}\right] = s^5 \times (s) - s^4 x(0) - s^3 x'(0) - s^2 x''(0) - s\, x'''(0) - x^{iv}(0)$$

(ii) $L\left[\dfrac{d^2y}{dt^2} - 3\dfrac{dy}{dt} + 5y(t)\right]$

$$= L\left[\frac{d^2y}{dt^2}\right] - 3L\left[\frac{dy}{dt}\right] + 5L[y(t)]$$

$$= \{s^2 Y(s) - y(0) - y'(0)\} - 3\{s\, Y(s) - y(0)\} + 5Y(s)$$

$$\text{[By results (12) and (13)]}$$

$$= \{s^2 Y(s) - s(2) - (-4)\} - 3\{s\, Y(s) - (2)\} + 5Y(s)$$

$$= (s^2 - 3s + 5)\, Y(s) - 2s + 10$$

Ex. 2 : *Obtain the Laplace transform of y(t), if* $\dfrac{d^3y}{dt^3} - \dfrac{d^2y}{dt^2} + 4\dfrac{dy}{dt} - 4y = t$, *given that* $y(0) = y'(0) = y''(0) = 1$.

Sol. : Taking Laplace transforms of both sides, we get

$$L\left[\frac{d^3y}{dt^3}\right] - L\left[\frac{d^2y}{dt^2}\right] + 4L\left[\frac{dy}{dt}\right] - 4L[y(t)] = L[t]$$

$$\therefore \quad \{s^3 Y(s) - s^2 y(0) - s\, y'(0) - y''(0)\} - \{s^2 Y(s) - s\, y(0) - y'(0)\}$$

$$+ 4\{s\, Y(s) - y(0)\} - 4Y(s) = \frac{1}{s^2}$$

$$\therefore \quad (s^3 - s^2 + 4s - 4)\, Y(s) + (-s^2 - s - 1) - (-s - 1) - 4 = \frac{1}{s^2}$$

$$\left\{\because\ y(0) = y'(0) = y''(0) = 1\right\}$$

$$\therefore \qquad (s^2 + 4)(s - 1)\, Y(s) = s^2 + 4 + \frac{1}{s^2}$$

$$\therefore \qquad Y(s) = \frac{1}{(s - 1)} + \frac{1}{s^2(s - 1)(s^2 + 4)}$$

(E) LAPLACE TRANSFORM OF INTEGRALS

Theorem : If $L[f(t)] = F(s)$, then

$$L\left[\int_0^t f(u)\,du\right] = \frac{1}{s}\,F(s)$$

Proof : Let $g(t) = \int_0^t f(u)\,du$,   then $g'(t) = f(t)$ and $g(0) = 0$

$$\left[\text{Since,}\ \frac{d}{dt}\,g(t) = \frac{d}{dt}\int_0^t f(u)\,du = f(t)\ \text{and}\ g(0) = \int_0^0 f(u)\,du = 0\right]$$

Taking the Laplace transform of both sides, we have

$$L[g'(t)] = L[f(t)]$$

$\therefore$ $\qquad s\,L[g(t)] - g(0) = F(s)$ $\qquad\qquad$ [By the result (12)]

$\therefore$ $\qquad s\,L[g(t)] = F(s)$ $\qquad\qquad$ [$\because g(0) = 0$]

$\therefore$ $\qquad L[g(t)] = \frac{1}{s}\,F(s)$

or $\qquad L\left[\int_0^t f(u)\,du\right] = \frac{1}{s}\,F(s)$

Hence

$$\boxed{L\left[\int_0^t f(u)\,du\right] = L\left[\int_0^t f(t)\,dt\right] = \frac{1}{s}\,L[f(t)] = \frac{1}{s}\,F(s)}\qquad \dots (16)$$

By using result (16), we can obtain

$$L\left[\int_0^t \int_0^t f(t)\,dt\,dt\right] = L\left[\int_0^t \phi(t)\,dt\right],\qquad\qquad \text{where } \phi(t) = \int_0^t f(t)\,dt$$

$$= \frac{1}{s}\,L[\phi(t)] = \frac{1}{s}\,L\left[\int_0^t f(u)\,du\right]$$

$$= \frac{1}{s}\left\{\frac{1}{s}\,F(s)\right\} = \frac{1}{s^2}\,F(s)$$

Thus

$$\boxed{L\left[\int_0^t \int_0^t f(t)\,dt\,dt\right] = \frac{1}{s^2}\,F(s)}\qquad \dots (17)$$

Remark 1 : Laplace transform of integral of f(t) over (0, t) corresponds to division of transform F(s) by s.

Remark 2 : In general, $\quad L\left[\int_0^t \int_0^t \ldots \int_0^t f(t)\, dt^n\right] = \dfrac{1}{s^n}\, F(s)$

ILLUSTRATIONS

Ex. 1 : *Obtain Laplace transform of* $\dfrac{d^2y}{dt^2} + 3\dfrac{dy}{dt} + 4y + 2\int_0^t y(t)\, dt.$

Sol. : $L\left[\dfrac{d^2y}{dt^2} + 3\dfrac{dy}{dt} + 4y + 2\int_0^t y(t)\, dt\right]$

$$= L\left[\dfrac{d^2y}{dt^2}\right] + 3\,L\left[\dfrac{dy}{dt}\right] + 4\,L\,[y(t)] + 2\,L\left[\int_0^t y(t)\, dt\right]$$

$$= \{s^2\,Y(s) - s\,y(0) - y'(0)\} + 3\,\{s\,Y(s) - y(0)\} + 4\,Y(s) + 2\dfrac{1}{s}\,Y(s)$$

$$= \left(s^2 + 3s + 4 + \dfrac{2}{s}\right)Y(s) - (s + 3)\,y(0) - y'(0)$$

Ex. 2 : Verify $L\left[\int_0^t u^2\, e^{-u}\, du\right] = \dfrac{1}{s}\,L\,[t^2\, e^{-t}]$

Sol. : L.H.S. $= L\left[\int_0^t u^2\, e^{-u}\, du\right] = L\left[\left\{u^2(-e^{-u}) - (2u)(e^{-u}) + (2)(-e^{-u})\right\}_0^t\right]$

$$= L\left[\left\{-(u^2 + 2u + 2)\, e^{-u}\right\}_0^t\right] = L\,[2 - (t^2 + 2t + 2)\, e^{-u}]$$

$$= 2\,L\,[1] - L\,[(t^2 + 2t + 2)\, e^{-u}] = \dfrac{2}{s} - \left\{\dfrac{2}{s^3} + \dfrac{2}{s^2} + \dfrac{2}{s}\right\}_{s \to s+1}$$

[By the First Shifting Theorem]

$$= \dfrac{2}{s} - 2\left\{\dfrac{1}{(s+1)^3} + \dfrac{1}{(s+1)^2} + \dfrac{1}{s+1}\right\} = \dfrac{2}{s\,(s+1)^3} \qquad \ldots \text{(i)}$$

$$\text{R.H.S.} = \dfrac{1}{s}\,L\,[t^2\, e^{-t}] = \dfrac{1}{s}\,L\,[e^{-t}(t^2)] = \dfrac{1}{s}\left\{\dfrac{2}{s^3}\right\}_{s \to s+1} = \dfrac{2}{s\,(s+1)^3} \quad \ldots \text{(ii)}$$

From (i) and (ii), L.H.S. = R.H.S. and hence the result is verified.

(F) MULTIPLICATION BY POWERS OF t

Theorem : If $L[f(t)] = F(s)$, then

$$L[t^n f(t)] = (-1)^n \frac{d^n}{ds^n} F(s)$$

Proof : By definition, we have

$$F(s) = \int_0^\infty e^{-st} f(t)\, dt$$

Differentiating both sides w.r.t. s, we get

$$\frac{d}{ds} F(s) = \frac{d}{ds} \int_0^\infty e^{-st} f(t)\, dt = \int_0^\infty \frac{\partial}{\partial s} e^{-st} f(t)\, dt \qquad \text{... (by DUIS rule)}$$

$$= \int_0^\infty -t\, e^{-st} f(t)\, dt = -\int_0^\infty e^{-st} \{t\, f(t)\}\, dt$$

$$= -L[t\, f(t)] \qquad\qquad \text{(By definition)}$$

Hence

$$\boxed{L[t\, f(t)] = -\frac{d}{ds} F(s)} \qquad\qquad \text{... (18)}$$

By using result (18), we can obtain

$$L[t^2 f(t)] = L[t \cdot t\, f(t)] = -\frac{d}{ds} L[t\, f(t)]$$

$$= -\frac{d}{ds} \left\{ -\frac{d}{ds} F(s) \right\} = (-1)^2 \frac{d^2}{ds^2} F(s)$$

Thus

$$\boxed{L[t^2 f(t)] = (-1)^2 \frac{d^2}{ds^2} F(s)} \qquad\qquad \text{... (19)}$$

etc. By using mathematical induction, we can obtain the following generalised result :

$$\boxed{L[t^n f(t)] = (-1)^n \frac{d^n}{ds^n} F(s)} \qquad\qquad \text{... (20)}$$

Note : The result (18) can be interpreted as the differentiation of the transform of a function f(t) corresponds to the multiplication of the function f(t) by $-t$.

ILLUSTRATIONS

Ex. 1 : *Obtain the Laplace transform of each of the following functions :*

(i) $\dfrac{t \sin at}{2a}$ *(ii)* $\dfrac{1}{2a^3} (\sin at - at \cos at)$ *(iii)* $\dfrac{1}{2a} (\sin at + at \cos at)$

Sol. : (i) We have

$$L\left[\frac{\sin at}{2a} \right] = \frac{1}{2a} L[\sin at] = \frac{1}{2}\frac{1}{s^2 + a^2}$$

$$\therefore \qquad L\left[t\ \frac{\sin at}{2a}\right] = (-1)\ \frac{d}{ds}\left\{\frac{1}{2}\left(\frac{1}{s^2 + a^2}\right)\right\} \qquad \text{[By result (18)]}$$

$$= (-1)\ \frac{1}{2}\ \frac{-2s}{(s^2 + a^2)^2} = \frac{s}{(s^2 + a^2)^2}$$

Another Method : We have

$$L\,[\cos at] = \int_0^\infty e^{-st}\,(\cos at)\,dt = \frac{s}{s^2 + a^2}$$

Differentiating with respect to the parameter a [using DUIS rule], we get

$$\frac{d}{da}\int_0^\infty e^{-st}\cos at\,dt = \int_0^\infty \frac{\partial}{\partial a}\,e^{-st}\,\cos at\,dt = \frac{d}{da}\,\frac{s}{s^2 + a^2}$$

$$\therefore \qquad \int_0^\infty e^{-st}\,(-t\sin at)\,dt = -\frac{2as}{(s^2 + a^2)^2}$$

$$\therefore \qquad -L\,[t\sin at] = -\frac{2as}{(s^2 + a^2)^2} \qquad\qquad \dots \text{(by def.)}$$

$$\text{Hence,} \qquad L\left[\frac{t\sin at}{2a}\right] = \frac{s}{(s^2 + a^2)^2}$$

(ii) $L\left[\dfrac{1}{2a^3}\,(\sin at - at\cos at)\right]$

$$= \frac{1}{2a^3}\,\{L\,[\sin at] - a\,L\,[t\cos at]\}$$

$$= \frac{1}{2a^3}\left[\frac{a}{(s^2 + a^2)} - a\,(-1)\,\frac{d}{ds}\,\frac{s}{s^2 + a^2}\right] \qquad \text{[By result (18)]}$$

$$= \frac{1}{2a^3}\left[\frac{a}{s^2 + a^2} + a\left\{\frac{(s^2 + a^2)\,(1) - s\,(2s)}{(s^2 + a^2)^2}\right\}\right]$$

$$= \frac{1}{2a^3}\left[\frac{a}{s^2 + a^2} + a\left\{\frac{a^2 - s^2}{(s^2 + a^2)^2}\right\}\right]$$

$$= \frac{1}{2a^3}\left[\frac{a\,(s^2 + a^2) + a\,(a^2 - s^2)}{(s^2 + a^2)^2}\right] = \frac{1}{(s^2 + a^2)^2}$$

(iii) $L\left[\dfrac{1}{2a}\,(\sin at + at\cos at)\right]$

$$= \frac{1}{2a}\,\{L\,[\sin at] + a\,L\,[t\cos at]\}$$

$$= \frac{1}{2a}\left[\frac{a}{s^2 + a^2} + a\,(-1)\,\frac{d}{ds}\,\frac{s}{s^2 + a^2}\right] \qquad \text{[By result (18)]}$$

$$= \frac{1}{2a}\left[\frac{a}{s^2+a^2} - a\left\{\frac{a^2-s^2}{(s^2+a^2)^2}\right\}\right]$$

$$= \frac{1}{2a}\left[\frac{a(s^2+a^2)-a(a^2-s^2)}{(s^2+a^2)^2}\right] = \frac{s^2}{(s^2+a^2)^2}$$

Ex. 2 : *Find the Laplace transform of each of the following functions :*

     (i) $t^2 \sin 4t$,   (ii) $t^2 \cos at$,   (iii) $t^3 e^{2t}$.

Sol. : (i) We have

$$L[\sin 4t] = \frac{4}{s^2+16}$$

$$\therefore \quad L[t^2 \sin 4t] = (-1)^2 \frac{d^2}{ds^2}\left(\frac{4}{s^2+16}\right) \qquad \text{[By result (19)]}$$

$$= 4\frac{d}{ds}\left[-\frac{2s}{(s^2+16)^2}\right] = -8\frac{d}{ds}\left[\frac{s}{(s^2+16)^2}\right]$$

$$= -8\left[\frac{(s^2+16)^2(1)-2(s^2+16)(2s)\cdot s}{(s^2+16)^4}\right] = -8\left[\frac{s^2+16-4s^2}{(s^2+16)^3}\right]$$

$$= \frac{24s^2-128}{(s^2+16)^3}$$

(ii) We have $L[\cos at] = \dfrac{s}{s^2+a^2}$

$$\therefore \quad L[t^2 \cos at] = (-1)^2 \frac{d^2}{ds^2}\left(\frac{s}{s^2+a^2}\right) \qquad \text{[By result (19)]}$$

$$= \frac{d}{ds}\left[\frac{(s^2+a^2)(1)-s(2s)}{(s^2+a^2)^2}\right] = \frac{d}{ds}\left[\frac{a^2-s^2}{(s^2+a^2)^2}\right]$$

$$= \left[\frac{(s^2+a^2)^2(-2s)-(a^2-s^2)\cdot 2(s^2+a^2)(2s)}{(s^2+a^2)^4}\right]$$

$$= \left[\frac{-2s^3-2a^2s-4a^2s+4s^3}{(s^2+a^2)^3}\right] = \frac{2s(s^2-3a^2)}{(s^2+a^2)^3}$$

(iii) $L[e^{2t}] = \dfrac{1}{s-2}$

$$\therefore \quad L[t^3 e^{2t}] = (-1)^3 \frac{d^3}{ds^3}\left(\frac{1}{s-2}\right) = -\frac{d^2}{ds^2}\left[-\frac{1}{(s-2)^2}\right] \text{ [By result (20)]}$$

$$= \frac{d}{ds}\left[-\frac{2}{(s-2)^3}\right] = \frac{6}{(s-2)^4}$$

(G) DIVISION BY t :

Theorem : If $\quad L[f(t)] = F(s)$, then

$$L\left[\frac{f(t)}{t}\right] = \int_{s}^{\infty} F(s)\, ds, \text{ provided } \lim_{t \to 0+} \frac{f(t)}{t} \text{ exists.}$$

Proof : By definition,

$$F(s) = \int_{0}^{\infty} e^{-st} f(t)\, dt$$

Integrating both sides w.r.t. s from s to ∞, we get

$$\int_{s}^{\infty} F(s)\, ds = \int_{s}^{\infty}\left[\int_{0}^{\infty} e^{-st} f(t)\, dt\right] ds$$

$$= \int_{0}^{\infty} f(t)\left[\int_{s}^{\infty} e^{-st}\, ds\right] dt, \quad \text{(changing the order of integration)}$$

$$= \int_{0}^{\infty} f(t)\left[\frac{e^{-st}}{-t}\right]_{s}^{\infty} dt = \int_{0}^{\infty} f(t)\left[0 + \frac{e^{-st}}{t}\right] dt$$

$$= \int_{0}^{\infty} e^{-st}\,\frac{f(t)}{t}\, dt = L\left[\frac{f(t)}{t}\right]$$

Hence
$$\boxed{L\left[\frac{f(t)}{t}\right] = \int_{s}^{\infty} F(s)\, ds} \qquad \qquad \dots (21)$$

By using result (21), we can obtain

$$L\left[\frac{f(t)}{t^2}\right] = L\left[\frac{1}{t} \cdot \frac{f(t)}{t}\right] = \int_{s}^{\infty} L\left[\frac{f(t)}{t}\right] ds = \int_{s}^{\infty} \int_{s}^{\infty} F(s)\, ds\, ds$$

Thus
$$\boxed{L\left[\frac{f(t)}{t^2}\right] = \int_{s}^{\infty} \int_{s}^{\infty} F(s)\, ds\, ds} \qquad \qquad \dots (22)$$

Repeating the above procedure, we can obtain the following generalised result :

$$\boxed{L\left[\frac{f(t)}{t^n}\right] = \underbrace{\int_{s}^{\infty} \int_{s}^{\infty} \dots \dots \int_{s}^{\infty}}_{\leftarrow\ n\text{ integrals }\rightarrow\ \ \leftarrow\ n\text{ times }\rightarrow} F(s)\, ds \cdot ds \dots \dots ds} \qquad \dots (23)$$

Note : The result (21) can be interpreted as the integration of the transform of a function f(t) corresponds to the division of the function f(t) by t.

ILLUSTRATIONS

Ex. 1 : *Find the Laplace transform of* $\dfrac{sin\ at}{t}$ *and hence show that* $\displaystyle\int_0^\infty \dfrac{sin\ t}{t}\ dt = \dfrac{\pi}{2}$.

Sol. : We have $\quad L\,[\sin at] \;=\; \dfrac{a}{s^2 + a^2}$

$$\therefore \qquad L\left[\dfrac{\sin at}{t}\right] \;=\; \int_s^\infty \dfrac{a}{s^2 + a^2}\ ds \;=\; \left[\tan^{-1}\dfrac{s}{a}\right]_s^\infty \qquad\qquad \text{[By result (21)]}$$

$$= \dfrac{\pi}{2} - \tan^{-1}\dfrac{s}{a} \;=\; \cot^{-1}\dfrac{s}{a}$$

When $a = 1$, we have

$$L\left[\dfrac{\sin t}{t}\right] \;=\; \cot^{-1} s$$

or $\qquad \displaystyle\int_0^\infty e^{-st}\,\dfrac{\sin t}{t}\ dt \;=\; \cot^{-1} s \qquad\qquad\qquad\qquad\qquad \text{(By definition)}$

On putting $s = 0$, we obtain

$$\int_0^\infty \dfrac{\sin t}{t}\ dt \;=\; \cot^{-1}(0) \;=\; \dfrac{\pi}{2}.$$

Ex. 2 : *Obtain the Laplace transforms of the following functions :*

(i) $\dfrac{e^{-at} - e^{-bt}}{t}$, **(Dec. 2014)** *(ii)* $\dfrac{cos\ at - cos\ bt}{t}$.

Sol. : (i) We have

$$L\,[e^{-at} - e^{-bt}] \;=\; \dfrac{1}{s + a} - \dfrac{1}{s + b}$$

$$\therefore \quad L\left[\dfrac{e^{-at} - e^{-bt}}{t}\right] \;=\; \int_s^\infty \left(\dfrac{1}{s + a} - \dfrac{1}{s + b}\right) ds \qquad\qquad \text{[By result (21)]}$$

$$= \big[\log (s + a) - \log (s + b)\big]_s^\infty \;=\; \left[\log \dfrac{s + a}{s + b}\right]_s^\infty \;=\; \left[\log \dfrac{1 + \dfrac{a}{s}}{1 + \dfrac{b}{s}}\right]_s^\infty$$

$$= \log 1 - \log \frac{1 + \dfrac{a}{s}}{1 + \dfrac{b}{s}} = 0 - \log \frac{s+a}{s+b} = \log \frac{s+b}{s+a}$$

$$\left[\text{Notice that } L\left[\frac{e^{-at}}{t}\right] \text{ or } L\left[\frac{e^{-bt}}{t}\right] \text{ does not exist since } \int_s^\infty \frac{1}{s+a}\, ds \text{ or } \int_s^\infty \frac{1}{s+b}\, ds \text{ does not exist.} \right]$$

(ii) We have

$$L\left[\cos at - \cos bt\right] = \frac{s}{s^2 + a^2} - \frac{s}{s^2 + b^2}$$

$$\therefore \quad L\left[\frac{\cos at - \cos bt}{t}\right] = \int_s^\infty \left(\frac{s}{s^2 + a^2} - \frac{s}{s^2 + b^2}\right) ds$$

$$= \left[\frac{1}{2}\, \log (s^2 + a^2) - \frac{1}{2}\, \log (s^2 + b^2)\right]_s^\infty$$

$$= \frac{1}{2}\left[\log \frac{s^2 + a^2}{s^2 + b^2}\right]_s^\infty = \frac{1}{2}\left[\log \frac{1 + \dfrac{a^2}{s^2}}{1 + \dfrac{b^2}{s^2}}\right]_s^\infty$$

$$= \frac{1}{2}\left[\log 1 - \log \frac{s^2 + a^2}{s^2 + b^2}\right] = \frac{1}{2}\, \log \frac{s^2 + b^2}{s^2 + a^2}$$

(H) THE CONVOLUTION THEOREM

Definition : The convolution of functions f(t) and g(t) is denoted by f(t) $*$ g(t) and

defined by
$$f(t) * g(t) = \int_0^t f(u)\, g(t-u)\, du \qquad\qquad \dots (24)$$

Note :
$$f(t) * g(t) = \int_0^t f(u)\, g(t-u)\, du \qquad \text{Put } t-u = v \quad \text{or} \quad u = t-v$$

$$\therefore \quad du = -dv \quad \text{and} \quad \begin{array}{|c|c|c|}\hline u & 0 & t \\\hline v & t & 0 \\\hline\end{array}$$

$$= \int_0^t f(t-v)\, g(v)\, dv = \int_0^t g(v)\, f(t-v)\, dv$$

$$= g(t) * f(t)$$

This shows that the convolution of f(t) and g(t) obeys the commutative law of algebra.

Similarly, the following properties of the convolution can be proved easily :

(i) $f(t) * [g(t) + h(t)] = f(t) * g(t) + f(t) * h(t)$ (Distributive Law)

(ii) $[f(t) * g(t)] * h(t) = f(t) * [g(t) * h(t)]$ (Associative Law)

Theorem : If $L[f(t)] = F(s)$ and $L[g(t)] = G(s),$ then

$$L[f(t) * g(t)] = L\left[\int_{0}^{t} f(u)\, g(t-u)\, du\right] = F(s)\, G(s)$$

Proof : $L[f(t) * g(t)] = L\left[\int_{0}^{t} f(u)\, g(t-u)\, du\right]$

$$= \int_{t=0}^{t=\infty} e^{-st} \left[\int_{u=0}^{u=t} f(u)\, g(t-u)\, du\right] dt$$

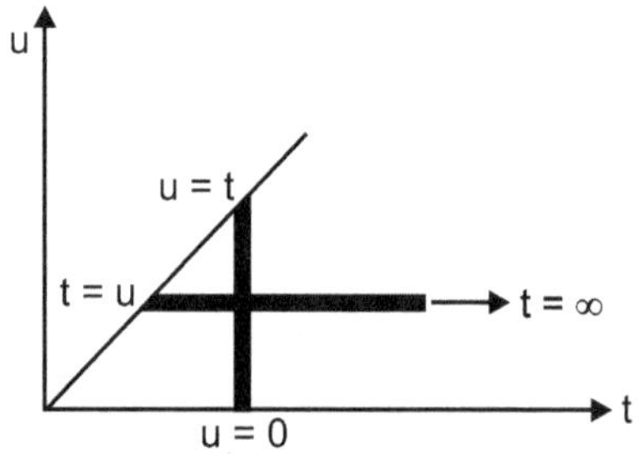

Fig. 4.3 : Region of Integration In The tu-Plane

Changing the order of integration, we get

$$= \int_{u=0}^{u=\infty} \left[\int_{t=u}^{t=\infty} e^{-st} f(u)\, g(t-u)\, dt\right] du = \int_{u=0}^{u=\infty} f(u) \left[\int_{t=u}^{t=\infty} e^{-st} g(t-u)\, dt\right] du$$

$$= \int_{u=0}^{u=\infty} f(u) \left[\int_{v=0}^{v=\infty} e^{-s(u+v)} g(v)\, dv\right] du \qquad \left\{ \begin{array}{l} \text{On putting} \\ t-u=v \ \therefore \ dt = dv \\ \text{and} \ \begin{array}{|c|c|c|} \hline t & u & \infty \\ \hline v & 0 & \infty \\ \hline \end{array} \end{array} \right.$$

$$= \int_{0}^{\infty} e^{-su} f(u)\, du \int_{0}^{\infty} e^{-sv} g(v)\, dv$$

$$= \int_{0}^{\infty} e^{-st} f(t)\, dt \int_{0}^{\infty} e^{-st} g(t)\, dt = F(s)\, G(s)$$

Hence $$\boxed{L[f(t) * g(t)] = L\left[\int_{0}^{t} f(u)\, g(t-u)\, du\right] = F(s)\, G(s)}$$ ... (25 a)

Note 1 : In words, this theorem states that Laplace transform of convolution of two functions is equal to product of their Laplace transforms.

Note 2 : Since convolution of f(t) and g(t) is commutative, we have from result (25 a)

$$\boxed{L\left[\int_0^t f(t-u)\,g(u)\,du\right] = F(s)\,G(s)} \qquad \ldots (25\ b)$$

Note 3 : The convolution theorem is useful to find inverse transformation.

ILLUSTRATIONS

Ex. 1 : *Verify the convolution theorem for the pair of functions f(t) = t, g(t) = e^{at}.*

Sol. : Here $\qquad f(t) = t \qquad \therefore \quad F(s) = \dfrac{1}{s^2}$

and $\qquad g(t) = e^{at} \qquad \therefore \quad G(s) = \dfrac{1}{s-a}$

$\therefore \qquad F(s)\,G(s) = \dfrac{1}{s^2\,(s-a)} \qquad \ldots (i)$

Now $\qquad L\,[f(t) * g(t)] = L\left[\int_0^t f(u)\,g(t-u)\,du\right] = L\left[\int_0^t u\,e^{a\,(t-u)}\,du\right]$

$$= L\left[e^{at}\int_0^t u\,e^{-au}\,du\right] = L\left[e^{at}\left\{u\left(\frac{e^{-au}}{-a}\right) - (1)\left(\frac{e^{-au}}{a^2}\right)\right\}_0^t\right]$$

$$= L\left[e^{at}\left\{\left(-\frac{te^{-at}}{a} - \frac{e^{-at}}{a^2}\right) - \left(0 - \frac{1}{a^2}\right)\right\}\right] = \frac{1}{a^2}\,L\,[e^{at} - at - 1]$$

$$= \frac{1}{a^2}\left[\frac{1}{s-a} - \frac{a}{s^2} - \frac{1}{s}\right] = \frac{1}{a^2}\left[\frac{s^2 - a\,(s-a) - s\,(s-a)}{s^2\,(s-a)}\right]$$

$$= \frac{1}{s^2\,(s-a)} \qquad \ldots (ii)$$

Since results (i) and (ii) are the same, convolution theorem is verified.

Ex. 2 : *Show that 1 * 1 = t, hence prove that*

$$1 * 1 * 1 \ldots\ldots * 1 = \frac{t^{n-1}}{(n-1)!}$$

$$\leftarrow n\text{-}ones \rightarrow$$

Sol. : $\qquad\qquad 1 * 1 = \int_0^t 1\cdot 1\,dt = t$

$$(1 * 1) * 1 \ = \ t * 1 \ = \ \int_0^t u \cdot 1 \, dt \ = \ \frac{t^2}{2}$$

$$(1 * 1 * 1) * 1 \ = \ \frac{t^2}{2} * 1 \ = \ \int_0^t \frac{u^2}{2} \cdot 1 \, dt \ = \ \frac{t^3}{3!}$$

$$\therefore \qquad 1 * 1 * 1 \ldots \ldots * 1 \ = \ \frac{t^{n-1}}{(n-1)!}$$

(I) INITIAL VALUE THEOREM

Theorem : If $\ L[f(t)] = F(s)$, then

$$\lim_{t \to 0} f(t) \ = \ \lim_{s \to \infty} s\,F(s)$$

provided these limits exist.

Proof : We have $\ L[f'(t)] \ = \ s\,F(s) - f(0)$ [By result (12)]

$$\text{or} \qquad \int_0^\infty e^{-st} f'(t) \, dt \ = \ s\,F(s) - f(0)$$

Taking the limit as $s \to \infty$, we get

$$\lim_{s \to \infty} \int_0^\infty e^{-st} f'(t) \, dt \ = \ \lim_{s \to \infty} [s\,F(s) - f(0)]$$

$$\left[\text{If } f'(t) \text{ is piecewise continuous and of exponential order, we have } \lim_{s \to \infty} \int_0^\infty e^{-st} f'(t) = 0. \right]$$

$$\therefore \qquad 0 \ = \ \lim_{s \to \infty} s\,F(s) - f(0)$$

$$\text{or} \qquad \lim_{s \to \infty} s\,F(s) \ = \ f(0) \ = \ \lim_{t \to 0} f(t)$$

$$\text{Hence} \qquad \boxed{\lim_{t \to 0} f(t) \ = \ \lim_{s \to \infty} s\,F(s)} \qquad \ldots (26)$$

ILLUSTRATION

Ex. 1 : *Verify the initial value theorem for the following functions :*

    (i) $t + \sin 3t$ *(ii)* $(3t + 4)^2$ *(iii)* $3 - 2 \cos t$

Sol. : (i) Let $\qquad f(t) \ = \ t + \sin 3t \qquad \therefore \ F(s) = \dfrac{1}{s^2} + \dfrac{3}{s^2 + 9}$

Now $\displaystyle\lim_{t\to 0} f(t) = \lim_{t\to 0} (t + \sin 3t) = 0$ ... (i)

and $\displaystyle\lim_{s\to\infty} s\,F(s) = \lim_{s\to\infty} s\left(\frac{1}{s^2} + \frac{3}{s^2+9}\right) = \lim_{s\to\infty}\left(\frac{1}{s} + \frac{3s}{s^2+9}\right)$

$$= \lim_{s\to\infty}\left(\frac{1}{s} + \frac{3/s}{1 + 9/s^2}\right) = 0 \qquad \text{... (ii)}$$

Since results (i) and (ii) are same, initial value theorem is verified.

(ii) Let $f(t) = (3t + 4)^2 = 9t^2 + 24t + 16 \qquad \therefore\ F(s) = \dfrac{18}{s^3} + \dfrac{24}{s^2} + \dfrac{16}{s}$

Now $\displaystyle\lim_{t\to 0} f(t) = \lim_{t\to 0} (3t + 4)^2 = 16$ ... (i)

and $\displaystyle\lim_{s\to\infty} s\,F(s) = \lim_{s\to\infty} s\left(\frac{18}{s^3} + \frac{24}{s^2} + \frac{16}{s}\right)$

$$= \lim_{s\to\infty}\left(\frac{18}{s^2} + \frac{24}{s} + 16\right) = 16 \qquad \text{... (ii)}$$

Since results (i) and (ii) are same, initial value theorem is verified.

(iii) Let $f(t) = 3 - 2\cos t \qquad \therefore\ F(s) = \dfrac{3}{s} - \dfrac{2s}{s^2+1}$

Now $\displaystyle\lim_{t\to 0} f(t) = \lim_{t\to 0} (3 - 2\cos t) = 1$ ... (i)

and $\displaystyle\lim_{s\to\infty} s\,F(s) = \lim_{s\to\infty} s\left(\frac{3}{s} - \frac{2s}{s^2+1}\right) = \lim_{s\to\infty}\left(3 - 2\frac{s^2}{s^2+1}\right)$

$$= \lim_{s\to\infty}\left(3 - 2\frac{1}{1 + 1/s^2}\right) = 1 \qquad \text{... (ii)}$$

Since results (i) and (ii) are same, initial value theorem is verified.

(J) FINAL VALUE THEOREM

Theorem : If $L[f(t)] = F(s)$, then

$$\lim_{t\to\infty} f(t) = \lim_{s\to 0} s\,F(s)$$

provided these limits exist.

Proof : We have $L[f'(t)] = s\,F(s) - f(0)$

or $\displaystyle\int_{0}^{\infty} e^{-st} f'(t)\, dt = s\,F(s) - f(0)$

Taking the limit as $s \to 0$, we get

$$\lim_{s\to 0} \int_{0}^{\infty} e^{-st} f'(t)\, dt = \lim_{s\to 0} [s\,F(s) - f(0)]$$

$$\int_0^\infty f'(t)\,dt = \lim_{s\to 0}[s\,F(s) - f(0)]$$

$$[f(t)]_0^\infty = \lim_{s\to 0}[s\,F(s) - f(0)]$$

$$\lim_{t\to\infty} f(t) - f(0) = \lim_{s\to 0} s\,F(s) - f(0)$$

$$\therefore \quad \lim_{t\to\infty} f(t) = \lim_{s\to 0} s\,F(s)$$

Hence

$$\boxed{\lim_{t\to\infty} f(t) = \lim_{s\to 0} s\,F(s)} \qquad \ldots (27)$$

Remark : The initial value theorem and final value theorem are useful in obtaining the initial and final values of a function from the limits of the transform functions.

ILLUSTRATIONS

Ex. 1 : *Verify the final value theorem for the following functions :*

(i) $4e^{-3t}$ *(ii)* $1 + e^{-t}(\sin 2t + \cos 2t)$ *(iii)* $t^2 e^{-t}$

Sol. : (i) Let $\quad f(t) = 4e^{-3t} \qquad\qquad \therefore \quad F(s) = \dfrac{4}{s+3}$

Now

$$\lim_{t\to\infty} f(t) = \lim_{t\to\infty}(4e^{-3t}) = 0 \qquad \ldots (i)$$

and

$$\lim_{s\to 0} s\,F(s) = \lim_{s\to 0} s\left(\frac{4}{s+3}\right) = \lim_{s\to 0}\frac{4s}{s+3} = 0 \qquad \ldots (ii)$$

Since results (i) and (ii) are same, final value theorem is verified.

(ii) Let $\quad f(t) = 1 + e^{-t}(\sin 2t + \cos 2t)$

$$\therefore \quad F(s) = \frac{1}{s} + \left\{\frac{2}{s^2+4} + \frac{s}{s^2+4}\right\}_{s\to s+1} \qquad \text{(By first shifting theorem)}$$

$$= \frac{1}{s} + \left\{\frac{2+s}{s^2+4}\right\}_{s\to s+1} = \frac{1}{s} + \left\{\frac{2+(s+1)}{(s+1)^2+4}\right\}$$

$$= \frac{1}{s} + \frac{3+s}{s^2+2s+5}$$

Now

$$\lim_{t\to\infty} f(t) = \lim_{t\to\infty}[1 + e^{-t}(\sin 2t + \cos 2t)] = 1 \qquad \ldots (i)$$

and

$$\lim_{s\to 0} s\,F(s) = \lim_{s\to 0} s\left\{\frac{1}{s} + \frac{3+s}{s^2+2s+5}\right\} = \lim_{s\to 0}\left\{1 + \frac{3s+s^2}{s^2+2s+5}\right\}$$

$$= 1 + 0 = 1 \qquad \ldots (ii)$$

Since results (i) and (ii) have same final value, final value theorem is verified.

(iii) Let $\qquad f(t) = t^2 e^{-t} \qquad \therefore \quad F(s) = \left\{\dfrac{2}{s^3}\right\}_{s \to s+1} = \dfrac{2}{(s+1)^3}$

Now $\qquad \lim\limits_{t \to \infty} f(t) = \lim\limits_{t \to \infty} t^2 e^{-t} = \lim\limits_{t \to \infty} \dfrac{t^2}{e^t} \qquad \left(\text{Form } \dfrac{\infty}{\infty}\right)$

$$= \lim\limits_{t \to \infty} \dfrac{2t}{e^t} = \lim\limits_{t \to \infty} \dfrac{2}{e^t} \qquad \text{(Applying L'Hospital's Rule)}$$

$$= 0 \qquad \qquad \dots \text{(i)}$$

and $\qquad \lim\limits_{s \to 0} s\, F(s) = \lim\limits_{s \to 0} s \left[\dfrac{2}{(s+1)^3}\right] = \lim\limits_{s \to 0} \left[\dfrac{2s}{(s+1)^3}\right] = 0 \qquad \dots \text{(ii)}$

Since results (i) and (ii) are same, final value theorem is verified.

In the following table, we have listed useful Laplace transform theorems for ready reference.

Table 4.2 : Table of Laplace Transform Theorems

	If $L[f(t)] = F(s)$, then
(A)	$L[e^{-at} f(t)] = F(s+a)$
(B)	$L\left[F(t) = \begin{cases} f(t-a) & t > a \\ 0 & t < a \end{cases}\right] = e^{-as} F(s)$
(C)	$L[f(at)] = \dfrac{1}{a} F\left(\dfrac{s}{a}\right)$
(D)	$L[f'(t)] = s\, F(s) - f(0)$
(E)	$L\left[\displaystyle\int_0^t f(u)\, du\right] = \dfrac{1}{s} F(s)$
(F)	$L[t\, f(t)] = (-1) \dfrac{d}{ds} F(s)$
(G)	$L\left[\dfrac{f(t)}{t}\right] = \displaystyle\int_s^\infty F(s)\, ds$
(H)	$L\left[\displaystyle\int_0^t f(u)\, g(t-u)\, du\right] = F(s)\, G(s)$
(I)	$\lim\limits_{t \to 0} f(t) = \lim\limits_{s \to \infty} s\, F(s)$
(J)	$\lim\limits_{t \to \infty} f(t) = \lim\limits_{s \to 0} s\, F(s)$

ILLUSTRATIONS ON LAPLACE TRANSFORM THEOREMS

Ex. 1 : *Find the Laplace transform of each of the following functions :*

(i) $e^{-3t}\, t^{-1/2}$ (ii) $e^{-2t}\,(4\cos 3t - 2\sinh t)$ (iii) $e^{-at}\,\dfrac{t^{n-1}}{(n-1)!}$

Sol. : (i) We have

$$L\,[t^{-1/2}] = \frac{\overline{|1/2}}{s^{1/2}} = \sqrt{\frac{\pi}{s}} \qquad \text{(From Table 4.1)}$$

$$\therefore \qquad L\,[e^{-3t}\, t^{-1/2}] = \left\{\sqrt{\frac{\pi}{s}}\right\}_{s\,\to\,s+3} \sqrt{\frac{\pi}{s+3}}$$

$$\text{(By the First Shifting Theorem)}$$

(ii) We have

$$L\,[4\cos 3t - 2\sinh t] = 4L\,[\cos 3t] - 2L\,[\sinh t]$$

$$= \frac{4s}{s^2 - 3^2} - \frac{2}{s^2 - 1} \qquad \text{(From Table 4.1)}$$

$$\therefore\ L\,[e^{-2t}\,(4\cos 3t - 2\sinh t)] = \left\{\frac{4s}{s^2 - 3^2} - \frac{2}{s^2 - 1}\right\}_{s\,\to\,s+2}$$

$$\text{(By the First Shifting Theorem)}$$

$$= \frac{4\,(s+2)}{(s+2)^2 - 9} - \frac{2}{(s+2)^2 - 1}$$

$$= \frac{4\,(s+2)}{s^2 + 4s - 5} - \frac{2}{s^2 + 4s + 3}$$

(iii) We have

$$L\left[\frac{t^{n-1}}{(n-1)!}\right] = \frac{1}{(n-1)!}\,L\,[t^{n-1}] = \frac{1}{(n-1)!}\,\frac{\overline{|n}}{s^n} \qquad \text{(From Table 4.1)}$$

$$= \frac{1}{(n-1)!}\,\frac{(n-1)!}{s^n} = \frac{1}{s^n}$$

$$\therefore \qquad L\left[e^{-at}\,\frac{t^{n-1}}{(n-1)!}\right] = \left\{\frac{1}{s^n}\right\}_{s\,\to\,s+a} = \frac{1}{(s+a)^n}$$

$$\text{(By the First Shifting Theorem)}$$

Ex. 2 : *Find* $L\,[F(t)]$ *if* $F(t) = \begin{cases} (t-1)^2 \,, & t > 1 \\ 0 \,, & 0 < t < 1 \end{cases}$.

Sol. : Here

$$f(t-a) = (t-1)^2 \qquad\qquad \text{where } a = 1$$

$$\therefore \qquad f(t) = t^2 \quad \text{and} \quad F(s) = \frac{2}{s^3}$$

Hence by the second shifting theorem [result (10)], with $a = 1$, we have

$$L\,[F(t)] = e^{-as}\,F(s) = e^{-s}\left(\frac{2}{s^3}\right)$$

Ex. 3 : *If $L [f(t)] = \dfrac{1}{s} e^{-1/s}$, find $L [e^{-t} f(3t)]$.*

Sol. : We have given that

$$L [f(t)] = \frac{1}{s} e^{-1/s}$$

By change of scale theorem [result (11)], with $a = 3$, we have

$$L [f(3t)] = \frac{1}{3} \left(\frac{1}{s/3} e^{-3/s} \right) = \frac{1}{s} e^{-3/s}$$

Hence, by the first shifting theorem, we get

$$L [e^{-t} f(3t)] = \left\{ \frac{1}{s} e^{-3/s} \right\}_{s \to s + 1} = \frac{e^{-3/(s + 1)}}{(s + 1)}$$

Ex. 4 : Given $\quad L \left[2 \sqrt{\dfrac{t}{\pi}} \right] = \dfrac{1}{s^{3/2}}$, show that $\quad L \left[\dfrac{1}{\sqrt{\pi t}} \right] = \dfrac{1}{\sqrt{s}}$

Sol. : Let $\qquad f(t) = 2 \sqrt{\dfrac{t}{\pi}} \implies f(0) = 0$

$\therefore \qquad f'(t) = \dfrac{2}{\sqrt{\pi}} \cdot \dfrac{1}{2} t^{-1/2} = \dfrac{1}{\sqrt{\pi t}}$

$\therefore \qquad L [f'(t)] = L \left[\dfrac{1}{\sqrt{\pi t}} \right] = s F(s) - f(0) \qquad\qquad$ [By result (12)]

$$= s \, \frac{1}{s^{3/2}} - 0 \qquad\qquad \left\{ \begin{array}{l} \because \text{ Given } F(s) = \dfrac{1}{s^{3/2}} \\[2mm] \text{ and } f(0) = 0 \end{array} \right.$$

$$= \frac{1}{\sqrt{s}}$$

Ex. 5 : *Given that $4 f''(t) + f(t) = 0$, $f(0) = 0$ and $f'(0) = 2$, show that $L [f(t)] = \dfrac{8}{4s^2 + 1}$.*

Sol. : Taking Laplace transforms of both sides, we get

$$4 L [f''(t)] + L [f(t)] = L [0]$$

$\therefore \quad 4 \{s^2 F(s) - s f(0) - f'(0)\} + F(s) = 0 \qquad\qquad$ [By results (12) and (13)]

$\therefore \quad 4 \{s^2 F(s) - s(0) - (2)\} + F(s) = 0 \qquad\qquad$ [as $f(0) = 0$ and $f'(0) = 2$]

$\therefore \qquad (4s^2 + 1) F(s) - 8 = 0$

$\therefore \qquad F(s) = L [f(t)] = \dfrac{8}{4s^2 + 1}$

Ex. 6 : *Use theorem on Derivative, to derive the following Laplace transforms :*

$$(i)\ L[e^{at}] = \frac{1}{s-a} \quad (ii)\ L[\sin at] = \frac{a}{(s^2 + a^2)}$$

Sol. : (i) Let $f(t) = e^{at}$. Then $f'(t) = a\,e^{at}$, $f(0) = 1$

Now $\qquad\qquad L[f'(t)] = s\,L[e^{at}] - f(0) \qquad\qquad$ [By result (12)]

$\therefore \qquad\qquad L[ae^{at}] = s\,L[e^{at}] - 1$

or $\qquad\qquad a\,L[e^{at}] = s\,L[e^{at}] - 1$

or $\qquad\qquad L[e^{at}] = \dfrac{1}{s-a}$

(ii) Let $f(t) = \sin at$. Then $f'(t) = a\cos at$, $f''(t) = -a^2 \sin at$, $f(0) = 0$, $f'(0) = a$.

Now $\qquad\qquad L[f''(t)] = s^2 L[f(t)] - s\,f(0) - f'(0) \qquad\qquad$ [By result (13)]

$\therefore \qquad\qquad L[-a^2 \sin at] = s^2 L[\sin at] - s(0) - a$

or $\qquad\qquad -a^2 L[\sin at] = s^2 L[\sin at] - a$

or $\qquad\qquad L[\sin at] = \dfrac{a}{s^2 + a^2}$

Ex. 7 : Find $\ L\left[\displaystyle\int_0^t \sin 2u\, du\right].$

Sol. : We have $\quad L[\sin 2t] = \dfrac{2}{s^2 + 4}$

$\therefore \qquad\qquad \displaystyle\int_0^t \sin 2u\, du = \dfrac{1}{s}\left(\dfrac{2}{s^2 + 4}\right) \qquad\qquad$ [By result (16)]

Ex. 8 : *Find the Laplace transforms of the following functions :*

$$(i)\ t\cos at \quad (ii)\ \frac{t\,\sinh at}{2a} \quad (iii)\ t\,\sin^3 t \qquad\qquad \textbf{(Dec. 2008)}$$

Sol. : (i) We have

$$L[\cos at] = \frac{s}{s^2 + a^2}$$

$\therefore \qquad L[t\cos at] = (-1)\dfrac{d}{ds}\left(\dfrac{s}{s^2 + a^2}\right) = -\left\{\dfrac{(s^2 + a^2)(1) - s\,(2s)}{(s^2 + a^2)^2}\right\}$ [By result (18)]

$$= \frac{s^2 - a^2}{(s^2 + a^2)^2}$$

(ii) We have

$$L\left[\frac{\sinh at}{2a}\right] = \frac{1}{2a}\,L[\sinh at] = \frac{1}{2}\,\frac{1}{s^2 - a^2}$$

$$\therefore \quad L\left[\frac{t\,\sinh at}{2a}\right] = (-1)\,\frac{d}{ds}\left\{\frac{1}{2}\,\frac{1}{(s^2-a^2)}\right\} = (-1)\,\frac{1}{2}\,\frac{-2s}{(s^2-a^2)^2} \quad \text{[By result (18)]}$$

$$= \frac{s}{(s^2-a^2)^2}$$

(iii) We have $\quad L\left[\sin^3 t\right] = L\left[\frac{3}{4}\,\sin t - \frac{1}{4}\,\sin 3t\right] \quad\quad \{\because\ \sin 3t = 3\,\sin t - 4\,\sin^3 t\}$

$$= \frac{3}{4}\,L\left[\sin t\right] - \frac{1}{4}\,L\left[\sin 3t\right] = \frac{3}{4}\left(\frac{1}{s^2+1} - \frac{1}{s^2+9}\right)$$

$$\therefore \quad L\left[t\,\sin^3 t\right] = (-1)\,\frac{d}{ds}\left[\frac{3}{4}\left(\frac{1}{s^2+1} - \frac{1}{s^2+9}\right)\right] = -\frac{3}{4}\left[\frac{(-2s)}{(s^2+1)^2} - \frac{(-2s)}{(s^2+9)^2}\right]$$

$$\text{[By result (18)]}$$

$$= \frac{3s}{2}\left[\frac{1}{(s^2+1)^2} - \frac{1}{(s^2+9)^2}\right]$$

Ex. 9 : *Find the Laplace transforms of the following functions :*

(i) $\dfrac{1-\cos t}{t}$ **(Dec. 2011)**   (ii) $\dfrac{1-\cos t}{t^2}$ (iii) $\dfrac{\sin^2 t}{t^2}$ **(May 2007, Dec. 2008)**

Sol. : (i) We have

$$L\left[1-\cos t\right] = \frac{1}{s} - \frac{s}{s^2+1}$$

$$\therefore \quad L\left[\frac{1-\cos t}{t}\right] = \int_{s}^{\infty}\left(\frac{1}{s} - \frac{s}{s^2+1}\right)ds \quad\quad\quad \text{[By result (21)]}$$

$$= \left[\log s - \frac{1}{2}\log(s^2+1)\right]_{s}^{\infty} = \frac{1}{2}\left[\log s^2 - \log(s^2+1)\right]_{s}^{\infty}$$

$$= \frac{1}{2}\left[\log\frac{s^2}{s^2+1}\right]_{s}^{\infty} = \frac{1}{2}\left[\log\frac{1}{1+1/s^2}\right]_{s}^{\infty}$$

$$= \frac{1}{2}\left[0 - \log\frac{s^2}{s^2+1}\right] \quad\quad\quad\quad (\because\ \log 1 = 0)$$

$$= \frac{1}{2}\,\log\frac{s^2+1}{s^2} \quad \text{or} \quad \log\frac{\sqrt{s^2+1}}{s}$$

$$\left[\text{Notice that } L\left[\frac{\cos t}{t}\right] \text{ does not exist since } \int_{s}^{\infty}\frac{s}{s^2+a^2}\,ds \text{ does not exist.}\right]$$

(ii) $\quad L\left[\dfrac{1-\cos t}{t^2}\right] = L\left[\dfrac{1}{t}\left(\dfrac{1-\cos t}{t}\right)\right] \quad\quad\quad\quad \text{[use result of (i) above]}$

$$= \int_{s}^{\infty}\frac{1}{2}\,\log\frac{s^2+1}{s^2}\,ds = \frac{1}{2}\int_{s}^{\infty}\left(\log\frac{s^2+1}{s^2}\right)\cdot 1\,ds$$

Integrating by parts, we have

$$= \frac{1}{2} \left[\left(\log \frac{s^2+1}{s^2} \right) \cdot s - \int \left\{ \frac{s^2}{s^2+1} \, \frac{s^2(2s)-(s^2+1)(2s)}{s^4} \right\} \cdot s \, ds \right]_0^{\infty}$$

$$= \frac{1}{2} \left[s \log \frac{s^2+1}{s^2} - \int \left\{ \frac{s^2}{s^2+1} \left(\frac{-2}{s^3} \right) \right\} s \, ds \right]_s^{\infty}$$

$$= \frac{1}{2} \left[s \log \frac{s^2+1}{s^2} + 2 \int \frac{1}{s^2+1} \, ds \right]_s^{\infty}$$

$$= \frac{1}{2} \left[s \log \frac{s^2+1}{s^2} + 2 \tan^{-1} s \right]_s^{\infty}$$

$$= \frac{1}{2} \left[\left\{ 0 + 2 \left(\frac{\pi}{2} \right) \right\} - \left\{ s \log \frac{s^2+1}{s^2} + 2 \tan^{-1} s \right\} \right]$$

$$\left\{ \because \lim_{s \to \infty} s \log \left(1 + \frac{1}{s^2} \right) = \lim_{s \to \infty} s \left(\frac{1}{s^2} - \frac{1}{2s^4} + \frac{1}{3s^6} \cdots \right) = 0 \right\}$$

$$= \frac{1}{2} \left[\pi - s \log \frac{s^2+1}{s^2} - 2 \tan^{-1} s \right]$$

$$= \frac{1}{2} s \log \frac{s^2}{s^2+1} + \cot^{-1} s \qquad \left(\because \frac{\pi}{2} - \tan^{-1} s = \cot^{-1} s \right)$$

(iii) We have $L[\sin^2 t] = L \left[\frac{1-\cos 2t}{2} \right] = \frac{1}{2} \left(\frac{1}{s} - \frac{s}{s^2+4} \right)$

$$\therefore \qquad L \left[\frac{\sin^2 t}{t} \right] = \frac{1}{2} \int_s^{\infty} \left(\frac{1}{s} - \frac{s}{s^2+4} \right) ds = \frac{1}{4} \log \frac{s^2+4}{s^2}$$

$$\therefore \qquad L \left[\frac{\sin^2 t}{t^2} \right] = L \left[\frac{1}{t} \left(\frac{\sin^2 t}{t} \right) \right] = \frac{1}{4} \int_s^{\infty} \left(\log \frac{s^2+4}{s^2} \right) \cdot (1) \, ds$$

$$= \frac{1}{4} \left[\left(\log \frac{s^2+4}{s^2} \right)(s) - \int \left(\frac{s^2}{s^2+4} \right) \left(-\frac{8}{s^3} \right)(s) \, ds \right]_s^{\infty}$$

$$= \frac{1}{4} \left[s \log \left(1 + \frac{4}{s^2} \right) + 8 \int \frac{1}{s^2+4} \, ds \right]_s^{\infty}$$

$$= \frac{1}{4} \left[s \log \left(1 + \frac{4}{s^2} \right) + \frac{8}{2} \tan^{-1} \frac{s}{2} \right]_{s}^{\infty}$$

$$= \frac{1}{4} \left[\left(0 + 4 \left(\frac{\pi}{2} \right) \right) - \left\{ s \log \left(\frac{s^2 + 4}{s^2} \right) + 4 \tan^{-1} \frac{s}{2} \right\} \right]$$

$$= \frac{1}{4} \left[4 \left(\frac{\pi}{2} - \tan^{-1} \frac{s}{2} \right) - s \log \left(\frac{s^2 + 4}{s^2} \right) \right]$$

$$= \frac{1}{4} \ s \log \frac{s^2}{s^2 + 4} + \cot^{-1} \frac{s}{2}$$

Ex. 10 : *Obtain the Laplace transform of each of the following functions :*

(i) $t \, e^{3t} \sin 2t$ **(Dec. 11, May 14)**

(ii) $t \, e^{-2t} \, (2 \cosh 3t - 4 \sinh 2t)$ **(Nov. 16)** (iii) $\dfrac{d}{dt} \left(\dfrac{\sin t}{t} \right)$

(iv) $\displaystyle\int_0^t \frac{\sin t}{t} \, dt$ **(May 05, 15)**   (v) $\displaystyle\int_0^t \frac{1 - e^{-x}}{x} \, dx$ **(May 09, Dec. 11)**

(vi) $\displaystyle\int_0^t u \cosh u \, du$

Sol. : (i) We have

$$L \, [\sin 2t] \ = \ \frac{2}{s^2 + 4} \qquad\qquad \text{[From Table 4.1]}$$

$$\therefore \qquad L \, [t \sin 2t] \ = \ (-1) \frac{d}{ds} \left(\frac{2}{s^2 + 4} \right) = \frac{4s}{(s^2 + 4)^2} \qquad \text{[By result (18)]}$$

$$\therefore \qquad L \, [e^{3t} t \sin 2t] \ = \ \left\{ \frac{4s}{(s^2 + 4)^2} \right\}_{s \to s - 3} \qquad \text{[By First Shifting Theorem, result (9)]}$$

$$= \ \frac{4 \, (s - 3)}{[(s - 3)^2 + 4]^2} \ = \ \frac{4 \, (s - 3)}{(s^2 - 6s + 13)^2}$$

(ii)   We have

$$L \, [2 \cosh 3t - 4 \sinh 2t] \ = \ \frac{2s}{s^2 - 9} - \frac{8}{s^2 - 4}$$

$$\therefore \quad L \, [t \, (2 \cosh 3t - 4 \sinh 2t)] \ = \ (-1) \frac{d}{ds} \left(\frac{2s}{s^2 - 9} - \frac{8}{s^2 - 4} \right) \qquad \text{[By result (18)]}$$

$$= \ -\left\{ \frac{(s^2 - 9)(2) - (2s)(2s)}{(s^2 - 9)^2} + \frac{16s}{(s^2 - 4)^2} \right\}$$

$$= \ \left\{ \frac{2 \, (s^2 + 9)}{(s^2 - 9)^2} - \frac{16s}{(s^2 - 4)^2} \right\}$$

$$\therefore \quad L\left[e^{-2t}\, t\, (2 \cosh 3t - 4 \sinh 2t)\right] \;=\; \left\{\frac{2\,(s^2+9)}{(s^2-9)^2} - \frac{16s}{(s^2-4)^2}\right\}_{s \to s+2}$$

$$= \left\{\frac{2\,(s+2)^2+18}{[(s+2)^2-9]^2} - \frac{16\,(s+2)}{[(s+2)^2-4]^2}\right\}$$

$$= \frac{2s^2+8s+26}{(s^2+4s-5)^2} - \frac{16\,(s+2)}{(s^2+4s)^2}$$

(iii) We have $\quad L\,[\sin t] \;=\; \dfrac{1}{s^2+1}$

$$\therefore \qquad L\left[\frac{\sin t}{t}\right] = \int_{s}^{\infty} \frac{1}{s^2+1}\ ds \;=\; \big[\tan^{-1} s\big]_{s}^{\infty} \qquad \text{[By result (21)]}$$

$$= \frac{\pi}{2} - \tan^{-1} s \;=\; \cot^{-1} s$$

$$\therefore \qquad L\left[\frac{d}{dt}\left(\frac{\sin t}{t}\right)\right] = s\, L\left[\frac{\sin t}{t}\right] - \lim_{t\to 0}\frac{\sin t}{t} \qquad \text{[By result (12)]}$$

$$= s \cot^{-1} s - 1$$

(iv) We have from result (iii) above

$$L\left[\frac{\sin t}{t}\right] = \cot^{-1} s$$

$$\therefore \qquad L\left[\int_{0}^{t} \frac{\sin t}{t}\, dt\right] = \frac{1}{s}\, \cot^{-1} s \qquad \text{[By result (16)]}$$

(v) We have $\quad L\,[1 - e^{-t}] \;=\; \dfrac{1}{s} - \dfrac{1}{s+1}$

$$\therefore \qquad L\left[\frac{1-e^{-t}}{t}\right] = \int_{s}^{\infty} \left(\frac{1}{s} - \frac{1}{s+1}\right) ds \qquad \text{[By result (21)]}$$

$$= \big[\log s - \log\,(s+1)\big]_{s}^{\infty} \;=\; \left[\log \frac{s}{s+1}\right]_{s}^{\infty}$$

$$= \left[\log \frac{1}{1+1/s} - \log \frac{s}{s+1}\right]_{s}^{\infty} \;=\; -\log \frac{s}{s+1} \;=\; \log \frac{s+1}{s}$$

$$\therefore \qquad L\left[\int_{0}^{t} \frac{1-e^{-x}}{x}\, dx\right] = L\left[\int_{0}^{t} \frac{1-e^{t}}{t}\, dt\right] = \frac{1}{s}\, \log \frac{s+1}{s} \qquad \text{[By result (16)]}$$

(vi) We have　　$L[\cosh t] = \dfrac{s}{s^2 - 1}$

$\therefore$ 　　　　$L[t \cosh t] = (-1)\dfrac{d}{ds}\left(\dfrac{s}{s^2 - 1}\right)$ 　　　　[By result (18)]

$$= (-1)\left\{\dfrac{(s^2 - 1)(1) - s(2s)}{(s^2 - 1)^2}\right\} = \dfrac{s^2 + 1}{(s^2 - 1)^2}$$

$\therefore$ 　　$L\left[\displaystyle\int_0^t u \cosh u \, du\right] = L\left[\displaystyle\int_0^t t \cosh t \, dt\right] = \dfrac{1}{s}\left\{\dfrac{s^2 + 1}{(s^2 - 1)^2}\right\}$ 　　[By result (16)]

Ex. 11 : *Obtain Laplace transforms of*

$$(i)\ t\int_0^t e^{-4t}\sin 3t \ dt \quad (ii)\ e^{-4t}\int_0^t t \sin 3t \, dt \quad (iii)\int_0^t t\, e^{-4t}\sin 3t \, dt$$

$$(iv)\ \cosh t \int_0^t e^t \cosh t \, dt \hspace{3cm} \textbf{(Dec. 07, 08, May 17)}$$

Sol. : (i) We have $L[\sin 3t] = \dfrac{3}{s^2 + 9}$ 　　　　[From Table (4.1)]

$\therefore$ 　　　$L[e^{-4t}\sin 3t] = \left\{\dfrac{3}{s^2 + 9}\right\}_{s \to s + 4}$ 　　　　[By result (9)]

$$= \dfrac{3}{(s + 4)^2 + 9} = \dfrac{3}{s^2 + 8s + 25}$$

$\therefore$ 　　$L\left[\displaystyle\int_0^t e^{-4t}\sin 3t\right] = \dfrac{1}{s}\left(\dfrac{3}{s^2 + 8s + 25}\right)$ 　　　[By result (16)]

$\therefore$ 　$L\left[t\displaystyle\int_0^t e^{-4t}\sin 3t\right] = (-1)\dfrac{d}{ds}\left\{\left(\dfrac{1}{s}\right)\left(\dfrac{3}{s^2 + 8s + 25}\right)\right\}$ 　[By result (18)]

$$= \dfrac{1}{s^2}\dfrac{3}{(s^2 + 8s + 25)} + \dfrac{1}{s}\dfrac{3(2s + 8)}{(s^2 + 8s + 25)^2}$$

$$= \dfrac{3(s^2 + 8s + 25) + 3s(2s + 8)}{s^2(s^2 + 8s + 25)^2}$$

$$= \dfrac{3(3s^2 + 16s + 25)}{s^2(s^2 + 8s + 25)^2}$$

$$\left\{\textbf{Note :}\ L\left[t\int_0^t e^{-4t}\sin 3t \, dt\right] = (-1)\dfrac{d}{ds}\left(\dfrac{1}{s}\{L[\sin 3t]\}_{s \to s + 4}\right)\right\}$$

(ii) We have $L[\sin 3t] = \dfrac{3}{s^2 + 9}$

$\therefore \qquad L[t \sin 3t] = (-1)\dfrac{d}{ds}\left(\dfrac{3}{s^2 + 9}\right) = \dfrac{6s}{(s^2 + 9)^2} \qquad$ [Multiplication by t]

$\therefore \qquad L\left[\displaystyle\int_0^t t \sin 3t\, dt\right] = \dfrac{1}{s}\dfrac{6s}{(s^2 + 9)^2} = \dfrac{6}{(s^2 + 9)^2} \qquad \left[L\displaystyle\int_0^t f(t)\, dt\right]$

$\therefore \qquad L\left[e^{-4t}\displaystyle\int_0^t t \sin 3t\, dt\right] = \left\{\dfrac{6}{(s^2 + 9)^2}\right\}_{s \to s + 4} \qquad$ [First Shifting Theorem]

$\qquad\qquad = \dfrac{6}{[(s + 4)^2 + 9]^2} = \dfrac{6}{(s^2 + 8s + 25)^2}$

(iii) We have $L[\sin 3t] = \dfrac{3}{s^2 + 9}$

$\therefore \qquad L[t \sin 3t] = (-1)\dfrac{d}{ds}\left(\dfrac{3}{s^2 + 9}\right) = \dfrac{6s}{(s^2 + 9)^2} \qquad$ [Multiplication by t]

$\therefore \qquad L[e^{-4t} t \sin 3t] = \left\{\dfrac{6s}{(s^2 + 9)^2}\right\}_{s \to s + 4} \qquad$ [First Shifting Theorem]

$\qquad\qquad = \dfrac{6(s + 4)}{[(s + 4)^2 + 9]^2} = \dfrac{6(s + 4)}{(s^2 + 8s + 25)^2}$

$\therefore \qquad L\left[\displaystyle\int_0^t e^{-4t} t \sin 3t\right] = \dfrac{1}{s}\dfrac{6(s + 4)}{(s^2 + 8s + 25)^2} \qquad \left[L\displaystyle\int_0^t f(t)\, dt\right]$

(iv) Let $f(t) = \displaystyle\int_0^t e^t \cosh t\, dt$

$\therefore \qquad F(s) = L\left[\displaystyle\int_0^t e^t \cosh t\, dt\right] = \dfrac{1}{s} L[e^t \cosh t]$

$\qquad\qquad = \dfrac{1}{s}\{L[\cosh t]\}_{s \to s - 1} = \dfrac{1}{s}\left\{\dfrac{s}{s^2 - 1}\right\}_{s \to s - 1}$

$\qquad\qquad = \dfrac{1}{s}\dfrac{s - 1}{[(s - 1)^2 - 1]} = \dfrac{s - 1}{s(s^2 - 2s)}$

$\qquad\qquad = \dfrac{s - 1}{s^2(s - 2)}$

Now $L\left[\cosh t \int_0^t e^t \cosh t\right] = L\left[\dfrac{e^t + e^{-t}}{2} f(t)\right]$ $\left\{\because \ \cosh t = \dfrac{e^t + e^{-t}}{2}\right.$

$$= \frac{1}{2}\ \{L\ [e^t\ f(t)] + L\ [e^{-t}\ f(t)]\}$$

$$= \frac{1}{2}\ [\{F(s)\}_{s\to s-1} + \{F(s)\}_{s\to s+1}]$$

$$= \frac{1}{2}\ \left\{\frac{(s-1)-1}{(s-1)^2\,[(s-1)-2]} + \frac{(s+1)-1}{(s+1)^2\,[(s+1)-2]}\right\}$$

$$= \frac{1}{2}\ \left\{\frac{s-2}{(s-1)^2\,(s-3)} + \frac{s}{(s+1)^2\,(s-1)}\right\}$$

Ex. 12 : *Obtain Laplace transforms of*

(i) $\dfrac{e^{-4t}\ sin\ 3t}{t}$ *(ii)* $\displaystyle\int_0^t \dfrac{e^{-4t}\ sin\ 3t}{t}\ dt$ *(iii)* $e^{-4t}\displaystyle\int_0^t \dfrac{sin\ 3t}{t}\ dt$

Sol. : (i) We have $L\ [\sin 3t] = \dfrac{3}{s^2 + 9}$

$\therefore$ $L\left[\dfrac{\sin 3t}{t}\right] = \displaystyle\int_s^\infty \dfrac{3}{s^2 + 9}\ ds = \left[\tan^{-1}\dfrac{s}{3}\right]_s^\infty$ [By result (21)]

$$= \frac{\pi}{2} - \tan^{-1}\frac{s}{3} = \cot^{-1}\frac{s}{3}$$

$\therefore$ $L\left[e^{-4t}\dfrac{\sin 3t}{t}\right] = \left\{\cot^{-1}\dfrac{s}{3}\right\}_{s\to s+4}$ [By result (9)]

$$= \cot^{-1}\frac{s+4}{3}$$

(ii) We have from result (i) above,

$$L\left[e^{-4t}\frac{\sin 3t}{t}\right] = \cot^{-1}\frac{s+4}{3}$$

$\therefore$ $L\left[\displaystyle\int_0^t e^{-4t}\dfrac{\sin 3t}{t}\ dt\right] = \dfrac{1}{s}\ \cot^{-1}\dfrac{s+4}{3}$ [By result (16)]

(iii) We have from result (i) above,

$$L\left[\frac{\sin 3t}{t}\right] = \cot^{-1}\frac{s}{3}$$

$$\therefore \quad L\left[\int_0^t \frac{\sin 3t}{t}\, dt\right] = \frac{1}{s}\cot^{-1}\frac{s}{3} \qquad \text{[By result (16)]}$$

$$\therefore \quad L\left[e^{-4t}\int_0^t \frac{\sin 3t}{t}\, dt\right] = \left\{\frac{1}{s}\cot^{-1}\frac{s}{3}\right\}_{s\,\to\,s+4} \qquad \text{[By result (9)]}$$

$$= \frac{1}{s+4}\cot^{-1}\frac{s+4}{3}$$

Ex. 13 : *Given $L\,[J_o(t)] = \dfrac{1}{\sqrt{s^2+1}}$, show that*

$$(i)\quad L\,[J_o(at)] = \frac{1}{\sqrt{s^2+a^2}} \qquad (ii)\quad L\,[e^{-at}J_o(at)] = \frac{1}{\sqrt{s^2+2as+2a^2}}$$

$$(iii)\quad L\,[t\,J_o(at)] = \frac{s}{(s^2+a^2)^{3/2}}$$

Sol. : (i) Given that

$$L\,[J_o(t)] = \frac{1}{\sqrt{s^2+1}}$$

$$\therefore \quad L\,[J_o(at)] = \frac{1}{a}\,\frac{1}{\sqrt{(s/a)^2+1}} = \frac{1}{\sqrt{(s^2+a^2)}}$$

[By result (11) of Change of Scale Theorem]

(ii) From result (i) above, we have

$$L\,[J_o(at)] = \frac{1}{\sqrt{s^2+a^2}}$$

$$\therefore \quad L\,[e^{-at}J_o(at)] = \left\{\frac{1}{\sqrt{s^2+a^2}}\right\}_{s\,\to\,s+a} \qquad \text{[By result (9) of First Shifting Theorem]}$$

$$= \frac{1}{\sqrt{(s+a)^2+a^2}} = \frac{1}{\sqrt{s^2+2as+2a^2}}$$

(iii) From result (i) above, we have

$$L\,[J_o(at)] = \frac{1}{\sqrt{s^2+a^2}}$$

$$\therefore \quad L\,[t\,J_o(at)] = (-1)\frac{d}{ds}\frac{1}{\sqrt{s^2+a^2}} \qquad \text{[By result (18)]}$$

$$= (-1)\left(\frac{-1}{2}\right)(s^2+a^2)^{-3/2}\,(2s)$$

$$= \frac{s}{(s^2+a^2)^{3/2}}$$

MISCELLANEOUS EXAMPLES

TYPE 1 : EVALUATION OF INTEGRALS

Laplace transformation is often useful in evaluating various integrals. This is illustrated in the following examples :

Ex. 14 : *Evaluate each of the following integrals :*

(i) $\displaystyle\int_0^\infty t\, e^{-3t} \sin t\, dt$ **(Dec. 2011)** *(ii)* $\displaystyle\int_0^\infty t^2\, e^{-t} \sin t\, dt$ *(iii)* $\displaystyle\int_0^\infty t^3\, e^{-t} \sin t\, dt$

(iv) $\displaystyle\int_0^\infty \frac{e^{-at} - e^{-bt}}{t}\, dt$ **(Dec. 2009, Nov. 2015)** *(v)* $\displaystyle\int_0^\infty \frac{\cos 6t - \cos 4t}{t}\, dt$

(vi) $\displaystyle\int_0^\infty e^{-2t}\, \frac{\sinh t}{t}\, dt$ *(vii)* $\displaystyle\int_0^\infty e^{-t}\, \frac{\sin t}{t}\, dt$ *(viii)* $\displaystyle\int_0^\infty e^{-2t} \sin^3 t\, dt$ **(Dec. 2005)**

Sol. : (i) We first obtain Laplace transform of $t \sin t$ using properties or theorems already proved.

$$L\,[t \sin t] \;=\; (-1)\frac{d}{ds}\, L\,[\sin t] \qquad\qquad \text{[By result (18)]}$$

$$=\; (-1)\frac{d}{ds}\, \frac{1}{s^2 + 1} \;=\; (-1)\frac{(-1)}{(s^2 + 1)^2}\,(2s)$$

$$=\; \frac{2s}{(s^2 + 1)^2}$$

$\therefore$ By definition of Laplace transform, we have

$$\int_0^\infty e^{-st}\, t \sin t\, dt \;=\; \frac{2s}{(s^2 + 1)^2}$$

Putting $s = 3$, we get

$$\int_0^\infty e^{-3t}\, t \sin t\, dt \;=\; \frac{2\,(3)}{(9 + 1)^2} \;=\; \frac{6}{100} \;=\; \frac{3}{50}$$

(ii) We have

$$L\,[t^2 \sin t] \;=\; L\,[t\,(t \sin t)]$$

$$=\; (-1)\frac{d}{ds}\, \frac{2s}{(s^2 + 1)^2} \;=\; (-1)\left[\frac{(s^2 + 1)^2\,(2) - (2s)\,2\,(s^2 + 1)\,(2s)}{(s^2 + 1)^4}\right]$$

$$=\; -\left[\frac{2 - 6s^2}{(s^2 + 1)^3}\right]$$

$\therefore$ By definition of Laplace transform, we have

$$\int_0^\infty e^{-st}\, t^2 \sin t\, dt = -\left[\frac{2 - 6s^2}{(s^2 + 1)^3}\right]$$

Putting $s = 1$, we get

$$\int_0^\infty e^{-t}\, t^2 \sin t\, dt = -\left[\frac{2 - 6\,(1)}{(1 + 1)^3}\right] = \frac{1}{2}$$

(iii) We have $L\,[t^3 \sin t] = L\,[t\,(t^2 \sin t)]$

$$= (-1)\frac{d}{ds}\left[-\left\{\frac{2 - 6s^2}{(s^2 + 1)^3}\right\}\right] \qquad \text{[By result (ii) above]}$$

$$= \left[\frac{(s^2 + 1)^3\,(-12s) - (2 - 6s^2)\,3\,(s^2 + 1)^2\,(2s)}{(s^2 + 1)^6}\right]$$

$$= \left[\frac{-12s\,(s^2 + 1) - 12s\,(1 - 3s^2)}{(s^2 + 1)^4}\right] = \frac{24s\,(s^2 - 1)}{(s^2 + 1)^4}$$

$\therefore$ By definition of Laplace transform, we have

$$\int_0^\infty e^{-st}\, t^3 \sin t\, dt = \frac{24s\,(s^2 - 1)}{(s^2 + 1)^4}$$

Putting $s = 1$, we get

$$\int_0^\infty e^{-t}\, t^3 \sin t\, dt = \frac{24\,(1)\,(1 - 1)}{(1 + 1)^4} = 0$$

(iv) We have $L\left[\dfrac{e^{-at} - e^{-bt}}{t}\right] = \displaystyle\int_s^\infty L\,[e^{-at} - e^{-bt}]\, ds$ [By result (21)]

$$= \int_s^\infty \left(\frac{1}{s + a} - \frac{1}{s + b}\right) ds = \left[\log\frac{s + a}{s + b}\right]_s^\infty$$

$$= 0 - \log\frac{s + a}{s + b} = \log\frac{s + b}{s + a}$$

$\therefore$ By definition of Laplace transform, we have

$$\int_0^\infty e^{-st}\left(\frac{e^{-at} - e^{-bt}}{t}\right) dt = \log\frac{s + b}{s + a}$$

Putting $s = 0$, we get

$$\int_0^\infty \frac{e^{-at} - e^{-bt}}{t}\, dt = \log\frac{0 + b}{0 + a} = \log\frac{b}{a}$$

(v) We have

$$L\left[\frac{\cos 6t - \cos 4t}{t}\right] = \int_s^\infty L\left[\cos 6t - \cos 4t\right] ds \qquad \text{[By result (21)]}$$

$$= \int_s^\infty \left(\frac{s}{s^2 + 36} - \frac{s}{s^2 + 16}\right) ds = \left[\frac{1}{2}\log(s^2 + 36) - \frac{1}{2}\log(s^2 + 16)\right]_s^\infty$$

$$= \left[\frac{1}{2}\log\frac{s^2 + 36}{s^2 + 16}\right]_s^\infty = \frac{1}{2}\log\frac{s^2 + 16}{s^2 + 36}$$

$\therefore$ By definition of Laplace transform, we have

$$\int_0^\infty e^{-st}\left(\frac{\cos 6t - \cos 4t}{t}\right) dt = \frac{1}{2}\log\frac{s^2 + 16}{s^2 + 36}$$

Putting $s = 0$, we get

$$\int_0^\infty \frac{\cos 6t - \cos 4t}{t}\, dt = \frac{1}{2}\log\frac{16}{36} = \log\frac{2}{3}$$

(vi) We have $L\left[\dfrac{\sinh t}{t}\right] = \displaystyle\int_s^\infty L\left[\sinh t\right] ds \qquad \text{[By result (21)]}$

$$= \int_s^\infty \frac{1}{(s^2 - 1)}\, ds = \frac{1}{2}\int_s^\infty \left(\frac{1}{s-1} - \frac{1}{s+1}\right) ds$$

$$= \frac{1}{2}\left[\log\frac{s-1}{s+1}\right]_s^\infty = \frac{1}{2}\log\frac{s+1}{s-1}$$

$\therefore$ By definition of Laplace transform, we have

$$\int_0^\infty e^{-st}\frac{\sinh t}{t}\, dt = \frac{1}{2}\log\frac{s+1}{s-1}$$

Putting $s = 2$, we get

$$\int_0^\infty e^{-2t}\frac{\sinh t}{t}\, dt = \frac{1}{2}\log\frac{2+1}{2-1} = \frac{1}{2}\log 3$$

(vii) We have $L\left[\dfrac{\sin t}{t}\right] = \displaystyle\int_s^\infty L\left[\sin t\right] ds \qquad \text{[By result (21)]}$

$$= \int_s^\infty \frac{1}{s^2 + 1}\, ds = \left[\tan^{-1} s\right]_s^\infty = \frac{\pi}{2} - \tan^{-1} s$$

$\therefore$ By definition of Laplace transform, we have

$$\int_0^\infty e^{-st} \frac{\sin t}{t}\, dt \;=\; \frac{\pi}{2} - \tan^{-1} s$$

Putting $s = 1$, we get

$$\int_0^\infty e^{-t} \frac{\sin t}{t} \;=\; \frac{\pi}{2} - \tan^{-1} 1 \;=\; \frac{\pi}{2} - \frac{\pi}{4} \;=\; \frac{\pi}{4}$$

(viii) We have $L[\sin^3 t] = \dfrac{1}{4} L[3\sin t - \sin 3t]$ $\qquad \{\because \sin 3t = 3\sin t - 4\sin^3 t\}$

$$= \frac{1}{4}\left(\frac{3}{s^2+1} - \frac{3}{s^2+9}\right) = \frac{6}{(s^2+1)(s^2+9)}$$

$\therefore$ By definition of Laplace transform, on LHS, we get

$$\int_0^\infty e^{-st} \sin^3 t\, dt \;=\; \frac{6}{(s^2+1)(s^2+9)}\;, \quad \text{and put } s = 2$$

$$\therefore \qquad \int_0^\infty e^{-2t} \sin^3 t\, dt \;=\; \frac{6}{(4+1)(4+9)} = \frac{6}{65}$$

TYPE 2 : LAPLACE TRANSFORM BY EXPANSION (SERIES METHOD)

If $f(t)$ has a power series expansion, its Laplace transform can be obtained by taking the sum of the Laplace transforms of each term in the series.

Ex. 15 : *Find Laplace transform of each of the following :*

(i) $\sin\sqrt{t}$ *(ii)* $\dfrac{\cos\sqrt{t}}{\sqrt{t}}$ **(May 2005, 2009)** *(iii)* $\sin t^2$ *(iv)* $\dfrac{t^{n-1}}{1-e^{-t}}$

Sol. : (i) Using infinite series (expansion), we have

$$\sin\sqrt{t} \;=\; \sqrt{t} - \frac{(\sqrt{t})^3}{3!} + \frac{(\sqrt{t})^5}{5!} - \frac{(\sqrt{t})^7}{7!} + \ldots\ldots$$

$$= t^{1/2} - \frac{t^{3/2}}{3!} + \frac{t^{5/2}}{5!} - \frac{t^{7/2}}{7!} + \ldots\ldots$$

Then the Laplace transform is

$$L\left[\sin\sqrt{t}\right] \;=\; L\left[t^{1/2} - \frac{t^{3/2}}{3!} + \frac{t^{5/2}}{5!} - \frac{t^{7/2}}{7!} + \ldots\right]$$

$$= L[t^{1/2}] - \frac{1}{3!}\, L[t^{3/2}] + \frac{1}{5!}\, L[t^{5/2}] - \frac{1}{7!}\, L[t^{7/2}] + \ldots\ldots\ldots$$

$$= \frac{\sqrt{3/2}}{s^{3/2}} - \frac{1}{3!}\frac{\sqrt{5/2}}{s^{5/2}} + \frac{1}{5!}\frac{\sqrt{7/2}}{s^{7/2}} - \frac{1}{7!}\frac{\sqrt{9/2}}{s^{9/2}} + \ldots\ldots$$

$$\left\{ \because L[t^n] = \frac{\sqrt{n+1}}{s^{n+1}} \text{ and using results } \overline{n+1} = n\,\overline{n}\,,\ \overline{1/2} = \sqrt{\pi} \right\}$$

$$= \frac{1/2\sqrt{\pi}}{s^{3/2}} - \frac{1}{3!}\frac{3/2\ \ 1/2\sqrt{\pi}}{s^{5/2}} + \frac{1}{5!}\frac{5/2\ \ 3/2\ \ 1/2\sqrt{\pi}}{s^{7/2}} - \frac{1}{7!}\frac{7/2\ \ 5/2\ \ 3/2\ \ 1/2\sqrt{\pi}}{s^{9/2}} + \ldots$$

$$= \frac{\sqrt{\pi}}{2s^{3/2}}\left\{ 1 - \left(\frac{1}{2^2\,s}\right) + \frac{(1/2^2\,s)^2}{2!} - \frac{(1/2^2\,s)^3}{3!} + \ldots \right\}$$

$$= \frac{\sqrt{\pi}}{2s^{3/2}}\,e^{-(1/2^2 s)} = \frac{\sqrt{\pi}}{2s^{3/2}}\,e^{-1/4s}$$

(ii) We have

$$\cos\sqrt{t} = 1 - \frac{(\sqrt{t})^2}{2!} + \frac{(\sqrt{t})^4}{4!} - \frac{(\sqrt{t})^6}{6!} + \ldots\ldots$$

$$= 1 - \frac{t}{2!} + \frac{t^2}{4!} - \frac{t^3}{6!} + \ldots\ldots$$

$$\therefore\qquad \frac{\cos\sqrt{t}}{\sqrt{t}} = t^{-1/2} - \frac{t^{1/2}}{2!} + \frac{t^{3/2}}{4!} - \frac{t^{5/2}}{6!} + \ldots\ldots$$

$$\therefore\quad L\left[\frac{\cos\sqrt{t}}{\sqrt{t}}\right] = L[t^{-1/2}] - \frac{1}{2!}L[t^{1/2}] + \frac{1}{4!}L[t^{3/2}] - \frac{1}{6!}L[t^{5/2}] + \ldots\ldots$$

$$= \frac{\sqrt{1/2}}{s^{1/2}} - \frac{1}{2!}\frac{\sqrt{3/2}}{s^{3/2}} + \frac{1}{4!}\frac{\sqrt{5/2}}{s^{5/2}} - \frac{1}{6!}\frac{\sqrt{7/2}}{s^{7/2}} + \ldots\quad \left\{ \because L[t^n] = \frac{\sqrt{n+1}}{s^{n+1}} \right.$$

$$= \frac{\sqrt{\pi}}{s^{1/2}} - \frac{1}{2!}\frac{1/2\sqrt{\pi}}{s^{3/2}} + \frac{1}{4!}\frac{3/2\cdot 1/2\sqrt{\pi}}{s^{5/2}} - \frac{1}{6!}\frac{5/2\cdot 3/2\cdot 1/2\sqrt{\pi}}{s^{7/2}} + \ldots$$

$$= \frac{\sqrt{\pi}}{s^{1/2}}\left\{ 1 - \frac{1}{(4s)} + \frac{1}{2!}\frac{1}{(4s)^2} - \frac{1}{3!}\frac{1}{(4s)^3} + \ldots \right\}$$

$$= \sqrt{\frac{\pi}{s}}\,e^{-1/4s}$$

Another Method :

Let $\qquad f(t) = \sin\sqrt{t}$.   Then $f'(t) = \dfrac{\cos\sqrt{t}}{2\sqrt{t}}$, $f(0) = 0.$

And $\qquad L[f'(t)] = s\,L[f(t)] - f(0)$ $\qquad\qquad\qquad$ [By result (12)]

$$\therefore \quad \frac{1}{2} L\left[\frac{\cos \sqrt{t}}{\sqrt{t}}\right] = s \left\{\frac{\sqrt{\pi}}{2\, s^{3/2}}\, e^{-1/4s}\right\} - 0 \qquad \text{[By result (i) above]}$$

$$\therefore \quad L\left[\frac{\cos \sqrt{t}}{\sqrt{t}}\right] = \sqrt{\frac{\pi}{s}}\; e^{-1/4s}$$

(iii) We have
$$\sin t^2 = t^2 - \frac{(t^2)^3}{3!} + \frac{(t^2)^5}{5!} - \frac{(t^2)^7}{7!} + \dots$$

$$= t^2 - \frac{t^6}{3!} + \frac{t^{10}}{5!} - \frac{t^{14}}{7!} + \dots\dots = \sum_{n=1}^{\infty} (-1)^{n-1} \frac{(t^2)^{2n-1}}{(2n-1)!}$$

$$\therefore \quad L[\sin t^2] = L\left[\sum_{n=1}^{\infty} (-1)^{n-1} \frac{t^{4n-2}}{(2n-1)!}\right] = \sum_{n=1}^{\infty} \frac{(-1)^{n-1}}{(2n-1)!}\, L\,[t^{4n-2}]$$

$$= \sum_{n=1}^{\infty} \frac{(-1)^{n-1}}{(2n-1)!}\, \frac{(4n-2)!}{s^{4n-1}} \qquad \left\{\because L\,[t^n] = \frac{\overline{n+1}}{s^{n+1}} = \frac{n!}{s^{n+1}}\right\}$$

(iv) We have
$$\frac{t^{n-1}}{1-e^{-t}} = t^{n-1}(1-e^{-t})^{-1}$$

$$= t^{n-1}(1 + e^{-t} + e^{-2t} + e^{-3t} + \dots) \qquad \left\{\begin{array}{l} \because (1-z)^{-1} \\ = 1 + z + z^2 + z^3 + \dots\end{array}\right\}$$

$$= \sum_{r=0}^{\infty} t^{n-1}\, e^{-rt}$$

$$\therefore \quad L\left[\frac{t^{n-1}}{1-e^{-t}}\right] = L\left[\sum_{r=0}^{\infty} t^{n-1}\, e^{-rt}\right]$$

$$= \sum_{r=0}^{\infty} L\,[e^{-rt}\, t^{n-1}] = \sum_{r=0}^{\infty} \{L\,[t^{n-1}]\}_{s\,\to\,s+r} \;\text{ (By First Shifting Theorem)}$$

$$= \sum_{r=0}^{\infty} \left\{\frac{\overline{n}}{s^n}\right\}_{s\,\to\,s+r} = \overline{n}\, \sum_{r=0}^{\infty} \frac{1}{(s+r)^n}$$

$$= \overline{n}\, \left\{\frac{1}{s^n} + \frac{1}{(s+1)^n} + \frac{1}{(s+2)^n} + \dots\dots\right\}$$

EXERCISE 4.2

1. Find the Laplace transform of each of the following functions :

   (i) $t^3 e^{-3t}$ (ii) $e^{at} (2 \cos bt - 3 \sin bt)$ (iii) $(1 + t\, e^{-t})^3$ (iv) $e^{-t} \{4t^3 + \cos (4t + 7)\}$

   (v) $2e^t \sin 4t \cos 2t$ (vi) $\sinh \dfrac{t}{2} \sin \dfrac{\sqrt{3}}{2} t$ (vii) $\cos at \sinh at$ (viii) $e^{4t} t^{3/2}$

   (ix) $\dfrac{\cosh at}{\sqrt{t}}$ (x) $e^{-t} \sin^3 t$

     Ans.   (i) $\dfrac{6}{(s + 3)^4}$ (ii) $\dfrac{2s - 2a - 2b}{(s - a)^2 + b^2}$ (iii) $\dfrac{1}{s} + \dfrac{3}{(s + 1)^2} + \dfrac{6}{(s + 2)^3} + \dfrac{6}{(s + 3)^4}$

           (iv) $\dfrac{24}{(s + 1)^4} + \dfrac{(s + 1) \cos 7 - 4 \sin 7}{s^2 + 2s + 17}$ (v) $\dfrac{6}{s^2 - 2s + 37} + \dfrac{2}{s^2 - 2s + 5}$

             (vi) $\dfrac{\sqrt{3}}{2} \dfrac{s}{s^4 + s^2 + 1}$ (vii) $\dfrac{a (s^2 - 2a^2)}{s^4 + 4a^2}$ (viii) $\dfrac{3}{4} \dfrac{\sqrt{\pi}}{(s - 4)^{5/2}}$

               (ix) $\dfrac{1}{2} \left[\sqrt{\dfrac{\pi}{s - a}} + \sqrt{\dfrac{\pi}{s + a}} \right]$ (x) $\left[\dfrac{6}{(s^2 + 2s + 2)(s^2 + 2s + 10)} \right]$

2. Find $L\,[F(t)]$ if (i) $F(t) = \begin{cases} \cos (t - \alpha) & t > \alpha \\ 0 & t < \alpha \end{cases}$

   (ii) $F(t) = \begin{cases} 5 \sin 3\,(t - \pi/4) & t > \pi/4 \\ 0 & t < \pi/4 \end{cases}$

                     Ans.   (i) $e^{-\alpha s} \dfrac{s}{s^2 + 1}$ (ii) $e^{-\pi s/4} \dfrac{15}{s^2 + 9}$

3. Verify change of scale theorem for $L\,[e^{2t} \cos 2t]$.   [**Hint :** Consider $f(t) = e^t \cos t$]

4. If $L\,[f(t)] = \dfrac{s^2 - s + 1}{(2s + 1)^2 (s - 1)}$, find $L\,[f(2t)]$.   **Ans.** $\dfrac{s^2 - 2s + 4}{4 (s + 1)^2 (s - 2)}$.

5. Given that $y'' + 2y' - 8y = 0$, $y(0) = 1$, $y'(0) = 8$, show that $L\,[y(t)] = \dfrac{2}{s - 2} - \dfrac{1}{s + 4}$.

6. Find $L\,[f'(t)]$ if (i) $f(t) = e^{-5t} \sin t$,   (ii) $f(t) = \sin^2 t$.

 Ans.   (i) $\dfrac{s}{s^2 + 10s + 26}$ (ii) $\dfrac{2}{(s^2 + 4)}$ $\left[\textbf{Hint :} f'(t) = \sin 2t, \text{ and } L\,[\sin 2t] = \dfrac{2}{s^2 + 4} \right]$

7. If $L\,[f''(t)] = \tan^{-1} \left(\dfrac{1}{s} \right)$, $f(0) = 2$ and $f'(0) = -1$, find $L\,[f(t)]$.

                           Ans. $\dfrac{2s - 1 + \tan^{-1}(1/s)}{s^2}$

8. Verify directly that $L\left[\int_0^t (u^2 - u + e^{-u})\, du\right] = \dfrac{1}{s} L\,[t^2 - t + e^{-t}]$

9. Find the Laplace transform of each of the following functions :

(i)　$t\,(3 \sin 2t - 2 \cos 2t)$　(ii)　$t \cos (4t + 3)$　(iii)　$t^2 \sin 2t$

(iv)　$t^2 \sinh t$　(v)　$(t^2 - 3t + 2) \sin 3t$　(vi)　$t^3 \cos t$.

$$\textbf{Ans.}\quad \text{(i)}\quad \frac{8 + 12s - 2s^2}{(s^2 + 4)^2}\quad \text{(ii)}\quad \frac{s^2 \cos 3 - 8s \sin 3 - 16 \cos 3}{(s^2 + 16)^2}\quad \text{(iii)}\quad \frac{4\,(3s^2 - 4)}{(s^2 + 4)^3}$$

$$\text{(iv)}\quad \frac{6s^2 + 2}{(s^2 - 1)^3}\quad \text{(v)}\quad \frac{6s^4 - 18s^3 + 126s^2 - 162s + 432}{(s^2 + 9)^3}\quad \text{(vi)}\quad \frac{6s^4 - 36s^2 + 6}{(s^2 + 1)^4}$$

10. If $L\left[\dfrac{1 - \cos at}{a^2}\right] = \dfrac{1}{s\,(s^2 + a^2)}$, show that $L\left[\dfrac{t\,(1 - \cos at)}{a^2}\right] = \dfrac{3s^2 + a^2}{s^2\,(s^2 + a^2)^2}$.

11. Find the Laplace transform of each of the following functions :

(i)　$\dfrac{\sinh t}{t}$　(ii)　$\dfrac{e^{2t} - 1}{t}$　(iii)　$\dfrac{1 - e^{-t}}{t}$　(iv)　$\dfrac{1 - \cos 3t}{t}$　(v)　$\dfrac{\cos 2t - \cos 3t}{t}$

$$\textbf{Ans.}\quad \text{(i)}\quad \frac{1}{2} \log \frac{s+1}{s-1}\quad \text{(ii)}\quad \log \frac{s}{s-2}\quad \text{(iii)}\quad \log \frac{s+1}{s}\quad \text{(iv)}\quad \log \frac{\sqrt{s^2 + 9}}{s}\quad \text{(v)}\quad \frac{1}{2} \log \frac{s^2 + 9}{s^2 + 4}$$

12. Obtain the Laplace transform of each of the following functions :　　　**(Dec. 2004)**

(i)　$t\, e^{3t} \cos 2t$　(ii)　$\int_0^t e^u u^3\, du$　(iii)　$\int_0^t e^x \cos x\, dx$　(iv)　$\int_0^t \dfrac{e^t - \cos 2t}{t}\, dt$

(May 12)

$$\textbf{Ans.}\quad \text{(i)}\quad \frac{s^2 - 6s + 5}{(s^2 - 6s + 13)^2}\quad \text{(ii)}\quad \frac{6}{s\,(s-1)^4}\quad \text{(iii)}\quad \frac{s-1}{s\,(s^2 - 2s + 2)}\quad \text{(iv)}\quad \frac{1}{s} \log \frac{\sqrt{s^2 + 4}}{(s-1)}$$

13. Obtain the Laplace transforms of

(i)　$t \int_0^t e^{-3t} \sin 2t\, dt$　(ii)　$e^{-3t} \int_0^t t \sin 2t\, dt$　(iii)　$\int_0^t t\, e^{-3t} \sin 2t\, dt$

(iv)　$\cosh t \int_0^t t \cosh t\, dt$

$$\textbf{Ans.}\quad \text{(i)}\quad \frac{6s^2 + 24s + 26}{s^2\,(s^2 + 6s + 13)^2}\quad \text{(ii)}\quad \frac{4}{(s^2 + 6s + 13)^2}\quad \text{(iii)}\quad \frac{1}{s}\, \frac{2\,(2s + 6)}{(s^2 + 6s + 13)^2}$$

$$\text{(iv)}\quad \frac{1}{2}\left[\frac{s^2 - 2s + 2}{(s-1)\,(s^2 - 2s)^2} + \frac{s^2 + 2s + 2}{(s+1)\,(s^2 + 2s)^2}\right]$$

14. Obtain the Laplace transforms of

(i) $\dfrac{e^{-3t}\,\sin 2t}{t}$ (ii) $\displaystyle\int_0^t \dfrac{e^{-3t}\,\sin 2t}{t}\,dt$ (iii) $e^{-3t}\displaystyle\int_0^t \dfrac{\sin 2t}{t}\,dt$

Ans.   (i) $\cot^{-1}\dfrac{s+3}{2}$ (ii) $\dfrac{1}{s}\cot^{-1}\dfrac{s+3}{2}$ (iii) $\dfrac{1}{s+3}\cot^{-1}\dfrac{s+3}{2}$

15. Find the following convolutions :

(i) $1 * 1$ (ii) $1 * e^t$ (iii) $1 * \cos t$ (iv) $(e^{-t} - e^{-2t}) * e^{-t}$

(v) $t * e^{at}$ (vi) $\cos t * \cos t$ (vii) $\sin t * \sin t$ (viii) $\sin t * \cos t$

Ans.   (i) t (ii) e^t (iii) $\sin t$ (iv) $e^{-2t} + (t-1)\,e^{-t}$ (v) $(e^{at} - 1)/a^2 - t/a$

(vi) $\dfrac{1}{2}\,(t\cos t + \sin t)$ (vii) $\dfrac{1}{2}\,(\sin t - t\cos t)$ (viii) $\dfrac{1}{2}\,t\sin t$.

Hint : Find $f(t) * g(t) = \displaystyle\int_0^t f(u)\,g(t-u)\,du$ or $f(t) * g(t) \displaystyle\int_0^t f(t-u)\,g(u)\,du$.

16. Verify the convolution theorem for the pair of following functions :

(i) $f(t) = t^2,\ \ g(t) = e^{-at}$ (ii) $f(t) = t,\ \ g(t) = \cos t$.

Hint : Show that $L\,[f(t) * g(t)] = F(s)\,G(s)$.

17. Verify the initial value theorem for the functions :

(i) $3e^{-2t}$ (ii) $5 + 2\cos 3t$ (iii) $(2t - 3)^2$.

Hint : Show that (i) $\displaystyle\lim_{t\to 0} f(t) = 3 = \lim_{s\to\infty} s\,F(s)$ (ii) $\displaystyle\lim_{t\to 0} f(t) = 7 = \lim_{s\to\infty} s\,F(s)$

(iii) $\displaystyle\lim_{t\to 0} f(t) = 9 = \lim_{s\to\infty} s\,F(s)$.

18. Verify the final value theorem for the functions :

(i) $3e^{-2t}$ (ii) $2 + 3e^{-2t}\sin 4t$ (iii) $t^3\,e^{-4t}$

Hint : Show that (i) $\displaystyle\lim_{t\to\infty} f(t) = 0 = \lim_{s\to 0} s\,F(s)$

(ii) $\displaystyle\lim_{t\to\infty} f(t) = 2 = \lim_{s\to 0} s\,F(s)$ (iii) $\displaystyle\lim_{t\to\infty} f(t) = 0 = \lim_{s\to 0} s\,F(s)$.

19. Using Laplace transform, evaluate each of the following integrals :

(i) $\displaystyle\int_0^\infty t\, e^{-2t} \cos t\, dt$ (ii) $\displaystyle\int_0^\infty t^2 e^{-3t} \sinh 2t\, dt$ (iii) $\displaystyle\int_0^\infty \frac{e^{-t} - e^{-3t}}{t}\, dt$

(iv) $\displaystyle\int_0^\infty \frac{e^{-3t} - e^{-6t}}{t}\, dt$ (v) $\displaystyle\int_0^\infty \frac{\cos 3t - \cos 2t}{t}\, dt$ (vi) $\displaystyle\int_0^\infty e^{3t}\, \frac{\sinh t}{t}\, dt$

(vii) $\displaystyle\int_0^\infty \frac{1 - \cos t}{t^2}\, dt$ (viii) $\displaystyle\int_0^t \frac{\sin^2 t}{t^2}\, dt$ (ix) $\displaystyle\int_0^\infty e^{-2t}\, \frac{\sinh t \sin t}{t}\, dt$

(x) $\displaystyle\int_0^\infty e^{3t} \cos^3 t\, dt$ (xi) $\displaystyle\int_0^\infty \frac{\sin^3 t}{t}\, dt$ (xii) $\displaystyle\int_0^\infty e^{-t}\, \frac{1 - \cos t}{t}\, dt$

Ans.   (i) $\dfrac{3}{25}$ (ii) $\dfrac{124}{125}$ (iii) $\log 3$ (iv) $\log 2$

(v) $\log \dfrac{2}{3}$ (vi) $-\log \sqrt{2}$

(vii) $\dfrac{\pi}{2}$ (viii) $\dfrac{\pi}{2}$ (ix) $\dfrac{1}{2} \tan^{-1}\!\left(\dfrac{1}{2}\right)$ (x) $\dfrac{4}{15}$ (xi) $\dfrac{\pi}{4}$ (xii) $\dfrac{1}{2}\log 2$

20. Given $L\,[J_0(t)] = \dfrac{1}{\sqrt{s^2 + 1}}$, show that

(i) $\displaystyle\int_0^\infty J_0(t)\, dt = 1$,   (ii) $\displaystyle\int_0^\infty e^{-t} J_0(t)\, dt = \dfrac{\sqrt{2}}{2}$,

(iii) $\displaystyle\int_0^\infty t\, e^{-3t} J_0\,(4t)\, dt = \dfrac{3}{125}$

21. Find $L\,[J_0(t)]$, where $J_0(t)$ is the Bessel function of order zero defined by

$$J_0(t) = 1 - \frac{t^2}{2^2} + \frac{t^4}{2^2\, 4^2} - \frac{t^6}{2^2\, 4^2\, 6^2}\, .$$

Ans. $\dfrac{1}{\sqrt{s^2 + 1}}$

22. Use infinite series to obtain Laplace transform of (i) $\cos\sqrt{t}$ (ii) $\displaystyle\int_0^t \frac{\sin u}{u}\,du$.

$$\textbf{Ans.} \quad \text{(i)} \quad \frac{1}{s}\left[1 - \left(\frac{1}{2s}\right) + \frac{(1/2s)^2}{3} - \frac{(1/2s)^3}{3.5} + \frac{(1/2s)^4}{3.5.7} - \frac{(1/2s)^5}{3.5.7.9} + \cdots\right]$$

$$\text{(ii)} \quad \text{(ii)}\ \frac{1}{s}\ \tan^{-1}\frac{1}{s}\ .$$

$$\textbf{Hint :} \quad \int_0^t \frac{\sin u}{u}\,du \ = \ t - \frac{t^3}{3\cdot 3!} + \frac{t^5}{5.5!} - \frac{t^7}{7\cdot 7!} + \cdots$$

MULTIPLE CHOICE QUESTIONS (MCQ's)

Type : General Theorems of Laplace Transform :

1. If $L[f(t)] = F(s)$ then $L[e^{-at} f(t)]$ is equal to (1)

    (A) $e^{-as} F(s)$ (B) $F(s+a)$

    (C) $\dfrac{1}{s+a} F(s)$ (D) $F(s-a)$

2. If $[f(t)] = F(s)$ and $F(t) = \begin{cases} f(t-a), & t>a \\ 0, & t<a \end{cases}$ then $L[f(t)]$ is equal to (1)

    (A) $e^{-as} F(s)$ (B) $F(s-a)$

    (C) $e^{as} F(s)$ (D) $F(s+a)$

3. If $L[f(t)] = F(s)$ then $L[f(at)]$ is equal to (1)

    (A) $e^{-as} F(s)$ (B) $F(s+a)$

    (C) $\dfrac{1}{a} F(as)$ (D) $\dfrac{1}{a} F\left(\dfrac{s}{a}\right)$

4. If $L[f(t)] = F(s)$ then $L\left[\dfrac{df}{dt}\right]$ is equal to (1)

    (A) $e^{-as} F(s)$ (B) $\dfrac{d}{ds} F(s)$

    (C) $s F(s) - f(0)$ (D) $s F(s) + f(0)$

5. If $L[f(t)] = F(s)$ then $L\left[\dfrac{d^2 f}{dt^2}\right]$ is equal to (1)

    (A) $s^2 F(s) + s f(0) + f'(0)$ (B) $s^2 F(s) - s f(0) - f'(0)$

    (C) $\dfrac{d^2}{ds^2} F(s)$ (D) $s^2 F(s) - s f(0)$

6. If $L[f(t)] = F(s)$ then $L\left[\int_0^t f(u)\, du\right]$ is equal to   (1)

(A) $s\, F(s) - f(0)$ (B) $s\, F(s)$

(C) $\dfrac{1}{s} F(s)$ (D) $\displaystyle\int_s^\infty F(s)\, ds$

7. If $L[f(t)] = F(s)$ then $L[t\, f(t)]$ is equal to   (1)

(A) $s\, F(s) - f(0)$ (B) $\displaystyle\int_s^\infty F(s)\, ds$

(C) $\dfrac{1}{s} F(s)$ (D) $-\dfrac{d}{ds} F(s)$

8. If $L[f(t)] = F(s)$ then $L[t^2\, f(t)]$ is equal to   (1)

(A) $(-1)^2 \dfrac{d^2}{ds^2} F(s)$ (B) $\displaystyle\int_s^\infty \int_s^\infty F(s)\, ds\, ds$

(C) $\dfrac{1}{s^2} F(s)$ (D) $s^2\, F(s) - s\, f(0) - f'(0)$

9. If $L[f(t)] = F(s)$ then $L\left[\dfrac{f(t)}{t}\right]$ is equal to   (1)

(A) $-\dfrac{d}{ds} F(s)$ (B) $\displaystyle\int_s^\infty F(s)\, ds$

(C) $\dfrac{1}{s} F(s)$ (D) $s\, F(s) - f(0)$

10. If $L[f(t)] = F(s)$ then $L\left[\dfrac{f(t)}{t^2}\right]$ is equal to   (1)

(A) $\displaystyle\int_s^\infty \int_s^\infty F(s)\, ds\, ds$ (B) $(-1)^2 \dfrac{d^2}{ds^2} F(s)$

(C) $\dfrac{1}{s^2} F(s)$ (D) $s^2\, F(s) - s\, f(0) - f'(0)$

11. The convolution of two functions $f(t)$ and $g(t)$, $f(t) * g(t)$ is defined as   (1)

(A) $\displaystyle\int_0^\infty f(u)\, g(t - u)\, dt$ (B) $\displaystyle\int_0^u f(u)\, g(u)\, du$

(C) $f(u)\, g(t - u)$ (D) $\displaystyle\int_0^t f(u)\, g(t - u)\, du$

12. The Laplace transform of convolution of two functions f(t) and g(t), L[f(t) * g(t)] is given by   (1)

(A) $\dfrac{F(s)}{G(s)}$ (B) $F(s)\,G(s)$

(C) $F(s) - G(s)$ (D) $F(z) + G(z)$

13. $L[e^{-2t}\sin 5t]$ is equal to   (2)

(A) $\dfrac{5}{(s+2)^2 + 25}$ (B) $\dfrac{5}{(S-2)^2 - 25}$

(C) $\dfrac{1}{(s+2)^2 + 5}$ (D) $\dfrac{5}{(s-2)^2 + 25}$

14. $L[e^{-t}\cos(4t+7)]$ is equal to   (2)

(A) $\sin 7\,\dfrac{s+1}{(s+1)^2 + 16} - \cos 7\,\dfrac{4}{(s+1)^2 + 16}$

(B) $\cos 7\,\dfrac{s+1}{(s+1)^2 + 16} + \sin 7\,\dfrac{4}{(s+1)^2 + 16}$

(C) $\cos 7\,\dfrac{s+1}{(s+1)^2 + 16} - \sin 7\,\dfrac{4}{(s+1)^2 + 16}$

(D) $\sin 7\,\dfrac{s+1}{(s+1)^2 + 16} + \cos 7\,\dfrac{4}{(s+1)^2 + 16}$

15. $L[e^{2t}\,t^3]$ is equal to   (2)

(A) $\dfrac{1}{(s-2)^3}$ (B) $\dfrac{6}{(s-2)^4}$

(C) $\dfrac{3}{(s-2)^5}$ (D) $\dfrac{2}{(s+2)^3}$

16. If $F(t) = \begin{cases} (t-2)^3, & t > 2 \\ 0, & t < 2 \end{cases}$ then L[f(t)] using second shifting theorem is   (2)

(A) $e^{-2s}\dfrac{2}{s^2}$ (B) $e^{-3s}\dfrac{6}{s^5}$

(C) $e^{-s}\dfrac{1}{s^4}$ (D) $e^{-2s}\dfrac{6}{s^4}$

17. If $F(t) = \begin{cases} \cos\left(t - \dfrac{2\pi}{3}\right), & t > \dfrac{2\pi}{3} \\ 0 & , t < \dfrac{2\pi}{3} \end{cases}$ then L[f(t)] using second shifting theorem is (2)

(A) $\dfrac{s}{s^2 + 1}$

(B) $e^{-s}\dfrac{s}{s^2 - 1}$

(C) $e^{-2\pi s}\dfrac{1}{s^2 + 1}$

(D) $e^{-\frac{2\pi}{3}s}\dfrac{s}{s^2 + 1}$

18. If $F(t) = \begin{cases} 5\sin 3\left(t - \dfrac{\pi}{4}\right), & t > \dfrac{\pi}{4} \\ 0 & , t < \dfrac{\pi}{4} \end{cases}$ then L[f(t)] using second shifting theorem is (2)

(A) $e^{-\frac{\pi}{4}s}\dfrac{15}{s^2 + 9}$

(B) $e^{\frac{\pi}{4}s}\dfrac{3}{s^2 + 9}$

(C) $e^{-\frac{\pi}{4}s}\dfrac{15s}{s^2 - 9}$

(D) $e^{\frac{\pi}{4}s}\dfrac{5s}{s^2 + 9}$

19. If $L[f(t)] = \dfrac{s}{s^2 + 10s + 26}$ then L[f(2t)] is equal to (2)

(A) $\dfrac{2s}{s^2 + 20s + 104}$

(B) $\dfrac{1}{s^2 + 20s + 104}$

(C) $\dfrac{s}{s^2 + 20s + 104}$

(D) $\dfrac{2s}{4s^2 + 20s + 26}$

20. If $L[f(t)] = \dfrac{1}{s}e^{-\frac{1}{s}}$ then $L[e^{-t}f(3t)]$ is equal to (2)

(A) $\dfrac{3}{s+1}e^{-\frac{3}{s+1}}$

(B) $\dfrac{1}{s+1}e^{-\frac{3}{s+1}}$

(C) $\dfrac{1}{s-1}e^{-\frac{3}{s-1}}$

(D) $(s+1)\,e^{-\frac{3}{s+1}}$

21. L[t cos 2t] is equal to (2)

(A) $\dfrac{4 + s^2}{(s^2 - 4)^2}$

(B) $\dfrac{s^2 - 4}{(s^2 + 4)^2}$

(C) $\dfrac{s^2 - 4}{(s^2 + 4)}$

(D) $\dfrac{4 - s^2}{(s^2 + 4)}$

22. L[t sin 3t] is equal to $\qquad$ (2)

(A) $\dfrac{6s}{(s^2 + 9)^2}$

(B) $\dfrac{6}{(s^2 + 9)^2}$

(C) $\dfrac{s^2 - 9}{(s^2 + 9)^2}$

(D) $\dfrac{6s}{(s^2 - 9)^2}$

23. $L\left[t\,\dfrac{\sin at}{2a}\right]$ is equal to $\qquad$ (2)

(A) $\dfrac{1}{(s^2 + a^2)^2}$

(B) $\dfrac{a}{(s^2 + a^2)^3}$

(C) $\dfrac{s}{(s^2 + a^2)^2}$

(D) $\dfrac{s}{(s^2 - a^2)^2}$

24. $L\left[\dfrac{\sin 3t}{t}\right]$ is equal to $\qquad$ (2)

(A) $\tan^{-1} s$

(B) $\cot^{-1} s$

(C) $\tan^{-1}\dfrac{s}{3}$

(D) $\cot^{-1}\dfrac{s}{3}$

25. $L\left[\dfrac{1 - \cos 3t}{t}\right]$ is equal to $\qquad$ (2)

(A) $\left[\log\dfrac{\sqrt{s^2 + 9}}{s}\right]_s^\infty$

(B) $\left[\log\dfrac{s}{\sqrt{s^2 + 9}}\right]_s^\infty$

(C) $\left[\log\dfrac{s}{s^2 + 9}\right]_s^\infty$

(D) $\left[\log s\sqrt{s^2 + 9}\right]_s^\infty$

26. If $L\left[\dfrac{\sin t}{t}\right] = \cot^{-1} s$ then $L\left[\dfrac{d}{dt}\left(\dfrac{\sin t}{t}\right)\right]$ is equal to $\qquad$ (2)

(A) $\cot^{-1} s + 1$

(B) $s\,\tan^{-1} s - 1$

(C) $s\,\cot^{-1} s$

(D) $s\,\cot^{-1} s - 1$

27. $L\left[\displaystyle\int_0^t (u^2 - e^{-u})\,du\right]$ is equal to $\qquad$ (2)

(A) $\dfrac{1}{s}\left(\dfrac{2}{s^3} - \dfrac{1}{s + 1}\right)$

(B) $s\left(\dfrac{2}{s^2} - \dfrac{1}{s + 1}\right)$

(C) $\dfrac{1}{s}\left(\dfrac{2}{s^3} + \dfrac{1}{s - 1}\right)$

(D) $\dfrac{1}{s}\left(\dfrac{1}{s^3} - \dfrac{1}{s - 1}\right)$

28. If $L[t \sin 2t] = \dfrac{4s}{(s^2 + 4)^2}$ then $L\left[\dfrac{d}{dt}(t \sin 2t)\right]$ is equal to   (2)

(A) $\dfrac{4s}{(s^2 + 4)^2}$

(B) $\dfrac{4s}{(s^2 + 4)}$

(C) $\dfrac{4s^2}{(s^2 + 4)^2}$

(D) $\dfrac{s}{(s^2 + 4)^2}$

29. If $L[t \sin 2t] = \dfrac{4s}{(s^2 + 4)^2}$ then $L\left[\displaystyle\int_0^t u \sin 2u \, du\right]$ is equal to   (2)

(A) $\dfrac{4s}{(s^2 + 4)^2}$

(B) $\dfrac{4s}{(s^2 + 4)}$

(C) $\dfrac{4}{(s^2 + 4)^2}$

(D) $\dfrac{s}{(s^2 - 4)^2}$

30. If $L\left[\dfrac{\sin 3t}{t}\right] = \cot^{-1}\left(\dfrac{s}{3}\right)$ then $L\left[\displaystyle\int_0^t e^{-4t}\left(\dfrac{\sin 3t}{t}\right) dt\right]$ is equal to   (2)

(A) $\dfrac{1}{s}\cot^{-1}\dfrac{s+4}{3}$

(B) $\cot^{-1}\dfrac{s+4}{3}$

(C) $\dfrac{1}{s}\cot^{-1}\dfrac{s}{3}$

(D) $\dfrac{1}{s}\cot^{-1}\dfrac{s-4}{3}$

31. If $L\left[\dfrac{\sin 3t}{t}\right] = \cot^{-1}\left(\dfrac{s}{3}\right)$ then $L\left[e^{-4t}\displaystyle\int_0^t\left(\dfrac{\sin 3t}{t}\right) dt\right]$ is equal to   (2)

(A) $\dfrac{1}{s}\cot^{-1}\dfrac{s+4}{3}$

(B) $\cot^{-1}\dfrac{s+4}{3}$

(C) $\dfrac{1}{s}\cot^{-1}\dfrac{s-4}{3}$

(D) $\dfrac{1}{s+4}\cot^{-1}\dfrac{s+4}{3}$

32. Laplace transform of convolution $f(t) * g(t)$ for the pair functions $f(t) = t$, $g(t) = e^{at}$ is   (2)

(A) $\dfrac{1}{s(s+a)}$

(B) $\dfrac{1}{s^2(s-a)}$

(C) $\dfrac{2}{s^3(s-a)}$

(D) $\dfrac{1}{s^2(s+a)}$

33. Laplace transform of convolution $f(t) * g(t)$ for the pair functions $f(t) = t$, $g(t) = \cos at$ is   (2)

(A) $\dfrac{1}{s(s+a)}$

(B) $\dfrac{a}{s^2(s^2 + a^2)}$

(C) $\dfrac{s}{s^2(s^2 + a^2)}$

(D) $\dfrac{1}{s^2(s+a)}$

34. $L [e^{-5t} \cos t]$ is equal to (2)

(A) $\dfrac{s}{(s-5)^2 + 1}$

(B) $\dfrac{s+5}{(s+5)^2 + 1}$

(C) $\dfrac{1}{(s+5)^2 + 1}$

(D) $\dfrac{s}{(s+5)^2 - 1}$

35. If $L\left[\dfrac{\sin t}{t}\right] = \dfrac{\pi}{2} - \tan^{-1} s$ then the value of integral $\displaystyle\int_0^\infty \dfrac{\sin t}{t}\, dt$ is equal to (2)

(A) $\dfrac{\pi}{2}$

(B) 0

(C) $\dfrac{\pi}{4}$

(D) 1

36. If $L\left[\dfrac{e^{-at} - e^{-bt}}{t}\right] = \log \dfrac{s+b}{s+a}$ then the value of integral $\displaystyle\int_0^\infty \dfrac{e^{-at} - e^{-bt}}{t}\, dt$ is equal to (2)

(A) $\log \dfrac{a}{b}$

(B) 0

(C) $\dfrac{\log b}{\log a}$

(D) $\log \dfrac{b}{a}$

37. If $L\left[\dfrac{\cos 6t - \cos 4t}{t}\right] = \dfrac{1}{2} \log \dfrac{s^2 + 16}{s^2 + 36}$ then the value of integral $\displaystyle\int_0^\infty \dfrac{\cos 6t - \cos 4t}{t}\, dt$ is

equal to (2)

(A) $\log \dfrac{3}{2}$

(B) 0

(C) $\dfrac{\log 2}{\log 3}$

(D) $\log \dfrac{2}{3}$

38. If $L[\sin^3 t] = \dfrac{6}{(s^2 + 1)(s^2 + 9)}$ then the value of integral $\displaystyle\int_0^\infty e^{-2t} \sin^3 t\, dt$ is equal to (2)

(A) $\dfrac{6}{25}$

(B) $\dfrac{6}{65}$

(C) $\dfrac{3}{50}$

(D) $\dfrac{2}{15}$

39. If $L[t \sin t] = \dfrac{2s}{(s^2 + 1)^2}$ then the value of integral $\displaystyle\int_0^\infty e^{-3t}\, t \sin t\, dt$ is equal to   (2)

  (A) $\dfrac{3}{100}$ (B) $\dfrac{2}{50}$

  (C) $\dfrac{3}{50}$ (D) $\dfrac{4}{25}$

40. If $L\left[\sin \sqrt{t}\right] = \dfrac{\sqrt{\pi}}{2s^{\frac{3}{2}}} e^{-\frac{1}{4s}}$ then $L\left[\dfrac{\cos \sqrt{t}}{\sqrt{t}}\right]$ is equal to   (2)

  (A) $\sqrt{\dfrac{\pi}{s}}\, e^{-\frac{1}{4s}}$ (B) $\dfrac{1}{\sqrt{s}}\, e^{-\frac{1}{4s}}$

  (C) $\dfrac{\pi}{s}\, e^{-\frac{1}{4s}}$ (D) $\dfrac{\sqrt{\pi}}{2s^{\frac{3}{2}}}\, e^{-\frac{1}{4s}}$

Answers

1. (B)	2. (A)	3. (D)	4. (C)	5. (B)	6. (C)	7. (D)	8. (A)
9. (B)	10. (A)	11. (D)	12. (B)	13. (A)	14. (C)	15. (B)	16. (D)
17. (D)	18. (A)	19. (C)	20. (B)	21. (B)	22. (A)	23. (C)	24. (D)
25. (B)	26. (D)	27. (A)	28. (C)	29. (C)	30. (A)	31. (D)	32. (B)
33. (C)	34. (B)	35. (A)	36. (D)	37. (D)	38. (B)	39. (D)	40. (A)

CHAPTER FIVE

INVERSE LAPLACE TRANSFORM

5.1 INTRODUCTION

We have so far discussed how to find Laplace transform of given function f(t). However, from the application point of view this will not be very useful unless we obtain inverse transform f(t) in time domain, of a given function F(s) in frequency domain.

In this chapter, we shall consider the inverse problem of finding f(t) for a given F(s) i.e. given a function F(s), to find a function f(t) of which F(s) is the Laplace transform. Applications of the Laplace transform to differential equations are also discussed in this chapter.

5.2 DEFINITION

If the Laplace transform of f(t) is F(s), i.e. L [f(t)] = F(s), then f(t) is called the inverse Laplace transform of F(s) and we write symbolically

$$\boxed{L^{-1} [F(s)] = f(t)} \qquad \qquad \dots (1)$$

where, L^{-1} is called inverse Laplace Transform Operator.

5.3 LINEARITY PROPERTY

Theorem : If c_1 and c_2 are any constants and $F_1(s)$ and $F_2(s)$ are the Laplace transforms of $f_1(t)$ and $f_2(t)$, respectively, then

$$L^{-1} [c_1 F_1(s) + c_2 F_2(s)] = c_1 L^{-1} [F_1(s)] + c_2 L^{-1} [F_2(s)]$$
$$= c_1 f_1(t) + c_2 f_2(t)$$

Proof : To prove this, we have given

$$F_1(s) = L [f_1(t)] \quad \text{and} \quad F_2(s) = L [f_2(t)]$$

We know by the Linearity property of Laplace transform (see Art. 4.5)

$$L [c_1 f_1(t) + c_2 f_2(t)] = c_1 L [f_1(t)] + c_2 L [f_2(t)]$$
$$= c_1 F_1(s) + c_2 F_2(s)$$

Therefore by definition (1) above, we have

$$L^{-1} [c_1 F_1(s) + c_2 F_2(s)] = c_1 f_1(t) + c_2 f_2(t)$$
$$= c_1 L^{-1} [F_1(s)] + c_2 L^{-1} [F_2(s)].$$

The result is easily extended to the addition of more than two functions.

Note : The property of Laplace transformation expressed in this theorem is, of course, the property of Linearity. In other words, the inverse Laplace transform is a Linear transform.

5.4 METHODS OF FINDING INVERSE TRANSFORMS

Following methods are used to find inverse Laplace transforms :

(I)   Use of Table of inverse Laplace transforms.

(II)   Use of Theorems of inverse Laplace transform.

(III)   Use of Partial fractions.

In what follows we shall illustrate these methods.

5.5 METHOD (I) : USE OF TABLE OF INVERSE LAPLACE TRANSFORMS

From the Table 4.1 (Art. 4.6) of Laplace transforms of elementary functions and by using definition and linearity property, we can obtain corresponding Table of inverse Laplace transform.

1. $\quad L[1] = \dfrac{1}{s}$ $\quad\therefore\quad$ $L^{-1}\left[\dfrac{1}{s}\right] = 1$

2. $\quad L[e^{at}] = \dfrac{1}{s-a}$ $\quad\therefore\quad$ $L^{-1}\left[\dfrac{1}{s-a}\right] = e^{at}$

$\quad L[e^{-at}] = \dfrac{1}{s+a}$ $\quad\therefore\quad$ $L^{-1}\left[\dfrac{1}{s+a}\right] = e^{-at}$

3. $\quad L[\sin at] = \dfrac{a}{s^2+a^2}$ $\quad\therefore\quad$ $L^{-1}\left[\dfrac{1}{s^2+a^2}\right] = \dfrac{1}{a}\sin at$

4. $\quad L[\cos at] = \dfrac{s}{s^2+a^2}$ $\quad\therefore\quad$ $L^{-1}\left[\dfrac{s}{s^2+a^2}\right] = \cos at$

5. $\quad L[\sinh at] = \dfrac{a}{s^2-a^2}$ $\quad\therefore\quad$ $L^{-1}\left[\dfrac{1}{s^2-a^2}\right] = \dfrac{1}{a}\sinh at$

6. $\quad L[\cosh at] = \dfrac{s}{s^2-a^2}$ $\quad\therefore\quad$ $L^{-1}\left[\dfrac{s}{s^2-a^2}\right] = \cosh at$

7. $\quad L[t^n] = \dfrac{\overline{|n+1}}{s^{n+1}}$ $\quad\therefore\quad$ $L^{-1}\left[\dfrac{1}{s^{n+1}}\right] = \dfrac{t^n}{\overline{|n+1}}$

$\quad L[t^{n-1}] = \dfrac{\overline{|n}}{s^n}$ $\quad\therefore\quad$ $L^{-1}\left[\dfrac{1}{s^n}\right] = \dfrac{t^{n-1}}{\overline{|n}}$

If n is a positive integer, $\overline{|n+1} = n!$ and $\overline{|n} = (n-1)!$, then we have

8. $\quad L[t^n] = \dfrac{n!}{s^{n+1}}$ $\quad\therefore\quad$ $L^{-1}\left[\dfrac{1}{s^{n+1}}\right] = \dfrac{t^n}{n!}$

$\quad L[t^{n-1}] = \dfrac{(n-1)!}{s^n}$ $\quad\therefore\quad$ $L^{-1}\left[\dfrac{1}{s^n}\right] = \dfrac{t^{n-1}}{(n-1)!}$

Note : For the units step functions $u(t) = \begin{cases} 0 \ , \ t < 0 \\ 1 \ , \ t \geq 0 \end{cases}$ and displaced unit steps function

$u(t - a) = \begin{cases} 0 \ , \ t < a \\ 1 \ , \ t \geq a \end{cases}$ we can also add the following results :

9. $\quad L\left[U(t - a)\right] \ = \ \dfrac{e^{-as}}{s} \qquad \therefore \qquad L^{-1}\left[\dfrac{e^{-as}}{s}\right] \ = \ U(t - a)$

$\quad L\left[U(t)\right] \ = \ \dfrac{1}{s} \qquad\qquad \therefore \qquad L^{-1}\left[\dfrac{1}{s}\right] \ = \ U(t)$

Similarly, for Dirac delta or unit impulse function $\delta(t - a) = \displaystyle\lim_{\varepsilon \to 0} F(t)$

where $F(t) = \begin{cases} 0 \ , & t < a \\ 1/\varepsilon \ , & a \leq t \leq a + \varepsilon \\ 0 \ , & t > a + \varepsilon \end{cases}$ we note that

10. $\quad L\left[\delta(t - a)\right] \ = \ e^{-as} \qquad \therefore \qquad L^{-1}\left[e^{-as}\right] \ = \ \delta(t - a)$

$\quad L\left[\delta(t)\right] \ = \ 1 \qquad\qquad \therefore \qquad L^{-1}\left[1\right] \ = \ \delta(t)$

The following table gives the inverse Laplace transforms of some elementary functions for ready reference.

Table 5.1
Table of Inverse Laplace Transforms

Sr. No.	$F(s)$	$f(t) = L^{-1}\left[F(s)\right]$
1	$\dfrac{1}{s}$	1
2	$\dfrac{1}{s - a}$	e^{at}
3	$\dfrac{1}{s^2 + a^2}$	$\dfrac{\sin at}{a}$
4	$\dfrac{s}{s^2 + a^2}$	$\cos at$
5	$\dfrac{1}{s^2 - a^2}$	$\dfrac{\sinh at}{a}$
6	$\dfrac{s}{s^2 - a^2}$	$\cosh at$
7	$\dfrac{1}{s^{n+1}}$	$\dfrac{t^n}{\overline{\lvert n + 1}}$
8	$\dfrac{1}{s^{n+1}}$ if n a positive integer	$\dfrac{t^n}{n!}$

ILLUSTRATIONS ON TABLE OF INVERSE LAPLACE TRANSFORMS

Ex. 1 : *Find the inverse Laplace transforms of the following functions :*

(i) $\dfrac{5}{s+3}$ (ii) $\dfrac{1}{2s-3}$ (iii) $\dfrac{4}{3s-1}$ (iv) $\dfrac{2s+1}{s(s+1)}$

Sol. : (i) $\quad L^{-1}\left[\dfrac{5}{s+3}\right] = 5\,L^{-1}\left[\dfrac{1}{s+3}\right] = 5e^{-3t}$

$$\begin{cases}\text{From Table of I.L.T.}\\ L^{-1}\left[\dfrac{1}{s+a}\right] = e^{-at}\end{cases}$$

(ii) $\quad L^{-1}\left[\dfrac{1}{2s-3}\right] = \dfrac{1}{2}\,L^{-1}\left[\dfrac{1}{s-3/2}\right] = \dfrac{1}{2}\,e^{(3/2)\,t}$

$$\begin{cases}\text{From Table of I.L.T.}\\ L^{-1}\left[\dfrac{1}{s-a}\right] = e^{at}\end{cases}$$

(iii) $\quad L^{-1}\left[\dfrac{4}{3s-1}\right] = \dfrac{4}{3}\,L^{-1}\left[\dfrac{1}{s-1/3}\right] = \dfrac{4}{3}\,e^{(1/3)\,t}$

(iv) $\quad L^{-1}\left[\dfrac{2s+1}{s(s+1)}\right] = L^{-1}\left[\dfrac{s+1+s}{s(s+1)}\right] = L^{-1}\left[\dfrac{1}{s}+\dfrac{1}{s+1}\right]$

$$= L^{-1}\left[\dfrac{1}{s}\right] + L^{-1}\left[\dfrac{1}{s+1}\right] = 1 + e^{-t} \quad \text{[By Linearity property]}$$

Ex. 2 : *Obtain the inverse Laplace transform of each of the following functions :*

(i) $\dfrac{2}{s^2+16}$ (ii) $\dfrac{4s}{s^2-16}$ (iii) $\dfrac{2s-5}{4s^2+25}$ (iv) $\dfrac{3s-12}{s^2+8}$ (v) $\dfrac{s-4}{s^2-4}$ (vi) $\dfrac{s\cos\alpha+\omega\sin\alpha}{s^2+\omega^2}$

Sol. : (i) $\quad L^{-1}\left[\dfrac{2}{s^2+16}\right] = 2\,L^{-1}\left[\dfrac{1}{s^2+16}\right] = 2\,L^{-1}\left[\dfrac{1}{s^2+4^2}\right]$

$$= 2\left(\dfrac{\sin 4t}{4}\right) = \dfrac{\sin 4t}{2}$$

$$\begin{cases}\text{From Table of I.L.T.}\\ L^{-1}\left[\dfrac{1}{s^2+a^2}\right] = \dfrac{\sin at}{a}\end{cases}$$

(ii) $\quad L^{-1}\left[\dfrac{4s}{s^2-16}\right] = 4\,L^{-1}\left[\dfrac{s}{s^2-16}\right] = 4\,L^{-1}\left[\dfrac{s}{s^2-4^2}\right]$

$$= 4\cosh 4t.$$

$$\begin{cases}\text{From Table of I.L.T.}\\ L^{-1}\left[\dfrac{s}{s^2-a^2}\right] = \cosh at\end{cases}$$

(iii) $\quad L^{-1}\left[\dfrac{2s-5}{4s^2+25}\right] = \dfrac{1}{4}\,L^{-1}\left[\dfrac{2s-5}{s^2+25/4}\right] = \dfrac{1}{4}\,L^{-1}\left[\dfrac{2s-5}{s^2+(5/2)^2}\right]$

$$= \dfrac{1}{2}\,L^{-1}\left[\dfrac{s}{s^2+(5/2)^2}\right] - \dfrac{5}{4}\,L^{-1}\left[\dfrac{1}{s^2+(5/2)^2}\right]$$

$$\text{[By Linearity Property]}$$

$$= \dfrac{1}{2}\cos\dfrac{5}{2}t - \dfrac{5}{4}\cdot\dfrac{2}{5}\sin\dfrac{5}{2}t = \dfrac{1}{2}\left(\cos\dfrac{5t}{2} - \sin\dfrac{5t}{2}\right).$$

(iv) $\quad L^{-1}\left[\dfrac{3s-12}{s^2+8}\right] = 3\,L^{-1}\left[\dfrac{s}{s^2+8}\right] - 12\,L^{-1}\left[\dfrac{1}{s^2+8}\right] \quad \text{[By Linearity Property]}$

$$= 3\,L^{-1}\left[\dfrac{s}{s^2+\left(2\sqrt{2}\right)^2}\right] - 12\,L^{-1}\left[\dfrac{1}{s^2+\left(2\sqrt{2}\right)^2}\right]$$

$$= 3 \cos\left(2\sqrt{2}\right) t - 12\frac{1}{2\sqrt{2}} \sin\left(2\sqrt{2}\right) t$$

$$= 3 \cos\left(2\sqrt{2}\right) t - 3\sqrt{2} \sin\left(2\sqrt{2}\right) t.$$

(v)
$$L^{-1}\left[\frac{s-4}{s^2-4}\right] = L^{-1}\left[\frac{s}{s^2-4}\right] - 4\,L^{-1}\left[\frac{1}{s^2-4}\right] \qquad \text{[By Linearity property]}$$

$$= \cosh 2t - 4\left(\frac{\sinh 2t}{2}\right)$$

$$= \cosh 2t - 2 \sinh 2t$$

(vi)
$$L^{-1}\left[\frac{s\cos\alpha + \omega\sin\alpha}{s^2+\omega^2}\right] = \cos\alpha\,L^{-1}\left[\frac{s}{s^2+\omega^2}\right] + \sin\alpha\,L^{-1}\left[\frac{\omega}{s^2+\omega^2}\right]$$

$$= \cos\alpha\cos\omega t + \sin\alpha\sin\omega t$$

$$= \cos\left(\omega t - \alpha\right)$$

Ex. 3 : *Find each of the following inverse Laplace transforms :*

(i) $L^{-1}\left[\dfrac{a_1}{s} + \dfrac{a_2}{s^2} + \dfrac{a_3}{s^3}\right]$ (ii) $L^{-1}\left[\dfrac{1}{s^4}\right]$ (iii) $L^{-1}\left[\dfrac{s+1}{s^{4/3}}\right]$ (iv) $L^{-1}\left[\dfrac{3\,(s^2-1)^2}{2s^5}\right]$

Sol. : (i) $L^{-1}\left[\dfrac{a_1}{s} + \dfrac{a_2}{s^2} + \dfrac{a_3}{s^3}\right] = a_1\,L^{-1}\left[\dfrac{1}{s}\right] + a_2\,L^{-1}\left[\dfrac{1}{s^2}\right] + a_3\,L^{-1}\left[\dfrac{1}{s^3}\right]$

$$\text{[By Linearity property]}$$

$$= a_1 + a_2 t + a_3\frac{t^2}{2!} = a_1 + a_2 t + \frac{a_3\,t^2}{2}.$$

$$\left\{\begin{array}{l}\text{From Table of I.L.T.}\\[4pt] L^{-1}\left[\dfrac{1}{s^{n+1}}\right] = \dfrac{t^n}{n!}\end{array}\right.$$

(ii)
$$L^{-1}\left[\frac{1}{s^4}\right] = \frac{t^3}{3!} = \frac{t^3}{6}$$

(iii)
$$L^{-1}\left[\frac{s+1}{s^{4/3}}\right] = L^{-1}\left[\frac{s}{s^{4/3}}\right] + L^{-1}\left[\frac{1}{s^{4/3}}\right] = L^{-1}\left[\frac{1}{s^{1/3}}\right] + L^{-1}\left[\frac{1}{s^{4/3}}\right]$$

$$= \frac{t^{-2/3}}{\lceil 1/3}\, + \frac{t^{1/3}}{\lceil 4/3} = \frac{1}{\lceil 1/3}\,(t^{-2/3} + 3t^{1/3}), \quad \left\{L^{-1}\left[\frac{1}{s^n} = \frac{t^{n-1}}{\lceil n}\right]\right\}$$

(iv)
$$L^{-1}\left[\frac{3\,(s^2-1)^2}{2s^5}\right] = \frac{3}{2}\,L^{-1}\left[\frac{s^4-2s^2+1}{s^5}\right] = \frac{3}{2}\,L^{-1}\left[\frac{1}{s} - \frac{2}{s^3} + \frac{1}{s^5}\right]$$

$$= \frac{3}{2}\left\{L^{-1}\left[\frac{1}{s}\right] - 2\,L^{-1}\left[\frac{1}{s^3}\right] + L^{-1}\left[\frac{1}{s^5}\right]\right\}$$

$$= \frac{3}{2}\left(1 - 2\frac{t^2}{2!} + \frac{t^4}{4!}\right) = \frac{3}{2}\left(1 - t^2 + \frac{t^4}{24}\right)$$

Ex. 4 : *Determine each of the following :*

(i) $L^{-1}\left[\dfrac{3}{s+2} - \dfrac{2s}{s^2+25} + \dfrac{3}{s^2+9}\right]$ (ii) $L^{-1}\left[\dfrac{5s+4}{s^3} - \dfrac{2s-18}{s^2+9} + \dfrac{24-30\sqrt{s}}{s^4}\right]$

(iii) $L^{-1}\left[\dfrac{6}{2s-3} - \dfrac{3+4s}{9s^2-16} + \dfrac{8-6s}{16s^2+9}\right]$

Sol. : (i) $L^{-1}\left[\dfrac{3}{s+2} - \dfrac{2s}{s^2+25} + \dfrac{3}{s^2+9}\right]$

$$= 3\,L^{-1}\left[\dfrac{1}{s+2}\right] - 2\,L^{-1}\left[\dfrac{s}{s^2+5^2}\right] + 3\,L^{-1}\left[\dfrac{1}{s^2+3^2}\right]$$

$$= 3\,e^{-2t} - 2\cos 5t + 3\left(\dfrac{\sin 3t}{3}\right) = 3\,e^{-2t} - 2\cos 5t + \sin 3t$$

(ii) $L^{-1}\left[\dfrac{5s+4}{s^3} - \dfrac{2s-18}{s^2+9} + \dfrac{24 - 30\sqrt{s}}{s^4}\right]$

$$= L^{-1}\left[\dfrac{5}{s^2} + \dfrac{4}{s^3} - \dfrac{2s}{s^2+9} + \dfrac{18}{s^2+9} + \dfrac{24}{s^4} - \dfrac{30}{s^{7/2}}\right]$$

$$= 5t + 4\left(\dfrac{t^2}{2!}\right) - 2\cos t + 18\left(\dfrac{\sin 3t}{3}\right) + 24\left(\dfrac{t^3}{3!}\right) - 30\left(\dfrac{t^{5/2}}{\overline{|7/2}}\right)$$

$$= 5t + 2t^2 - 2\cos t + 6\sin 3t + 4t^3 - \dfrac{16t^{5/2}}{\sqrt{\pi}}$$

$$\left\{\because \ \overline{|7/2} = \dfrac{5}{2}\cdot\dfrac{3}{2}\cdot\dfrac{1}{2}\,\overline{|1/2} = \dfrac{15}{8}\sqrt{\pi}\right\}$$

(iii) $L^{-1}\left[\dfrac{6}{2s-3} - \dfrac{3+4s}{9s^2-16} + \dfrac{8-6s}{16s^2+9}\right]$

$$= L^{-1}\left[\dfrac{3}{s-3/2} - \dfrac{1}{3}\left(\dfrac{1}{s^2-16/9}\right) - \dfrac{4}{9}\left(\dfrac{s}{s^2-16/9}\right) + \dfrac{1}{2}\left(\dfrac{1}{s^2+9/16}\right) - \dfrac{3}{8}\left(\dfrac{s}{s^2+9/16}\right)\right]$$

$$= 3\,e^{3t/2} - \dfrac{1}{4}\sinh\dfrac{4t}{3} - \dfrac{4}{9}\cosh\dfrac{4t}{3} + \dfrac{2}{3}\sin\dfrac{3t}{4} - \dfrac{3}{8}\cos\dfrac{3t}{4}.$$

EXERCISE 5.1

1. Find the inverse Laplace transforms of the following functions :

(i) $\dfrac{3}{s+4}$ (ii) $\dfrac{1}{2s-5}$ (iii) $\dfrac{12}{4-3s}$ (iv) $\dfrac{2\pi}{s+\pi}$

Ans. (i) $3e^{-4t}$ (ii) $\dfrac{1}{2}e^{5t/2}$ (iii) $-4e^{4t/3}$ (iv) $2\pi\,e^{-\pi s}$

2. Obtain the inverse Laplace transform of each of the following functions :

(i) $\dfrac{7s}{s^2+4}$ (ii) $\dfrac{3}{s^2-7}$ (iii) $\dfrac{4s+15}{16s^2-25}$ (iv) $\dfrac{3s+5\sqrt{2}}{s^2+8}$ (v) $\dfrac{2s+6}{s^2+4}$ (vi) $\dfrac{5s-10}{9s^2-16}$

Ans. (i) $7\cos 2t$ (ii) $\dfrac{3}{\sqrt{7}}\sinh\sqrt{7}\,t$ (iii) $\dfrac{1}{4}\left(\cosh\dfrac{5t}{4} + 4\sinh\dfrac{5t}{4}\right)$

(iv) $3\cos 2\sqrt{2}\,t + \dfrac{5}{2}\sin 2\sqrt{2}\,t$ (v) $2\cos 2t + 3\sin 2t$

(vi) $\dfrac{5}{9}\cosh\dfrac{4}{3}t - \dfrac{5}{6}\sinh\dfrac{4t}{3}.$

3. Find each of the following inverse Laplace transforms :

(i) $L^{-1}\left[\dfrac{s^2+s+1}{s^{9/2}}\right]$ (ii) $L^{-1}\left[\dfrac{1}{s^5}\right]$ (iii) $L^{-1}\left[\left(\dfrac{1-\sqrt{s}}{s^2}\right)^2\right]$ (iv) $L^{-1}\left[\dfrac{7\,(s^2+1)^2}{5s^5}\right]$

Ans. (i) $\dfrac{t^{3/2}}{\lfloor 9/2}\left(\dfrac{35}{4}+\dfrac{7}{2}t+t^2\right)$ (ii) $\dfrac{t^4}{24}$ (iii) $\dfrac{t^3}{6}+\dfrac{t^2}{2}-\dfrac{16}{15\sqrt{\pi}}\,t^{5/2}$

(iv) $\dfrac{7}{5}\left(1+t^2+\dfrac{t^4}{24}\right)$

4. Determine each of the following :

(i) $L^{-1}\left[\dfrac{3s-2}{s^{5/2}}-\dfrac{7}{3s+2}+\dfrac{5s}{s^2-1}\right]$ (ii) $L^{-1}\left[\dfrac{3s-8}{s^2+4}-\dfrac{4s-24}{s^2-16}\right]$

(iii) $L^{-1}\left[\dfrac{3\,(s^2-1)^2}{s^5}+\dfrac{4s-18}{9-s^2}+\dfrac{(s+1)\,(2-s^{3/2})}{s^{7/2}}\right]$

Ans. (i) $\sqrt{\dfrac{t}{\pi}}\left(6-\dfrac{8}{3}\,t\right)-\dfrac{7}{3}e^{-2t/3}+5\cosh t$

(ii) $3\cos 2t-4\sin 2t-4\cosh 4t+6\sinh 4t$

(iii) $2-t-3t^2+\dfrac{t^4}{8}+\dfrac{t^{3/2}}{\lfloor 7/2}\,(5+2t)-4\cosh 3t+6\sinh 3t.$

MULTIPLE CHOICE QUESTIONS (MCQ's)

Type : Use of Inverse Laplace Transform Table of Elementary Functions :

1. If $F(s)=\dfrac{1}{s}$ then $L^{-1}\left[\dfrac{1}{s}\right]$ is equal to (1)

(A) e^t　　　　　　　　　　　　　(B) 1

(C) t　　　　　　　　　　　　　(D) sin t

2. If $F(s)=\dfrac{1}{s-a}$, $s>a$ then $L^{-1}\left[\dfrac{1}{s-a}\right]$ is equal to (1)

(A) e^{-at}　　　　　　　　　　　(B) cos at

(C) e^{at}　　　　　　　　　　　(D) sin at

3. If $F(s)=\dfrac{1}{s+a}$, $s>-a$ then $L^{-1}\left[\dfrac{1}{s+a}\right]$ is equal to (1)

(A) cos at　　　　　　　　　　　(B) e^{at}

(C) sinh at　　　　　　　　　　　(D) e^{-at}

4. If $F(s) = \dfrac{1}{s - a \log c}$, $s > a \log c$, $c > 0$ then $L^{-1}\left[\dfrac{1}{s - a \log c}\right]$ is equal to   (1)

(A) c^{at} (B) $\cos at$

(C) e^{-at} (D) $\sinh at$

5. If $F(s) = \dfrac{a}{s^2 + a^2}$, $s > 0$ then $L^{-1}\left[\dfrac{a}{s^2 + a^2}\right]$ is equal to   (1)

(A) $\cos at$ (B) e^{-at}

(C) $\sinh at$ (D) $\sin at$

6. If $F(s) = \dfrac{s}{s^2 + a^2}$, $s > 0$ then $L^{-1}\left[\dfrac{s}{s^2 + a^2}\right]$ is equal to   (1)

(A) t^n (B) e^{-at}

(C) $\cos at$ (D) $\sin at$

7. If $F(s) = \dfrac{a}{s^2 - a^2}$, $s > |a|$ then $L^{-1}\left[\dfrac{a}{s^2 - a^2}\right]$ is equal to   (1)

(A) $\cos at$ (B) $\sinh at$

(C) t^n (D) e^{-at}

8. If $F(s) = \dfrac{s}{s^2 - a^2}$, $s > |a|$ then $L^{-1}\left[\dfrac{s}{s^2 - a^2}\right]$ is equal to   (1)

(A) $\cosh at$ (B) $\sinh at$

(C) $\cos at$ (d) e^{-at}

9. If $F(s) = \dfrac{\overline{|n + 1}}{s^{n+1}}$, $s > 0$ then $L^{-1}\left[\dfrac{\overline{|n + 1}}{s^{n+1}}\right]$ is equal to   (1)

(A) $\cosh at$ (B) t^n

(C) $\cos at$ (D) e^{-at}

10. $L^{-1}\left[\dfrac{5}{s + 3}\right]$ is equal to   (1)

(A) $5e^{-3t}$ (B) $5e^{3t}$

(C) $\dfrac{e^{-3t}}{5}$ (D) e^{-3t}

11. $L^{-1}\left[\dfrac{4s}{s^2 - 16}\right]$ is equal to   (1)

(A) $\cosh 4t$ (B) $4 \sinh 4t$

(C) $4 \cos 4t$ (D) $4 \cosh 4t$

12. $L^{-1}\left[\dfrac{2}{s^2+9}\right]$ is equal to   (1)

(A) $2\sin 3t$ (B) $\dfrac{2}{9}\sin 9t$

(C) $\dfrac{2}{3}\sin 3t$ (D) $\dfrac{2}{3}\cos 3t$

13. $L^{-1}\left[\dfrac{1}{s^4}\right]$ is equal to   (1)

(A) $\dfrac{t^2}{2}$ (B) $\dfrac{t^3}{6}$

(C) $\dfrac{t^3}{4}$ (D) $\dfrac{t^4}{24}$

14. $L^{-1}\left[\dfrac{s-4}{s^2-4}\right]$ is equal to   (2)

(A) $\cosh 2t - 2\sinh 2t$ (B) $\cosh 2t - 4\sinh 4t$
(C) $\cos 2t - 2\sin 2t$ (D) $\sinh 2t - 2\cosh 2t$

15. $L^{-1}\left[\dfrac{1}{2s-3}\right]$ is equal to   (2)

(A) $\dfrac{1}{2}e^{-\frac{2}{3}t}$ (B) $e^{\frac{3}{2}t}$

(C) $\dfrac{1}{2}e^{\frac{3}{2}t}$ (D) $\dfrac{1}{2}e^{-\frac{3}{2}t}$

16. $L^{-1}\left[\dfrac{3}{s+2}-\dfrac{2s}{s^2+25}\right]$ is equal to   (2)

(A) $3e^{-2t} - 2\sin 5t$ (B) $e^{-2t} - \cos 5t$
(C) $3e^{2t} - 2\cos 25t$ (D) $3e^{-2t} - 2\cos 5t$

17. $L^{-1}\left[\dfrac{(s+1)^2}{s^3}\right]$ is equal to   (2)

(A) $t + \dfrac{t^2}{2} + \dfrac{t^3}{3}$ (B) $1 + 2t + \dfrac{t^2}{2}$

(C) $t + \dfrac{t^2}{2}$ (D) $1 + t + t^2$

18. $L^{-1}\left[\dfrac{3s+5\sqrt{2}}{s^2+8}\right]$ is equal to   (2)

(A) $3\cos\sqrt{8}\,t + \dfrac{5\sqrt{2}}{\sqrt{8}}\sin\sqrt{8}\,t$ (B) $3\cosh\sqrt{8}\,t + \dfrac{5\sqrt{2}}{\sqrt{8}}\sinh\sqrt{8}\,t$

(C) $3\cos\sqrt{8}\,t + 5\sqrt{2}\sin\sqrt{8}\,t$ (D) $3\sin\sqrt{8}\,t + \dfrac{5\sqrt{2}}{\sqrt{8}}\cos\sqrt{8}\,t$

19. $L^{-1}\left[\dfrac{4s + 15}{16s^2 - 25}\right]$ is equal to   (2)

(A) $\dfrac{1}{4}\cos\dfrac{5}{4}t + \dfrac{3}{4}\sin\dfrac{5}{4}t$

(B) $\cosh\dfrac{5}{4}t + \sinh\dfrac{5}{4}t$

(C) $\dfrac{1}{4}\cosh 5t + \dfrac{3}{4}\sinh 5t$

(D) $\dfrac{1}{4}\cosh\dfrac{5}{4}t + \dfrac{3}{4}\sinh\dfrac{5}{4}t$

20. $L^{-1}\left[\dfrac{3s - 2}{s^{\frac{5}{2}}}\right]$ is equal to   (2)

(A) $\dfrac{\left|\frac{3}{2}\right.}{t^{\frac{1}{2}}} - 2\dfrac{\left|\frac{5}{2}\right.}{t^{\frac{3}{2}}}$

(B) $\dfrac{t^{\frac{1}{2}}}{\left|\frac{1}{2}\right.} - 2\dfrac{t^{\frac{3}{2}}}{\left|\frac{3}{2}\right.}$

(C) $3\dfrac{t^{\frac{1}{2}}}{\left|\frac{3}{2}\right.} - 2\dfrac{t^{\frac{3}{2}}}{\left|\frac{5}{2}\right.}$

(D) $t^{\frac{1}{2}} - 2t^{\frac{3}{2}}$

Answers

1. (B)	2. (C)	3. (D)	4. (A)	5. (D)	6. (C)	7. (B)	8. (A)
9. (B)	10. (A)	11. (D)	12. (C)	13. (B)	14. (A)	15. (C)	16. (D)
17. (B)	18. (A)	19. (D)	20. (C)				

5.6 METHOD II : USE OF THEOREMS OF INVERSE LAPLACE TRANSFORM

Analogous to the theorems proved in Sec. 4.8, we have the following theorems of Inverse Laplace transform.

(A) FIRST SHIFTING THEOREM

Theorem : If $\qquad L^{-1}[F(s)] = f(t),$ then
$$L^{-1}[f(s + a)] = e^{-at} f(t)$$

Proof : We have proved in the first shifting theorem of Laplace transform [result (9) in chapter 4] that
$$L[e^{-at} f(t)] = F(s + a)$$
$$\therefore \qquad L^{-1}[F(s + a)] = e^{-at} f(t)$$

Hence $\boxed{L^{-1}[F(s + a)] = e^{-at} f(t)}$ … (2)

Remark 1 : In words, this theorem states that the replacement of s by s + a in F(s) corresponds to multiplication of original function f(t) by e^{-at}.

Remark 2 : In practice, to obtain inverse Laplace transform of F(s + a), obtain that of F(s) first (i.e. first obtain $L^{-1}[F(s)]$) and then multiply it by e^{-at}.

ILLUSTRATION

Ex. 1 : *Obtain the inverse Laplace transforms of the following functions :*

(i) $\dfrac{1}{(s+4)^6}$ (ii) $\dfrac{s}{(s-3)^5}$ (iii) $\dfrac{3s+1}{(s+1)^4}$ (iv) $\dfrac{s}{s^2+6s+25}$

Sol. : (i) $\quad L^{-1}\left[\dfrac{1}{(s+4)^6}\right] = e^{-4t}\,L^{-1}\left[\dfrac{1}{s^6}\right]$ $\qquad$ [By the First Shifting Theorem]

$$= e^{-4t}\,\frac{t^5}{5!} = e^{-4t}\,\frac{t^5}{120} \qquad \left\{\text{By } L^{-1}\left[\frac{1}{s^{n+1}}\right] = \frac{t^n}{n!}\right\}$$

(ii) $\quad L^{-1}\left[\dfrac{s}{(s-3)^5}\right] = L^{-1}\left[\dfrac{(s-3)+3}{(s-3)^5}\right] = L^{-1}\left[\dfrac{1}{(s-3)^4}\right] + 3\,L^{-1}\left[\dfrac{1}{(s-3)^5}\right]$

$$= e^{3t}\,L^{-1}\left[\frac{1}{s^4}\right] + 3e^{3t}\,L^{-1}\left[\frac{1}{s^5}\right] = e^{3t}\,\frac{t^3}{3!} + 3e^{3t}\,\frac{t^4}{4!}$$

[By result (2)]

$$= e^{3t}\,t^3\left(\frac{1}{6}+\frac{t}{8}\right)$$

(iii) $\quad L^{-1}\left[\dfrac{3s+1}{(s+1)^4}\right] = L^{-1}\left[\dfrac{3(s+1)-2}{(s+1)^4}\right] = 3\,L^{-1}\left[\dfrac{1}{(s+1)^3}\right] - 2\,L^{-1}\left[\dfrac{1}{(s+1)^4}\right]$

$$= 3e^{-t}\,L^{-1}\left[\frac{1}{s^3}\right] - 2e^{-t}\,L^{-1}\left[\frac{1}{s^4}\right] = 3\,e^{-t}\frac{t^2}{2!} - 2e^{-t}\frac{t^3}{3!}$$

[By result (2)]

$$= e^{-t}\,t^2\left(\frac{3}{2}-\frac{t}{3}\right)$$

(iv) $\quad L^{-1}\left[\dfrac{s}{s^2+6s+25}\right] = L^{-1}\left[\dfrac{s+3-3}{s^2+6s+9+16}\right] = L^{-1}\left[\dfrac{(s+3)-3}{(s+3)^2+4^2}\right]$

$$= L^{-1}\left[\frac{s+3}{(s+3)^2+4^2}\right] - 3\,L^{-1}\left[\frac{1}{(s+3)^2+4^2}\right]$$

$$= e^{-3t}\,L^{-1}\left[\frac{s}{s^2+4^2}\right] - 3e^{-3t}\,L^{-1}\left[\frac{1}{s^2+4^2}\right]$$

$$= e^{-3t}\,(\cos 4t) - 3e^{-3t}\left(\frac{\sin 4t}{4}\right)$$

$$= e^{-3t}\left(\cos 4t - \frac{3}{4}\,\sin 4t\right)$$

(B) SECOND SHIFTING THEOREM

Theorem : If $L^{-1}[F(s)] = f(t)$, then

$$L^{-1}[e^{-as} F(s)] = \begin{cases} f(t-a), & t > a \\ 0, & t < a \end{cases}$$

Proof : We have proved in second shifting theorem of Laplace transform [result (10) in chapter 4] that

$$L[F(t)] = e^{-as} F(s), \text{ where } F(t) = \begin{cases} f(t-a), & t > a \\ 0, & t < a \end{cases}$$

$\therefore$ $$L^{-1}[e^{-as} F(s)] = F(t) = \begin{cases} f(t-a), & t > a \\ 0, & t < a \end{cases}$$

Hence $$\boxed{L^{-1}[e^{-as} F(s)] = \begin{cases} f(t-a), & t > a \\ 0, & t < a \end{cases}}$$ ... (3 a)

Note : Since we can write $F(t)$ in terms of Heaviside unit step functions as $f(t-a)\,U(t-a)$, we have the following equivalent result for the second shifting theorem.

$$\boxed{L^{-1}[e^{-as} F(s)] = f(t-a)\,U(t-a)}$$ ... (3 b)

Remark 1 : In words, this theorem states that suppressing the factor e^{-as} in a transform requires that the inverse of what remains be shifted a units to the right and cut-off to the left of the point $t = a$.

Remark 2 : In practice, to obtain inverse Laplace transform of $e^{-as} F(s)$, we first obtain inverse transform of $F(s)$, say $f(t)$ (i.e. factor e^{-as} is dropped initially), then to account for the factor e^{-as}, replace t by $t - a$ throughout in $f(t)$ and multiply this result by $U(t-a)$.

ILLUSTRATIONS

Ex. : *Obtain the inverse Laplace transforms of the following functions :*

(i) $\dfrac{e^{-\pi s}}{s + a}$ (ii) $\dfrac{s\, e^{-4\pi s/5}}{s^2 + 25}$ (iii) $\dfrac{e^{-3s}}{(s-2)^4}$ (iv) $\dfrac{e^{-\pi s/2} + e^{-3\pi s/2}}{s^2 + 1}$.

Sol. : (i) We have $L^{-1}\left[\dfrac{1}{s + a}\right] = e^{-at}$ (Dropping $e^{-\pi s}$)

Hence by the second shifting theorem, with $a = \pi$, we get

$$L^{-1}\left[\dfrac{e^{-\pi s}}{s + a}\right] = \begin{cases} f(t-a), & t > a \\ 0, & t < a \end{cases} = \begin{cases} e^{-a(t-\pi)}, & t > \pi \\ 0, & t < \pi \end{cases}$$

or $$L^{-1}\left[\dfrac{e^{-\pi s}}{s + a}\right] = f(t-a)\,U(t-a) = e^{-a(t-\pi)}\,U(t-\pi)$$

(ii) We have $\quad L^{-1}\left[\dfrac{s}{s^2+25}\right] = \cos 5t$

Hence by the second shifting theorem, with $a = 4\pi/5$, we get

$$L^{-1}\left[\frac{e^{-4\pi s/5}\,s}{s^2+25}\right] = \begin{cases} \cos 5\,(t-4\pi/5) & , \quad t > 4\pi/5 \\ 0 & , \quad t < 4\pi/5 \end{cases}$$

or $\quad L^{-1}\left[\dfrac{e^{-4\pi/5}\,s}{s^2+25}\right] = \cos 5\,(t-4\pi/5)\,U(t-4\pi/5)$

(iii) We have $\quad L^{-1}\left[\dfrac{1}{(s-2)^4}\right] = e^{2t}\,L^{-1}\left[\dfrac{1}{s^4}\right] = \dfrac{t^3}{3!}$ (By the First Shifting Theorem)

Hence by the second shifting theorem, with $a = 3$, we get

$$L^{-1}\left[\frac{e^{-3s}}{(s-2)^4}\right] = \begin{cases} e^{2\,(t-3)}\left[\dfrac{(t-3)^3}{6}\right], & t > 3 \\ 0, & t < 3 \end{cases}$$

or $\quad L^{-1}\left[\dfrac{e^{-3s}}{(s-2)^4}\right] = e^{2\,(t-3)}\left[\dfrac{(t-3)^3}{6}\right]U(t-3)$

(iv) We have $\quad L^{-1}\left[\dfrac{1}{s^2+1}\right] = \sin t$

$\therefore \quad L^{-1}\left[\dfrac{e^{-\pi s/2}+e^{-3\pi s/2}}{s^2+1}\right] = L^{-1}\left[\dfrac{e^{-\pi s/2}}{s^2+1}\right] + L^{-1}\left[\dfrac{e^{-3\pi s/2}}{s^2+1}\right]$

Hence by the second shifting theorem, we get

$$L^{-1}\left[\frac{e^{-\pi s/2}+e^{-3\pi s/2}}{s^2+1}\right] = \sin\,(t-\pi/2)\,U(t-\pi/2) + \sin\,(t-3\pi/2)\,U(t-3\pi/2)$$

$$= -\cos t\,U(t-\pi/2) + \cos t\,U(t-3\pi/2)$$

$$= \cos t\,[U(t-3\pi/2) - U(t-\pi/2)]$$

(C) CHANGE OF SCALE THEOREM

Theorem : If $\quad L^{-1}\,[F(s)] = f(t),$ then

$$L^{-1}\,[F(ks)] = \frac{1}{k}\,f\left(\frac{t}{k}\right)$$

Proof : We have proved in change of scale theorem of Laplace transform [result (11), chapter 4] that

$$L\,[f(at)] = \frac{1}{a}\,F\left(\frac{s}{a}\right)$$

$\therefore \quad L^{-1}\left[\dfrac{1}{a}\,F\left(\dfrac{s}{a}\right)\right] = f(at)$

Putting $\dfrac{1}{a} = k$, we get

$$L^{-1} [kF(ks)] = f\left(\dfrac{t}{k}\right)$$

Hence

$$\boxed{L^{-1} [F(ks)] = \dfrac{1}{k}\, f\left(\dfrac{t}{k}\right)} \qquad \dots (4)$$

ILLUSTRATIONS

Ex. 1 : Prove that $L^{-1}\left[\dfrac{s}{a^2 s^2 + b^2}\right] = \dfrac{1}{a^2} \cos\left(\dfrac{b\,t}{a}\right)$

Sol. : We have $\quad L^{-1}\left[\dfrac{s}{s^2 + b^2}\right] = \cos bt$

$$\therefore \qquad L^{-1}\left[\dfrac{as}{(as)^2 + b^2}\right] = \dfrac{1}{a} \cos b\left(\dfrac{t}{a}\right) \qquad \text{[By Change of Scale Theorem]}$$

$$\therefore \qquad L^{-1}\left[\dfrac{s}{a^2 s^2 + b^2}\right] = \dfrac{1}{a^2} \cos\left(\dfrac{b\,t}{a}\right)$$

Ex. 2 : If $L^{-1}\left[\dfrac{1}{\sqrt{s^2 + 1}}\right] = J_0(t)$, then prove that $L^{-1}\left[\dfrac{1}{\sqrt{s^2 + a^2}}\right] = J_0(at)$

Sol. : Since $\qquad L^{-1}\left[\dfrac{1}{\sqrt{s^2 + 1}}\right] = J_0(t)$

$$\therefore \qquad L^{-1}\left[\dfrac{1}{\sqrt{(s/a)^2 + 1}}\right] = \dfrac{1}{1/a}\, J_0\left(\dfrac{t}{1/a}\right) \qquad \text{[By Change of Scale Theorem]}$$

$$\therefore \qquad L^{-1}\left[\dfrac{a}{\sqrt{s^2 + a^2}}\right] = a\, J_0(at)$$

$$\therefore \qquad L^{-1}\left[\dfrac{1}{\sqrt{s^2 + a^2}}\right] = J_0(at)$$

[**Note :** $J_0(t)$ is a Bessel's function]

(D) INVERSE LAPLACE TRANSFORMS OF DERIVATIVES

Statement : If $\quad L^{-1} [F(s)] = f(t)$, then

$$L^{-1}\left[\dfrac{d}{ds} F(s)\right] = -t\, f(t)$$

Proof : Since $\qquad L[t\, f(t)] = -\dfrac{d}{ds} F(s) \qquad \text{[By result (18), Chapter 4]}$

$$\therefore \qquad L^{-1}\left[-\dfrac{d}{ds} F(s)\right] = t\, f(t) \quad \text{or} \quad L^{-1}\left[\dfrac{d}{ds} F(s)\right] = -t\, f(t)$$

Hence,

$$\boxed{L^{-1}\left[\dfrac{d}{ds} F(s)\right] = -t\, f(t)} \qquad \dots (5a)$$

The generalization to higher order derivatives is

$$\boxed{L^{-1}\left[\frac{d^n}{ds^n}\, F(s)\right] = (-1)^n\, t^n\, f(t)}$$
     ... (5b)

Remark 1 : The result (5 a) can be interpreted as the differentiation of the transform corresponds to multiplication of the function by $-t$.

Remark 2 : This theorem is often useful when the inverse of the transform cannot conveniently be found but the inverse of the derivative of the transform is known. In particular, when F(s) involves logarithmic or inverse circular functions.

ILLUSTRATION

Ex. 1 : *Find the inverse Laplace transform of each of the following functions :*

$$(i)\ \ cot^{-1}s \qquad (ii)\ \ log\left(\frac{s+b}{s+a}\right) \textbf{(May 2007, 2015)} \quad (iii)\ \ \frac{s}{(s^2+a^2)^2} \qquad \textbf{(Dec. 2009)}$$

Sol. : (i) Let

$$L^{-1}\left[cot^{-1}s\right] = f(t)$$

$\therefore$
$$L^{-1}\left[\frac{d}{ds}\,cot^{-1}s\right] = -t\,f(t) \qquad \text{[By result (5a)]}$$

$\therefore$
$$L^{-1}\left[-\frac{1}{s^2+1}\right] = -t\,f(t)$$

$\therefore$
$$\sin t = t\,f(t)$$

$\therefore$
$$\frac{\sin t}{t} = f(t)$$

Hence
$$L^{-1}\left[cot^{-1}s\right] = f(t) = \frac{\sin t}{t}$$

(ii) Let
$$L^{-1}\left[log\left(\frac{s+b}{s+a}\right)\right] = f(t)$$

$\therefore$
$$L^{-1}\left[log\,(s+b) - log\,(s+a)\right] = f(t)$$

$\therefore L^{-1}\left[\dfrac{d}{ds}\,\{log\,(s+b) - log\,(s+a)\}\right] = -t\,f(t) \qquad \text{[By result (5a)]}$

$\therefore$
$$L^{-1}\left[\frac{1}{s+b} - \frac{1}{s+a}\right] = -t\,f(t)$$

$\therefore$
$$e^{-bt} - e^{-at} = -t\,f(t)$$

or
$$\frac{e^{-at} - e^{-bt}}{t} = f(t)$$

Hence
$$L^{-1}\left[log\,\frac{s+b}{s+a}\right] = f(t) = \frac{e^{-at} - e^{-bt}}{t}$$

(iii) [**Note** : Since $\dfrac{d}{ds}\left(\dfrac{1}{s^2+a^2}\right) = \dfrac{-2s}{(s^2+a^2)^2}$ or $-\dfrac{1}{2}\dfrac{d}{ds}\left(\dfrac{1}{s^2+a^2}\right) = \dfrac{s}{(s^2+a^2)^2}$, we use result (5a), to obtain required transform.]

We know that,
$$L^{-1}\left[\frac{1}{s^2+a^2}\right] = \frac{\sin at}{a}$$

$$\therefore \qquad L^{-1}\left[\frac{d}{ds}\frac{1}{s^2+a^2}\right] = \frac{-t\sin at}{a}$$

$$\therefore \qquad L^{-1}\left[-\frac{2s}{(s^2+a^2)^2}\right] = \frac{-t\sin at}{a}$$

$$\text{or} \qquad L^{-1}\left[\frac{s}{(s^2+a^2)^2}\right] = \frac{t\sin at}{2a}$$

Another Method : Differentiating w.r.t. parameter a, we find

$$\frac{d}{da}\frac{s}{s^2+a^2} = \frac{-2as}{(s^2+a^2)^2}$$

Hence
$$L^{-1}\left[\frac{d}{da}\left(\frac{s}{s^2+a^2}\right)\right] = L^{-1}\left[\frac{-2as}{(s^2+a^2)^2}\right]$$

or
$$\frac{d}{da}L^{-1}\left[\frac{s}{s^2+a^2}\right] = -2a\,L^{-1}\left[\frac{s}{(s^2+a^2)^2}\right]$$

or
$$\frac{d}{da}(\cos at) = -2a\,L^{-1}\left[\frac{s}{(s^2+a^2)^2}\right]$$

or
$$-t\sin at = -2a\,L^{-1}\left[\frac{s}{(s^2+a^2)^2}\right]$$

i.e.
$$L^{-1}\left[\frac{s}{(s^2+a^2)^2}\right] = \frac{t\sin at}{2a}$$

(E) INVERSE LAPLACE TRANSFORM OF INTEGRALS :

Theorem : If
$$L^{-1}[F(s)] = f(t), \text{ then}$$

$$L^{-1}\left[\int_{s}^{\infty} F(s)\,ds\right] = \frac{f(t)}{t}$$

Proof : Since
$$L\left[\frac{f(t)}{t}\right] = \int_{s}^{\infty} F(s)\,ds \qquad \text{[By result (21), Chapter 4]}$$

Hence,
$$\boxed{L^{-1}\left[\int_{s}^{\infty} F(s)\,ds\right] = \frac{f(t)}{t}} \qquad \dots (6a)$$

We can generalise the above result as

$$L^{-1}\left[\int_s^\infty \int_s^\infty \ldots\ldots \int_s^\infty F(s)\, ds \cdot ds \ldots\ldots\ldots ds\right] = \frac{f(t)}{t^n} \qquad \ldots (6b)$$

Remark 1 : The result (6a) can be interpreted as the integration of the transform of a function corresponds to division of the function by t.

Remark 2 : This theorem is often useful when the integral of a transform is simpler to work.

ILLUSTRATION

Ex. 1 : *Find the inverse Laplace transform of*

$(i)\ \dfrac{2s}{(s^2-4)^2} \quad (ii)\ \dfrac{2s+1}{(s^2+s+1)^2}$ **(May 2012)** $(iii)\ \dfrac{s}{(s^2+a^2)^2}$

Sol. : (i) Let

$$L^{-1}\left[\frac{2s}{(s^2-4)^2}\right] = f(t)$$

$\therefore$
$$L^{-1}\left[\int_s^\infty \frac{2s}{(s^2-4)^2}\, ds\right] = \frac{f(t)}{t} \qquad \text{[By result (6a)]}$$

$\therefore$
$$L^{-1}\left[\left\{-\frac{1}{(s^2-4)}\right\}_s^\infty\right] = \frac{f(t)}{t}$$

$\therefore$
$$L^{-1}\left[\frac{1}{s^2-4}\right] = \frac{f(t)}{t}$$

$\therefore$
$$\frac{\sinh 2t}{2} = \frac{f(t)}{t}$$

Hence
$$L^{-1}\left[\frac{2s}{(s^2-4)^2}\right] = f(t) = \frac{t \sinh 2t}{2}$$

(ii) Let
$$L^{-1}\left[\frac{2s+1}{(s^2+s+1)^2}\right] = f(t)$$

$\therefore$
$$L^{-1}\left[\int_s^\infty \frac{2s+1}{(s^2+s+1)^2}\, ds\right] = \frac{f(t)}{t} \qquad \text{[By result (6a)]}$$

$\therefore$
$$L^{-1}\left[\left\{-\frac{1}{(s^2+s+1)}\right\}_s^\infty\right] = \frac{f(t)}{t}$$

$\therefore$
$$L^{-1}\left[\frac{1}{s^2+s+1}\right] = \frac{f(t)}{t}$$

or $\qquad L^{-1}\left[\dfrac{1}{(s + 1/2)^2 + (\sqrt{3}/2)^2}\right] = \dfrac{f(t)}{t}$ $\qquad$ [Note this step]

$\therefore \qquad e^{-t/2}\, L^{-1}\left[\dfrac{1}{s^2 + (\sqrt{3}/2)^2}\right] = \dfrac{f(t)}{t}$ $\qquad$ [By the First Shifting Theorem]

$\therefore \qquad e^{-t/2}\, \dfrac{2}{\sqrt{3}}\, \sin\dfrac{\sqrt{3}}{2}\, t = \dfrac{f(t)}{t}$

or $\qquad \dfrac{2t}{\sqrt{3}}\, e^{-t/2} \sin\dfrac{\sqrt{3}}{2}\, t = f(t)$

Hence $\qquad L^{-1}\left[\dfrac{2s + 1}{(s^2 + s + 1)^2}\right] = f(t) = \dfrac{2t}{\sqrt{3}}\, e^{-t/2} \sin\dfrac{\sqrt{3}}{2}\, t$

(iii) Let $\qquad L^{-1}\left[\dfrac{s}{(s^2 + a^2)^2}\right] = f(t)$

$\therefore \qquad L^{-1}\left[\displaystyle\int_{s}^{\infty} \dfrac{s}{(s^2 + a^2)^2}\, ds\right] = \dfrac{f(t)}{t}$ $\qquad$ [By result (6 a)]

$\therefore \qquad \dfrac{1}{2}\, L^{-1}\left[\left\{-\dfrac{1}{s^2 + a^2}\right\}_{s}^{\infty}\right] = \dfrac{f(t)}{t}$

$\therefore \qquad \dfrac{1}{2}\, L^{-1}\left[\dfrac{1}{s^2 + a^2}\right] = \dfrac{f(t)}{t}$

$\therefore \qquad \dfrac{1}{2}\left(\dfrac{\sin at}{a}\right) = \dfrac{f(t)}{t}$

Hence $\qquad L^{-1}\left[\dfrac{s}{(s^2 + a^2)^2}\right] = f(t) = \dfrac{t \sin at}{2a}$

(F) MULTIPLICATION BY POWERS OF s :

Theorem : If $\qquad L^{-1}\,[F(s)] = f(t)$ and $f(0) = 0$, then

$\qquad L^{-1}\,[s\, F(s)] = f'(t)$

Proof : Since $\qquad L\,[f'(t)] = s\, F(s) - f(0)$ $\qquad$ [By result (12), Chapter 4]

$\qquad = s\, F(s)$ $\qquad \left\{\because\ f(0) = \lim_{t\to 0} f(t) = 0\right.$

$\therefore \qquad L^{-1}\,[s\, F(s)] = f'(t)$

Hence $\qquad \boxed{L^{-1}\,[s\, F(s)] = f'(t)\,,\ \text{if } f(0) = 0}$ $\qquad$ ... (7)

Generalisations to $L^{-1}\,[s^n\, F(s)]$, $n = 2, 3, \ldots\ldots$, are possible.

Remark 1 : The result (7) can be interpreted as multiplication of the transform by s corresponds to differentiation of a function of t w.r. to t.

Remark 2 : If the Laplace transform of unknown function f(t) contains the factor s, the inverse of that transform can be found by dropping (suppressing) the factor s, determining the inverse of the remaining portion of the transform and finally differentiating that inverse with respect to t.

ILLUSTRATION

Ex. 1 : *Use result (7), to find*

(i) $L^{-1}\left[\dfrac{s}{s^2+4}\right]$, given that $L^{-1}\left[\dfrac{1}{s^2+4}\right] = \dfrac{\sin 2t}{2}$

(ii) $L^{-1}\left[\dfrac{s}{s^2-4}\right]$, given that $L^{-1}\left[\dfrac{1}{s^2-4}\right] = \dfrac{\sinh 2t}{2}$

Sol. : (i) Given that $\quad L^{-1}\left[\dfrac{1}{s^2+4}\right] = \dfrac{\sin 2t}{2}$

$$\therefore \qquad L^{-1}\left[s \cdot \dfrac{1}{s^2+4}\right] = \dfrac{d}{dt}\left(\dfrac{\sin 2t}{2}\right) = \dfrac{2\cos 2t}{2} \qquad [\because \sin(0) = 0]$$

Hence, $\qquad L^{-1}\left[\dfrac{s}{s^2+4}\right] = \cos 2t \qquad$ [By result (7)]

(ii) Given that $\qquad L^{-1}\left[\dfrac{1}{s^2-4}\right] = \dfrac{\sinh 2t}{2}$

$$\therefore \qquad L^{-1}\left[s \cdot \dfrac{1}{s^2-4}\right] = \dfrac{d}{dt}\left(\dfrac{\sinh 2t}{2}\right) = \dfrac{2\cosh 2t}{2} \qquad [\because \sinh(0) = 0]$$

Hence, $\qquad L^{-1}\left[\dfrac{s}{s^2-4}\right] = \cosh 2t \qquad$ [By result (7)]

(G) DIVISION BY S :

Theorem : If $\qquad L^{-1}[F(s)] = f(t)$, then

$$L^{-1}\left[\dfrac{F(s)}{s}\right] = \int_0^t f(t)\, dt$$

Proof : Since $\qquad L\left[\int_0^t f(t)\, dt\right] = \dfrac{F(s)}{s} \qquad$ [By result (16), Chapter 4]

Hence, $\qquad \boxed{L^{-1}\left[\dfrac{F(s)}{s}\right] = \int_0^t f(t)\, dt} \qquad \qquad \dots (8)$

Generalisations to $L^{-1}\left[\dfrac{F(s)}{s^n}\right]$, $n = 2, 3, \dots\dots$, are possible.

Remark 1 : The result (8) can be interpreted as the division of the transform by s corresponds to integration of function of t.

Remark 2 : If the Laplace transform contains the factor $\dfrac{1}{s}$, the inverse of that transform can be found by dropping (suppressing) the factor 1/s, determining the inverse of the remaining portion of the transform, and finally integrating that inverse with respect to t from 0 to t.

$$\boxed{\textbf{ILLUSTRATIONS}}$$

Ex. 1 : *Obtain the inverse Laplace transform of the following functions :*

(i) $\dfrac{1}{s\,(s+2)}$　　(ii) $\dfrac{1}{s\,(s^2+4)}$　　(iii) $\dfrac{1}{s^3\,(s^2+1)}$　　　　**(Nov. 2013)**

Sol. : (i) We have 　$L^{-1}\left[\dfrac{1}{s+2}\right] = e^{-2t}$　　　　[Dropping the factor 1/s]

$\therefore$　　$L^{-1}\left[\dfrac{1}{s}\cdot\dfrac{1}{s+2}\right] = \displaystyle\int_0^t e^{-2t}\,dt = \left[\dfrac{e^{-2t}}{-2}\right]_0^t$　　　　[By result (8)]

$$= \dfrac{1-e^{-2t}}{2}\ .$$

(ii) We have 　$L^{-1}\left[\dfrac{1}{s^2+4}\right] = \dfrac{\sin 2t}{2}$

$\therefore$　　$L^{-1}\left[\dfrac{1}{s}\cdot\dfrac{1}{s^2+4}\right] = \displaystyle\int_0^t \dfrac{\sin 2t}{2}\,dt = \dfrac{1}{2}\left[\dfrac{-\cos 2t}{2}\right]_0^t$　　　　[By result (8)]

$$= \dfrac{1-\cos 2t}{4} = \dfrac{1}{2}\sin^2 t$$

(iii) We have 　$L^{-1}\left[\dfrac{1}{s^2+1}\right] = \sin t$

$\therefore$　$L^{-1}\left[\dfrac{1}{s}\cdot\dfrac{1}{s^2+1}\right] = \displaystyle\int_0^t \sin t\,dt = \left[-\cos t\right]_0^t = 1-\cos t$　　　　[By result (8)]

$$= f(t)\ (\text{say}),\qquad\text{where } F(s) = \dfrac{1}{s\,(s^2+1)}$$

$\therefore$　$L^{-1}\left[\dfrac{1}{s}\cdot F(s)\right] = \displaystyle\int_0^t f(t)\,dt = \int_0^t (1-\cos t)\,dt$　　　　[By result (8)]

$$= \left[t-\sin t\right]_0^t = t-\sin t = \phi(t)\ (\text{say}),$$

$$\text{where } \Phi(s) = \dfrac{1}{s^2\,(s+1)}$$

$$\therefore \quad L^{-1}\left[\frac{1}{s} \cdot \Phi(s)\right] = \int_0^t \phi(t)\, dt = \int_0^t (t - \sin t)\, dt \qquad \text{[By result (8)]}$$

$$\text{Hence, } L^{-1}\left[\frac{1}{s^3 (s^2 + 1)}\right] = \left[\frac{t^2}{2} + \cos t\right]_0^t = \frac{t^2}{2} + \cos t - 1$$

(H) USE OF CONVOLUTION THEOREM

If the function H(s) can be expressed as product of two functions F(s) and G(s) whose inverses f(t) and g(t) respectively are known, then the inverse of the product H(s) = F(s) G(s) can be obtained by using convolution theorem.

Theorem : If $L^{-1}[F(s)] = f(t)$, $L^{-1}[G(s)] = g(t)$ and $H(s) = F(s)\,G(s)$, then

$$L^{-1}[H(s)] = L^{-1}[F(s)\,G(s)] = \int_0^t f(u)\, g(t - u)\, du = f(t) * g(t)$$

Proof : Since

$$L[f(t) * g(t)] = L\left[\int_0^t f(u)\, g(t - u)\, du\right]$$

$$= F(s)\,G(s) = H(s) \qquad \text{[By result (25 a), Chapter 4]}$$

Hence,

$$\boxed{L^{-1}[H(s)] = L^{-1}[F(s)\,G(s)] = \int_0^t f(u)\, g(t - u)\, du = f(t) * g(t)} \qquad \dots (9\ a)$$

Note 1 : Since convolution of f(t) and g(t) is commutative, f(t) and g(t) are interchangeable in the above result.

Hence

$$\boxed{L^{-1}[H(s)] = L^{-1}[F(s)\,G(s)] = \int_0^t f(t - u)\, g(u)\, du = f(t) * g(t)} \qquad \dots (9\ b)$$

Note 2 : If $L^{-1}[F(s)] = f(t)$ and $L^{-1}[G(s)] = L^{-1}\left[\dfrac{1}{s}\right] = 1$, then by result (9 a), we get

$$L^{-1}\left[\frac{F(s)}{s}\right] = \int_0^t f(u) \cdot 1\, du, \text{ (same as result (8))}$$

ILLUSTRATION

Ex. 1 : *Use the convolution theorem to find inverse Laplace transform of the following functions :*

(i) $\dfrac{1}{s (s^2 + a^2)}$ (ii) $\dfrac{s^2}{(s^2 + a^2)(s^2 + b^2)}$, $a \neq b$ (iii) $\dfrac{1}{(s + 1)(s^2 + 1)}$ (iv) $\dfrac{1}{s\sqrt{s + 4}}$

(Nov. 2013, May 2005, 2009)

Sol. : (i) We can write $\dfrac{1}{s\,(s^2 + a^2)} = \dfrac{1}{s} \cdot \dfrac{1}{s^2 + a^2}$.

Let $\quad F(s) = \dfrac{1}{s} \quad$ and $\quad G(s) = \dfrac{1}{s^2 + a^2}$,

so that $\quad f(t) = L^{-1}\left[\dfrac{1}{s}\right] = 1 \quad$ and $\quad g(t) = L^{-1}\left[\dfrac{1}{s^2 + a^2}\right] = \dfrac{\sin at}{a}$

Hence by convolution theorem, we have

$$L^{-1}\left[\dfrac{1}{s\,(s^2 + a^2)}\right] = 1 * \dfrac{\sin at}{a} = \int_0^t 1 \cdot \dfrac{\sin au}{a}\,du \quad\text{[Using result (9b)]}$$

$$= \left[\dfrac{-\cos au}{a^2}\right]_0^t = \dfrac{1 - \cos at}{a^2}$$

(ii) We can write $\dfrac{s^2}{(s^2 + a^2)\,(s^2 + b^2)} = \dfrac{s}{s^2 + a^2} \cdot \dfrac{s}{s^2 + b^2}$

Let $\quad F(s) = \dfrac{s}{s^2 + a^2} \quad$ and $\quad G(s) = \dfrac{s}{s^2 + b^2}$,

so that $\quad f(t) = L^{-1}\left[\dfrac{s}{s^2 + a^2}\right] = \cos at \quad$ and $\quad g(t) = L^{-1}\left[\dfrac{s}{s^2 + b^2}\right] = \cos bt$

Hence by convolution theorem, we have

$$L^{-1}\left[\dfrac{s^2}{(s^2 + a^2)\,(s^2 + b^2)}\right] = \cos at * \cos bt = \int_0^t \cos au \cos b\,(t - u)\,du$$

$$= \dfrac{1}{2} \int_0^t [\cos (au + bt - bu) + \cos (au - bt + bu)]\,du$$

$$[\because\ 2 \cos A \cos B = \cos (A + B) + \cos (A - B)]$$

$$= \dfrac{1}{2} \int_0^t [\cos \{(a - b)\,u + bt\} + \cos \{(a + b)\,u - bt\}]\,du$$

$$= \dfrac{1}{2} \left[\dfrac{\sin \{(a - b)\,u + bt\}}{a - b} + \dfrac{\sin \{(a + b)\,u - bt\}}{a + b}\right]_0^t$$

$$= \dfrac{1}{2} \left[\dfrac{\sin at - \sin bt}{a - b} + \dfrac{\sin at + \sin bt}{a + b}\right]$$

$$= \dfrac{a \sin at - b \sin bt}{a^2 - b^2}$$

(iii) We can write $\dfrac{1}{(s+1)(s^2+1)} = \dfrac{1}{(s+1)} \cdot \dfrac{1}{(s^2+1)}$.

Let $\qquad F(s) = \dfrac{1}{s+1} \qquad$ and $\qquad G(s) = \dfrac{1}{s^2+1}$

so that $\qquad f(t) = L^{-1}\left[\dfrac{1}{s+1}\right] = e^{-t} \qquad$ and $\qquad g(t) = L^{-1}\left[\dfrac{1}{s^2+1}\right] = \sin t.$

Hence by convolution theorem, we have

$$L^{-1}\left[\frac{1}{(s+1)(s^2+1)}\right] = e^{-t} * \sin t = \int_0^t e^{-u} \sin(t-u)\, du$$

$$\int_0^t e^{-u} \sin(t-u)\, du = \left[\frac{e^{-u}}{(-1)^2+(-1)^2}\left(-\sin(t-u)+\cos(t-u)\right)\right]_{u=0}^{t}$$

$$= \frac{e^{-t}}{2}(0+1) - \frac{1}{2}(-\sin t + \cos t)$$

$$= \frac{1}{2}\left[\sin t - \cos t + e^{-t}\right]$$

(iv) We can write $\dfrac{1}{s\sqrt{s+4}} = \dfrac{1}{s} \cdot \dfrac{1}{\sqrt{s+4}}$.

Let $\qquad\qquad F(s) = \dfrac{1}{s} \quad$ and $\quad G(s) = \dfrac{1}{\sqrt{s+4}}$

so that $\qquad\qquad f(t) = 1 \quad$ and $\quad g(t) = L^{-1}\left[\dfrac{1}{\sqrt{s+4}}\right] = \dfrac{e^{-4t}}{\sqrt{\pi t}}$

Hence by convolution theorem, we have

$$L^{-1}\left[\frac{1}{s\sqrt{s+4}}\right] = 1 * \frac{e^{-4t}}{\sqrt{\pi t}} = \int_0^t \frac{e^{-4u}}{\sqrt{\pi u}}\, du$$

$$= \frac{1}{\sqrt{\pi}} \int_0^{2\sqrt{t}} e^{-y^2}\, dy$$

$$= \frac{1}{2}\,\mathrm{erf}\,(2\sqrt{t})$$

Put $\quad 4u = y^2 \;\therefore\; du = \dfrac{1}{2}\,y\,dy$

$$\begin{array}{c|cc} u & 0 & t \\ y & 0 & 2\sqrt{t} \end{array}$$

In the following table, we have listed useful inverse Laplace transform theorems for ready reference.

Table 5.2

Table of Theorems of Inverse Laplace Transform

	If $L^{-1}[F(s)] = f(t)$, then
A	$L^{-1}[F(s + a)] = e^{-at} f(t)$
B	$L^{-1}[e^{-as} F(s)] = f(t - a)\, U(t - a) = \begin{cases} f(t - a) & t > a \\ 0 & t < a \end{cases}$
C	$L^{-1}[F(ks)] = \dfrac{1}{k}\, f\!\left(\dfrac{t}{k}\right)$
D	$L^{-1}\left[\dfrac{d}{ds}\, F(s)\right] = -t\, f(t)$
E	$L^{-1}\left[\displaystyle\int_{s}^{\infty} F(s)\, ds\right] = \dfrac{f(t)}{t}$
F	$L^{-1}[s\, F(s)] = f'(t)$, if $f(0) = 0$
G	$L^{-1}\left[\dfrac{F(s)}{s}\right] = \displaystyle\int_{0}^{t} f(u)\, du$
H	$L^{-1}[F(s)\, G(s)] = \displaystyle\int_{0}^{t} f(u)\, g(t - u)\, du = f(t) * g(t)$

5.7 METHOD III : USE OF PARTIAL FRACTIONS

In case where $F(s)$ is a rational algebraic fraction, it is often convenient to find inverse Laplace transform by expressing $F(s)$ in terms of partial fractions.

Consider a rational function $F(s) = \dfrac{N(s)}{D(s)}$, where $N(s)$ and $D(s)$ are polynomials with the degree of $N(s)$ less than that of $D(s)$ (i.e. proper fraction). Then $F(s) = \dfrac{N(s)}{D(s)}$ can be resolved into the sum of rational functions (called *partial fractions*) having the form $\dfrac{A}{(as + b)^r}$, $\dfrac{As + B}{(as^2 + bs + c)^r}$, where $r = 1, 2, 3 \ldots$ By finding the inverse Laplace transform of each of the partial fractions, we can find $L^{-1}[F(s)]$.

Example 1 : When the denominator has non-repeated linear factors, we write

$$L^{-1} \frac{11s^2 - 2s + 5}{(s - 2)(2s - 1)(s + 1)} = \frac{A}{s - 2} + \frac{B}{2s - 1} + \frac{C}{s + 1}$$

Example 2 : When the denominator has repeated linear factors, we write

$$\frac{2s - 5}{(3s - 4)(2s + 1)^3} = \frac{A}{3s - 2} + \frac{B}{(2s + 1)} + \frac{C}{(2s + 1)^2} + \frac{D}{(2s + 1)^3}$$

Example 3 : When the denominator has non-repeated quadratic factors, we write

$$\frac{s^2 + 2s - 4}{(s^2 + 2s + 5)(s^2 + 2s + 2)} = \frac{As + B}{(s^2 + 2s + 5)} + \frac{Cs + D}{(s^2 + 2s + 2)}$$

Example 4 : When the denominator has repeated quadratic factors, we write

$$\frac{3s^2 - 4s + 2}{(s^2 + 2s + 4)^2(s - 5)} = \frac{As + B}{(s^2 + 2s + 4)} + \frac{Cs + D}{(s^2 + 2s + 4)^2} + \frac{E}{s - 5}$$

The constants A, B, C etc., can be obtained by clearing of fractions (i.e. by multiplying both sides by the denominator of the given fraction) and equating coefficients of like powers of s on both sides or by using special methods [see solved examples].

For non-repeated linear factors, we have more simple method for finding the constants [see solved examples].

Note : Quadratic factor can also be written as product of linear factors with complex conjugate roots and apply above method.

ILLUSTRATION

Ex. 1 : *Using partial fractions, find the inverse Laplace transforms of :*

(i) $\dfrac{3s + 7}{s^2 - 2s - 3}$ **(Dec. 2009, May 2011)** *(ii)* $\dfrac{11s^2 - 2s + 5}{(s - 2)(2s - 1)(s + 1)}$ **(May 09, Dec. 05)**

(iii) $\dfrac{21s - 9}{(s + 1)(s - 2)^3}$ *(iv)* $\dfrac{3s + 1}{(s - 1)(s^2 + 1)}$ **(Dec. 14, Nov. 2015)** *(v)* $\dfrac{2s^2 - 1}{(s^2 + 1)(s^2 + 4)}$

(vi) $\dfrac{s}{s^4 + 4a^4}$

Sol. : (i) We have $\dfrac{3s + 7}{s^2 - 2s - 3} = \dfrac{3s + 7}{(s - 3)(s + 1)}$.

Here denominator has non-repeated linear factors.

Let $\qquad \dfrac{3s + 7}{(s - 3)(s + 1)} = \dfrac{A}{(s - 3)} + \dfrac{B}{(s + 1)}$ ... (i)

Multiplying both sides of (i) by $(s - 3)(s + 1)$, we obtain

$$3s + 7 = A(s + 1) + B(s - 3) = (A + B)s + A - 3B$$

Equating coefficients of like powers of s, we have

$$A + B = 3 \quad \text{and} \quad A - 3B = 7$$

$$\therefore \qquad A = 4 \quad \text{and} \quad B = -1$$

Hence
$$\frac{3s+7}{(s-3)(s+1)} = \frac{4}{s-3} - \frac{1}{s+1}$$

and
$$L^{-1}\left[\frac{3s+7}{(s-3)(s+1)}\right] = 4\,L^{-1}\left[\frac{1}{s-3}\right] - L^{-1}\left[\frac{1}{s+1}\right] = 4\,e^{3t} - e^{-t}$$

Another Method : Multiplying both sides of (i) by $(s-3)(s+1)$, we have
$$3s+7 = A(s+1) + B(s-3)$$

Putting $s = 3$, we get $16 = A(4)$ $\qquad \therefore \quad A = 4$

Putting $s = -1$, we get $4 = B(-4)$ $\qquad \therefore \quad B = -1$ etc.

Note : It should be noted that the second method is less tedious. It can be used whenever the denominator has non-repeated linear factors.

(ii) We have $\dfrac{11s^2 - 2s + 5}{(s-2)(2s-1)(s+1)}$

Here the denominator has non-repeated linear factors.

Let
$$\frac{11s^2 - 2s + 5}{(s-2)(2s-1)(s+1)} = \frac{A}{s-2} + \frac{B}{(2s-1)} + \frac{C}{s+1} \qquad \ldots \text{(i)}$$

Multiplying both sides of (i) by $(s-2)(2s-1)(s+1)$, we obtain
$$11s^2 - 2s + 5 = A(2s-1)(s+1) + B(s-2)(s+1) + C(s-2)(2s-1)$$

Putting $s = 2$, we get $\quad 11(4) - 2(2) + 5 = A(4-1)(2+1) \qquad \therefore \qquad A = 5$

Putting $s = 1/2$, we get $\quad 11(1/4) - 2(1/2) + 5 = B(1/2 - 2)(1/2 + 1) \quad \therefore \quad B = -3$

Putting $s = -1$, we get $\quad 11(-1) - 2(-1) + 5 = C(-3)(-3) \qquad \therefore \qquad C = 2$

$$\text{Hence } L^{-1}\left[\frac{11s^2 - 2s + 5}{(s-2)(2s-1)(s+1)}\right] = L^{-1}\left[\frac{5}{s-2} + \frac{-3}{2s-1} + \frac{2}{s+1}\right]$$

$$= 5\,L^{-1}\left[\frac{1}{s-2}\right] - \frac{3}{2}\,L^{-1}\left[\frac{1}{s-1/2}\right]$$

$$+ 2\,L^{-1}\left[\frac{1}{s+1}\right]$$

$$= 5\,e^{2t} - \frac{3}{2}\,e^{t/2} + 2e^{-t}$$

(iii) We have $\dfrac{21s-9}{(s+1)(s-2)^3}$

Here the denominator has repeated linear factors.

$$\text{Given : } F(s) = \frac{21s-9}{(s+1)(s-2)^3} = \frac{A}{s+1} + \frac{B}{s-2} + \frac{C}{(s-2)^2} + \frac{D}{(s-2)^3} , \text{ (say)} \quad \ldots \text{(i)}$$

$$\therefore\ 21s - 9 = A(s-2)^3 + B(s+1)(s-2)^2 + C(s+1)(s-2) + D(s+1)$$

$$= A(s^3 - 2s^2 + 4s - 8) + B(s+1)(s^2 - 4s + 4) + C(s^2 - s - 2) + D(s+1)$$

$$= s^3[A+B] + s^2[-2A - 3B + C] + s[4A - C + D]$$

$$+ [-8A + 4B - 2C + D]$$

Equating coefficients of identical powered terms of s from both sides

$$\therefore \qquad 0 = A + B$$
$$0 = -2A - 3B + C$$
$$21 = 4A - C + D$$
$$\text{and} \qquad -9 = -8A + 4B - 2C + D$$

On solving simultaneously we get

$$-A = B = C = -2 \text{ and } D = 11$$

$\therefore$ Equation (i) $\Rightarrow$ $F(s) = \dfrac{2}{s+1} - \dfrac{2}{s-2} - \dfrac{2}{(s-2)^2} + \dfrac{11}{(s-2)^3}$ ... (ii)

Taking inverse Laplace transform using

$$L^{-1}\left[G(s+a)\right] = e^{-at}\, g(t) \text{ and } L^{-1}\left[\frac{1}{s^n}\right] = \frac{t^{n-1}}{(n-1)!}$$

$\therefore$ Equation (ii) $\Rightarrow$ $f(t) = L^{-1}\left[\dfrac{2}{s+1}\right] + L^{-1}\left\{\dfrac{-2}{s} - \dfrac{2}{s^2} + \dfrac{11}{s^3}\right\}_{s \to s-2}$

$$= 2e^{-t} + e^{2t}\left\{-2 - 2t + 11\,\frac{t^2}{2}\right\}$$

(iv) Here denominator has one linear factor and one quadratic factor.

Let $\qquad \dfrac{3s+1}{(s-1)(s^2+1)} = \dfrac{A}{s-1} + \dfrac{Bs+C}{s^2+1}$ ... (i)

Multiplying both sides of (i) by $(s-1)(s^2+1)$, we obtain

$$3s + 1 = A(s^2+1) + (Bs+C)(s-1) \qquad ... \text{(ii)}$$

Putting s = 1, we get $\;4 = A(2) \qquad \therefore \quad A = 2$

To determine B and C, equate coefficients of like powers of s^2 and constant terms in (ii), then

$$0 = A + B \text{ and } 1 = A - C$$
$$\therefore \qquad B = -A = -2 \text{ and } C = A - 1 = 1$$

Thus $\quad L^{-1}\left[\dfrac{3s+1}{(s-1)(s^2+1)}\right] = L^{-1}\left[\dfrac{2}{s-1} + \dfrac{-2s+1}{s^2+1}\right]$

$$= 2L^{-1}\left[\frac{1}{s-1}\right] - 2L^{-1}\left[\frac{s}{s^2+1}\right] + L^{-1}\left[\frac{1}{s^2+1}\right]$$

$$= 2e^t - 2\cos t + \sin t$$

Another method : Since A = 2, we have from (i)

$$\dfrac{3s+1}{(s-1)(s^2+1)} = \dfrac{2}{s-1} + \dfrac{Bs+C}{s^2+1} \qquad ... \text{(iii)}$$

To determine B and C we can substitute two values for s, say $\;s = 0$ and $s = 2$ (for example) in (iii); then

$$-1 = -2 + C \qquad \text{and} \qquad \frac{7}{5} = 2 + \frac{2B+C}{5}$$

$$\therefore \qquad C = 1 \qquad\qquad \text{and} \qquad B = -2 \text{ ... etc.}$$

(v) We have $\dfrac{s}{s^4 + 4a^4}$. Here denominator has non-repeated quadratic factors.

Let $$\frac{2s^2 - 1}{(s^2 + 1)\,(s^2 + 4)} = \frac{As + B}{(s^2 + 1)} + \frac{Cs + D}{(s^2 + 4)} \qquad \dots \text{(i)}$$

Multiplying both sides of (i) by $(s^2 + 1)\,(s^2 + 4)$, we have

$$2s^2 - 1 = (As + B)\,(s^2 + 4) + (Cs + D)\,(s^2 + 1)$$
$$= (A + C)\,s^3 + (B + D)\,s^2 + (4A + C)\,s + 4B + D \qquad \dots \text{(ii)}$$

To determine A, B, C and D, equate like powers of s^3, s^2, s and constant terms in (ii),
then $\quad A + C = 0, \quad B + D = 2, \quad 4A + C = 0, \quad 4B + D = -1$

$\therefore \ \ A = 0, \ B = -1, \ C = 0, \ D = 3.$

Thus $\quad L^{-1}\left[\dfrac{2s^2 - 1}{(s^2 + 1)\,(s^2 + 4)}\right] = L^{-1}\left[\dfrac{-1}{s^2 + 1} + \dfrac{3}{s^2 + 4}\right]$

$$= -L^{-1}\left[\frac{1}{s^2 + 1}\right] + 3\,L^{-1}\left[\frac{1}{s^2 + 4}\right] = -\sin t + 3\,\frac{\sin 2t}{2}$$

Another method : Since fraction involves only even powers of s, we put $s^2 = p$ so that
the given fraction becomes $\dfrac{2p - 1}{(p + 1)\,(p + 4)}$ which has only non-repeated linear factors in
the denominator.

Let $$\frac{2p - 1}{(p + 1)\,(p + 4)} = \frac{A}{p + 1} + \frac{B}{p + 4} \qquad \dots \text{(iii)}$$

Multiplying both sides of (iii) by $(p + 1)\,(p + 4)$, we get

$$2p - 1 = A\,(p + 4) + B\,(p + 1)$$

Putting $p = -1$, we get $\quad -3 = A\,(3) \qquad \therefore \quad A = -1$

Putting $p = -4$, we get $\ -9 = B\,(-3) \qquad \therefore \quad B = 3 \ \dots$ etc.

(vi) Since $\quad s^4 + 4a^4 = (s^2 + 2a^2)^2 - (2as)^2$
$$= (s^2 + 2as + 2a^2)\,(s^2 - 2as + 2a^2)$$

Let $$\frac{s}{s^4 + 4a^4} = \frac{As + B}{(s^2 + 2as + 2a^2)} + \frac{Cs + D}{(s^2 - 2as + 2a^2)} \qquad \dots \text{(i)}$$

Multiplying both sides by $s^4 + a^4$, we get

$$s = (As + B)\,(s^2 - 2as + 2a^2) + (Cs + D)\,(s^2 + 2as + 2a^2)$$
$$= (A + C)\,s^3 + (-2a\,A + B + 2aC + D)\,s^2$$
$$+ (2a^2\,A - 2a\,B + 2a^2\,C + 2a\,D)\,s + 2a^2\,B + 2a^2\,D \qquad \dots \text{(ii)}$$

Equating coefficients of s^3, s^2, s and constant terms in (ii), we have

$A + C = 0, \quad -2aA + B + 2aC + D = 0, \quad 2a^2A - 2aB + 2a^2\,C + 2aD = 1,$
$2a^2\,B + 2a^2\,D = 0.$

$\therefore \ \ A = 0, \qquad B = \dfrac{-1}{4a}, \qquad C = 0, \qquad D = \dfrac{1}{4a}$

$\therefore \qquad L^{-1}\left[\dfrac{s}{s^4 + 4a^4}\right] = \dfrac{1}{4a}\,L^{-1}\left[-\dfrac{1}{s^2 + 2as + 2a^2} + \dfrac{1}{s^2 - 2as + 2a^2}\right]$

$$= \frac{1}{4a}\left\{-L^{-1}\left[\frac{1}{(s+a)^2+a^2}\right]+L^{-1}\left[\frac{1}{(s-a)^2+a^2}\right]\right\}$$

$$= \frac{1}{4a}\left\{-e^{-at}L^{-1}\left[\frac{1}{s^2+a^2}\right]+e^{at}L^{-1}\left[\frac{1}{s^2+a^2}\right]\right\}$$

[By the First Shifting Theorem]

$$= \frac{1}{4a}\left\{-e^{-at}\left(\frac{\sin at}{a}\right)+e^{at}\left(\frac{\sin at}{a}\right)\right\}$$

$$= \frac{1}{2a^2}\sin at\left(\frac{e^{at}-e^{-at}}{2}\right) = \frac{1}{2a^2}\sin at\,\sinh at$$

Note : In certain cases, with a little insight, the partial fractions can be written directly.

Thus
$$\frac{s}{(s^2+2as+2a^2)\,(s^2-2as+2a^2)} = \frac{1}{4a}\left[\frac{-1}{s^2+2as+2a^2}+\frac{1}{s^2-2as+2a^2}\right]$$

ILLUSTRATIONS ON THEOREMS OF INVERSE LAPLACE TRANSFORM AND PARTIAL FRACTIONS METHOD

Ex. 1 : *Find the inverse Laplace transforms of the following functions :*

(i) $\dfrac{3s+5}{(4s^2+12s+9)}$ *(ii)* $\dfrac{2s+5}{s^2+4s+13}$ **(Dec. 2011)** *(iii)* $\dfrac{s+7}{s^2+2s+2}$

(iv) $\dfrac{5s-2}{3s^2+4s+8}$ *(v)* $\dfrac{s-1}{s^2-6s+25}$ *(vi)* $\dfrac{1}{\sqrt{7s+6}}$ **(May 2005)**

Sol. : (i) $L^{-1}\left[\dfrac{3s+5}{4s^2+12s+9}\right] = L^{-1}\left[\dfrac{3\,(s+3/2)-9/2+5}{4\,(s^2+3s+9/4)}\right]$

$$= \frac{1}{4}\,L^{-1}\left[\frac{3\,(s+3/2)+1/2}{(s+3/2)^2}\right]$$

$$= \frac{3}{4}\,L^{-1}\left[\frac{1}{(s+3/2)}\right] + \frac{1}{8}\,L^{-1}\left[\frac{1}{(s+3/2)^2}\right]$$

$$= \frac{3}{4}\,e^{-3t/2}\,L^{-1}\left[\frac{1}{s}\right] + \frac{1}{8}\,e^{-3t/2}\,L^{-1}\left[\frac{1}{s^2}\right]$$

[By the First Shifting Theorem]

$$= \frac{3}{4}\,e^{-3t/2}\,(1) + \frac{1}{8}\,e^{-3t/2}\,(t) = \frac{e^{-3t/2}}{4}\left(3+\frac{t}{2}\right)$$

(ii) $L^{-1}\left[\dfrac{2s+5}{s^2+4s+13}\right] = L^{-1}\left[\dfrac{2\,(s+2)-4+5}{(s+2)^2+3^2}\right] = L^{-1}\left[\dfrac{2\,(s+2)+1}{(s+2)^2+3^2}\right]$

$$= 2\,L^{-1}\left[\frac{(s+2)}{(s+2)^2+3^2}\right] + L^{-1}\left[\frac{1}{(s+2)^2+3^2}\right]$$

$$= 2\,e^{-2t}\,L^{-1}\left[\frac{s}{s^2+3^2}\right] + e^{-2t}\,L^{-1}\left[\frac{1}{s^2+3^2}\right]$$

$$= 2\,e^{-2t}\,(\cos 3t) + e^{-2t}\left(\frac{\sin 3t}{3}\right)$$

$$= e^{-2t}\left(2\cos 3t + \frac{1}{3}\sin 3t\right)$$

(iii) $\qquad L^{-1}\left[\dfrac{s+7}{s^2+2s+2}\right] = L^{-1}\left[\dfrac{(s+1)+6}{(s+1)^2+1}\right]$

$$= L^{-1}\left[\frac{s+1}{(s+1)^2+1}\right] + 6\,L^{-1}\left[\frac{1}{(s+1)^2+1}\right]$$

$$= e^{-t}\,L^{-1}\left[\frac{s}{s^2+1}\right] + 6e^{-t}\,L^{-1}\left[\frac{1}{s^2+1}\right]$$

$$= e^{-t}\,(\cos t) + 6\,e^{-t}\,(\sin t) = e^{-t}\,(\cos t + 6\sin t)$$

(iv) $\qquad L^{-1}\left[\dfrac{5s-2}{3s^2+4s+8}\right] = L^{-1}\left[\dfrac{5s-2}{3\left(s^2+\dfrac{4}{3}s+\dfrac{8}{3}\right)}\right]$

$$= \frac{1}{3}\,L^{-1}\left[\frac{5\,(s+2/3)-10/3-2}{(s+2/3)^2+20/9}\right]$$

$$= \frac{5}{3}\,L^{-1}\left[\frac{(s+2/3)}{(s+2/3)^2+(2\sqrt{5}/3)^2}\right] - \frac{16}{9}\,L^{-1}\left[\frac{1}{(s+2/3)^2+(2\sqrt{5}/3)^2}\right]$$

$$= \frac{5}{3}\,e^{-2t/3}\,L^{-1}\left[\frac{s}{s^2+(2\sqrt{5}/3)^2}\right] - \frac{16}{9}\,e^{-2t/3}\,L^{-1}\left[\frac{1}{s^2+(2\sqrt{5}/3)^2}\right]$$

$$= \frac{5}{3}\,e^{-2t/3}\left(\cos\frac{2\sqrt{5}}{3}\,t\right) - \frac{16}{9}\,e^{-2t/3}\left(\frac{3}{2\sqrt{5}}\sin\frac{2\sqrt{5}}{3}\,t\right)$$

$$= e^{-2t/3}\left(\frac{5}{3}\cos\frac{2\sqrt{5}\,t}{3} - \frac{8}{3\sqrt{5}}\sin\frac{2\sqrt{5}\,t}{3}\right).$$

(v) $L^{-1}\left[\dfrac{s-1}{s^2-6s+25}\right] = L^{-1}\left[\dfrac{(s-3)+3-1}{(s-3)^2+16}\right] = L^{-1}\left[\dfrac{(s-3)+2}{(s-3)^2+4^2}\right]$

$$= L^{-1}\left[\frac{(s-3)}{(s-3)^2+4^2}\right] + 2\,L^{-1}\left[\frac{1}{(s-3)^2+4^2}\right]$$

$$= e^{3t}\,L^{-1}\left[\frac{s}{s^2+4^2}\right] + 2\,e^{3t}\,L^{-1}\left[\frac{1}{s^2+4^2}\right]$$

$$= e^{3t}\,(\cos 4t) + 2e^{3t}\left(\frac{\sin 4t}{4}\right) = e^{3t}\left(\cos 4t + \frac{1}{2}\sin 4t\right)$$

(vi) $\quad L^{-1}\left[\dfrac{1}{\sqrt{7s+6}}\right] = \dfrac{1}{\sqrt{7}}\,L^{-1}\left[\dfrac{1}{\sqrt{s+6/7}}\right] = \dfrac{1}{\sqrt{7}}\,L^{-1}\left[\dfrac{1}{(s+6/7)^{1/2}}\right]$

$$= \frac{1}{\sqrt{7}} \; e^{-6t/7} \, L^{-1}\left[\frac{1}{s^{1/2}}\right] = \frac{1}{\sqrt{7}} \; e^{-6t/7} \frac{t^{1/2 - 1}}{\overline{|1/2}}$$

$$= \frac{e^{-6t/7}}{\sqrt{7\pi \, t}} \qquad\qquad \left\{ \because \; L^{-1}\left[\frac{1}{s^n}\right] = \frac{t^{n-1}}{\overline{|n}} \; \text{ and } \; \overline{|1/2} = \sqrt{\pi} \right\}$$

Ex. 2 : *Obtain the inverse Laplace transforms of the following functions :*

(i) $\dfrac{e^{-as}}{(s + b)^{5/2}}$ (ii) $\dfrac{e^{3 - 2s}}{(s + 4)^{5/2}}$ (iii) $\dfrac{e^{-3s}}{s^2 + 8s + 25}$ (iv) $\dfrac{e^{-2s}}{\sqrt{s + 5}}$

Sol. : (i) We have

$$L^{-1}\left[\frac{1}{(s + b)^{5/2}}\right] = e^{-bt} \, L^{-1}\left[\frac{1}{s^{5/2}}\right] = e^{-bt} \frac{t^{3/2}}{\overline{|5/2}} \qquad \text{(Dropping } e^{-as}\text{)}$$

$$= \frac{4}{3\sqrt{\pi}} \; e^{-bt} \, t^{3/2}$$

Hence by the second shifting theorem, we get

$$L^{-1}\left[\frac{e^{-as}}{(s + b)^{5/2}}\right] = \begin{cases} \dfrac{4}{3\sqrt{\pi}} e^{b\,(t - a)}\,(t - a)^{3/2} & , \; t > a \\[2ex] 0 & , \; t < a \end{cases}$$

$$= \left\{ \frac{4}{3\sqrt{\pi}} e^{b\,(t - a)}\,(t - a)^{3/2} \right\} \, U(t - a)$$

(ii) We can write $\quad L^{-1}\left[\dfrac{e^{3 - 2s}}{(s + 4)^{5/2}}\right] = e^3 \, L^{-1}\left[\dfrac{e^{-2s}}{(s + 4)^{5/2}}\right]$

Also we have $\quad L^{-1}\left[\dfrac{1}{(s + 4)^{5/2}}\right] = \dfrac{4\,e^{-4t}\,t^{3/2}}{3\sqrt{\pi}}$

Hence by the second shifting theorem, with a = 2, we get

$$L^{-1}\left[\frac{e^{3 - 2s}}{(s + 4)^{5/2}}\right] = \begin{cases} e^3 \left[\dfrac{4}{3\sqrt{\pi}} e^{-4\,(t - 2)}\,(t - 2)^{3/2}\right] & , \; t > 2 \\[2ex] 0 & , \; t < 2 \end{cases}$$

$$= e^3 \left\{ \frac{4}{3\sqrt{\pi}} e^{-4\,(t - 2)}\,(t - 2)^{3/2} \right\} \, U(t - 2)$$

(iii) We have

$$L^{-1}\left[\frac{1}{s^2 + 8s + 25}\right] = L^{-1}\left[\frac{1}{(s+4)^2 + 3^2}\right] = e^{-4t}\, L^{-1}\left[\frac{1}{s^2 + 3^2}\right]$$

$$= e^{-4t}\left(\frac{\sin 3t}{3}\right) = \frac{1}{3}\, e^{-4t}\, \sin 3t$$

Hence by the second shifting theorem, with a = 3, we get

$$L^{-1}\left[\frac{e^{-3s}}{s^2 + 8s + 25}\right] = \begin{cases} \dfrac{1}{3}\, e^{-4(t-3)}\, \sin 3\,(t-3) & , \quad t > 3 \\[2mm] 0 & , \quad t < 3 \end{cases}$$

$$= \left\{\frac{1}{3}\, e^{-4(t-3)}\, \sin 3\,(t-3)\right\}\, U(t-3)$$

(iv) We have

$$L^{-1}\left[\frac{1}{\sqrt{s+5}}\right] = e^{-5t}\, L^{-1}\left[\frac{1}{\sqrt{s}}\right] = e^{-5t}\left(\frac{t^{-1/2}}{\overline{|1/2}}\right)$$

$$= \frac{e^{-5t}}{\sqrt{\pi t}}$$

Hence by the second shifting theorem, with a = 2, we get

$$L^{-1}\left[\frac{e^{-2s}}{\sqrt{s+5}}\right] = \begin{cases} \dfrac{e^{-5(t-2)}}{\sqrt{\pi (t-2)}} & , \quad t > 2 \\[2mm] 0 & , \quad t < 2 \end{cases}$$

$$= \frac{e^{-5(t-2)}}{\sqrt{\pi (t-2)}}\, U(t-2)$$

Ex. 3 : If $L^{-1}\left[\dfrac{e^{-1/s}}{s^{1/2}}\right] = \dfrac{\cos 2\sqrt{t}}{\sqrt{\pi t}}$, find $L^{-1}\left[\dfrac{e^{-a/s}}{s^{1/2}}\right]$ where $a > 0$.

Sol. : Given that

$$L^{-1}\left[\frac{e^{-1/s}}{s^{1/2}}\right] = \frac{\cos 2\sqrt{t}}{\sqrt{\pi t}}$$

$$\therefore \quad L^{-1}\left[\frac{e^{-1/ks}}{(ks)^{1/2}}\right] = \frac{1}{k}\, \frac{\cos 2\sqrt{t/k}}{\sqrt{\pi (t/k)}} = \frac{1}{\sqrt{k}}\, \frac{\cos 2\sqrt{t/k}}{\sqrt{\pi t}} \qquad \text{[By the Change of Scale Theorem]}$$

or $$L^{-1}\left[\frac{e^{-1/ks}}{s^{1/2}}\right] = \frac{\cos 2\sqrt{t/k}}{\sqrt{\pi t}}$$

Putting $k = 1/a$, we get

$$L^{-1}\left[\frac{e^{-as}}{s^{1/2}}\right] = \frac{\cos 2\sqrt{at}}{\sqrt{\pi t}}.$$

Ex. 4 : *Find the inverse Laplace transforms of the following :*

$(i)\ \cot^{-1}\left(\frac{s-2}{3}\right)$ **(May 17)**　　　$(ii)\ \log\left(1 + \frac{a^2}{s^2}\right)$ **(May 2012)**

$(iii)\ \log\left(\frac{s^2 + a^2}{s^2 + b^2}\right)$ **(Dec. 2011)**　$(iv)\ \frac{s+1}{(s^2 + 2s + 1)^2}$　**(Dec. 2004, 2006; May 2008)**

Sol. : (i) Let　　$L^{-1}\left[\cot^{-1}\left(\frac{s-2}{3}\right)\right] = f(t)$

$\therefore\qquad L^{-1}\left[\frac{d}{ds}\cot^{-1}\left(\frac{s-2}{3}\right)\right] = -t\,f(t)$　　　　　　　　[By result (5 a)]

$\therefore\qquad L^{-1}\left[\frac{-1/3}{1 + (s-2)^2/3^2}\right] = -t\,f(t)$　　　$\left\{\because\ \cot^{-1}\left(\frac{s-2}{3}\right) = \frac{\pi}{2} - \tan^{-1}\left(\frac{s-2}{3}\right)\right\}$

or$\qquad L^{-1}\left[\frac{-3}{(s-2)^2 + 9}\right] = -t\,f(t)$

$\therefore\qquad e^{2t}\,L^{-1}\left[\frac{3}{s^2 + 9}\right] = -t\,f(t)$　　　　　[By the First Shifting Theorem]

$\therefore\qquad e^{2t}\,(\sin 3t) = t\,f(t)$

Hence$\qquad L^{-1}\left[\cot^{-1}\left(\frac{s-2}{3}\right)\right] = f(t) = \frac{e^{2t}\sin 3t}{t}$

(ii) Let$\qquad L^{-1}\left[\log\left(1 + \frac{a^2}{s^2}\right)\right] = f(t)$

$\therefore\qquad L^{-1}\left[\frac{d}{ds}\log\left(\frac{s^2 + a^2}{s^2}\right)\right] = -t\,f(t)$

or $\ L^{-1}\left[\frac{d}{ds}\{\log(s^2 + a^2) - \log s^2\}\right] = -t\,f(t)$

$\therefore\qquad L^{-1}\left[\frac{2s}{s^2 + a^2} - \frac{2}{s}\right] = -t\,f(t)$

$\therefore\qquad 2(\cos at - 1) = -t\,f(t)$

or$\qquad \frac{2(1 - \cos at)}{t} = f(t)$

Hence$\qquad L^{-1}\left[\log\left(1 + \frac{a^2}{s^2}\right)\right] = \frac{2(1 - \cos at)}{t}$

(iii) Let $\quad L^{-1}\left[\log\left(\dfrac{s^2+a^2}{s^2+b^2}\right)\right] = f(t)$

$\therefore\ L^{-1}\left[\dfrac{d}{ds}\{\log(s^2+a^2)-\log(s^2+b^2)\}\right] = -t\,f(t)$

$\therefore \quad L^{-1}\left[\dfrac{2s}{s^2+a^2}-\dfrac{2s}{s^2+b^2}\right] = -t\,f(t)$

$\therefore \quad 2\,(\cos at - \cos bt) = -t\,f(t)$

or $\quad \dfrac{2\,(\cos bt - \cos at)}{t} = f(t)$

Hence $\quad L^{-1}\left[\log\left(\dfrac{s^2+a^2}{s^2+b^2}\right)\right] = \dfrac{2\,(\cos bt - \cos at)}{t}$

(iv) [**Note :** Since $\dfrac{d}{ds}\left(\dfrac{1}{s^2+2s+1}\right)=\dfrac{-2\,(s+1)}{(s^2+2s+1)^2}$ or $-\dfrac{1}{2}\dfrac{d}{ds}\left(\dfrac{1}{s^2+2s+1}\right)=\dfrac{s+1}{(s^2+2s+1)^2}$,

we use result 5 (a), to obtain required transform.]

We know that $\quad L^{-1}\left[\dfrac{1}{s^2+2s+1}\right] = L^{-1}\left[\dfrac{1}{(s+1)^2}\right] = e^{-t}L^{-1}\left[\dfrac{1}{s^2}\right] = e^{-t}\,t$

$\therefore \quad L^{-1}\left[\dfrac{d}{ds}\left(\dfrac{1}{s^2+2s+1}\right)\right] = -t\,(e^{-t}\,t)$

$\therefore \quad L^{-1}\left[\dfrac{-2\,(s+1)}{(s^2+2s+1)^2}\right] = -t\,(e^{-t}\,t)$

or $\quad L^{-1}\left[\dfrac{s+1}{(s^2+2s+1)^2}\right] = \dfrac{1}{2}\,t^2\,e^{-t}$

Ex. 5 : *Find the inverse Laplace transforms of the following functions :*

$(i)\ \dfrac{s+2}{(s^2+4s+5)^2}$ $\quad (ii)\ \dfrac{s+1}{(s^2+2s+2)^2}$ $\quad (iii)\ \dfrac{s^2}{(s+a)^3}$ $\hspace{2cm}$ **(Dec. 2004)**

Sol. : (i) Let $\quad L^{-1}\left[\dfrac{s+2}{(s^2+4s+5)^2}\right] = f(t)$

$\therefore \quad L^{-1}\left[\displaystyle\int_s^{\infty}\dfrac{s+2}{(s^2+4s+5)^2}\,ds\right] = \dfrac{f(t)}{t}$ $\hspace{2cm}$ [By result (6 a)]

$\therefore \quad L^{-1}\left[\left\{-\dfrac{1}{2\,(s^2+4s+5)}\right\}_s^{\infty}\right] = \dfrac{f(t)}{t}$

$\therefore \quad \dfrac{1}{2}\,L^{-1}\left[\dfrac{1}{s^2+4s+5}\right] = \dfrac{f(t)}{t}$

or
$$\frac{1}{2}\, L^{-1}\left[\frac{1}{(s+2)^2+1}\right] = \frac{f(t)}{t}$$

$\therefore$
$$\frac{1}{2}\, e^{-2t}\, L^{-1}\left[\frac{1}{s^2+1}\right] = \frac{f(t)}{t} \qquad \text{[By the First Shifting Theorem]}$$

$\therefore$
$$\frac{1}{2}\, e^{-2t}\, (\sin t) = \frac{f(t)}{t}$$

Hence
$$L^{-1}\left[\frac{s+2}{(s^2+4s+5)^2}\right] = f(t) = \frac{1}{2}\, t\, e^{-2t} \sin t$$

(ii) Let
$$L^{-1}\left[\frac{s+1}{(s^2+2s+2)^2}\right] = f(t)$$

$\therefore$
$$L^{-1}\left[\int_{s}^{\infty} \frac{s+1}{(s^2+2s+2)^2}\, ds\right] = \frac{f(t)}{t}$$

$\therefore$
$$L^{-1}\left[\left\{-\frac{1}{2\,(s^2+2s+2)}\right\}_{s}^{\infty}\right] = \frac{f(t)}{t}$$

$\therefore$
$$L^{-1}\left[\frac{1}{2}\,\frac{1}{(s^2+2s+2)}\right] = \frac{f(t)}{t}$$

$\therefore$
$$\frac{1}{2}\, L^{-1}\left[\frac{1}{(s+1)^2+1}\right] = \frac{f(t)}{t}$$

$\therefore$
$$\frac{1}{2}\, e^{-t}\left[\frac{1}{s^2+1}\right] = \frac{f(t)}{t}$$

$\therefore$
$$\frac{1}{2}\, e^{-t} \sin t = \frac{f(t)}{t}$$

Hence
$$L^{-1}\left[\frac{s+1}{(s^2+2s+2)^2}\right] = f(t) = \frac{1}{2}\, t\, e^{-t} \sin t$$

(iii) We have
$$L^{-1}\left[\frac{1}{(s+a)^3}\right] = e^{-at}\, L^{-1}\left[\frac{1}{s^3}\right] = e^{-at}\,\frac{t^2}{2} \qquad \text{[By the First Shifting Theorem]}$$

$\therefore$
$$L^{-1}\left[s\,\frac{1}{(s+a)^3}\right] = \frac{d}{dt}\left(\frac{1}{2}\, e^{-at}\, t^2\right) = \frac{1}{2}\, e^{-at}\, (2t - at^2) \qquad \text{[By result (7)]}$$

$$= \phi\,(t)\ (\text{say}), \qquad \text{where } \Phi(s) = \frac{s}{(s+a)^2} \text{ and } \phi(0) = 0$$

$\therefore$
$$L^{-1}\,[s\,\Phi(s)] = \frac{d}{dt}\,\phi(t) = \frac{d}{dt}\left\{\frac{1}{2}\, e^{-at}\, (2t - at^2)\right\}$$

$$= \frac{1}{2}\, e^{-at}\, (2 - 4\,at + a^2\,t^2)$$

Hence,
$$L^{-1}\left[\frac{s^2}{(s+a)^3}\right] = e^{-at}\left(1 - 2at + \frac{1}{2}\, a^2 t^2\right)$$

Ex. 6 : *Find the inverse of each of the following transforms :*

(i) $\dfrac{1}{s^2\,(s+1)}$ (ii) $\dfrac{s^2+2}{s\,(s^2+4)}$ (iii) $\dfrac{1}{s\,(s+1)^3}$

Sol. : (i) We have

$$L^{-1}\left[\frac{1}{s+1}\right] = e^{-t} \qquad\qquad \text{[Dropping the factor } 1/s^2\text{]}$$

$$\therefore \quad L^{-1}\left[\frac{1}{s}\cdot\frac{1}{s+1}\right] = \int_0^t e^{-t}\,dt = \left[-e^{-t}\right]_0^t = 1 - e^{-t} \qquad \text{[By result (8)]}$$

$$= \phi(t)\ (\text{say}), \qquad \text{where } \Phi(s) = \frac{1}{s\,(s+1)}$$

$$\therefore \quad L^{-1}\left[\frac{1}{s}\cdot\Phi(s)\right] = \int_0^t \phi(t)\,dt = \int_0^t (1-e^{-t})\ dt \qquad \text{[By result (8)]}$$

$$\text{Hence,} \quad L^{-1}\left[\frac{1}{s^2\,(s+1)}\right] = \left[t+e^{-t}\right]_0^t = t + e^{-t} - 1$$

(ii) $$L^{-1}\left[\frac{s^2+2}{s\,(s^2+4)}\right] = L^{-1}\left[\frac{s^2+4-2}{s\,(s^2+4)}\right] = L^{-1}\left[\frac{1}{s} - \frac{2}{s\,(s^2+4)}\right]$$

$$= L^{-1}\left[\frac{1}{s}\right] - L^{-1}\left[\frac{2}{s\,(s^2+4)}\right] = 1 - \int_0^t L^{-1}\left[\frac{2}{s^2+4}\right]\,dt$$

$$\text{[By result (8)]}$$

$$= 1 - \int_0^t \sin 2t\,dt = 1 - \left[-\frac{\cos 2t}{2}\right]_0^t$$

$$= 1 + \frac{\cos 2t}{2} - \frac{1}{2} = \frac{1+\cos 2t}{2} = \cos^2 t$$

(iii) We have

$$L^{-1}\left[\frac{1}{(s+1)^3}\right] = e^{-t}\,L^{-1}\left[\frac{1}{s^3}\right] = e^{-t}\,\frac{t^2}{2}$$

$$\therefore \quad L^{-1}\left[\frac{1}{s}\cdot\frac{1}{(s+1)^3}\right] = \frac{1}{2}\int_0^t e^{-t}\,t^2\,dt = \frac{1}{2}\left[t^2\,(-e^{-t}) - (2t)\,(e^{-t}) + (2)\,(-e^{-t})\right]_0^t$$

$$= \frac{1}{2}\left[(-t^2 e^{-t} - 2t\,e^{-t} - 2e^{-t}) - (-2)\right] = 1 - e^{-t}\left(\frac{t^2}{2} + t + 1\right)$$

Ex. 7 : *Find the inverse Laplace transforms of each of the following functions :*

(i) $\dfrac{s^2}{(s^2+a^2)^2}$ (ii) $\dfrac{1}{(s^2+a^2)^2}$ (iii) $\dfrac{1}{s}\,\log\left(\dfrac{s+3}{s+2}\right)$ (iv) $\dfrac{1}{s}\,\log\left(\dfrac{s^2+a^2}{s^2+b^2}\right)$.

(May 2005, Dec. 2005)

Sol. : (i) We have

$$L^{-1}\left[\frac{1}{s^2 + a^2}\right] = \frac{\sin at}{a}$$

$$\therefore \quad L^{-1}\left[\frac{d}{ds}\frac{1}{s^2 + a^2}\right] = \frac{-t \sin at}{a} \qquad \text{[By result (5 a)]}$$

$$\therefore \quad L^{-1}\left[-\frac{2s}{(s^2 + a^2)^2}\right] = \frac{-t \sin at}{a}$$

$$\text{or} \quad L^{-1}\left[\frac{s}{(s^2 + a^2)^2}\right] = \frac{1}{2a} t \sin at$$

$$\therefore \quad L^{-1}\left[s \cdot \frac{s}{(s^2 + a^2)^2}\right] = \frac{1}{2a}\frac{d}{dt}(t \sin at)$$

$$\text{[By result (7) and } \because (t \sin at)_{t=0} = 0]$$

$$= \frac{1}{2a}(\sin at + at \cos at)$$

$$\text{Hence} \quad L^{-1}\left[\frac{s^2}{(s^2 + a^2)^2}\right] = \frac{1}{2a}(\sin at + at \cos at)$$

(ii) We have $\quad L^{-1}\left[\dfrac{1}{s^2 + a^2}\right] = \dfrac{\sin at}{a}$

$$\therefore \quad L^{-1}\left[\frac{d}{ds}\frac{1}{s^2 + a^2}\right] = \frac{-t \sin at}{a} \qquad \text{[By result (5 a)]}$$

$$\therefore \quad L^{-1}\left[\frac{s}{(s^2 + a^2)^2}\right] = \frac{1}{2a} t \sin at$$

$$\therefore \quad L^{-1}\left[\frac{1}{s} \cdot \frac{s}{(s^2 + a^2)^2}\right] = \frac{1}{2a}\int_0^t t \sin at\, dt \qquad \text{[By result (8)]}$$

$$= \frac{1}{2a}\left[t\left(-\frac{\cos at}{a}\right) - (1)\left(-\frac{\sin at}{a^2}\right)\right]_0^t$$

$$= \frac{1}{2a}\left(\frac{\sin at}{a^2} - \frac{t \cos at}{a}\right) = \frac{1}{2a^3}(\sin at - at \cos at)$$

$$\text{Hence} \quad L^{-1}\left[\frac{1}{(s^2 + a^2)^2}\right] = \frac{1}{2a^3}(\sin at - at \cos at)$$

(iii) Let $\quad L^{-1}\left[\log\left(\dfrac{s + 3}{s + 2}\right)\right] = f(t)$

$$\therefore \quad L^{-1}\left[\frac{d}{ds}\{\log(s + 3) - \log(s + 2)\}\right] = -t\, f(t) \qquad \text{[By result (5 a)]}$$

$$\therefore \quad L^{-1}\left[\frac{1}{s + 3} - \frac{1}{s + 2}\right] = -t\, f(t)$$

$\therefore \qquad\qquad (e^{-3t} - e^{-2t}) = -t\, f(t)$

or $\qquad\qquad \dfrac{e^{-2t} - e^{-3t}}{t} = f(t)$

Hence $\qquad L^{-1}\left[\dfrac{1}{s}\, \log\left(\dfrac{s+3}{s+2}\right)\right] = \displaystyle\int_0^t \dfrac{e^{-2t} - e^{-3t}}{t}\, dt$ [By result (8)]

(iv) Let $\qquad L^{-1}\left[\log\left(\dfrac{s^2+a^2}{s^2+b^2}\right)\right] = f(t)$

$\therefore \qquad L^{-1}\left[\dfrac{d}{ds}\{\log(s^2+a^2) - \log(s^2+b^2)\}\right] = -t\, f(t)$ [By result (5 a)]

$\therefore \qquad L^{-1}\left[\dfrac{2s}{s^2+a^2} - \dfrac{2s}{s^2+b^2}\right] = -t\, f(t)$

or $\qquad\qquad \dfrac{2(\cos bt - \cos at)}{t} = f(t)$

Hence $\qquad L^{-1}\left[\dfrac{1}{s}\, \log\left(\dfrac{s^2+a^2}{s^2+b^2}\right)\right] = \displaystyle\int_0^t \dfrac{2(\cos bt - \cos at)}{t}\, dt$ [By result (8)]

Ex. 8 : *Find the inverse Laplace transforms of the following functions :*

(i) $\dfrac{(s+2)^2}{(s^2+4s+8)^2}$ (ii) $\dfrac{s^2-a^2}{(s^2+a^2)^2}$ (iii) $\dfrac{1}{(s-2)^4(s+3)}$ **(Dec. 2008, Dec. 2010)**

(iv) $\tan^{-1}\dfrac{2}{s^2}$

Sol. : (i) $L^{-1}\left[\dfrac{(s+2)^2}{(s^2+4s+8)^2}\right] = L^{-1}\left[\dfrac{(s+2)^2}{[(s+2)^2+4]^2}\right]$

$\qquad\qquad\qquad\qquad = e^{-2t}\, L^{-1}\left[\dfrac{s^2}{(s^2+4)^2}\right]$

Using the result of $L^{-1}\left[\dfrac{s^2}{(s^2+a^2)^2}\right]$ from Ex. 7 (i), we have

$L^{-1}\left[\dfrac{(s+2)^2}{(s^2+4s+8)^2}\right] = e^{-2t}\left\{\dfrac{1}{4}(\sin 2t + 2t \cos 2t)\right\}$

(ii) $\qquad L^{-1}\left[\dfrac{s^2-a^2}{(s^2+a^2)^2}\right] = L^{-1}\left[\dfrac{s^2}{(s^2+a^2)^2} - \dfrac{a^2}{(s^2+a^2)^2}\right]$

$\qquad\qquad\qquad\qquad = L^{-1}\left[\dfrac{s^2}{(s^2+a^2)^2}\right] - a^2 L^{-1}\left[\dfrac{1}{(s^2+a^2)^2}\right]$

Using results of Ex. 7 (i) and (ii), we get

$L^{-1}\left[\dfrac{s^2-a^2}{(s^2+a^2)^2}\right] = \dfrac{1}{2a}(\sin at + at \cos at) - a^2\left\{\dfrac{1}{2a^3}(\sin at - at \cos at)\right\}$

$\qquad\qquad\qquad\qquad = \dfrac{1}{2a}(2at \cos at) = t \cos at$

(iii) $\quad L^{-1}\left[\dfrac{1}{(s-2)^4(s+3)}\right] = L^{-1}\left[\dfrac{1}{(s+3-5)^4(s+3)}\right] = e^{-3t}\, L^{-1}\left[\dfrac{1}{s\,(s-5)^4}\right]$

$$= e^{-3t}\int_0^t L^{-1}\left[\dfrac{1}{(s-5)^4}\right]dt = e^{-3t}\int_0^t e^{5t}\,\dfrac{t^3}{3!}\,dt$$

$$= \dfrac{e^{-3t}}{6}\int_0^t t^3\,e^{5t}\,dt$$

$$= \dfrac{e^{-3t}}{6}\left[t^3\left(\dfrac{e^{5t}}{5}\right) - 3t^2\left(\dfrac{e^{5t}}{25}\right) + 6t\left(\dfrac{e^{5t}}{125}\right) - 6\left(\dfrac{e^{5t}}{625}\right)\right]_0^t$$

$$= \dfrac{e^{-3t}}{6}\left[e^{5t}\left(\dfrac{t^3}{5} - \dfrac{3t^2}{25} + \dfrac{6t}{125} - \dfrac{6}{625}\right) + \dfrac{6}{625}\right]$$

$$= e^{-3t}\left\{\dfrac{e^{5t}}{30}\left(t^3 - \dfrac{3t^2}{5} + \dfrac{6t}{25} - \dfrac{6}{125}\right) + \dfrac{1}{625}\right\}$$

$$= \dfrac{e^{2t}}{30}\left(t^3 - \dfrac{3t^2}{5} + \dfrac{6t}{25} - \dfrac{6}{125}\right) + \dfrac{e^{-3t}}{625}$$

(iv) Let $\qquad L^{-1}\left[\tan^{-1}\dfrac{2}{s^2}\right] = f(t)$

$\therefore \qquad L^{-1}\left[\dfrac{d}{ds}\tan^{-1}\dfrac{2}{s^2}\right] = -t\,f(t)$

$\therefore \qquad L^{-1}\left[\dfrac{1}{1+4/s^4}\left(-\dfrac{4}{s^3}\right)\right] = -t\,f(t)$

or $\qquad L^{-1}\left[\dfrac{4s}{s^4+4}\right] = t\,f(t)$

or $\quad L^{-1}\left[\dfrac{4s}{(s^2-2s+2)(s^2+2s+2)}\right] = t\,f(t)$

$$\{\because\ s^4+4 = s^4+4s^2+4-4s^2 = (s^2+2)^2-(2s)^2\}$$

or $\quad L^{-1}\left[\dfrac{1}{s^2-2s+2} - \dfrac{1}{s^2+2s+2}\right] = t\,f(t)$

or $\quad L^{-1}\left[\dfrac{1}{(s-1)^2+1} - \dfrac{1}{(s+1)^2+1}\right] = t\,f(t)$

$\therefore \qquad e^t\sin t - e^{-t}\sin t = t\,f(t)$

Hence $\qquad L^{-1}\left[\tan^{-1}\dfrac{2}{s^2}\right] = f(t) = \dfrac{2}{t}\sin t \sinh t$

Ex. 9 : *Using the convolution theorem, find the inverse of each of the following transforms :*

(i) $\dfrac{s^2}{(s^2+a^2)^2}$ $\quad$ (ii) $\dfrac{1}{(s^2+a^2)^2}$ $\quad$ (iii) $\dfrac{s}{(s^2+a^2)^2}$ $\quad$ (iv) $\dfrac{1}{(s^2+1)^3}$ $\qquad\qquad$ **(Dec. 2005)**

Sol. : (i) We can write $\dfrac{s^2}{(s^2+a^2)^2} = \dfrac{s}{s^2+a^2} \cdot \dfrac{s}{s^2+a^2}$

Let $\qquad F(s) = \dfrac{s}{s^2+a^2}$ and $G(s) = \dfrac{s}{s^2+a^2}$,

so that $\qquad f(t) = \cos at$ and $g(t) = \cos at$

Hence by convolution theorem, we have

$$L^{-1}\left[\frac{s^2}{(s^2+a^2)^2}\right] = \cos at * \cos at$$

$$= \int_0^t \cos au \cos a(t-u)\, du = \frac{1}{2}\int_0^t [\cos at + \cos a(2u-t)]\, du$$

$$[\because\ 2\cos A \cos B = \cos(A+B) + \cos(A-B)]$$

$$= \frac{1}{2}\left[\cos at\,(u) + \frac{\sin a(2u-t)}{2a}\right]_0^t$$

$$= \frac{1}{2}\left[\{(\cos at)(t) - 0\} + \left\{\frac{\sin at}{2a} - \frac{\sin a(-t)}{2a}\right\}\right]$$

$$= \frac{1}{2}\left(t\cos at + \frac{\sin at}{2a} + \frac{\sin at}{2a}\right) = \frac{1}{2a}(\sin at + at\cos at)$$

(ii) We can write $\dfrac{1}{(s^2+a^2)^2} = \dfrac{1}{s^2+a^2} * \dfrac{1}{s^2+a^2}$.

Let $\qquad F(s) = \dfrac{1}{s^2+a^2}$ and $G(s) = \dfrac{1}{s^2+a^2}$,

so that $\qquad f(t) = \dfrac{\sin at}{a}$ and $g(t) = \dfrac{\sin at}{a}$

Hence by the convolution theorem, we have

$$L^{-1}\left[\frac{1}{(s^2+a^2)^2}\right] = \frac{\sin at}{a} * \frac{\sin at}{a}$$

$$= \int_0^t \frac{\sin au}{a} \cdot \frac{\sin a(t-u)}{a}\, du$$

$$= \frac{1}{2a^2}\int_0^t [\cos a(2u-t) - \cos at]\, du$$

$$[\because\ 2\sin A \sin B = \cos(A-B) - \cos(A+B)]$$

$$= \frac{1}{2a^2}\left[\frac{\sin a(2u-t)}{2a} - \cos at\,(u)\right]_0^t$$

$$= \frac{1}{2a^2} \left[\left\{ \frac{\sin at}{2a} - \frac{\sin a\,(-t)}{2a} \right\} - \{(\cos at)\,(t) - 0\} \right]$$

$$= \frac{1}{2a^2} \left(\frac{\sin at}{a} - t \cos at \right) = \frac{1}{2a^3} (\sin at - at \cos at)$$

(iii) We can write $\dfrac{s}{(s^2 + a^2)^2} = \dfrac{s}{s^2 + a^2} \cdot \dfrac{1}{s^2 + a^2}$.

Let $\qquad\qquad F(s) = \dfrac{s}{s^2 + a^2} \quad$ and $\quad G(s) = \dfrac{1}{s^2 + a^2}$,

so that $\qquad\qquad f(t) = \cos at \quad$ and $\quad g(t) = \dfrac{\sin at}{a}$

Hence by the convolution theorem, we have

$$L^{-1} \left[\frac{s}{(s^2 + a^2)^2} \right] = \cos at * \frac{\sin at}{a}$$

$$= \int_0^t \cos au \cdot \frac{\sin a\,(t - u)}{a}\, du = \frac{1}{2a} \int_0^t [\sin at - \sin a\,(2u - t)]\, dt$$

$$[\because\ 2 \cos A \sin B = \sin (A + B) - \sin (A - B)]$$

$$= \frac{1}{2a} \left[\sin at\,(u) + \frac{\cos a\,(2u - t)}{2a} \right]_0^t$$

$$= \frac{1}{2a} \left[\{(\sin at)\,(t) - 0\} + \left\{ \frac{\cos at}{2a} - \frac{\cos a\,(-t)}{2a} \right\} \right]$$

$$= \frac{1}{2a} (t \sin at)$$

(iv) We can write $\dfrac{1}{(s^2 + 1)^3} = \dfrac{1}{(s^2 + 1)^2} \cdot \dfrac{1}{(s^2 + 1)}$.

Let $\qquad\qquad F(s) = \dfrac{1}{(s^2 + 1)^2} \quad$ and $\quad G(s) = \dfrac{1}{(s^2 + 1)}$

so that $\qquad\qquad f(t) = L^{-1} \left[\dfrac{1}{(s^2 + 1)^2} \right]$ and $\quad g(t) = \sin t$

Hence by the convolution theorem, we have

$$L^{-1} \left[\frac{1}{(s^2 + 1)^3} \right] = f(t) * \sin t \qquad\qquad\qquad \dots \text{(i)}$$

$$\text{Now } f(t) = L^{-1} \left[\frac{1}{(s^2 + 1)^2} \right] = L^{-1} \left[\frac{1}{s^2 + 1} \cdot \frac{1}{s^2 + 1} \right]$$

$$= \sin t * \sin t$$

$$= \int_0^t \sin u \, \sin(t-u) \, du = \frac{1}{2} \int_0^t [\cos(2u-t) - \cos t] \, du$$

$$[\because \; 2 \sin A \sin B = \cos(A-B) - \cos(A+B)]$$

$$= \frac{1}{2} \left[\frac{\sin(2u-t)}{2} - \cos t \,(u) \right]_0^t$$

$$= \frac{1}{2} \left[\left\{ \frac{\sin t}{2} - \frac{\sin(-t)}{2} \right\} - \{(\cos t \,(t) - 0)\} \right]$$

$$= \frac{1}{2} (\sin t - t \cos t) \qquad\qquad \text{... (ii)}$$

Hence from (i),

$$L^{-1} \left[\frac{1}{(s^2+1)^3} \right] = \frac{1}{2} (\sin t - t \cos t) \, * \sin t$$

$$= \int_0^t \frac{1}{2} (\sin u - u \cos u) \cdot \sin(t-u) \, du$$

$$= \frac{1}{2} \left[\int_0^t \sin u \, \sin(t-u) \, du - \int_0^t u \cos u \, \sin(t-u) \, du \right]$$

$$= \frac{1}{2} \left[\frac{1}{2} (\sin t - t \cos t) - \frac{1}{2} \int_0^t u \, \{\sin t - \sin(2u-t)\} \, du \right] \qquad \text{[From result (ii)]}$$

$$= \frac{1}{4} \left[(\sin t - t \cos t) - \int_0^t u \sin t + \int_0^t u \sin(2u-t) \, du \right]$$

$$= \frac{1}{4} \left[(\sin t - t \cos t) - \left\{ \sin t \left(\frac{u^2}{2} \right) \right\}_0^t + \left\{ u \left(-\frac{\cos(2u-t)}{2} \right) - (1) \left(-\frac{\sin(2u-t)}{t} \right) \right\}_0^t \right]$$

$$= \frac{1}{4} \left[(\sin t - t \cos t) - (\sin t) \left(\frac{t^2}{2} \right) + \left\{ \left(\frac{-t \cos t}{2} - 0 \right) - \left(-\frac{\sin t}{4} - \frac{\sin t}{4} \right) \right\} \right]$$

$$= \frac{1}{4} \left(\sin t - t \cos t - \frac{t^2}{2} \sin t - \frac{t \cos t}{2} + \frac{\sin t}{2} \right) = \frac{1}{8} \left[(3 - t^2) \sin t - 3t \cos t \right]$$

Ex. 10 : *Use the convolution theorem to find inverse Laplace transform of each of the following :*

(i) $\dfrac{1}{s^2(s+1)^2}$ *(ii)* $\dfrac{1}{(s-2)^4(s+3)}$ *(iii)* $\dfrac{s+2}{s^2(s-1)^2}$ *(iv)* $\dfrac{s+29}{(s+4)(s^2+9)}$

Sol. : (i) We can write $\dfrac{1}{s^2(s+1)^2} = \dfrac{1}{s^2} \cdot \dfrac{1}{(s+1)^2}$

Let $\qquad\qquad F(s) = \dfrac{1}{s^2} \qquad$ and $\qquad G(s) = \dfrac{1}{(s+1)^2}$,

so that $\qquad\qquad f(t) = t \qquad$ and $\qquad g(t) = t\,e^{-t}$

Hence by the convolution theorem, we have

$$L^{-1}\left[\dfrac{1}{s^2(s+1)^2}\right] = t * t\,e^{-t} = t\,e^{-t} * t$$

$$= \int_0^t (u e^{-u})\,(t-u)\ du = \int_0^t (ut - u^2)\,e^{-u}\,du$$

$$= \left[(ut - u^2)\,(-e^{-u}) - (t - 2u)\,(e^{-u}) + (-2)\,(-e^{-u})\right]_0^t$$

$$= t\,e^{-t} + 2\,e^{-t} + t - 2$$

Check : $L[t e^{-t} + 2e^{-t} + t - 2] = \dfrac{1}{(s+1)^2} + \dfrac{2}{s+1} + \dfrac{1}{s^2} - \dfrac{2}{s}$

$$= \dfrac{s^2 + 2s^2(s+1) + (s+1)^2 - 2s(s+1)^2}{s^2(s+1)^2} = \dfrac{1}{s^2(s+1)^2}$$

(ii) $\qquad L^{-1}\left[\dfrac{1}{(s-2)^4(s+3)}\right] = L^{-1}\left[\dfrac{1}{(s-2)^4(s-2+5)}\right]$ **(May 2014)** (Note the step)

$$= e^{2t}\,L^{-1}\left[\dfrac{1}{s^4(s+5)}\right] \qquad\qquad\qquad \dots\text{(i)}$$

Now to find $L^{-1}\left[\dfrac{1}{s^4(s+5)}\right]$, we use the convolution theorem.

Let $\qquad\qquad F(s) = \dfrac{1}{s^4} \qquad\qquad$ and $\qquad\qquad G(s) = \dfrac{1}{(s+5)}$

so that $\qquad\qquad f(t) = \dfrac{t^3}{6} \qquad\qquad$ and $\qquad\qquad g(t) = e^{-5t}$

$\therefore \qquad L^{-1}\left[\dfrac{1}{s^4(s+5)}\right] = \dfrac{t^3}{6} * e^{-5t}$

$$= \int_0^t \dfrac{u^3}{6}\,e^{-5(t-u)}\,du = \dfrac{e^{-5t}}{6}\int_0^t u^3\,e^{5u}\,du$$

$$= \dfrac{e^{-5t}}{6}\left[u^3\left(\dfrac{e^{5u}}{5}\right) - 3u^2\left(\dfrac{e^{5u}}{25}\right) + 6u\left(\dfrac{e^{5u}}{125}\right) - 6\left(\dfrac{e^{5u}}{625}\right)\right]_0^t$$

$$= \dfrac{e^{-5t}}{6}\left[\left(t^3\dfrac{e^{5t}}{5} - 3t^2\dfrac{e^{5t}}{25} + 6t\dfrac{e^{5t}}{125} - \dfrac{6e^{5t}}{625}\right) + \dfrac{6}{625}\right]$$

$$= \dfrac{1}{30}\left(t^3 - \dfrac{3t^2}{5} + \dfrac{6t}{25} - \dfrac{6}{125}\right) + \dfrac{e^{-5t}}{625} \qquad\qquad \dots\text{(ii)}$$

Hence from (i) and (ii), we get

$$L^{-1}\left[\frac{1}{(s-2)^4(s+3)}\right] = e^{2t}\,L^{-1}\left[\frac{1}{s^4(s+5)}\right]$$

$$= \frac{e^{2t}}{30}\left(t^3 - \frac{3}{5}t^2 + \frac{6}{25}t - \frac{6}{125}\right) + \frac{e^{-3t}}{625}$$

(iii)　$L^{-1}\left[\dfrac{s+2}{s^2(s-1)^2}\right] = L^{-1}\left[\dfrac{1}{s(s-1)^2}\right] + 2\,L^{-1}\left[\dfrac{1}{s^2(s-1)^2}\right]$　　… (i)

Now　$L^{-1}\left[\dfrac{1}{s(s-1)^2}\right] = L^{-1}\left[\dfrac{1}{s}\cdot\dfrac{1}{(s-1)^2}\right] = 1 * t\,e^t$

$$= \int_0^t 1 \cdot u\,e^u\,du = \left[u\,e^u - e^u\right]_0^t$$

$$= 1 + e^t(t-1) \qquad\qquad\qquad\text{… (ii)}$$

And　$L^{-1}\left[\dfrac{1}{s^2(s-1)^2}\right] = L^{-1}\left[\dfrac{1}{s}\left\{\dfrac{1}{s(s-1)^2}\right\}\right] = \int_0^t [1 + e^t(t-1)]\,dt$　　[Using (ii)]

$$= \left[t + \{(t-1)\,e^t - e^t\}\right]_0^t$$

$$= \left[(t + (t-1)\,e^t - e^t) - (0 - 1 - 1)\right]$$

$$= 2 + t + e^t(t-2) \qquad\qquad\qquad\text{… (iii)}$$

Using (i), (ii) and (iii), we get

$$L^{-1}\left[\frac{s+2}{s^2(s-1)^2}\right] = 1 + e^t(t-1) + 2\,[2 + t + e^t(t-2)]$$

$$= 5 + 2t + e^t(3t-5)$$

(iv)　We can write $\dfrac{s+29}{(s+4)(s^2+9)} = \dfrac{1}{s+4}\cdot\dfrac{s+29}{s^2+9}$.

Let　　　　　$F(s) = \dfrac{1}{s+4}$　　and　　$G(s) = \dfrac{s+29}{s^2+9}$

so that　　　$f(t) = e^{-4t}$　　and　　$g(t) = \cos 3t + \dfrac{29}{3}\sin 3t$

Hence by the convolution theorem, we have

$$L^{-1}\left[\frac{s+29}{(s+4)(s^2+9)}\right] = e^{-4t} * \left(\cos 3t + \frac{29}{3}\sin 3t\right)$$

$$= \int_0^t e^{-4(t-u)}\left(\cos 3u + \frac{29}{3}\sin 3u\right)du$$

$$= e^{-4t} \left[\int_0^t e^{4u} \cos 3u \, du + \frac{29}{3} \int_0^t e^{4u} \sin 3u \, du \right]$$

$$= e^{-4t} \left[\left\{ \frac{e^{4u}}{16+9} (4 \cos 3u + 3 \sin 3u) \right\}_0^t + \frac{29}{3} \left\{ \frac{e^{4u}}{16+9} (4 \sin 3u - 3 \cos 3u) \right\}_0^t \right]$$

$$= e^{-4t} \left[\left\{ \frac{e^{4t}}{25} (4 \cos 3t + 3 \sin 3t) - \frac{4}{25} \right\} + \frac{29}{3} \left\{ \frac{e^{4t}}{25} (4 \sin 3t - 3 \cos 3t) + \frac{3}{25} \right\} \right]$$

$$= e^{-4t} \left(\frac{-4+29}{25} \right) + \frac{1}{25} (4 \cos 3t + 3 \sin 3t + \frac{116}{3} \sin 3t - 29 \cos 3t)]$$

$$= e^{-4t} + \frac{1}{25} \left(\frac{125}{3} \sin 3t - 25 \cos 3t \right) = e^{-4t} + \frac{5}{3} \sin 3t - \cos 3t$$

Ex. 11 : *Show that* $\displaystyle \int_0^t \int_0^t \int_0^t f(t) \, dt^3 = \int_0^t \frac{(t-u)^2}{2!} f(u) \, du.$

Sol. : Consider inverse Laplace transform of $\dfrac{1}{s^3} F(s)$ as

$$L^{-1} \left[\frac{1}{s^3} F(s) \right] = \int_0^t \int_0^t \int_0^t f(t) \, dt^3 \qquad \dots \text{(i)}$$

and by the convolution theorem, we have

$$L^{-1} \left[\frac{1}{s^3} \cdot F(s) \right] = L^{-1} \left[\frac{1}{s^3} \right] * L^{-1} [F(s)] = \frac{t^2}{2!} * f(t)$$

$$= \int_0^t \frac{(t-u)^2}{2!} f(u) \, du \qquad \dots \text{(ii)}$$

Equating (i) and (ii), we get the required result.

Ex. 12 : *If* $L [J_o(t)] = \dfrac{1}{\sqrt{s^2 + 1}}$, *then show that* $\displaystyle \int_0^t J_o(u) \, J_o(t-u) \, du = \sin t$

Sol. : Let $\displaystyle h(t) = \int_0^t J_o(u) \, J_o(t-u) \, du$

Then by the convolution theorem, we have

$$L[h(t)] = L \left[\int_0^t J_o(u) \, J_o(t-u) \, du \right] = L [J_o(t)] \, L [J_o(t)]$$

$$= \left(\frac{1}{\sqrt{s^2 + 1}} \right) \left(\frac{1}{\sqrt{s^2 + 1}} \right) = \frac{1}{s^2 + 1}$$

Hence $\qquad h(t) = L^{-1}\left[\dfrac{1}{s^2+1}\right] = \sin t$

or $\quad \displaystyle\int_0^t J_0(u)\, J_0(t-u)\, du = \sin t$

[**Note :** This $J_0(t)$ is known as Bessel's function.]

Ex. 13 : Prove that $B(m, n) = \displaystyle\int_0^1 x^{m-1}(1-x)^{n-1}\, dx = \dfrac{\overline{|m}\;\overline{|n}}{\overline{|m+n}}$, where $m > 0$ and $n > 0$.

Sol. : Consider, $\qquad h(t) = \displaystyle\int_0^t x^{m-1}(t-x)^{n-1}\, dx = t^{m-1} * t^{n-1}$

Then by the convolution theorem, we have

$$L[h(t)] = L\left[\int_0^t x^{m-1}(t-x)^{n-1}\, dx\right] = L[t^{m-1}]\, L[t^{n-1}]$$

$$= \frac{\overline{|m}}{s^m} \cdot \frac{\overline{|n}}{s^n} = \frac{\overline{|m}\;\overline{|n}}{s^{m+n}}$$

Hence $\qquad h(t) = L^{-1}\left[\dfrac{\overline{|m}\;\overline{|n}}{s^{m+n}}\right] = \dfrac{\overline{|m}\;\overline{|n}}{\overline{|m+n}}\, t^{m+n-1}$

or $\quad \displaystyle\int_0^t x^{m-1}(t-x)^{n-1}\, dx = \dfrac{\overline{|m}\;\overline{|n}}{\overline{|m+n}}\, t^{m+n-1}$

On putting $t = 1$, we get

$$B(m, n) = \int_0^1 x^{m-1}(1-x)^{n-1} = \frac{\overline{|m}\;\overline{|n}}{\overline{|m+n}}$$

Ex. 14 : *Using partial fractions, find the inverse Laplace transform of :*

(i) $\dfrac{2s^2-6s+5}{s^3-6s^2+11s-6}$ *(Dec. 2006, May 2007)* (ii) $\dfrac{3s^3+s^2+12s+2}{(s-3)(s+1)^3}$

(iii) $\dfrac{1}{(s+2)(s^2+2s+2)}$ *(Dec. 2004)*

(iv) $\dfrac{s^2+2s+3}{(s^2+2s+2)(s^2+2s+5)}$ (v) $\dfrac{s^3}{s^4-a^4}$ (vi) $\dfrac{s}{s^4+s^2+1}$

(vii) $\dfrac{1}{s^3+a^3}$ (viii) $\dfrac{s-2}{s(s+1)^3}$ (ix) $\dfrac{s^2-2s+3}{(s-1)^2(s+1)}$ *(Nov. 16)*

Sol. : (i) We have $\dfrac{2s^2 - 6s + 5}{s^3 - 6s^2 + 11s - 6} = \dfrac{2s^2 - 6s + 5}{(s-1)\,(s-2)\,(s-3)}$

Here denominator has non-repeated factors.

Let $\dfrac{2s^2 - 6s + 5}{(s-1)\,(s-2)\,(s-3)} = \dfrac{A}{(s-1)} + \dfrac{B}{(s-2)} + \dfrac{C}{(s-3)}$

Multiplying both sides by $(s-1)\,(s-2)\,(s-3)$, we get

$\quad 2s^2 - 6s + 5 = A\,(s-2)\,(s-3) + B\,(s-1)\,(s-3) + C\,(s-1)\,(s-2)$

Putting $s = 1$,   we get $A = 1/2$

Putting $s = 2$,   we get $B = -1$

Putting $s = 3$,   we get $C = 5/2$

$\therefore \quad L^{-1}\left[\dfrac{2s^2 - 6s + 5}{(s-1)\,(s-2)\,(s-3)}\right] = L^{-1}\left[\dfrac{1/2}{s-1} - \dfrac{1}{s-2} + \dfrac{5/2}{s-3}\right]$

$$= \dfrac{1}{2}\,e^t - e^{2t} + \dfrac{5}{2}\,e^{3t}$$

(ii) Let $\dfrac{3s^3 + s^2 + 12s + 2}{(s-3)\,(s+1)^3} = \dfrac{A}{s-3} + \dfrac{B}{s+1} + \dfrac{C}{(s+1)^2} + \dfrac{D}{(s+1)^3}$

Multiplying both sides by $(s-3)\,(s+1)^3$, we get

$\quad 3s^3 + s^2 + 12s + 2 = A\,(s+1)^3 + B\,(s-3)\,(s+1)^2 + C\,(s-3)\,(s+1) + D\,(s-3)$

Putting $s = 3$,   we get $A = 2$

Putting $s = -1$, we get $D = 3$

To determine B and C, equating coefficients of like powers of s^3 and s^2, we have

$\quad\quad\quad A + B = 3 \quad\quad$ and $\quad\quad 3A - B + C = 1$

$\therefore \quad\quad\quad\quad\quad B = 1 \quad\quad$ and $\quad\quad C = -4$

$\therefore \quad L^{-1}\left[\dfrac{3s^3 + s^2 + 12s + 2}{(s-3)\,(s+1)^3}\right] = L^{-1}\left[\dfrac{2}{s-3} + \dfrac{1}{s+1} - \dfrac{4}{(s+1)^2} + \dfrac{3}{(s+1)^3}\right]$

$$= 2e^{3t} + e^{-t} - 4e^{-t}\,(t) + 3e^{-t}\left(\dfrac{t^2}{2!}\right)$$

$$= 2e^{3t} + e^{-t} - 4t\,e^{-t} + \dfrac{3}{2}\,e^{-t}\,t^2$$

(iii) Here in denominator, quadratic factor can be written as product of linear factors with complex conjugate roots as

$$\dfrac{1}{(s+2)\,(s^2 + 2s + 2)} = \dfrac{1}{(s+2)\,(s+1+i)\,(s+1-i)}$$

Let $\dfrac{1}{(s+2)\,(s+1+i)\,(s+1-i)} = \dfrac{A}{s+2} + \dfrac{B}{s+1+i} + \dfrac{C}{s+1-i}$

Multiplying both sides by $(s+2)\,(s^2 + 2s + 2)$, we get

$\quad 1 = A\,(s^2 + 2s + 2) + B\,(s+2)\,(s+1-i) + C\,(s+2)\,(s+1+i)$

Putting $s = -2$, we get　　　　$A = \dfrac{1}{2}$

Putting $s = -1 - i$, we get　　　$B = \dfrac{1}{(1 - i)(-2i)} = -\dfrac{1}{4}(1 - i)$

Putting $s = -1 + i$, we get　　　$C = \dfrac{1}{(1 + i)(2i)} = -\dfrac{1}{4}(1 + i)$

$$\therefore \quad L^{-1}\left[\frac{1}{(s + 2)(s^2 + 2s + 2)}\right] = L^{-1}\left[\frac{1/2}{s + 2} + \left\{\frac{-\frac{1}{4}(1 - i)(s + 1 - i) - \frac{1}{4}(1 + i)(s + 1 + i)}{(s + 1 + i)(s + 1 - i)}\right\}\right]$$

$$= \frac{1}{2} L^{-1}\left[\frac{1}{s + 2}\right] - \frac{1}{4} L^{-1}\left[\frac{2s}{s^2 + 2s + 2}\right]$$

$$= \frac{1}{2} e^{-2t} - \frac{1}{2} L^{-1}\left[\frac{(s + 1) - 1}{(s + 1)^2 + 1}\right]$$

$$= \frac{1}{2} e^{-2t} - \frac{1}{2} e^{-t} L^{-1}\left[\frac{s - 1}{s^2 + 1}\right]$$

[By the First Shifting Theorem]

$$= \frac{1}{2} e^{-2t} - \frac{1}{2} e^{-t}(\cos t - \sin t)$$

Another method : We can write

$$\frac{1}{(s + 2)(s^2 + 2s + 2)} = \frac{A}{s + 2} + \frac{Bs + C}{s^2 + 2s + 2}$$

$$\therefore \quad 1 = A(s^2 + 2s + 2) + (Bs + C)(s + 2)$$

Equating coefficients of s^2, s and constant terms and after solving, we get $A = 1/2$, $B = -1/2$ and $C = 0$. Using these values we have the same result in above method.

(iv) Let $\dfrac{s^2 + 2s + 3}{(s^2 + 2s + 2)(s^2 + 2s + 5)} = \dfrac{p + 3}{(p + 2)(p + 5)}$　where $p = s^2 + 2s$

$$= \frac{1}{3(p + 2)} + \frac{2}{3}\frac{1}{(p + 5)}$$

$$= \frac{1}{3(s^2 + 2s + 2)} + \frac{2}{3}\frac{1}{(s^2 + 2s + 5)}$$

$$\therefore L^{-1}\left[\frac{s^2 + 2s + 3}{(s^2 + 2s + 2)(s^2 + 2s + 5)}\right] = \frac{1}{3} L^{-1}\left[\frac{1}{s^2 + 2s + 2}\right] + \frac{2}{3} L^{-1}\left[\frac{1}{s^2 + 2s + 5}\right]$$

$$= \frac{1}{3} L^{-1}\left[\frac{1}{(s + 1)^2 + 1}\right] + \frac{2}{3} L^{-1}\left[\frac{1}{(s + 1)^2 + 4}\right]$$

$$= \frac{1}{3} e^{-t} L^{-1}\left[\frac{1}{s^2 + 1}\right] + \frac{2}{3} e^{-t}\left[\frac{1}{s^2 + 4}\right]$$

$$= \frac{1}{3} e^{-t}(\sin t) + \frac{2}{3} e^{-t}\left(\frac{\sin 2t}{2}\right)$$

$$= \frac{1}{3} e^{-t}(\sin t + \sin 2t)$$

Note : We can also write

$$L^{-1}\left[\frac{s^2+2s+3}{(s^2+2s+2)(s^2+2s+5)}\right] = L^{-1}\left[\frac{As+B}{s^2+2s+2}+\frac{Cs+D}{s^2+2s+5}\right]$$

Then determining A, B, C and D, we can obtain the same result in above method.

(v) We have
$$\frac{s^3}{s^4-a^4} = s\left[\frac{s^2}{(s^2-a^2)\times(s^2+a^2)}\right] = \frac{s}{2}\left[\frac{1}{s^2-a^2}+\frac{1}{s^2+a^2}\right]$$

$$= \frac{1}{2}\left[\frac{s}{s^2-a^2}+\frac{s}{s^2+a^2}\right]$$

$$\therefore \qquad L^{-1}\left[\frac{s^3}{s^4-a^4}\right] = \frac{1}{2}L^{-1}\left[\frac{s}{s^2-a^2}\right] + \frac{1}{2}L^{-1}\left[\frac{s}{s^2+a^2}\right]$$

$$= \frac{1}{2}\cosh at + \frac{1}{2}\cos at = \frac{1}{2}(\cosh at + \cos at)$$

(vi) Since
$$s^4+s^2+1 = (s^2+1)^2-s^2 = (s^2+s+1)(s^2-s+1)$$

$$\therefore \qquad \frac{s}{s^4+s^2+1} = \frac{s}{(s^2+s+1)(s^2-s+1)}$$

$$= \frac{As+B}{s^2+s+1} + \frac{Cs+D}{s^2-s+1}$$

$$= \frac{-1/2}{s^2+s+1} + \frac{1/2}{s^2-s+1}$$

Hence
$$L^{-1}\left[\frac{s}{s^4+s^2+1}\right] = \frac{1}{2}\left\{-L^{-1}\left[\frac{1}{s^2+s+1}\right]+L^{-1}\left[\frac{1}{s^2-s+1}\right]\right\}$$

$$= \frac{1}{2}\left\{-L^{-1}\left[\frac{1}{(s+1/2)^2+(\sqrt{3}/2)^2}\right]+L^{-1}\left[\frac{1}{(s-1/2)^2+(\sqrt{3}/2)^2}\right]\right\}$$

$$= \frac{1}{2}\left\{-e^{-t/2}L^{-1}\left[\frac{1}{s^2+(\sqrt{3}/2)^2}\right]+e^{t/2}L^{-1}\left[\frac{1}{s^2+(\sqrt{3}/2)^2}\right]\right\}$$

$$= \frac{1}{2}\left\{-e^{-t/2}\left(\frac{\sin\sqrt{3}/2\,t}{\sqrt{3}/2}\right)+e^{t/2}\left(\frac{\sin\sqrt{3}/2\,t}{\sqrt{3}/2}\right)\right\}$$

$$= \frac{2}{\sqrt{3}}\sin\frac{\sqrt{3}}{2}t\left(\frac{e^{t/2}-e^{-t/2}}{2}\right)$$

$$= \frac{2}{\sqrt{3}}\sin\frac{\sqrt{3}}{2}t\,\sinh\frac{t}{2}$$

(vii) We have
$$\frac{1}{s^3+a^3} = \frac{1}{(s+a)(s^2-as+a^2)}$$

Let
$$\frac{1}{(s+a)(s^2-as+a^2)} = \frac{A}{s+a} + \frac{Bs+C}{s^2-as+a^2} \qquad \dots \text{(i)}$$

Multiplying both sides by $(s+a)(s^2-as+a^2)$, we get

$$1 = A(s^2-as+a^2) + (Bs+C)(s+a) \qquad \dots \text{(ii)}$$

Putting $s = -a$,   we get $A = \dfrac{1}{3a^2}$

To determine B and C, we equate the coefficients of like powers of s^2 and s, and we obtain

$$A + B = 0 \qquad\text{and}\quad -aA + aB + C = 0$$

$\therefore \qquad\qquad B = -A = -\dfrac{1}{3a^2} \quad\text{and}\quad C = \dfrac{2}{3a}$

$\therefore \qquad L^{-1}\left[\dfrac{1}{(s+a)(s^2-as+a^2)}\right] = L^{-1}\left[\dfrac{1/3a^2}{(s+a)} + \dfrac{(-1/3a^2)\,s + 2/3a}{s^2-as+a^2}\right]$

$$= \dfrac{1}{3a^2}\,L^{-1}\left[\dfrac{1}{s+a}\right] - \dfrac{1}{3a^2}\,L^{-1}\left[\dfrac{s-2a}{s^2-as+a^2}\right]$$

$$= \dfrac{1}{3a^2}\,e^{-at} - \dfrac{1}{3a^2}\,L^{-1}\left[\dfrac{(s-a/2)-3a/2}{(s-a/2)^2+3a^2/4}\right]$$

$$= \dfrac{1}{3a^2}\,e^{-at} - \dfrac{1}{3a^2}\,e^{at/2}\,L^{-1}\left[\dfrac{s-3a/2}{s^2+(\sqrt{3}\,a/2)^2}\right]$$

$$= \dfrac{1}{3a^2}\,e^{-at} - \dfrac{1}{3a^2}\,e^{at/2}\left(\cos\dfrac{\sqrt{3}\,a}{2}t - \sin\dfrac{\sqrt{3}\,a}{2}t\right)$$

(viii) $L^{-1}\left[\dfrac{s-2}{s\,(s+1)^3}\right] = L^{-1}\left[\dfrac{(s+1)-3}{(s+1-1)\,(s+1)^3}\right]$

$$= e^{-t}L^{-1}\left[\dfrac{s-3}{(s-1)\,s^3}\right] \quad\text{[By the First Shifting Theorem]}$$

$$= e^{-t}L^{-1}\left[\dfrac{1}{s^3}\left(\dfrac{s-3}{s-1}\right)\right]$$

$$\text{(Dividing } -3+s \text{ by } -1+s\text{) (Note this step)}$$

$$= e^{-t}L^{-1}\left[\dfrac{1}{s^3}(3 + 2s + 2s^2 - 2s^3)\right]$$

$$= e^{-t}L^{-1}\left[\dfrac{3}{s^3} + \dfrac{2}{s^2} + \dfrac{2}{s} - \dfrac{2}{s-1}\right]$$

$$= e^{-t}\left[3\left(\dfrac{t^2}{2!}\right) + 2\,(t) + 2 - 2\,e^t\right]$$

$$= e^{-t}\left(2 + 2t + \dfrac{3t^2}{2}\right) - 2$$

Note 1 : Before applying the method of partial fractions (to obtain inverse Laplace transform), it is advisable to find out whether the expression can be simplified by first shifting theorem.

Note 2 : It should be noted that the method given above is less tedious than writing the given expression as

$$\dfrac{s-2}{s\,(s+1)^3} = \dfrac{A}{s} + \dfrac{B}{s+1} + \dfrac{C}{(s+1)^2} + \dfrac{D}{(s+1)^3}$$

and then determining the coefficients A, B, C, D to obtain inverse Laplace transform.

(ix) $\quad L^{-1}\left[\dfrac{s^2-2s+3}{(s-1)^2(s+1)}\right] = L^{-1}\left[\dfrac{(s-1)^2+2}{(s-1)^2(s-1+2)}\right] = e^t L^{-1}\left[\dfrac{s^2+2}{s^2(s+2)}\right]$

$$= e^t\, L^{-1}\left[\dfrac{1}{s^2}\left(\dfrac{2+s^2}{2+s}\right)\right] \text{[By the First Shifting Theorem]}$$

$\qquad\qquad$ (Dividing $2+s^2$ by $2+s$) $\qquad\qquad\qquad\qquad$ (Note this step)

$$= e^t L^{-1}\left[\dfrac{1}{s^2}\left(1-\dfrac{s}{2}+\dfrac{3s^2/2}{2+s}\right)\right]$$

$$= e^t L^{-1}\left[\dfrac{1}{s^2}-\dfrac{1}{2s}+\dfrac{3}{2}\dfrac{1}{s+2}\right]$$

$$= e^t\left(t-\dfrac{1}{2}+\dfrac{3}{2}\,e^{-2t}\right) = \left(t-\dfrac{1}{2}\right)e^t+\dfrac{3}{2}\,e^{-t}$$

EXERCISE 5.2

1. Find the Inverse Laplace transform of each of the following functions :

(i) $\dfrac{s}{(s+a)^2}$ (ii) $\dfrac{1}{(s+4)^{3/2}}$ (iii) $\dfrac{s+7}{s^2+2s+2}$ (iv) $\dfrac{6s-4}{s^2-4s+20}$ (v) $\dfrac{8s+20}{s^2-12s+32}$

(vi) $\dfrac{2s+5}{s^2-2s-3}$ (vii) $\dfrac{1}{\sqrt{2s+3}}$ (viii) $\dfrac{1}{3\sqrt{8s-27}}$

Ans.   (i) $e^{-at}(1-at)$ (ii) $2e^{-4t}\dfrac{\sqrt{t}}{\sqrt{\pi}}$ (iii) $e^{-t}(\cos t+6\sin t)$

(iv) $2e^{2t}(3\cos 4t+\sin 4t)$

(v) $2e^{6t}(4\cosh 2t+17\sinh 2t)$ or $(21\,e^{8t}-13\,e^{4t})$

(vi) $e^t\left(2\cosh 2t+\dfrac{7}{2}\sinh 2t\right)$ or $\left(\dfrac{11}{4}\,e^{3t}-\dfrac{3\,e^{-t}}{4}\right)$

(vii) $\dfrac{e^{-3t/2}}{\sqrt{2\pi t}}$ (viii) $\dfrac{e^{27t/8}\,t^{-2/3}}{2\,\lfloor 1/3}$.

2. Obtain the Inverse Laplace transforms of the following functions :

(i) $\dfrac{e^{-5s}}{(s-2)^4}$ (ii) $\dfrac{e^{4-3s}}{(s+4)^{5/2}}$ (iii) $\dfrac{e^{-3s}}{s^2-9}$ (iv) $\dfrac{e^{-s}}{\sqrt{s+1}}$ (v) $\dfrac{s\,e^{-s/2}+\pi e^{-s}}{s^2+\pi^2}$

(vi) $\dfrac{s\,e^{-\pi s}}{s^2-4s+29}$ (vii) $\dfrac{(s+1)\,e^{-\pi s}}{s^2+s+1}$ (viii) $\dfrac{e^{-s}+e^{-2s}}{s^2-3s+2}$ (ix) $\dfrac{(1-\sqrt{s})\,e^{-s}}{s^{3/2}}$

(x) $\dfrac{(1-\sqrt{s})^2\,e^{-s}}{s^3}$ (xi) $\dfrac{e^{-s}(1-e^{-s})}{s(s^2+1)}$

Ans.   Notation used for displaced unit step function is $U(t - a) = \begin{cases} 0, & t < a \\ 1, & t \geq a \end{cases}$

(i) $\frac{1}{6} (t - 5)^3 \, e^{2(t-5)} \, U(t - 5)$ (ii) $\frac{4 (t - 3)^{3/2} \, e^{-4(t-4)}}{3 \sqrt{\pi}} \, U(t - 3)$

(iii) $\frac{1}{3} \sinh 3 (t - 3) \, U(t - 3)$ (iv) $\frac{e^{-(t-1)}}{\sqrt{\pi (t - 1)}} \, U(t - 1)$

(v) $\sin \pi t \, [U(t - 1/2) - U(t - 1)]$

(vi) $e^{2(t-\pi)} \left\{ \cos 5 (t - \pi) + \frac{2}{5} \sin 5 (t - \pi) \right\} U(t - \pi)$

(vii) $\frac{e^{-(t-\pi)/2}}{\sqrt{3}} \left\{ \sqrt{3} \cos \frac{\sqrt{3}}{2} (t - \pi) + \sin \frac{\sqrt{3}}{2} (t - \pi) \right\} U(t - \pi)$

(viii) $\{ e^{2(t-1)} - e^{(t-1)} \} \, U(t - 1) + \{ e^{2(t-2)} - e^{(t-2)} \} \, U(t - 2)$

(ix) $\left\{ \frac{2 \sqrt{t - 1}}{\sqrt{\pi}} - 1 \right\} U(t - 1)$ (x) $\left\{ \frac{(t - 1)^2}{2} - \frac{8}{3} \frac{(t - 1)^{3/2}}{\sqrt{\pi}} + (t - 1) \right\} U(t - 1)$

(xi) $\{ 1 - \cos (t - 1) \} \, U(t - 1) - \{ 1 - \cos (t - 2) \} \, U(t - 2)$.

3.   Find the Inverse Laplace transforms of the following functions :

(i) $\tan^{-1} \frac{1}{s}$ (ii) $\tan^{-1} (s + 1)$ **(Dec. 2005, May 2009)**

(iii) $\log \left(\frac{s + 2}{s + 1} \right)$ (iv) $\frac{1}{2} \log \frac{s - 1}{s + 1}$ (v) $\log \left(\frac{1 + s}{s} \right)$

(vi) $\log \left(\frac{s}{s - 1} \right)$ (vii) $\frac{1}{2} \log \left(\frac{s^2 - a^2}{s^2} \right)$ (viii) $\frac{1}{2} \log \frac{s^2 + b^2}{(s - a)^2}$

(ix) $s \log \frac{s}{\sqrt{s^2 + 1}} + \cot^{-1} s$

Ans.   (i) $\frac{\sin t}{t}$ (ii) $-e^{-t} \frac{\sin t}{t}$ (iii) $\frac{e^{-t} - e^{-2t}}{t}$ (iv) $\frac{\sinh t}{t}$ (v) $\frac{1 - e^{-t}}{t}$ (vi) $\frac{e^t - 1}{t}$

(vii) $\frac{1 - \cosh at}{t}$ (viii) $\frac{e^{-at} - \cos bt}{t}$ (ix) $\frac{1 - \cos t}{t^2}$

4.   Use theorem on Inverse Laplace transform of derivative, to find

(i) $L^{-1} [1/(s - a)^3]$,   given that $L^{-1} [1/(s - a)] = e^{at}$.

(ii) $L^{-1} [s/(s^2 - a^2)^2]$,   given that $L^{-1} [1/(s^2 - a^2)] = \sinh at/a$.

5.   Given that $L^{-1} \left[\frac{s}{(s^2 + 1)^2} \right] = \frac{1}{2} t \sin t$,   find $L^{-1} \left[\frac{1}{(s^2 + 1)^2} \right]$.

[**Hint** : $L^{-1} \left[\frac{1}{(s^2 + 1)^2} \right] = L^{-1} \left[\frac{1}{s} \cdot \frac{s}{(s^2 + 1)^2} \right] = \int_0^t \frac{1}{2} u \sin u \, du = \frac{1}{2} (\sin t - t \cos t) \,]$

6. Find the Inverse of each of the following transforms :

(i) $\dfrac{1}{s^2 + s}$ (ii) $\dfrac{1}{s^2(s^2 + \omega^2)}$ (iii) $\dfrac{s + 2}{s^2(s + 3)}$ **(Dec. 10)** (iv) $\dfrac{1}{s^4 - 2s^3}$ (v) $\dfrac{1}{s}\left(\dfrac{s - a}{s + a}\right)$

(vi) $\dfrac{1}{s^2}\left(\dfrac{s - a}{s + a}\right)$ (vii) $\dfrac{1}{s^2}\left(\dfrac{s + 1}{s^2 + 1}\right)$ (viii) $\dfrac{1}{s^3(s + 1)}$

Ans. (i) $1 - e^{-t}$ (ii) $\dfrac{1}{\omega^2}\left(t - \dfrac{\sin \omega t}{\omega}\right)$ (iii) $\dfrac{2}{3}\,t + \dfrac{1}{9} - \dfrac{1}{9}\,e^{-3t}$ (iv) $(e^{2t} - 1 - 2t - 2t^2)/8$

(v) $2e^{-at} - 1$ (vi) $\dfrac{2}{a} - \dfrac{2}{a}\,e^{-at} - t$ (vii) $1 + t - \cos t - \sin t$ (viii) $1 - t + \dfrac{1}{2}\,t^2 - e^{-t}$.

7. Find the Inverse Laplace transforms of the following functions :

(i) $\dfrac{s^2}{(s^2 - a^2)^2}$ (ii) $\dfrac{1}{(s - 1)^5(s + 2)}$ (iii) $\dfrac{s}{(s - 2)^5(s + 1)^2}$ (iv) $\log\dfrac{s^2 + 1}{s^2 + s}$ **(Dec. 10)**

Ans. (i) $\dfrac{1}{2a}(\sinh at + at \cosh at)$ (ii) $\dfrac{e^t}{72}\left(t^4 - \dfrac{4}{3}\,t^3 + \dfrac{4}{3}\,t^2 - \dfrac{8}{9}\,t + \dfrac{8}{27}\right) - \dfrac{e^{-2t}}{243}$

(iii) $e^{2t}\left(\dfrac{t^4}{36} + \dfrac{t^3}{54} - \dfrac{t^2}{54} + \dfrac{t}{81} - \dfrac{1}{243}\right) + \dfrac{e^{-t}}{243}$ (iv) $\dfrac{1}{t}(1 + e^{-t} - 2\cos t)$

8. Use the convolution theorem to find Inverse Laplace transforms of the following :

(i) $\dfrac{1}{(s - 1)(s - 2)}$ (ii) $\dfrac{1}{(s + 3)(s - 1)}$ (iii) $\dfrac{1}{s^2(s - a)}$ (iv) $\dfrac{1}{(s + 2)^2(s - 2)}$

(v) $\dfrac{s^2}{(s^2 + 4)^2}$ (vi) $\dfrac{1}{(s^2 + 9)^2}$ (vii) $\dfrac{s}{(s^2 + 4)^3}$ (viii) $\dfrac{1}{s^4 - a^4}$

Ans. (i) $e^{2t} - e^t$ (ii) $\dfrac{1}{4}(e^t - e^{-3t})$ (iii) $\dfrac{1}{a^2}(e^{at} - at - 1)$ (iv) $\dfrac{1}{16}(e^{2t} - c^{-2t} - 4t\,e^{-2t})$

(v) $\dfrac{1}{2}\,t\cos 2t + \dfrac{1}{4}\sin 2t$ (vi) $\dfrac{1}{18}\left(\dfrac{\sin 3t}{3} - t\cos 3t\right)$ (vii) $\dfrac{1}{64}\,t(\sin 2t - 2t\cos 2t)$

(viii) $\dfrac{1}{2a^3}\sinh at - \dfrac{1}{2a^4}\sin at$.

9. Show that $\displaystyle\int_0^t \int_0^t \ldots\ldots\ldots \int_0^t f(t)\,dt^n = \int_0^t \dfrac{(t - u)^{n-1}}{(n - 1)\,!}\,f(u)\,du$.

[**Hint :** Consider Inverse Laplace transform of $\dfrac{1}{s^n}\,F(s)$ by division by $\dfrac{1}{s^n}$ and convolution theorem.]

10. Using partial fractions, find the inverse Laplace transforms of the following :

(i) $\dfrac{4s-5}{s^2-s-2}$ (ii) $\dfrac{s}{(s-1)(s-2)(s-3)}$ **(May 2016)** (iii) $\dfrac{2s^2-4}{(s+1)(s-2)(s-3)}$

(iv) $\dfrac{s^2+2s-3}{s(s-3)(s+2)}$ **(May 2008)** (v) $\dfrac{s+2}{(s+3)(s+1)^3}$ (vi) $\dfrac{2s+1}{(s+2)^2(s-1)^2}$

(vii) $\dfrac{s+2}{s^3(s-1)^2}$ (viii) $\dfrac{3s+1}{(s+1)^4}$

Ans.(i) $e^{2t}+3e^{-t}$ (ii) $\dfrac{1}{2}e^t-\dfrac{1}{2}e^{2t}+\dfrac{3}{2}e^{3t}$ (iii) $\dfrac{1}{6}e^{-t}-\dfrac{4}{3}e^{2t}+\dfrac{7}{2}e^{3t}$ (iv) $\dfrac{1}{2}t+\dfrac{4}{5}e^{3t}-\dfrac{3}{10}e^{-2t}$

(v) $\dfrac{1}{8}(2t^2+2t-1)e^{-t}+\dfrac{1}{8}e^{-3t}$ (vi) $\dfrac{1}{3}t(e^t-e^{-2t})$ (vii) $(3t-8)e^t+t^2+5t+8$

(viii) $e^{-t}\left(\dfrac{3}{2}t^2-\dfrac{1}{3}t^3\right)$

11. Using partial fractions, find the inverse Laplace transforms of the following :

(i) $\dfrac{5s+3}{(s-1)(s^2+2s+5)}$ **(May 2012)** (ii) $\dfrac{s^2-3}{(s+2)(s-3)(s^2+2s+5)}$

(iii) $\dfrac{27s-12s}{(s+4)(s^2+9)}$

(iv) $\dfrac{s^2+2s-4}{(s^2+2s+5)(s^2+2s+2)}$ (v) $\dfrac{s}{(s^2+1)(s^2+2)}$ (vi) $\dfrac{1}{(s^2+2s+5)^2}$

(vii) $\dfrac{s^3+3s^2-s-3}{(s^2+2s+5)^2}$ (viii) $\dfrac{s}{s^4+4}$ (ix) $\dfrac{a(s^2-2a^2)}{s^4+4a^4}$ (x) $\dfrac{1}{s^3-a^3}$ (xi) $\dfrac{s^3}{s^4+64}$

(xii) $\dfrac{s^3+16s-24}{s^4+20s^2+64}$

Ans. (i) $e^t-e^{-t}\cos 2t+\dfrac{3}{2}e^{-t}\sin 2t$ (ii) $\dfrac{3}{50}e^{3t}-\dfrac{1}{25}e^{-2t}-\dfrac{1}{50}e^{-t}(\cos 2t-18\sin 2t)$

(iii) $3(e^{-4t}-\cos 3t)$ (iv) $\dfrac{3}{2}e^{-t}\sin 2t-2e^{-t}\sin t$ (v) $\dfrac{1}{2}\sin t-\dfrac{1}{2}te^{-t}$

(vi) $\dfrac{1}{16}e^{-t}(\sin 2t-2t\cos 2t)$ (vii) $e^{-t}(\cos 2t-2t\sin 2t)$ (viii) $\dfrac{1}{2}\sinh t\sin t$

(ix) $\cos at\sinh at$ (x) $\dfrac{1}{3a^2}\left[e^{at}-e^{-at/2}\left\{\cos\dfrac{\sqrt{3}}{2}at+\sqrt{3}\sin\dfrac{\sqrt{3}}{2}at\right\}\right]$

(xi) $\cosh 2t\cos 2t$ (xii) $\dfrac{1}{2}\sin 4t+\cos 2t-\sin 2t$

MULTIPLE CHOICE QUESTIONS (MCQ's)

Type : Use of Theorems of Inverse Laplace Transforms :

1. If $L^{-1}[F(s)] = f(t)$ then $L^{-1}[F(s + a)]$ is equal to (1)

    (A) $e^{at} f(t)$ (B) $F(t) = \begin{cases} f(t-a), & t > a \\ 0 & , t < a \end{cases}$

    (C) $-t\, f(t)$ (D) $e^{-at} f(t)$

2. If $L^{-1}[F(s)] = f(t)$ then $L^{-1}[e^{-as} F(s)]$ is equal to (1)

    (A) $F(t) \begin{cases} f(t+a), & t < a \\ 0 & , t > a \end{cases}$ (B) $F(t) = \begin{cases} f(t-a), & t > a \\ 0 & , t < a \end{cases}$

    (C) $e^{-at} f(t)$ (D) $-t\, f(t)$

3. If $L^{-1}[F(s)] = f(t)$ then $L^{-1}[F(ks)]$ is equal to (1)

    (A) $\dfrac{1}{k} f\left(\dfrac{t}{k}\right)$ (B) $-t\, f(t)$

    (C) $e^{-k} f(t)$ (D) $F(t) = \begin{cases} f(t-k), & t > k \\ 0 & , t < k \end{cases}$

4. If $L^{-1}[F(s)] = f(t)$ then $L^{-1}\left[\dfrac{d}{ds} F(s)\right]$ is equal to (1)

    (A) $e^{-at} f(t)$ (B) $F(t) = \begin{cases} f(t-a), & t > a \\ 0 & , t < a \end{cases}$

    (C) $-t\, f(t)$ (D) $\dfrac{1}{t} f(t)$

5. If $L^{-1}[F(s)] = f(t)$ then $L^{-1}\left[\dfrac{d^2}{ds^2} F(s)\right]$ is equal to (1)

    (A) $-t\, f(t)$ (B) $t^2 f(t)$

    (C) $e^{-at} f(t)$ (D) $e^{at} f(t)$

6. If $L^{-1}[F(s)] = f(t)$ then $L^{-1}\left[\displaystyle\int_{s}^{\infty} F(s)\, ds\right]$ is equal to (1)

    (A) $-t\, f(t)$ (B) $\displaystyle\int_{0}^{t} f(t)\, dt$

    (C) $\dfrac{1}{t} f(t)$ (D) $\dfrac{d}{dt} f(t)$

7. If $L^{-1}[F(s)] = f(t)$ then $L^{-1}\left[\displaystyle\int_{s}^{\infty}\int_{s}^{\infty} F(s)\, ds\, ds\right]$ is equal to (1)

    (A) $\dfrac{1}{t^2} f(t)$ (B) $(-1)^2 \dfrac{d^2}{dt^2} f(t)$

    (C) $-t\, f(t)$ (D) $\displaystyle\int_{s}^{t} f(t)\, dt$

8. If $L^{-1}[F(s)] = f(t)$ and $f(0) = 0$ then $L^{-1}[s\,F(s)]$ is equal to   (1)

(A) $(-1)^2 \dfrac{d^2}{dt^2} f(t)$ (B) $\displaystyle\int_0^t f(t)\,dt$

(C) $\dfrac{1}{t} f(t)$ (D) $\dfrac{d}{dt} f(t)$

9. If $L^{-1}[F(s)] = f(t)$ then $L^{-1}\left[\dfrac{F(s)}{s}\right]$ is equal to   (1)

(A) $\dfrac{d}{dt} f(t)$ (B) $-t\,f(t)$

(C) $\displaystyle\int_0^t f(u)\,du$ (D) $\dfrac{1}{t} f(t)$

10. If $L^{-1}[F(s)] = f(t)$, $L^{-1}[G(s)] = g(t)$ and $H(s) = F(s)\,G(s)$ then
$L^{-1}[H(s)] = L^{-1}[F(s)\,G(s)]$ is equal to   (1)

(A) $f(t) * g(t)$ (B) $f(t)\,g(t)$

(C) $\dfrac{f(t)}{g(t)}$ (D) $f(t) - g(t)$

11. $L^{-1}\left[\dfrac{s}{(s-3)^5}\right]$ is equal to   (2)

(A) $e^{-3t}\left(\dfrac{t^3}{6} - \dfrac{t^4}{8}\right)$ (B) $e^{-3t}\left(\dfrac{t^3}{3} - 3\dfrac{t^4}{4}\right)$

(C) $e^{3t}\left(\dfrac{t^4}{24} + \dfrac{t^4}{40}\right)$ (D) $e^{3t}\left(\dfrac{t^3}{6} + \dfrac{t^4}{8}\right)$

12. $L^{-1}\left[\dfrac{s}{s^2 + 2s + 1}\right]$ is equal to   (2)

(A) $e^t\,(1 - t)$ (B) $e^{-t}\,(1 - t)$

(C) $e^t\,(1 + t)$ (D) $e^{-t}\,(1 + t)$

13. $L^{-1}\left[\dfrac{1}{\sqrt{2s + 3}}\right]$ is equal to   (2)

(A) $\dfrac{1}{\sqrt{2}}\, e^{-\frac{3}{2}t}\, \dfrac{1}{\sqrt{\pi t}}$ (B) $e^{\frac{3}{2}t}\, \dfrac{1}{\sqrt{\pi t}}$

(C) $e^{-\frac{3}{2}t}\, \dfrac{\sqrt{t}}{\sqrt{\pi}}$ (D) $\dfrac{1}{\sqrt{2}}\, e^{-\frac{3}{2}t}\, \sqrt{t}$

14. $L^{-1}\left[\dfrac{e^{-\pi s}}{s+a}\right]$ is equal to   (2)

(A) $\begin{cases} e^{-a(t-\pi)}, & t<\pi \\ 0, & t>\pi \end{cases}$

(B) $\begin{cases} e^{(t-\pi)}, & t>a \\ 0, & t<a \end{cases}$

(C) $\begin{cases} e^{-a(t-\pi)}, & t>\pi \\ 0, & t<\pi \end{cases}$

(D) $\begin{cases} e^{a(t-\pi)}, & t>\pi \\ 0, & t<\pi \end{cases}$

15. $L^{-1}\left[\dfrac{e^{-3s}}{s^2-9}\right]$ is equal to   (2)

(A) $\begin{cases} \sin 3(t-3), & t>3 \\ 0, & t<3 \end{cases}$

(B) $\begin{cases} \dfrac{1}{3}\sinh 3(t-3), & t>3 \\ 0, & t<3 \end{cases}$

(C) $\begin{cases} \dfrac{1}{3}\cosh 3(t-3), & t>3 \\ 0, & t<3 \end{cases}$

(D) $\begin{cases} \cos 3(t-3), & t>3 \\ 0, & t<3 \end{cases}$

16. $L^{-1}\left[\dfrac{e^{-3s}}{s^2+8s+17}\right]$ is equal to   (2)

(A) $\begin{cases} e^{-4(t-3)}\cos (t-3), & t<3 \\ 0, & t>3 \end{cases}$

(B) $\begin{cases} e^{4(t-3)}\sinh (t-3), & t>3 \\ 0, & t<3 \end{cases}$

(C) $\begin{cases} e^{-4t}\sinh (t-3), & t>3 \\ 0, & t<3 \end{cases}$

(D) $\begin{cases} e^{-4(t-3)}\sin (t-3), & t>3 \\ 0, & t<3 \end{cases}$

17. $L^{-1}\left[\log \dfrac{s^2+a^2}{s^2+b^2}\right]$ is equal to   (2)

(A) $2\left(\dfrac{\cos bt - \cos at}{t}\right)$

(B) $2\left(\dfrac{\sin bt - \sin at}{t}\right)$

(C) $2\left(\dfrac{\cosh bt - \cosh at}{t}\right)$

(D) $\left(\dfrac{\cos bt + \cos at}{t}\right)$

18. $L^{-1}\left[\log \dfrac{s^2+a^2}{s^2}\right]$ is equal to   (2)

(A) $\dfrac{1+\cos at}{t}$

(B) $\dfrac{1-\sin at}{t}$

(C) $2\left(\dfrac{1-\cos at}{t}\right)$

(D) $\dfrac{1-\cosh at}{t}$

19. $L^{-1}\left[\cot^{-1} s\right]$ is equal to   (2)

(A) $\sin t$

(B) $\dfrac{\sin t}{t}$

(C) $\dfrac{\cos t}{t}$

(D) $\dfrac{\sinh t}{t}$

20. $L^{-1}\left[\log\dfrac{s+b}{s+a}\right]$ is equal to   (2)

(A) $t\,(e^{-at} - e^{-bt})$

(B) $\left(\dfrac{e^{at} - e^{bt}}{t}\right)$

(C) $\left(\dfrac{e^{-bt} + e^{-at}}{t}\right)$

(D) $\left(\dfrac{e^{-at} - e^{-bt}}{t}\right)$

21. $L^{-1}\left[\dfrac{s}{(s^2 + a^2)^2}\right] = \dfrac{t\sin at}{2a}$ then $L^{-1}\left[s\left\{\dfrac{s}{(s^2 + a^2)^2}\right\}\right]$ is equal to   (2)

(A) $\dfrac{1}{2a}\,(\sin at - a\cos at)$

(B) $\dfrac{1}{2a}\,(\sin at + at\cos at)$

(C) $(\sin at - at\cos at)$

(D) $\dfrac{1}{2a}\,(\sinh at + \cosh at)$

22. $L^{-1}\left[\dfrac{1}{(s + a)^3}\right] = \dfrac{t^2 e^{-at}}{2}$ then $L^{-1}\left[s\left\{\dfrac{1}{(s + a)^3}\right\}\right]$ is equal to   (2)

(A) $\dfrac{1}{2}\,e^{-at}\,(2t + at^2)$

(B) $\dfrac{1}{2}\,e^{at}\,(2t - at^2)$

(C) $\dfrac{1}{2}\,e^{-at}\,(2t - at^2)$

(D) $e^{at}\,(2t + at^2)$

23. $L^{-1}\left[\dfrac{1}{s + 1}\right] = e^{-t}$ then $L^{-1}\left[\dfrac{1}{s}\left\{\dfrac{1}{(s + 1)}\right\}\right]$ is equal to

(A) $1 - e^{-t}$

(B) $e^{-t} - 1$

(C) $1 + e^{-1}$

(D) $1 - e^{t}$

24. $L^{-1}\left[\dfrac{1}{(s + 1)^2}\right] = t\,e^{-t}$ then $L^{-1}\left[\dfrac{1}{s}\left\{\dfrac{1}{(s + 1)^2}\right\}\right]$ is equal to   (2)

(A) $e^{-t}\,(t - 1) + 1$

(B) $\dfrac{e^{-t}}{2}\,(t + 1) + 1$

(C) $e^{t}\,(t - 1)$

(D) $-e^{-t}\,(t + 1) + 1$

25. $L^{-1}\left[\dfrac{2}{s^2 + 4}\right] = \sin 2t$ then $L^{-1}\left[\dfrac{1}{s}\left\{\dfrac{2}{(s^2 + 4)}\right\}\right]$ is equal to   (2)

(A) $\dfrac{1 + \cos 2t}{2}$

(B) $\dfrac{1 + \sin 2t}{2}$

(C) $\dfrac{1 - \cos 2t}{2}$

(D) $\dfrac{\cos 2t}{2}$

26. Using convolution theorem $L^{-1}\left[\dfrac{s^2}{(s^2 + a^2)^2}\right]$ is equal to   (2)

(A) $\displaystyle\int_0^t \cos au \, \cos a(t - u)\, du$

(B) $\displaystyle\int_0^\infty \cos au \, \cos a(t - u)\, du$

(B) $\displaystyle\int_0^t \sin au \, \cos a(t - u)\, du$

(D) $\displaystyle\int_0^\infty \cos au \, \sin a(t - u)\, du$

27. Using convolution theorem $L^{-1}\left[\dfrac{1}{(s^2 + a^2)^2}\right]$ is equal to   (2)

    (A) $\displaystyle\int_0^t \cos au\,\cos a(t-u)\,du$ (B) $\dfrac{1}{a^2}\displaystyle\int_0^t \sin au\,\sin a(t-u)\,du$

    (C) $\displaystyle\int_0^\infty \sin au\,\cos a(t-u)\,du$ (D) $\displaystyle\int_0^\infty \cos au\,\sin a(t-u)\,du$

28. Using convolution theorem $L^{-1}\left[\dfrac{1}{s^4(s+5)}\right]$ is equal to   (2)

    (A) $\displaystyle\int_0^\infty \dfrac{u^3}{6}\,e^{-5(t-u)}\,du$ (B) $\displaystyle\int_0^t \dfrac{u^4}{24}\,e^{-5(t-u)}\,du$

    (C) $\displaystyle\int_0^\infty \dfrac{u^4}{24}\,e^{-5(t-u)}\,du$ (D) $\displaystyle\int_0^t \dfrac{u^3}{6}\,e^{-5(t-u)}\,du$

29. $L^{-1}\left[\dfrac{1}{s(s^2+1)}\right]$ is equal to   (2)

    (A) $-\cos t + 1$ (B) $-\cos t$

    (C) $-\sin t + 1$ (D) $-\cosh t + 1$

30. The inverse Laplace transform of the function $\dfrac{1}{s(s+1)}$

    (A) $e^{-t} - 1$ (B) $1 - e^{-t}$ (C) $1 + e^{t}$ (D) e^{-t}

31. $L^{-1}\left[\dfrac{1}{(s+1)(s+2)}\right]$ is equal to   (2)

    (A) $e^{t} - e^{2t}$ (B) $e^{-2t} - e^{-t}$

    (C) $e^{-t} - e^{-2t}$ (D) $e^{t} + e^{2t}$

32. $L^{-1}\left[\dfrac{3}{(s^2+4)(s^2+1)}\right]$ is equal to   (2)

    (A) $e^{t} - e^{2t}$ (B) $-\dfrac{1}{2}\sinh 2t + \sinh t$

    (C) $e^{-t} - e^{-2t}$ (D) $-\dfrac{1}{2}\sin 2t + \sin t$

33. $L^{-1}\left[\dfrac{3s+7}{(s-3)(s+1)}\right]$ is equal to   (2)

    (A) $4e^{3t} - e^{-t}$ (B) $4e^{3t} + e^{-t}$

    (C) $e^{-t} - 4e^{3t}$ (D) $4e^{-3t} + e^{-t}$

34. $L^{-1}\left[\dfrac{1}{s^2(s^2+1)}\right]$ is equal to   (2)

    (A) $t + \sin t$ (B) $t - \sin t$

    (C) $t - \cos t$ (D) $\dfrac{t^2}{2} - \sinh t$

Answers

1. (D)	2. (B)	3. (A)	4. (C)	5. (B)	6. (C)	7. (A)	8. (D)
9. (C)	10. (A)	11. (D)	12. (B)	13. (A)	14. (C)	15. (B)	16. (D)
17. (A)	18. (C)	19. (B)	20. (D)	21. (B)	22. (C)	23. (A)	24. (D)
25. (C)	26. (A)	27. (B)	28. (D)	29. (A)	30. (B)	31. (C)	32. (D)
33. (A)	34. (B)						

5.10 APPLICATIONS TO DIFFERENTIAL EQUATIONS

The Laplace transform is useful in solving differential equations and corresponding initial and boundary value problems. The solution of differential equations involving functions of an impulsive type can also be solved by the use of Laplace transform in a very efficient manner. The general process of solution consists of three main steps :

1. The given differential equation is transformed into an simple algebraic equation (called subsidiary equation).
2. The subsidiary equation is solved by pure algebraic manipulations.
3. The solution of the subsidiary equation is then transformed back to obtain the solution of the given differential equation.

In this way, the Laplace transform method reduces the problem of solving differential equation to an algebraic problem. Another advantage of this method over the classical method is that it solves initial value problem directly without first finding general solution (complete solution) and then evaluating the arbitrary constants. We shall now illustrate this method in the following applications.

Note :

(i) $$L\left[\frac{dy}{dt}\right] = L\,[y'] = s\,Y(s) - y(0)$$

(ii) $$L\left[\frac{d^2y}{dt^2}\right] = L\,[y''] = s^2\,Y(s) - s\,y(0) - y'(0)$$

(iii) $$L\left[\frac{d^3y}{dt^3}\right] = L\,[y'''] = s^3\,Y(s) - s^2\,y(0) - s\,y'(0) - y''(0)$$

(iv) $$L\left[\frac{d^4y}{dt^4}\right] = L\,[y^{iv}] = s^4\,Y(s) - s^3\,y(0) - s^2\,y'(0) - s\,y''(0) - y'''(0) \text{ etc.}$$

5.11 SOLUTION OF ORDINARY DIFFERENTIAL EQUATIONS WITH CONSTANT COEFFICIENT

ILLUSTRATIONS

Ex. 1 : *Find the solution of each of the following differential equations which satisfy the given conditions :*

(i) $y'' - 3y' + 2y = 12\,e^{-2t}$, (**Nov. 15**) $y(0) = 2$, $y'(0) = 6$. (**Dec. 05, 13, 14**)

(ii) $y'' + y = t$, $y(0) = 1$, $y'(0) = -2$. (**May 11**)

(iii) $y'' + 2y' + y = t\,e^{-t}$, $y(0) = 1$, $y'(0) = -2$. (**May 05, 17**)

(iv) $y''' - 3y'' + 3y' - y = t^2\,e^t$, $y(0) = 1$, $y'(0) = 0$, $y''(0) = -2$.

(v) $y''' - y = e^t$, $y(0) = y'(0) = y''(0) = 0$. (**May 09**)

Sol. : (i) Note : In the usual notation, given equation is

$$\frac{d^2y}{dt^2} - 3\frac{dy}{dt} + 2y\,(t) = 12\ e^{-2t}$$

Taking the Laplace transform of both sides of the differential equation, we have

$$L\left[\frac{d^2y}{dt^2}\right] - 3\,L\left[\frac{dy}{dt}\right] + 2\,L\,[y(t)] \;=\; 12\,L\,[e^{-2t}]$$

$$\therefore \{s^2\,Y(s) - s\,y(0) - y'(0)\} - 3\{s\,Y(s) - y(0)\} + 2Y(s) = \frac{12}{s+2}$$

Substituting the given conditions $y(0) = 2$, $y'(0) = 6$, we get

$$\{s^2\,Y(s) - s(2) - 6\} - 3\,\{s\,Y(s) - 2\} + 2\,Y(s) \;=\; \frac{12}{s+2}$$

or
$$(s^2 - 3s + 2)\ Y(s) - 2s \;=\; \frac{12}{s+2}$$

$$\therefore \qquad (s^2 - 3s + 2)\ Y(s) \;=\; + 2s + \frac{12}{s+2} \;=\; \frac{2s^2 + 4s + 12}{s+2}$$

$$\therefore \qquad Y(s) \;=\; \frac{2s^2 + 4s + 12}{(s^2 - 3s + 2)\,(s+2)} \;=\; \frac{2s^2 + 4s + 12}{(s-1)\,(s-2)\,(s+2)}$$

Using the method of partial fractions, we can express $Y(s)$ in the form

$$Y(s) \;=\; -\frac{6}{s-1} + \frac{7}{s-2} + \frac{1}{s+2}$$

Taking the inverse Laplace transform of both sides, we get

$$y(t) \;=\; -6\ e^{t} + 7\ e^{2t} + e^{-2t}$$

which is the required solution.

Check :

$$\because y = -6\ e^{t} + 7\ e^{2t} + e^{-2t} \therefore y' = -6\ e^{t} + 14\ e^{2t} - 2\ e^{-2t} \text{ and } y'' = -6\ e^{t} + 28\ e^{2t} + 4\ e^{-2t}$$

Then $y'' - 3y'' + 2y = 12\ e^{-2t}$, $y(0) = 2$, $y'(0) = 6$ and the function $y(t)$ obtained is the required solution.

Note : Classical method will give the solution as

$$y \;=\; C_1\,e^{t} + C_2\,e^{2t} + e^{-2t}$$

where, C_1 and C_2 are to be evaluated from given conditions.

(ii) Taking the Laplace transform of both sides of the differential equation, we have

$$L\,[y''] + L\,[y(t)] \;=\; L\,[t]$$

$$\therefore \{s^2\,Y(s) - s\,y(0) - y'(0)\} + Y(s) \;=\; \frac{1}{s^2}$$

Substituting the given conditions $y(0) = 1$, $y'(0) = -2$, we get

$$\{s^2\,Y(s) - s(1) - (-2)\} + Y(s) = \frac{1}{s^2}$$

or $\qquad (s^2 + 1)\,Y(s) - s + 2 = \dfrac{1}{s^2}$

$\therefore \qquad (s^2 + 1)\,Y(s) = s - 2 + \dfrac{1}{s^2}$

$\therefore \qquad Y(s) = \dfrac{s-2}{s^2+1} + \dfrac{1}{s^2(s^2+1)}$

$$= \frac{s}{s^2+1} - \frac{2}{s^2+1} + \frac{1}{s^2} - \frac{1}{s^2+1} \text{ [By partial fractions]}$$

$$= \frac{1}{s^2} + \frac{s}{s^2+1} - \frac{3}{s^2+1}$$

Taking the Inverse Laplace transform of both sides, we get

$$y(t) = t + \cos t - 3\sin t$$

which can be verified as the solution.

(iii) Taking Laplace transform of both sides, we have

$$L\,[y''] + 2\,[y'] + L\,[y(t)] = L\,[t\,e^{-t}]$$

$$\therefore \{s^2\,Y(s) - s\,y(0) - y'(0)\} + 2\,\{s\,Y(s) - y(0)\} + Y(s) = \frac{1}{(s+1)^2}$$

Using the given conditions $y(0) = 1$, $y'(0) = -2$, it reduces to

$$\{s^2\,Y(s) - s(1) - (-2)\} + 2\,\{s\,Y(s) - 1\} + Y(s) = \frac{1}{(s+1)^2}$$

or $\qquad (s^2 + 2s + 1)\,Y(s) - s = \dfrac{1}{(s+1)^2}$

$\therefore \qquad (s^2 + 2s + 1)\,Y(s) = s + \dfrac{1}{(s+1)^2}$

or $\qquad Y(s) = \dfrac{s}{(s+1)^2} + \dfrac{1}{(s+1)^4} = \dfrac{s+1-1}{(s+1)^2} + \dfrac{1}{(s+1)^4}$

$$= \frac{1}{(s+1)} - \frac{1}{(s+1)^2} + \frac{1}{(s+1)^4}$$

Taking the inverse Laplace transform of both sides, we get

$$y(t) = e^{-t} - t\,e^{-t} + \frac{t^3\,e^{-t}}{3!}$$

(iv) Taking the Laplace transform of both sides, we have

$$L\,[y'''] - 3\,L\,[y''] + 3\,L\,[y'] - L\,[y(t)] = L\,[t^2\,e^t]$$

$$\{s^3\,Y(s) - s^2\,y(0) - s\,y'(0) - y''(0)\} - 3\,\{s^2\,Y(s) - s\,y(0) - y'(0)\}$$

$$+ 3\,\{s\,Y(s) - y(0)\} - Y(s) = \frac{2}{(s-1)^3}$$

Using the given conditions $y(0) = 1$, $y'(0) = 0$, $y''(0) = -2$, we get

$$(s^3 - 3s^2 + 3s - 1)\, Y(s) - s^2 + 3s - 1 = \frac{2}{(s-1)^3}$$

$$\therefore \qquad Y(s) = \frac{s^2 - 3s + 1}{s^3 - 3s^2 + 3s - 1} + \frac{2}{(s^3 - 3s^2 + 3s - 1)\,(s-1)^3}$$

$$= \frac{s^2 - 3s + 1}{(s-1)^3} + \frac{2}{(s-1)^6}$$

$$= \frac{s^2 - 2s + 1 - s}{(s-1)^3} + \frac{2}{(s-1)^6}$$

$$= \frac{(s-1)^2 - (s-1) - 1}{(s-1)^3} + \frac{2}{(s-1)^6}$$

$$= \frac{1}{s-1} - \frac{1}{(s-1)^2} - \frac{1}{(s-1)^3} + \frac{2}{(s-1)^6}$$

and
$$y(t) = e^t - t\,e^t - \frac{t^2 e^t}{2} + \frac{t^5 e^t}{60}, \qquad \text{which is a particular solution.}$$

Remark : If we assume $y(0) = A$, $y'(0) = B$, $y''(0) = C$, we find

$$Y(s) = \frac{As^2 + (B - 3A)\,s + 3A - 3B + C}{(s-1)^3} + \frac{2}{(s-1)^6}$$

Since A, B, C are arbitrary, so also is the polynomial in the numerator of the first term on the right. We can thus write

$$Y(s) = \frac{C_1}{(s-1)^3} + \frac{C_2}{(s-1)^2} + \frac{C_3}{s-1} + \frac{2}{(s-1)^6}$$

Taking inverse, we obtain general solution as

$$y(t) = \frac{C_1 t^2 e^t}{2} + C_2 t\,e^t + C_3 e^t + \frac{t^5 e^t}{60}.$$

It should be noted that finding the general solution is easier than finding the particular solution. Since we avoid the necessity of determining the constants in the partial fraction expansion.

(v) Taking the Laplace transform of both sides, we have

$$L\,[y'''] - L\,[y(t)] = L\,[e^t]$$

$$\therefore \quad \{s^3\,Y(s) - s^2\,y(0) - s\,y'(0) - y''(0)\} - Y(s) = \frac{1}{s-1}$$

Using the given conditions $y(0) = y'(0) = y''(0) = 0$, we get

$$(s^3 - 1)\,Y(s) = \frac{1}{s-1}$$

$$\therefore \qquad Y(s) = \frac{1}{(s^3 - 1)\,(s-1)} = \frac{1}{(s-1)^2\,(s^2 + s + 1)}$$

Using the method of partial fractions, we can express Y(s) in the form

$$Y(s) = \frac{-1/3}{s-1} + \frac{1/3}{(s-1)^2} + \frac{s/3 + 1/3}{s^2 + s + 1}$$

$$= -\frac{1}{3}\frac{1}{s-1} + \frac{1}{3}\frac{1}{(s-1)^2} + \frac{1}{3}\frac{(s+1/2) - 1/2}{(s+1/2)^2 + (\sqrt{3}/2)^2}$$

Taking inverse Laplace transform of both sides, we get

$$y(t) = -\frac{1}{3}\,e^t + \frac{1}{3}\,t\,e^t + \frac{1}{3}\,e^{-t/2}L^{-1}\left[\frac{s-1/2}{s^2 + (\sqrt{3}/2)^2}\right]$$

$$= -\frac{1}{3}\,e^t + \frac{1}{3}\,t\,e^t + \frac{1}{3}\,e^{-t/2}\left\{\cos\frac{\sqrt{3}}{2}\,t + \frac{1}{\sqrt{3}}\sin\frac{\sqrt{3}}{2}\,t\right\}$$

Ex. 2 : *Solve each of the following by using Laplace transforms :*

(i) $\dfrac{d^2x}{dt^2} + 9x(t) = 18\,t$, $x(0) = 0$, $x(\pi/2) = 0$.   **(May 2007, 2015)**

(ii) $\dfrac{d^2y}{dt^2} + 2\dfrac{dy}{dt} + 5y = e^{-t}\sin t$, $y(0) = 0$, $y'(0) = 1$.   **(Dec. 2008, May 2014)**

(iii) $y'' + 4y' + 13y = \dfrac{1}{3}e^{-2t}\sin 3t$, $y(0) = 1$, $y'(0) = -2$.

(iv) $(D^2 + n^2)x = a\sin(nt + \alpha)$, $x(0) = x'(0) = 0$.

Sol. : (i) Taking Laplace transform of both sides, we get

$$L\left[\frac{d^2x}{dt^2}\right] + 9\,L[x(t)] = 18\,L[t]$$

$$\{s^2 X(s) - s\,x(0) - x'(0)\} + 9\,X(s) = \frac{18}{s^2}$$

Since x'(0) is not known, let x'(0) = A. Then

$$\{s^2 X(s) - s(0) - A\} + 9\,X(s) = \frac{18}{s^2} \qquad\qquad \{\because x(0) = 0\}$$

or $$(s^2 + 9)\,X(s) = A + \frac{18}{s^2}$$

$$X(s) = \frac{A}{s^2 + 9} + \frac{18}{s^2(s^2 + 9)}$$

$$= \frac{A}{s^2 + 9} + \frac{18 + 2s^2 - 2s^2}{s^2(s^2 + 9)}$$

$$= \frac{A}{s^2 + 9} - \frac{2}{s^2 + 9} + \frac{2(s^2 + 9)}{s^2(s^2 + 9)}$$

$$= \frac{(A - 2)}{s^2 + 9} + \frac{2}{s^2}$$

Thus $$x(t) = \left(\frac{A - 2}{3}\right)\sin 3t + 2t$$

To determine A, we put $t = \pi/2$ and obtain

$$x\left(\frac{\pi}{2}\right) = \left(\frac{A-2}{3}\right)\sin 3\pi/2 + 2\pi/2$$

$$0 = \left(\frac{A-2}{3}\right)(-1) + \pi \quad \text{or} \quad \left(\frac{A-2}{3}\right) = \pi$$

$$\therefore \qquad x = \pi \sin 3t + 2t$$

(ii) Taking Laplace transform of both sides, we get

$$L\left[\frac{d^2y}{dt^2}\right] + 2\,L\left[\frac{dy}{dt}\right] + 5\,L\,[y(t)] = L\,[e^{-t}\sin t]$$

$$\therefore \ \{s^2\,Y(s) - s\,y(0) - y'(0)\} + 2\,\{s\,Y(s) - y(0)\} + 5\,Y(s) = \frac{1}{(s+1)^2+1}$$

$$\therefore \quad \{s^2\,Y(s) - s(0) - 1\} + 2\,\{s\,Y(s) - 0\} + 5\,Y(s) = \frac{1}{s^2+2s+2}$$

$$\left\{\because\ y(0) = 0,\ y'(0) = 1\right\}$$

$$\therefore \quad \{s^2\,Y(s) - s(0) - 1\} + 2\,\{s\,Y(s) - 0\} + 5\,Y(s) = \frac{1}{s^2+2s+2}$$

$$\therefore \qquad (s^2+2s+5)\,Y(s) - 1 = \frac{1}{s^2+2s+2}$$

$$\therefore \qquad Y(s) = \frac{1}{(s^2+2s+5)} + \frac{1}{(s^2+2s+2)\,(s^2+2s+5)}$$

$$= \frac{s^2+2s+3}{(s^2+2s+2)\,(s^2+2s+5)}$$

$$\therefore \qquad y(t) = \frac{1}{3}\,e^{-t}\,(\sin t + \sin 2t) \ \text{[Refer solved example 14 (iv), sec. 5.9]}$$

(iii) Taking Laplace transform of each side, we have

$$L\,[y''] + 4\,L\,[y'] + 13\,L\,[y(t)] = \frac{1}{3}\,L\,[e^{-2t}\sin 3t]$$

$$\therefore \ \{s^2\,Y(s) - s\,y(0) - y'(0)\} + 4\,\{s\,Y(s) - y(0)\} + 13\,Y(s) = \frac{1}{3}\cdot\frac{3}{(s+2)^2+9}$$

$$\therefore \ \{s^2\,Y(s) - s(1) - (-2)\} + 4\,\{s\,Y(s) - 1\} + 13\,Y(s) = \frac{1}{(s+2)^2+9}$$

$$\left\{\because\ y(0) = 1,\ y'(0) = -2\right\}$$

$$\text{or} \qquad (s^2+4s+13)\,Y(s) - s - 2 = \frac{1}{(s+2)^2+9}$$

$$\text{or} \qquad Y(s) = \frac{s+2}{s^2+4s+13} + \frac{1}{(s^2+4s+13)\,[(s+2)^2+9]}$$

$$= \frac{s+2}{(s+2)^2+9} + \frac{1}{[(s+2)^2+9]^2}$$

Taking inverse Laplace transform, we get

$$y(t) = L^{-1}\left[\frac{s+2}{(s+2)^2+9}\right] + L^{-1}\left[\frac{1}{\{(s+2)^2+9\}^2}\right]$$

$$= e^{-2t}\left[\frac{s}{s^2+9}\right] + e^{-2t}L^{-1}\left[\frac{1}{(s^2+9)^2}\right]$$

$$= e^{-2t}\cos 3t + e^{-2t}L^{-1}\left[\frac{1}{s^2+9}\cdot\frac{1}{s^2+9}\right]$$

$$= e^{-2t}\cos 3t + e^{-2t}\left\{\frac{\sin 3t}{3}\cdot\frac{\sin 3t}{3}\right\} \qquad \text{(By the convolution theorem)}$$

$$= e^{-2t}\cos 3t + \frac{e^{-2t}}{9}\int_0^t \sin 3u \sin 3(t-u)\,du$$

$$= e^{-2t}\cos 3t + \frac{e^{-2t}}{9}\int_0^t \frac{\cos(6u-3t)-\cos 3t}{2}\,du$$

$$= e^{-2t}\cos 3t + \frac{e^{-2t}}{18}\left[\frac{\sin(6u-3t)}{6} - u\cos 3t\right]_0^t$$

$$= e^{-2t}\cos 3t + \frac{e^{-2t}}{18}\left(\frac{\sin 3t}{3} - t\cos 3t\right)$$

$$= e^{-2t}\cos 3t + \frac{e^{-2t}}{54}(\sin 3t - 3t\cos 3t).$$

(iv) Given equation is $x''(t) + n^2 x(t) = a\sin nt\cos\alpha + a\cos nt\sin\alpha$.

Taking Laplace transform of the equation, we have

$$L[x''(t)] + n^2 L[x(t)] = a\cos\alpha\, L[\sin nt] + a\sin\alpha\, L[\cos nt]$$

$$\{s^2 X(s) - s\,x(0) - x'(0)\} + n^2 X(s) = a\cos\alpha\left(\frac{n}{s^2+n^2}\right) + a\sin\alpha\left(\frac{s}{s^2+n^2}\right)$$

Using the given conditions $x(0) = x'(0) = 0$, we get

$$(s^2+n^2)X(s) = a\cos\alpha\left(\frac{n}{s^2+n^2}\right) + a\sin\alpha\left(\frac{s}{s^2+n^2}\right)$$

$$\therefore \quad X(s) = a\cos\alpha\left[\frac{n}{(s^2+n^2)^2}\right] + a\sin\alpha\left[\frac{s}{(s^2+n^2)^2}\right]$$

$$\text{Thus} \quad x(t) = (a\cos\alpha)\,L^{-1}\left[\frac{n}{(s^2+n^2)^2}\right] + (a\sin\alpha)\,L^{-1}\left[\frac{s}{(s^2+n^2)^2}\right]$$

$$= (a\cos\alpha)\left\{\frac{n}{2n^3}(\sin nt - nt\cos nt)\right\} + (a\sin\alpha)\left\{\frac{t\sin nt}{2n}\right\}$$

$$= \frac{a\cos\alpha}{2n^2}(\sin nt - nt\cos nt) + \frac{a\sin\alpha}{2n}(t\sin nt)$$

$$\Big[\textbf{Note : } \text{(i)} \quad L^{-1}\left[\frac{1}{s^2+n^2}\right] = \frac{\sin nt}{n} \quad \therefore \ L^{-1}\left[-\frac{d}{ds}\frac{1}{s^2+n^2}\right] = \frac{t \sin nt}{n}$$

$$\therefore \qquad L^{-1}\left[\frac{2s}{(s^2+n^2)^2}\right] = \frac{t \sin nt}{n} \quad \text{or} \quad L^{-1}\left[\frac{s}{(s^2+n^2)^2}\right] = \frac{t \sin nt}{2n}$$

$$\text{(ii)} \qquad L^{-1}\left[\frac{1}{s}\cdot\frac{s}{(s^2+n^2)^2}\right] = \int_0^t \frac{t \sin nt}{2n}\,dt = \frac{1}{2n^3}(\sin nt - nt \cos nt)\,\Big]$$

Ex. 3 : *Solve the differential equation*

$$y'' + 4y = f(t), \quad y(0) = 0, \quad y'(0) = 1.$$

Sol. : Taking Laplace transform of both sides, we have

$$L[y''] + 4 L[y(t)] = L[f(t)]$$

$$\{s^2 Y(s) - s\,y(0) - y'(0)\} + 4 Y(s) = F(s)$$

Using the given conditions $y(0) = 0$, $y'(0) = 1$, we get

$$\{s^2 Y(s) - s(0) - 1\} + 4 Y(s) = F(s)$$

or

$$(s^2 + 4) Y(s) - 1 = F(s)$$

$$\therefore \qquad Y(s) = \frac{1}{s^2+4} + \frac{F(s)}{s^2+4} \qquad \qquad \ldots \text{(i)}$$

Then using the convolution theorem, we have

$$y(t) = \sin t + f(t) * \frac{\sin 2t}{2} = \sin t + \frac{1}{2}\int_0^t f(u) \sin 2(t-u)\,du.$$

[Note that in this case, actual Laplace transform of $f(t)$ does not enter into final solution.]

Ex. 4 : *Using the Laplace transform, solve the following differential equations :*

(i) $\dfrac{dy}{dt} + 3y\,(t) + 2\displaystyle\int_0^t y(t)\,dt = t,$ *given* $y(0) = 0$ **(Dec. 04, 06; May 09)**

(ii) $\dfrac{dy}{dt} + 2y\,(t) + \displaystyle\int_0^t y(t)\,dt = \sin t,$ *given* $y(0) = 1$ **(Nov. 16)**

Sol. : (i) We have $L\left[\dfrac{dy}{dt}\right] + 3 L[y(t)] + 2 L\left[\displaystyle\int_0^t y(t)\,dt\right] = L[t]$

$$\therefore \quad \{s\,Y(s) - y(0)\} + 3 Y(s) + \frac{2}{s} Y(s) = \frac{1}{s^2}$$

Using given condition $y(0) = 0$, it reduces to

$$\left(s + 3 + \frac{2}{s}\right) Y(s) = \frac{1}{s^2}$$

$$\therefore \qquad Y(s) = \frac{s}{s^2 (s^2 + 3s + 2)} = \frac{1}{s (s + 1) (s + 2)} = \frac{1/2}{s} - \frac{1}{s + 1} + \frac{1/2}{s + 2}$$

$$\therefore \qquad y(t) = \frac{1}{2} - e^{-t} + \frac{1}{2} e^{-2t}$$

(ii) We have $L\left[\dfrac{dy}{dt}\right] + 2\, L\, [y(t)] + L\left[\displaystyle\int_0^t y(t)\, dt\right] = L\, [\sin t]$

$$\therefore \qquad \{s\, Y(s) - y(0)\} + 2\, Y(s) + \frac{1}{s}\, Y(s) = \frac{1}{s^2 + 1}$$

Using given condition, it reduces to

$$\left(s + 2 + \frac{1}{s}\right) Y(s) = 1 + \frac{1}{s^2 + 1}$$

$$\therefore \qquad Y(s) = \frac{s}{s^2 + 2s + 1} + \frac{s}{(s^2 + 2s + 1)\,(s^2 + 1)}$$

$$= \frac{s}{(s + 1)^2} + \frac{s}{(s + 1)^2\,(s^2 + 1)}$$

$$= \frac{1}{s + 1} - \frac{1}{(s + 1)^2} + \frac{-1/2}{(s + 1)^2} + \frac{1/2}{s^2 + 1} \qquad \text{(By partial fraction)}$$

$$= \frac{1}{s + 1} - \frac{3/2}{(s + 1)^2} + \frac{1/2}{s^2 + 1}$$

$$\therefore \qquad y(t) = e^{-t} - \frac{3}{2}\, t\, e^{-t} + \frac{1}{2}\, \sin t$$

Note : Differential equations in Ex. 4 (i) and (ii) are called integrodifferential equations, since an integral as well as a derivative of the dependent variables appears in these equations.

Remark : The Laplace transform can also be used to solve some ordinary differential equations with variable coefficients. We can use the following result :

$$L\, [t^m\, y^{(n)}(t)] = (-1)^m\, \frac{d^m}{ds^m}\, L\, [y^{(n)}\, (t)]$$

EXERCISE 5.3

1. Find the solution of each of the following differential equations which satisfy the given conditions :

(i) $y'' + y = 0$, $\quad y(0) = 1$, $\quad y'(0) = 2$. **Ans.** $y(t) = \cos t + 2 \sin t$

(ii) $y'' - 3y' = 9$, $\quad y(0) = y'(0) = 0$ **Ans.** $y(t) = e^{3t} - 3t - 1$

(iii) $y'' - 3y' + 2y = 4e^{2t}$, $y(0) = -3$, $y'(0) = 5$ **(May 16)** **Ans.** $y(t) = -7e^t + 4e^{2t} + 4t\,e^{2t}$

(iv) $y'' + 4y' + 13y = 2e^{-t}$, $y(0) = y'(0) = 0$

$$\textbf{Ans. } y(t) = \frac{1}{5}\,e^{-t} - \frac{1}{5}\,e^{-2t}\left[\cos 3t + \frac{1}{3}\sin 3t\right]$$

(v) $y'' + 4y + 8y = 1$, $\quad y(0) = 0$, $\quad y'(0) = 1$ **(Dec. 2010)**

$$\textbf{Ans. } y(t) = \frac{1}{8} - \frac{1}{8}\,e^{-2t}(\cos 2t - 3\sin 2t)$$

(vi) $y'' - 2y' + y = e^{-2t}$, $y(0) = y'(0) = 0$ **(Dec. 11)** **Ans.** $y(t) = \dfrac{-1}{9}\,e^t + \dfrac{1}{3}\,t\,e^t + \dfrac{1}{9}\,e^{-2t}$

(vii) $y'' + 2y' + y = 6t\,e^{-t}$, $\quad y(0) = 2$, $y'(0) = 5$ **(May 2008)**

$$\textbf{Ans. } y(t) = e^{-t}\,(t^3 + 7t + 2)$$

(viii) $y'' - 7y' + 10y = e^{2t} + 10$, $\quad y(0) = 0$, $y'(0) = \dfrac{-1}{3}$

$$\textbf{Ans. } y(t) = 2 + \frac{4}{3}\,e^{5t} - \frac{10}{3}\,e^{2t} - \frac{t\,e^{2t}}{3}$$

(ix) $y''' + y' = 2$, $\quad y(0) = 3$, $\quad y'(0) = 1$, $\quad y''(0) = 2$

$$\textbf{Ans. } y(t) = 5 + 2t - \sin t - 2\cos t$$

(x) $y'' + 4y' + 3y = 10\sin t$, $\quad y(0) = y'(0) = 0$

$$\textbf{Ans. } y(t) = \frac{5}{2}\,e^{-t} - \frac{1}{2}\,e^{-3t} + \sin t - 2\cos t \textbf{ (Dec. 95)}$$

(xi) $y'' + 9y = \cos 2t$, $\quad y(0) = 1$, $\quad y(\pi/2) = -1$

$$\textbf{Ans. } y(t) = \frac{4}{5}\cos 3t + \frac{4}{5}\sin 3t + \frac{1}{5}\cos 2t$$

(xii) $y'' + 2y' + 2y = 2 \cos 2t - 4 \sin 2t,\quad y(0) = 0,\quad y'(0) = 1$

$$\textbf{Ans. } y(t) = \frac{3}{5} \cos 2t + \frac{4}{5} \sin 2t - \frac{3}{5} e^{-t} (\cos t + 2 \sin t)$$

(xiii) $y'' + y' - 2y = 3 \cos 3t - 11 \sin 3t,\quad y(0) = 0,\quad y'(0) = 6.$

$$\textbf{Ans. } y(t) = e^t - e^{-2t} + \sin 3t$$

(xiv) $y'' + y' - 2y = 2(1 + t - t^2),\quad y(0) = 0,\ y'(0) = 3 \qquad \textbf{Ans. } y(t) = t^2 - e^{-2t} + e^t$

(xv) $y'' + y = t \cos 2t,\quad y(0) = y'(0) = 0 \quad \textbf{Ans. } y(t) = \frac{4}{9} \sin 2t - \frac{5}{9} \sin t - \frac{1}{3} t \cos 2t$

(xvi) $y^{iv} + y'' - 2y = 0,\quad y(0) = 0,\ y'(0) = -1,\ y''(0) = 0,\ y'''(0) = 1.$

$$\textbf{Ans. } y(t) = -\frac{1}{3} \left(\sqrt{2} \sin \sqrt{2}\, t + \sinh t \right)$$

(xvii) $y^{iv} + 2y'' + y = \sin t,\quad y(0) = y'(0) = y''(0) = y'''(0) = 0.$

$$\textbf{Ans. } y(t) = \frac{1}{8} \{ (3 - t^2) \sin t - 3t \cos t \}$$

2. Solve each of the following by using Laplace transform :

(i) $\dfrac{d^2y}{dt^2} + 3 \dfrac{dy}{dt} + 2y = f(t),\quad y(0) = y'(0) = 0$

where $f(t) = \begin{cases} 1 & , \quad 0 < t < 1 \\ 0 & , \qquad t > 1 \end{cases}$

$$\textbf{Ans. } \frac{1}{2} - e^{-t} + \frac{1}{2} e^{-2t} - \left\{ \frac{1}{2} - e^{-(t-1)} + \frac{1}{2} e^{-2(t-1)} \right\} U(t - 1)$$

(ii) $\dfrac{d^2y}{dt^2} + n^2 y = f(t),\quad y(0) = y'(0) = 0,\quad (n \neq 1)$

where $f(t) = \begin{cases} 0 & , \quad 0 < t < \pi \\ \sin t & , \quad \pi < t < 2\pi \\ 0 & , \quad t > 2\pi \end{cases}$

$$\textbf{Ans. } \frac{1}{n(n^2 - 1)} (1 + \cos n\pi)\, \sin nt,\quad \pi < t < 2\pi$$

(iii) $y(t) + \displaystyle\int_0^t y(t)\, dt = 1 - e^{-t}.$ $\qquad\qquad\qquad$ $\textbf{Ans. } y = t\, e^{-t}$

(iv) $\dfrac{dy}{dt} + 4y(t) + 5 \displaystyle\int_0^t y(t)\, dt = e^{-t}$, $y(0) = 0$

$$\textbf{(May 12) Ans. } y(t) = -\frac{1}{2} e^{-t} + \frac{e^{-2t}}{2}(\cos t + 3 \sin t)$$

(v) $\dfrac{dy}{dt} + y(t) - 2 \displaystyle\int_0^t y(t)\, dt = \dfrac{t^2}{2}$, $y(0) = 1$, $y(0) = -2$.

$$\textbf{Ans. } y(t) = \frac{1}{3} e^{t} + \frac{11}{12} e^{-2t} - \frac{t}{2} - \frac{1}{4}$$

3. A particle moves along a line so that its displacement x from a fixed point O at any time t is given by $\dfrac{d^2x}{dt^2} + 4\dfrac{dx}{dt} + 5x = 80 \sin 5t$.

If at $t = 0$, the particle is at rest at $x = 0$, find the displacement at any time $t > 0$.

$$\textbf{Ans. } x(t) = 2e^{-2t}(\cos t + 7 \sin t) - 2(\sin 5t + \cos 5t)$$

MULTIPLE CHOICE QUESTIONS (MCQ's)

Type : Application of Laplace Transform to Solve Differential Equations :

1. If $L[y(t)] = Y(s)$ then using Laplace transform, the differential equation $\dfrac{d^2y}{dt^2} + y = t$, with $y(0) = 1$, $y'(0) = -2$ is transformed into   (2)

(A) $Y(s) - \dfrac{s-2}{s^2+1} + \dfrac{1}{s^2(s^2+1)}$
(B) $Y(s) = \dfrac{s-2}{s^2-1} + \dfrac{1}{s^2(s-1)}$

(C) $Y(s) = \dfrac{s+2}{s^2+1} + \dfrac{1}{(s+1)}$
(D) $Y(s) = \dfrac{s}{s^2+1} + \dfrac{1}{s(s+1)}$

2. If $L[y(t)] = Y(s)$ then using Laplace transform, the differential equation $\dfrac{d^3y}{dt^3} - y = e^{t}$, with $y(0) = y'(0) = y''(0) = 0$ is transformed into   (2)

(A) $Y(s) = \dfrac{1}{s^3(s-1)}$
(B) $Y(s) = \dfrac{1}{s(s^3-1)}$

(C) $Y(s) = \dfrac{1}{(s^3+1)(s+1)}$
(D) $Y(s) = \dfrac{1}{(s^3-1)(s-1)}$

3. If $L[y(t)] = Y(s)$ then using Laplace transform, the differential equation

$$\frac{dy}{dt} + 3y(t) + 2\int_0^t y(t)\, dt = t, \text{ with } y(0) = 0 \text{ is transformed into}$$ (2)

  (A) $Y(s) = \dfrac{s+2}{s(s^2 + 3s + 2)}$ (B) $Y(s) = \dfrac{1}{s(s^2 + 3s + 2)}$

  (C) $Y(s) = \dfrac{1}{s(s^2 - 3s - 2)}$ (D) $Y(s) = \dfrac{1}{(s^2 + 3s + 2)}$

4. If $L[y(t)] = Y(s)$ then using Laplace transform, the differential equation

$$\frac{d^2y}{dt^2} + 9\, y = \cos 2t \text{ with } y(0) = 0,\ y'(0) = 0 \text{ is transformed into}$$ (2)

  (A) $Y(s) = \dfrac{s}{(s^2 - 9)\,(s^2 - 4)}$ (B) $Y(s) = \dfrac{s}{(s^2 + 9)\,(s^2 - 4)}$

  (C) $Y(s) = \dfrac{s}{(s^2 + 9)\,(s^2 + 4)}$ (D) $Y(s) = \dfrac{4}{(s^2 + 9)\,(s^2 + 4)}$

5. Taking Laplace transform on both sides of the differential equation $\dfrac{d^2x}{dt^2} + 9x(t) = 18t$,

with $x(0) = x'(0) = 0$, the value of $X(s)$ is $(L[x(t)] = X(s))$ (2)

  (A) $X(s) = \dfrac{1}{s^2\,(s^2 + 9)}$ (B) $X(s) = \dfrac{18}{s^2\,(s^2 + 9)}$

  (C) $X(s) = \dfrac{18}{s^2\,(s^2 - 9)}$ (D) $X(s) = \dfrac{18}{s(s^2 + 9)}$

6. By using Laplace transform the solution of differential equation $\dfrac{dx}{dt} + x(t) = e^t$, $x(0) = 0$ is (2)

  (A) $x(t) = \sinh t$ (B) $x(t) = \cosh t$

  (C) $x(t) = \sin t$ (D) $x(t) = \cos t$

7. By using Laplace transform the solution of differential equation $\dfrac{dy}{dt} + y(t) = e^{-t}$, given $y(0) = 0$ is (2)

  (A) $y(t) = t\, e^t$ (B) $y(t) = \sin t$

  (C) $y(t) = t\, e^{-t}$ (D) $y(t) = \dfrac{t^2}{2}\, e^{-t}$

8. By using Laplace transform the solution of differential equation $\dfrac{dy}{dt} + y(t) = 1$, $y(0) = 0$ is   (2)

(A) $y(t) = 1 + e^{-t}$ (B) $y(t) = -1 - e^{t}$

(C) $y(t) = 1 - e^{t}$ (D) $y(t) = 1 - e^{-t}$

9. By using Laplace transform the solution of differential equation $\dfrac{d^2y}{dt^2} + y(t) = 0$, given $y(0) = 1$, $y'(0) = 2$ is   (2)

(A) $y(t) = e^{t} + e^{2t}$ (B) $y(t) = \cos t + 2 \sin t$

(C) $y(t) = \cos t - \sin t$ (D) $y(t) = \sin t + 2 \cos t$

10. On taking Laplace transform of differential equation $\dfrac{d^2y}{dt^2} + 4y(t) = \sin t$, with $y(0) = 0$, $y'(0) = 0$, the subsidiary equation is $(s^2 + 4) \, Y(s) = \dfrac{1}{(s^2 + 1)}$. The solution of differential equation is   (2)

(A) $y(t) = \dfrac{1}{3}\left(\sin t - \dfrac{1}{2}\sin 2t\right)$ (B) $y(t) = \dfrac{1}{3}\left(\cos t - \dfrac{1}{2}\cos 2t\right)$

(C) $y(t) = \dfrac{1}{3}(\cos t + \cos 2t)$ (D) $y(t) = \dfrac{1}{3}(\sin t + \sin 2t)$

11. On applying Laplace transform to differential equation $\dfrac{d^2y}{dt^2} + 4\dfrac{dy}{dt} + 4y = e^{-2t}$, with $y(0) = 0$, $y'(0) = 0$, the subsidiary equation is $(s^2 + 4s + 4) \, Y(s) = \dfrac{1}{(s + 2)}$. The solution of differential equation is   (2)

(A) $y(t) = e^{2t}\dfrac{t^3}{3!}$ (B) $y(t) = e^{-2t}\dfrac{t^2}{2!}$

(C) $y(t) = e^{-2t}\, t^2$ (D) $y(t) = e^{-2t}\dfrac{2!}{t^2}$

12. On applying Laplace transform to differential equation $\dfrac{d^2y}{dt^2} + 9y = 6\cos 3t$, with $y(0) = 0$, $y'(0) = 0$, the subsidiary equation is $(s^2 + 9) \, Y(s) = \dfrac{6s}{(s^2 + 9)}$. The solution of differential equation is   (2)

(A) $y(t) = t \sin 9t$ (B) $y(t) = -\dfrac{1}{3}(t \sin 3t)$

(C) $y(t) = \dfrac{\sin 3t}{t}$ (D) $y(t) = t \sin 3t$

13. On applying Laplace transform to differential equation $\dfrac{d^2x}{dt^2} + 9x = 18t$, with $x(0) = 0$, $x'(0) = 0$, the subsidiary equation is $(s^2 + 9)\, Y(s) = \dfrac{18}{s^2}$. The solution of differential equation is   (2)

(A) $x(t) = \left[t + \dfrac{\sin 3t}{3} \right]$

(B) $x(t) = 2\left[\dfrac{t^2}{2} - \dfrac{\cos 3t}{3} \right]$

(C) $x(t) = 2\left[t - \dfrac{\sin 3t}{3} \right]$

(D) $x(t) = 2\left[t + \dfrac{\sinh 3t}{3} \right]$

Answers

1. (A)	2. (D)	3. (B)	4. (C)	5. (B)	6. (A)	7. (C)	8. (D)
9. (B)	10. (A)	11. (B)	12. (D)	13. (C)			

CHAPTER SIX

FOURIER TRANSFORM

6.1 INTRODUCTION

Transformation is an operation which converts a mathematical expression into a different form with the help of which problems are either solved easily or methods of solution become simple. For example, Logarithmic transformation reduces multiplication, division and one expression raised to power another expression into addition, subtraction and simple multiplication. Transfer of origin and/or axes convert equations of curves and surfaces in simple or standard forms from which useful informations and important properties can be obtained. Similarly, elementary transformations in matrices are useful in solving various problems by simple methods.

Fourier series are powerful tools in treating various problems involving periodic functions. However, in many practical problems, the impressed force or voltage is non-periodic rather than periodic, a single unrepeated pulse, for instance. A suitable representation for non-periodic functions can be obtained by considering the limiting form of Fourier series when the fundamental period is made infinite. We shall find that in such a case, the Fourier series becomes a Fourier integral. Using symmetry, Fourier integral can conveniently be expressed in terms of Fourier transform which transforms a non-periodic function, say f(t) in time domain, into a function $F(\lambda)$ in frequency domain.

The Fourier integrals and transforms are useful in solving boundary value problems arising in science and engineering e.g. Conduction of Heat, Wave Propagation, Theory of Communication, etc.

6.2 COMPLEX EXPONENTIAL FORM OF FOURIER SERIES

If f(x) is a periodic function of period 2L, defined in the interval $-L < x < L$, and satisfies Dirichlet's conditions then f(x) can be represented by Fourier series :

$$f(x) = \frac{a_0}{2} + \sum_{n=1}^{\infty} \left(a_n \cos \frac{n\pi x}{L} + b_n \sin \frac{n\pi x}{L} \right) \qquad \dots \text{(i)}$$

where

$$\left. \begin{aligned} a_n &= \frac{1}{L} \int_{-L}^{L} f(u) \cos \frac{n\pi u}{L} \, du \\ b_n &= \frac{1}{L} \int_{-L}^{L} f(u) \sin \frac{n\pi u}{L} \, du \end{aligned} \right\} \qquad \dots \text{(ii)}$$

Using exponential equivalent of cosine and sine terms

$$\cos\theta = \frac{e^{i\theta} + e^{-i\theta}}{2} \quad \text{and} \quad \sin\theta = \frac{e^{i\theta} - e^{-i\theta}}{2i} = \frac{-i}{2}(e^{i\theta} - e^{-i\theta})$$

result (i) can be expressed as

$$f(x) = \frac{a_0}{2} + \sum_{n=1}^{\infty}\left[a_n\frac{1}{2}(e^{in\pi x/L} + e^{-in\pi x/L}) + b_n\left(-\frac{i}{2}\right)(e^{in\pi x/L} - e^{-in\pi x/L})\right]$$

$$= \frac{a_0}{2} + \sum_{n=1}^{\infty}\left[\left(\frac{a_n - i\,b_n}{2}\right)e^{in\pi x/L} + \left(\frac{a_n + i\,b_n}{2}\right)e^{-in\pi x/L}\right]$$

If we now define $c_0 = \dfrac{a_0}{2}$, $\qquad c_n = \dfrac{a_n - i\,b_n}{2}$, $\qquad c_{-n} = \dfrac{a_n + i\,b_n}{2}$

then the above series can be written in more symmetric form

$$f(x) = \sum_{n=-\infty}^{\infty} c_n\, e^{in\pi x/L} \qquad\qquad \ldots\text{(iii)}$$

where $\qquad c_0 = \dfrac{a_0}{2}$

$$c_n = \frac{1}{2}(a_n - ib_n) = \frac{1}{2}\left[\frac{1}{L}\int_{-L}^{L} f(u)\cos\frac{n\pi u}{L}\,du - i\frac{1}{L}\int_{-L}^{L} f(u)\sin\frac{n\pi u}{L}\,du\right]$$

$$= \frac{1}{2L}\int_{-L}^{L} f(u)\left[\cos\frac{n\pi u}{L} - i\sin\frac{n\pi u}{L}\right]du$$

$$= \frac{1}{2L}\int_{-L}^{L} f(u)\, e^{-in\pi u/L}\,du.$$

Similarly, $\qquad c_{-n} = \dfrac{1}{2L}\displaystyle\int_{-L}^{L} f(u)\, e^{in\pi u/L}\,du.$

Clearly, the index n is positive, negative or zero, c_n is correctly given by the single formula

$$c_n = \frac{1}{2L}\int_{-L}^{L} f(u)\, e^{-in\pi u/L}\,du \qquad\qquad \ldots\text{(iv)}$$

Thus the complex exponential form of a Fourier series is given by

$$\boxed{\begin{aligned} f(x) &= \sum_{n=-\infty}^{\infty} c_n\, e^{in\pi x/L}\\[2mm] \textbf{where} \quad c_n &= \frac{1}{2L}\int_{-L}^{L} f(u)\, e^{-in\pi u/L}\,du \end{aligned}} \qquad \ldots\text{(1)}$$

6.3 FOURIER INTEGRAL

We shall now consider the limiting form of Fourier series for periodic function of period 2 L, when $L \to \infty$.

For convenience, we start with the complex exponential form of a Fourier series

$$[\text{result (1)}] \qquad f(x) = \sum_{n=-\infty}^{\infty} c_n \, e^{in\pi x/L} \qquad\qquad \dots \text{(i)}$$

$$\text{where,} \qquad c_n = \frac{1}{2L} \int_{-L}^{L} f(u) \, e^{-in\pi u/L} \, du \qquad\qquad \dots \text{(ii)}$$

Substituting for c_n from (ii) in (i), we obtain

$$f(x) = \sum_{n=-\infty}^{\infty} \left[\frac{1}{2L} \int_{-L}^{L} f(u) \, e^{-in\pi u/L} \, du \right] e^{in\pi x/L}$$

$$= \sum_{n=-\infty}^{\infty} \left[\frac{1}{2\pi} \int_{-L}^{L} f(u) \, e^{-in\pi (u-x)/L} \, du \right] \left(\frac{\pi}{L} \right) \qquad\qquad \dots \text{(iii)}$$

Now, let us denote $\lambda = \dfrac{n\pi}{L}$ 　　　　　　(frequency of general term)

$$\therefore \qquad \Delta\lambda = \frac{(n+1)\pi}{L} - \frac{n\pi}{L} = \frac{\pi}{L} \qquad \left(\begin{array}{l} \text{difference in frequency between} \\ \qquad\qquad\qquad \text{successive terms} \end{array} \right)$$

Then f(x) can be written as

$$f(x) = \sum_{n=-\infty}^{\infty} \left[\frac{1}{2\pi} \int_{-L}^{L} f(u) \, e^{-i\lambda(u-x)} \, du \right] \Delta\lambda \qquad\qquad \dots \text{(iv)}$$

Now if $L \to \infty$, then $\Delta\lambda \to 0$ and the expression (iv) gives

$$f(x) = \lim_{L \to \infty} \sum_{n=-\infty}^{\infty} \left[\frac{1}{2\pi} \int_{-L}^{L} f(u) \, e^{-i\lambda(u-x)} \, du \right] \Delta\lambda$$

$$= \lim_{\Delta\lambda \to 0} \sum_{n=-\infty}^{\infty} \left[\frac{1}{2\pi} \int_{-\infty}^{\infty} f(u) \, e^{-i\lambda(u-x)} \, du \right] \Delta\lambda$$

$$= \frac{1}{2\pi} \int_{-\infty}^{\infty} \left[\int_{-\infty}^{\infty} f(u) \, e^{-i\lambda(u-x)} \, du \right] d\lambda$$

[By definition of integral as limit of sum]

Thus the Fourier integral representation of $f(x)$, where $-\infty < x < \infty$ is given by

$$f(x) = \frac{1}{2\pi} \int_{\lambda=-\infty}^{\lambda=\infty} \int_{u=-\infty}^{u=\infty} f(u)\, e^{-i\lambda(u-x)}\, du\, d\lambda \qquad \ldots (2)$$

The result (2) is also known as **Fourier integral theorem.**

The limitations on $f(x)$ for validity of the result (2) are as follows :

(i) In every finite interval, $f(x)$ satisfies the Dirichlet's conditions.

(ii) The integral $\int_{-\infty}^{\infty} |f(x)|\, dx$ exists.

Note that the above conditions are sufficient but not necessary.

Remark 1 : The result (2) holds if x is a point of continuity of $f(x)$. At a point of discontinuity $x = x_0$, the value of the Fourier integral equals the average value of the left-hand and right-hand limit of $f(x)$ at $x = x_0$ i.e. at $f(x_0) = \frac{1}{2}\,[f(x_0 + 0) + f(x_0 - 0)]$ as in the case of Fourier series.

Remark 2 : The result (2) can also be written as

$$f(x) = \frac{1}{2\pi} \int_{-\infty}^{\infty} e^{i\lambda x}\, d\lambda \int_{-\infty}^{\infty} f(u)\, e^{-i\lambda u}\, du \qquad \ldots (2\,a)$$

Remark 3 : Example of a periodic function $f(x)$ of period T and the limiting non-periodic function whose period becomes infinite.

Consider the function

$$f_T(x) = \begin{cases} 0, & -T/2 < x < -1 \\ 1, & -1 < x < 1 \\ 0, & 1 < x < T/2 \end{cases}$$

having period $T > 2$. For $T \to \infty$, we obtain a function which is no longer periodic [See Fig. 6.1]. Non-periodic function could be assumed to have infinite period.

$$f(x) = \lim_{T \to \infty} f_T(x) = \begin{cases} 1, & -1 < x < 1 \\ 0, & \text{otherwise} \end{cases}$$

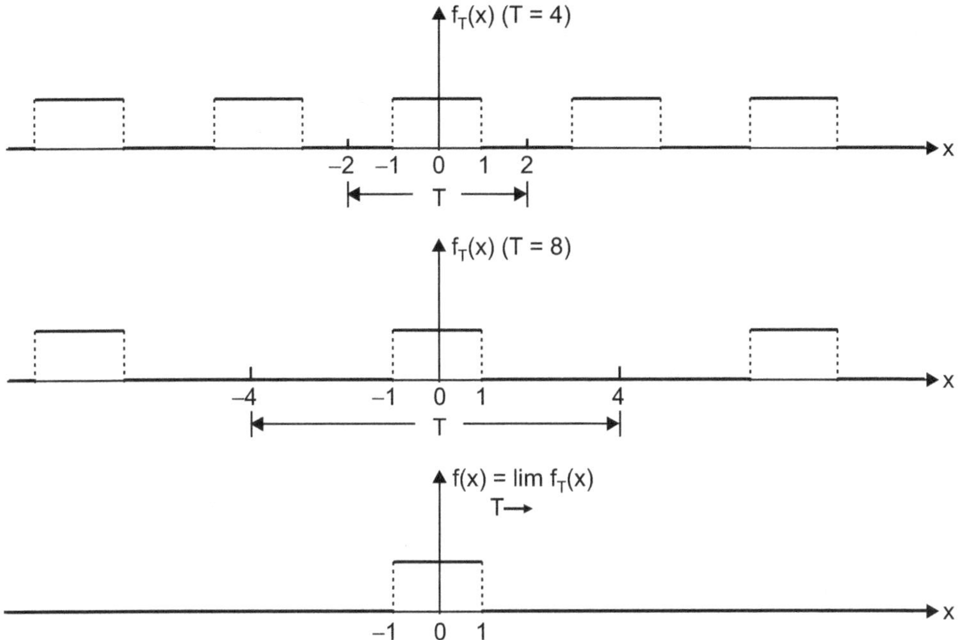

Fig. 6.1 : The Non-Periodic Limit of Sequence of Periodic

Function Whose Period Becomes Infinite

Remark 4 : We note that when we extend a function into Fourier series in certain range then the function is defined by the series outside this range in a periodic manner. However, by the Fourier integral, we obtain analytical expression for functions that represent the function throughout the infinite range $-\infty < x < \infty$.

6.4 EQUIVALENT FORMS OF FOURIER INTEGRAL

The Fourier integral can be written in various forms :

From result (2), we have

$$f(x) \;=\; \frac{1}{2\pi} \int_{-\infty}^{\infty} \int_{-\infty}^{\infty} f(u)\, e^{-i\lambda(u-x)}\, du\, d\lambda \qquad \dots (i)$$

Replacing the exponential by its trigonometric equivalent, we get

$$= \frac{1}{2\pi} \int_{-\infty}^{\infty} \int_{-\infty}^{\infty} f(u)\, [\cos\lambda(u-x) - i\sin\lambda(u-x)]\, du\, d\lambda$$

$$= \frac{1}{2\pi} \int_{-\infty}^{\infty} \int_{-\infty}^{\infty} f(u)\cos\lambda(u-x)\, du\, d\lambda - i\frac{1}{2\pi} \int_{-\infty}^{\infty} \int_{-\infty}^{\infty} f(u)\sin\lambda(u-x)\, du\, d\lambda \;\dots (ii)$$

Since $\sin \lambda (u - x)$ is an odd function of λ in $-\infty < \lambda < \infty$, we have $\int_{-\infty}^{\infty} \sin \lambda (u - x) \, d\lambda = 0$ and second integral is always zero. Then the expression (ii) gives equivalent form of result (2) as

$$f(x) = \frac{1}{2\pi} \int_{-\infty}^{\infty} \int_{-\infty}^{\infty} f(u) \cos \lambda (u - x) \, du \, d\lambda \qquad \dots (3)$$

Again since the $\cos \lambda (u - x)$ of result (3) is even function of λ in $-\infty < \lambda < \infty$, we have

$$\int_{-\infty}^{\infty} \cos \lambda (u - x) \, d\lambda = 2 \int_{0}^{\infty} \cos \lambda (u - x) \, d\lambda$$

and we get modified form of the result (3) as

$$f(x) = \frac{1}{\pi} \int_{\lambda = 0}^{\lambda = \infty} \int_{u = -\infty}^{u = \infty} f(u) \cos \lambda (u - x) \, du \, d\lambda \qquad \dots (4)$$

Expanding the factor $\cos \lambda (u - x)$ in the integrand of the result (4), we obtain

$$f(x) = \frac{1}{\pi} \int_{\lambda = 0}^{\lambda = \infty} \int_{u = -\infty}^{u = \infty} f(u) [\cos \lambda u \cos \lambda x + \sin \lambda u \sin \lambda x] \, du \, d\lambda$$

Hence another equivalent form of the result (4) is

$$f(x) = \int_{0}^{\infty} [A(\lambda) \cos \lambda x + B(\lambda) \sin \lambda x] \, d\lambda$$

where

$$A(\lambda) = \frac{1}{\pi} \int_{-\infty}^{\infty} f(u) \cos \lambda u \, du \qquad \dots (5)$$

$$B(\lambda) = \frac{1}{\pi} \int_{-\infty}^{\infty} f(u) \sin \lambda u \, du$$

6.5 SINE AND COSINE INTEGRALS

If a function defined in the interval $-\infty < x < \infty$ is either an even function or an odd function, then the Fourier integral representation becomes simpler than in the case of arbitrary function.

Case 1 : When f(x) is an even function, then in the result (5), we have

$$B(\lambda) = \frac{1}{\pi} \int_{-\infty}^{\infty} f(u) \sin \lambda u \, du = 0 \qquad \text{[product f(u) sin λu is odd]}$$

and

$$A(\lambda) = \frac{1}{\pi} \int_{-\infty}^{\infty} f(u) \cos \lambda u \, du = \frac{2}{\pi} \int_{0}^{\infty} f(u) \cos \lambda u \, du$$

$$\text{[product f(u) cos λu is even]}$$

Hence result (5) reduces to the following simpler form

$$\boxed{f(x) = \frac{2}{\pi} \int_{0}^{\infty} \int_{0}^{\infty} f(u) \cos \lambda u \cos \lambda x \, du \, d\lambda} \qquad \ldots (6)$$

The result (6) is called the **Fourier cosine integral** of f(x).

Case 2 : When f(x) is an odd function, then in the result (5), we have

$$A(\lambda) = \frac{1}{\pi} \int_{-\infty}^{\infty} f(u) \cos \lambda u \, du = 0 \qquad \text{[product f(u) cos λu is odd]}$$

and $B(\lambda) = \dfrac{1}{\pi} \displaystyle\int_{-\infty}^{\infty} f(u) \sin \lambda u \, du = \dfrac{2}{\pi} \displaystyle\int_{0}^{\infty} f(u) \sin \lambda u \, du$ [product f(u) sin λu is even]

Hence result (5) reduces to the following simpler form

$$\boxed{f(x) = \frac{2}{\pi} \int_{0}^{\infty} \int_{0}^{\infty} f(u) \sin \lambda u \sin \lambda x \, du \, d\lambda} \qquad \ldots (7)$$

The result (7) is called the **Fourier sine integral** of f(x).

Note : If a function f(x) is defined in the interval $0 < x < \infty$, then considering f(x) to be either an even or an odd function of x in $-\infty < x < \infty$, we can express f(x) as a Fourier cosine integral or Fourier sine integral respectively.

These simplifications are quite similar to half range cosine and half range sine expansions of even and odd periodic functions respectively.

6.6 FOURIER TRANSFORMS

From result (2), we have

$$f(x) = \frac{1}{2\pi} \int_{-\infty}^{\infty} \int_{-\infty}^{\infty} f(u) \, e^{-i\lambda (u-x)} \, du \, d\lambda$$

$$= \frac{1}{2\pi} \int_{-\infty}^{\infty} \left[\int_{-\infty}^{\infty} f(u) \, e^{-i\lambda u} \, du \right] e^{i\lambda x} \, d\lambda \qquad \ldots (i)$$

If we write $\quad F(\lambda) = \displaystyle\int_{-\infty}^{\infty} f(u)\, e^{-i\lambda u}\, du$ ... (ii)

then from (i), we get

$$f(x) = \frac{1}{2\pi} \int_{-\infty}^{\infty} F(\lambda)\, e^{i\lambda x}\, d\lambda \qquad \text{... (iii)}$$

The function $F(\lambda)$ is called the *Fourier transform* of $f(x)$ (and is written as $F(\lambda) = F\,[f(x)])$, while the function $f(x)$ is the *inverse Fourier transform* of $F(\lambda)$.

Hence Fourier transform of $f(x)$ is defined as

$$\boxed{F(\lambda) = \int_{-\infty}^{\infty} f(u)\, e^{-i\lambda u}\, du} \qquad \text{... (8)}$$

and Inverse Fourier transform is given by

$$\boxed{f(x) = \frac{1}{2\pi} \int_{-\infty}^{\infty} F(\lambda)\, e^{i\lambda x}\, d\lambda} \qquad \text{... (9)}$$

Note 1 : It is sometimes convenient to associate the factor $\dfrac{1}{2\pi}$ with the integral for $F(\lambda)$ instead with the integral for $f(x)$. It is also possible to achieve more symmetric form by associating the factor $1/\sqrt{2\pi}$ with each of the integrals.

Hence the results (8) and (9) can be written as :

$$\boxed{F(\lambda) = \frac{1}{\sqrt{2\pi}} \int_{-\infty}^{\infty} f(u)\, e^{-i\lambda u}\, du} \qquad \text{... (8 a)}$$

and $\qquad \boxed{f(x) = \dfrac{1}{\sqrt{2\pi}} \displaystyle\int_{-\infty}^{\infty} F(\lambda)\, e^{i\lambda x}\, d\lambda} \qquad \text{... (9 a)}$

Note 2 : To find Fourier integral representation of a function $f(x)$, first find $F(\lambda)$ from result (8) and then substitute this value of $F(\lambda)$ in (9).

Note 3 : Symmetrical expressions $f(x)$ and its corresponding function $F(\lambda)$ constitute a *Fourier Transform pair*.

6.7 FOURIER SINE AND COSINE TRANSFORMS

1. Fourier cosine transform :

If a function f(x) defined in the interval $-\infty < x < \infty$ is an *even function*, then from Fourier cosine integral [result (6)], we have

$$f(x) = \frac{2}{\pi} \int_0^\infty \int_0^\infty f(u) \cos \lambda u \cos \lambda x \, du \, d\lambda$$

$$= \frac{2}{\pi} \int_0^\infty \left[\int_0^\infty f(u) \cos \lambda u \, du \right] \cos \lambda x \, d\lambda \qquad \ldots \text{(i)}$$

If we write $\quad F_c(\lambda) = \int_0^\infty f(u) \cos \lambda u \, du \qquad \ldots \text{(ii)}$

then from (i), it follows that

$$f(x) = \frac{2}{\pi} \int_0^\infty F_c(\lambda) \cos \lambda x \, d\lambda \qquad \ldots \text{(iii)}$$

We call $F_c(\lambda)$ the Fourier cosine transform of f(x), while f(x) is the *Inverse Fourier cosine transform* of $F_c(\lambda)$.

Hence the Fourier cosine transform of f(x) is defined as

$$\boxed{F_c(\lambda) = \int_0^\infty f(u) \cos \lambda u \, du} \qquad \ldots \text{(10)}$$

and the Inverse Fourier cosine transform of $F_c(\lambda)$ is given by

$$\boxed{f(x) = \frac{2}{\pi} \int_0^\infty F_c(\lambda) \cos \lambda x \, d\lambda} \qquad \ldots \text{(11)}$$

2. Fourier sine transform :

If a function f(x) defined in the interval $-\infty < x < \infty$ is an *odd function*, then from Fourier sine integral [result (7)], we have

$$f(x) = \frac{2}{\pi} \int_0^\infty \int_0^\infty f(u) \sin \lambda u \sin \lambda x \, du \, d\lambda$$

$$= \frac{2}{\pi} \int_0^\infty \left[\int_0^\infty f(u) \sin \lambda u \, du \right] \sin \lambda x \, d\lambda \qquad \ldots \text{(i)}$$

If we write $\quad F_s(\lambda) = \int_0^\infty f(u)\sin\lambda u\,du \qquad\qquad\qquad\qquad \ldots\text{(ii)}$

then from (i), it follows that

$$f(x) = \frac{2}{\pi}\int_0^\infty F_s(\lambda)\sin\lambda x\,d\lambda \qquad\qquad\qquad\qquad \ldots\text{(iii)}$$

We call $F_s(\lambda)$ the *Fourier sine transform* of $f(x)$, while $f(x)$ is the *Inverse Fourier sine transform* of $F_s(\lambda)$.

Hence the Fourier sine transform of $f(x)$ is defined as

$$\boxed{\;F_s(\lambda) \;=\; \int_0^\infty f(u)\sin\lambda u\,du\;} \qquad\qquad\qquad\qquad \ldots\text{(12)}$$

and the Inverse Fourier sine transform of $F_s(\lambda)$ is given by

$$\boxed{\;f(x) \;=\; \frac{2}{\pi}\int_0^\infty F_s(\lambda)\sin\lambda x\,d\lambda\;} \qquad\qquad\qquad\qquad \ldots\text{(13)}$$

Note :

1. If a function $f(x)$ is defined in the interval $0 < x < \infty$, then we can extend $f(x)$ in the interval $-\infty < x < 0$ so that $f(x)$ becomes an even function in the interval $-\infty < x < \infty$. Thus for even function defined in $-\infty < x < \infty$, Fourier cosine transform and Inverse Fourier cosine transform are given by results (10) and (11) respectively.

2. If a function $f(x)$ is defined in the interval $0 < x < \infty$, then we can also extend $f(x)$ in the interval $-\infty < x < 0$, so that $f(x)$ becomes an odd function in the interval $-\infty < x < \infty$. Thus for odd function defined in $-\infty < x < \infty$, Fourier sine transform and Inverse Fourier sine transform are given by results (12) and (13) respectively.

3. These simplifications are quite similar to those in the case of Fourier series.

4. Results (10) and (11) of Fourier cosine transform and Inverse Fourier cosine transform can be written in more symmetric forms as

$$\boxed{\;F_c(\lambda) \;=\; \sqrt{\frac{2}{\pi}}\int_0^\infty f(u)\cos\lambda u\,du\;} \qquad\qquad \ldots\text{(10 (a))}$$

$$\text{and}\qquad\boxed{\;f(x) \;=\; \sqrt{\frac{2}{\pi}}\int_0^\infty F_c(\lambda)\cos\lambda x\,d\lambda\;} \qquad\qquad \ldots\text{(11 (a))}$$

Similarly, results (12) and (13) of Fourier sine transform and Inverse Fourier sine transform can be written in more symmetrical forms as

$$F_s(\lambda) = \sqrt{\frac{2}{\pi}} \int_0^\infty f(u) \sin \lambda u \, du \qquad \qquad \text{... (12 (a))}$$

and

$$f(x) = \sqrt{\frac{2}{\pi}} \int_0^\infty F_s(\lambda) \sin \lambda x \, d\lambda \qquad \qquad \text{... (13 (a))}$$

In the following table, we have listed Fourier transform pairs for ready reference.

Table 6.1
Table of Fourier Transforms and Inverse Transforms

Sr. No.	Name of the transform	Interval	Expression for the transform	Inverse transform
1.	Fourier	$-\infty < x < \infty$	$F(\lambda) = \int_{-\infty}^\infty f(u)\, e^{-i\lambda u}\, du$	$f(x) = \dfrac{1}{2\pi} \int_{-\infty}^\infty F(\lambda)\, e^{i\lambda x}\, d\lambda$
2.	Fourier cosine (for even function)	$-\infty < x < \infty$	$F_c(\lambda) = \int_0^\infty f(u) \cos \lambda u\, du$	$f(x) = \dfrac{2}{\pi} \int_0^\infty F_c(\lambda) \cos \lambda x\, d\lambda$
3.	Fourier sine (for odd function)	$-\infty < x < \infty$	$F_s(\lambda) = \int_0^\infty f(u) \sin \lambda u\, du$	$f(x) = \dfrac{2}{\pi} \int_0^\infty F_s(\lambda) \sin \lambda x\, d\lambda$
4.	Fourier cosine	$0 < x < \infty$	$F_c(\lambda) = \int_0^\infty f(u) \cos \lambda u\, du$	$f(x) = \dfrac{2}{\pi} \int_0^\infty F_c(\lambda) \cos \lambda x\, d\lambda$
5.	Fourier sine	$0 < x < \infty$	$F_s(\lambda) = \int_0^\infty f(u) \sin \lambda u\, du$	$f(x) = \dfrac{2}{\pi} \int_0^\infty F_s(\lambda) \sin \lambda x\, d\lambda$

6.8 USEFUL RESULTS FOR EVALUATING THE INTEGRALS IN FOURIER TRANSFORMS

The following results are quite useful in evaluating the integrals :

1. $B(m, n) = \dfrac{\overline{|m}\ \overline{|n}}{\overline{|m+n}}$

2. $\overline{|n+1} = n\,\overline{|n}\ $, $\ \overline{|n+1} = n!$ if n is positive integer, $\overline{|1/2} = \sqrt{\pi}$

3. Rule of differentiation under the integral sign (DUIS) :

$$\text{If } I(\alpha) = \int_a^b f(x, \alpha)\, dx, \quad \text{where a and b are constants, then}$$

$$\frac{d\, I(\alpha)}{d\alpha} = \frac{d}{d\alpha} \int_a^b f(x, \alpha)\, dx = \int_a^b \frac{\partial}{\partial \alpha}\, f(x, \alpha)\, dx$$

4. $e^{ix} = \cos x + i \sin x \quad$ and $\quad e^{-ix} = \cos x - i \sin x$

5. $\left| x \right| \le a \;\Rightarrow\; -a \le x \le a \quad$ and $\quad \left| x \right| \ge a \Rightarrow x \ge a \text{ and } x \le -a$

6. $\displaystyle \int e^{ax} \sin bx\; dx = \frac{e^{ax}}{a^2 + b^2}\, (a \sin bx - b \cos bx)$

$$\int e^{ax} \cos bx\; dx = \frac{e^{ax}}{a^2 + b^2}\, (a \cos bx + b \sin bx)$$

7. $\displaystyle \int_0^\infty \frac{\sin ax}{x}\; dx = \begin{cases} \pi/2 & \text{if a is positive} \\[4pt] -\pi/2 & \text{if a is negative} \end{cases}$

6.9 ILLUSTRATIONS ON FOURIER INTEGRALS AND FOURIER TRANSFORMS

Type 1 : Problems on Fourier integral representation

Ex. 1 : *Find the Fourier integral representation of the function*

$$f(x) = \begin{cases} 1, & \left| x \right| < 1 \\[4pt] 0, & \left| x \right| > 1 \end{cases}$$

and hence

(a) evaluate $\displaystyle \int_0^\infty \frac{\sin \lambda \cos \lambda x}{\lambda}\, d\lambda$

(b) deduce the value of $\displaystyle \int_0^\infty \frac{\sin \lambda}{\lambda}\, d\lambda.$

(c) Find the value of above integrals at $\left| x \right| = 1$, *which are points of discontinuity of* $f(x)$. **(Dec. 2007)**

Sol. : Here the given function f(x) is

$$f(x) = \begin{cases} 1, & -1 < x < 1 \\[4pt] 0, & \left| x \right| > 1 \end{cases} \qquad \dots \text{(i)}$$

This shows that $f(-x) = f(x)$ i.e. $f(x)$ is an even function in the interval $-\infty < x < \infty$ [See Fig. 6.2].

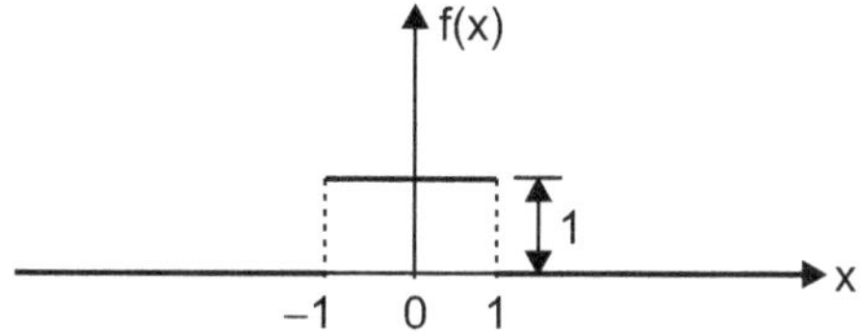

Fig. 6.2

Hence by result (10), the Fourier cosine transform for even function $f(x)$ in the interval $-\infty < x < \infty$ is given by

$$F_c(\lambda) \;=\; \int_0^\infty f(u) \cos \lambda u \; du \;=\; \int_0^1 \cos \lambda u \; du \qquad \text{[from (i)]}$$

$$=\; \left[\frac{\sin \lambda u}{\lambda}\right]_0^1 \;=\; \frac{\sin \lambda}{\lambda} \qquad \qquad \dots \text{(ii)}$$

By using inverse transform [result (11)], the Fourier integral representation is given by

$$f(x) \;=\; \frac{2}{\pi} \int_0^\infty F_c(\lambda) \cos \lambda x \; d\lambda \;=\; \frac{2}{\pi} \int_0^\infty \frac{\sin \lambda}{\lambda} \cos \lambda x \; d\lambda \quad \text{[substituting } F_c(\lambda) \text{ from (ii)]}$$

$$=\; \frac{2}{\pi} \int_0^\infty \frac{\sin \lambda \cos \lambda x}{\lambda} \; dx \qquad \qquad \dots \text{(iii)}$$

which is the required Fourier integral representation.

The result (iii) can be expressed as

$$\int_0^\infty \frac{\sin \lambda \cos \lambda x}{\lambda} \; d\lambda \;=\; \frac{\pi}{2} f(x), \quad \text{where } f(x) = \begin{cases} 1, & |x| < 1 \\ 0, & |x| > 1 \end{cases}$$

$$\therefore \quad \int_0^\infty \frac{\sin \lambda \cos \lambda x}{\lambda} \; d\lambda \;=\; \begin{cases} \dfrac{\pi}{2}, & |x| < 1 \\ 0, & |x| > 1 \end{cases} \qquad \qquad \dots \text{(iv)}$$

Now, if we put $x = 0$ (which lies in $-1 < x < 1$) in (iv), we have

$$\int_0^\infty \frac{\sin \lambda}{\lambda} \; d\lambda \;=\; \frac{\pi}{2} \qquad \qquad \dots \text{(v)}$$

At $|x| = 1$, which are points of discontinuity, the value of the Fourier integral equals to average of left-hand and right-hand limit of $f(x)$ at $|x| = 1$.

Thus,

$$\left[\int_0^\infty \frac{\sin \lambda \cos \lambda x}{\lambda} dx\right]_{|x| = 1} = \frac{\frac{\pi}{2} + 0}{2} = \frac{\pi}{4}.$$

Note 1 : We note that the integral in (v) is the limit of the so-called *sine integral*

$$S_i(t) = \int_0^t \frac{\sin \lambda}{\lambda} d\lambda \quad \text{as} \quad t \to \infty.$$

Note 2 : The Fourier integral representation can also be obtained directly by using result (4) in section 6.4. Thus,

$$f(x) = \frac{1}{\pi} \int_{\lambda = 0}^{\lambda = \infty} \int_{u = -\infty}^{u = \infty} f(u) \cos \lambda (u - x) \, du \, d\lambda$$

$$= \frac{1}{\pi} \int_{\lambda = 0}^{\lambda = \infty} \left[\int_{u = -1}^{u = 1} \cos \lambda (u - x) \, du\right] d\lambda \qquad (\because f(u) = 1 \text{ for } -1 < u < 1)$$

$$= \frac{1}{\pi} \int_{\lambda = 0}^{\lambda = \infty} \left[\frac{\sin \lambda (u - x)}{\lambda}\right]_{-1}^{1} d\lambda$$

$$= \frac{1}{\pi} \int_{\lambda = 0}^{\lambda = \infty} \left[\frac{\sin \lambda (1 - x) + \sin \lambda (1 + x)}{x}\right] d\lambda$$

$$= \frac{2}{\pi} \int_{\lambda = 0}^{\lambda = \infty} \frac{\sin \lambda \cos \lambda x}{\lambda} d\lambda. \left\{\because \sin A + \sin B = 2 \sin \frac{A + B}{2} \cos \frac{A - B}{2}\right.$$

Ex. 2 : *Find the Fourier integral for the function*

$$f(x) = \begin{cases} 0, & x < 0 \\ e^{-x}, & x > 0 \\ 1/2, & x = 0 \end{cases}$$

Sol. : Note that the given function $f(x)$ is neither an even function nor an odd function. Hence the Fourier integral representation can be obtained by first finding Fourier transform $F(\lambda)$ using result (8) and then substituting this value of $F(\lambda)$ in result (9).

Thus from result (8), we have

$$F(\lambda) = \int_{-\infty}^{\infty} f(u)\, e^{-i\lambda u}\, du = \int_{-\infty}^{0} f(u)\, e^{-i\lambda u}\, du + \int_{0}^{\infty} f(u)\, e^{-i\lambda u}\, du$$

$$= \int_{-\infty}^{0} (0)\, e^{-i\lambda u}\, du + \int_{0}^{\infty} e^{-u}\, e^{-i\lambda u}\, du$$

$$= \int_{0}^{\infty} e^{-(1+i\lambda)u}\, du = \left[\frac{e^{-(1+i\lambda)u}}{-(1+i\lambda)}\right]_{0}^{\infty}$$

$$= \frac{1}{1+i\lambda} = \frac{1-i\lambda}{1+\lambda^2} \qquad \qquad \dots \text{(i)}$$

By using inverse transform [result (9)], the Fourier integral representation of f(x) is

given by, $\qquad f(x) = \dfrac{1}{2\pi} \displaystyle\int_{-\infty}^{\infty} F(\lambda)\, e^{i\lambda x}\, d\lambda = \dfrac{1}{2\pi} \displaystyle\int_{-\infty}^{\infty} \dfrac{1-i\lambda}{1+\lambda^2}\, [\cos \lambda x + i \sin \lambda x]\, d\lambda$

$$= \frac{1}{2\pi} \int_{-\infty}^{\infty} \left[\frac{\cos \lambda x + \lambda \sin \lambda x}{1+\lambda^2} + i\, \frac{-\lambda \cos \lambda x + \sin \lambda x}{1+\lambda^2}\right] d\lambda \quad \dots \text{(ii)}$$

If $\ \phi_1(\lambda) = \dfrac{\cos \lambda x + \lambda \sin \lambda x}{1+\lambda^2}$, then since $\phi_1(-\lambda) = \phi_1(\lambda)$, $\phi_1(\lambda)$ is an even function of λ

and hence, we have

$$\int_{-\infty}^{\infty} \frac{\cos \lambda x + \lambda \sin \lambda}{1+\lambda^2}\, d\lambda = 2 \int_{0}^{\infty} \frac{\cos \lambda x + \lambda \sin \lambda x}{1+\lambda^2}\, d\lambda \qquad \qquad \dots \text{(iii)}$$

and if $\ \phi_2(\lambda) = \dfrac{-\lambda \cos \lambda x + \sin \lambda x}{1+\lambda^2}$, then since $\phi_2(-\lambda) = -\phi_2(\lambda)$, $\phi_2(\lambda)$ is an odd

function of λ, we have

$$\int_{-\infty}^{\infty} \frac{-\lambda \cos \lambda x + \lambda \sin \lambda x}{1+\lambda^2}\, d\lambda = 0 \qquad \qquad \dots \text{(iv)}$$

Substituting (iii) and (iv) in (ii), we get

$$f(x) = \frac{1}{\pi} \int_{0}^{\infty} \frac{\cos \lambda x + \lambda \sin \lambda x}{1+\lambda^2}\, d\lambda$$

which is the required Fourier integral representation.

Ex. 3 : *By considering Fourier sine and cosine integrals of e^{-mx} ($m > 0$), prove that*

(a) $\displaystyle\int_0^\infty \frac{\lambda \sin \lambda x}{\lambda^2 + m^2}\, d\lambda = \frac{\pi}{2}\, e^{-mx}, \qquad m > 0,\ x > 0;\quad and$

(b) $\displaystyle\int_0^\infty \frac{\cos \lambda x}{\lambda^2 + m^2}\, d\lambda = \frac{\pi}{2m}\, e^{-mx}, \qquad m > 0,\ x > 0.$ **(May 2015)**

Sol. : Let $f(x) = e^{-mx}$, $m > 0$, $x > 0$, then since $f(x)$ is defined in the half range $0 < x < \infty$, the function $f(x)$ can have either a Fourier sine transform or a Fourier cosine transform.

(a) Taking Fourier sine transform [using result (12)] of $f(x) = e^{-mx}$, we have

$$F_s(\lambda) = \int_0^\infty f(u) \sin \lambda u\, du = \int_0^\infty e^{-mu} \sin \lambda u\, du$$

$$= \left[\frac{e^{-mu}}{m^2 + \lambda^2}(-m \sin \lambda u - \lambda \cos \lambda u)\right]_0^\infty = \frac{\lambda}{m^2 + \lambda^2} \qquad \dots \text{(i)}$$

Using result (13), inverse sine transform of $F_s(\lambda)$ is given by

$$f(x) = \frac{2}{\pi} \int_0^\infty F_s(\lambda) \sin \lambda x\, d\lambda = \frac{2}{\pi} \int_0^\infty \frac{\lambda}{m^2 + \lambda^2} \sin \lambda x\, d\lambda$$

$$= \frac{2}{\pi} \int_0^\infty \frac{\lambda \sin \lambda x}{m^2 + \lambda^2}\, d\lambda \qquad \dots \text{(ii)}$$

The result (ii) can be expressed as

$$\int_0^\infty \frac{\lambda \sin \lambda x}{\lambda^2 + m^2}\, d\lambda = \frac{\pi}{2}\, f(x) = \frac{\pi}{2}\, e^{-mx}, \qquad x > 0,\ m > 0 \qquad \dots \text{(iii)}$$

(b) Taking Fourier cosine transform [using result (10)] of $f(x) = e^{-mx}$, we have

$$F_c(\lambda) = \int_0^\infty f(u) \cos \lambda u\, du = \int_0^\infty e^{-mu} \cos \lambda u\, du$$

$$= \left[\frac{e^{-mu}}{m^2 + \lambda^2}(-m \cos \lambda u + \lambda \sin \lambda u)\right]_0^\infty = \frac{m}{m^2 + \lambda^2} \qquad \dots \text{(iv)}$$

Using result (11), inverse cosine transform of $F_c(\lambda)$ is given by

$$f(x) = \frac{2}{\pi} \int_0^\infty F_c(\lambda) \cos \lambda x\, d\lambda = \frac{2}{\pi} \int_0^\infty \frac{m}{m^2 + \lambda^2} \cos \lambda x\, d\lambda$$

$$= \frac{2m}{\pi} \int_0^\infty \frac{\cos \lambda x}{m^2 + \lambda^2}\, d\lambda \qquad \dots \text{(v)}$$

The result (v) can be expressed as

$$\int_0^\infty \frac{\cos \lambda x}{\lambda^2 + m^2} \, d\lambda \;=\; \frac{\pi}{2m} \, f(x) \;=\; \frac{\pi}{2m} \, e^{-mx}.$$

Ex. 4 : *If* $f(x) = \begin{cases} \sin x, & \text{when } 0 < x < \pi \\ 0, & \text{when } x < 0 \text{ or } x > \pi \end{cases}$ **(Dec. 2010)**

then prove that

$$f(x) \;=\; \frac{1}{\pi} \int_0^\infty \frac{\cos \lambda x + \cos [\lambda (\pi - x)]}{1 - \lambda^2} \, d\lambda.$$

Hence deduce that $\displaystyle \int_0^\infty \frac{\cos \lambda \, \pi/2}{1 - \lambda^2} \, d\lambda = \frac{\pi}{2}\,.$

Sol. : Here $f(x)$ is defined over the interval $-\infty < x < \infty$ and is neither an even function nor an odd function, hence the Fourier transform of $f(x)$ is given by [result (8)],

$$F(\lambda) \;=\; \int_{-\infty}^{\infty} f(u) \, e^{-i\lambda u} \, du \;=\; \int_0^\pi \sin u \, e^{-i\lambda u} \, du$$

$$= \left[\frac{e^{-i\lambda u}}{(-i\lambda)^2 + 1} \, (-i\lambda \sin u - \cos u) \right]_0^\pi$$

$$= \left[\frac{e^{-i\lambda \pi}}{-\lambda^2 + 1} \, (-\cos \pi) - \frac{1}{-\lambda^2 + 1} \, (-\cos 0) \right]$$

$$= \frac{e^{-i\lambda \pi} + 1}{1 - \lambda^2} \;=\; \frac{(1 + \cos \lambda \pi) - i \sin \lambda \pi}{1 - \lambda^2} \qquad \ldots \text{(i)}$$

Using result (9), inverse transform of $F(\lambda)$ is given by

$$f(x) \;=\; \frac{1}{2\pi} \int_{-\infty}^{\infty} F(\lambda) \, e^{i\lambda x} \, d\lambda$$

$$= \frac{1}{2\pi} \int_{-\infty}^{\infty} \left[\frac{(1 + \cos \lambda \pi) - i \sin \lambda \pi}{1 - \lambda^2} \right] (\cos \lambda x + i \sin \lambda x) \, d\lambda$$

$$= \frac{1}{2\pi} \left[\int_{-\infty}^{\infty} \left[\frac{1 + \cos \lambda\pi}{1 - \lambda^2} \right] \cos \lambda x \, d\lambda + i \int_{-\infty}^{\infty} \left[\frac{1 + \cos \lambda\pi}{1 - \lambda^2} \right] \sin \lambda x \, d\lambda \right.$$

$$\left. - i \int_{-\infty}^{\infty} \frac{\sin \lambda\pi \cos \lambda x}{1 - \lambda^2} \, d\lambda + \int_{-\infty}^{\infty} \frac{\sin \lambda\pi \sin \lambda x}{1 - \lambda^2} \, d\lambda \right]$$

$$= \frac{1}{2\pi} \left[2 \int_{0}^{\infty} \left(\frac{1 + \cos \lambda\pi}{1 - \lambda^2} \right) \cos \lambda x \, d\lambda + 2 \int_{0}^{\infty} \frac{\sin \lambda\pi \sin \lambda x}{1 - \lambda^2} \, d\lambda \right]$$

$$\begin{cases} \because \left(\dfrac{1 + \cos \lambda\pi}{1 - \lambda^2} \right) \cos \lambda x \text{ is an even function of } \lambda, \ \sin \lambda\pi \cos \lambda x \text{ is an odd function of } \lambda \\ \text{and } \left(\dfrac{1 + \cos \lambda\pi}{1 - \lambda^2} \right) \sin \lambda x \text{ is an odd function of } \lambda, \ \sin \lambda\pi \sin \lambda x \text{ is an even function of } \lambda \end{cases}$$

$$= \frac{1}{\pi} \int_{0}^{\infty} \frac{\cos \lambda x + \cos \lambda\pi \cos \lambda x + \sin \lambda\pi \sin \lambda x}{1 - \lambda^2} \, d\lambda$$

$$\therefore \qquad f(x) = \frac{1}{\pi} \int_{0}^{\infty} \frac{\cos \lambda x + \cos [\lambda (\pi - x)]}{1 - \lambda^2} \, d\lambda \qquad \qquad \dots \text{(ii)}$$

Putting $\quad x = \dfrac{\pi}{2}\quad$ in (ii), we obtain

$$f\left(\frac{\pi}{2} \right) = \frac{1}{\pi} \int_{0}^{\infty} \frac{\cos \lambda \, \pi/2 + \cos [\lambda (\pi - \pi/2)]}{1 - \lambda^2} \, d\lambda$$

$$\sin \frac{\pi}{2} = \frac{1}{\pi} \int_{0}^{\infty} \frac{2 \cos \lambda \, \pi/2}{1 - \lambda^2} \, d\lambda \qquad \therefore \quad \int_{0}^{\infty} \frac{\cos \lambda \, \pi/2}{1 - \lambda^2} \, d\lambda = \frac{\pi}{2}$$

which is the required deduction.

Ex. 5 : *Find the Fourier cosine integral representation for the function*

$$f(x) = \begin{cases} x^2, & 0 < x < a \\ 0, & x > a \end{cases}$$

Sol. : Using result (10), Fourier cosine transform of $f(x)$ is given by

$$F_c (\lambda) = \int_{0}^{\infty} f(u) \cos \lambda u \, du = \int_{0}^{a} u^2 \cos \lambda u \, du$$

$$= \left[u^2 \left(\frac{\sin \lambda u}{\lambda} \right) - (2u) \left(-\frac{\cos \lambda u}{\lambda^2} \right) + (2) \left(-\frac{\sin \lambda u}{\lambda^3} \right) \right]_{0}^{a}$$

(using generalised rule of integration by parts)

$$= \frac{a^2 \sin \lambda a}{\lambda} + \frac{2a \cos \lambda a}{\lambda^2} - \frac{2 \sin \lambda a}{\lambda^3}$$

and using result (11), corresponding inverse transform is given by

$$f(x) = \frac{2}{\pi} \int_0^\infty F_c(\lambda) \cos \lambda x \, d\lambda$$

$$= \frac{2}{\pi} \int_0^\infty \left[\frac{a^2 \sin a\lambda}{\lambda} + \frac{2a \cos a\lambda}{\lambda^2} - \frac{2 \sin a\lambda}{\lambda^3} \right] \cos \lambda x \, d\lambda.$$

Ex. 6 : *Using Fourier integral representation, show that*

(a) $\displaystyle \int_0^\infty \frac{\lambda^3 \sin \lambda x}{\lambda^4 + 4} \, d\lambda = \frac{\pi}{2} e^{-x} \cos x$, where $x > 0$ **(Dec. 05, 08, May 17)**

(b) $\displaystyle \int_0^\infty \frac{\cos \frac{\pi\lambda}{2} \cos \lambda x}{1 - \lambda^2} \, d\lambda = \begin{cases} \dfrac{\pi}{2} \cos x, & |x| \leq \dfrac{\pi}{2} \\[2mm] 0, & |x| > \dfrac{\pi}{2} \end{cases}$ **(Nov. 15)**

(c) $\displaystyle \int_0^\infty \frac{\cos \lambda x + \lambda \sin \lambda x}{1 + \lambda^2} \, d\lambda = \begin{cases} 0, & x < 0 \\[2mm] \dfrac{\pi}{2}, & x = 0 \\[2mm] \pi e^{-x}, & x > 0 \end{cases}$ **(Dec. 04, May 07)**

(d) $\displaystyle \int_0^\infty \frac{1 - \cos \pi\lambda}{\lambda} \sin \lambda x \, d\lambda = \begin{cases} \dfrac{\pi}{2}, & 0 < x < \pi \\[2mm] 0, & x > \pi \end{cases}$.

Sol. : (a) To prove the result, consider R.H.S. which defines the function

$$f(x) = \frac{\pi}{2} e^{-x} \cos x, \quad x > 0 \qquad \dots (i)$$

Here the function $f(x)$ is defined in the half range $0 < x < \infty$ and since the integral on L.H.S. involves a term $\sin \lambda x$, indicates that, we are required to find the Fourier sine transform of $f(x)$.

Thus from result (12), we have

$$F_s(\lambda) = \int_0^\infty f(u) \sin \lambda u \, du = \int_0^\infty \frac{\pi}{2} e^{-u} \cos u \sin \lambda u \, du \qquad \text{[from (i)]}$$

$$= \frac{\pi}{4} \int_0^\infty e^{-u} [\sin (\lambda + 1) u + \sin (\lambda - 1) u] \, du$$

$$= \frac{\pi}{4} \left[\int_0^\infty e^{-u} \sin (\lambda + 1)\, u \, du + \int_0^\infty e^{-u} \sin (\lambda - 1)\, u \, du \right]$$

$$= \frac{\pi}{4} \left[\frac{e^{-u}}{1 + (\lambda + 1)^2} \left\{ - \sin (\lambda + 1)\, u - (\lambda + 1)\, \cos (\lambda + 1)\, u \right\} \right.$$

$$\left. + \frac{e^{-u}}{1 + (\lambda - 1)^2} \left\{ - \sin (\lambda - 1)\, u - (\lambda - 1) \cos (\lambda - 1)\, u \right\} \right]_0^\infty$$

$$= \frac{\pi}{4} \left[\frac{\lambda + 1}{\lambda^2 + 2\lambda + 2} + \frac{\lambda - 1}{\lambda^2 - 2\lambda + 2} \right] = \frac{\pi}{4} \left[\frac{2\lambda^3}{(\lambda^2 + 2)^2 - 4\lambda^2} \right]$$

$$= \frac{\pi}{2} \frac{\lambda^3}{\lambda^4 + 4} \qquad \ldots \text{(ii)}$$

Now using result (13), inverse sine transform of $F_s (\lambda)$ is given by

$$f(x) \; = \; \frac{2}{\pi} \int_0^\infty F_s (\lambda) \sin \lambda x \, d\lambda = \frac{2}{\pi} \int_0^\infty \frac{\pi}{2} \frac{\lambda^3}{\lambda^4 + 4} \; \sin \lambda x \, d\lambda$$

$$= \int_0^\infty \frac{\lambda^3 \sin \lambda x}{\lambda^4 + 4} d\lambda \qquad \ldots \text{(iii)}$$

The result (iii) can be expressed as

$$\int_0^\infty \frac{\lambda^3 \sin \lambda x}{\lambda^4 + 4} \; = \; f(x) \; = \; \frac{\pi}{2} \; e^{-x} \cos x \qquad \qquad \text{[from (i)]}$$

which is the required result.

(b) To prove the result, consider the function

$$f(x) \; = \; \begin{cases} \dfrac{\pi}{2} \cos x, & |x| \le \dfrac{\pi}{2} \\[3mm] 0, & |x| > \dfrac{\pi}{2} \end{cases} \qquad \ldots \text{(i)}$$

Here $f(x)$ is an even function of x defined in the interval $-\infty < x < \infty$ and since cosine terms are present in the integral, we find Fourier cosine transform.

Thus from result (10), we have

$$F_c (\lambda) \; = \; \int_0^\infty f(u) \cos \lambda u \, du = \int_0^{\pi/2} \frac{\pi}{2} \cos u \cos \lambda u \, du + \int_{\pi/2}^\infty (0) \cos \lambda u \, du$$

$$= \frac{\pi}{4} \int_0^{\pi/2} [\cos (\lambda + 1)\, u + \cos (\lambda - 1)\, u] \, du$$

$$= \frac{\pi}{4} \left[\frac{\sin (\lambda + 1) \, u}{\lambda + 1} + \frac{\sin (\lambda - 1) \, u}{\lambda - 1} \right]_0^{\pi/2}$$

$$\left\{ \because 2 \cos A \cos B = \cos (A + B) + \cos (A - B) \right\}$$

$$= \frac{\pi}{4} \left[\frac{\sin (\lambda + 1) \, \pi/2}{\lambda + 1} + \frac{\sin (\lambda - 1) \, \pi/2}{\lambda - 1} \right]$$

$$= \frac{\pi}{4} \left[\frac{\cos \lambda \pi/2}{\lambda + 1} - \frac{\cos \lambda \pi/2}{\lambda - 1} \right] \qquad \left\{ \because \sin \frac{(\lambda + 1) \, \pi}{2} = \cos \frac{\lambda \pi}{2} \right\}$$

$$= \frac{\pi}{4} \left[\frac{2 \cos \lambda \pi/2}{1 - \lambda^2} \right] = \frac{\pi}{2} \frac{\cos \lambda \pi/2}{1 - \lambda^2} \qquad \ldots \text{(ii)}$$

Using inverse Fourier cosine transform given by result (11), we have

$$f(x) = \frac{2}{\pi} \int_0^\infty F_c (\lambda) \cos \lambda x \, d\lambda = \frac{2}{\pi} \int_0^\infty \frac{\pi}{2} \frac{\cos \lambda \, \pi/2}{1 - \lambda^2} \cos \lambda x \, d\lambda$$

$$= \int_0^\infty \frac{\cos \dfrac{\lambda \pi}{2} \cos \lambda x}{1 - \lambda^2} \, d\lambda \qquad \ldots \text{(iii)}$$

The result (iii) can be expressed as

$$\int_0^\infty \frac{\cos \dfrac{\lambda \pi}{2} \cos \lambda x}{1 - \lambda^2} \, d\lambda = f(x) = \begin{cases} \dfrac{\pi}{2} \cos x, & |x| \leq \dfrac{\pi}{2} \\[3mm] 0, & |x| > \dfrac{\pi}{2} \end{cases}$$

which is the required result.

(c) To prove the result, consider the function

$$f(x) = \begin{cases} 0, & x < 0 \\ \pi \, e^{-x}, & x > 0 \end{cases} \qquad \ldots \text{(i)}$$

This function is defined in $-\infty < x < \infty$ and since the terms $\sin \lambda x$ and $\cos \lambda x$ are present in the integrand, we find general Fourier transform. Also note that f(x) is neither an even function nor an odd function.

Thus from result (8), we have

$$F(\lambda) = \int_{-\infty}^\infty f(u) \, e^{-i\lambda u} \, du = \int_{-\infty}^0 0 \, e^{-i\lambda u} \, du + \int_0^\infty \pi \, e^{-u} \, e^{-i\lambda u} \, du$$

$$= \pi \int_0^\infty e^{-(1 + i\lambda) \, u} \, du = \pi \left[\frac{e^{-(1 + i\lambda) \, u}}{-(1 + i\lambda)} \right]_0^\infty$$

$$= \pi \left[\frac{1}{1 + i\lambda} \right] = \pi \left[\frac{1 - i\lambda}{1 + \lambda^2} \right] \qquad \ldots \text{(ii)}$$

Now using result (9), inverse Fourier transform of $F(\lambda)$ is given by

$$f(x) \;=\; \frac{1}{2\pi} \int_{-\infty}^{\infty} F(\lambda)\, e^{i\lambda x}\, d\lambda \;=\; \frac{1}{2\pi} \int_{-\infty}^{\infty} \pi\left(\frac{1 - i\lambda}{1 + \lambda^2}\right) [\cos \lambda x + i \sin \lambda x]\, d\lambda$$

$$=\; \frac{1}{2} \int_{-\infty}^{\infty} \left[\frac{\cos \lambda x + \lambda \sin \lambda x}{1 + \lambda^2} + i\,\frac{-\lambda \cos \lambda x + \sin \lambda x}{1 + \lambda^2}\right] d\lambda$$

$$=\; \frac{1}{2}\left[2\int_{0}^{\infty} \frac{\cos \lambda x + \lambda \sin \lambda x}{1 + \lambda^2}\, d\lambda\right] \qquad \begin{cases} \because \displaystyle\int_{-\infty}^{\infty} \dfrac{\lambda \cos \lambda x + \sin \lambda}{1 + \lambda^2} = 0 \\[2pt] \text{since integrand is odd} \\ \text{function of } \lambda \text{ (refer Ex. 2)} \end{cases}$$

$$=\; \int_{0}^{\infty} \frac{\cos \lambda x + \lambda \sin \lambda x}{1 + \lambda^2}\, d\lambda \qquad\qquad\qquad\qquad \dots \text{(iii)}$$

The result (iii) can be expressed as

$$\int_{0}^{\infty} \frac{\cos \lambda x + \lambda\ \sin \lambda x}{1 + \lambda^2}\, d\lambda = f(x) \;=\; \begin{cases} 0, & x < 0 \\ \pi\, e^{-x}, & x > 0 \end{cases} \qquad\qquad \dots \text{(iv)}$$

To find the value of the integral at $x = 0$ i.e. $f(0)$, put $x = 0$ in (iv), we get

$$f(0) \;=\; \int_{0}^{\infty} \frac{1}{1 + \lambda^2}\, d\lambda \;=\; \left[\tan^{-1}\lambda\right]_{0}^{\infty} \;=\; \frac{\pi}{2} \qquad\qquad \dots \text{(v)}$$

Hence from (iv) and (v), we get

$$\int_{0}^{\infty} \frac{\cos \lambda x + \lambda \sin \lambda x}{1 + \lambda^2}\, d\lambda = \begin{cases} 0, & x < 0 \\ \pi/2, & x = 0 \\ \pi\, e^{-x}, & x > 0 \end{cases}$$

which is the required result.

(d)   To prove the result, consider the function

$$f(x) \;=\; \begin{cases} \dfrac{\pi}{2}, & 0 < x < \pi \\[6pt] 0, & x > \pi \end{cases} \qquad\qquad \dots \text{(i)}$$

Here the function is defined in $0 < x < \infty$ and since the integral on L.H.S. involves a term $\sin \lambda x$, we find Fourier sine transform of $f(x)$.

Thus from result (12), we have

$$F_s(\lambda) \;=\; \int_0^\infty f(u)\,\sin\lambda u\,du = \int_0^\pi \frac{\pi}{2}\,\sin\lambda u\,du + \int_\pi^\infty (0)\,\sin\lambda u\,du$$

$$= \frac{\pi}{2}\left[\frac{-\cos\lambda u}{\lambda}\right]_0^\pi = \frac{\pi}{2}\left[\frac{1-\cos\lambda\pi}{\lambda}\right] \qquad \ldots \text{(ii)}$$

Now using result (13), inverse sine transform of $F_s(\lambda)$ is given by

$$f(x) \;=\; \frac{2}{\pi}\int_0^\infty F_s(\lambda)\,\sin\lambda x\,d\lambda = \frac{2}{\pi}\int_0^\infty \frac{\pi}{2}\left[\frac{1-\cos\lambda\pi}{\lambda}\right]\sin\lambda x\,d\lambda$$

$$= \int_0^\infty \frac{1-\cos\lambda\pi}{\lambda}\,\sin\lambda x\,d\lambda \qquad \ldots \text{(iii)}$$

Result (iii) can be expressed as

$$\int_0^\infty \frac{1-\cos\lambda\pi}{\lambda}\,\sin\lambda x\,d\lambda = f(x) = \begin{cases} \dfrac{\pi}{2}, & 0 < x < \pi \\[2mm] 0, & x > \pi \end{cases}$$

which is the required result.

Type 2 : Problems on Fourier Transforms

Ex. 7 : *Find the Fourier transforms of* **(May 2014, Dec. 2014)**

$$f(x) \;=\; \begin{cases} 1, & |x| < a \\ 0, & |x| > a \end{cases}$$

Also graph f(x) and its Fourier transform for a = 3.

Sol. : The Fourier transform of f(x) is [refer result (8)]

$$F(\lambda) \;=\; \int_{-\infty}^\infty f(u)\,e^{-i\lambda u}\,du = \int_{-\infty}^a (1)\,e^{-i\lambda u}\,du = \left[\frac{e^{-i\lambda u}}{-i\lambda}\right]_{-a}^a$$

$$= \frac{e^{i\lambda a}-e^{-i\lambda a}}{i\lambda} = \frac{2\sin\lambda a}{\lambda}\,,\ \lambda \neq 0 . \qquad \ldots \text{(i)}$$

For $\lambda = 0$, we obtain $F(\lambda) = 2a$.

The graphs of f(x) and F(λ) for a = 3 are shown in Figs. 6.3 and 6.4 respectively.

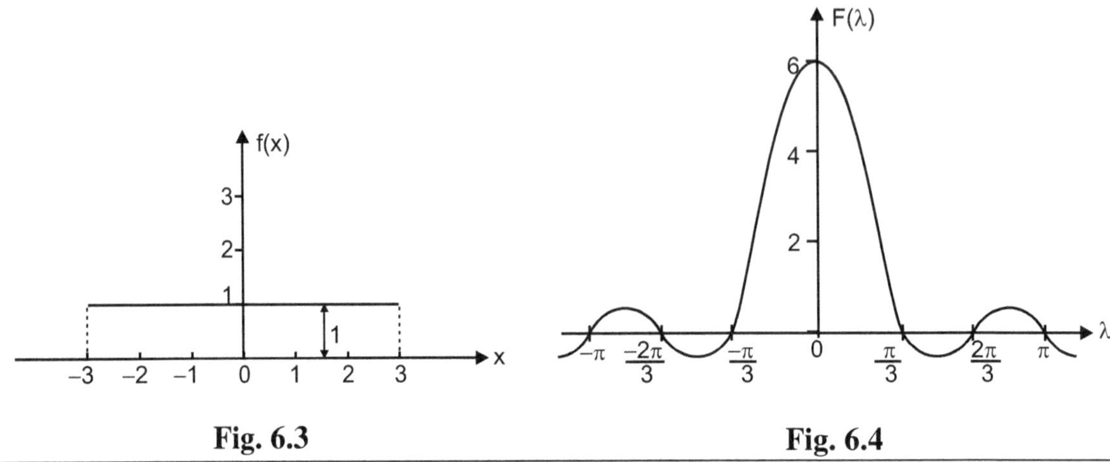

Fig. 6.3   **Fig. 6.4**

Ex. 8 : *Find the Fourier transform of*

$$f(x) \;=\; \begin{cases} 1 - x^2, & |x| \le 1 \\ 0, & |x| > 1 \end{cases}$$

and hence evaluate $\displaystyle\int_0^\infty \left(\frac{x \cos x - \sin x}{x^3}\right) \cos \frac{x}{2}\; dx$ **(May 2005)**

Sol. : The function f(x) is given by

$$f(x) \;=\; \begin{cases} 1 - x^2, & -1 \le x \le 1 \\ 0, & |x| > 1 \end{cases} \qquad \dots \text{(i)}$$

This shows that f(–x) = f(x) i.e. f(x) is an even function in the interval $-\infty < x < \infty$. Hence by result (10), the Fourier cosine transform of f(x) is

$$F_c(\lambda) \;=\; \int_0^\infty f(u) \cos \lambda u\, du \;=\; \int_0^1 (1 - u^2)\, \cos \lambda u\, du + \int_1^\infty (0)\, \cos \lambda u\, du$$

$$[\text{from (i)}]$$

$$= \left[(1 - u^2)\left(\frac{\sin \lambda u}{\lambda}\right) - (-2u)\left(\frac{-\cos \lambda u}{\lambda^2}\right) + (-2)\left(\frac{-\sin \lambda u}{\lambda^3}\right)\right]_0^1$$

$$= 2\left(\frac{\sin \lambda - \lambda \cos \lambda}{\lambda^3}\right) \qquad \dots \text{(ii)}$$

By using inverse transform [result (11)], the Fourier integral representation is given by

$$f(x) \;=\; \frac{2}{\pi} \int_0^\infty F_c(\lambda) \cos \lambda x \, d\lambda = \frac{2}{\pi} \int_0^\infty 2\left(\frac{\sin \lambda - \lambda \cos \lambda}{\lambda^3}\right) \cos \lambda x \, d\lambda$$

$$= \frac{4}{\pi} \int_0^\infty \left(\frac{\sin \lambda - \lambda \cos \lambda}{\lambda^3}\right) \cos \lambda x \, d\lambda \qquad \qquad \text{... (iii)}$$

The result (iii) can be expressed as

$$\int_0^\infty \left(\frac{\sin \lambda - \lambda \cos \lambda}{\lambda^3}\right) \cos \lambda x \, d\lambda = \frac{\pi}{4} \; f(x) = \begin{cases} \dfrac{\pi}{4}(1 - x^2), & |x| \le 1 \\[2mm] 0, & |x| > 1 \end{cases} \qquad \text{... (iv)}$$

Putting $x = \dfrac{1}{2}$, which lies in $-1 \le x \le 1$ i.e. in $|x| \le 1$, we get

$$\int_0^\infty \left(\frac{\sin \lambda - \lambda \cos \lambda}{\lambda^3}\right) \cos \frac{\lambda}{2} \, d\lambda = \frac{\pi}{4}\left(1 - \frac{1}{4}\right) = \frac{3\pi}{16} \qquad \qquad \text{... (v)}$$

Since variable of integration in definite integral is of no importance, replacing λ by x in (v), we have

$$\int_0^\infty \left(\frac{\sin x - x \cos x}{x^3}\right) \cos \frac{x}{2} \, dx \;=\; \frac{3\pi}{16}$$

$$\text{or} \quad \int_0^\infty \left(\frac{x \cos x - \sin x}{x^3}\right) \cos \frac{x}{2} \, dx \;=\; -\frac{3\pi}{16} .$$

Ex. 9 : *Find the Fourier cosine transform of the function* **(May 2016)**

$$f(x) \;=\; \begin{cases} \cos x, & 0 < x < a \\ 0, & x > a \end{cases}$$

Sol. : Using result (10), cosine transform of $f(x)$ is

$$F_c(\lambda) \;=\; \int_0^\infty f(u) \cos \lambda u \, du = \int_0^a \cos u \cos \lambda u \, du + \int_a^\infty (0) \cos \lambda u \, du$$

$$= \frac{1}{2} \int_0^a [\cos (\lambda + 1) u + \cos (\lambda - 1) u] \, du$$

$$= \frac{1}{2} \left[\frac{\sin (\lambda + 1) u}{\lambda + 1} + \frac{\sin (\lambda - 1) u}{\lambda - 1} \right]_0^a$$

$$= \frac{1}{2} \left[\frac{\sin (\lambda + 1) a}{\lambda + 1} + \frac{\sin (\lambda - 1) a}{\lambda - 1} \right]$$

Note : If we use result [10 (a)] for Fourier cosine transform,

$$F_c (\lambda) = \sqrt{\frac{2}{\pi}} \int_0^\infty f(u) \cos \lambda u \, du$$

we get the result

$$F_c (\lambda) = \sqrt{\frac{2}{\pi}} \cdot \frac{1}{2} \left[\frac{\sin (\lambda + 1) a}{\lambda + 1} + \frac{\sin (\lambda - 1) a}{\lambda - 1} \right].$$

Ex. 10 : *Show that :*

(a)   *the Fourier transform of* $f(x) = e^{-|x|}$ *is* $\dfrac{2}{1 + \lambda^2}$.

(b)   *the Fourier transform of* $f(x) = e^{-x^2/2}$ *is* $e^{-\lambda^2/2}$ **(Dec. 2005)**

(c)   *the Fourier cosine transform of* $f(x) = e^{-x^2}$ *is* $\dfrac{1}{\sqrt{2}} e^{-\lambda^2/4}$ **(May 2008)**

(d)   *the Fourier cosine transform of* $f(x) = e^{-x} + e^{-2x} \, (x > 0)$ *is* $\dfrac{6 + 3\lambda^2}{4 + 5\lambda^2 + \lambda^4}$

Sol. : (a) Fourier transform of $f(x) = e^{-|x|}$ in the interval $-\infty < x < \infty$ is given by

$$F(\lambda) = \int_{-\infty}^\infty f(u) \, e^{-i\lambda u} \, du = \int_{-\infty}^\infty e^{-|u|} \, e^{-i\lambda u} \, du$$

$$= \int_{-\infty}^\infty e^{-|u|} (\cos \lambda u - i \sin \lambda u) \, du$$

$$= \int_{-\infty}^\infty e^{-|u|} \cos \lambda u \, du - i \int_{-\infty}^\infty e^{-|u|} \sin \lambda u \, du$$

Since the integrand in the second integral is odd and hence integral is zero.

$$\therefore \qquad F(\lambda) = 2 \int_0^\infty e^{-u} \cos \lambda u \, du = 2 \left[\frac{e^{-u}}{1 + \lambda^2} (- \cos \lambda u + \lambda \sin \lambda u) \right]_0^\infty$$

$$= \frac{2}{1 + \lambda^2}$$

Note : We can also obtain Fourier cosine transform of $f(x)$ directly, since it is an even function.

(b)   Here $f(x) = e^{-x^2/2}$ is an even function of x defined in the interval $-\infty < x < \infty$, hence to obtain the required result, we use formula (10 a) for the Fourier cosine transform.

$$F_c (\lambda) = \sqrt{\frac{2}{\pi}} \int_0^\infty f(u) \cos \lambda u \, du = \sqrt{\frac{2}{\pi}} \int_0^\infty e^{-u^2/2} \cos \lambda u \, du \qquad \dots (i)$$

Let $\quad I(\lambda) = \displaystyle\int_0^\infty e^{-u^2/2} \cos \lambda u \, du \qquad \qquad \dots \text{(ii)}$

$\therefore \quad \dfrac{dI(\lambda)}{d\lambda} = \displaystyle\int_0^\infty \dfrac{\partial}{\partial \lambda} e^{-u^2/2} \cos \lambda u \, du \qquad \left[\begin{array}{l}\text{Using rule of differentiation}\\ \text{under the integral sign}\end{array}\right]$

$$= \int_0^\infty -(u\, e^{-u^2/2}) \sin \lambda u \, du$$

Integrating by parts, we have

$$= \left[e^{-u^2/2} \sin \lambda u\right]_0^\infty - \int_0^\infty e^{-u^2/2} \lambda \cos \lambda u \, du \left\{\begin{array}{l}\because \int - u\, e^{-u^2/2} \, du, \ [u^2/2 = t]\\[2mm] = -\int e^{-t} \, dt = + e^{-t} = + e^{-u^2/2}\end{array}\right.$$

$$= 0 - \lambda \int_0^\infty e^{-u^2/2} \cos \lambda u \, du.$$

$$= -\lambda \, I(\lambda), \qquad \text{where, } I(\lambda) = \int_0^\infty e^{-u^2/2} \cos \lambda u \, du \qquad \dots \text{(iii)}$$

$\therefore \quad \dfrac{dI}{d\lambda} = -\lambda \, I \qquad \qquad \text{(In variable separable form)}$

$\therefore \quad I = A\, e^{-\lambda^2/2} \qquad \qquad \dots \text{(iv)}$

To find constant A, put $\lambda = 0$ in (iv), then

$$[I(\lambda)]_{\lambda=0} = A\, e^0 = A \qquad \qquad \dots \text{(v)}$$

The value of $[I(\lambda)]$ at $\lambda = 0$ is obtained by putting $\lambda = 0$ in (ii),

$$[I(\lambda)]_{\lambda=0} = \int_0^\infty e^{-u^2/2} \, du, \text{ putting } u^2 = 2t \text{ or } u = \sqrt{2}\, t^{1/2}$$

$$= \int_0^\infty e^{-t} \frac{1}{\sqrt{2}} t^{-1/2} \, dt = \frac{1}{\sqrt{2}} \int_0^\infty e^{-t} \, t^{-1/2} \, dt$$

$$= \frac{1}{\sqrt{2}} \overline{\lvert 1/2} = \frac{1}{\sqrt{2}} \sqrt{\pi} = \sqrt{\frac{\pi}{2}}.$$

Thus from (v), we have $A = \sqrt{\dfrac{\pi}{2}}$ and hence from (iv) and (ii), we have

$$I(\lambda) = \int_0^\infty e^{-u^2/2} \cos \lambda u = \sqrt{\frac{\pi}{2}} \, e^{-\lambda^2/2} \qquad \qquad \dots \text{(vi)}$$

Substituting (vi) in (i), we get

$$F(\lambda) = \sqrt{\frac{2}{\pi}} \ \sqrt{\frac{\pi}{2}} \ e^{-\lambda^2/2} = e^{-\lambda^2/2}$$

Note : If we use result (10) for finding Fourier cosine transform, we get

$$F(\lambda) = \sqrt{\frac{\pi}{2}} \ e^{-\lambda^2/2}$$

(c)   Here $f(x) = e^{-x^2}$ is defined in the interval $-\infty < x < \infty$. To obtain required result, we use formula (10 a) for Fourier cosine transform.

$$F_c(\lambda) = \sqrt{\frac{2}{\pi}} \int_0^\infty f(u) \cos \lambda u \, du = \sqrt{\frac{2}{\pi}} \int_0^\infty e^{-u^2} \cos \lambda u \, du \qquad \ldots \text{(i)}$$

Let

$$I(\lambda) = \int_0^\infty e^{-u^2} \cos \lambda u \, du \qquad \ldots \text{(ii)}$$

$$I'(\lambda) = \int_0^\infty \frac{\partial}{\partial \lambda} e^{-u^2} \cos \lambda u \, du = \int_0^\infty (-u \, e^{-u^2}) \sin \lambda u \, du$$

[Using the rule of differentiation under the integral sign]

Integrating by parts, we have

$$= \left[\frac{1}{2} e^{-u^2} \sin \lambda u \right]_0^\infty - \int_0^\infty \frac{1}{2} e^{-u^2} \lambda \cos \lambda u \, du \begin{cases} \because \int -u \, e^{-u^2} \, du \ [-u^2 = t] \\ = \int \frac{1}{2} e^t \, dt = \frac{1}{2} \, e^{-u^2} \end{cases}$$

$$= 0 - \frac{\lambda}{2} \int_0^\infty e^{-u^2} \cos \lambda u \, du$$

$$= -\frac{\lambda}{2} I(\lambda), \qquad\qquad \text{where, } I(\lambda) = \int_0^\infty e^{-u^2} \cos \lambda u \, du \ \ldots \text{(iii)}$$

$$\therefore \qquad \frac{dI}{I} = -\frac{\lambda}{2} \, d\lambda \qquad\qquad \text{(In variable separable form)}$$

Integrating, we have

$$I = A \, e^{-\lambda^2/4} \qquad \ldots \text{(iv)}$$

To find the constant A, put $\lambda = 0$ in (iv), then

$$[I(\lambda)]_{\lambda=0} = A \qquad \ldots \text{(v)}$$

The value of $[I(\lambda)]_{\lambda=0}$ is obtained by putting $\lambda = 0$ in (ii),

$$[I(\lambda)]_{\lambda=0} = \frac{\sqrt{\pi}}{2}, \qquad\qquad \text{(refer to similar part of previous example)}$$

Thus from (v), we have $A = \dfrac{\sqrt{\pi}}{2}$; and hence from (iv) and (ii), we have

$$I(\lambda) = \int_0^\infty e^{-u^2} \cos \lambda u \, du = \frac{\sqrt{\pi}}{2} e^{-\lambda^2/4} \qquad \dots \text{(vi)}$$

Substituting (iv) in (i), we get

$$F(\lambda) = \sqrt{\frac{2}{\pi}} \; \frac{\sqrt{\pi}}{2} e^{-\lambda^2/4} = \frac{1}{\sqrt{2}} e^{-\lambda^2/4} .$$

Note : If we use result (10) for finding Fourier cosine transform, we get

$$F(\lambda) = \frac{\sqrt{\pi}}{2} e^{-\lambda^2/4}$$

(d) Here $f(x) = e^{-x} + e^{-2x}, \; 0 < x < \infty.$
The Fourier cosine transform of $f(x)$ is

$$F_c(\lambda) = \int_0^\infty f(u) \cos \lambda u \, du = \int_0^\infty (e^{-u} + e^{-2u}) \cos \lambda u \, du$$

$$= \left[\frac{e^{-u}}{1 + \lambda^2} (- \cos \lambda u + \lambda \sin \lambda u) + \frac{e^{-2u}}{4 + \lambda^2} (- 2 \cos \lambda u + \lambda \sin \lambda u) \right]_0^\infty$$

$$= \frac{1}{1 + \lambda^2} + \frac{2}{4 + \lambda^2} = \frac{6 + 3 \lambda^2}{4 + 5 \lambda^2 + \lambda^4} .$$

Ex. 11 : *Find the Fourier sine transform of* $\dfrac{1}{x}$.

Sol. : Using result (12), we have

$$F_s(\lambda) = \int_0^\infty f(u) \sin \lambda u \, du = \int_0^\infty \frac{1}{u} \sin \lambda u \, du$$

$$= \int_0^\infty \frac{\lambda}{t} (\sin t) \frac{dt}{\lambda}, \quad \text{putting } \lambda u = t \text{ or } u = \frac{t}{\lambda} \text{ and } du = \frac{dt}{\lambda}.$$

$$= \int_0^\infty \frac{\sin t}{t} \, dt = \frac{\pi}{2} .$$

Note : If we use result 12 (a), we would get

$$F_s(\lambda) \;=\; \sqrt{\frac{2}{\pi}} \int\limits_0^\infty f(u)\,\sin\lambda u\,du = \sqrt{\frac{2}{\pi}} \cdot \frac{\pi}{2} = \sqrt{\frac{\pi}{2}}.$$

Ex. 12 : *Find the Fourier sine transform of $\dfrac{e^{-ax}}{x}$ & hence evaluate $\displaystyle\int\limits_0^\infty \tan^{-1}\dfrac{x}{a}\,\sin x\,dx$.*

$$\textbf{(May 2006, Dec. 2008)}$$

Sol. : Using result (12), we have

$$F_s(\lambda) \;=\; \int\limits_0^\infty f(u)\,\sin\lambda u\,du = \int\limits_0^\infty \frac{e^{-au}}{u}\,\sin\lambda u\,du \qquad \ldots \text{(i)}$$

Let

$$I(\lambda) \;=\; \int\limits_0^\infty \frac{e^{-au}}{u}\,\sin\lambda u\,du \qquad \ldots \text{(ii)}$$

$$\therefore \qquad \frac{dI}{d\lambda} \;=\; \int\limits_0^\infty \frac{\partial}{\partial\lambda}\frac{e^{-au}}{u}\,\sin\lambda u\,du \qquad\qquad \text{[Using DUIS rule]}$$

$$=\; \int\limits_0^\infty \frac{e^{-au}}{u}\,(u\cos\lambda u)\,du = \int\limits_0^\infty e^{-au}\cos\lambda u\,du$$

$$=\; \left[\frac{e^{-au}}{a^2+\lambda^2}(-a\cos\lambda u + \lambda\sin\lambda u)\right]_0^\infty \;=\; \frac{a}{\lambda^2+a^2}$$

$$\therefore \qquad \frac{dI}{d\lambda} \;=\; \frac{a}{\lambda^2+a^2} \qquad \ldots \text{(iii)}$$

Integrating, we have

$$I(\lambda) \;=\; \int \frac{a}{\lambda^2+a^2}\,d\lambda + A \;=\; \tan^{-1}\frac{\lambda}{a} + A \qquad \ldots \text{(iv)}$$

To find constant A, we put $\lambda = 0$ in (iv), we get

$$[I(\lambda)]_{\lambda=0} \;=\; 0 + A$$

or

$$\left[\int\limits_0^\infty \frac{e^{-au}}{u}\sin\lambda u\,du\right]_{\lambda=0} \;=\; 0 + A \quad\Rightarrow\quad \boxed{A = 0} \qquad \ldots \text{(by (ii))}$$

$$\therefore \text{(iv)} \Rightarrow \quad I(\lambda) \;=\; \int\limits_0^\infty \frac{e^{-au}}{u}\sin\lambda u\,du \;=\; \tan^{-1}\frac{\lambda}{a} \qquad \ldots \text{(v)}$$

Substituting (v) in (i), we get

$$F_s(\lambda) = \tan^{-1}\frac{\lambda}{a} \qquad \qquad \ldots \text{(vi)}$$

Using result (13), inverse sine transform is given by

$$f(x) = \frac{2}{\pi}\int_0^\infty F_s(\lambda)\sin\lambda x\, d\lambda = \frac{2}{\pi}\int_0^\infty \tan^{-1}\frac{\lambda}{a}\sin\lambda x\, d\lambda$$

$$\therefore \quad \int_0^\infty \tan^{-1}\frac{\lambda}{a}\sin\lambda x\, d\lambda = \frac{\pi}{2}\, f(x) = \frac{\pi}{2}\frac{e^{-ax}}{x} \qquad \qquad \ldots \text{(vii)}$$

Putting $x = 1$ in (vii), we get

$$\int_0^\infty \tan^{-1}\frac{\lambda}{a}\sin\lambda\, d\lambda = \frac{\pi}{2}\, e^{-a}$$

or $\qquad \qquad \displaystyle\int_0^\infty \tan^{-1}\frac{x}{a}\sin x\, dx = \frac{\pi}{2}\, e^{-a}.$

Ex. 13 : *Find the Fourier sine and cosine transforms of the function $f(x) = e^{-x}$ and hence show that $\displaystyle\int_0^\infty \frac{\cos mx}{1+x^2}\, dx = \frac{\pi}{2}\, e^{-m}$ and $\displaystyle\int_0^\infty \frac{x\sin mx}{1+x^2}\, dx = \frac{\pi}{2}\, e^{-m}.$*

Sol. : Fourier Cosine Transform : Using result (10), we have

$$F_c(\lambda) = \int_0^\infty f(u)\cos\lambda u\, du = \int_0^\infty e^{-u}\cos\lambda u\, du$$

$$= \left[\frac{e^{-u}}{1+\lambda^2}(-\cos\lambda u + \lambda\sin\lambda u)\right]_0^\infty$$

$$= \frac{1}{1+\lambda^2} \qquad \qquad \ldots \text{(i)}$$

Now using result (11), inverse cosine transform is given by

$$f(x) = \frac{2}{\pi}\int_0^\infty F_c(\lambda)\cos\lambda x\, d\lambda = \frac{2}{\pi}\int_0^\infty \frac{1}{1+\lambda^2}\cos\lambda x\, d\lambda$$

$$\therefore \quad \int_0^\infty \frac{\cos\lambda x}{1+\lambda^2}\, d\lambda = \frac{\pi}{2}\, f(x) = \frac{\pi}{2}\, e^{-x} \qquad \qquad \ldots \text{(ii)}$$

Putting $x = m$ in (ii), we have

$$\int_0^\infty \frac{\cos\lambda m}{1+\lambda^2}\, d\lambda = \frac{\pi}{2}\, e^{-m} \qquad \qquad \ldots \text{(iii)}$$

Since variable of integration is immaterial in the definite integral,

hence,
$$\int_0^\infty \frac{\cos mx}{1 + x^2} \, dx = \frac{\pi}{2} e^{-m}.$$

Fourier Sine Transform : Using result (12), we have

$$F_s(\lambda) = \int_0^\infty f(u) \sin \lambda u \, du = \int_0^\infty e^{-u} \sin \lambda u \, du$$

$$= \left[\frac{e^{-u}}{1 + \lambda^2} (-\sin \lambda u - \lambda \cos \lambda u) \right]_0^\infty$$

$$= \frac{\lambda}{1 + \lambda^2} \qquad \qquad \ldots (i)$$

Now using result (13), inverse sine transform is given by

$$f(x) = \frac{2}{\pi} \int_0^\infty F_s(\lambda) \sin \lambda x \, d\lambda = \frac{2}{\pi} \int_0^\infty \frac{\lambda}{1 + \lambda^2} \sin \lambda x \, d\lambda$$

$$\therefore \quad \int_0^\infty \frac{\lambda \sin \lambda x}{1 + \lambda^2} \, d\lambda = \frac{\pi}{2} f(x) = \frac{\pi}{2} e^{-x} \qquad \qquad \ldots (ii)$$

Putting x = m in (ii), we have

$$\int_0^\infty \frac{\lambda \, \sin \lambda m}{1 + \lambda^2} \, d\lambda = \frac{\pi}{2} e^{-m} \qquad \qquad \ldots (iii)$$

Since variable of integration is immaterial in the definite integral,

hence
$$\int_0^\infty \frac{x \sin mx}{1 + x^2} \, dx = \frac{\pi}{2} e^{-m}.$$

Ex. 14 : *Find the Fourier sine and cosine transforms of the following function*

$$f(x) = \begin{cases} x, & 0 \le x \le 1 \\ 2 - x, & 1 \le x \le 2 \\ 0, & x > 2 \end{cases} \qquad \textbf{(May 2009, Dec. 2009, May 2011)}$$

Sol. : Fourier Cosine Transform : Using result (10), we have

$$F_c(\lambda) = \int_0^\infty f(u) \cos \lambda u \, du$$

$$= \int_0^1 (u) \cos \lambda u \, du + \int_1^2 (2 - u) \cos \lambda u \, du + \int_2^\infty (0) \cos \lambda u \, du$$

$$= \left[u \frac{\sin \lambda u}{\lambda} + \frac{\cos \lambda u}{\lambda^2} \right]_0^1 + \left[(2 - u) \frac{\sin \lambda u}{\lambda} - \frac{\cos \lambda u}{\lambda^2} \right]_1^2$$

$$= \left[\frac{\sin \lambda}{\lambda} + \frac{\cos \lambda}{\lambda^2} - \frac{1}{\lambda^2} \right] + \left[-\frac{\cos 2\lambda}{\lambda^2} - \frac{\sin \lambda}{\lambda} + \frac{\cos \lambda}{\lambda^2} \right]$$

$$= \frac{2 \cos \lambda - (1 + \cos 2\lambda)}{\lambda^2} = \frac{2 \cos \lambda \, (1 - \cos \lambda)}{\lambda^2}.$$

Fourier Sine Transform : Using result (12), we have

$$F_s (\lambda) = \int_0^\infty f(u) \sin \lambda u \, du$$

$$= \int_0^1 (u) \, \sin \lambda u \, du + \int_1^2 (2 - u) \, \sin \lambda u \, du + \int_2^\infty (0) \, \sin \lambda u \, du$$

$$= \left[- u \, \frac{\cos \lambda u}{\lambda} + \frac{\sin \lambda u}{\lambda^2} \right]_0^1 + \left[- (2 - u) \, \frac{\cos \lambda u}{\lambda} - \frac{\sin \lambda u}{\lambda^2} \right]_1^2$$

$$= \left[- \frac{\cos \lambda}{\lambda} + \frac{\sin \lambda}{\lambda^2} \right] + \left[- \frac{\sin 2\lambda}{\lambda^2} + \frac{\cos \lambda}{\lambda} + \frac{\sin \lambda}{\lambda^2} \right]$$

$$= \frac{2 \sin \lambda - \sin 2\lambda}{\lambda^2} = \frac{2 \sin \lambda \, (1 - \cos \lambda)}{\lambda^2}.$$

Ex. 15 : *Find the Fourier sine and cosine transforms of the function f(x) = x^{m–1}.*

(May 2005, 2007)

Sol. : The given function $f(x) = x^{m-1}$ using results (10) and (12), Fourier cosine and sine transforms are given by

$$F_c (\lambda) = \int_0^\infty f(u) \cos \lambda u \, du = \int_0^\infty u^{m-1} \cos \lambda u \, du \qquad \text{... (i)}$$

$$F_s (\lambda) = \int_0^\infty f(u) \sin \lambda u \, du = \int_0^\infty u^{m-1} \sin \lambda u \, du \qquad \text{... (ii)}$$

Now by definition of Gamma function, we have

$$\overline{|m} = \int_0^\infty e^{-x} \, x^{m-1} \, dx$$

Putting $\quad x = i\lambda u, \quad i = \cos \dfrac{\pi}{2} + i \sin \dfrac{\pi}{2} = e^{i\pi/2}$, we get

$$\overline{|m} = \int_0^\infty e^{-i\lambda u} (i\lambda u)^{m-1} (i\lambda) \, du = (e^{i\pi/2})^m \, \lambda^m \int_0^\infty u^{m-1} \, e^{-i\lambda u} \, du$$

$$\therefore \quad \int_0^\infty u^{m-1} e^{-i\lambda u}\, du = \frac{\sqrt{m}}{\lambda^m}\, e^{-im\pi/2}$$

$$\therefore \quad \int_0^\infty u^{m-1} (\cos \lambda u - i \sin \lambda u)\, du = \frac{\sqrt{m}}{\lambda^m}\left(\cos \frac{m\pi}{2} - i \sin \frac{m\pi}{2}\right)$$

Equating real and imaginary parts on both sides, we get

$$F_c(\lambda) = \int_0^\infty u^{m-1} \cos \lambda u\, du = \frac{\sqrt{m}}{\lambda^m}\, \cos \frac{m\pi}{2}$$

$$\text{and} \quad F_s(\lambda) = \int_0^\infty u^{m-1} \sin \lambda u\, du = \frac{\sqrt{m}}{\lambda^m}\, \sin \frac{m\pi}{2}.$$

Ex. 16 : *Find the Fourier cosine transform of $f_1(x) = \dfrac{1}{1 + x^2}$ and hence find the Fourier sine transform of $f_2(x) = \dfrac{x}{1 + x^2}$.*

Sol. : We know that Fourier cosine transform of $f_1(x) = \dfrac{1}{1 + x^2}$ is given by [result (10)],

$$F_c(\lambda) = \int_0^\infty f_1(u) \cos \lambda u\, du = \int_0^\infty \frac{1}{1 + u^2} \cos \lambda u\, du \qquad \ldots \text{(i)}$$

$$\text{Let} \quad I(\lambda) = \int_0^\infty \frac{1}{1 + u^2} \cos \lambda u\, du \qquad \ldots \text{(ii)}$$

Differentiating both sides w.r.t. λ using the rule of DUIS, we get

$$\frac{dI}{d\lambda} = I'(\lambda) = \int_0^\infty \frac{\partial}{\partial \lambda} \frac{1}{1 + u^2} \cos \lambda u\, du = \int_0^\infty -\frac{u}{1 + u^2} \sin \lambda u\, du$$

$$= \int_0^\infty -\frac{u^2}{u\,(1 + u^2)} \sin \lambda u\, du = \int_0^\infty \frac{-(u^2 + 1 - 1)}{u\,(1 + u^2)} \sin \lambda u\, du$$

$$= \int_0^\infty \left(\frac{1}{u\,(1 + u^2)} - \frac{1}{u}\right) \sin \lambda u\, du = \int_0^\infty \frac{\sin \lambda u}{u\,(1 + u^2)}\, du - \int_0^\infty \frac{\sin \lambda u}{u}\, du$$

$$= \int_0^\infty \frac{\sin \lambda u}{u\,(1 + u^2)}\, du - \int_0^\infty \frac{\sin t}{t}\, dt, \qquad \begin{cases} \text{Putting } \lambda u = t \text{ in the} \\ \text{second integral} \end{cases}$$

$$= \int_0^\infty \frac{\sin \lambda u}{u\,(1 + u^2)}\, du - \frac{\pi}{2}, \qquad \left(\because \int_0^\infty \frac{\sin t}{t}\, dt = \frac{\pi}{2}\right) \quad \ldots \text{(iii)}$$

Again differentiating both sides w.r.t. λ using the rule of DUIS, we get

$$I''(\lambda) = \int_0^\infty \frac{\partial}{\partial \lambda} \frac{\sin \lambda u}{u\,(1 + u^2)}\ du - 0 = \int_0^\infty \frac{u \cos \lambda u}{u\,(1 + u^2)}\ du$$

$$= \int_0^\infty \frac{\cos \lambda u}{1 + u^2}\ du = I(\lambda) \qquad\qquad \text{[from (i)]}$$

$$\therefore \qquad I''(\lambda) - I(\lambda) = 0 \qquad\qquad\qquad\qquad \dots \text{(iv)}$$

General solution of (iv) is given by

$$I(\lambda) = A\,e^\lambda + B\,e^{-\lambda} \qquad\qquad\qquad\qquad \dots \text{(v)}$$

Now to evaluate constants A and B, differentiating (v), w.r.t. λ, we get

$$I'(\lambda) = A\,e^\lambda - B\,e^{-\lambda} \qquad\qquad\qquad\qquad \dots \text{(vi)}$$

Putting $\lambda = 0$ in (v) and (vi), we obtain

$$I(0) = \left[\int_0^\infty \frac{\cos \lambda u}{1 + u^2}\ du\right]_{\lambda = 0} = A + B \qquad\qquad \text{[from (ii)]} \ \dots \text{(vii)}$$

and

$$I'(0) = \left[\int_0^\infty \frac{\sin \lambda u}{u\,(1 + u^2)}\ du - \frac{\pi}{2}\right]_{\lambda = 0} = A - B \qquad\qquad \text{[from (iii)]} \ \dots \text{(viii)}$$

From (vii) and (viii), we obtain

$$A + B = \frac{\pi}{2} \qquad\qquad\qquad \left\{ \because \int_0^\infty \frac{1}{1 + u^2}\ du = \left[\tan^{-1} u\right]_0^\infty = \frac{\pi}{2} \right\}$$

and

$$A - B = -\frac{\pi}{2} \qquad\qquad\qquad \left\{ \because \int_0^\infty \frac{\sin \lambda u}{u\,(1 + u^2)}\ du = 0 \text{ at } \lambda = 0 \right\}$$

Solving for A and B, we get $A = 0$ and $B = \frac{\pi}{2}$ and substituting these values of A and B in result (v), we have

$$I(\lambda) = \frac{\pi}{2}\ e^{-\lambda}$$

$$\therefore \qquad F_c(\lambda) = \int_0^\infty f_1(u) \cos \lambda u\ du = \int_0^\infty \frac{1}{1 + u^2}\ \cos \lambda u\ du = \frac{\pi}{2}\ e^{-\lambda} \qquad \dots \text{(ix)}$$

Now to find Fourier sine transform of $f_2(x) = \dfrac{x}{1 + x^2}$, we differentiate result (ix) with

respect to λ, we get $\displaystyle -\int_0^\infty \frac{u}{1 + u^2}\ \sin \lambda u\ du = -\frac{\pi}{2}\ e^{-\lambda}$

$$\therefore \qquad F_s(\lambda) = \int_0^\infty f_2(u) \sin \lambda u\ du = \int_0^\infty \frac{u}{1 + u^2}\ \sin \lambda u\ du = \frac{\pi}{2}\ e^{-\lambda}$$

Type 3 : Problems on Inverse Fourier transforms

Ex. 17 : *Using inverse sine transform, find f(x) if*

$$F_s(\lambda) = \frac{1}{\lambda}\, e^{-a\lambda} \qquad\qquad \textbf{(Dec. 2005, 2007, 2009)}$$

Sol. : By result (13), inverse sine transform of $F_s(\lambda)$ is given by

$$f(x) = \frac{2}{\pi} \int_0^\infty F_s(\lambda)\, \sin \lambda x\, d\lambda = \frac{2}{\pi} \int_0^\infty \frac{1}{\lambda}\, e^{-a\lambda} \sin \lambda x\, d\lambda \qquad \ldots \text{(i)}$$

Let

$$I(x) = \int_0^\infty \frac{e^{-a\lambda}}{\lambda}\, \sin \lambda x\, d\lambda \qquad \ldots \text{(ii)}$$

$$\therefore \qquad I'(x) = \int_0^\infty \frac{\partial}{\partial x} \frac{e^{-a\lambda}}{\lambda}\, \sin \lambda x\, d\lambda \qquad\qquad \text{[Using DUIS rule]}$$

$$= \int_0^\infty e^{-a\lambda} \cos \lambda x\, d\lambda = \left[\frac{e^{-a\lambda}}{a^2 + x^2} (- a \cos \lambda x + x \sin \lambda x) \right]_0^\infty$$

$$= \frac{a}{a^2 + x^2} \qquad \ldots \text{(iii)}$$

Integrating, we get

$$I(x) = \int \frac{a}{x^2 + a^2}\, dx + A = \tan^{-1}\frac{x}{a} + A \qquad \ldots \text{(iv)}$$

Putting x = 0, we get

$$[I(x)]_{x=0} = A \qquad \ldots \text{(v)}$$

The value of $[I(x)]_{x=0}$ is obtained from (ii), when x = 0.

$$[I(x)]_{x=0} = \left[\int_0^\infty \frac{e^{-a\lambda}}{\lambda} \sin \lambda x\, d\lambda \right]_{x=0} = 0 \qquad \therefore\ A = 0$$

Hence from (iv), we have

$$I(x) = \tan^{-1}\frac{x}{a} \qquad \ldots \text{(vi)}$$

Thus from (i) and using (vi), we have

$$f(x) = \frac{2}{\pi}\, I(x) = \frac{2}{\pi}\, \tan^{-1}\frac{x}{a} .$$

Note : If we use result (13 a), we get $f(x) = \sqrt{\dfrac{2}{\pi}}\, \tan^{-1}\dfrac{x}{a} .$

Ex. 18 : *What is the function f(x), whose Fourier cosine transform is* $\dfrac{\sin a\lambda}{\lambda}$ *?*

(Dec. 2006)

Sol. : Given that $F_c(\lambda) = \dfrac{\sin a\lambda}{\lambda}$ and we are required to find f(x). Using result (11), inverse cosine transform is given by

$$f(x) \;=\; \frac{2}{\pi} \int_0^\infty F_c(\lambda) \cos \lambda x \, d\lambda = \frac{2}{\pi} \int_0^\infty \frac{\sin a\lambda}{\lambda} \cos \lambda x \, d\lambda$$

$$= \frac{1}{\pi} \int_0^\infty \frac{\sin (a+x)\,\lambda + \sin (a-x)\,\lambda}{\lambda} \, dx$$

$$= \frac{1}{\pi} \left[\int_0^\infty \frac{\sin (a+x)\,\lambda}{\lambda} \, d\lambda + \int_0^\infty \frac{\sin (a-x)\,\lambda}{\lambda} \, d\lambda \right]$$

$$= \begin{cases} \dfrac{1}{\pi}\left[\dfrac{\pi}{2} + \dfrac{\pi}{2}\right], & a+x>0 \text{ and } a-x>0 \\[2mm] 0, & a+x>0 \text{ and } a-x<0 \end{cases} \qquad \left[\begin{aligned} &\because \int_0^\infty \frac{\sin ax}{x}\,dx \\[1mm] &= \begin{cases} \pi/2 & a>0 \\ -\pi/2 & a<0 \end{cases} \end{aligned} \right]$$

$$= \begin{cases} 1, & 0<x<a \\ 0, & x>a \end{cases}$$

Ex. 19 : *Solve the following integral equations :*

(a) $\displaystyle \int_0^\infty f(x) \sin \lambda x \, dx = \begin{cases} 1-\lambda, & 0 \le \lambda \le 1 \\ 0, & \lambda \ge 1 \end{cases}$ **(Dec. 2008, May 2009, Dec. 2010)**

(b) $\displaystyle \int_0^\infty f(x) \sin \lambda x \, dx = \begin{cases} 1, & 0 \le \lambda < 1 \\ 2, & 1 \le \lambda < 2 \\ 0, & \lambda \ge 2 \end{cases}$ **(Dec. 2011)**

(c) $\displaystyle \int_0^\infty f(x) \cos \lambda x \, dx = e^{-\lambda},\ \lambda > 0.$ **(May 2007)**

Sol. : (a) Since the term $\sin \lambda x$ is present in the integral, using result (12), the Fourier sine transform of f(x) is given by

$$F_s(\lambda) \;=\; \int_0^\infty f(u) \sin \lambda u \, du \;=\; \begin{cases} 1-\lambda, & 0 \le \lambda \le 1 \\ 0, & \lambda \ge 1 \end{cases} \qquad \dots \text{(i)}$$

To find f(x), we obtain inverse Fourier sine transform [by result (13)]. Thus

$$f(x) \;=\; \frac{2}{\pi} \int_0^\infty F_s(\lambda) \sin \lambda x \, d\lambda = \frac{2}{\pi} \int_0^1 (1-\lambda) \sin \lambda x \, d\lambda \qquad \text{[from (i)]}$$

$$= \frac{2}{\pi} \left[(1-\lambda) \left(\frac{-\cos \lambda x}{x} \right) - (-1) \left(-\frac{\sin \lambda x}{x^2} \right) \right]_0^1$$

$$= \frac{2}{\pi} \left[-\frac{\sin x}{x^2} + \frac{1}{x} \right] = \frac{2}{\pi} \left(\frac{x - \sin x}{x^2} \right)$$

which is the required result.

Note : If we use (13 a) for inverse sine transform, we would get

$$f(x) \;=\; \sqrt{\frac{2}{\pi}} \left(\frac{x - \sin x}{x^2} \right).$$

(b)   Since the term $\sin \lambda x$ is present in the integral, using result (12), Fourier sine transform is given by

$$F_s(\lambda) \;=\; \int_0^\infty f(u) \sin \lambda u \, du = \begin{cases} 1, & 0 \le \lambda < 1 \\ 2, & 1 \le \lambda < 2 \\ 0, & \lambda \ge 2 \end{cases} \qquad \dots \text{(i)}$$

Now to find f(x), we use result (13) and obtain Inverse Fourier sine transform. Thus

$$f(x) \;=\; \frac{2}{\pi} \int_0^\infty F_s(\lambda) \sin \lambda x \, d\lambda$$

$$= \frac{2}{\pi} \left[\int_0^1 (1) \sin \lambda x \, d\lambda + \int_1^2 (2) \sin \lambda x \, d\lambda + \int_2^\infty (0) \sin \lambda x \, d\lambda \right]$$

$$= \frac{2}{\pi} \left[\left(-\frac{\cos \lambda x}{x} \right)_0^1 + 2 \left(-\frac{\cos \lambda x}{x} \right)_1^2 \right] \qquad \text{[from (i)]}$$

$$= \frac{2}{\pi} \left[\left(\frac{1 - \cos x}{x} \right) + 2 \left(\frac{\cos x - \cos 2x}{x} \right) \right]$$

$$= \frac{2}{\pi} \left(\frac{1 + \cos x - 2 \cos 2x}{x} \right)$$

(c)   Presence of $\cos \lambda x$ in the integral indicates that, we have to find inverse Fourier cosine transform.

Using result (10), Fourier cosine transform of f(x) is given by

$$F_c(\lambda) \;=\; \int_0^\infty f(u) \cos \lambda u \, du = e^{-\lambda}, \qquad \text{(given) } \dots \text{(i)}$$

Hence using result (11), we have

$$f(x) = \frac{2}{\pi} \int_0^\infty F_c(\lambda) \cos \lambda x \, d\lambda = \frac{2}{\pi} \int_0^\infty e^{-\lambda} \cos \lambda x \, d\lambda \qquad \text{[from (i)]}$$

$$= \frac{2}{\pi} \left[\frac{e^{-\lambda}}{1 + x^2} (- \cos \lambda x + x \sin \lambda x) \right]_0^\infty = \frac{2}{\pi} \left(\frac{1}{1 + x^2} \right).$$

Ex. 20 : *Solve the integral equation*

$$\int_0^\infty f(x) \cos \lambda x \, dx = \begin{cases} 1 - \lambda, & 0 \le \lambda \le 1 \\ 0, & \lambda \ge 1 \end{cases}$$

and hence show that $\displaystyle \int_0^\infty \frac{\sin^2 z}{z^2} \, dz = \frac{\pi}{2}$ **(May 2005, 2008)**

Sol. : Since the term $\cos \lambda x$ is present in the integral, using result (10), the Fourier cosine transform is given by

$$F_c(\lambda) = \int_0^\infty f(u) \cos \lambda u \, du = \begin{cases} 1 - \lambda, & 0 \le \lambda \le 1 \\ 0, & \lambda \ge 1 \end{cases} \qquad \dots \text{(i)}$$

To find $f(x)$, we use inverse Fourier cosine transform given by result (11). Thus

$$f(x) = \frac{2}{\pi} \int_0^\infty F_c(\lambda) \cos \lambda x \, d\lambda$$

$$= \frac{2}{\pi} \left[\int_0^1 (1 - \lambda) \cos \lambda x \, d\lambda + \int_1^\infty (0) \cos \lambda x \, d\lambda \right]$$

$$= \frac{2}{\pi} \left[(1 - \lambda) \left(\frac{\sin \lambda x}{x} \right) - (-1) \left(- \frac{\cos \lambda x}{x^2} \right) \right]_0^1$$

$$= \frac{2}{\pi} \left[- \frac{\cos x}{x^2} + \frac{1}{x^2} \right] = \frac{2}{\pi} \left(\frac{1 - \cos x}{x^2} \right) \qquad \dots \text{(ii)}$$

Now from (i), we have

$$F_c(\lambda) = \int_0^\infty f(u) \cos \lambda u \, du = \frac{2}{\pi} \int_0^\infty \left(\frac{1 - \cos u}{u^2} \right) \cos \lambda u \, du$$

$$= \frac{2}{\pi} \int_0^\infty \frac{2 \sin^2 u/2}{u^2} \cos \lambda u \, du \qquad \dots \text{(iii)}$$

At $\lambda = 0$, we have from result (iii),

$$[F_c(\lambda)]_{\lambda = 0} = \frac{2}{\pi} \int_0^\infty \frac{2 \sin^2 u/2}{u^2} (1) \, du \qquad [\because \cos 0 = 1]$$

$$1 = \frac{2}{\pi} \int_0^\infty \frac{2 \sin^2 u/2}{u^2} \, du \qquad \text{[from (i)]}$$

Putting $u/2 = z$ or $u = 2z$, we have

$$1 = \frac{2}{\pi} \int_0^\infty \frac{2 \sin^2 z}{(2z)^2} \, 2 \, dz$$

$$\therefore \qquad \int_0^\infty \frac{\sin^2 z}{z^2} \, dz = \frac{\pi}{2}$$

which is the required result.

EXERCISE 6.1

1. **(a)** Find the Fourier cosine integral representation for the following functions :

(i) $\quad f(x) = \begin{cases} x, & 0 \le x \le a \\ 0, & x > a \end{cases}$ $\qquad$ **Ans.** $f(x) = \dfrac{2}{\pi} \displaystyle\int_0^\infty \left(\dfrac{a \sin a\lambda}{\lambda} + \dfrac{\cos a\lambda - 1}{\lambda^2} \right) \cos \lambda x \, d\lambda$

(ii) $\quad f(x) = \begin{cases} x^2, & 0 \le x \le 1 \\ 0, & x > 1 \end{cases}$ $\qquad$ **Ans.** $f(x) = \dfrac{2}{\pi} \displaystyle\int_0^\infty \dfrac{1}{\lambda^3} \{(\lambda^2 - 2) \sin \lambda + 2 \lambda \cos \lambda\} \cos \lambda x \, d\lambda$

(iii) $\quad f(x) = \begin{cases} 1, & 0 \le x \le 1 \\ 0, & x > 1 \end{cases}$ $\qquad$ **Ans.** $f(x) = \dfrac{2}{\pi} \displaystyle\int_0^\infty \dfrac{\sin \lambda}{\lambda} \cos \lambda x \, du \, d\lambda$

(iv) $f(x) = e^{-x} + e^{-2x}$, $x \ge 0$ **(Nov. 16)** $\qquad$ **Ans.** $f(x) = \dfrac{6}{\pi} \displaystyle\int_0^\infty \dfrac{\lambda^2 + 2}{\lambda^4 + 5 \lambda^2 + 4} \cos \lambda x \, d\lambda$

(v) $\quad f(x) = \dfrac{1}{1 + x^2}$, $x \ge 0$

$$\textbf{Ans. } f(x) = \frac{2}{\pi} \int_0^\infty \int_0^\infty \frac{\cos \lambda u \cos \lambda x}{1 + u^2} \, du \, d\lambda = \int_0^\infty e^{-\lambda} \cos \lambda x \, d\lambda$$

(b) Represent the following functions in the Fourier integral form :

(i) $\quad f(x) = \begin{cases} \dfrac{\pi}{2} \sin x, & |x| \le \pi \\ 0, & |x| > \pi \end{cases}$ $\qquad$ **Ans.** $f(x) = \displaystyle\int_0^\infty \dfrac{\sin \lambda\pi \sin \lambda x}{1 - \lambda^2} \, d\lambda$

(ii) $\quad f(x) = \begin{cases} \dfrac{\pi}{2} \cos x, & |x| \le \pi \\ 0, & |x| > \pi \end{cases}$ $\qquad$ **Ans.** $f(x) = \displaystyle\int_0^\infty \dfrac{\lambda \sin \lambda\pi}{1 - \lambda^2} \cos \lambda x \, d\lambda$

(iii) $\quad f(x) = \begin{cases} 0, & x < -a \\ 1, & -a \le x \le a \\ 0, & x > a \end{cases}$ $\qquad$ **Ans.** $f(x) = \dfrac{2}{\pi} \displaystyle\int_0^\infty \dfrac{2 \sin \lambda a \cos \lambda x}{\lambda} \, d\lambda$

(iv) $f(x) = e^{-|x|}, -\infty < x < \infty$

Ans. $f(x) = \dfrac{2}{\pi} \displaystyle\int_0^\infty \dfrac{1}{1+\lambda^2} \cos \lambda x \, d\lambda$

(v) $f(x) = e^{-x^2/2}, -\infty < x < \infty$

Ans. $f(x) = \dfrac{2}{\pi} \displaystyle\int_0^\infty e^{-\lambda^2/2} \cos \lambda x \, d\lambda$

2. If $f(x) = \begin{cases} 1, & |x| < 1 \\ \dfrac{1}{2}, & |x| = 1 \\ 0, & |x| > 1 \end{cases}$ then prove that for every x in $-\infty < x < \infty$,

$$f(x) = \frac{1}{\pi} \int_0^\infty \frac{\sin [\lambda (1 + x)] + \sin [\lambda (1 - x)]}{\lambda} \, d\lambda = \frac{2}{\pi} \int_0^\infty \frac{\sin \lambda \cos \lambda x}{\lambda} \, d\lambda.$$

3. By applying the Fourier sine integral formula to the function

$$f(x) = \begin{cases} 1, & 0 < x < k \\ \dfrac{1}{2}, & x = k \\ 0, & x > k \end{cases}$$

obtain the representation

$$f(x) = \frac{2}{\pi} \int_0^\infty \frac{1 - \cos k\lambda}{\lambda} \sin \lambda x \, d\lambda, \; x > 0.$$

4. Find the Fourier integral for f(x), where

$$f(x) = e^{-kx}, \; (x > 0)$$

in the following cases : (i) $f(-x) = f(x)$,   (ii) $f(-x) = -f(x)$.

Ans. (i) $f(x) = \dfrac{2}{\pi} \displaystyle\int_0^\infty \dfrac{k \cos \lambda x}{\lambda^2 + k^2} \, d\lambda$,   (ii) $f(x) = \dfrac{2}{\pi} \displaystyle\int_0^\infty \dfrac{\lambda \sin \lambda x}{\lambda^2 + k^2} \, d\lambda$

5. Using the Fourier integral representation, show that :

(i) $\displaystyle\int_0^\infty \frac{\sin \pi\lambda \, \sin \lambda x}{1 - \lambda^2} \, d\lambda = \begin{cases} \dfrac{\pi}{2} \sin x, & 0 \le x \le \pi \\ 0, & x > \pi \end{cases}$

(ii) $\displaystyle\int_0^\infty \frac{\sin \lambda \cos \lambda x}{\lambda} \, d\lambda = \begin{cases} \dfrac{\pi}{2}, & 0 \le x < 1 \\ \dfrac{\pi}{4}, & x = 1 \\ 0, & x > 1. \end{cases}$

6. Establish the following representations :

(i) $e^{-x} - e^{-2x} = \dfrac{6}{\pi} \displaystyle\int_0^\infty \dfrac{\lambda \, \sin \lambda x}{(\lambda^2 + 1)(\lambda^2 + 4)} \, d\lambda, \ x > 0$

(ii) $e^{-x} \sin x = \dfrac{2}{\pi} \displaystyle\int_0^\infty \dfrac{2\lambda \sin \lambda x}{\lambda^4 + 4} \, d\lambda, x > 0.$ **(May 2012)**

(iii) $e^{-3x} \sinh x = \dfrac{12}{\pi} \displaystyle\int_0^\infty \dfrac{\lambda \sin \lambda x}{(\lambda^2 + 4)(\lambda^2 + 16)} \, d\lambda$

7. Find the Fourier transforms of the following functions :

(i) $f(x) = \begin{cases} x, & |x| \le a \\ 0, & |x| > a \end{cases}$ **Ans.** $F(\lambda) = 2i \left(\dfrac{\sin a\lambda}{\lambda^2} - \dfrac{a \cos a\lambda}{\lambda} \right), \ F_s(\lambda) = \left(\dfrac{\sin a\lambda}{\lambda^2} - \dfrac{a \cos a\lambda}{\lambda} \right)$

(ii) $f(x) = \begin{cases} x^2, & |x| \le a \\ 0, & |x| > a \end{cases}$ **Ans.** $\dfrac{2}{\lambda^3} \left\{ (a^2 \lambda^2 - 2) \sin a\lambda + 2a\lambda \cos a\lambda \right\}$

(iii) $f(x) = \begin{cases} \dfrac{\pi}{2} \cos x, & |x| \le \pi \\ 0, & |x| > \pi \end{cases}$ **Ans.** $\pi \, \dfrac{\lambda \sin \lambda \pi}{1 - \lambda^2}$

8. Find the Fourier sine transforms of the following functions :

(i) $f(x) = \begin{cases} \sin x, & 0 \le x < a \\ 0, & x > a \end{cases}$ **Ans.** $\dfrac{1}{2} \left[\dfrac{\sin (1-\lambda) a}{1 - \lambda} - \dfrac{\sin (1+\lambda) a}{1 + \lambda} \right]$

(ii) $f(x) = \begin{cases} 0, & 0 \le x < a \\ x, & a \le x \le b \\ 0, & x > b \end{cases}$ **Ans.** $\left(\dfrac{a \cos \lambda a - b \cos \lambda b}{\lambda} \right) + \left(\dfrac{\sin \lambda b - \sin \lambda a}{\lambda^2} \right)$

9. Find the Fourier sine transform of $e^{-|x|}$. Hence evaluate $\displaystyle\int_0^\infty \dfrac{x \sin mx}{1 + x^2} \, dx.$

Ans. $\dfrac{\lambda}{1 + \lambda^2}, \ \dfrac{\pi}{2} \ e^{-m}$

10. Find the Fourier cosine transforms of the following functions :

(i) $f(x) = 2 e^{-5x} + 5 e^{-2x}$ **Ans.** $10 \left(\dfrac{1}{\lambda^2 + 5} + \dfrac{1}{\lambda^2 + 4} \right)$

(ii) $f(x) = e^{-2x} + 4 e^{-3x}$ **Ans.** $2 \left(\dfrac{1}{\lambda^2 + 4} + \dfrac{6}{\lambda^2 + 9} \right)$

(iii) $f(x) = \begin{cases} x, & 0 < x < \dfrac{1}{2} \\ 1 - x, & 1/2 < x < 1 \\ 0, & x > 1 \end{cases}$ **Ans.** $\left(\dfrac{-\cos \lambda + 2 \cos \lambda/2 - 1}{\lambda^2} \right)$

11. Find the Fourier sine and cosine transforms of the following functions :

(i) $f(x) = \begin{cases} 1, & 0 \le x \le 1 \\ 0, & x > 1 \end{cases}$ **Ans.** $\dfrac{1 - \cos \lambda}{\lambda}, \; \dfrac{\sin \lambda}{\lambda}$

(ii) $f(x) = \begin{cases} x^2, & 0 \le x \le 1 \\ 0, & x > 0 \end{cases}$

Ans. $\dfrac{1}{\lambda^3} \{2\lambda \sin \lambda - \lambda^2 \cos \lambda + 2 (\cos \lambda - 1)\}, \; \dfrac{1}{\lambda^3} \{2\lambda \cos \lambda + \lambda^2 \sin \lambda - 2 \sin \lambda\}$

12. Find the Fourier sine transform of

$$f(x) = \begin{cases} 1, & 0 \le x \le 1 \\ 0, & x > 1 \end{cases}$$

and hence evaluate $\displaystyle \int_0^\infty \frac{\sin^3 x}{x} \, dx$.

Hint : $\displaystyle F_s(\lambda) = \int_0^\infty f(u) \sin \lambda u \, du = \int_0^1 \sin \lambda u \, du = \left[-\frac{\cos \lambda u}{\lambda} \right]_0^1$

$$= \frac{1 - \cos \lambda}{\lambda} = \frac{2 \sin^2 \lambda/2}{\lambda}$$

$$f(x) = \frac{2}{\pi} \int_0^\infty F_s(\lambda) \sin \lambda n \, d\lambda = \frac{2}{\pi} \int_0^\infty \frac{2 \sin^2 \lambda/2}{2 (\lambda/2)} \sin \lambda x \, d\lambda$$

Putting $\lambda/2 = t, \;\; f(x) = \dfrac{4}{\pi} \displaystyle\int_0^\infty \frac{\sin^2 t}{t} \sin 2tx \, dt$

Again putting $x = 1/2, \;\; f\left(\dfrac{1}{2}\right) = 1 = \dfrac{4}{\pi} \displaystyle\int_0^\infty \frac{\sin^3 t}{t} dt$ **Ans.** $\dfrac{\pi}{4}$

13. Using inverse Fourier cosine transform, find $f(x)$, if

$$F_c(\lambda) = \begin{cases} \sqrt{2/\pi}\left(a - \dfrac{\lambda}{2}\right), & \lambda \le 2a \\ 0, & \lambda > 2a \end{cases}$$ **Ans.** $\dfrac{2 \sin^2 ax}{\pi x^2}$

14. Using inverse Fourier sine transform, find $f(x)$, if

$$F_s(\lambda) = \frac{\lambda}{1 + \lambda^2}$$ **Ans.** e^{-x}

Hint : $f(x) = \dfrac{2}{\pi} \displaystyle\int_0^\infty F_s(\lambda) \sin \lambda x \, d\lambda = \dfrac{2}{\pi} \int_0^\infty \frac{\lambda}{1 + \lambda^2} \sin \lambda x \, d\lambda = \dfrac{2}{\pi} \int_0^\infty \frac{\lambda^2 + 1 - 1}{\lambda (1 + \lambda^2)} \sin \lambda x \, d\lambda$

$$= \frac{2}{\pi}\left[\frac{\pi}{2} - \int_0^\infty \frac{\sin \lambda x}{\lambda (1 + \lambda)^2} \, d\lambda \right] = 1 - \frac{2}{\pi} \int_0^\infty \frac{\sin \lambda x}{\lambda (1 + \lambda^2)} \, d\lambda$$

Using DUIS Rule,

$$f'(x) = 0 - \frac{2}{\pi} \int_0^\infty \frac{\partial}{\partial x} \frac{\sin \lambda x}{\lambda (1 + \lambda^2)} \, d\lambda = -\frac{2}{\pi} \int_0^\infty \frac{\cos \lambda x}{1 + \lambda^2} \, d\lambda$$

Again using DUIS Rule,

$$f''(x) = \frac{2}{\pi} \int_0^\infty \frac{\lambda \sin \lambda x}{1 + \lambda^2} \, d\lambda = f(x) \qquad\qquad \therefore \quad f''(x) - f(x) = 0$$

G.S. $= f(x) = c_1 e^x + c_2 e^{-x}$ and $f'(x) = c_1 e^x - c_2 e^{-x}$.

Taking $f(0) = 1$ and $f'(0) = 1$, gives $c_1 = 0$, $c_2 = 1$.

15. Find the function $f(x)$, satisfying the integral equation

$$\int_0^\infty f(x) \sin \lambda x \, dx = \frac{\lambda}{\lambda^2 + k^2} \,.$$ **Ans.** $f(x) = e^{-kx}$, $x > 0$

MULTIPLE CHOICE QUESTIONS (MCQ's)

Type I : Fourier Integral Representation Fourier Transform and Inverse Fourier Transform

1. The fourier integral representation of $f(x)$ defined in the interval $-\infty < x < \infty$ is   (1)

(A) $\dfrac{1}{2\pi} \displaystyle\int_{-\infty}^{\infty} \int_{-\infty}^{\infty} f(u) \, e^{-i\lambda(u - x)} \, du \, d\lambda$ (B) $\displaystyle\int_{-\infty}^{\infty} \int_{-\infty}^{\infty} f(u) \, e^{-i\lambda(u - x)} \, du \, d\lambda$

(C) $\dfrac{1}{2\pi} \displaystyle\int_{-\infty}^{\infty} \int_{-\infty}^{\infty} f(u) \, e^{i\lambda u} \, du \, dx$ (D) $\dfrac{2}{\pi} \displaystyle\int_{-\infty}^{\infty} \int_{-\infty}^{\infty} f(u) \, e^{i\lambda(u - x)} \, du \, d\lambda$

2. The Fourier transform $F(\lambda)$ of function $f(x)$ defined in the interval $-\infty < x < \infty$ is   (1)

(A) $\displaystyle\int_{-\infty}^{\infty} f(u) \, e^{iu} \, du$ (B) $\displaystyle\int_{-\infty}^{\infty} f(u) \, e^{-\lambda u} \, du$

(C) $\displaystyle\int_{-\infty}^{\infty} f(u) \, e^{-i\lambda u} \, du$ (D) $\displaystyle\int_{0}^{\infty} f(u) \, e^{-i\lambda u} \, du$

3. The inverse Fourier transform $f(x)$ defined in $-\infty < x < \infty$ of $F(\lambda)$ is   (1)

(A) $\dfrac{1}{2\pi} \displaystyle\int_{-\infty}^{\infty} F(\lambda) \, e^{i\lambda x} \, d\lambda$ (B) $\dfrac{2}{\pi} \displaystyle\int_{-\infty}^{\infty} F(\lambda) \, e^{-i\lambda x} \, d\lambda$

(C) $\dfrac{1}{2\pi} \displaystyle\int_{-\infty}^{0} F(\lambda) \, e^{ix} \, d\lambda$ (D) $\dfrac{1}{2\pi} \displaystyle\int_{0}^{\infty} F(\lambda) \, e^{i\lambda x} \, dx$

4. In the Fourier integral representation of $\dfrac{1}{2\pi}\displaystyle\int_{-\infty}^{\infty}\left(\dfrac{1-i\lambda}{1+\lambda^2}\right)e^{i\lambda x}\,d\lambda = \begin{cases}0 & , & x<0 \\ e^{-x} & , & x>0\end{cases}$, $F(\lambda)$ is

(1)

(A) $\dfrac{1+\lambda^2}{1-i\lambda}$ (B) $\dfrac{\sin\lambda}{1+\lambda^2}$

(C) $\dfrac{\cos\lambda}{1+\lambda^2}$ (D) $\dfrac{1-i\lambda}{1+\lambda^2}$

5. In the Fourier integral representation of

$$\dfrac{1}{2\pi}\int_{-\infty}^{\infty}\left(\dfrac{e^{-i\lambda\pi}+1}{1-\lambda^2}\right)e^{i\lambda x}\,d\lambda = \begin{cases}\sin x\,, & 0<x<\pi \\ 0 & ,\; x<0 \text{ and } x>\pi\end{cases}, \; F(\lambda) \text{ is} \qquad (1)$$

(A) $\dfrac{1+\lambda^2}{1-i\lambda}$ (B) $\dfrac{e^{-i\lambda}}{1-\lambda^2}$

(C) $\dfrac{e^{-i\lambda\pi}+1}{1-\lambda^2}$ (D) $\dfrac{\sin\lambda}{1-\lambda^2}$

6. In the Fourier integral representation $\dfrac{1}{2\pi}\displaystyle\int_{-\infty}^{\infty}\pi\left(\dfrac{1-i\lambda}{1+\lambda^2}\right)e^{i\lambda x}\,d\lambda = \begin{cases}0 & , & x<0 \\ e^{-x} & , & x>0\end{cases}$, $F(\lambda)$ is

(2)

(A) $\dfrac{1+\lambda^2}{1-i\lambda}$ (B) $\dfrac{\sin\lambda}{1+\lambda^2}$

(C) $\dfrac{\cos\lambda}{1+\lambda^2}$ (D) $\pi\dfrac{1-i\lambda}{1+\lambda^2}$

7. The Fourier transform $F(\lambda)$ of $f(x) = \begin{cases}1\,, & x>0 \\ 0\,, & x<0\end{cases}$ is   (2)

(A) $i\lambda$ (B) $\dfrac{1}{i\lambda}$

(C) $\dfrac{1}{\lambda}$ (D) λ

8. The Fourier transform $F(\lambda)$ of $f(x) = \begin{cases}1\,, & |x|<a \\ 0\,, & |x|>a\end{cases}$ is   (2)

(A) $\dfrac{2\sin\lambda a}{\lambda}$ (B) $\dfrac{e^{-i\lambda a}}{\lambda}$

(C) $\dfrac{e^{i\lambda a}}{\lambda}$ (D) $\dfrac{2\cos\lambda a}{\lambda}$

9. The Fourier transform $F(\lambda)$ of $f(x) = \begin{cases} e^{-x}, & x > 0 \\ 0, & x < 0 \end{cases}$ is   (2)

(A) $\dfrac{1 - \lambda}{1 + \lambda^2}$ (B) $\dfrac{1 - i\lambda}{1 + \lambda^2}$

(C) $\dfrac{1 - i\lambda}{1 - \lambda^2}$ (D) $\dfrac{1}{1 + \lambda^2}$

10. The Fourier transform $F(\lambda)$ of $f(x) = e^{-|x|}$ is given by   (2)

(A) $\dfrac{1}{1 + \lambda^2}$ (B) $\dfrac{1}{1 - \lambda^2}$

(C) $\dfrac{2}{1 - \lambda^2}$ (D) $\dfrac{2}{1 + \lambda^2}$

11. If $f(x) = \begin{cases} \sin x, & 0 < x < \pi \\ 0, & x < 0 \text{ and } x > \pi \end{cases}$ then Fourier transform $F(\lambda)$ of $f(x)$ is   (2)

(A) $\dfrac{e^{i\lambda\pi} + 1}{1 + \lambda^2}$ (B) $\dfrac{e^{i\lambda\pi} + 1}{1 - \lambda^2}$

(C) $\dfrac{e^{-i\lambda\pi} + 1}{1 - \lambda^2}$ (D) $\dfrac{e^{-i\lambda\pi} + 1}{1 + \lambda^2}$

12. The Fourier transform $F(\lambda)$ of $f(x) = \begin{cases} \cos x, & x > 0 \\ 0, & x < 0 \end{cases}$ is   (2)

(A) $\dfrac{i\lambda}{1 - \lambda^2}$ (B) $-\dfrac{i\lambda}{1 - \lambda^2}$

(C) $-\dfrac{i\lambda}{1 + \lambda^2}$ (D) $\dfrac{i\lambda}{1 + \lambda^2}$

13. The Fourier transform $F(\lambda)$ of $f(x) = \begin{cases} \sin x, & x > 0 \\ 0, & x < 0 \end{cases}$ is   (2)

(A) $\dfrac{1}{1 - \lambda^2}$ (B) $\dfrac{1}{1 + \lambda^2}$

(C) $\dfrac{i\lambda}{1 - \lambda^2}$ (D) $\dfrac{i\lambda}{1 + \lambda^2}$

14. The Fourier transform $F(\lambda)$ of $f(x) = \begin{cases} x, & x > 0 \\ 0, & x < 0 \end{cases}$ is   (2)

(A) 0 (B) $\dfrac{1}{\lambda^2}$

(C) λ^2 (D) $-\dfrac{1}{\lambda^2}$

15. If $f(x) = \begin{cases} 2, & |x| < 1 \\ 0, & |x| > 1 \end{cases}$ then Fourier transform $F(\lambda)$ of $f(x)$ is given by (2)

(A) $\dfrac{4\cos\lambda}{\lambda^2}$ 　　　　　　　　(B) $\dfrac{4\sin\lambda}{\lambda}$

(C) $\dfrac{2\sin 2\lambda}{\lambda}$ 　　　　　　　　(D) $\dfrac{\sin\lambda}{\lambda}$

16. The Fourier transform $F(\lambda)$ of $f(x) = \begin{cases} x^2, & x > 0 \\ 0, & x < 0 \end{cases}$ is (2)

(A) $-\dfrac{2i}{\lambda^3}$ 　　　　　　　　(B) $\dfrac{1}{i\lambda^3}$

(C) $\dfrac{2i}{\lambda^3}$ 　　　　　　　　(D) $-\dfrac{1}{i\lambda^3}$

17. The Fourier transform $F(\lambda)$ of $f(x) = \begin{cases} x - x^2, & x > 0 \\ 0, & x < 0 \end{cases}$ is (2)

(A) $\dfrac{2}{\lambda^2} + i\,\dfrac{1}{\lambda^3}$ 　　　　　　　　(B) $\dfrac{1}{\lambda^2} - i\,\dfrac{2}{\lambda^3}$

(C) $\dfrac{1}{\lambda^2} + i\,\dfrac{2}{\lambda^3}$ 　　　　　　　　(D) $-\dfrac{1}{\lambda^2} - i\,\dfrac{2}{\lambda^3}$

18. The Fourier transform $F(\lambda)$ of $f(x) = \begin{cases} 1 - x^2, & |x| \le 1 \\ 0, & |x| > 1 \end{cases}$ is (2)

(A) $-\dfrac{4}{\lambda^3}(\sin\lambda - \lambda\cos\lambda)$ 　　　　(B) $\dfrac{4}{\lambda^3}(\sin\lambda - \lambda\cos\lambda)$

(C) $\dfrac{4}{\lambda^2}(\sin\lambda - \lambda\cos\lambda)$ 　　　　(D) $\dfrac{4}{\lambda^3}(\sin\lambda + \lambda\cos\lambda)$

19. The Fourier transform $F(\lambda)$ of $f(x) = \begin{cases} 2 + x, & x > 0 \\ 0, & x < 0 \end{cases}$ is (2)

(A) $-\dfrac{1}{\lambda^2} - i\,\dfrac{2}{\lambda}$ 　　　　　　　　(B) $\dfrac{1}{\lambda^2} - i\,\dfrac{2}{\lambda}$

(C) $\dfrac{1}{\lambda^2} + i\,\dfrac{2}{\lambda}$ 　　　　　　　　(D) $-\dfrac{1}{\lambda^2} + i\,\dfrac{2}{\lambda}$

20. The inverse Fourier transform, f(x) defined in $-\infty < x < \infty$ of $F(\lambda) = \left[\dfrac{1 - i\lambda}{1 + \lambda^2}\right]$ is   (2)

(A) $\dfrac{1}{2\pi} \displaystyle\int_{-\infty}^{\infty} \left[i\,\dfrac{-\lambda\cos\lambda x + \sin\lambda x}{1 + \lambda^2}\right] d\lambda$

(B) $\dfrac{1}{2\pi} \displaystyle\int_{-\infty}^{\infty} \left[\dfrac{\cos\lambda x - \lambda\sin\lambda x}{1 + \lambda^2} + i\,\dfrac{-\lambda\cos\lambda x - \sin\lambda x}{1 + \lambda^2}\right] d\lambda$

(C) $\dfrac{1}{2\pi} \displaystyle\int_{-\infty}^{\infty} \left[\dfrac{\cos\lambda x + \lambda\sin\lambda x}{1 + \lambda^2} + i\,\dfrac{-\lambda\cos\lambda x + \sin\lambda x}{1 + \lambda^2}\right] d\lambda$

(D) $\dfrac{1}{2\pi} \displaystyle\int_{-\infty}^{\infty} \left[\dfrac{\cos\lambda x + \lambda\sin\lambda x}{1 - \lambda^2} + i\,\dfrac{-\lambda\cos\lambda x + \sin\lambda x}{1 - \lambda^2}\right] d\lambda$

21. The inverse Fourier transform f(x) defined in $-\infty < x < \infty$ of $F(\lambda) = \pi\left[\dfrac{1 - i\lambda}{1 + \lambda^2}\right]$ is   (2)

(A) $\dfrac{1}{2} \displaystyle\int_{0}^{\infty} \left[\dfrac{\cos\lambda x + \lambda\sin\lambda x}{1 + \lambda^2} + i\,\dfrac{-\lambda\cos\lambda x + \sin\lambda x}{1 + \lambda^2}\right] d\lambda$

(B) $\dfrac{1}{2} \displaystyle\int_{-\infty}^{\infty} \left[\dfrac{\cos\lambda x + \lambda\sin\lambda x}{1 + \lambda^2} + i\,\dfrac{-\lambda\cos\lambda x + \sin\lambda x}{1 + \lambda^2}\right] d\lambda$

(C) $\dfrac{1}{2} \displaystyle\int_{-\infty}^{\infty} \left[i\,\dfrac{-\lambda\cos\lambda x + \sin\lambda x}{1 + \lambda^2}\right] d\lambda$

(D) $\dfrac{1}{2} \displaystyle\int_{-\infty}^{\infty} \left[\dfrac{\cos\lambda x + \lambda\sin\lambda x}{1 - \lambda^2} + i\,\dfrac{-\lambda\cos\lambda x + \sin\lambda x}{1 - \lambda^2}\right] d\lambda$

22. The inverse Fourier transform f(x) defined in $-\infty < x < \infty$ of $F(\lambda) = \dfrac{e^{-i\lambda\pi} + 1}{1 - \lambda^2}$ is   (2)

(A) $\dfrac{1}{2\pi} \displaystyle\int_{-\infty}^{\infty} \left[\dfrac{1 + \cos\lambda x}{1 - \lambda^2}\right] (\cos\lambda x + i\sin\lambda x)\, d\lambda$

(B) $\dfrac{1}{2\pi} \displaystyle\int_{0}^{\infty} \left[\dfrac{(1 + \cos\lambda x) - i\sin\lambda\pi}{1 - \lambda^2}\right] (\cos\lambda x + i\sin\lambda x)\, d\lambda$

(C) $\dfrac{1}{2\pi} \displaystyle\int_{-\infty}^{\infty} \left[\dfrac{(1 + \cos\lambda\pi) - i\sin\lambda\pi}{1 - \lambda^2}\right] (\cos\lambda x + i\sin\lambda x)\, d\lambda$

(D) $\dfrac{1}{2\pi} \displaystyle\int_{-\infty}^{\infty} \left[\dfrac{\sin\lambda\pi}{1 - \lambda^2}\right] (\cos\lambda x + i\sin\lambda x)\, d\lambda$

23. If the Fourier integral representation of f(x) is

$$\frac{2}{\pi} \int_0^\infty \frac{\sin \lambda \cos \lambda x}{\lambda}\, d\lambda = \begin{cases} 1, & |x| < 1 \\ 0, & |x| > 1 \end{cases}$$ then value of integral $\int_0^\infty \frac{\sin \lambda}{\lambda}\, d\lambda$ is   (2)

(A) $\dfrac{\pi}{4}$ (B) $\dfrac{\pi}{2}$ (C) 0   (D) 1

24. If the Fourier integral representation of f(x) is

$$\frac{1}{\pi} \int_0^\infty \frac{\cos \lambda x + \cos [\lambda(\pi - x)]}{1 - \lambda^2}\, d\lambda = \begin{cases} \sin x, & 0 < x < \pi \\ 0, & x < 0 \text{ and } x > \pi \end{cases}$$ then value of the integral

$$\int_0^\infty \frac{\cos \dfrac{\lambda \pi}{2}}{1 - \lambda^2}\, d\lambda$$ is   (2)

(A) $\dfrac{\pi}{4}$ (B) 1   (C) 0   (D) $\dfrac{\pi}{2}$

Answers

1. (A)	2. (C)	3. (A)	4. (D)	5. (C)	6. (D)	7. (B)	8. (A)
9. (B)	10. (D)	11. (C)	12. (A)	13. (A)	14. (D)	15. (B)	16. (C)
17. (D)	18. (B)	19. (A)	20. (C)	21. (B)	22. (C)	23. (B)	24. (D)

Type II : Fourier Sine and Cosine Integral Representations, Transform and Inverse Transform

1. The Fourier consine integral representation of an even function f(x) defined in the interval $-\infty < x < \infty$ is   (1)

(A) $\int_0^\infty \int_0^\infty f(u) \cos \lambda u \sin \lambda x\, du\, d\lambda$ (B) $\dfrac{2}{\pi} \int_0^\infty \int_0^\infty f(u) \cos \lambda u \cos \lambda x\, du\, d\lambda$

(C) $\dfrac{2}{\pi} \int_0^\infty \int_0^\infty f(u) \sin \lambda u \cos \lambda x\, du\, d\lambda$ (D) $\dfrac{2}{\pi} \int_0^\infty \int_0^\infty f(u) \sin \lambda u \sin \lambda x\, du\, d\lambda$

2. The Fourier sine integral representation of an odd function f(x) defined in the interval $-\infty < x < \infty$ is   (1)

(A) $\int_0^\infty \int_0^\infty f(u) \sin \lambda u \cos \lambda x\, du\, d\lambda$ (B) $\int_0^\infty \int_0^\infty f(u) \cos \lambda u \sin \lambda x\, du\, d\lambda$

(C) $\dfrac{2}{\pi} \int_0^\infty \int_0^\infty f(u) \cos \lambda u \cos \lambda x\, du\, d\lambda$ (D) $\dfrac{2}{\pi} \int_0^\infty \int_0^\infty f(u) \sin \lambda u \sin \lambda x\, du\, d\lambda$

3. The Fourier cosine transform $F_c(\lambda)$ of an even function f(x) defined in the interval $-\infty < x < \infty$ is   (1)

(A) $\int_0^\infty f(u) \sec \lambda u\, du$ (B) $\int_0^\infty f(u) \cos \lambda u\, d\lambda$

(C) $\int_0^\infty f(u) \cos \lambda u\, du$ (D) $\int_0^\infty f(u) \sin \lambda u\, du$

4. The Fourier sine transform $F_s(\lambda)$ of an odd function $f(x)$ defined in the interval $-\infty < x < \infty$ is (1)

(A) $\displaystyle\int_0^\infty f(u) \sin \lambda u\, du$

(B) $\displaystyle\int_0^\infty f(u) \operatorname{cosec} \lambda u\, du$

(C) $\displaystyle\int_0^\infty f(u) \sin \lambda u\, d\lambda$

(D) $\displaystyle\int_0^\infty f(u) \cos \lambda u\, du$

5. The inverse Fourier cosine transform $f(x)$ of $F_c(\lambda)$ is (1)

(A) $\displaystyle\int_0^\infty F_c(\lambda) \sin \lambda x\, d\lambda$

(B) $\displaystyle\frac{2}{\pi}\int_0^\infty F_c(\lambda) \cos \lambda x\, dx$

(C) $\displaystyle\int_0^\infty F_c(\lambda) \sec \lambda x\, d\lambda$

(D) $\displaystyle\frac{2}{\pi}\int_0^\infty F_c(\lambda) \cos \lambda x\, d\lambda$

6. The inverse Fourier sine transform $f(x)$ of $F_s(\lambda)$ is (1)

(A) $\displaystyle\frac{2}{\pi}\int_0^\infty F_s(\lambda) \sin \lambda x\, d\lambda$

(B) $\displaystyle\frac{2}{\pi}\int_0^\infty F_s(\lambda) \cos \lambda x\, d\lambda$

(C) $\displaystyle\frac{2}{\pi}\int_0^\infty F_s(\lambda) \operatorname{cosec} \lambda x\, d\lambda$

(D) $\displaystyle\int_0^\infty F_s(\lambda) \sin \lambda x\, dx$

7. For the Fourier sine integral representation $e^{-x} \cos x = \dfrac{2}{\pi}\displaystyle\int_0^\infty \dfrac{\lambda^3}{\lambda^4 + 4} \sin \lambda x\, d\lambda$, $F_s(\lambda)$ is

(1)

(A) $\dfrac{\lambda}{\lambda^4 + 4}$

(B) $\dfrac{\lambda^3}{\lambda^4 + 4}$

(C) $\dfrac{\lambda^4 + 4}{\lambda^3}$

(D) $\dfrac{1}{\lambda^4 + 4}$

8. For the Fourier cosine integral representation

$$\frac{2}{\pi}\int_0^\infty \frac{\cos \dfrac{\pi\lambda}{2}}{1 - \lambda^2} \cos \lambda x\, d\lambda = \begin{cases} \cos x, & |x| \le \dfrac{\pi}{2} \\ 0, & |x| > \dfrac{\pi}{2} \end{cases}$$, then Fourier cosine transform $F_c(\lambda)$ is (1)

(A) $\dfrac{1 - \lambda^2}{\cos \dfrac{\pi\lambda}{2}}$

(B) $\dfrac{\sin \dfrac{\pi\lambda}{2}}{1 - \lambda^2}$

(C) $\dfrac{\cos \dfrac{\pi\lambda}{2}}{1 - \lambda^2}$

(D) $\dfrac{\cos \dfrac{\pi\lambda}{2}}{1 + \lambda^2}$

9. For the Fourier sine integral representation

$$\frac{2}{\pi} \int_0^\infty \frac{1 - \cos \pi\lambda}{\lambda} \sin \lambda x \, d\lambda = \begin{cases} 1, & 0 < x < \pi \\ 0, & x > \pi \end{cases}, \; F_s(\lambda) \text{ is} \qquad (1)$$

(A) $\dfrac{1 - \cos \pi\lambda}{\lambda^2}$ (B) $\dfrac{\lambda}{1 - \cos \pi\lambda}$

(C) $\dfrac{1 - \sin \pi\lambda}{\lambda}$ (D) $\dfrac{1 - \cos \pi\lambda}{\lambda}$

10. For the Fourier sine integral representation

$$\frac{2}{\pi} \int_0^\infty \frac{\sin \pi\lambda}{1 - \lambda^2} \sin \lambda x \, d\lambda = \begin{cases} \sin x, & |x| \le \pi \\ 0, & |x| > \pi \end{cases}, \; F_s(\lambda) \text{ is} \qquad (1)$$

(A) $\dfrac{\sin \pi\lambda}{1 - \lambda^2}$ (B) $\dfrac{1 - \cos \pi\lambda}{1 - \lambda^2}$

(C) $\dfrac{\sin \pi\lambda}{1 + \lambda^2}$ (D) $\dfrac{1 - \lambda^2}{\sin \lambda\pi}$

11. For the Fourier sine integral representation

$$\frac{6}{\pi} \int_0^\infty \frac{\lambda \sin \lambda x}{(\lambda^2 + 1)(\lambda^2 + 4)} \, d\lambda = e^{-x} - e^{-2x}, \; x > 0, \; F_s(\lambda) \text{ is} \qquad (1)$$

(A) $\dfrac{(\lambda^2 + 1)(\lambda^2 + 4)}{3\lambda}$ (B) $\dfrac{\lambda}{(\lambda^2 + 1)(\lambda^2 + 4)}$

(C) $\dfrac{3\lambda}{(\lambda^2 + 1)(\lambda^2 + 4)}$ (D) $\dfrac{\lambda \sin \lambda x}{(\lambda^2 + 1)(\lambda^2 + 4)}$

12. For the Fourier sine integral representation $\dfrac{2}{\pi} \displaystyle\int_0^\infty \dfrac{2\lambda \sin \lambda x}{\lambda^4 + 4} \, d\lambda = e^{-x} \sin x, \; x > 0, \; F_s(\lambda)$ is $\qquad (1)$

(A) $\dfrac{\lambda^4 + 4}{2\lambda \sin \lambda x}$ (B) $\dfrac{2\lambda}{\lambda^4 + 4}$

(C) $\dfrac{2\lambda \sin \lambda x}{\lambda^4 + 4}$ (D) $\dfrac{2\lambda \cos \lambda x}{\lambda^4 + 4}$

13. For the Fourier sine integral representation

$$\frac{12}{\pi} \int_0^\infty \frac{\lambda \sin \lambda x}{(\lambda^2 + 4)(\lambda^2 + 16)} \, d\lambda = e^{-3x} \sinh x, \; x > 0, \; F_s(\lambda) \text{ is} \qquad (1)$$

(A) $\dfrac{6\lambda}{(\lambda^2 + 4)(\lambda^2 + 16)}$ (B) $\dfrac{\lambda}{(\lambda^2 + 4)(\lambda^2 + 16)}$

(C) $\dfrac{6 \cos \lambda x}{(\lambda^2 + 4)(\lambda^2 + 16)}$ (D) $\dfrac{1}{(\lambda^2 + 4)(\lambda^2 + 16)}$

14. For the Fourier cosine integral representation

$$\frac{2}{\pi} \int_0^\infty \frac{\lambda \sin \pi\lambda}{1 - \lambda^2} \cos \lambda x \, d\lambda = \begin{cases} \cos x, & |x| \le \pi \\ 0, & |x| > \pi \end{cases}, \; F_c(\lambda) \text{ is}$$

(1)

(A) $\dfrac{\sin \pi\lambda}{1 - \lambda^2}$

(B) $\dfrac{\lambda \sin \pi\lambda}{1 - \lambda^2}$

(C) $\dfrac{\lambda \cos \pi\lambda}{1 - \lambda^2}$

(D) $\dfrac{1 - \lambda^2}{\sin \lambda\pi}$

15. For the Fourier cosine integral representation

$$\frac{20}{\pi} \int_0^\infty \left(\frac{1}{\lambda^2 + 5} + \frac{1}{\lambda^2 + 4} \right) \cos \lambda x \, d\lambda = 2e^{-5x} + 5e^{-2x}, \; F_c(\lambda) \text{ is}$$

(1)

(A) $2e^{-5\lambda} + 5e^{-2\lambda}$

(B) $\left(\dfrac{1}{\lambda^2 + 5} + \dfrac{1}{\lambda^2 + 4} \right) \cos \lambda x$

(C) $\left(\dfrac{1}{\lambda^2 + 5} + \dfrac{1}{\lambda^2 + 4} \right)$

(D) $10 \left(\dfrac{1}{\lambda^2 + 5} + \dfrac{1}{\lambda^2 + 4} \right)$

16. For the Fourier sine transform of $f(x) = e^{-mx}$, $m > 0$, $x > 0$ is $F_s(\lambda) = \dfrac{\lambda}{\lambda^2 + m^2}$ then its inverse Fourier sine transform is

(1)

(A) $\dfrac{2}{\pi} \int_0^\infty \dfrac{\lambda}{\lambda^2 + m^2} \sin \lambda x \, dm$

(B) $\dfrac{2}{\pi} \int_0^\infty \dfrac{\lambda}{\lambda^2 + m^2} \sin \lambda x \, dx$

(C) $\dfrac{2}{\pi} \int_0^\infty \dfrac{\lambda}{\lambda^2 + m^2} \cos \lambda x \, d\lambda$

(D) $\dfrac{2}{\pi} \int_0^\infty \dfrac{\lambda}{\lambda^2 + m^2} \sin \lambda x \, d\lambda$

17. If the Fourier cosine integral representation of $f(x) = \begin{cases} 1, & |x| < 1 \\ 0, & |x| > 1 \end{cases}$ is

$$f(x) = \frac{2}{\pi} \int_0^\infty \frac{\sin \lambda \cos \lambda x}{\lambda} \, d\lambda$$ then the value of integral $\int_0^\infty \dfrac{\sin \lambda}{\lambda} \, d\lambda$ is equal to

(1)

(A) $\dfrac{\pi}{2}$

(B) $\dfrac{2}{\pi}$

(C) 1

(D) 0

18. The Fourier sine transform $F_s(\lambda)$ of $f(x) = \begin{cases} \pi/2, & 0 < x < \pi \\ 0, & x > \pi \end{cases}$ is

(2)

(A) $\dfrac{\pi}{2} \left(\dfrac{1 - \sin \lambda\pi}{\lambda} \right)$

(B) $\dfrac{\pi}{2} \left(\dfrac{\cos \lambda\pi - 1}{\lambda} \right)$

(C) $\dfrac{\pi}{2} \left(\dfrac{1 - \cos \lambda\pi}{\lambda} \right)$

(D) $\left(\dfrac{\cos \lambda\pi}{\lambda} \right)$

19. The Fourier sine transform $F_s(\lambda)$ of $f(x) = \begin{cases} 1, & 0 \le x \le 1 \\ 0, & x > 1 \end{cases}$ is   (2)

(A) $\left(\dfrac{\cos \lambda\pi - 1}{\lambda} \right)$

(B) $\left(\dfrac{1 - \cos \lambda}{\lambda} \right)$

(C) $\left(\dfrac{1 - \sin \lambda}{\lambda} \right)$

(D) $\left(\dfrac{\cos \lambda\pi}{\lambda} \right)$

20. If $f(x) = \begin{cases} x, & 0 < x < 1 \\ 0, & x > 1 \end{cases}$ then Fourier cosine transform $F_c(\lambda)$ of $f(x)$ is given by   (2)

(A) $\dfrac{\lambda \sin \lambda + \cos \lambda - 1}{\lambda^2}$

(B) $\dfrac{\cos \lambda - \lambda \sin\lambda - 1}{\lambda^2}$

(C) $\dfrac{\cos \lambda - \lambda \sin \lambda + 1}{\lambda^2}$

(D) $\dfrac{\lambda \sin \lambda + 1}{\lambda^2}$

21. If $f(x) = \begin{cases} x, & 0 < x < 1 \\ 0, & x > 1 \end{cases}$ then Fourier sine transform $F_s(\lambda)$ of $f(x)$ is given by   (2)

(A) $\dfrac{\lambda \cos \lambda + \sin \lambda}{\lambda^2}$

(B) $\dfrac{-\lambda \cos \lambda - \sin \lambda}{\lambda^2}$

(C) $\dfrac{-\lambda \cos \lambda + \sin \lambda}{\lambda^2}$

(D) $\dfrac{\cos \lambda}{\lambda^2}$

22. If $f(x) = \begin{cases} x^2, & 0 < x < 1 \\ 0, & x > 1 \end{cases}$ then Fourier cosine transform $F_c(\lambda)$ of $f(x)$ is given by   (2)

(A) $\dfrac{-\lambda^2 \sin \lambda + 2\lambda \cos \lambda - 2 \sin \lambda}{\lambda^3}$

(B) $\dfrac{\lambda^2 \sin \lambda - 2\lambda \cos \lambda - 2 \sin \lambda}{\lambda^3}$

(C) $\dfrac{\lambda^2 \sin \lambda - 2\lambda \cos \lambda + 2 \sin \lambda}{\lambda^3}$

(D) $\dfrac{\lambda^2 \sin \lambda + 2\lambda \cos \lambda - 2 \sin \lambda}{\lambda^3}$

23. If $f(x) = \begin{cases} x^2, & 0 < x < 1 \\ 0, & x > 1 \end{cases}$ then Fourier sine transform $F_s(\lambda)$ of $f(x)$ is given by   (2)

(A) $\dfrac{-\lambda^2 \cos \lambda + 2\lambda \sin\lambda + 2(\cos \lambda - 1)}{\lambda^3}$

(B) $\dfrac{\lambda^2 \cos \lambda + 2\lambda \sin \lambda + 2(\cos \lambda - 1)}{\lambda^3}$

(C) $\dfrac{\lambda^2 \cos \lambda - 2\lambda \sin \lambda + 2(\cos \lambda - 1)}{\lambda^3}$

(D) $\dfrac{\lambda^2 \cos \lambda - 2\lambda \sin \lambda - 2(\cos \lambda - 1)}{\lambda^3}$

24. The Fourier cosine transform $F_c(\lambda)$ of $f(x) = \begin{cases} 1 - x^2, & |x| \le 1 \\ 0, & |x| > 1 \end{cases}$ is	(2)

(A) $-\dfrac{2}{\lambda^3}(\sin \lambda - \lambda \cos \lambda)$

(B) $\dfrac{2}{\lambda^3}(\sin \lambda - \lambda \cos \lambda)$

(C) $\dfrac{2}{\lambda^2}(\sin \lambda - \lambda \cos \lambda)$

(D) $\dfrac{2}{\lambda^3}(\sin \lambda + \lambda \cos \lambda)$

25. The Fourier cosine transform $f_c(\lambda)$ of $f(x) = \begin{cases} \pi/2, & 0 < x < \pi \\ 0, & x > \pi \end{cases}$ is	(2)

(A) $\dfrac{\pi}{2}\left(\dfrac{1 - \sin \lambda\pi}{\lambda}\right)$

(B) $\left(\dfrac{1 - \sin \lambda\pi}{\lambda}\right)$

(C) $\left(\dfrac{\pi \sin \lambda\pi}{2\lambda}\right)$

(D) $\left(\dfrac{\sin \lambda\pi}{\lambda}\right)$

26. The Fourier sine transform $F_s(\lambda)$ of $f(x) = e^{-x}$, $x > 0$ is given by	(2)

(A) $\dfrac{3\lambda}{1 + \lambda^2}$

(B) $\dfrac{\lambda}{1 - \lambda^2}$

(C) $\dfrac{\lambda}{1 + \lambda^2}$

(D) $\dfrac{\lambda}{1 - \lambda^2}$

27. The Fourier cosine transform $F_c(\lambda)$ of $f(x) = e^{-x}$, $x > 0$ is given by	(2)

(A) $\dfrac{2}{1 - \lambda^2}$

(B) $\dfrac{1}{1 - \lambda^2}$

(C) $\dfrac{2}{1 + \lambda^2}$

(D) $\dfrac{1}{1 + \lambda^2}$

28. If $f(x) = e^{-kx}$, $x > 0$, $k > 0$ then Fourier sine transform $F_s(\lambda)$ of $f(x)$ is given by	(2)

(A) $\dfrac{\lambda}{k^2 + \lambda^2}$

(B) $\dfrac{k}{k^2 + \lambda^2}$

(C) $\dfrac{1}{k^2 + \lambda^2}$

(D) $-\dfrac{k}{k^2 + \lambda^2}$

29. If $f(x) = e^{-kx}$, $x > 0$ then Fourier cosine transform $F_c(\lambda)$ of $f(x)$ is given by	(2)

(A) $-\dfrac{k}{k^2 + \lambda^2}$

(B) $\dfrac{k}{k^2 + \lambda^2}$

(C) $\dfrac{\lambda}{k^2 + \lambda^2}$

(D) $\dfrac{1}{k^2 + \lambda^2}$

30. The Fourier cosine transform $F_c(\lambda)$ of $f(x) = e^{-|x|}$, $-\infty < x < \infty$ is   (2)

(A) $\dfrac{\lambda}{1 + \lambda^2}$

(B) $\dfrac{1}{1 + \lambda^2}$

(C) $\dfrac{1}{1 - \lambda^2}$

(D) $-\dfrac{1}{1 + \lambda^2}$

31. The Fourier sine transform $F_s(\lambda)$ of $f(x) = e^{-|x|}$, $-\infty < x < \infty$ is   (2)

(A) $\dfrac{\lambda}{1 + \lambda^2}$

(B) $\dfrac{1}{1 + \lambda^2}$

(C) $\dfrac{1}{1 - \lambda^2}$

(D) $-\dfrac{1}{1 + \lambda^2}$

32. If $f(x) = \begin{cases} 1, & 0 < x < 1 \\ 0, & x > 1 \end{cases}$ then Fourier cosine transform $F_c(\lambda)$ of $f(x)$ is given by   (2)

(A) $\dfrac{\cos \lambda}{\lambda}$

(B) $\dfrac{\cos 2\lambda}{\lambda}$

(C) $\dfrac{\sin \lambda}{\lambda}$

(D) $\dfrac{\sin 2\lambda}{\lambda}$

33. The Fourier cosine transform $F_c(\lambda)$ of $f(x) = \begin{cases} 1, & |x| < a \\ 0, & |x| > a \end{cases}$ is   (2)

(A) $\dfrac{1 - \cos \lambda a}{\lambda}$

(B) $\dfrac{\cos \lambda a - 1}{\lambda}$

(C) $\dfrac{\sin \lambda a}{a}$

(D) $\dfrac{\sin \lambda a}{\lambda}$

34. The Fourier sine transform $F_s(\lambda)$ of $f(x) = \begin{cases} 1, & |x| < a \\ 0, & |x| > a \end{cases}$ is

(A) $\dfrac{1 - \cos \lambda a}{\lambda}$

(B) $\dfrac{\sin \lambda a}{\lambda}$

(C) $\dfrac{\cos \lambda a - 1}{\lambda}$

(D) $\dfrac{\sin \lambda a}{a}$

35. The Fourier cosine transform $F_c(\lambda)$ of $f(x) = \begin{cases} \sin x, & 0 < x < \pi \\ 0, & x > \pi \end{cases}$ is   (2)

(A) $\dfrac{1}{2}\left[-\dfrac{\sin (1 + \lambda)u}{1 + \lambda} - \dfrac{\sin (1 - \lambda)u}{1 - \lambda} \right]_0^{\pi}$

(B) $\dfrac{1}{2}\left[-\dfrac{\cos (1 + \lambda)u}{1 + \lambda} - \dfrac{\sin (1 - \lambda)u}{1 - \lambda} \right]_0^{\pi}$

(C) $\dfrac{1}{2}\left[-\dfrac{\cos (1 + \lambda)u}{1 + \lambda} - \dfrac{\cos (1 - \lambda)u}{1 - \lambda} \right]_0^{\pi}$

(D) $\dfrac{1}{2}\left[-\dfrac{\sin (1 + \lambda)u}{1 + \lambda} - \dfrac{\cos (1 - \lambda)u}{1 - \lambda} \right]_0^{\pi}$

36. The Fourier sine transform $F_s(\lambda)$ of $f(x) = \begin{cases} \sin x, & 0 < x < \pi \\ 0, & x > \pi \end{cases}$ is (2)

(A) $\dfrac{1}{2}\left[-\dfrac{\cos(1+\lambda)u}{1+\lambda} - \dfrac{\sin(1-\lambda)u}{1-\lambda}\right]_0^\pi$

(B) $\dfrac{1}{2}\left[\dfrac{\sin(1-\lambda)u}{1-\lambda} - \dfrac{\sin(1+\lambda)u}{1+\lambda}\right]_0^\pi$

(C) $\dfrac{1}{2}\left[-\dfrac{\cos(1+\lambda)u}{1+\lambda} - \dfrac{\cos(1-\lambda)u}{1-\lambda}\right]_0^\pi$

(D) $\dfrac{1}{2}\left[-\dfrac{\sin(1+\lambda)u}{1+\lambda} - \dfrac{\cos(1-\lambda)u}{1-\lambda}\right]_0^\pi$

37. The Fourier cosine transform $F_c(\lambda)$ of $f(x) = \begin{cases} \cos x, & 0 < x < \pi \\ 0, & x > \pi \end{cases}$ is (2)

(A) $\dfrac{1}{2}\left[\dfrac{\sin(1-\lambda)u}{1-\lambda} - \dfrac{\cos(1+\lambda)u}{1+\lambda}\right]_0^\pi$

(B) $\dfrac{1}{2}\left[-\dfrac{\cos(1+\lambda)u}{1+\lambda} - \dfrac{\sin(1-\lambda)u}{1-\lambda}\right]_0^\pi$

(C) $\dfrac{1}{2}\left[-\dfrac{\cos(1+\lambda)u}{1+\lambda} - \dfrac{\cos(1-\lambda)u}{1-\lambda}\right]_0^\pi$

(D) $\dfrac{1}{2}\left[\dfrac{\sin(1+\lambda)u}{1+\lambda} + \dfrac{\sin(1-\lambda)u}{1-\lambda}\right]_0^\pi$

38. The Fourier sine transform $F_s(\lambda)$ of $f(x) = \begin{cases} \cos x, & 0 < x < \pi \\ 0, & x > \pi \end{cases}$ is (2)

(A) $\dfrac{1}{2}\left[\dfrac{\sin(1-\lambda)u}{1-\lambda} - \dfrac{\cos(1+\lambda)u}{1+\lambda}\right]_0^\pi$

(B) $\dfrac{1}{2}\left[-\dfrac{\cos(\lambda+1)u}{\lambda+1} - \dfrac{\cos(\lambda-1)u}{\lambda-1}\right]_0^\pi$

(C) $\dfrac{1}{2}\left[-\dfrac{\cos(1+\lambda)u}{1+\lambda} - \dfrac{\sin(1-\lambda)u}{1-\lambda}\right]_0^\pi$

(D) $\dfrac{1}{2}\left[\dfrac{\sin(1+\lambda)u}{1+\lambda} - \dfrac{\sin(1-\lambda)u}{1-\lambda}\right]_0^\pi$

39. The Fourier cosine transform $F_c(\lambda)$ of $f(x) = \begin{cases} \cos x, & 0 < x < a \\ 0, & x > a \end{cases}$ is (2)

(A) $\dfrac{1}{2}\left[\dfrac{\sin(\lambda+1)a}{\lambda+1} - \dfrac{\sin(\lambda-1)a}{\lambda-1}\right]$

(B) $\dfrac{1}{2}\left[\dfrac{\sin(\lambda-1)a}{\lambda-1} - \dfrac{\sin(\lambda+1)a}{\lambda+1}\right]$

(C) $\dfrac{1}{2}\left[\dfrac{\sin(\lambda+1)a}{\lambda+1} + \dfrac{\sin(\lambda-1)a}{\lambda-1}\right]$

(D) $\dfrac{\sin(\lambda+1)a}{\lambda+1}$

40. The solution $f(x)$ of integral equation $\displaystyle\int_0^\infty f(x)\cos\lambda x\,dx = e^{-\lambda}$, $\lambda > 0$ is (2)

(A) $\dfrac{2}{\pi}\left(\dfrac{e^{-x}}{1+x^2}\right)$

(B) $\dfrac{2}{\pi}\left(\dfrac{x}{1+x^2}\right)$

(C) $\dfrac{2}{\pi}\left(\dfrac{1}{1-x^2}\right)$

(D) $\dfrac{2}{\pi}\left(\dfrac{1}{1+x^2}\right)$

41. The solution of integral equation $\int_0^\infty f(x) \sin \lambda x \, dx = \begin{cases} 1 - \lambda, & 0 \le \lambda \le 1 \\ 0, & \lambda \ge 1 \end{cases}$ is

$f(x) = \dfrac{2}{\pi} \int_0^1 (1 - \lambda) \sin \lambda x \, d\lambda$ then the value of $f(x)$ is equal to   (2)

(A) $\dfrac{2}{\pi} \left(\dfrac{1}{x} - \dfrac{\sin x}{x^2} \right)$ (B) $\dfrac{2}{\pi} \left(\dfrac{1}{x} - \dfrac{\cos x}{x^2} \right)$

(C) $\dfrac{2}{\pi} \left(\dfrac{1}{x} + \dfrac{\sin x}{x^2} \right)$ (D) $\dfrac{2}{\pi} \left(-\dfrac{1}{x} + \dfrac{\sin x}{x^2} \right)$

42. The solution of integral equation $\int_0^\infty f(x) \cos \lambda x \, dx = \begin{cases} 1 - \lambda, & 0 \le \lambda \le 1 \\ 0, & \lambda \ge 1 \end{cases}$ is

$f(x) = \dfrac{2}{\pi} \int_0^1 (1 - \lambda) \sin \lambda x \, d\lambda$ then the value of $f(x)$ is equal to   (2)

(A) $\dfrac{2}{\pi} \left(\dfrac{1 + \cos x}{x^2} \right)$ (B) $\dfrac{2}{\pi} \left(\dfrac{1 - \cos x}{x^2} \right)$

(C) $\dfrac{2}{\pi} \left(\dfrac{1 + \sin x}{x^2} \right)$ (D) $\dfrac{2}{\pi} \left(\dfrac{1 - \sin x}{x^2} \right)$

43. The solution $f(x)$ of integral $\int_0^\infty f(x) \sin \lambda x \, dx = \begin{cases} 1, & 0 \le \lambda \le 1 \\ 2, & 1 \le \lambda < 2 \\ 0, & \lambda \ge 2 \end{cases}$ is   (2)

(A) $\dfrac{2}{\pi} \left[\left(\dfrac{1 - \sin x}{x} \right) + 2 \left(\dfrac{\sin x - \sin 2x}{x} \right) \right]$

(B) $\dfrac{2}{\pi} \left[\left(\dfrac{-1 + \cos x}{x} \right) + 2 \left(\dfrac{-\cos x + \cos 2x}{x} \right) \right]$

(C) $\dfrac{2}{\pi} \left[\left(\dfrac{1 - \cos x}{x} \right) + 2 \left(\dfrac{\cos x - \cos 2x}{x} \right) \right]$

(D) $\dfrac{2}{\pi} \left[\left(\dfrac{1 - \cos x}{x^2} \right) + 2 \left(\dfrac{\cos x - \cos 2x}{x^2} \right) \right]$

44. The solution $f(x)$ of integral equation $\int_0^\infty f(x) \sin \lambda x \, dx = \begin{cases} 1, & 0 \le \lambda \le 1 \\ 0, & \lambda \ge 1 \end{cases}$ is   (2)

(A) $\dfrac{2}{\pi} \left(\dfrac{1 + \cos x}{x} \right)$ (B) $\dfrac{2}{\pi} \left(\dfrac{1 + \sin x}{x} \right)$

(C) $\dfrac{2}{\pi} \left(\dfrac{1 - \sin x}{x} \right)$ (D) $\dfrac{2}{\pi} \left(\dfrac{1 - \cos x}{x} \right)$

45. The solution f(x) of integral equation $\int\limits_{0}^{\infty} f(x) \cos \lambda x \, dx = \begin{cases} 1, & 0 \le \lambda \le 1 \\ 0, & \lambda \ge 1 \end{cases}$ is   (2)

(A) $\dfrac{2}{\pi} \left(\dfrac{\sin x}{x} \right)$

(B) $\dfrac{2}{\pi} \left(\dfrac{\cos x}{x} \right)$

(C) $\dfrac{2}{\pi} \left(\dfrac{1 - \cos x}{x} \right)$

(D) $\dfrac{2}{\pi} \left(\dfrac{1 + \sin x}{x} \right)$

46. The inverse Fourier cosine transform f(x) of $F_c(\lambda) = \dfrac{\sin a\lambda}{\lambda}$ is   (2)

(A) $\dfrac{1}{\pi} \int\limits_{0}^{\infty} \dfrac{\cos (a + x)\lambda + \sin (a - x)\lambda}{\lambda} \, d\lambda$

(B) $\dfrac{1}{\pi} \int\limits_{0}^{\infty} \dfrac{\cos (a + x)\lambda + \cos (a - x)\lambda}{\lambda} \, d\lambda$

(C) $\dfrac{1}{\pi} \int\limits_{0}^{\infty} \dfrac{\sin (a + x)\lambda + \sin (a - x)\lambda}{\lambda} \, d\lambda$

(D) $\dfrac{1}{\pi} \int\limits_{0}^{\infty} \dfrac{\sin (a + x)\lambda + \cos (a - x)\lambda}{\lambda} \, d\lambda$

47. If the Fourier cosine integral representation of $f(x) = \begin{cases} 1 - x^2, & 0 < x < 1 \\ 0, & x > 1 \end{cases}$ is

$$f(x) = \dfrac{4}{\pi} \int\limits_{0}^{\infty} \left(\dfrac{\sin \lambda - \lambda \cos \lambda}{\lambda^3} \right) \cos \lambda x \, d\lambda \text{ then the value of integral}$$

$$\int\limits_{0}^{\infty} \left(\dfrac{\sin \lambda - \lambda \cos \lambda}{\lambda^3} \right) \cos \dfrac{\lambda}{2} \, d\lambda \text{ is equal to}$$ (2)

(A) $-\dfrac{3\pi}{16}$

(B) $\dfrac{3\pi}{16}$

(C) $\dfrac{3\pi}{8}$

(D) $\dfrac{3\pi}{4}$

48. Given that $\int\limits_{0}^{\infty} \dfrac{\sin t}{t} \, dt = \dfrac{\pi}{2}$, then Fourier sine transform $F_s(\lambda)$ of $f(x) = \dfrac{1}{x}$, x > 0 is given by   (2)

(A) π

(B) $\dfrac{\pi}{4}$

(C) $\dfrac{\pi}{2}$

(D) $-\pi$

49. For the Fourier cosine transform $\displaystyle\int_0^\infty \left(\frac{1-\cos u}{u^2}\right)\cos \lambda u \; du = \begin{cases} \pi/2\,(1-\lambda), & 0 < \lambda < 1 \\ 0, & \lambda > 1 \end{cases}$

the value of integral $\displaystyle\int_0^\infty \frac{\sin^2 z}{z^2}\, dz$ is   (2)

(A) 1 (B) $\dfrac{\pi}{2}$

(C) 0 (D) $\dfrac{\pi}{4}$

50. For the Fourier sine integral representation

$\displaystyle\frac{2}{\pi}\int_0^\infty \left(\frac{1-\cos\lambda}{\lambda}\right)\sin\lambda x \; d\lambda = \begin{cases} 1, & 0<\lambda<1 \\ 0, & \lambda>1 \end{cases}$, the value of integral $\displaystyle\int_0^\infty \frac{\sin^3 t}{t}\, dt$ is   (2)

(A) $\dfrac{\pi}{2}$ (B) 1

(C) 0 (D) $\dfrac{\pi}{4}$

51. Given that $\displaystyle F_c(\lambda) = \int_0^\infty u^{m-1}\cos\lambda u \; du = \frac{\sqrt{m}}{\lambda^m}\cos\frac{m\pi}{2}$, then Fourier cosine transform

$F_c(\lambda)$ of $f(x) = x^3,\ x > 0$ is given by   (2)

(A) $\dfrac{6}{\lambda^4}$ (B) $\dfrac{3}{\lambda^3}$

(C) $\dfrac{4}{\lambda^2}$ (D) $\dfrac{1}{\lambda^2}$

52. Given that $\displaystyle F_s(\lambda) = \int_0^\infty u^{m-1}\sin\lambda u \; du = \frac{\sqrt{m}}{\lambda^m}\sin\frac{m\pi}{2}$, then Fourier cosine transform

$F_c(\lambda)$ of $f(x) = x^2,\ x > 0$ is given by   (2)

(A) $\dfrac{2}{\lambda^3}$ (B) $-\dfrac{2}{\lambda^3}$

(C) $\dfrac{3}{\lambda^2}$ (D) $-\dfrac{3}{\lambda^2}$

Answers

1. (B)	2. (D)	3. (C)	4. (A)	5. (D)	6. (A)	7. (B)	8. (C)
9. (D)	10. (A)	11. (C)	12. (B)	13. (A)	14. (B)	15. (D)	16. (D)
17. (A)	18. (C)	19. (B)	20. (A)	21. (C)	22. (D)	23. (A)	24. (B)
25. (C)	26. (C)	27. (D)	28. (A)	29. (B)	30. (B)	31. (A)	32. (C)
33. (D)	34. (A)	35. (C)	36. (B)	37. (D)	38. (B)	39. (C)	40. (D)
41. (A)	42. (B)	43. (C)	44. (D)	45. (A)	46. (C)	47. (B)	48. (C)
49. (B)	50. (D)	51. (A)	52. (B)				

CHAPTER SEVEN

STATISTICS, CORRELATION AND REGRESSION

7.1 INTRODUCTION

In recent decades, the growth of statistic has made itself felt in almost every major phase of human activity, particularly so in the field of Engineering and Science. Everything dealing with the collection, processing, analysis and interpretation of numerical data belongs to the field of statistics. Collection and processing of data is usually referred to as statistical survey. Before any major project work is undertaken, the statistical survey is a must. Only when statistical survey gives green signal, actual start of the work is undertaken. For example, if a Dam is to be constructed on a river, many aspects have to be taken into account. Foremost is the selection of dam site. For making a proper choice, it may be necessary to consider average rainfull in the catchment area for the past say 100 years, the extent of the area which may be submerged, the population which is going to be benefitted, the availability of labour and many other aspects. Good statistical survey should be able to answer all these questions. All such considerations and statistical survey have to be made whenever a new industry is to be started. The success of such projects depends to a great extent upon sound statistical survey. Apart from these basic considerations, modern statistical techniques are widely used in the fields of statistical work, Quality control, reliability needs of the highly complex products of space technology and operation research.

Aim of this work is to introduce to the readers, the simple aspects of collection, classification and enumeration of numerical data, which are so very essential for development of modern statistical techniques, used in engineering fields.

7.2 COLLECTION AND CLASSIFICATION OF DATA

Data collected in a statistical survey as a result of some kind of experimentation is usually large in size and is in the form which is not very useful for arriving at any specific conclusions. The first task is to present this data in a proper form. As a first step, this data which is generally in the form of numerical observations, is arranged either in the ascending or descending order. For example, the set of observations 45, 35, 0, 10, 0, 51, 81, 71, 95, 17, 97, 21, 26, 86, 100, 55, 46, 56, 37, 92 (which are in all 20) is rearranged in ascending order as 0, 0, 10, 17, 21, 26, 35, 37, 45, 51, 55, 56, 71, 81, 86, 92, 95, 97, 100.

This way of presentation immediately reveals that the minimum value of the observation is 0 and maximum is 100. It also indicates that observations are well spread out in the interval (0, 100). In different experiments, these observations could carry different meanings. In some experiments, these figures may indicate the number of syntax errors committed by a group of 20 students in their first attempt to write a computer program. In yet another experiment, these figures may indicate marks obtained out of 100 by a group of 20 students in the paper of numerical computational methods. In an altogether different context, these figures may indicate Rainfall in centimeters in a certain catchment area for the past 20 year. For development of statistical techniques it is unimportant, what is exactly represented by these observations. In presentation of data, these observations are represented by symbol x, called in statistical language, a variate (variable).

After arranging the data in ascending or descending order, to make it more compact, it is presented in a tabular form consisting of columns headed by symbols x and f. The column headed by x consists of various observations recorded out of experimentation, arranged in proper order, and column headed by f contains entries which indicate number of times particular value of x occur.

Consider the Table 7.1, which shows various values of x and f. It shows that the value of x = 1 is recorded twice, x = 4 occurs six times, x = 8 occurs four times, etc.

Table 7.1

x	f
1	2
2	3
3	5
4	6
5	10
6	6
7	4
8	4
9	3
10	2
–	$\Sigma f = 45$

The total numbers of observations being $\Sigma f = 45$. In statistical language, this table means x = 1 has frequency 2, x = 4 has frequency 6 and so on. This way of arrangement of data is called *frequency distribution*. In the above example, the range of variate is from x = 1 to x = 10. When the range is wide and the total number of observations is very large, the data can be expressed in still more compact form by dividing the range in class intervals.

Consider the table given on next page (Table 7.2). Here the range of variate (0, 100) is divided into 10 class intervals each of width 10. The class interval 0 – 10 has width 10, the lower limit 0 and the upper limit 10.

$\dfrac{10 + 0}{2}$ = 5 is the middle value of the class interval and 16 is the frequency corresponding to this class interval. The middle value x = 5 represents the class interval (0 – 10) of f = 16 is taken as frequency of variate x. This way of representing the data is called *Grouped frequency distribution*. In such type of presentation, the class intervals must be well defined. One such way of defining the class interval is that, all the values of x = 0 and above but less than 10 are included in the class interval 0 – 10. The total frequency of all such observations is 16 and is the frequency of class interval 0 – 10 or is the frequency of variate x = 5.

Table 7.2

C.I. (Class interval)	Mid-value x	Frequency f
0 – 10	5	16
10 – 20	15	18
20 – 30	25	20
30 – 40	35	22
40 – 50	45	40
50 – 60	55	45
60 – 70	65	35
70 – 80	75	20
80 – 90	85	19
90 – 100	95	15
Total	–	**$\Sigma f = 250$**

Similarly all the observations having the value x = 10 and above but less than 20 are included in the class interval 10 – 20 and so on. Slight change in the definition of last class interval is made. Here all the values of x = 90 and above and less than or equal to 100 are included in the class interval 90 – 100. $\Sigma f = 250$ gives the total frequency which is sometimes denoted by N.

In presenting the data in Grouped frequency distribution form, the following points must be noted :

(i)   The class interval must be well defined that is there must not be any ambiguity about the inclusion of value of *x* in one or the other class interval. In the Table 7.2, the way of defining class interval enables us to put x = 10 in the class interval 10 – 20 while x = 100 is put in the interval 90 – 100.

(ii) The class intervals must be exhaustive that is no observation should escape classification. For this, the entire range of observations should be divided into well defined class intervals.

(iii) The width of the class interval should be uniform as far as possible.

(iv) The number of class intervals should neither be too large nor too small. Depending upon the range of variate x and the total frequency of observations, the total number of class intervals is divided into about 10 to 25 class intervals.

Sometimes the additional column of cumulative frequency (c.f.) suppliments the grouped frequency distribution or frequency distribution table.

In the Table 7.3, the number 76 against x = 35 shows the total frequency upto and including the observation x = 35 which is the middle value of the interval (30 – 40).

Table 7.3

C.I.	Mid-value x	Frequency f	Cumulative frequency c.f.
0 – 10	5	16	16
10 – 20	15	18	34
20 – 30	25	20	54
30 – 40	35	22	76
40 – 50	45	40	116
50 – 60	55	45	161
60 – 70	65	35	196
70 – 80	75	20	216
80 – 90	85	19	235
90 – 100	95	15	250
Total	–	**Σf = 250**	**N = 250**

Graphical Representation of Data

To observe the data at a glance, it is exhibited by following graphical methods :

1.　Histogram : A Histogram is drawn by constructing rectangles over the class intervals, such that the areas of rectangles are proportional to the class frequencies.

If the class intervals are of equal width, the heights of the rectangles will be proportional to the class frequencies themselves, otherwise these would be proportional to the ratios of the frequencies to the width of the classes (See Fig. 7.1).

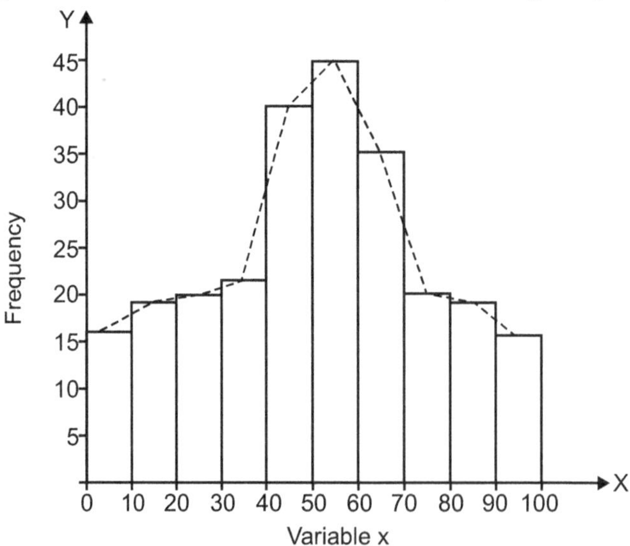

Fig. 7.1

2. Frequency Polygon : Consider the set of points (x, f), where x is the middle value of the class interval and f is the corresponding frequency. If these set of points are joined by straight lines, they form a frequency polygon. It is shown by dotted lines in Fig. 7.1.

3. Cumulative Frequency Curve or The Ogive : Taking upper limit of classes of x co-ordinate and corresponding cumulative frequency as y co-ordinate, if the points are plotted and then joined by free hand curve, it gives what is called as ogive (See Fig. 7.2).

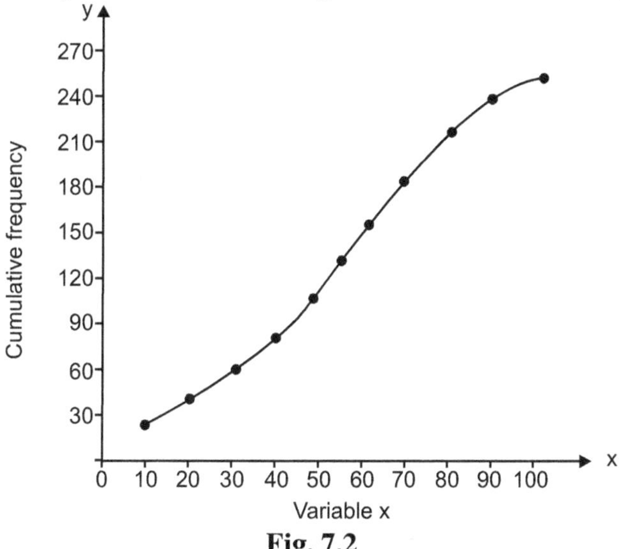

Fig. 7.2

7.3 LOCATION OF CENTRAL TENDENCY

After collecting the data and arranging it in the proper order in the form of frequency distribution or grouped frequency distribution, next task is to study this data carefully and to draw valid conclusions. If data collected relates to marks obtained by the students in Mathematics paper, it should be able to reveal the general performance of the students. Whether the class contains large number of good students or the overall calibre of students is medicore, all this must be inferred from the data. If the numerical data collected relates to the industrial project, the whole success of the project will depend upon the appropriate conclusions drawn from the study of this data. The first step in this direction is the location of central tendency. It means what is represented by data by and large. Whether the data is favourable to a particular project or not will depend upon the criterion that is decided upon. But overall picture must be exhibited. This overall picture or central tendency of the data is known by obtaining what we call the Mean or Average. There are various methods to calculate the mean or the average. Depending upon the project under study, the particular method is selected. Various types of measures of central tendency are as given below :

(1) Arithmetic mean   (2) Geometric mean

(3) Harmonic mean   (4) Median   (5) Mode.

Out of these, Arithmetic mean is of greater importance and serves the purpose in many cases. Now, we see how these measures are calculated.

7.3.1 Arithmetic Mean

Consider the variate x which takes n values $x_1, x_2, x_3 \ldots\ldots x_n$, then the Arithmetic mean (A.M.) is denoted by $\bar{x}$ and is given by,

$$\bar{x} = \frac{x_1 + x_2 + x_3 + \ldots\ldots + x_n}{n}$$

If the data is presented in the form of frequency distribution

x	x_1	x_2	x_3	......	x_n
f	f_1	f_2	f_3	......	f_n

then arithmetic mean $\bar{x}$ is given by

$$\bar{x} = \frac{f_1 x_1 + f_2 x_2 + \ldots + f_n x_n}{f_1 + f_2 + f_3 + \ldots + f_n}$$

$$= \frac{\sum fx}{N}$$

where $N = f_1 + f_2 + \ldots\ldots + f_n$ is the total frequency

ILLUSTRATIONS

Ex. 1 : *Find the Arithmetic mean for the following distribution :*

x	0	1	2	3	4	5	6	7	8	9	10
f	4	5	12	12	13	16	15	13	12	5	6

Sol. : Writing the tabulated values as :

x	f	x × f
0	4	0
1	5	5
2	12	24
3	12	36
4	13	52
5	16	80
6	15	90
7	13	91
8	12	96
9	5	45
10	6	60
Total	$\Sigma f = 113$	$\Sigma fx = 579$

$$\bar{x} = \frac{\sum fx}{\sum f} = \frac{579}{113} = 5.12 \text{ (approximately)}$$

To reduce the calculations, we consider the variable $d = x - A$.

Where, A is middle value or value near to it in the range of variable x, A is sometimes called assumed mean.

Now we can write

$$f \times d = f \times x - f \times A$$

Or

$$\sum fd = \sum fx - \sum fA$$

Dividing by $\sum f$ throughout

$$\frac{\sum fd}{\sum f} = \frac{\sum fx}{\sum f} - \frac{\sum fA}{\sum f}$$

i.e.

$$\frac{\sum fd}{\sum f} = \bar{x} - \frac{A \sum f}{\sum f}$$

(A being constant is taken outside the $\sum$ notation)

$$\frac{\sum fd}{\sum f} = \bar{x} - A$$

Or

$$\bar{x} = A + \frac{\sum fd}{\sum f} = A + \bar{d} \qquad [\bar{d} \text{ is the mean of the variable d}]$$

fd and $\sum fd$ are smaller numbers as compared to fx and $\sum fx$, which result in the reduction of the calculations.

Further reduction in calculations can be achieved by taking

$$u = \frac{x - A}{h} \text{ or } \frac{d}{h}$$

that gives

$$hu = x - A$$

Then proceeding as before, we get

$$h \frac{\sum fu}{\sum f} = \bar{x} - A$$

Or

$$\bar{x} = A + h \frac{\sum fu}{\sum f}$$

This formula is mostly used in grouped frequency distribution, where, h is chosen to be equal to the width of the class interval.

Ex. 2 : *Marks obtained in a paper of statistics are given in the following table.*

Marks obtained	No. of students
0 – 10	8
10 – 20	20
20 – 30	14
30 – 40	16
40 – 50	20
50 – 60	25
60 – 70	13
70 – 80	10
80 – 90	5
90 – 100	2

Find the Arithmetic mean of the distribution.

Sol. : Preparing the table as : A = 45, h = 10.

C.I.	Mid-value x	f	$u = \dfrac{x-45}{10}$	f × u
0 – 10	5	8	– 4	– 32
10 – 20	15	20	– 3	– 60
20 – 30	25	14	– 2	– 28
30 – 40	35	16	– 1	– 16
40 – 50	45	20	0	0
50 – 60	55	25	1	25
60 – 70	65	13	2	26
70 – 80	75	10	3	30
80 – 90	85	5	4	20
90 – 100	95	2	5	10
Total	–	**$\Sigma f = 133$**	–	**$\Sigma fu = -25$**

$$\bar{x} = A + h \frac{\Sigma fu}{\Sigma f} = 45 + 10 \left(\frac{-25}{133}\right)$$

$$= 45 + 10 \left(\frac{-25}{133}\right) = 45 - \frac{250}{133} = 43.12$$

Joint Arithmetic Mean (Mean of composite series)

Consider two sets of data

1. $x_1, x_2, \ldots, x_{n_1}$ containing n_1 items

2. $y_1, y_2, \ldots, y_{n_2}$ containing n_2 items

$\therefore$ $\bar{x}$, the mean of first set is given by

$$\bar{x} = \frac{x_1 + x_2 + x_3 + \ldots + x_n}{n_1}$$

$\therefore$ $n_1 \bar{x} = x_1 + x_2 + \ldots + x_{n_1}$

and the mean of second set is given by

$$\bar{y} = \frac{y_1 + y_2 + y_3 + \ldots + y_{n_2}}{n_2}$$

$\therefore$ $n_2 \bar{y} = y_1 + y_2 + \ldots + y_{n_2}$

Hence, by definition the joint arithmetic mean $\bar{z}$ is given by

$$\bar{z} = \frac{(x_1 + x_2 + x_3 + \ldots + x_{n_1}) + (y_1 + y_2 + y_3 + \ldots + y_{n_2})}{n_1 + n_2}$$

$\therefore$ $$\bar{z} = \frac{n_1 \bar{x} + n_2 \bar{y}}{n_1 + n_2} \qquad \ldots (A)$$

(A) gives joint Arithmetic Mean (A.M.) of the composite series.

Same type of formula holds good for sets of data presented in frequency distribution form. Consider two sets of data :

Set 1	
x	**f**
x_1	f_1
x_2	f_2
x_3	f_3
...	...
...	...
x_{n_1}	f_{n_1}
	$\Sigma f = N_1$

Set 2	
y	**f**
y_1	f_1
y_2	f_2
y_3	f_3
...	...
...	...
y_{n_1}	f_{n_1}
	$\Sigma f = N_2$

Means $\bar{x}$, $\bar{y}$ for two sets are given by

$$\bar{x} = \frac{\Sigma fx}{N_1} \qquad\qquad N_1\,\bar{x} = \Sigma fx$$

$$\bar{y} = \frac{\Sigma fy}{N_2} \qquad\qquad N_2\,\bar{y} = \Sigma fy$$

Hence $\bar{z}$, the joint mean given by

$$\bar{z} = \frac{\Sigma fx + \Sigma fy}{N_1 + N_2} = \frac{N_1\,\bar{x} + N_2\,\bar{y}}{N_1 + N_2} \qquad\qquad \dots (A)$$

Ex. 3 : *Marks obtained in paper of Applied Mechanics by a group of Computer and Electronics students are as given in following tables :*

Group (A) of Computer students :

Marks obtained	No. of students
0 – 10	5
10 – 20	6
20 – 30	15
30 – 40	15
40 – 50	9
	$\Sigma f = 50$

Group (B) of Electronics students :

Marks obtained	No. of students
0 – 10	8
10 – 20	15
20 – 30	18
30 – 40	13
40 – 50	6
	$\Sigma f = 60$

Find the Joint mean of the two groups.

Sol. : For group (A) :

C.I.	Mid-value x	f	f × x
0 – 10	5	5	25
10 – 20	15	6	90
20 – 30	25	15	375
30 – 40	35	15	525
40 – 50	45	9	405
Total	–	$N_1 = \sum f = 50$	$\sum fx = 1420$

For group (B) :

C.I.	Mid-value x	f	f × x
0 – 10	5	8	40
10 – 20	15	15	225
20 – 30	25	18	450
30 – 40	35	13	455
40 – 50	45	6	270
Total	–	$N_2 = \sum f = 60$	$\sum fy = 1440$

Mean $\bar{x}$ of group (A) is given by,

$$\bar{x} = \frac{\sum fx}{\sum f} \Rightarrow \bar{x} \sum f = N_1 \bar{x} = \sum fx = 1420$$

Mean $\bar{y}$ of group (B) is given by,

$$\bar{y} = \frac{\sum fy}{\sum f} \Rightarrow \bar{y} \sum f = N_2 \bar{y} = \sum fy = 1440$$

Common mean $\bar{z}$ is given by,

$$\bar{z} = \frac{N_1 \bar{x} + N_2 \bar{y}}{N_1 + N_2} = \frac{1420 + 1440}{50 + 60}$$

$$= \frac{2860}{110} = 26$$

Ex. 4 : *Calculate arithmetic mean for the following frequency distribution :*

Observations (x)	*103*	*110*	*112*	*118*	*95*
Frequency (f)	*4*	*6*	*10*	*12*	*3*

Solution : We solve the problem by both the methods.

1. Direct Method

x	f	fx
103	4	$103 \times 4 = 412$
110	6	$110 \times 6 = 660$
112	10	$112 \times 10 = 1120$
118	12	$118 \times 12 = 1416$
95	3	$95 \times 3 = 285$
Total	**N = 35**	$\boldsymbol{\sum f_i x_i = 3893}$

$$\therefore \qquad \bar{x} = \frac{\sum fx}{\sum f} = \frac{3893}{35} = 111.2286$$

Ex. 5 : *Arithmetic mean of weight of 100 boys is 50 kg and the arithmetic mean of 50 girls is 45 kg. Calculate the arithmetic mean of combined group of boys and girls.*

Solution : Let $\bar{X}_1$ and N_1 be the mean and size of group of boys and $\bar{Y}$ and N_2 be the mean and size of group of girls. So $N_1 = 100$, $\bar{X} = 50$, $N_2 = 50$, $\bar{Y} = 45$. Hence, combined mean is

$$Z = \frac{N_1 \bar{X} + N_2 \bar{Y}}{N_1 + N_2} = \frac{(100 \times 50) + (50 \times 45)}{100 + 50} = \frac{7250}{150} = 48.3333$$

Ex. 6 : *The mean weekly salary paid to 300 employees of a firm is ₹ 1,470. There are 200 male employees and the remaining are females. If mean salary of males is ₹ 1,505, obtain the mean salary of females.*

Solution : Suppose $\bar{X}$ and N_1 are mean and group size of males. $\bar{Y}$ and N_2 are mean and size of group of females, $\bar{x}_c$ mean of all the employees considered together.

$$\text{Now,} \qquad Z = \frac{N_1 \bar{X} + N_2 \bar{Y}}{N_1 + N_2}$$

$$\therefore \qquad 1470 = \frac{(200 \times 1505) + (100 \times \bar{Y})}{200 + 100}$$

$$\therefore \qquad 1470 = \frac{301000 + 100\bar{Y}}{300}$$

$$\therefore \qquad 441000 = 301000 + 100Y$$

$$\therefore \qquad 4410 = 3010 + Y$$

$$\therefore \qquad \bar{Y} = 1,400 \text{ ₹}$$

7.3.2 Geometric Mean

Geometric mean of a set of an observations x_1, x_2, ..., x_n is given by n^{th} root of their product.

Thus Geometric Mean (G.M.) is given by,

$$\text{G.M.} = (x_1 \cdot x_2 \cdot x_3 \dots x_n)^{1/n}$$

In case of frequency distribution

x	x_1	x_2	.... x_n
f	f_1	f_2	.... f_n

$$\text{G.M.} = \left(x_1^{f1} \cdot x_2^{f2} \cdot x_3^{f3} \dots x_n^{fn}\right)^{1/N}$$

where, $N = \Sigma f$

To calculate it, denoting G.M. by G and taking logarithms of both sides

$$\log G = \frac{1}{N}\left[\log \left(x_1^{f1} \cdot x_2^{f2} \cdot x_3^{f3} \dots x_n^{fn}\right)^{1/N}\right]$$

$$= \frac{1}{N}[f_1 \log x_1 + f_2 \log x_2 \dots + f_n \log x_n]$$

$$= \frac{1}{N} \Sigma f \log x$$

$$\text{or} \quad G = \text{antilog}\left(\frac{1}{N} \Sigma f \log x\right)$$

It is seen that logarithm of G is the arithmetic mean of the logarithms of the given values.

In case of grouped frequency distribution, x is taken as mid-value of the class interval.

For two sets of observations $(x_1, x_2, \dots, x_{n_1})$, $(y_1, y_2, \dots, y_{n_2})$ with geometric means G_1, G_2 it can be established that

$$\log G = \frac{n_1 \log G_1 + n_2 \log G_2}{n_1 + n_2}$$

where, G is the joint or common geometric mean of the two series.

It may be noted here that if one of the observations is zero, geometric mean becomes zero and if one of the observations is negative, geometric mean becomes imaginary. Naturally, calculation of geometric mean becomes meaningless in such cases.

7.3.3 Harmonic Mean

(H.M.) Harmonic mean of set of observations $(x_1, x_2, \dots, x_n)$ is the reciprocal of the arithmetic mean of the reciprocals of the given values. Thus H.M. or H is given by,

$$H = \frac{1}{\dfrac{1}{n}\left(\dfrac{1}{x_1} + \dfrac{1}{x_2} + \dfrac{1}{x_3} + \dots + \dfrac{1}{x_n}\right)}$$

In case of frequency distribution (x, f),

$$H = \cfrac{1}{\cfrac{1}{N} \Sigma \, (f / x)} \qquad \text{where, } N = \Sigma \, f$$

7.3.4 Median

Median of a distribution is the value of the variable (or variate) which divides it into two equal parts. It is the value such that the number of observations above it is equal to the number of observations below it. Sometimes, Median is called positional average.

In case of ungrouped data, if the number of observations is odd, then the median is the middle value of the set of observations after they are arranged in ascending or descending order. For even number of observations, it is the arithmetic mean of the two middle terms. Thus for the observations

$x = 1, 5, 9, 11, 21, 24, 27, 30$, the middle terms are 11 and 21 and median $= \dfrac{11 + 21}{2} = 16$.

For a data presented in the form of frequency distribution :

x	x_1	x_2	.... x_n
f	f_1	f_2	.... f_n

$\Sigma f = N$

We prepare the cumulative frequency column. Then consider cumulative frequency (c.f.) equal to $\dfrac{N}{2}$ or just greater than $\dfrac{N}{2}$, the corresponding value of x is the median.

ILLUSTRATIONS

Ex. 1 : *Obtain the median of the distribution :*

x	*1*	*3*	*5*	*7*	*9*	*11*	*13*	*15*	*17*
f	*3*	*6*	*8*	*12*	*16*	*16*	*15*	*10*	*5*

Sol. : Preparing the table as :

x	**f**	**c.f.**
1	3	3
3	6	9
5	8	17
7	12	29
9	16	45
11	16	61
13	15	76
15	10	86
17	5	91
Total	$\Sigma f = 91$	–

Here the total frequency $N = 91$; $\dfrac{N}{2} = 45.5$.

The value of c.f. just greater than 45.5 is 61, the corresponding value of x is 11 and thus median is 11. In case of grouped frequency distribution, the class corresponding to the c.f. just greater than $\dfrac{N}{2}$ is called the median class and the value of median is obtained by the formula :

$$\text{Median} = l + \frac{h}{f}\left(\frac{N}{2} - c\right)$$

where,

l is the lower limit of the median class

f is the frequency of the median class

h is the width of the median class

c is the c.f. of the class preceding the median class

Ex. 2 : *Wages earned in Rupees per day by the labourers are given by the table :*

Wages in ₹	*10 – 20*	*20 – 30*	*30 – 40*	*40 – 50*	*50 – 60*
No. of labourers	*5*	*8*	*13*	*10*	*8*

Find the median of the distribution.

Sol. :

Wages in ₹ C.I.	No. of labourers f	(c.f.)
10 – 20	5	5
20 – 30	8	13
30 – 40	13	26
40 – 50	10	36
50 – 60	8	44
Total	**Σf = N = 44**	–

Here $\dfrac{N}{2} = \dfrac{44}{2} = 22$

Cumulative frequency (c.f.) just greater than 22 is 26 and the corresponding class is $30 – 40$.

Using formula to calculate median,

$l = 30,\ f = 13,\ h = 10,\ \dfrac{N}{2} = 22,\ c = 13$

$$\text{Median} = 30 + \frac{10}{13}\,(22 - 13)$$

$$= 30 + \frac{10}{13}\,(9) = 30 + \frac{90}{13} = 36.923$$

7.3.5 Mode

It is the value of the variate which occurs most frequently in a set of observations, or is the value of variate corresponding to maximum frequency.

In case of grouped frequency distribution, Mode is given by the formula :

$$\text{Mode} = l + \frac{h\,(f_1 - f_0)}{(f_1 - f_0) - (f_2 - f_1)}$$

$$= l + \frac{h\,(f_1 - f_0)}{2\,f_1 - f_0 - f_2}$$

Here,

l is the lower limit of the modal class

h is the width of the modal class

f_1 is the frequency of the modal class

f_0 is the frequency of the class preceding to the modal class

f_2 is the frequency of the class succeeding to the modal class.

ILLUSTRATION

Ex. 9 : *Find the Mode for the following distribution :*

C.I.	0 – 10	10 – 20	20 – 30	30 – 40	40 – 50	50 – 60	60 – 70
f	4	7	8	12	25	18	10

Sol. : Here C.I. 40 – 50 corresponding to which f = 25 is maximum, is the modal class.

$l = 40,\ h = 10,\ f_1 = 25,\ f_0 = 12,\ f_2 = 18$

$$\text{Mode} = 40 + \frac{10\,(25 - 12)}{(2 \times 25 - 12 - 18)}$$

$$= 40 + \frac{130}{20} = 40 + 6.5 = 46.5$$

So far we have considered various ways in which average can be calculated. It is clear that no single average is suitable for all types of data. Arithmetic mean, Geometric mean and Harmonic mean are rigidly defined and are based on all the observations, they are suitable for further mathematical treatment. They are not much affected by fluctuations of sampling. In fact among all the averages, Arithmetic mean is least affected by fluctuations. Geometric mean becomes zero if any one of the observations is zero. Geometric and Harmonic means are not easy to understand and are difficult to compute. They give greater importance to small items and are useful when small items have to be given a very high weightage. Median and Mode are not amenable to algebraic treatment. Their main advantage is that they are not affected by extreme values, but compared to Arithmetic mean they are affected much by fluctuations of sampling. All the averages have merits and demerits, but Arithmetic mean because of its simplicity and its stability is much more familiar to a lyman. It has wide applications in statistical theory and is considered as best among all the averages.

7.4 DISPERSION

After calculation of the average using any of the five methods discussed in previous section, question arises whether the average calculated gives correct information about the central tendency of the data, the purpose for which it is calculated. Main point to be discussed is whether the average is true representative of the data or not. As an illustration, consider the two sets of observations :

(i)   5, 10, 15, 20, 25.

(ii)   13, 14, 15, 16, 17.

The Arithmetic mean of both these sets is 15. It is obvious that 15 is better average for second than the first, because the observations in the second set are much closer to the value 15 as compared to the first set. In the second set, the values of the variate are much less scattered or dispersed from the mean as compared to the first. There are two widely accepted ways of measuring the degree of scatteredness from the mean. These are :

(i)   Mean deviation

(ii)   Standard deviation.

These are the measures of dispersion, which decide whether the average truely represents the given data or not. Besides these two standard measures, there are other measures such as Range and Quartile deviation or semi-interquartile range. But these are not as much of consequence. We shall now discuss about the two measures of dispersion mentioned earlier.

(i) Mean Deviation :   For a frequency distribution

x	x_1	x_2	....	x_n
f	f_1	f_2	....	f_n

mean deviation from the average A (usually Arithmetic mean or at most median or mode) is given by,

$$\text{Mean deviation} = \frac{1}{N} \Sigma f \, |x - A|$$

where, $N = \Sigma f$ is the total frequency, $|x - A|$ represents the modulus or the absolute value of the deviation $(x - A)$ ignoring the $-$ ve sign. It can be broadly stated that when deviation is a small number, the average is good.

ILLUSTRATION

Ex. 1 : *Calculate Arithmetic mean and Mean deviation of the following frequency distribution :*

x	*1*	*2*	*3*	*4*	*5*	*6*
f	*3*	*4*	*8*	*6*	*4*	*2*

Sol. : Preparing the table :

x	f	x × f	x – A	|x – A|	f × |x – A|
1	3	3	– 2.37	2.37	7.11
2	4	8	– 1.37	1.37	5.48
3	8	24	– 0.37	0.37	2.96
4	6	24	0.63	0.63	3.78
5	4	20	1.63	1.63	6.52
6	2	12	2.63	2.63	5.26
Total	**Σf = 27**	**Σfx = 91**	–	–	**Σf × |x – A| = 31.11**

$$\text{A.M.} = A = \frac{\sum fx}{\sum f} = \frac{91}{27} = 3.37 \text{ (approximately)}$$

$$\text{Mean deviation} = \frac{\sum f \times |x - A|}{\sum f} = \frac{31.11}{27} = 1.152 \text{ (approximately).}$$

(ii) Standard Deviation : *It is defined as the positive square root of the arithmetic mean of the squares of the deviations of the given values from their arithmetic mean.* It is denoted by the symbol σ.

For a frequency distribution (x, f),

$$\sigma = \sqrt{\frac{1}{N} \sum f \left(x - \bar{x}\right)^2}$$

where, $\bar{x}$ is A.M. of the distribution and $N = \sum f$.

The square of the standard deviation is called variance, denoted by V.

Thus,　　　　$$V = \sigma^2 = \frac{1}{N} \sum f \cdot \left(x - \bar{x}\right)^2$$

The step of squaring the deviations $\left(x - \bar{x}\right)$ overcomes the drawback of ignoring the signs in Mean deviation. Standard deviation is also suitable for further mathematical treatment. Moreover among all the measures of dispersion, standard deviation is affected by least fluctuations of sampling, hence it is considered as most reliable measure of dispersion.

Root mean square deviation is given by

$$S = \sqrt{\frac{1}{N} \sum f \ (x - A)^2}$$

where, A is any arbitrary number.

S^2 is called Mean square deviation. When $A = \bar{x}$, the Arithmetic mean, Root mean square deviation becomes equal to the standard deviation.

(iii) Relation Between σ and S : By definition, we have

$$S^2 = \frac{1}{N} \Sigma f (x - A)^2$$

$$= \frac{1}{N} \Sigma f \left(x - \bar{x} + \bar{x} - A\right)^2$$

$$= \frac{1}{N} \Sigma f \left[\left(x - \bar{x}\right)^2 + 2 \left(x - \bar{x}\right) \left(\bar{x} - A\right) + \left(\bar{x} - A\right)^2\right]$$

$$= \frac{1}{N} \Sigma f \left(x - \bar{x}\right)^2 + 2 \left(\bar{x} - A\right) \frac{1}{N} \Sigma f \left(x - \bar{x}\right) + \left(\bar{x} - A\right)^2 \frac{\Sigma f}{N}$$

Note that $\left(\bar{x} - A\right)$ being constant, is taken outside the summation.

Now since $\frac{1}{N} \Sigma f \left(x - \bar{x}\right) = \frac{1}{N} \Sigma fx - \bar{x} . \frac{1}{N} \Sigma f = \bar{x} - \bar{x} = 0$

$$\therefore \qquad S^2 = \frac{1}{N} \Sigma f \left(x - \bar{x}\right)^2 + \left(\bar{x} - A\right)^2, \quad \text{as } \Sigma f = N$$

Thus, $\qquad S^2 = \sigma^2 + d^2, \ d = \bar{x} - A$

If $\bar{x} = A$, thus S^2 would be least as $d = 0$.

Thus Mean square deviation (S^2) and consequently Root mean square (S) deviation are least when deviations are taken from $A = \bar{x}$.

(iv) Method of Calculating σ :

$$\sigma^2 = \frac{1}{N} \Sigma f \left(x - \bar{x}\right)^2$$

$$= \frac{1}{N} \Sigma f \left(x^2 - 2x\bar{x} + \bar{x}^2\right)$$

$$= \frac{1}{N} \Sigma f x^2 - \frac{2\bar{x}}{N} \Sigma fx + \bar{x}^2 . \frac{\Sigma f}{N}$$

$$= \frac{1}{N} \Sigma f x^2 - 2\bar{x}^2 + \bar{x}^2 \left[\frac{\Sigma fx}{N} = \bar{x}, \ \frac{\Sigma f}{N} = 1\right]$$

$$= \frac{1}{N} \Sigma f x^2 - \bar{x}^2$$

$$= \frac{1}{N} \Sigma f x^2 - \left(\frac{1}{N} \Sigma f x\right)^2$$

Usually, product terms fx and fx^2 are large, hence to reduce the volume of calculations, we proceed as follows :

$$\sigma^2 = \frac{1}{N} \Sigma f \left(x - \bar{x}\right)^2$$

$$= \frac{1}{N} \Sigma f \left(x - A + A - \bar{x}\right)^2, \qquad \text{(where A is arbitrary number)}$$

$$= \frac{1}{N} \Sigma f \left[(x - A)^2 + 2(x - A)\left(A - \bar{x}\right) + \left(A - \bar{x}\right)^2\right]$$

$$= \frac{1}{N} \Sigma f (x - A)^2 + \frac{2}{N} \Sigma \left(A - \bar{x}\right) \Sigma f (x - A) + \left(A - \bar{x}\right)^2 \frac{\Sigma f}{N}$$

Let $d = x - A$ then using

$$\bar{x} = A + \frac{1}{N} \Sigma fd$$

$$\sigma^2 = \frac{1}{N} \Sigma fd^2 + \frac{2}{N} \left[A - A - \frac{1}{N} \Sigma fd\right] \Sigma fd + \left[A - A - \frac{1}{N} \Sigma fd\right]^2 \cdot 1$$

$$= \frac{1}{N} \Sigma fd^2 - \frac{2}{N^2} \left(\Sigma fd\right)^2 + \frac{1}{N^2} \left(\Sigma fd\right)^2$$

$$= \frac{1}{N} \Sigma fd^2 - \frac{1}{N^2} \left(\Sigma fd\right)^2$$

$$= \frac{1}{N} \Sigma fd^2 - \left(\frac{\Sigma fd}{N}\right)^2$$

$$\text{Or} \qquad \sigma = \sqrt{\frac{1}{N} \Sigma f d^2 - \left(\frac{\Sigma fd}{N}\right)^2} \qquad \qquad \dots \text{(A)}$$

Terms fd, fd^2 are numerically smaller as compared to fx, fx^2 and use of formula (A) reduces the calculations considerably in obtaining σ.

To reduce the calculations further, and in dealing with data presented in grouped frequency distribution form, we put $u = \dfrac{x - A}{h}$, where h is generally taken as width of class interval

Thus $\qquad\qquad u = \dfrac{d}{h}$ or $d = hu$ putting $d = hu$ in formula (A)

$$\sigma = \sqrt{\frac{1}{N} \Sigma f h^2 u^2 - \left(\frac{\Sigma f hu}{N}\right)^2}$$

$$= h \sqrt{\frac{1}{N} \Sigma f u^2 - \left(\frac{\Sigma f u}{N}\right)^2} \qquad\qquad \dots \text{(B)}$$

Formula (B) is quite useful for data presented in grouped frequency distribution form.

ILLUSTRATION

Ex. 1 : *Calculate standard deviation for the following frequency distribution. Decide whether A.M. is good average.*

Wages in Rupees earned per day	0 – 10	10 – 20	20 – 30	30 – 40	40 – 50	50 – 60
No. of labourers	5	9	15	12	10	3

Sol. : Preparing the table for the purpose of calculations.

Wages earned C.I.	Mid-value x	Frequency f	$u = \dfrac{x - 25}{10}$	fu	fu^2
0 – 10	5	5	– 2	– 10	20
10 – 20	15	9	– 1	– 9	9
20 – 30	25	15	0	0	0
30 – 40	35	12	1	12	12
40 – 50	45	10	2	20	40
50 – 60	55	3	3	9	27
Total	–	$\Sigma f = 54$	–	$\Sigma fu = 22$	$\Sigma fu^2 = 108$

Using formula (B),

$$\sigma = 10 \sqrt{\frac{1}{54} \times 108 - \left(\frac{22}{54}\right)^2}$$

$$= 10 \sqrt{2 - 0.166} = 13.54 \text{ approximately}$$

In this problem,

$$\text{A.M.} = 25 + h \frac{\Sigma fu}{N} = 25 + 10 \,(0.4074) = 29.074$$

$\sigma = 13.54$ is quite a large value and Arithmetic mean 29.074 is not a good average.

Ex. 2 : *Prove that for any discrete distribution standard deviation, σ is greater than or equal to Mean deviation from the mean.*

$$\sigma^2 = \frac{1}{N} \Sigma f \left(x - \bar{x}\right)^2, \quad M.D. = \frac{1}{N} \Sigma f \left|x - \bar{x}\right|$$

Sol. : Required result implies

$$\frac{1}{N} \Sigma f \left(x - \bar{x}\right)^2 \geq \left(\frac{1}{N} f \left|x - \bar{x}\right|\right)^2$$

Putting

$$\left|x - \bar{x}\right| = z$$

which means

$$\left(x - \bar{x}\right)^2 = z^2$$

We have to prove that $\dfrac{1}{N} \Sigma f z^2 \geq \left(\dfrac{1}{N} \Sigma f z\right)^2$

i.e. $\dfrac{1}{N} \Sigma f z^2 - \left(\dfrac{1}{N} \Sigma f z\right)^2 \geq 0$

i.e. $\dfrac{1}{N} \Sigma f \left(z - \bar{z}\right)^2 \geq 0$　　　　　　[Refer article 7.4 (i)]

which is always true.

Hence the required results.

Ex. 3 : *Two sets containing n_1 and n_2 items have means m_1 and m_2 and standard deviations σ_1 and σ_2 respectively. Show that combined group has variance given by :*

$$\sigma^2 = \frac{n_1\,\sigma_1^2 + n_2\,\sigma_2^2}{n_1 + n_2} + \frac{n_1\,n_2}{(n_1 + n_2)}\,(m_1 - m_2)^2$$

Sol. : Let the variates in two series be denoted by x and y respectively. The first series contains n_1 values of variate x and the second series contains n_2 values of variate y.

By definition,

$$m_1 = \frac{\Sigma x}{n_1}, \quad m_2 = \frac{\Sigma y}{n_2}$$

$$\sigma_1^2 = \frac{1}{n_1} \Sigma (x - m_1)^2, \quad \sigma_2^2 = \frac{1}{n_2} \Sigma (y - m_2)^2$$

By formula (A) of section 7.3.

The A.M. $\bar{z}$ of combined series is given by,

$$\bar{z} = \frac{n_1\,m_1 + n_2\,m_2}{n_1 + n_2}$$

The variance σ^2 of combined series is given by

$$\sigma^2 = \frac{1}{n_1 + n_2} \left[\Sigma \left(x - \bar{z}\right)^2 + \Sigma \left(y - \bar{z}\right)^2\right]$$

Now, $\Sigma \left(x - \bar{z}\right)^2 = \Sigma \left(x - m_1 + m_1 - \bar{z}\right)^2$

$$= \Sigma (x - m_1)^2 + 2 (x - m_1) \left(m_1 - \bar{z}\right) + \left(m_1 - \bar{z}\right)^2$$

$$= \Sigma (x - m_1)^2 + 2 \left(m_1 - \bar{z}\right) \Sigma (x - m_1) + \Sigma \left(m_1 - \bar{z}\right)^2$$

$$\Sigma (x - m_1) = \Sigma x - \Sigma m_1$$

$$= n_1\,m_1 - n_1\,m_1 = 0$$

Let
$$d_1 = m_1 - \bar{z}$$

$$\sum \left(x - \bar{z}\right)^2 = \sum (x - m_1)^2 + n_1\, d_1^2$$

$$= n_1\, \sigma_1^2 + n_1\, d_1^2$$

Similarly, we can show that

$$\sum \left(y - \bar{z}\right)^2 = n_2\, \sigma_2^2 + n_2\, d_2^2$$

where
$$d_2 = m_2 - \bar{z}$$

Thus,
$$\sigma^2 = \frac{1}{n_1 + n_2} \left[n_1\, \sigma_1^2 + n_1\, d_1^2 + n_2\, \sigma_2^2 + n_2\, d_2^2 \right]$$

$$= \frac{1}{n_1 + n_2} \left[n_1\, \sigma_1^2 + n_1\, d_1^2 + n_2\, \sigma_2^2 + n_2\, d_2^2 \right]$$

To express it in required form :

$$d_1 = m_1 - \bar{z} = m_1 - \frac{n_1\, m_1 + n_2\, m_2}{n_1 + n_2} = \frac{n_2\, (m_1 - m_2)}{n_1 + n_2}$$

$$d_2 = m_2 - \bar{z} = m_2 - \frac{n_1\, m_1 + n_2\, m_2}{n_1 + n_2} = \frac{n_1\, (m_1 - m_2)}{n_1 + n_2}$$

$$\sigma^2 = \frac{1}{n_1 + n_2} \left[n_1\, \sigma_1^2 + n_2\, \sigma_2^2 + n_1\, d_1^2 + n_2\, d_2^2 \right]$$

$$= \frac{n_1\, \sigma_1^2 + n_2\, \sigma_2^2}{n_1 + n_2} + \frac{1}{n_1 + n_2} \left[\frac{n_1\, n_2^2\, (m_1 - m_2)^2}{(n_1 + n_2)^2} + \frac{n_2\, n_1^2\, (m_1 - m_2)^2}{(n_1 + n_2)^2} \right]$$

$$= \frac{n_1\, \sigma_1^2 + n_2\, \sigma_2^2}{n_1 + n_2} + \frac{n_1\, n_2\, (m_1 - m_2)^2}{(n_1 + n_2)^3}\, (n_2 + n_1)$$

$$= \frac{n_1\, \sigma_1^2 + n_2\, \sigma_2^2}{n_1 + n_2} + \frac{n_1\, n_2\, (m_1 - m_2)^2}{(n_1 + n_2)^2}$$

which is the required result.

Ex. 4 : *Fluctuations in the Aggregate of marks obtained by two groups of students are given below. Find out which of the two shows greater variability.*

Group A	518	519	530	530	544	542	518	550	527	527	531	550	550	529	528
Group B	825	830	830	819	814	814	844	842	842	826	832	835	835	840	840

(Dec. 2010)

Sol. : To solve this problem, we have to determine coefficient of variation $\dfrac{\sigma}{\text{A.M.}} \times 100$ in each case. First we present the data in frequency distribution form.

For Group A :

x	f	d = x − 530	d²	fd	fd²
518	2	− 12	144	− 24	288
519	1	− 11	121	− 11	121
527	2	− 3	9	− 6	18
528	1	− 2	4	− 2	4
529	1	− 1	1	− 1	1
530	2	0	0	0	0
531	1	1	1	1	1
542	1	12	144	12	144
544	1	14	196	14	196
550	3	20	400	60	1200
Total	**$\sum f = 15$**	–	–	**$\sum fd = 43$**	**1973**

$$\text{A.M.} = 530 + \frac{\sum fd}{\sum f}$$

$$= 530 + \frac{43}{15} = 532.866$$

$$\sigma = \sqrt{\frac{1}{N} \sum fd^2 - \left(\frac{\sum fd}{N}\right)^2}$$

$$= \sqrt{\frac{1973}{15} - \left(\frac{43}{15}\right)^2}$$

$$= \sqrt{131.533 - 8.218}$$

$$= 11.105$$

$$\text{Coefficient of variation} = \frac{\sigma}{\text{A.M.}} \times 100$$

$$= \frac{11.105}{532.866} \times 100 = 2.0840$$

For Group B :

x	f	d = x − 830	d²	fd	fd²
814	2	− 16	256	− 32	512
819	1	− 11	121	− 11	121
825	1	− 5	25	− 5	25
826	1	− 4	16	− 4	16
830	2	0	0	0	0
832	1	2	4	2	4
835	2	5	25	10	50
840	2	10	100	20	200
842	2	12	144	24	288
844	1	14	196	14	196
Total	$\sum f = 15$	–	–	$\sum fd = 18$	$\sum fd^2 = 1412$

$$\text{A.M.} = 830 + \frac{18}{15} = 831.2$$

$$\sigma = \sqrt{\frac{1412}{15} - \left(\frac{18}{15}\right)^2} = \sqrt{94.133 - 1.44} = 9.628$$

$$\text{Coefficient of variation} = \frac{9.628}{831.2} \times 100 = 1.158$$

Coefficient of variation of group A is greater than that of group B.

$\therefore$ Group A has greater variability, or Group B is more consistent.

***Ex. 5** : Runs scored in 10 matches of current IPL season by two batsmen A and B are tabulated as under*

Batsman A	46	34	52	78	65	81	26	46	19	47
Batsman B	59	25	81	47	73	78	42	35	42	10

Decide who is better batsman and who is more consistent.

Sol.: For Batsman A

x	d = x − 46	d²
46	0	0
34	−12	144
52	6	36
78	32	1024
65	19	361
81	35	1225
26	−20	400
46	0	0
19	−27	729
47	1	1
	$\sum d = 34$	$\sum d^2 = 3920$

$$\overline{x}_A = 46 + \frac{\Sigma d}{10} = 46 + 3.4 = 49.4$$

$$\sigma_A = \sqrt{\frac{\Sigma d^2}{N} - \left(\frac{\Sigma d}{N}\right)^2} = \sqrt{392 - 11.56} = 19.50 \quad (N = 10)$$

Coefficient of variation for A $= \dfrac{\sigma_A}{\text{A.M.}} \times 100 = \dfrac{19.50}{49.4} \times 100 = 39.47$

For Batsman B

x	d = x – 42	d²
59	17	289
25	–17	289
81	39	1521
47	5	25
73	31	961
78	36	1296
42	0	0
35	–7	49
42	0	0
10	–32	1024
	$\Sigma d = 72$	$\Sigma d^2 = 5454$

$$\overline{x}_B = 42 + \frac{\Sigma d}{10} = 42 + 7.2 = 49.2$$

$$\sigma_B = \sqrt{\frac{\Sigma d^2}{N} - \left(\frac{\Sigma d}{N}\right)^2} = \sqrt{545.4 - 51.84} - \sqrt{493.56} = 22.22$$

Coefficient of variation for B $= \dfrac{\sigma_B}{\text{A.M.}} \times 100 = \dfrac{22.22}{49.2} \times 100 = 45.16$

Conclusion : A.M. for A is slightly higher than B A.M. for B so A is slightly better and coefficient of variation for A is less than that of B.

$\therefore$ A is more consistent.

Ex. 6 *: Arithmetic mean and standard deviation of 30 items are 20 and 3 respectively out of these 30 items, item 22 and 15 are dropped. Find new A.M. and S.D.. Calculate A.M. and S.D. if item 22 is replaced by 8 and 15 is replaced by 17.*

Sol.: $\overline{x} = \dfrac{\Sigma x}{30}$, $\overline{x} = 20$ $\therefore$ $\Sigma x = 20 \times 30 = 600$

Since items 22 and 15 are dropped. Now $\Sigma x = 600 - (22 + 15)$

Now $\qquad \sum x = 563,$ and total item are 28

Now $\qquad \bar{x} = \dfrac{563}{28} = 20.107$

Again $\qquad V = \sigma^2 = \dfrac{\sum x^2}{N} - \left(\dfrac{\sum x}{N}\right)^2$ where N = No. of items = 30

$$\sigma^2 = \dfrac{\sum x^2}{30} - 400$$

$\therefore \qquad 9 = \dfrac{\sum x^2}{30} - 400$

$\therefore \qquad \sum x^2 = 30 \times 9 + 30 \times 400 = 12270.$

Items 22 and 15 are dropped.

Now $\qquad \sum x^2 = 12270 - (22)^2 - (15)^2 = 12270 - 709 = 11561$

Now $\qquad$ S.D. $= \sqrt{\dfrac{11561}{28} - (20.107)^2} = 2.933$

In the second case if items are replaced

Now $\qquad \sum x = 600 - (22 - 8) + (17 - 15) = 600 - 14 + 2 = 588 \,, \; N = 30$

$\therefore$ Now $\qquad \bar{x} = \dfrac{588}{30} = 19.6$

Now $\qquad \sum x^2 = 12270 - (14)^2 + 4 = 12078$

Now $\qquad$ S.D. $= \sqrt{\dfrac{12078}{30} - (19.6)^2} = 4.294$

7.5   MOMENTS, SKEWNESS AND KURTOSIS

7.5.1 Moments

The rth moment about the mean of a distribution is denoted by μ_r and is given by,

$$\mu_r = \frac{1}{N} \sum f \left(x - \bar{x}\right)^r, \quad N = \sum f$$

where $\bar{x}$ is A.M. of the distribution. Putting $r = 0, 1, 2$ etc., we get

$$\mu_0 = \frac{1}{N} \sum f = 1,$$

$\mu_1 = \dfrac{1}{N} \sum f \left(x - \bar{x}\right) = \bar{x} - \bar{x} = 0$ gives first moment of distribution about the mean.

$\mu_2 = \dfrac{1}{N} \sum f \left(x - \bar{x}\right)^2 = \sigma^2 = V =$ variance gives second moment of the distribution about the mean.

$\mu_3 = \dfrac{1}{N} \Sigma f \left(x - \bar{x}\right)^3$ gives 3rd moment of the distribution about the mean and so on.

Since actual evaluation of rth moment μ_r about the mean $\bar{x}$ is numerically complicated, we find r^{th} moments $\mu_r^{'}$ of the distribution about convenient mean A with much less calculation (Refer Art. 7.4).

The rth moment about any number A (assumed or convenient arbitrary mean) is denoted by μ'_r and is given by

$$\mu'_r = \dfrac{1}{N} \Sigma f (x - A)^r, \text{ it can be seen on putting } r = 0, 1, 2, \ldots \text{etc. that}$$

$$\mu'_0 = 1, \quad \mu'_1 = \dfrac{1}{N} \Sigma f (x - A) = \dfrac{1}{N} \Sigma f x - \dfrac{\Sigma f}{N} A$$

$$\mu'_1 = \bar{x} - A$$

$$\mu'_2 = \dfrac{1}{N} \Sigma f (x - A)^2 = S^2 \text{ the mean square deviation}$$

$$\mu'_3 = \dfrac{1}{N} \Sigma f (x - A)^3 \text{ etc.}$$

Relation Between μ_r and μ'_r :

We know by definition of μ_r

$$\mu_r = \dfrac{1}{N} \Sigma f \left(x - \bar{x}\right)^r = \dfrac{1}{N} \Sigma f \left(x - A + A - \bar{x}\right)^r$$

Let $d = x - A$ and hence

$$\therefore \quad \bar{d} = \dfrac{\Sigma fd}{N} = \dfrac{\Sigma fx}{N} - \dfrac{A \cdot \Sigma f}{N} \quad \text{or} \quad \bar{d} = \bar{x} - A = \mu'_1$$

Thus,

$$\mu_r = \dfrac{1}{N} \Sigma f \left(d - \bar{d}\right)^r$$

On expanding $\left(d - \bar{d}\right)^r$ binomially, we obtain

$$\mu_r = \dfrac{1}{N} \Sigma f \left(d^r - {}^rC_1 \, d^{r-1} \, \bar{d} + {}^rC_2 \, d^{r-2} \, \bar{d}^2 \ldots + (-1)^r \, \bar{d}^r \right)$$

where $\quad {}^rC_1 = r, {}^rC_2 = \dfrac{r(r-1)}{2!}, \quad {}^rC_3 = \dfrac{r(r-1)(r-2)}{3!}$ etc.

$$\therefore \quad \mu_r = \dfrac{1}{N} \Sigma fd^r - {}^rC_1 \dfrac{1}{N} \Sigma fd^{r-1} \, \bar{d} + {}^rC_2 \dfrac{1}{N} \Sigma fd^{r-2} \, \bar{d}^2$$

$$- {}^rC_3 \dfrac{1}{N} \Sigma fd^{r-3} \, \bar{d}^3 \ldots (-1)^r \dfrac{1}{N} \Sigma f \bar{d}^r$$

Using, $\frac{1}{N} \Sigma f \, d^r = \mu'_r$　and　$\bar{d} = \mu'_1$, relation between μ_r and μ'_r is

$\therefore$

$$\boxed{\mu_r = \mu'_r - {}^rC_1 \; \mu'_{r-1} \; \mu'_1 + {}^rC_2 \; \mu'_{r-2} \; {\mu'_1}^2 + \dots + (-1)^r \; (\mu'_1)^r}$$

We have already seen that $\mu_0 = 1$, $\mu_1 = 0$.

Putting $r = 2, 3, 4$ etc., we get

$$\begin{aligned}
\mu_2 &= \mu'_2 - {}^2C_1 \, \mu'_1 \, \mu'_1 + {}^2C_2 \, \mu'_0 \, \mu'_1 \\
&= \mu'_2 - 2 {\mu'_1}^2 + {\mu'_1}^2 = \mu'_2 - {\mu'_1}^2 && \dots \text{(A)} \\
\mu_3 &= \mu'_3 - {}^2C_1 \, \mu'_2 \, \mu'_1 + {}^3C_2 \, \mu'_1 \, {\mu'_1}^2 - {\mu'_1}^3 \\
&= \mu'_3 - {}^3C_1 \, \mu'_2 + {}^3C_2 \, \mu'_1 \, {\mu'_1}^2 - {\mu'_1}^3 \\
\mu_3 &= \mu'_3 - 3 \, \mu'_2 \, \mu'_1 + 2 \, {\mu'_1}^3 && \dots \text{(B)} \\
\mu_4 &= \mu'_4 - {}^4C_1 \mu'_3 \, \mu'_1 + {}^4C_2 \, \mu'_2 \, {\mu'_1}^2 - {}^4C_2 \, \mu'_1 \, {\mu'_1}^3 + {}^4C_4 \, {\mu'_1}^4 \\
&= \mu'_4 - 4 \mu'_3 \, \mu'_1 + 6 \mu'_2 \, {\mu'_1}^2 - 4 {\mu'_1}^4 + {\mu'_1}^4 \\
\mu_4 &= \mu'_4 - 4 \mu'_3 \, \mu'_1 + 6 \mu'_2 \, {\mu'_1}^2 - 3 {\mu'_1}^4 && \dots \text{(C)}
\end{aligned}$$

The moments of higher order μ_5, μ_6 etc. can be similarly expressed.

To reduce the calculation of μ'_r further while dealing with data presented in group frequency distribution, we use the following procedure.

Put $u = \dfrac{x - A}{h}$ where, h is taken generally width of class interval, then the expressions

for the moments μ_r about any point A (arbitrary assumed convenient mean) are given by

$$\begin{aligned}
\mu'_r &= \frac{1}{N} \Sigma f \, (x - A)^r, && N = \Sigma f \\
&= \frac{1}{N} \Sigma f \, (hu)^r \\
&= h^r \frac{1}{N} \Sigma f \, u^r, && r = 1, 2, 3, \dots \quad \dots \text{(D)}
\end{aligned}$$

We know that first moment about mean $\bar{x}$ is $\mu_1 = 0$. The second, third and fourth moments about the mean $\bar{x}$ are obtained using relations (A), (B) and (C).

Remark :

(i)　Change of Origin Property : The central moments are invariant to the change of origin. If $u = x - A$ then $(\mu_r \text{ of } u) = (\mu_r \text{ of } x)$.

(ii)　Change of Origin and Scale : If $u = \dfrac{x - A}{h}$ then $(\mu_r \text{ or } u) = \dfrac{1}{h^r} (\mu_r \text{ of } x)$.

Sheppard's Correction for Moments : In case of grouped frequency distribution, we take mid-values of class intervals to represent the class interval. This involves some error in calculation of moments. W.F. Sheppard suggested some corrective formulae :

$$\mu_2 \text{ (corrected)} = \mu_2 - \frac{1}{12} h^2$$

$$\mu_3 = \mu_3$$

$$\mu_4 \text{ (corrected)} = \mu_4 - \frac{1}{2} h^2 \mu_1 + \frac{7}{240} h^4$$

where, h is the width of class interval.

7.5.2 Skewness

Skewness signifies departure from symmetry. We study skewness to have an idea about the shape of the curve which we draw with the given data.

If the frequency curve stretches to the right as in Fig. 7.3 (a) i.e. the mean is to the right of the mode then the distribution is right skewed or is said to have positive skewness. If the curve stretches to left or mode is to the right of the mean then the distribution is said to have negative skewness.

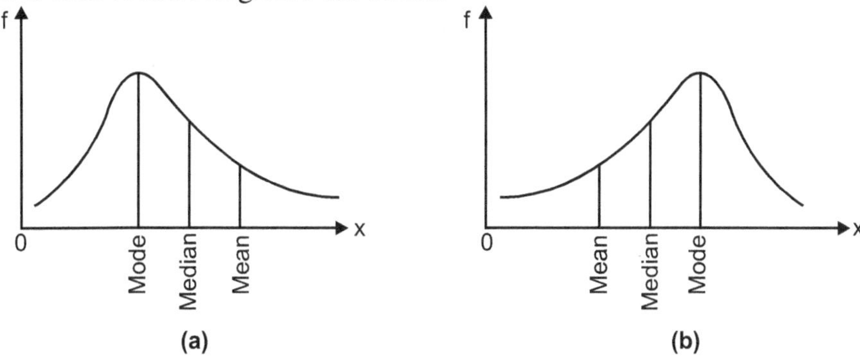

Fig. 7.3

The different measures of skewness are :

(i)   Skewness $= \dfrac{3 \,(\text{Mean} - \text{Median})}{\text{Standard deviation}}$

(ii)   Coefficient of skewness, $\beta_1 = \dfrac{\mu_3^2}{\mu_2^3}$

The distribution is positively skewed if skewness or coefficient of skewness β_1 is positive. If coefficient of skewness is negative the distribution is negatively skewed. It is also clear from (i). Now to decide the sign of β_1, We introduce the parameter $\gamma_1 = \pm \sqrt{\beta_1}$.

Now $\beta_1 = \dfrac{\mu_3^2}{\mu_2^3}$ where both numerator and denominator are positive. To decide the sign of γ_1, we associate with sign of μ_3. It μ_3 is negative, we take γ_1 as negative and μ_3 is positive, we take γ_1 as positive. In short distribution is positively skewed if μ_3 is positive and it is negatively skewed if μ_3 is negative.

7.5.3 Kurtosis

To get complete idea of the distribution in addition to the knowledge of mean, dispersion and skewness, we should have an idea of the flatness or peakedness of the curve. It is measured by the coefficient β_2 given by,

$$\beta_2 = \frac{\mu_4}{\mu_2^2}$$

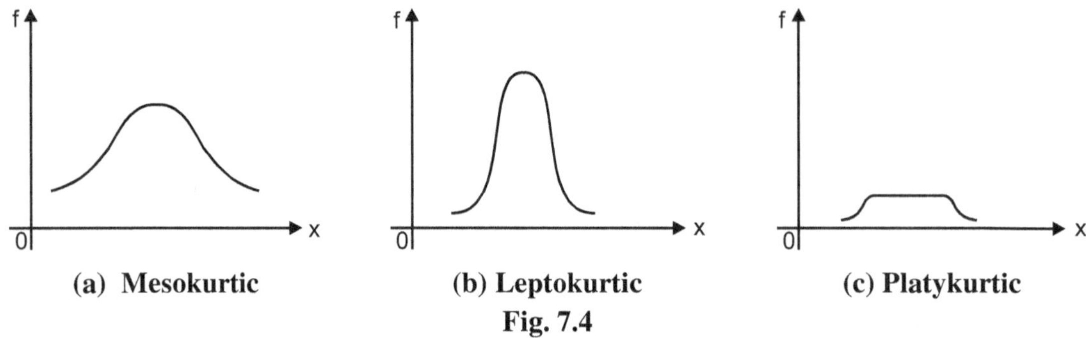

(a) **Mesokurtic**   (b) **Leptokurtic**   (c) **Platykurtic**

Fig. 7.4

The curve of Fig. 7.4 (a) which is neither flat nor peaked is called the normal curve or Mesokurtic curve. $\gamma_2 = \beta_2 - 3$ gives the excess of kurtosis. For a normal distribution, $\beta_2 = 3$ and the excess is zero. The curve of Fig. 7.4 (c) which is flatter than the normal curve is called Platykurtic and that of Fig. 7.4 (b) which is more peaked is called Leptokurtic. For Platykurtic curves $\beta_2 < 3$, for Leptokurtic curves $\beta_2 > 3$.

Ex. 7 : *Calculate the first four moments about the mean of the given distribution. Also find β_1 and β_2.*   **(Dec. 2010, 2011, May 2015)**

x	2.0	2.5	3.0	3.5	4.0	4.5	5.0
f	4	36	60	90	70	40	10

Sol. : Taking A = 3.5, h = 0.5 and $u = \dfrac{x - 3.5}{0.5}$

We prepare the table for calculating μ'_1, μ'_2, μ'_3 and μ'_4.

x	f	$u = \dfrac{x - 3.5}{0.5}$	fu	fu²	fu³	fu⁴
2.0	4	-3	-12	36	-108	342
2.5	36	-2	-72	144	-288	576
3.0	60	-1	-60	60	-60	60
3.5	90	0	0	0	0	0
4.0	70	1	70	70	70	70
4.5	40	2	80	160	320	640
5.0	10	3	30	90	270	810
Total	$\Sigma f = 310$		$\Sigma fu = 36$	$\Sigma fu^2 = 560$	$\Sigma fu^3 = 204$	$\Sigma fu^4 = 2480$

For moments about arbitrary mean A = 3.5, we use formula (D).

$$\mu'_r = h^r\, \frac{\Sigma\, fu^r}{\Sigma f}$$

$$\mu'_1 = h\, \frac{\Sigma\, fu}{\Sigma f} = (0.5)\, \frac{36}{310} = 0.058064$$

$$\mu'_2 = h^2 \, \frac{\Sigma \, fu^2}{\Sigma \, f} = (0.5)^2 \, \frac{560}{310} = 0.451612$$

$$\mu'_3 = h^3 \, \frac{\Sigma \, fu^3}{\Sigma \, f} = (0.5)^3 \, \frac{204}{310} = 0.082259$$

$$\mu'_4 = h^4 \, \frac{\Sigma \, fu^4}{\Sigma \, f} = (0.5)^4 \, \frac{2480}{310} = 0.5$$

Using relations A, B, C of section 7.5 central moments are

$$\mu_1 = 0$$

$$\mu_2 = \mu'_2 - \mu'^2_1 = (0.451612) - (0.058064)^2 = 0.44824$$

$$\mu_3 = \mu'_3 - 3\,\mu'_2\,\mu'_1 + 2\,\mu'^3_1$$

$$= (0.082259) - 3\,(0.451612)\,(0.058064) + 2\,(0.058064)^3$$

$$= 0.082259 - 0.078668 + 0.0003916$$

$$= 3.9826 \times 10^{-3} = 0.0039826$$

$$\mu_4 = \mu'_4 - 4\,\mu'_3\,\mu'_1 + 6\,\mu'_2\,(\mu'_1)^2 - 3\,(\mu'_1)^4$$

$$= 0.5 - 0.01911 + 0.009136 - 0.0000341$$

$$= 0.48999$$

$$\beta_1 = \frac{\mu_3^2}{\mu_2^3} = \frac{0.0000159}{0.0900599} = 1.76549$$

$$\beta_2 = \frac{\mu_4}{\mu_2^2} = \frac{0.48999}{0.20092} = 2.43874$$

Ex. 8 : *Compute the first four central moments for the following frequencies :*

No. of jobs completed	0-10	10-20	20-30	30-40	40-50
No. of workers	6	26	47	15	6

Sol. :

Class	Mid-Pts. (x)	Freq. (f)	$u = \dfrac{x-25}{10}$	fu	fu^2	fu^3	fu^4
0-10	5	6	− 2	− 12	24	− 48	96
10-20	15	26	− 1	− 26	26	− 26	26
20-30	25	47	0	0	0	0	0
30-40	35	15	1	15	15	15	15
40-50	45	6	2	12	24	48	96
Total	−	**100**	−	**− 11**	**89**	**− 11**	**233**

For moments about arbitrary mean A = 25 we use the formula (D)

$$\mu'_r = h^r \frac{\sum fu^r}{\sum f}$$

$$\therefore \quad \mu'_1 = h \frac{\sum fu}{\sum f} = 10\left(\frac{-11}{100}\right) = 10\,(-0.11) = -1.1$$

$$\mu'_2 = h^2 \frac{\sum fu^2}{\sum f} = (10)^2 \left(\frac{89}{100}\right) = 100\,(0.89) = 89$$

$$\mu'_3 = h^3 \frac{\sum fu^3}{\sum f} = (10)^3 \left(\frac{-11}{100}\right) = (1000)\,(-0.11) = -110$$

$$\mu'_4 = h^4 \frac{\sum fu^4}{\sum f} = (10)^4 \left(\frac{233}{100}\right) = (10)^4\,(2.33) = 23300$$

Using relations A, B, C of section 7.5 central moments are

$$\mu_1 = 0$$

$$\begin{aligned}
\mu_2 &= \mu'_2 - \mu'^{\,2}_1 \\
&= 89 - (-1.1)^2 \\
&= 89 - (1.21) = 87.79
\end{aligned}$$

$$\begin{aligned}
\mu_3 &= \mu'_3 - 3\,\mu'_2\,\mu'_1 + 2\,\mu'^{\,3}_1 \\
&= -110 - 3\,(89)\,(-1.1) + 2\,(-1.1)^3 \\
&= -110 + 293.7 + 2\,(-1.331) \\
&= -110 + 293.7 - 2.662 \\
&= 181.038
\end{aligned}$$

$$\begin{aligned}
\mu_4 &= \mu'_4 - 4\,\mu'_3\,\mu'_1 + 6\,\mu'_2\,(\mu'_1)^2 - 3\,(\mu'_1)^4 \\
&= 23300 - 4\,(-110)\,(-1.1) + 6\,(89)\,(-1.1)^2 - 3\,(-1.1)^4 \\
&= 23300 - 484 + 646.14 - 4.3923 \\
&= 23457.7477
\end{aligned}$$

Ex. 9 : *If $\sum f = 27$, $\sum fx = 91$, $\sum fx^2 = 359$, $\sum fx^3 = 1567$, $\sum fx^4 = 7343$. Find first four moments about origin. Find A.M., S.D., μ_3 and μ_4. Find coefficients of skewness and kurtosis. Comment on skewness and kurtosis.* **(May 2017)**

Sol.:

$$\mu'_1 = \frac{\sum fx}{\sum f} = \frac{91}{27} = 3.37$$

$$\mu'_2 = \frac{\sum fx^2}{\sum f} = \frac{359}{27} = 13.297$$

$$\mu'_3 = \frac{\sum fx^3}{\sum f} = \frac{1567}{27} = 58.04$$

$$\mu'_4 = \frac{\sum fx^4}{\sum f} = \frac{7343}{27} = 271.963$$

$$\text{A.M.} = \mu'_1 = 3.37$$

$$\mu_2 = \mu'_2 - \mu'^2_1 = 13.297 - (3.37)^2 = 1.94$$

$$\text{S.D.} = \sqrt{\mu_2} = 1.3928$$

$$\mu_3 = \mu'_3 - 3\,\mu'_1\,\mu'_2 + 2\,(\mu'_1)^3$$

$$= 58.04 - 3 \times 3.37 \times 13.297 + 2 \times (3.37)^3$$

$$= 58.04 - 134.43267 + 38.2727 \times 2$$

$$= 58.04 - 134.43267 + 76.5455 = 0.15283$$

$$\mu_4 = \mu'_4 - 4\,\mu'_1\,\mu'_2 + 6(\mu'_1)^2\,\mu'_2 - 3\,\mu'^4_1$$

$$= 271.963 - 4 \times 58.04 \times 3.37 + 6(13.37)^2 \times 13.297 - 3 \times (3.37)^4$$

$$= 8.7311$$

$$\beta_1 = \text{coefficient of skewness} = \frac{\mu_3^2}{\mu_2^3} = 0.003197$$

Skewness is very small and curve is symmetrical

$$\beta_2 = \text{coefficient of kurtosis} = \frac{\mu_4}{\mu_2^2} = 2.3198$$

$$\gamma_2 = \beta_2 - 3 \text{ given excess of kurtosis, which is small}$$

Since $\beta_2 < 3$, it is playtikurtic type curve.

Ex. 10 : *Calculate the first four moments about the mean of the given distribution. Find β_1, β_2 and comment on skewness and kurtosis.*

x	5	7	13	24	29	36	40	45	50
f	4	6	17	25	18	12	9	3	2

Sol.: Taking A = 24, d = x – 24

x	f	d = x – 24	fd	fd^2	fd^3	fd^4
5	4	–19	–76	1444	–27436	521284

7	6	−17	−102	1734	−29478	501126
13	17	−11	−187	2057	−22627	248897
24	25	0	0	0	0	0
29	18	5	90	450	2250	11250
36	12	12	144	1728	20736	248832
40	9	16	144	2304	36864	589924
45	3	21	63	1323	27783	583443
50	2	26	52	1352	35152	913952
	$\sum f = 96$		$\sum fd = 128$	$\sum fd^2 =$ 12392	$\sum fd^3 =$ 43244	$\sum fd^4 =$ 3618608

$$\mu_1' = \frac{\sum fd}{\sum f} = 1.33, \quad \mu_2' = \frac{\sum fd^2}{\sum f} = 129.08, \quad \mu_3' = \frac{\sum fd^3}{\sum f} = 450.46$$

$$\mu_4' = \frac{\sum fd^4}{\sum f} = 37693.83$$

$$\mu_1 = 0, \qquad \mu_2 = \mu_2' - \mu_1'^2 = 127.31$$

$$\mu_3 = \mu_3' - 3\mu_2' \mu_1' + 2\mu_1'^3 = -59.86$$

$$\mu_4 = \mu_4' - 4\mu_3' \mu_1' + 6 \mu_2' \mu_1'^2 - 3\mu_1'^4$$

$$= 36657.97$$

$$\beta_1 = \frac{\mu_3^2}{\mu_2^3} = 0.001736$$

$$\beta_2 = \frac{\mu_4}{\mu_2^2} = 2.262$$

β_1 is very small, so the curve is symmetrical, skewness is negative.

$$\beta_2 = 2.262 < 3, \text{ curve is playticurtic type.}$$

Ex. 11 : *For the following distribution, find (i) first 4 moments about the mean, (ii) β_1 and β_2, (iii) arithmetic mean, (iv) standard deviation.*   **(Dec. 2014)**

x	2	2.5	3	3.5	4	4.5	5
f	5	38	65	92	70	40	10

Sol. : Let $u = \dfrac{x - 3.5}{0.5}$, $A = 3.5$, $h = 0.5$.

x	f	u	fu	fu^2	fu^3	fu^4
2	5	-3	-15	45	-135	405
2.5	38	-2	-76	152	-304	608
3	65	-1	-65	65	-65	65
3.5	92	0	0	0	0	0
4	70	1	70	70	70	70
4.5	40	2	80	160	320	640
5	10	3	30	90	270	810
Total	**320**	–	**24**	**582**	**156**	**2598**

(i) Moment about the mean M.

When assumed mean is A $=$ 3.5 and using (D), we have

$$\mu'_1 = h\,\frac{\sum fu}{\sum f} = 0.5\left(\frac{24}{320}\right) = 0.0375$$

$$\mu'_2 = h^2\,\frac{\sum fu^2}{\sum f} = (0.5)^2\left(\frac{582}{320}\right) = 0.4546$$

$$\mu'_3 = h^3\,\frac{\sum fu^3}{\sum f} = (0.5)^3\left(\frac{156}{320}\right) = 0.0609$$

$$\mu'_4 = h^4\,\frac{\sum fu^4}{\sum f} = (0.5)^4\left(\frac{2598}{320}\right) = 0.5074$$

Using results (A), (B), (C), we have four moments about the mean M

$$\mu_1 = 0$$

$$\mu_2 = \mu'_2 - {\mu'_1}^2 = (0.4546) - (0.0375)^2, \; [d = \mu'_1] = 0.453$$

$$\mu_3 = \mu'_3 - 3\,\mu'_2\,\mu'_1 + 2\,{\mu'_1}^3$$

$$= (0.0609) - 3\,(0.4546)\,(0.0375) + 2\,(0.0375)^3$$

$$= 0.0600$$

$$\mu_4 = \mu'_4 - 4\,\mu'_3\,\mu'_1 + 6\,{\mu'_1}^2\,\mu'_2 - 3\,{\mu'_1}^4$$

$$= (0.5074) - 4\,(0.0609)\,(0.0375) + 6\,(0.0375)^2\,(0.4546)$$

$$- 3\,(0.0375)^4$$

$$= 0.502$$

(ii) By definition of β_1 and β_2, we have

$$\beta_1 = \frac{\mu_3^2}{\mu_2^3} = \frac{(0.0600)^2}{(0.453)^3} = 0.0387$$

$$\beta_2 = \frac{\mu_4}{\mu_2^2} = \frac{0.502}{(0.453)^2} = 2.4463$$

Since $\beta_2 < 3$, the distribution is platy kurtic i.e. it is flatter than the normal distribution.

(iii) Arithmetic Mean : Using result (B), we have

$$A = \frac{\Sigma\,fu}{\Sigma\,f} = \frac{24}{320} = 0.075$$

(iv) Standard Deviation :

$$\sigma^2 = h^2 \left\{ \frac{\Sigma\,fu^2}{\Sigma\,f} - \left(\frac{\Sigma\,fu}{\Sigma\,f}\right)^2 \right\}$$

$$= (0.5)^2 \left\{ \frac{582}{320} - \left(\frac{24}{320}\right)^2 \right\} = 0.453$$

$$\sigma = 0.673$$

Ex. 12 : *The first four moments about the working mean 30.2 of a distribution are 0.255, 6.222, 30.211 and 400.25. Calculate the first four moments about the mean. Also evaluate β_1, β_2 and comment upon the skewness and kurtosis of the distribution.*

(Dec. 2005, May 2012)

Sol. : Given : The first four moments about the arbitrary origin 30.2 are

$$\mu_1' = 0.255, \quad \mu_2' = 6.222, \quad \mu_3' = 30.211, \quad \mu_4' = 400.25$$

$$\therefore \qquad \mu_1' = \frac{1}{N}\Sigma\,f_i\,(x_i - 30.2) = \frac{1}{N}\,\Sigma\,f_i\,x_i - 30.2 = \bar{x} - 30.2 = 0.255$$

Or $\qquad \bar{x} = 30.455$

$$\mu_2 = \mu_2' - \mu_1'^2 = 6.222 - (0.255)^2 = 6.15698$$

$$\mu_3 = \mu_3' - 3\mu_2'\,\mu_1' + 2\,\mu_1'^3 = 30.211 - 3\,(6.222)\,(0.255) + 2\,(0.255)^3$$

$$= 30.211 - 4.75983 + 0.03316275$$

$$\mu_3 = 25.48433$$

$$\mu_4 = \mu_4' - 4\mu_3'\,\mu_1' + 6\,\mu_2'\,\mu_1'^2 - 3\,\mu_1'^4$$

$$= 440.25 - 4\,(30.211)\,(0.255) + 6\,(6.222)\,(0.255) - 3\,(0.255)^4$$

$$\mu_4 = 378.9418$$

$$\therefore \qquad \beta_1 = \frac{\mu_3^2}{\mu_2^3} = \frac{(25.48433)^2}{(6.15698)^3} = 2.78255$$

$$\beta_2 = \frac{\mu_4}{\mu_2^2} = \frac{378.9418}{(6.15698)^2}$$

$$\beta_2 = 9.99625$$

$$\therefore \quad \gamma_1 = \sqrt{\beta_1} = \sqrt{2.78255} = 1.6681$$

which indicates considerable positive skewness of the distribution.

$$\gamma_2 = \beta_2 - 3 = 9.99625 - 3 = 6.99625$$

which shows that the distribution is leptokurtic.

Ex. 13 : *The first four moments of a distribution about the value 5 are 2, 20, 40 and 50. From the given information obtain the first four central moments, mean, standard deviation and coefficient of skewness and kurtosis.* **(Dec. 2007)**

Sol. : $A = 5$, $\mu_1' = 2$, $\mu_2' = 20$, $\mu_3' = 40$ and $\mu_4' = 50$.

On the basis of given information we can calculate the various central moments, mean, standard deviation and coefficient of skewness and kurtosis.

The first moment about zero gives the value of the distribution.

$$\therefore \quad \text{Mean} = \overline{x} = A + \mu_1' = 5 + 2 = 7$$

Now we calculate central moments.

$$\mu_1 = 0$$

$$\mu_2 = \mu_2' - (\mu_1')^2 = 20 - (2)^2 = 16$$

$$\mu_3 = \mu_3' - 3\,\mu_1'\,\mu_2' + 2\,(\mu_1')^3 = 40 - 3\,(2)\,(20) + 2\,(2)^3$$
$$= 40 - 120 + 16$$
$$= -64$$

$$\mu_4 = \mu_4' - 4\,\mu_1'\,\mu_3' + 6\,(\mu_1')^2\,\mu_2' - 3\,(\mu_1')^4$$
$$= 50 - 4\,(2)\,(40) + 6\,(2)^2\,(20) - 3\,(2)^4 = 50 - 320 + 480 - 48$$
$$= 162$$

The second central moment gives the value of variance.

$$\therefore \quad \text{Variance} = \mu_2 = 16$$

$$\therefore \quad \text{Standard deviation} = \sqrt{\mu_2} = \sqrt{16} = 4$$

Coefficient of skewness is given by,

$$\beta_1 = \frac{\mu_3^2}{\mu_2^3} = \frac{(-64)^2}{(16)^3} = 1$$

Since μ_3 is negative, the distribution is negatively skewed. Coefficient of kurtosis is given by,

$$\beta_2 = \frac{\mu_4}{\mu_2^2} = \frac{162}{(16)^2} = 0.63$$

Since the value of β_2 is less than 3, hence the distribution is platykurtic.

Ex. 14 : *The first four central moments of distribution are 0, 2.5, 0.7 and 18.75. Comment on the skewness and kurtosis of the distribution.*   **(May 2009)**

Sol. : Testing of Skewness : $\mu_1 = 0$, $\mu_2 = 2.5$, $\mu_3 = 0.7$ and $\mu_4 = 18.75$

Coefficient of skewness is given by,

$$\beta_1 = \frac{\mu_3^2}{\mu_2^3} = \frac{(0.7)^2}{(2.5)^3} = 0.0314$$

Since, μ_3 is positive, the distribution is positively skewed slightly.

Testing of kurtosis : Coefficient of kurtosis is given by

$$\beta_2 = \frac{\mu_4}{\mu_2^2}$$

$$\beta_2 = \frac{\mu_4}{\mu_2^2} = \frac{18.75}{(2.5)^2} = 3$$

Since, β_2 is exactly three, the distribution is mesokurtic.

EXERCISE 7.1

1. Find the Arithmetic Mean, Median and Standard deviation for the following frequency distribution.

x	5	9	12	15	20	24	30	35	42	49
f	3	6	8	8	9	10	8	7	6	2

Ans. $\bar{x} = 22.9851$,   M = 20, $\sigma = 11.3538$

2. Following table gives the Marks obtained in a paper of statistics out of 50, by the students of two divisions :

C.I.	0 – 5	5 – 10	10 – 15	15 – 20	20 – 25	25 – 30	30 – 35	35 – 40	40 – 45	45 – 50
Div. A f	2	6	8	8	15	18	12	11	9	4
Div. B f	3	5	7	9	12	16	11	5	6	2

Find out which of the two divisions show greater variability.

Also find the common mean and standard deviation.

Ans. B has greater variability

$$\bar{x} = 26.1458$$

$$\sigma = 11.1267$$

3. Calculate the first four moments about the mean of the following distribution. Find the coefficient of Skewness and Kurtosis.

x	1	2	3	4	5	6	7	8	9	10
f	6	15	23	42	62	60	40	24	13	5

Ans. $\mu_1 = 0, \mu_2 = 3.703$

$$\mu_3 = 0.04256, \mu_4 = 37.5$$

$$\beta_1 = 0.00005572, \ \beta_2 = 2.8411$$

4. The Mean and Standard deviation of 25 items is found to be 11 and 3 respectively. It was observed that one item 9 was incorrect. Calculate the Mean and Standard deviation if :

(i) the wrong item is omitted.

(ii) it is replaced by 13. **(May 2012)**

Ans. (i) $\bar{x} = 11.08, \sigma = 3.345$

(ii) $\bar{x} = 11.16, \sigma = 2.9915$

5. Age distribution of 150 life insurance policy-holders is as follows :

Age as on nearest birthday	Number
15 – 19.5	10
20 – 24.5	20
25 – 29.5	14
30 – 34.5	30
35 – 39.5	32
40 – 44.5	14
45 – 49.5	15
50 – 54.5	10
55 – 59.5	5

Calculate mean deviation from median age.

Ans. M.D. = 8.4284

MULTIPLE CHOICE QUESTIONS (MCQ's)

Type : Measures of Central Tendencies and Dispersion :

1. If the data is presented in the forms of frequency distribution then arithmetic mean $\bar{x}$ is given by ($N = \sum f$)   (1)

   (A) $\dfrac{\sum fx}{N}$ (b) $\dfrac{1}{N}\sum f\,|x - A|$

   (C) $N \sum fx$ (D) $\dfrac{\sum fx^2}{N}$

2. For the data presented in the form of frequency distribution, mean deviation (M.D.) from the average A is given by ($N = \sum f$)   (1)

   (A) $\dfrac{\sum fx}{N}$ (B) $\sum f\,|x - A|$

   (C) $\dfrac{1}{N}\sum f\,|x - A|$ (D) $\dfrac{1}{N}\sum f\,|x - A|^2$

3. If the data is presented in the form of frequency distribution then standard deviation σ is given by ($\bar{x}$ is arithmetic mean and $N = \sum f$)   (1)

   (A) $\dfrac{1}{N}\sum f\,(x - \bar{x})^2$ (B) $\sqrt{\dfrac{1}{N}\sum f(x - \bar{x})^2}$

   (C) $\dfrac{\sum fx}{N}$ (D) $\dfrac{1}{N}\sum f\,|x - \bar{x}|$

4. If the data is presented in the form of frequency distribution then variance V is given by ($\bar{x}$ is arithmetic mean and $N = \sum f$)   (1)

   (A) $\dfrac{1}{N}\sum f\,|x - \bar{x}|$ (B) $\sqrt{\dfrac{1}{N}\sum f(x - \bar{x})^2}$

   (C) $\dfrac{\sum fx}{N}$ (D) $\dfrac{1}{N}\sum f\,(x - \bar{x})^2$

5. To compare the variability of two or more than two series, coefficient of variation (C.V.) is obtained using ($\bar{x}$ is arithmetic mean and σ is standard deviation).   (1)

   (A) $\dfrac{\bar{x}}{\sigma} \times 100$ (B) $\dfrac{\sigma}{\bar{x}} \times 100$

   (C) $\sigma \times \bar{x} \times 100$ (D) $\dfrac{\bar{x}}{\sigma^2} \times 100$

6. If the data is presented in the form of frequency distribution then r^{th} moment μ_r about the arithmetic mean $\bar{x}$ of distribution is given by ($N = \sum f$)   (1)

(A) $\dfrac{1}{N} \sum f (x + \bar{x})^r$

(B) $N \times \sum f (x - \bar{x})^r$

(C) $\dfrac{1}{N} \sum f (x - \bar{x})$

(D) $\dfrac{1}{N} \sum f (x - \bar{x})^r$

7. If the data is presented in the form of frequency distribution then 1st moment μ_1 about the arithmetic mean $\bar{x}$ of distribution is ($N = \sum f$)   (1)

(A) 1

(B) σ^2

(C) 0

(D) $\dfrac{1}{N} \sum f (x - \bar{x})^3$

8. If μ_1' and μ_2' are the first two moments of the distribution about certain number then second moment μ_2 of the distribution about the arithmetic mean is given by   (1)

(A) $\mu_2' - (\mu_1')^2$

(B) $2\mu_2' - \mu_1'$

(C) $\mu_2' + (\mu_1')^2$

(D) $\mu_2' + 2(\mu_1')^2$

9. If μ_1', μ_2', μ_3' are the first three moments of the distribution about certain number then third moment μ_3 of the distribution about the arithmetic mean is given by   (1)

(A) $\mu_3' - 3\mu_2' \mu_1' + 2(\mu_1')^3$

(B) $\mu_3' - 3\mu_1' + (\mu_2')^3$

(C) $\mu_3' + 2\mu_2' \mu_1' + (\mu_3')^3$

(D) $\mu_3' + 3\mu_2' \mu_1' + (\mu_1')^2$

10. If μ_1', μ_2', μ_3', μ_4' are the first four moments of the distribution about certain number then fourth moment μ_4 of the distribution about the arithmetic mean is given by   (1)

(1) $\mu_4' + 4\mu_3' \mu_1' + 6\mu_2' (\mu_1')^4 + 3(\mu_1')^4$

(B) $\mu_4' - 4\mu_3' \mu_1' + 6\mu_2' (\mu_1')^2 - 3(\mu_1')^4$

(C) $\mu_4' + 4\mu_3' \mu_1' - 6\mu_2' (\mu_1')^4 - 3(\mu_1')^4$

(D) $\mu_4' + 2\mu_3' \mu_1' - 6\mu_2' (\mu_1')^2 - 3(\mu_1')^4$

11. If μ_1' be the first moment of the distribution about any number A then arithmetic mean $\bar{x}$ is given by   (1)

(A) $\mu_1' + A$

(B) μ_1'

(C) $\mu_1' - A$

(D) $\mu_1' A$

12. Second moment μ_2 about mean is   (1)

(A) Mean

(B) Standard deviation

(C) Variance

(D) Mean deviation

13. Coefficient of skewness β_1 is given by   (1)

(A) $\dfrac{\mu_2^3}{\mu_3^2}$

(B) $\dfrac{\mu_1^2}{\mu_2^3}$

(C) $\dfrac{\mu_2^2}{\mu_3^2}$

(D) $\dfrac{\mu_3^2}{\mu_2^3}$

14. Coefficient of kurtosis β_2 is given by   (1)

(A) $\dfrac{\mu_4}{\mu_3}$

(B) $\dfrac{\mu_4}{\mu_2^2}$

(C) $\dfrac{\mu_3}{\mu_2^2}$

(D) $\dfrac{\mu_4}{\mu_2^3}$

15. For a distribution coefficient of kurtosis $\beta_2 = 2.5$, this distribution is   (1)

(A) Leptokurtic

(B) Mesokurtic

(C) Platykurtic

(D) None of these

16. For a distribution coefficient of kurtosis $\beta_2 = 3.9$, this distribution is   (1)

(A) Leptokurtic

(B) Mesokurtic

(C) Platykurtic

(D) None of these

17. The first four moments of a distribution about the mean are 0, 16, −64 and 162. Standard deviation of a distribution is   (1)

(A) 21

(B) 12

(C) 16

(D) 4

18. Standard deviation of three numbers 9, 10, 11 is   (2)

(A) $\dfrac{2}{3}$

(B) $\dfrac{1}{3}$

(C) $\sqrt{\dfrac{2}{3}}$

(D) $\sqrt{2}$

19. Standard deviation of four numbers 9, 11, 13, 15 is   (2)

(A) 2

(B) 4

(C) $\sqrt{6}$

(D) $\sqrt{5}$

20. From the given information $\sum x = 235$, $\sum x^2 = 6750$, $n = 10$. Standard deviation of x is   (2)

(A) 11.08

(B) 13.08

(C) 8.08

(D) 7.6

21. Coefficient of variation of the data 1, 3, 5, 7, 9 is   (2)
(A) 54.23   (B) 56.57
(C) 55.41   (D) 60.19

22. The standard deviation and arithmetic mean of the distribution are 12 and 45.5 respectively. Coefficient of variation of the distribution is   (2)
(A) 26.37   (B) 32.43
(C) 12.11   (D) 22.15

23. The Standard Deviation and Arithmetic Mean of three distribution x, y, z are as follow:

	Arithmetic mean	Standard deviation
x	18.0	5.4
y	22.5	4.5
z	24.0	6.0

The more stable distribution is   (2)

(A) x   (B) y
(C) z   (D) x and z

24. The standard deviation and arithmetic mean of scores of three batsman x, y, z in ten inning during a certain season are

	Arithmetic mean	Standard deviation
x	50	24.43
y	46	25.495
z	40	27

The more consistent batsman is   (2)

(A) y and z   (B) y
(C) z   (D) x

25. The standard deviation and arithmetic mean of aggregate marks obtained three group of students x, y, z are as follow :

	Arithmetic mean	Standard deviation
x	532	11
y	831	9
z	650	10

The more variable group is   (2)

(A) y and z   (B) z
(C) y   (D) x

26. Arithmetic mean of four numbers is 16, one item 20 is replaced by 24, what is the new arithmetic mean　　　　(2)

(A) 15　　　　　　　　　　(B) 17

(C) 18　　　　　　　　　　(D) 16

27. The first moment of the distribution about the value 5 is 2. Arithmetic mean of the distribution is　　　　(2)

(A) 5　　　　　　　　　　(B) 2

(C) 4　　　　　　　　　　(D) 7

28. The first and second moments of the distribution about the value 3 are 2 and 20. Second moment about the mean is　　　　(2)

(A) 12　　　　　　　　　　(B) 14

(C) 16　　　　　　　　　　(D) 20

29. The first three moments of a distribution about the value 5 are 2, 20 and 40. Third moment about the mean is　　　　(2)

(A) −64　　　　　　　　　　(B) 64

(C) 32　　　　　　　　　　(D) −32

30. The first four moments of a distribution about the value 5 are 2, 20, 40 and 50. Fourth moment about the mean is　　　　(2)

(A) 160　　　　　　　　　　(B) 162

(C) 210　　　　　　　　　　(D) 180

31. The first moments of a distribution about the value 2 are −2, 12, −20 and 100. Fourth moment about the mean is　　　　(2)

(A) 200　　　　　　　　　　(B) 190

(C) 170　　　　　　　　　　(D) 180

32. The first three moments of a distribution about the value 2 are −2, 12, −20. Third moment about the mean is　　　　(2)

(A) 36　　　　　　　　　　(B) 30

(C) 22　　　　　　　　　　(D) 8

33. The first and second moments of the distribution about the value 2 are 1 and 16. Variance of the distribution is　　　　(2)

(A) 12　　　　　　　　　　(B) 3

(C) 15　　　　　　　　　　(D) 17

34. The second and third moments of a distribution about the arithmetic mean are 16 and −64 respectively. Coefficient of skewness β_1 is given by　　　　(2)

    (A) −0.25　　　　　　　　　　　　(B) 1

    (C) 4　　　　　　　　　　　　　(D) −1

35. The second and fourth moments of a distribution about the arithmetic mean are 16 and 162 respectively. Coefficient of kurtosis β_2 is given by　　　　(2)

    (A) 1　　　　　　　　　　　　　(B) 1.51

    (C) 0.63　　　　　　　　　　　　(D) 1.69

Answers

1. (A)	2. (C)	3. (B)	4. (D)	5. (B)	6. (D)	7. (C)	8. (A)
9. (A)	10. (B)	11. (A)	12. (C)	13. (D)	14. (B)	15. (C)	16. (A)
17. (D)	18. (C)	19. (D)	20. (A)	21. (B)	22. (A)	23. (B)	24. (D)
25. (D)	26. (B)	27. (D)	28. (C)	29. (A)	30. (B)	31. (D)	32. (A)
33. (C)	34. (B)	35. (C)					

7.6 CORRELATION

We have already considered distributions involving one variable or what we call as univariate distributions. In many problems of practical nature, we are required to deal with two or more variables. If we consider the marks obtained by a group of students in two or more subjects, the distribution will involve two or more variables. Distributions using two variables are called *Bivariate distributions*. In such distributions, we are often interested in knowing whether there exists some kind of relationship between the two variables involved. In language of statistics, this means whether there is correlation or co-variance between the two variables. If the change in one variable affects the change in the other variable, the variables are said to be correlated. For example, change in rainfall will affect the crop output and thus the variables 'Rainfall recorded' and 'crop output' are correlated. Similarly for a group of workers, the variables 'income' and 'expenditure' would be correlated. If the increase (or decrease) in one variable causes corresponding increase (or decrease) in the other, the correlation is said to be *positive* or *direct*. On the other hand, if increase in the value of one variable shows a corresponding decrease in the value of the other or vice versa, the correlation is called *negative* or *inverse*. As the income of a worker increases, as a natural course his expenditure also increases, hence the correlation between income and expenditure is positive or direct. Correlation between heights and weights of a group of students will also be positive. If we consider the price and demand of a certain commodity then our experience tells us that as the price of a commodity rises, its demand falls and thus the correlation between these variables is negative or inverse. Several such examples can be given. Correlation can also be classified as linear and non-linear. It is based upon the constancy of the ratio of change between the two variables. As an example, consider the values assumed by variables x and y.

x	5	8	11	15	17	19	20
y	10	16	22	30	34	38	40

Here the ratio $\dfrac{y}{x}$ is equal to 2 for all the values of x and y.

Correlation in such case is called *linear*.

When the amount of change in one variable is not in a constant ratio to the amount of change in other variable, the correlation is called *non-linear*. In such a case, the relationship between the variables x and y is not of the form y = mx (or of the form y = mx + c). In practical situations, the correlation is generally non-linear, but its analysis is quite complicated. Usually, it is assumed that the relation between x and y is linear and further analysis is made. There are different methods to determine whether the two variables are correlated. Some of these methods such as 'Scatter Diagram' are graphical methods and give rough idea about the correlation. These methods are not suitable if the number of observations is large. There are mathematical methods such as *'Karl Pearson's Coefficient of Correlation'*, 'Concurrent Deviation Method' etc. which are more suitable. We shall discuss *'Karl Pearson's* Coefficient of Correlation' which is widely used in practice.

7.7 KARL PEARSON'S COEFFICIENT OF CORRELATION

To measure the intensity or degree of linear relationship between two variables, Karl Pearson developed a formula called *correlation coefficient*.

Correlation coefficient between two variables x and y denoted by r (x, y) is defined as

$$r\,(x,\,y) \;=\; \frac{\operatorname{cov}\,(x,\,y)}{\sigma_x\,\sigma_y}$$

In bivariate distribution if $(x_i,\,y_i)$ take the values $(x_1,\,y_1)\,(x_2,\,y_2)\,\ldots\,(x_n,\,y_n)$

$$\operatorname{cov}\,(x,\,y) \;=\; \frac{1}{n}\,\sum\,(x_i - \overline{x})\,(y_i - \overline{y})$$

where $\overline{x}$, $\overline{y}$ are arithmetic means for x and y series respectively.

Similarly, $\quad \sigma_x = \sqrt{\dfrac{1}{n}\,\sum\,(x_i - \overline{x})^2}\quad$ and $\quad \sigma_y = \sqrt{\dfrac{1}{n}\,\sum\,(y_i - \overline{y})^2}$

which are the standard deviations for x and y series.

$$\operatorname{cov}\,(x,\,y) \;=\; \frac{1}{n}\,\sum\,(x_i - \overline{x})\,(y_i - \overline{y})$$

$$=\; \frac{1}{n}\,\sum\,(x_i\,y_i - x_i\,\overline{y} - \overline{x}\,y_i + \overline{x}\,\overline{y})$$

$$=\; \frac{1}{n}\,\sum x_i\,y_i - \overline{y}\,\frac{1}{n}\,\sum x_i - \overline{x}\,\frac{1}{n}\,\sum y_i + \frac{1}{n}\,\sum \overline{x}\,\overline{y}$$

$$= \frac{1}{n} \sum x_i y_i - \bar{y}\,\bar{x} - \bar{x}\,\bar{y} + \frac{1}{n}(n\bar{x}\,\bar{y})$$

$$= \frac{1}{n} \sum x_i y_i - \bar{x}\,\bar{y}$$

$$\sigma_x^2 = \frac{1}{n} \sum (x_i - \bar{x})^2 = \frac{1}{n} \sum x_i^2 - 2x_i\bar{x} + \bar{x}^2$$

$$= \frac{1}{n} \sum x_i^2 - 2\frac{\bar{x}}{n} \sum x_i + \frac{1}{n} \sum \bar{x}^2$$

$$= \frac{1}{n} \sum x_i^2 - 2\bar{x}^2 + \frac{1}{n}(n\bar{x}^2) = \frac{1}{n} \sum x_i^2 - \bar{x}^2$$

Similarly,
$$\sigma_y^2 = \frac{1}{n} \sum y_i^2 - \bar{y}^2$$

$$r(x, y) = \frac{\text{cov}(x, y)}{\sigma_x \sigma_y} \quad \text{can then be calculated.}$$

If we put
$$u_i = x_i - A \quad \text{or} \quad \frac{x_i - A}{h}$$

and
$$v_i = y_i - B \quad \text{or} \quad \frac{y_i - B}{k}$$

then
$$\text{cov}(u, v) = \frac{1}{n} \sum u_i v_i - \bar{u}\,\bar{v} \qquad \sigma_u^2 = \frac{1}{n} \sum u_i^2 - \bar{u}^2$$

$$\sigma_v^2 = \frac{1}{n} \sum v_i^2 - \bar{v}^2$$

$r(u, v)$ is given by, $r(u, v) = \dfrac{\text{cov}(u, v)}{\sigma_u \sigma_v}$

It can be established that $r(x, y) = r(u, v)$.

Calculation of $r(u, v)$ is simpler as compared to $r(x, y)$.

ILLUSTRATIONS

Ex. 1 : *Following are the values of import of raw material and export of finished product in suitable units.*

Export	10	11	14	14	20	22	16	12	15	13
Import	12	14	15	16	21	26	21	15	16	14

Calculate the coefficient of correlation between the import values and export values.

(Dec. 2010, May 2014)

Solution : Let X : Quantity exported, Y : Quantity imported, Preparing table as follows calculations can be made simple.

x	y	x^2	y^2	xy
10	12	100	144	120
11	14	121	196	154
14	15	196	225	210
14	16	196	256	224
20	21	400	441	420
22	26	484	676	572
16	21	256	441	336
12	15	144	225	180
15	16	225	256	240
13	14	169	196	182
Total = 147	**170**	**2291**	**3056**	**2638**

Here, n = 10, hence

$$\bar{x} = \frac{\sum x}{N} = \frac{147}{10} = 14.7$$

and

$$\bar{y} = \frac{\sum y}{N} = \frac{170}{10} = 17$$

$$r = \frac{\sum x\,y - n\,\bar{x}\,\bar{y}}{\sqrt{(\sum x^2 - n\bar{x}^2) \times (\sum y^2 - n\bar{y}^2)}}$$

$$= \frac{2638 - 10 \times 14.7 \times 17}{\sqrt{(2291 - 10 \times 14.7^2)(3056 - 10 \times 17^2)}}$$

$$= \frac{139}{\sqrt{130.1 \times 166}} = 0.9458$$

Ex. 2 : *From a group of 10 students, marks obtained by each in papers of Mathematics and Applied Mechanics are given as :*

x Marks in Maths	*23*	*28*	*42*	*17*	*26*	*35*	*29*	*37*	*16*	*46*
y Marks in App. Mech.	*25*	*22*	*38*	*21*	*27*	*39*	*24*	*32*	*18*	*44*

Calculate Karl Pearson's Coefficient of correlation.

Sol. : The data is tabulated as :

x	y	u = x – 35	v = y – 39	u²	v²	uv
16	18	– 19	– 21	361	441	399
17	21	– 18	– 18	324	324	324
23	25	– 12	– 14	144	196	168
26	27	– 09	– 12	81	144	108
28	22	– 07	– 17	49	289	119
29	24	– 06	– 15	36	225	90
35	39	– 00	00	00	00	00
37	32	02	– 07	04	49	– 14
42	38	07	– 01	49	01	– 07
46	44	11	05	121	25	55
Total		$\sum u = -51$	$\sum v = -100$	$\sum u^2 = 1169$	$\sum v^2 = 1694$	$\sum uv = 1242$

$$\bar{u} = \frac{-51}{10} = -5.1, \qquad \bar{u}^2 = 26.01$$

$$\bar{v} = \frac{-100}{10} = -10, \qquad \bar{v}^2 = 100$$

$$\text{cov}(u, v) = \frac{1}{n} \sum u_i v_i - \bar{u}\,\bar{v}$$

$$= \frac{1}{10}(1242) - 51 = 73.2$$

$$\sigma_u^2 = \frac{1}{n} \sum u_i^2 - \bar{u}^2 = \frac{1169}{10} - 26.01 = 90.89$$

$$\sigma_u = \sqrt{90.89} = 9.534$$

$$\sigma_v^2 = \frac{1}{n} \sum v_i^2 - \bar{v}^2 = \frac{1694}{10} - 100 = 69.4$$

$$\sigma_v = \sqrt{69.4} = 8.33$$

$$r(x, y) = r(u, v) = \frac{\text{cov}(u, v)}{\sigma_u \, \sigma_v} = \frac{73.2}{9.534 \times 8.33} = 0.9217$$

Ex. 3 : *Compute correlation coefficient between supply and price of commodity using following data.*

Supply	152	158	169	182	160	166	182
Price	198	178	167	152	180	170	162

Sol. : Let x = Supply, u = x – 150, y = price, v = y – 160

x	y	u	v	u^2	v^2	uv
152	198	2	38	4	1444	76
158	178	8	18	64	324	144
169	167	19	7	361	49	133
182	152	32	– 8	1024	64	– 256
160	180	10	20	100	400	200
166	170	16	10	256	100	160
182	162	32	2	1024	4	64
Total	**–**	**119**	**87**	**2833**	**2385**	**521**

Here, n = 7, $\sum u = 119$, $\sum v = 87$, $\sum u^2 = 2833$, $\sum v^2 = 2385$, $\sum uv = 521$

$\therefore \qquad \bar{u} = 17, \ \bar{v} = 12.4286$

$$r = \frac{\sum uv - n\,\bar{u}\,\bar{v}}{\sqrt{(\sum u^2 - n\bar{u}^2) \times (\sum v^2 - n\bar{v}^2)}}$$

$$r = \frac{521 - 7 \times 17 \times 12.4286}{\sqrt{(2833 - 7 \times 17^2)\,(2.385 - 7 \times 12.4286)^2}}$$

$$r = \frac{-958}{\sqrt{810 \times 1303.7142}} = \frac{-958}{1027.6227}$$

$$= -0.9322$$

Interpretation : There is high negative correlation between supply and price.

Ex. 4 : *Calculate the coefficient of correlation for the following distribution.*

x	5	9	15	19	24	28	32
y	7	9	14	21	23	29	30
f	6	9	13	20	16	11	7

Sol. : Tabulating the data as   (Dec. 2008)

x	y	f	u = x–19	v = y–21	fu	fv	fu^2	fv^2	fuv
5	7	6	– 14	– 14	– 84	– 84	1176	1176	1176
9	9	9	– 10	– 12	– 90	– 108	900	1296	1080
15	14	13	– 4	– 7	– 52	– 91	208	637	364
19	21	20	0	0	0	0	0	0	0
24	23	16	5	2	80	32	400	64	160
28	29	11	9	8	99	88	891	704	792
32	30	7	13	9	91	63	1183	567	819
Total		**$\sum f = 82$**			**$\sum fu = 44$**	**$\sum fv = -100$**	**$\sum fu^2 = 4758$**	**$\sum fv^2 = 4444$**	**$\sum fuv = 4391$**

$$\bar{u} = \frac{\sum fu}{\sum f} = \frac{44}{82} = 0.5366; \quad \bar{u}^2 = 0.288$$

$$\bar{v} = \frac{\sum fv}{\sum f} = \frac{-100}{82} = 1.2195; \quad \bar{v}^2 = 1.4872$$

$$\text{cov}(u, v) = \frac{1}{\sum f} \sum fu_i v_i - \bar{u}\,\bar{v} = \frac{4391}{82} - 0.6544 = 52.89$$

$$\sigma_u^2 = \frac{1}{\sum f} \sum fu_i^2 - \bar{u}^2 = \frac{758}{82} - 0.288 = 57.7364$$

$$\sigma_v^2 = \frac{1}{\sum f} \sum fv_i^2 - \bar{v}^2 = \frac{4444}{82} - 1.4872 = 52.708$$

$$\sigma_u = 7.598$$

$$\sigma_v = 7.26$$

$$r(u, v) = \frac{\text{cov}(u, v)}{\sigma_u\,\sigma_v} = \frac{52.89}{55.16} = 0.9588$$

$\therefore$ Coefficient of correlation $= r(x, y) = 0.9588$

Ex. 5 : *Find correlation coefficient between X and Y, given that,*

$n = 25$, $\sum x = 75$, $\sum y = 100$, $\sum x^2 = 250$, $\sum y^2 = 500$, $\sum xy = 325$.

Solution : Here $\bar{x} = \dfrac{75}{25} = 3$, $\quad \bar{y} = \dfrac{100}{25} = 4$.

$\therefore \qquad$
$$r = \frac{\sum xy - n\bar{x}\,\bar{y}}{\sqrt{(\sum x^2 - n\bar{x}^2) \times \sum(y^2 - n\bar{y}^2)}}$$

$$r = \frac{325 - 25 \times 3 \times 4}{\sqrt{(250 - 25 \times 9)(500 - 25 \times 16)}} = \frac{25}{\sqrt{25 \times 100}} = \frac{25}{50} = 0.5$$

7.9 REGRESSION

After having established that the two variables are correlated, we are generally interested in estimating the value of one variable for a given value of the other variable. For example, if we know that rainfall affects the crop output then it is possible to predict the crop output at the end of a rainy season. If the variables in a bivariate distribution are related, the points in scatter diagram cluster round some curve called the curve of regression or the regression curve. If the curve is a straight line, it is called the line of regression and in such case the regression between two variables is linear. The line of regression gives best estimate for the value of one variable for some specified value of the other variable. Being the line of best fit, the regression line is obtained by using the method of least squares.

Consider the set of values of (x_i, y_i), $i = 1, 2, \ldots n$. Let the line of regression of y on x be $y = mx + c$

From the method of least squares, the normal equations for estimating m and c are given by

$$\sum y_i = nc + m \sum x_i \qquad \ldots (1)$$

$$\sum x_i y_i = c \sum x_i + m \sum x_i^2 \qquad \ldots (2)$$

Dividing (1) by n, we get

$$\frac{1}{n} \sum y_i = c + m \left(\frac{1}{n} \sum x_i \right)$$

i.e. $$\overline{y} = c + m \overline{x} \qquad \ldots(3)$$

which shows that the point $(\overline{x}, \overline{y})$ lies on the line of regression.

We know that $$\mu_{11} = \text{cov}(x, y) = \frac{1}{n} \sum x_i y_i - \overline{x}\, \overline{y}$$

$\therefore$ $$\frac{1}{n} \sum x_i y_i = \mu_{11} + \overline{x}\, \overline{y} \qquad \ldots (4)$$

Also $$\sigma_x^2 = \frac{1}{n} \sum x_i^2 - \overline{x}^2$$

$\therefore$ $$\frac{1}{n} \sum x_i^2 = \sigma_x^2 + \overline{x}^2 \qquad \ldots(5)$$

Dividing (2) by n, we get

$$\frac{1}{n} \sum x_i y_i = c \frac{\sum x_i}{n} + m \frac{\sum x_i^2}{n} \qquad \ldots (6)$$

Substituting from (4) and (5) in (6),

$$\mu_{11} + \overline{x}\, \overline{y} = c \overline{x} + m \left(\sigma_x^2 + \overline{x}^2 \right) \qquad \ldots (7)$$

Multiplying (3) by $\overline{x}$ and subtracting from (7), we get

$$\mu_{11} = m \sigma_x^2$$

$$m = \frac{\mu_{11}}{\sigma_x^2}$$

Equation of regression line which passes through $(\overline{x}, \overline{y})$ and which has slope $\dfrac{\mu_{11}}{\sigma_x^2}$ is

thus given by the equation

$$y - \overline{y} = \frac{\mu_{11}}{\sigma_x^2} (x - \overline{x}) \qquad \ldots (8)$$

This equation gives regression line of y on x.

Similarly, if we start with regression line of x on y as

$$x = my + c$$

same procedure will give

$$x - \bar{x} = \frac{\mu_{11}}{\sigma_y^2} (y - \bar{y}) \qquad \dots (9)$$

Now,
$$r(x, y) = \frac{\text{cov}(x, y)}{\sigma_x \sigma_y}$$

Or
$$r = \frac{\mu_{11}}{\sigma_x \sigma_y}$$

Putting for μ_{11} in (8) and (9), we have

$$y - \bar{y} = \frac{r \sigma_x \sigma_y}{\sigma_x^2} (x - \bar{x})$$

Or
$$y - \bar{y} = r \frac{\sigma_y}{\sigma_x} (x - \bar{x}) = b_{yx} (x - \bar{x}) \qquad \dots (10)$$

which is the regression line of y on x.

Similarly,
$$x - \bar{x} = r \frac{\sigma_x}{\sigma_y} (y - \bar{y}) = b_{xy} (y - \bar{y}) \qquad \dots (11)$$

is the regression line of x on y.

For obtaining (10) and (11) we have to calculate $r = r(x, y)$ the correlation coefficient, which can be determined using change of scale property.

Thus,
$$r = r(x, y) = \frac{\text{cov}(x, y)}{\sigma_x \sigma_y} = \frac{\text{cov}(u, v)}{\sigma_u \sigma_v}$$

If
$$u = \frac{x - a}{h}, \quad v = \frac{y - b}{k}$$

then
$$\sigma_x = h \sigma_u, \quad \sigma_v = k \sigma_v$$

where
$$\sigma_u^2 = \frac{1}{n} \sum u_i^2 - \bar{u}^2 \quad \text{and} \quad \sigma_v^2 = \frac{1}{n} \sum v_i^2 - \bar{v}^2$$

In particular, if
$$u = x - a, \quad v = y - b$$

then
$$h = k = 1$$

and
$$\sigma_x = \sigma_u \quad \text{and} \quad \sigma_y = \sigma_v$$

Similarly,
$$\bar{x} = a + h\bar{u}, \qquad \bar{y} = b + k\bar{v}$$

These results help us to determine (10) and (11).

ILLUSTRATIONS

Ex. 1 : *Find the lines of regression for the following data :*

x	10	14	19	26	30	34	39
y	12	16	18	26	29	35	38

and estimate y for x = 14.5 and x for y = 29.5.

Sol. : Tabulating the data as :

x	y	$u = x - 26$	$v = y - 26$	u^2	v^2	uv
10	12	– 16	– 14	256	196	224
14	16	– 12	– 10	144	100	120
19	18	– 7	– 8	49	64	56
26	26	0	0	0	0	0
30	29	4	3	16	9	12
34	35	8	9	64	81	72
39	38	13	12	169	144	156
Total	–	$\sum u = -10$	$\sum v = -8$	$\sum u^2 = 698$	$\sum v^2 = 594$	$\sum uv = 640$

Here n = 7, $\bar{u} = \dfrac{-10}{7} = -1.429,$ $\bar{v} = \dfrac{-8}{7} = -1.143$

$$\bar{u}^2 = 2.042, \qquad \bar{v}^2 = 1.306$$

$$\text{cov}(u, v) = \frac{1}{n} \sum uv - \bar{u}\,\bar{v}$$

$$= \frac{1}{7}(640) - (1.429)(1.143) = 89.795$$

$$\sigma_u^2 = \frac{1}{n} \sum u_i^2 - \bar{u}^2 = \frac{1}{7}(698) - 2.042 = 97.672$$

$$\therefore \quad \sigma_u = 9.883$$

$$\sigma_v^2 = \frac{1}{n} \sum v_i^2 - \bar{v}^2 = \frac{1}{7}(594) - 1.306 = 83.551$$

$$\therefore \quad \sigma_v = 9.14$$

$$r = r(x, y) = r(u, v) = \frac{\text{cov}(u, v)}{\sigma_u\, \sigma_v} = \frac{89.795}{9.883 \times 9.14}$$

$$= \frac{89.795}{90.33062} = 0.9941$$

$$r \times \frac{\sigma_y}{\sigma_x} = r \times \frac{\sigma_v}{\sigma_u} = 0.9941 \times \frac{9.14}{9.883} = 0.9194$$

$$r \times \frac{\sigma_x}{\sigma_y} = r \times \frac{\sigma_u}{\sigma_v} = 0.9941 \times \frac{9.883}{9.14} = 1.0749$$

$$\bar{x} = a + \bar{u} = 26 - 1.429 = 24.571$$

$$\bar{y} = b + \bar{v} = 26 - 1.143 = 24.857$$

Regression line of y on x is given by equation (10)

$$y - 24.857 = 0.9194 (x - 24.571) \qquad \text{... (i)}$$

Regression line of x on y is given by equation (ii)

$$x - 24.571 = 1.0749 (y - 24.857) \qquad \text{... (ii)}$$

To estimate y for x = 14.5

put x = 14.5 in (i), $\therefore$ y = 24.857 + 0.9194 (14.5 – 24.571) = 15.5977

Estimate of x for y = 29.5 is obtained from (ii).

$$x = 24.571 + 1.0749 (29.5 - 24.857)$$

$$= 29.56176$$

Ex. 2 : *Obtain regression lines for the following data :*   **(Nov. 2015, May 2016)**

X	2	3	5	7	9	10	12	15
Y	2	5	8	10	12	14	15	16

Find estimate of (i) Y when X = 6 and (ii) X when Y = 20.

Solution : To find regression lines we require to calculate regression coefficients b_{xy} and b_{yx}. These coefficients depend upon Σx, Σy, Σx^2, Σy^2, Σxy. So we prepare the following table and simplify the calculations :

x_i	y_i	x_i^2	y_i^2	$x_i y_i$
2	2	4	4	4
3	5	9	25	15
5	8	25	64	40
7	10	49	100	70
9	12	81	144	108
10	14	100	196	140
12	15	144	225	180
15	16	225	256	240
Total = 63	**82**	**637**	**1014**	**797**

$$n = \text{number of pairs of observations} = 8$$

$$\bar{x} = \frac{\Sigma x_i}{n} = \frac{63}{8} = 7.875$$

$$\sigma_x^2 = \frac{\sum x_i^2}{n} - (\bar{x})^2$$

$$= \frac{637}{8} - (7.875)^2 = 17.6094$$

$$\bar{y} = \frac{\sum y_i}{n} = \frac{82}{8} = 10.25$$

$$\sigma_y^2 = \frac{\sum y_i^2}{n} - (\bar{y})^2$$

$$= \frac{1014}{8} - (10.25)^2 = 21.6875$$

$$\text{Cov}(x, y) = \frac{\sum x_i y_i}{n} - \bar{x}\,\bar{y} = \frac{797}{8} - 7.875 \times 10.25$$

$$= 18.9063$$

$$b_{yx} = \frac{\text{Cov}(x, y)}{\sigma_x^2} = \frac{18.9063}{17.6094} = 1.0736$$

$$b_{xy} = \frac{\text{Cov}(x, y)}{\sigma_y^2} = \frac{18.9063}{21.6875} = 0.8718$$

Regression line of Y on X : $Y - \bar{Y} = b_{yx}(X - \bar{X})$

$$y - 10.25 = 1.0736(X - 7.875)$$

$$Y = 1.0736\,X + 1.7954$$

(i) Estimate of y for $x = 6$ can be obtained by substituting $x = 6$ in the above regression equation.

$$\therefore \qquad Y = 1.0736 \times 6 + 1.7954 = 8.237$$

Regression line of X on Y :

$$X - \bar{X} = b_{xy}(Y - \bar{Y})$$

$$X - 7.875 = 0.8718(Y - 10.25)$$

$$X = 0.8718\,Y - 1.06095$$

(ii) Estimate of x can be obtained by substituting $y = 20$ in the above equation.

$$X = 16.37505$$

Note : For estimation of x and estimation of y, separate equations are to be used.

Ex. 3 : *The table below gives the respective heights x and y of a sample of 10 fathers and their sons :*

(i)   *Find regression line of y on x.*

(ii)   *Find regression line of x on y.*

(iii)   *Estimate son's height if father's height is 65 inches.*

(iv)   *Estimate father's height if son's height is 60 inches.*

(v)   *Compute correlation coefficient between x and y.*

(vi)   *Find the angle between the regression lines.*

Height of father x (inches)	65	63	67	64	68	62	70	66	68	67
Height of son y (inches)	68	66	68	65	69	66	68	65	71	67

Sol. : Let $u = x - 62$, $v = y - 65$. We prepare the table to simplify the computations.

x	y	u	v	u^2	v^2	uv
65	68	3	3	9	9	9
63	66	1	1	1	1	1
67	68	5	3	25	9	15
64	65	2	0	4	0	0
68	69	6	4	36	16	24
62	66	0	1	0	1	0
70	68	8	3	64	9	24
66	65	4	0	16	0	0
68	71	6	6	36	36	36
67	67	5	2	25	4	10
Total		**40**	**23**	**216**	**85**	**119**

$$n = \text{Number of pairs} = 10$$

$$\bar{u} = \frac{40}{10} = 4, \quad \sigma_u^2 = \frac{216}{10} - 4^2 = 5.6$$

$$\bar{v} = \frac{23}{10} = 2.3, \quad \sigma_v^2 = \frac{85}{10} - (2.3)^2 = 3.21$$

$$\text{Cov}(u, v) = \frac{119}{10} - 4 \times 2.3 = 2.7$$

$$\therefore \qquad b_{xy} = b_{uv} = \frac{2.7}{3.21} = 0.8411, \quad \text{and} \quad b_{yx} = b_{vu} = \frac{2.7}{5.6} = 0.4821$$

$$\bar{x} = \bar{u} + 62 = 66, \quad \bar{y} = \bar{v} + 65 = 67.3$$

(i)   Regression line of y on x is $Y - \bar{Y} = b_{yx}(X - \bar{X})$

$\therefore$ $Y - 67.3 = 0.4821(X - 66)$

$\therefore$ $Y = 0.4821X + 35.4814$

(ii)   Regression line of x on y is $X - \bar{X} = b_{xy}(Y - \bar{Y})$

$\therefore$ $X - 66 = 0.8411(Y - 67.3)$

$\therefore$ $X = 0.8411\,Y + 9.3940$

(iii)   Estimate of son's height Y for x = 65

$$Y = 0.4821 \times 65 + 35.4814$$

$$= 66.8179 \text{ inches}$$

(iv)   Estimate of father's height x for y = 60

$$X = 0.8411 \times 60 + 9.394 = 59.86 \text{ inches}$$

(v)   Correlation coefficient,

$$r = \sqrt{b_{xy} \cdot b_{yx}}$$

$$= \sqrt{0.8411 \times 0.4821} = 0.63678$$

We choose positive square root because regression coefficients are positive.

(vi)   The acute angle between the regression lines is given by

$$\tan\theta = \frac{1 - r^2}{|r|} \cdot \frac{\sigma_x\,\sigma_y}{\sigma_x^2 + \sigma_y^2}$$

$$= \frac{1 - (0.63678)^2}{0.63678} \times \frac{\sqrt{5.6 \times 3.21}}{(5.6 + 3.21)}$$

$$= 0.933621 \times \frac{4.2398}{8.81} = 0.4493$$

$\therefore$ $\theta = \tan^{-1}(0.4493) = 24.19^{\circ}$

Ex. 4 : *Calculate the correlation coefficient for the following weights (in kg) of husband (x) and wife (y).*

x	65	66	67	67	68	69	70	72
y	55	58	72	55	66	71	70	50

Sol. :

x	y	x^2	y^2	xy
65	55	4225	3025	3575
66	58	4356	3364	3828
67	72	4489	5184	4824
67	55	4489	3025	3685
68	66	4624	4354	4488
69	71	4761	5041	4899
70	70	4900	4900	4900
72	50	5184	2500	3600
544	**497**	**37028**	**31393**	**33799**

$$\bar{x} = \frac{\sum x}{n} = \frac{544}{8} = 68$$

$$\bar{y} = \frac{\sum y}{n} = \frac{497}{8} = 62.125$$

Correlation coefficient between x and y is given by

$$r\,(x, y) = \frac{\text{Cov}\,(x, y)}{\sigma_x\,\sigma_y} = \frac{\dfrac{1}{n}\sum xy - \bar{x}\,\bar{y}}{\sqrt{\left[\dfrac{1}{n}\sum x^2 - (\bar{x})^2\right]\left[\dfrac{1}{n}\sum y^2 - (\bar{y})^2\right]}}$$

$$= \frac{\dfrac{1}{8}\,(33799) - 68\,(62.125)}{\sqrt{\left[\dfrac{37028}{8} - (68)^2\right]\left[\dfrac{31398}{8} - (62.125)^2\right]}}$$

$$= \frac{4224.875 - 4224.5}{\sqrt{(4628.5 - 4624)\,(3924.125 - 3859.52)}}$$

$$= \frac{0.375}{\sqrt{4.5 \times 64.605}} = \frac{0.375}{\sqrt{290.7225}} = \frac{0.375}{17.051}$$

$$r\,(x, y) = 0.022$$

Ex. 5 : *Obtain correlation coefficient between population density (per square miles) and death rate (per thousand persons) from data related to 5 cities.* **(May 2005)**

Population density	200	500	400	700	800
Death rate	12	18	16	21	10

Sol. : Let x = Population density and y = Death rate.

Let, $u = x - a$ and $v = y - b$

$= x - 500$ $= y - 15$

x	y	u = x – 500	v	u^2	v^2	uv
200	12	– 300	– 3	90000	9	900
500	18	0	3	0	9	0
400	16	– 100	1	10000	1	– 100
700	21	200	6	40000	36	1200
800	10	300	– 5	90000	25	– 1500
Total	–	**100**	**2**	**230000**	**80**	**500**

Here, $n = 5$, $\sum u = 100$, $\sum v = 2$, $\sum u^2 = 230000$, $\sum v = 80$, $\sum uv = 500$

$$\bar{u} = \frac{\sum u}{n} = \frac{100}{5} = 20$$

$$\bar{v} = \frac{\sum v}{n} = \frac{2}{5} = 0.4$$

$$r(u, v) = \frac{\sum uv - n\,\bar{u}\,\bar{v}}{\sqrt{[\sum u^2 - n\,(\bar{u})^2]\ [\sum v^2 - n\,(\bar{v})^2]}}$$

$$= \frac{500 - 5\,(20)\,(0.4)}{\sqrt{230000 - 5\,(20)^2}\ \sqrt{80 - 5\,(0.4)^2}}$$

$$= \frac{460}{\sqrt{228000}\ \sqrt{79.2}}$$

$$= \frac{460}{4249.42} = 0.1082$$

Ex. 6 : *Calculate the coefficient of correlation from the following information.*

$n = 10$, $\sum x = 40$, $\sum x^2 = 190$, $\sum y^2 = 200$, $\sum xy = 150$, $\sum y = 40$.

Sol. : Here, $$\bar{x} = \frac{\sum x}{n} = \frac{40}{10} = 4$$

$$\bar{y} = \frac{\sum y}{n} = \frac{40}{10} = 4$$

Coefficient of correlation is given by,

$$r = \frac{\sum xy - n\,\bar{x}\,\bar{y}}{\sqrt{(\sum x^2 - n\,(\bar{x})^2) \times (\sum y^2 - n\,(\bar{y})^2)}}$$

$$r = \frac{150 - 10\,(4)\,(4)}{\sqrt{190 - 10\,(4)^2}\ \sqrt{200 - 10\,(4)^2}}$$

$$= \frac{150 - 160}{\sqrt{30}\ \sqrt{40}} = \frac{-10}{34.6410} = -0.2886$$

Ex. 7 : *Given : $r = 0.9$, $\sum XY = 70$, $\sigma_y = 3.5$, $\sum X^2 = 100$.*

Find the number of items, if X and Y are deviations from arithmetic mean.

Sol. : $\sum X^2 = 100$ $\sum XY = 70$

   $r = 0.9$ $\sigma_y = 3.5$

We have to find the value of n

$$\sigma_x^2 = \frac{1}{n} \sum (x - \bar{x})^2 = \frac{1}{n} \sum X^2 = \frac{100}{n}$$

$$r = \frac{\sum (x - \bar{x})(y - \bar{y})}{n\,\sigma_x\,\sigma_y} = \frac{\sum XY}{n\,\sigma_x\,\sigma_y}$$

Squaring we get, $$r^2 = \frac{(\sum XY)^2}{n^2\,\sigma_x^2\,\sigma_y^2}$$

$$(0.9)^2 = \frac{(70)^2}{n^2 \times \left(\dfrac{100}{n}\right) \times (3.5)^2}$$

$$0.81 = \frac{4900}{1225 \cdot n}$$

$$0.81 \times 1225\ n = 4900$$

$$992.25\ n = 4900$$

$$n = 4.9383$$

$$n \approx 5$$

Ex. 8 : *Given : $n = 6$, $\sum (x - 18.5) = -3$, $\sum (y - 50) = 20$, $\sum (x - 18.5)^2 = 19$, $\sum (y - 50)^2 = 850$, $\sum (x - 18.5)(y - 50) = -120$.*

Calculate coefficient of correlation.

Sol. : Let $u = x - 18.5$ and $v = y - 50$

$$\bar{u} = \frac{-3}{6} = -0.5$$

and $$\bar{v} = \frac{20}{6} = 3.33$$

From the given data $\sum u = -3$, $\sum v = 20$, $\sum u^2 = 19$, $\sum v^2 = 850$ and $\sum uv = -120$.

Coefficient of correlation is given by

$$r = \frac{\sum uv - n\,\bar{u}\,\bar{v}}{\sqrt{[\sum u^2 - n\,(\bar{u})^2]\, \times\, [\sum v^2 - n\,(\bar{v})^2]}}$$

$$= \frac{-120 - 6\,(-0.5) \times (3.33)}{\sqrt{[19 - 6\,(-0.5)^2] \times [850 - 6\,(3.33)^2]}}$$

$$= \frac{-120 + 9.99}{\sqrt{(17.5)\,(783.47)}} = \frac{-110.01}{117.0928}$$

$$r = -0.9395$$

Ex. 9 : *Obtain regression lines for the following data :*

x	6	2	10	4	8
y	9	11	5	8	7

(Dec. 06, 07, 08, 11, Nov. 15, 16; May 09, 17)

Sol. : To find regression lines we require to calculate regression coefficient b_{xy} and b_{yx}. These coefficients depend upon $\sum x$, $\sum y$, $\sum x^2$, $\sum y^2$ and $\sum xy$. So we prepare the following table and simplify the calculations.

x_i	y_i	x_i^2	y_i^2	$x_i\,y_i$
6	9	36	81	54
2	11	4	121	22
10	5	100	25	50
4	8	16	64	32
8	7	64	49	56
$\sum x_i = 30$	$\sum y_i = 40$	$\sum x_i^2 = 220$	$\sum y_i^2 = 340$	$\sum x_i\,y_i = 214$

No. of observations $= n = 5$

$$\bar{x} = \frac{\sum x_i}{n} = \frac{30}{5} = 6 \quad \text{and} \quad \bar{y} = \frac{\sum y_i}{n} = \frac{40}{5} = 8$$

$$\sigma_x^2 = \frac{\sum x_i^2}{n} - (\bar{x})^2 = \frac{220}{5} - (6)^2 = 44 - 36 = 8$$

$$\sigma_y^2 = \frac{\sum y_i^2}{n} - (\bar{y})^2 = \frac{340}{5} - (8)^2 = 68 - 64 = 4$$

$$\text{Cov}\,(x, y) = \frac{\sum (x_i\,y_i)}{n} - \bar{x}\,\bar{y}$$

$$= \frac{214}{5} - 6 \times 8$$

$$\text{Cov}(x, y) = 42.8 - 48 = -5.2$$

$$b_{yx} = \frac{\text{Cov}(x, y)}{\sigma_x^2} = \frac{-5.2}{8} = -0.65$$

$$b_{xy} = \frac{\text{Cov}(x, y)}{\sigma_y^2} = \frac{-5.2}{6} = -1.3$$

Regression line of Y on X is

$$y - \overline{y} = b_{yx}(x - \overline{x})$$
$$y - 8 = -0.65(x - 6)$$
$$y = -0.65\,x + 3.9 + 8$$
$$y = -0.65\,x + 11.9$$

Regression line of X on Y is

$$x - \overline{x} = b_{xy}(y - \overline{y})$$
$$x - 6 = -1.3(y - 8)$$
$$x - 6 = -1.3\,y + 10.4$$
$$x = -1.3\,y + 10.4 + 6$$
$$x = -1.3\,y + 16.4$$

Ex. 10 : *Find the coefficient of correlation for distribution in which S.D. of x = 4, and S.D. of y = 1.8. Coefficient of regression of y on x is 0.32.*

Sol. : $\sigma_x = 4$, $\sigma_y = 1.8$ and $b_{yx} = 0.32$

We have,
$$b_{yx} = r\frac{\sigma_y}{\sigma_x}$$

$$0.32 = r \times \frac{1.8}{4}$$

$$\therefore \qquad r = \frac{0.32 \times 4}{1.8} = 0.711$$

Ex. 11 : *Given the following information*

	Variable x	Variable y
Arithmetic mean	8.2	12.4
Standard deviation	6.2	20

Coefficient of correlation between x and y is 0.9. Find the linear regression estimate of x, given y = 10.

Sol. : Given that $\overline{x} = 8.2$, $\overline{y} = 12.4$, $\sigma_x = 6.2$, $\sigma_y = 20$ and $r_{xy} = 0.9$. We want to find x for y = 10.

Line of regression of x on y is

$$x - \overline{x} = b_{xy}(y - \overline{y})$$

$$b_{xy} = r \cdot \frac{\sigma_x}{\sigma_y} = 0.9 \times \frac{6.2}{20} = 0.279$$

Substituting value of $\bar{x}$, $\bar{y}$ and b_{xy} in above equation, we get

$$x - 8.2 = 0.279\,(y - 12.4)$$
$$x = 0.279\,y - 3.4596 + 8.2$$
$$x = 0.279\,y + 4.7404$$

Putting $y = 10$ in equation, we get

$$x = 0.279 \times 10 + 4.7404$$
$$x = 7.5304$$

Ex. 12 : *The following are marks obtained by 10 students in Statistics and Economics.*

No.	1	2	3	4	5	6	7	8	9	10
Marks in Economics	25	28	35	32	31	36	29	38	34	32
Marks in Statistics	43	46	49	41	36	32	31	30	33	39

Marks are out of 50. Obtain regression equation to estimate marks in Statistics if marks in Economics are 30.   **(Dec. 2005)**

Sol. : $n = 10$. Let us denote marks in Economics by x and marks in Statistics by y.

Let $u = x - 30$ and $v = y - 35$.

x	y	$u = x - 30$	$v = y - 35$	u^2	v^2	uv
25	43	– 5	8	25	64	– 40
28	46	– 2	11	4	121	– 22
35	49	5	14	25	196	70
32	41	2	6	4	36	12
31	36	1	1	1	1	1
36	32	6	– 3	36	9	– 18
29	31	– 1	– 4	1	16	4
38	30	8	– 5	64	25	– 40
34	33	4	– 2	16	4	– 8
32	39	2	4	4	16	8
–	–	$\sum u = 2$	$\sum v = 30$	$\sum u^2 = 180$	$\sum v^2 = 488$	$\sum uv = -33$

$$\bar{u} = \frac{\sum u}{n} = \frac{20}{10} = 2 \quad \text{and} \quad \bar{v} = \frac{\sum v}{n} = \frac{30}{10} = 3$$

$$u = x - 30 \quad \therefore \quad u = \bar{x} - 30$$

$$\therefore \quad \bar{x} = \bar{u} - 30 = 2 + 30 = 32$$

$v = y - 35$ $\therefore$ $\bar{v} = \bar{y} - 35$

$\therefore$ $\bar{y} = \bar{v} + 35 = 3 + 35 = 38$

$$\sigma_u^2 = \frac{\sum u^2}{n} - (\bar{u})^2 = \frac{180}{10} - (2)^2 = 18 - 4 = 14$$

$$\sigma_v^2 = \frac{\sum v^2}{n} - (\bar{v})^2 = \frac{488}{10} - (3)^2 = 48.8 - 9 = 39.8$$

$\therefore$ $\sigma_u = 3.742$ and $\sigma_v = 6.309$

Standard deviation is invariant to the change of origin.

$\therefore$ $\sigma_x = 3.742$ and $\sigma_y = 6.309$

$\therefore$ $\sigma_x^2 = 14$ and $\sigma_y^2 = 39.8$

$$\text{Cov}(u, v) = \frac{\sum uv}{n} - \bar{u}\,\bar{v} = \frac{-33}{10} - 2\,(3) = -3.3 - 6$$

$\therefore$ $\text{Cov}(u, v) = -9.3$

Covariance is invariant to the change of origin.

$\therefore$ $\text{Cov}(x, y) = \text{Cov}(u, v) = -9.3$

We have to find regression equation of y on x. It is given by

$$y - \bar{y} = b_{yx}(x - \bar{x})$$

$$b_{yx} = \frac{\text{Cov}(x, y)}{\sigma_x^2} = \frac{-9.3}{14} = -0.664$$

$\therefore$ Regression equation becomes,

$$y - 38 = -0.664\,(x - 32)$$
$$y = -0.664\,x + 21.248 + 38$$
$$y = -0.664\,x + 59.248$$

Now, we have to estimate marks in Statistics if marks in Economics are 30, i.e. we have to find value of y when x = 30.

Substituting x = 30 in above equation, we get

$$y = -0.664 \times 30 + 59.248$$
$$y = 39.328$$

$\therefore$ Marks in Economics are 39.328 i.e. approximately 39.

Ex. 13 : *If the two lines of regression are $9x + y - \lambda = 0$ and $4x + y = \mu$ and the means of x and y are 2 and –3 respectively, find the values of λ, μ and the coefficient of correlation between x and y.*   **(May 09)**

Sol. : $\bar{x} = 2$ and $\bar{y} = -3$.

The lines of regression are $9x + y = \lambda$ and $4x + y = \mu$.

The point of intersection of two regression lines is (x, y) i.e. $(\overline{x}, \overline{y})$ lies on both the regression lines.

$$9\overline{x} + \overline{y} = \lambda \qquad \qquad \dots (1)$$

$$4\overline{x} + \overline{y} = \mu \qquad \qquad \dots (2)$$

Substituting values of $\overline{x}$ and $\overline{y}$, we get

$$9\,(2) + (-3) = \lambda$$

$$\lambda = 18 - 3 = 15$$

and

$$4\,(2) + (-3) = \mu$$

$$\therefore \qquad \mu = 8 - 3 = 5$$

Thus, the regression lines are,

$$9x + y = 15 \quad \text{and} \quad 4x + y = 5$$

Let $9x + y = 15$ be the regression line of x on y, so it can be written as

$$x = \frac{15}{9} - \frac{y}{9}$$

$$\therefore \qquad b_{xy} = -\frac{1}{9} = -0.11$$

Let $4x + y = 5$ be the regression line of y on x. So it can be written as $y = 5 - 4x$.

$$\therefore \qquad b_{yx} = -4$$

Correlation coefficient between x and y is given as,

$$r = \sqrt{b_{yx} \cdot b_{xy}} = \sqrt{(-4) \times (-0.11)} = \sqrt{0.44} = 0.663$$

Since both the regression coefficients are negative, we take $r = -0.663$.

Ex. 14 : *The regression equations are 8x – 10y + 66 = 0 and 40x – 18y = 214. The value of variance of x is 9. Find :*

(1) The mean values of x and y.

(2) The correlation x and y and

(3) The standard deviation of y. **(May 06, Dec. 2009)**

Sol. : (1) Since both the regression lines pass through the point $(\overline{x}, \overline{y})$, we have

$$8\,\overline{x} - 10\,\overline{y} + 66 = 0 \quad \text{and} \quad 40\,\overline{x} - 18\,\overline{y} = 214$$

Solving these two equations, we get

$$\overline{x} = 13 \quad \text{and} \quad \overline{y} = 17$$

(2) Let $8x - 10y + 66 = 0$ be the line of regression of y on x and $40x - 18y = 214$ be the line of regression of x on y. These equations can be written in the form

$$y = \frac{8}{10}\,x + \frac{66}{10} \quad \text{and} \quad x = \frac{18}{40}\,y + \frac{214}{40}$$

i.e. $\qquad y = 0.8\,x + 6.6$ and $x = 0.45\,y + 5.35$

$\therefore \qquad b_{yx}$ = Regression coefficient of y on x

$\qquad\qquad = 0.8$

and $\qquad b_{xy}$ = Regression coefficient of x on y

$\qquad\qquad = 0.45$

Correlation coefficient between x and y is given by

$$r = \sqrt{b_{xy} \times b_{yx}} = \sqrt{0.45 \times 0.8} = \pm 0.6$$

But since both the regression coefficients are positive, we take

$$r = +0.6$$

(3) Variance of x $= 9$, i.e. $\sigma_x^2 = 9$

$\therefore \qquad\qquad \sigma_x = 3$

We have, $\qquad\qquad b_{yx} = r \cdot \dfrac{\sigma_y}{\sigma_x}$

$$0.8 = 0.6 \times \frac{\sigma_y}{3}$$

$$\sigma_y = 4$$

7.10 RELIABILITY OF REGRESSION ESTIMATES

Standard Error of Regression Estimate :

In order to study the reliability of regression estimate, we require to know its standard error. For further statistical analysis such as testing the significance of regression coefficient, standard error is required.

Suppose $\{(x_i, y_i), i = 1, 2, \ldots, n\}$ is a sample on the variables X and Y. The sample variances of X and Y are σ_x^2 and σ_y^2 respectively. The sample correlation coefficient between X and Y is r. The regression line of Y on X is given by $y - \bar{y} = b_{yx}\,(x - \bar{x})$. We can write it as $y = b_{yx}\,(x - \bar{x}) + \bar{y}$. Clearly, the error in estimation is (observed value of y) – (regression estimate of y). The positive square root of the mean sum of squares of error is called as *standard error of regression estimate*. We denote it by S_y.

If y_i is observed value of y; and $\hat{y}_i$ is the regression estimate for given x_i then $y_i = b_{yx}\,(x_i - \bar{x}) + \bar{y}$.

$$\text{Therefore,} \quad S_y^2 = \frac{\displaystyle\sum_{i=1}^{n} (y_i - \hat{y}_i)^2}{n} = \frac{1}{n} \sum_{i=1}^{n} [y_i - b_{yx}\,(x_i - \bar{x}) - \bar{y}]^2$$

$$= \frac{1}{n} \sum_{i=1}^{n} [(y_i - \bar{y}) - b_{yx}\,(x_i - \bar{x})]^2$$

$$= \frac{1}{n}\left[\sum (y_i - \bar{y})^2 + b_{yx}^2 \sum (x_i - \bar{x})^2 - 2\,b_{yx} \sum (x_i - \bar{x})\,(y_i - \bar{y})\right]$$

$$= \sigma_y^2 + b_{yx}^2\,\sigma_x^2 - 2\,b_{yx}\,\text{cov}\,(x,\,y)$$

$$\left(\because\ b_{yx} = r\frac{\sigma_y}{\sigma_x},\ \text{cov}\,(x,\,y) = r\,\sigma_x\,\sigma_y\right)$$

$$= \sigma_y^2 + r^2\,\sigma_y^2 - 2r^2\,\sigma_y^2 = \sigma_y^2\,(1 - r^2)$$

Hence the standard error of regression estimate of y on x is

$$S_y = \sigma_y\sqrt{1 - r^2}$$

Note that larger the value of r^2, smaller is the error. Hence the regression estimates are close to the actual values of y_i for large r^2. If $r = \pm 1$, the correlation is perfect and the standard error is zero, which means observed values and estimated values of y agree.

The standard error of regression estimate of x on y is given by,

$$S_x = \sigma_x\sqrt{1 - r^2}$$

Note : The above discussion leads to conclusion that rather than r we should consider r^2 for testing reliability of regression estimates. Therefore, regression analysis claims validity if r^2 is sufficiently large. The quantity r^2 is called as the coefficient of determination.

EXERCISE 7.2

1. Find Karl Pearson's coefficient of correlation for the following data and determine the probable error.

x	20	22	23	25	25	28	29	30	30	34
y	18	20	22	24	21	26	26	25	27	29

[**Hint :** Probable error $= 0.6745\left(\dfrac{1 - r^2}{\sqrt{N}}\right)$

where, r is the coefficient correlation and N the number of pairs of observations.]

Ans. 0.952, 0.02.

2. For the following tabulated data, find the coefficient of correlation.

y \ x	18	19	20	21	Total
10 – 20	4	2	2	–	8
20 – 30	5	4	6	4	19
30 – 40	6	8	10	11	35
40 – 50	4	4	6	8	22
50 – 60	–	2	4	4	10
60 – 70	–	2	3	1	6
Total	**19**	**22**	**31**	**28**	**100**

Ans. 0.25

3. Two examiners A and B independently award marks to seven students.

R. No.	1	2	3	4	5	6	7
Marks by A	40	44	28	30	44	38	31
Marks by B	32	39	26	30	38	34	28

Obtain the equations of regression lines. If examiner A awards 36 marks to Roll No. 8, what would be the marks expected to be awarded by examiner B to the same candidate ?

Ans. $y = 11.885 + 0.587\, x$, 33.017.

4. Determine the equations of regression lines for the following data :

x	1	2	3	4	5	6	7	8	9
y	9	8	10	12	11	13	14	16	15

and obtain an estimate of y for x = 4.5.   **(May 2012)**

Ans. $0.95\, x + 7.25$, $x = 0.957 - 6.4 = 11.525$.

5. Determine the reliability of estimates for the data :

x	10	14	19	26	30	34	39
y	12	16	18	26	29	35	38

Ans. $r^2 = 0.988$ high.

6. The following marks have been obtained by a group of students in Engineering Mathematics.

Paper I	80	45	55	56	58	60	65	68	70	75	85
Paper II	82	56	50	48	60	62	64	65	70	74	90

Calculate the coefficient of correlation.

Ans. 9277

7. Coefficient of correlation between two variables X and Y is 0.8. Their covariance is 20. The variance of X is 16. Find the standard deviation of Y series.

Ans. 1.5625.

8. Find the coefficient of correlation for the following table : **(Dec. 06, 2014, May 2015)**

x	10	14	18	22	26	30
y	18	12	24	6	30	36

Ans. $r = 0.6013$

9. The two regression equations of the variables x and y are

$$x = 19.13 - 0.87\, y \qquad y = 11.64 - 0.50\, x$$

Find (i) $\bar{x}$, $\bar{y}$, (ii) The correlation coefficient between x and y.   **(Dec. 2006)**

Ans. $\bar{x} = 15.935$, $\bar{y} = 3.673$, $r = 0.6595$

10. If θ is the acute angle between the two regression lines in the case of two variables x and y, show that

$$\tan \theta = \frac{1 - r^2}{r} \cdot \frac{\sigma_x \, \sigma_y}{\sigma_x^2 + \sigma_y^2}$$

MULTIPLE CHOICE QUESTIONS (MCQ's)

Type : Correlation and Regression :

1. Covariance between two variables x and y is given by   (1)

   (A) $\dfrac{1}{n}\sum (x - \bar{x})(y - \bar{y})$

   (B) $\dfrac{1}{n}\sum (x + \bar{x})(y + \bar{y})$

   (C) $n \sum (x - \bar{x})(y - \bar{y})$

   (D) $\dfrac{1}{n}\sum [(x - \bar{x}) + (y - \bar{y})]$

2. Correlation coefficient r between two variables x and y is given by   (1)

   (A) $\dfrac{\text{cov}(x, y)}{\sigma_x^2 \, \sigma_y^2}$

   (B) $\dfrac{\sigma_y}{\sigma_x}$

   (C) $\dfrac{\sigma_x}{\sigma_y}$

   (D) $\dfrac{\text{cov}(x, y)}{\sigma_x \, \sigma_y}$

3. Range of coefficient of correlation r is   (1)

   (A) $-\infty < \dfrac{1}{r} < \infty$

   (B) $-\infty < r < \infty$

   (C) $-1 \le r \le 1$

   (D) $0 \le r \le 1$

4. Probable error of coefficient of correlation r is   (1)

   (A) $0.6745 \left(\dfrac{1 + r^2}{\sqrt{N}} \right)$

   (B) $0.6745 \left(\dfrac{1 - r^2}{\sqrt{N}} \right)$

   (C) $0.6745 \left(\dfrac{1 - r^2}{N} \right)$

   (D) $0.6547 \left(\dfrac{1 - r^2}{N} \right)$

5. Line of regression y on x is   (1)

   (A) $y + \bar{y} = r \dfrac{\sigma_x}{\sigma_y}(x + \bar{x})$

   (B) $x - \bar{x} = r \dfrac{\sigma_x}{\sigma_y}(y - \bar{y})$

   (C) $y - \bar{y} = r \dfrac{\sigma_y}{\sigma_x}(x - \bar{x})$

   (D) $y - \bar{y} = r \dfrac{\sigma_x}{\sigma_y}(x - \bar{x})$

6. Line of regression x on y is   (1)

   (A) $y - \bar{y} = r \dfrac{\sigma_y}{\sigma_x}(x - \bar{x})$

   (B) $x + \bar{x} = r \dfrac{\sigma_x}{\sigma_y}(y + \bar{y})$

   (C) $x - \bar{x} = r \dfrac{\sigma_y}{\sigma_x}(y - \bar{y})$

   (D) $x - \bar{x} = r \dfrac{\sigma_x}{\sigma_y}(y - \bar{y})$

7. Slope of regression line of y on x is　　　　　　　　　　(1)

(A) $r\,(x,\,y)$　　　　　　　　　　(B) $r\,\dfrac{\sigma_y}{\sigma_x}$

(C) $r\,\dfrac{\sigma_x}{\sigma_y}$　　　　　　　　　　(D) $\dfrac{\sigma_y}{\sigma_x}$

8. Slope of regression line of x on y is　　　　　　　　　　(1)

(A) $r\,\dfrac{\sigma_x}{\sigma_y}$　　　　　　　　　　(B) $r\,(x,\,y)$

(C) $\dfrac{\sigma_x}{\sigma_y}$　　　　　　　　　　(D) $r\,\dfrac{\sigma_y}{\sigma_x}$

9. In regression line y on x, b_{yx} is given by　　　　　　　　　　(1)

(A) $\text{cov}\,(x,\,y)$　　　　　　　　　　(B) $r\,(x,\,y)$

(C) $\dfrac{\text{cov}\,(x,\,y)}{\sigma_x^2}$　　　　　　　　　　(D) $\dfrac{\text{cov}\,(x,\,y)}{\sigma_y^2}$

10. In regression line x on y, b_{xy} is given by　　　　　　　　　　(1)

(A) $\text{cov}\,(x,\,y)$　　　　　　　　　　(B) $r\,(x,\,y)$

(C) $\dfrac{\text{cov}\,(x,\,y)}{\sigma_x^2}$　　　　　　　　　　(D) $\dfrac{\text{cov}\,(x,\,y)}{\sigma_y^2}$

11. If b_{xy} and b_{yx} are the regression coefficient x on y and y on x respectively then the coefficient of correlation $r(x,\,y)$ is given by　　　　　　　　　　(1)

(A) $\sqrt{b_{xy} + b_{yx}}$　　　　　　　　　　(B) $b_{xy}\,b_{yx}$

(C) $\sqrt{\dfrac{b_{xy}}{b_{yx}}}$　　　　　　　　　　(D) $\sqrt{b_{xy}\,b_{yx}}$

12. If θ is the acute angle between the regression line of y on x and the regression line of x on y, then $\tan\theta$ is　　　　　　　　　　(1)

(A) $\dfrac{(1-r^2)}{|r|}\;\dfrac{\sigma_x\sigma_y}{\sigma_x^2 + \sigma_y^2}$　　　　　　　　　　(B) $\dfrac{|r|}{(1-r^2)}\;\dfrac{\sigma_x\sigma_y}{\sigma_x^2 + \sigma_y^2}$

(C) $|r|\;\dfrac{\sigma_x\sigma_y}{\sigma_x^2 + \sigma_y^2}$　　　　　　　　　　(D) $\dfrac{1}{|r|}\;\dfrac{\sigma_x^2 + \sigma_y^2}{\sigma_x\sigma_y}$

13. If $\sum xy = 2638$, $\bar{x} = 14$, $\bar{y} = 17$, $n = 10$ then cov (x, y) is   (1)

    (A) 24.2   (B) 25.8

    (C) 23.9   (D) 20.5

14. If $\sum xy = 1242$, $\bar{x} = -5.1$, $\bar{y} = -10$, $n = 10$, then cov (x, y) is   (2)

    (A) 67.4   (B) 83.9

    (C) 58.5   (D) 73.2

15. If $\sum x^2 = 2291$, $\sum y^2 = 3056$, $\sum (x + y)^2 = 10623$, $n = 10$, $\bar{x} = 14.7$, $\bar{y} = 17$ then cov (x, y) is   (2)

    (A) 1.39   (B) 13.9

    (C) 139   (D) -13.9

16. If the two regression coefficient are 0.16 and 4 then the correlation coefficient is   (2)

    (A) 0.08   (B) -0.8

    (C) 0.8   (D) 0.64

17. If the two regression coefficient are $-\dfrac{8}{15}$ and $-\dfrac{5}{6}$ then the correlation coefficient is   (2)

    (A) -0.667 (B) 0.5

    (C) -1.5 (D) 0.537

18. If covariance between x and y is 10 and the variance of x and y are 16 and 9 respectively then coefficient of correlation r(x, y) is   (2)

    (A) 0.833   (B) 0.633

    (C) 0.527   (D) 0.745

19. If cov (x, y) = 25.8 $\sigma_x = 6$, $\sigma_y = 5$ then correlation coefficient r(x, y) is equal to   (2)

    (A) 0.5   (B) 0.75

    (C) 0.91   (D) 0.86

20. If $\sum xy = 190$, $\bar{x} = 4$, $\bar{y} = 4$, $n = 10$, $\sigma_x = 1.732$, $\sigma_y = 2$ then correlation coefficient r(x, y) is equal to   (2)

    (A) 0.91287   (B) 0.8660

    (C) 0.7548   (D) 0.5324

21. If $\sum xy = 2800$, $\bar{x} = 16$, $\bar{y} = 16$, $n = 10$, variance of x is 36 and variance of y is 25 then correlation coefficient r(x, y) is equal to   (2)

    (A) 0.95   (B) 0.73   (C) 0.8   (D) 0.65

22. The correlation coefficient for the following data

$n = 10, \sum x = 140, \sum y = 150, \sum x^2 = 1980, \sum y^2 = 2465, \sum xy = 2160$ is   (2)

(A) 0.753   (B) 0.4325   (C) 0.556   (D) 0.9013

23. You are given the following information related to a distribution comprising 10 observation $\bar{x} = 5.5, \bar{y} = 4, \sum x^2 = 385, \sum y^2 = 192, \sum (x + y)^2 = 947$. The correlation coefficient $r(x, y)$ is   (2)

(A) -0.924 (B) -0.681 (C) -0.542 (D) -0.813

24. Given the following data

$r = 0.022, \sum xy = 33799, \sigma_x = 4.5, \sigma_y = 64.605, \bar{x} = 68, \bar{y} = 62.125$. The value of n (number of observation) is   (2)

(A) 5   (B) 7   (C) 8   (D) 10

25. Given the following data $r = 0.5, \sum xy = 350, \sigma_x = 1, \sigma_y = 4, \bar{x} = 3, \bar{y} = 4$. The value of n (number of observation) is   (2)

(A) 25   (B) 5   (C) 20   (D) 15

26. Coefficient of correlation between the variables x and y is 0.8 and their covariance is 20, the variance of x is 16. Standard deviation of y is   (2)

(A) 6.75   (B) 6.25   (C) 7.5   (D) 8.25

27. Line of regression y on x is $8x - 10y + 66 = 0$. Lie of regression x on y is

$40x - 18y - 214 = 0$. Mean values of x and y are   (2)

(A) $\bar{x} = 12, \bar{y} = 15$ (B) $\bar{x} = 10, \bar{y} = 11$

(C) $\bar{x} = 13, \bar{y} = 17$ (D) $\bar{x} = 9, \bar{y} = 8$

28. If the two lines of regression of $9x + y - \lambda = 0$ and $4x + y = \mu$ and the mean of x and y are 2 and −3 respectively then the values of λ and μ are   (2)

(A) $\lambda = 15$ and $\mu = 5$ (B) $\lambda = -15$ and $\mu = -5$

(C) $\lambda = 5$ and $\mu = 15$ (D) $\lambda = 15$ and $\mu = -5$

29. Line of regression y on x is $8x - 10y + 66 = 0$. Line of regression x on y is $40x - 18y - 214 = 0$. Correlation coefficient $r(x, y)$ is given by(2)

(A) 0.6   (B) 0.5   (C) 0.75   (D) 0.45

30. The regression lines are $9x + y = 15$ and $4x + y = 5$. Correlation $r(x, y)$ is given by (2)

(A) 0.444   (B) -0.11 (C) 0.663   (D) 0.7

31. Line of regression y on x is $8x - 10y + 66 = 0$. Line of regression x on y is $40x - 18y - 214 = 0$. The value of variance of x is 9. The standard deviation of y is equal to   (2)

(A) 2   (B) 5   (C) 6   (D) 4

32. Line of regression y on x is $8x - 10y + 66 = 0$. Line of regression x on y is $40x - 18y - 214 = 0$. The value of variance of y is 16. The standard deviation of x is equal to   (2)

(A) 3   (B) 2   (C) 6   (D) 7

33. Line of regression y on x is $3x + 2y = 26$, line of regression x on y is $6x + y = 31$. The value of variance of x is 25. Then the standard deviation of y is   (2)

(A) – 15   (B) 15   (C) 1.5   (D) – 1.5

34. The correlation coefficient between two variable x and y is 0.6. If $\sigma_x = 1.5$, $\sigma_y = 2.00$, $\bar{x} = 10$, $\bar{y} = 20$ then the lines of regression are   (2)

(A) $x = 0.45y + 12$ and $y = 0.8x + 1$

(B) $x = 0.45y + 1$ and $y = 0.8x + 12$

(C) $x = 0.65y + 10$ and $y = 0.4x + 12$

(D) $x = 0.8y + 1$ and $y = 0.45x + 12$

35. The correlation coefficient between two variable x and y is 0.711. If $\sigma_x = 4$, $\sigma_y = 1.8$, $\bar{x} = 5$, $\bar{y} = 4$ then the lines of regression are   (2)

(A) $x - 5 = 1.58 (y - 4)$ and $y - 4 = 0.32 (x - 5)$

(B) $x + 5 = 1.58 (y + 4)$ and $y + 4 = 0.32 (x + 5)$

(C) $x - 5 = 0.32 (y - 4)$ and $y - 4 = 1.58 (x - 5)$

(D) $x - 4 = 1.58 (y - 5)$ and $y - 5 = 0.32 (x - 4)$

36. Your are given below the following information about advertisement expenditure and sales

	Adv. Expenditure (X) ₹ (Crore)	Sales (Y) ₹ (Crore)
Mean	10	90
Standard Deviation	3	12

Correlation coefficient $= 0.8$

The two lines of regression are   (2)

(A) $x = 58 + 3.2y$ and $y = -8 + 0.2x$ (B) $x = -8 + 2.2y$ and $y = 8 + 1.2x$

(C) $x = -8 + 3.2y$ and $y = 58 + 0.2x$ (D) $x = -8 + 0.2y$ and $y = 58 + 3.2x$

37. You are given below the following information about rainfall and production of rice

	Rainfall (X) in inches	**Production of Rice (Y) in Kg**
Mean	30	500
Standard Deviation	5	100

Correlation coefficient = 0.8

The two lines of regression are   (2)

(A) $x + 30 = 0.04 (y + 500)$ and $y + 500 = 6 (x + 30)$

(B) $x - 30 = 0.4 (y - 500)$ and $y - 500 = 1.6 (x - 30)$

(C) $x - 30 = 0.04 (y - 500)$ and $y - 500 = 16 (x - 30)$

(D) $x - 30 = 16 (y - 500)$ and $y - 500 = 0.04 (x - 30)$

38. Given $b_{xy} = 0.85$, $b_{yx} = 0.89$ and the standard deviation of x is 6 then the value of correlation coefficient $r(x, y)$ and standard deviation of y is   (2)

(A) $r = 0.87, \sigma_y = 6.14$ (B) $r = -0.87, \sigma_y = 0.614$

(C) $r = 0.75, \sigma_y = 6.14$ (D) $r = 0.89, \sigma_y = 4.64$

39. Given $b_{xy} = 0.8411$, $b_{yx} = 0.4821$ and the standard deviation of y is 1.7916 then the value of correlation coefficient $r(x, y)$ and standard deviation of x is   (2)

(A) $r = -0.6368$ and $\sigma_x = -2.366$ (B) $r = 0.63678$ and $\sigma_x = 2.366$

(C) $r = 0.40549$ and $\sigma_x = 2.366$ (D) $r = 0.63678$ and $\sigma_x = 5.6$

40. For a given set of Bivariate data $\bar{x} = 53.2$, $\bar{y} = 27.9$ Regression coefficient of y on x = -1.5. By using line of regression y on x the most probable value of y when x is 60 is   (2)

(A) 15.7   (B) 13.7

(C) 17.7   (D) 21.7

41. Given the following data $\bar{x} = 36$, $\bar{y} = 85$, $\sigma_x = 11$, $\sigma_y = 8$, $r = 0.66$. By using line of regression x on y, the most probable value of x when $y = 75$ is   (2)

(A) 29.143   (B) 24.325

(C) 31.453   (D) 26.925

42. For a given set of Bivariate data $\bar{x} = 2$, $\bar{y} = -3$ Regression coefficient of x on y = -0.11. By using line of regression x on y the most probable value of x when y is 10 is   (2)

(A) 0.77   (B) 0.57   (C) 1.77   (D) 0.87

Answers

1. (A)	2. (D)	3. (C)	4. (B)	5. (C)	6. (D)	7. (B)	8. (A)
9. (C)	10. (D)	11. (D)	12. (A)	13. (B)	14. (D)	15. (B)	16. (C)
17. (A)	18. (A)	19. (D)	20. (B)	21. (C)	22. (D)	23. (B)	24. (C)
25. (A)	26. (B)	27. (C)	28. (A)	29. (A)	30. (C)	31. (D)	32. (A)
33. (B)	34. (B)	35. (A)	36. (D)	37. (C)	38. (A)	39. (B)	40. (C)
41. (D)	42. (B)						

CHAPTER EIGHT

PROBABILITY AND PROBABILITY DISTRIBUTIONS

8.1 INTRODUCTION

Theory of Probability had its origin in Mid-eighteenth century studies in games of chance related to dice throw gambling. Galileo was the first man to attempt at a quantitative measure of probability. The first foundation of Modern Mathematical theory of probability was laid down by French Mathematicians B. Pascal and P. Fermat. J. Bernoulli, Demoivre, T. Bayes, P. S. Laplace alongwith many others did considerable work in this field. Almost every human activity involves some kind of chance element and the role for the theory of probability to play. The subject of statistics originated much earlier than probability and dealt mainly with the collection and organisation of data. With the advent of probability, it was realized that statistics could be used in drawing valid conclusions and making reasonable decisions on the basis of analysis of data, such as in sampling theory and prediction of forecasting. As time progressed, probability theory found its way into many applications not only in Engineering and Science but also in the fields like Actuarial Science, Agriculture, Commerce, Medicine and Psychology.

The scope of this work is to introduce to the readers the modern concept of probability and the subject of probability distribution, which forms the basis of the modern theory of probability.

8.2 TERMINOLOGY

Before we take-up the subject matter, we shall define and explain certain terms which are encountered so very often.

(i) Experiment : Students of Science and Engineering are familiar with experiments which when performed repeatedly under the same conditions give identical results. In theory of probability, our interest is centred around the kind of experiment, which though repeated under essentially identical conditions, does not give unique results but may result in any one of the several possible outcomes. Such an experiment is also called a trial and the outcome an event or a case. For example, the throw of a coin is an experiment or a trial which can result in one of the two outcomes a Head or a Tail. Drawing a card from a well shuffled pack is a trial which may result in any one of 52 outcomes.

(ii) Equally Likely : The outcomes of a trial are said to be equally likely if any one of them cannot be expected to occur in preference to another. In tossing an unbiased coin, the outcomes Head or Tail are equally likely.

(iii) Mutually Exclusive : The outcomes of a trial are said to be mutually exclusive, if the occurrence of one of them precludes the occurrence of all other outcomes. In the experiment of throw of a die, the occurrence of number 1 at uppermost face will exclude automatically the occurrence of numbers 2, 3, 4, 5 and 6.

In tossing a coin, events Head or Tail are mutually exclusive.

(iv) Exhaustive : All possible outcomes of a trial form exhaustive set of cases or events. In throw of a coin, the events Head and Tail constitute exhaustive set of events. In throw of a die, appearance of numbers 1, 2, 3, 4, 5, 6 constitute exhaustive set of events.

(v) Sample Space : A set of all possible outcomes of a trial which are exhaustive is called a sample space. In a throw with two dice, sample space consists of following outcomes :

$$
\begin{array}{llllll}
(1,1), & (1,2), & (1,3), & (1,4), & (1,5), & (1,6) \\
(2,1), & (2,2), & (2,3), & (2,4), & (2,5), & (2,6) \\
(3,1), & (3,2), & (3,3), & (3,4), & (3,5), & (3,6) \\
(4,1), & (4,2), & (4,3), & (4,4), & (4,5), & (4,6) \\
(5,1), & (5,2), & (5,3), & (5,4), & (5,5), & (5,6) \\
(6,1), & (6,2), & (6,3), & (6,4), & (6,5), & (6,6)
\end{array}
$$

which forms a sample space.

(vi) Independent : Events A and B are said to be independent if happening of A has nothing to do with the happening of B and vice-a-versa. If a coin is thrown twice, the event 'Occurrence of Head in first throw' has nothing to do with the event '*Occurrence of Head in second throw*'. The two successive throws, or for that matter n successive throws, are considered as independent trials, which result in independent outcomes. Note that independent events are quite different from mutually exclusive events.

If the occurrence of event B is affected by the occurrence of event A, then such events are Dependent events. For example, if two cards are drawn successively from a well shuffled pack of cards *without replacement*, then the event of appearance of king at second draw will certainly depend upon the result of the first draw.

8.3 DEFINITION OF PROBABILITY AND RELATED EXAMPLES

Question of defining Probability is quite delicate. In Modern Axiomatic approach, the term 'Probability' is left undefined. However, we shall give two definitions of probability, which have got their limitations, but serve the purpose in many cases.

(1) Classical or 'a *priori*' Probability : If a trial results in n exhaustive cases which are mutually exclusive and equally likely and out of which m are favourable to the happening of event A, then the probability P of the happening of event A also denoted by P (A) is given by,

$$
p = P(A) = \frac{m}{n}
$$

If $\overline{A}$ indicates non-happening of A, then the number of cases favourable to this event are obviously n – m and

$$q = P(\overline{A}) = \frac{n-m}{n} = 1 - \frac{m}{n}$$

$$\therefore \qquad P(\overline{A}) = 1 - P(A)$$

Or $\qquad P(A) + P(\overline{A}) = 1 \qquad$ i.e. $\quad p + q = 1$

If an event A is certain to happen

$$P(\overline{A}) = 0 \text{ and } P(A) = 1.$$

(2) Statistical or Empirical Definition : If a trial be repeated for a large number of times, say n, under the same conditions and a certain event A occurs on $p \times n$ occasions, then, the probability of happening of event A is given by

$$P(A) = \lim_{n \to \infty} \frac{p \times n}{n} = p$$

The classical definition of probability gives the relative frequency of favourable cases to the total number of cases, which in the empirical definition is the limit of the relative frequency of the happening of the event.

Note that $\qquad 0 \leq P(A) \leq 1.$

$P(A) = \dfrac{m}{n}$ is sometimes expressed by saying that the odds in favour of A are m : (n – m) or the odds against A are (n – m) : n.

ILLUSTRATIONS

Ex. 1 : *Find the probability of drawing the king from a well shuffled pack of cards.*

Sol. : *Here the total number of outcomes is n = 52 and there are four kings in the pack of cards.*

$$\therefore \quad \textit{Required probability} = p = \frac{m}{n} = \frac{4}{52} = \frac{1}{13}$$

Ex. 2 : *If 3 of 20 tubes are defective and 4 of them are randomly chosen for inspection (i.e. each tube has the same chance of being selected), then what is the probability that only one of the defective tubes will be included ?*

Sol. : 4 tubes can be selected out of 20 in $^{20}C_4$ ways.

$$\therefore \qquad n = {}^{20}C_4 = \frac{20 \cdot 19 \cdot 18 \cdot 17}{1 \cdot 2 \cdot 3 \cdot 4} = 4845$$

One defective tube can be chosen in $^3C_1$ ways and each of which should be associated with 3 non-defective tubes which can be selected in $^{17}C_3$ ways.

Thus
$$m = {}^3C_1 \times {}^{17}C_3 = 3 \times \frac{17 \cdot 16 \cdot 15}{1 \cdot 2 \cdot 3} = 2040$$

$$p = \frac{m}{n} = \frac{2040}{4845} = \frac{8}{19} = 0.42 \text{ approximately.}$$

Ex. 3 : *A throw is made with two dice. Find the probability of getting a score of*

(i)   10 points; (ii) At least 10 points; (iii) At most 10 points.

Sol. : All possible outcomes are sample space.

(1, 1),   (1, 2),   (1, 3),   (1, 4),   (1, 5),   (1, 6)
(2, 1),   (2, 2),   (2, 3),   (2, 4),   (2, 5),   (2, 6)
(3, 1),   (3, 2),   (3, 3),   (3, 4),   (3, 5),   (3, 6)
(4, 1),   (4, 2),   (4, 3),   (4, 4),   (4, 5),   (4, 6)
(5, 1),   (5, 2),   (5, 3),   (5, 4),   (5, 5),   (5, 6)
(6, 1),   (6, 2),   (6, 3),   (6, 4),   (6, 5),   (6, 6)

(1) The total number of outcomes are $n = 36$, the number of cases favourable to the event.

(i)   of total of 10 points are (4, 6), (5, 5), (6, 4) i.e. $m = 3$

$\therefore$ p (score of 10 points) $= \dfrac{3}{36} = \dfrac{1}{12}.$

(ii) The number of cases favourable to the event score of at least 10 points are the score with 10, 11 and 12 points.

These are (4, 6), (5, 5), (6, 4), (5, 6), (6, 5), (6, 6) i.e. $m = 6$

$\therefore$ p (at least 10 points) $= \dfrac{6}{36} = \dfrac{1}{6}$.

(iii) The number of cases favourable to the event at most 10 points are the score with less than or equal to 10 points. These are all the first four rows of sample space containing 24 cases, 5 cases from fifth row and 4 cases from fourth row.

$$m = 24 + 5 + 4 = 33$$

$\therefore$ p (at most 10 points) $= \dfrac{33}{36} = \dfrac{11}{12}$

Ex. 4 : *What is the probability that a leap year selected at random will contain 53 Mondays ?*

Sol. : Leap year will have 366 days, 52 Mondays will be contained in 364 days. Now the extra two days could be

(1) Sunday, Monday, (2) Monday, Tuesday, (3) Tuesday, Wednesday, (4) Wednesday, Thursday, (5) Thursday, Friday, (6) Friday, Saturday or (7) Saturday, Sunday. Thus there are seven possible ways in which two extra days can occur i.e. n = 7 out of these, first two cases contain Monday.

Thus in m = 2 cases, there will be extra Monday.

Thus required probability,

$$p = \frac{2}{7}$$

Ex. 5 : *From a well shuffled pack of cards, three cards are drawn at random. Find the probability that they form a King, Queen, Jack combination.*

Sol. : 3 cards can be drawn in $^{52}C_3$ ways.

$$n = {}^{52}C_3 = \frac{52 \cdot 51 \cdot 50}{1 \cdot 2 \cdot 3}$$

King, Queen and Jack each can be chosen in $^4C_1$ ways.

The combination can be chosen in

$$^4C_1 \times {}^4C_1 \times {}^4C_1 = 64$$

$$m = 64$$

$$p = p\,(KQJ) = \frac{64}{\dfrac{52 \cdot 51 \cdot 50}{1 \cdot 2 \cdot 3}} = \frac{64}{26 \cdot 17 \cdot 50} = \frac{16}{5525}$$

Ex. 6 : *Among six books, there are two volume of one book. These books are arranged in a random order on a shelf. Find the probability that the two volumes are always together.*

Sol. : Six books can be arranged on a shelf in 6! = 720 ways, thus n = 720.

If first two places are occupied by same volume and remaining by other four books, this can happen in 2! × 4! = 48 ways.

Two volume can come together if they occupy 1st and 2nd, 2nd and 3rd, 3rd and 4th, 4th and 5th or 5th and 6th positions. Each of which can happen in 48 ways.

Thus

$$m = 48 \times 5 = 240$$

$$\therefore \qquad p = \frac{m}{n} = \frac{240}{720} = \frac{1}{3}$$

8.4 ALGEBRA OF SETS

We discuss below elementary ideas about sets, Venn diagrams and operations on sets.

Set : Set can be thought of as a well-defined collection of objects, called members or elements of the set. In order for a set to be well-defined, we must be able to determine whether a particular object does or does not belong to the set. Elements of the set can be enumerated by roster method or by the property method. The set of all vowels in the English alphabet can be defined by the roster method as (a, e, i, o, u). In this method, we actually list all the elements. The set of all natural numbers can be written as $\{1, 2, 3, ...\}$. Here we do not list all the elements, but write the elements in such a way that the complete description is evident. Set of vowels can be described as $\{x \mid x$ is a vowel$\}$ which reads as, the set of all elements x and that x is a vowel. This is a property method to define a set. If an element a belongs to the set D, we write $a \in D$. If a does not belong to D, we write $a \notin D$.

Subsets : If each element of set A also belongs to a set B then we call A as subset of B, written as $A \subset B$ or $B \supset A$ and 'A is contained in B' or 'B contains A' respectively.

It follows that for all sets A, we have $A \subset A$.

If $A \subset B$ and $B \subset A$ then we call A and B equal and write $A = B$. In such a case, A and B have exactly the same elements.

If A is not equal to B i.e. if A and B do not have exactly the same elements, then we write $A \neq B$.

If $A \subset B$ but $A \neq B$, then we call A a proper subset of B. For example, if $A = \{1, 2, 5\}$, $B = \{1, 2, 3, 4, 5\}$ then $A \neq B$ and $A \subset B$. Thus A is proper subset of B.

It can be easily established that if $A \subset B$ and $B \subset C$ then $A \subset C$.

Universal Set and Empty Set : For many purposes, we restrict our discussion to subsets of some particular set called the universal set denoted by U.

It is also useful to consider a set having no elements at all. This is called the empty set or null set and it is denoted by ϕ. It is a subset of any set.

In dealing with a problem of throw of a die, the universal set is $\{1, 2, 3, 4, 5, 6\}$. The set of outcomes consisting of faces 8 or 10 on a single die is the null set.

In dealing with problems on probability, the sample space S usually constitutes a Universal set.

Venn Diagrams : A universal set U can be represented geometrically by the set of points inside a rectangle. In such a case, subsets of U (such as A and B shown shaded in Fig. 8.1) are represented by sets of points inside circles. Such diagrams called Venn diagrams, often serve to provide geometric intuition regarding possible relationships between sets.

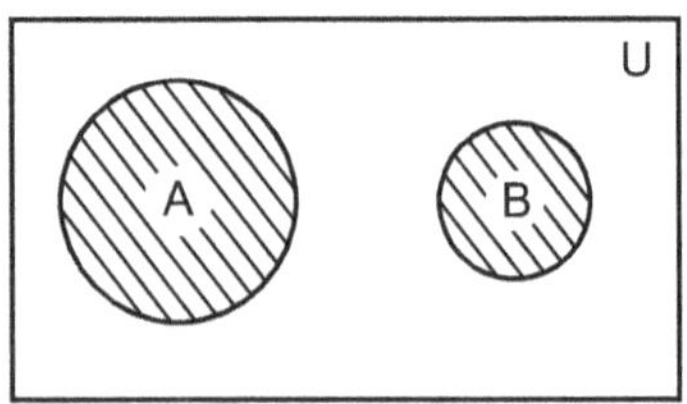

Fig. 8.1

Set Operations :

1. Union : The set of all elements (or points) which belong to either A or B or both A and B is called the union of A and B and is denoted by $A \cup B$, shown by shaded region in Fig. 8.2.

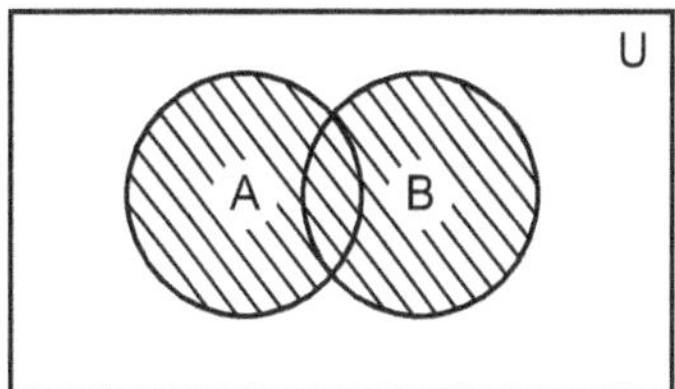

Fig. 8.2

2. Intersection : The set of all elements which belong to both A and B is called the intersection of A and B and is denoted by $A \cap B$, shown by shaded region in Fig. 8.3.

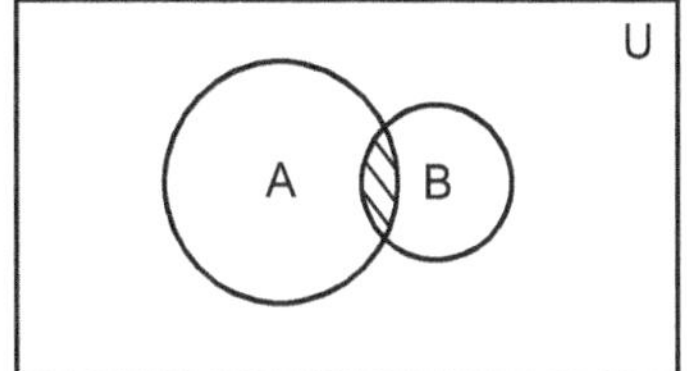

Fig. 8.3

Two sets A and B such that $A \cap B = \phi$ i.e. which have no elements in common are called disjoint sets. In Fig. 8.1, A and B are disjoint.

3. Difference : The set consisting of all the elements of A which do not belong to B is called the difference of A and B, denoted by $A - B$, shown by shaded region in Fig. 8.4.

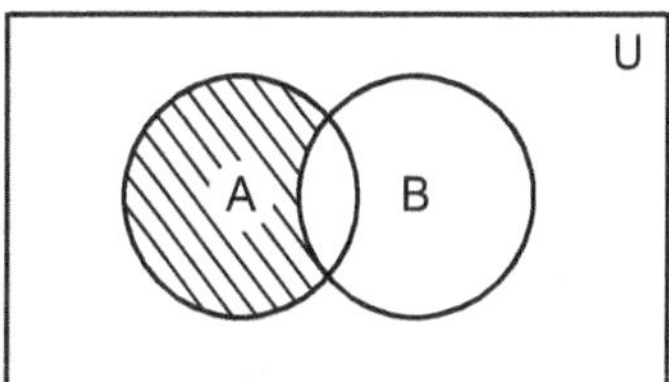

Fig. 8.4

4. Complement : If $B \subset A$ then $A - B$ is called the complement of B relative to A and is denoted by B'_A , shown by shaded region in Fig. 8.5.

If $A = U$, the universal set, we refer to $U - B$ as simply the complement of B and denote it by B', shown shaded in Fig. 8.6. The complement of $A \cup B$ is denoted by $(A \cup B)'$.

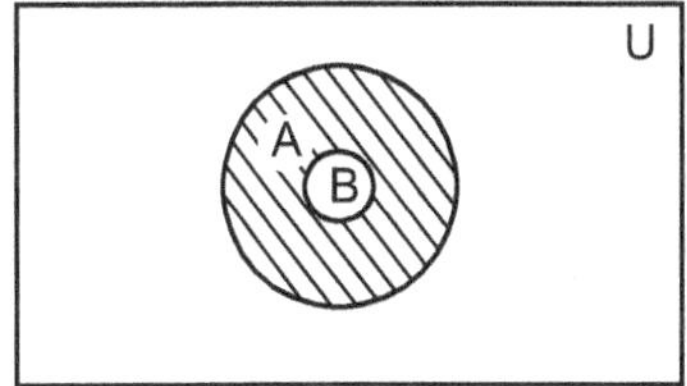

Fig. 8.5

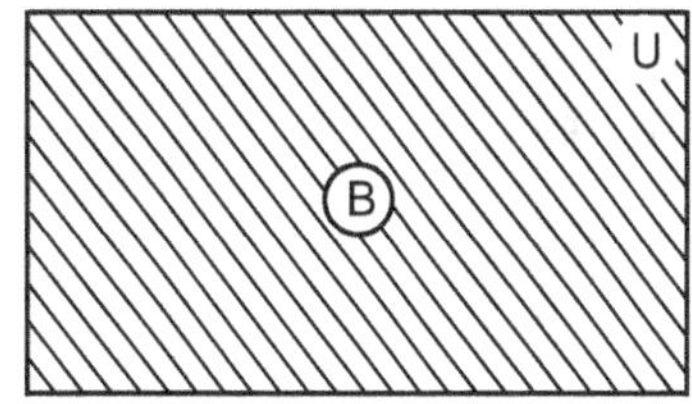

Fig. 8.6

Operations Involving Sets

1. Commutative law for Unions $\qquad A \cup B = B \cup A$
2. Associative law for Unions $\qquad A \cup (B \cup C) = (A \cup B) \cup C = A \cup B \cup C$
3. Commutative law for intersections $\quad A \cap B = B \cap A$

4. Associative law for intersections $\quad A \cap (A \cap C) = (A \cap B) \cap C = A \cap B \cap C$

5. First Distributive law $\quad A \cap (B \cup C) = (A \cap B) \cup (A \cap C)$

6. Second Distributive law $\quad A \cup (B \cap C) = (A \cup B) \cap (A \cup C)$

7. $A - B = A \cap B'$

8. If $A \subset B$, then $A' \supset B'$ or $B' \subset A'$

9. $A \cup \phi = A,\ A \cap \phi = \phi$

10. $A \cup U = U,\ A \cap U = A$

11. Demorgan's first law $\quad (A \cap B)' = A' \cup B'$

12. Demorgan's second law $\quad (A \cap B)' = A' \cup B'$

13. For any sets A and B $\quad A = (A \cap B) \cup (A \cap B')$

An event is a subset A of the sample space S, i.e. it is a set of all possible outcomes. If the outcome of an experiment is an element of A, then we say that the event A has occurred.

If A and B are any two events, then

1. $A \cup B$ is the event either A or B or both, sometimes this is denoted by $A + B$.

2. $A \cap B$ is the event both A and B, alternatively it is denoted by AB.

3. A' or $\overline{A}$ is the event not A.

4. $A - B$ is the event A but not B.

If the sets corresponding to events A and B are disjoint i.e. $A \cap B = \phi$, then we often say that the events are mutually exclusive.

8.5 THEOREMS ON PROBABILITY

(1) **Theorem of Total probability :** If A and B are any two events then

$$P(A \cup B) = P(A) + P(B) - P(A \cap B)$$

Proof : Consider the sample space containing n cases, out of which m_1 are favourable to the event A, m_2 are favourable to the event B and m_3 are favourable to the event $A \cap B$ (or AB).

$n(A) = m_1,\ n(B) = m_2,\ n(A \cap B) = m_3$

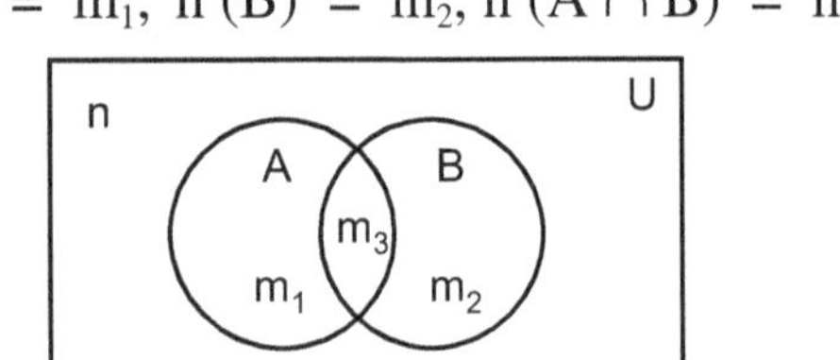

Fig. 8.7

∴ Total number of cases favourable to the event $A \cup B$ (or $A + B$) are $m_1 + m_2 - m_3$ (Because addition of m_1 and m_2 cases includes m_3 twice).

$$\therefore \quad P(A \cup B) = \frac{m_1 + m_2 - m_3}{n} = \frac{m_1}{n} + \frac{m_2}{n} - \frac{m_3}{n}$$

$$= P(A) + P(B) - P(A \cap B)$$

If the events A, B, are mutually exclusive then $P(A \cap B) = 0$

$\therefore \qquad P(A \cup B) = P(A) + P(B)$

Similarly for three events A, B, C, it can be proved that

$$P(A \cup B \cup C) = P(A) + P(B) + P(C) - P(A \cap B) - P(B \cap C)$$
$$- P(C \cap A) + P(A \cap B \cap C)$$

Generalization of this theorem for n events $A_1, A_2, A_3 \ldots A_n$ can also be made.

In particular if $A_1, A_2, A_3 \ldots A_n$ are mutually exclusive event, then

$$P(A_1 \cup A_2 \cup A_3 \cup \ldots \cup A_n) = P(A_1) + P(A_2) + \ldots + P(A_n).$$

(2) Theorem of Compound Probability :

$$P(A \cap B) = P(A)\, P(B|A)$$

where, B|A means occurrence of event B, subject to the condition that A has already occurred.

Proof : Consider the sample space containing n cases, out of which m_1 are favourable to the event A and out of these m_1 cases, m_2 are favourable to the event B $(B \subset A)$.

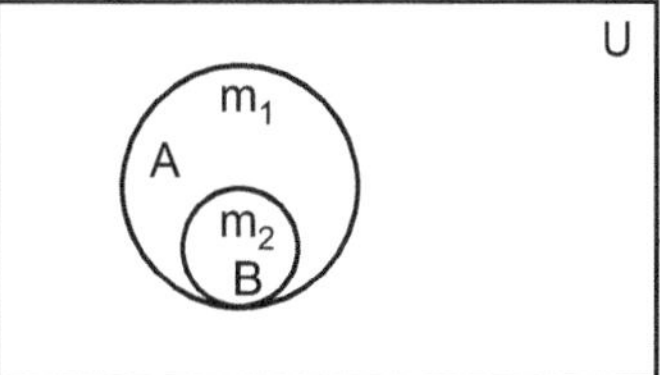

Fig. 8.8

Thus m_2 cases correspond to the event $A \cap B$.

Now we can write, $\qquad \dfrac{m_2}{n} = \dfrac{m_2}{m_1} \cdot \dfrac{m_1}{n}$

It is clear that $\qquad \dfrac{m_2}{m_1} = P(B|A)$

$\therefore \qquad \dfrac{m_2}{n} = P(A \cap B)$

$\qquad \dfrac{m_1}{n} = P(A)$

$\therefore \qquad P(A \cap B) = P(B|A) \cdot P(A)$

Similarly, if $A \subset B$ then $\quad P(A \cap B) = P(A|B) \cdot P(B)$

If A and B are independent events, then

$$P(B|A) = P(B) \text{ or } P(A|B) = P(A)$$

and we have $\quad P(A \cap B) = P(A) \cdot P(B)$

Similarly, it can be proved that for any three events A_1, A_2, A_3

$$P(A_1 \cap A_2 \cap A_3) = P(A_1)\, P(A_2|A_1)\, P(A_3|A_1 \cap A_2)$$

In particular if A_1, A_2, A_3 are independent events, then

$$P(A_1 \cap A_2 \cap A_3) = P(A_1) \cdot P(A_2) \cdot P(A_3)$$

(3) Baye's theorem : If A_1, A_2, ..., A_n are mutually exclusive events whose union is the sample space and A is any event, then

$$P(A_k|A) = \frac{P(A_k)\, P(A|A_k)}{\sum\limits_{k=1}^{n} P(A_k)\, P(A|A_k)}$$

Proof :

$$P(A) = P(A_1)\, P(A|A_1) + P(A_2)\, P(A|A_2) + \ldots + P(A_n)\, P(A|A_n)$$

$$= \sum\limits_{k=1}^{n} P(A_k)\, P(A|A_k)$$

Thus,

$$P(A_k|A) = \frac{P(A_k \cap A)}{P(A)} = \frac{P(A_k)\, P(A|A_k)}{\sum\limits_{k=1}^{n} P(A_k)\, P(A|A_k)}$$

This proves the theorem.

ILLUSTRATIONS

Ex. 1 : *Two cards are drawn from a well shuffled pack of 52 cards. Find the probability that they are both kings if*

(i) the first card drawn is replaced, (ii) first card drawn is not replaced.

Sol. : (i) First card drawn is replaced : Let A_1 be event of king on first draw and A_2 be the event of king on second draw. $A_1 \cap A_2$ is the event of king at both draws.

If first card drawn is replaced before the second draw then A_1, A_2 are independent.

$\therefore$

$$P(A_1 \cap A_2) = P(A_1) \cdot P(A_2)$$

$$P(A_1) = \frac{4}{52} = \frac{1}{13} \text{ (as there are four kings)}$$

$$P(A_2) = \frac{4}{52} = \frac{1}{13}$$

$\therefore$

$$P(A_1 \cap A_2) = \frac{1}{13} \cdot \frac{1}{13} = \frac{1}{169}$$

(ii) First card drawn is not replaced : In this case, the two events are dependent.

$$P (A_1 \cap A_2) = P (A_1) \cdot P (A_2 | A_1)$$

$$\therefore \qquad P (A_1) = \frac{4}{52} = \frac{1}{13}$$

If first draw is king then for second draw, 3 kings are left to be chosen out of 51 cards.

$$P (A_2 | A_1) = \frac{3}{51} = \frac{1}{17}$$

$$\therefore \qquad P (A_1 \cap A_2) = \frac{1}{13} \cdot \frac{1}{17} = \frac{1}{221}$$

Ex. 2 : *A can hit the target 1 out of 4 times, B can hit the target 2 out of 3 times, C can hit the target 3 out of 4 times. Find the probability of at least two hit the target.*

(Dec. 2005)

Sol. : Let A be the event of A hitting the target, B the event of B hitting the target, C the event of C hitting the target.

$$P (A) = \frac{1}{4}, \qquad P (\bar{A}) = 1 - \frac{1}{4} = \frac{3}{4}$$

$$P (B) = \frac{2}{3}, \qquad P (\bar{B}) = \frac{1}{3}$$

$$P (C) = \frac{3}{4}, \qquad P (\bar{C}) = \frac{1}{4}$$

The required event 'at least two hitting the target' can occur in following mutually exclusive cases : $A \cap B \cap \bar{C}$, $A \cap \bar{B} \cap C$, $\bar{A} \cap B \cap C$, $A \cap B \cap C$

P (at least two hitting the target)

$$= P (A \cap B \cap \bar{C}) + P (A \cap \bar{B} \cap C) + P (\bar{A} \cap B \cap C) + P (A \cap B \cap C)$$

Now A, B, $\bar{C}$ etc. are all independent.

$$\therefore \qquad P (A \cap B \cap \bar{C}) = P (A) P (B) P (\bar{C}) = \frac{1}{4} \times \frac{2}{3} \times \frac{1}{4} = \frac{1}{24}$$

$$P (A \cap \bar{B} \cap C) = P (A) P (\bar{B}) P (C) = \frac{1}{4} \times \frac{1}{3} \times \frac{3}{4} = \frac{1}{16}$$

$$P (\bar{A} \cap B \cap C) = P (\bar{A}) P (B) P (C) = \frac{3}{4} \times \frac{2}{3} \times \frac{3}{4} = \frac{3}{8}$$

$$P (A \cap B \cap C) = P (A) P (B) P (C) = \frac{1}{4} \times \frac{2}{3} \times \frac{3}{4} = \frac{1}{8}$$

P (at least two hit the target)

$$= \frac{1}{24} + \frac{1}{16} + \frac{3}{8} + \frac{1}{8} = \frac{2 + 3 + 18 + 6}{48} = \frac{29}{48}$$

Ex. 3 : _An envelope contains 6 tickets with numbers 1, 2, 3, 5, 6, 7. Another envelope contains 4 tickets with numbers 1, 3, 5, 7. An envelope is chosen at random and ticket is drawn from it. Find the probability that the ticket bears the numbers (i) 2 or 5, (ii) 2._

(Dec. 2008)

Sol. : (i) Required event can happen in the following mutually exclusive ways.

(1) First envelope is chosen and then ticket is drawn.

(2) Second envelope is chosen and then ticket is drawn. Probability of choosing an envelope is 1/2.

Required probability p is

$$p = p(1) + p(2) = \frac{1}{2} \times \frac{2}{6} + \frac{1}{2} \times \frac{1}{4} = \frac{1}{6} + \frac{1}{8} = \frac{4+3}{24} = \frac{7}{24}$$

(ii)

$$p = p(1) + p(2) = \frac{1}{2} \times \frac{1}{6} + \frac{1}{2} \times 0 = \frac{1}{12}$$

Ex. 4 : _An urn contains 6 white and 8 red balls. Second urn contains 9 white and 10 red balls. One ball is drawn at random from the first urn and put into the second urn without noticing its colour. A ball is then drawn at random from the second urn. What is the probability that it is red ?_

Sol. : There are two mutually exclusive cases.

(i) The white ball is transferred from the first urn to the second and then red ball is drawn from it.

(ii) The red ball is transferred from the first urn to the second and then ball is drawn from it.

Let A be the event of transferring a white ball from the first urn, B be the event of transferring a red ball from the first urn, and C the event of drawing a red ball from the second urn.

$$P(A) = \frac{6}{14} = \frac{3}{7}$$

$$P(B) = \frac{8}{14} = \frac{4}{7}$$

$$P(C|A) = \frac{10}{20} = \frac{1}{2}$$

(In this, second urn will contain 10 white and 10 red)

$$P(C|B) = \frac{11}{20} \quad \text{(In this case, second urn will contain 9 white and 11 red)}$$

$$\therefore \qquad P(i) = P(A \cap C) = P(A)\,P(C|A) = \frac{3}{7} \times \frac{1}{2} = \frac{3}{14}$$

$$\therefore \qquad P(ii) = P(B \cap C)$$

$$= P(B) \cdot P(C|B) = \frac{4}{7} \times \frac{11}{20} = \frac{11}{35}$$

Required probability P is given by

$$P = P(i) + P(ii) = \frac{3}{14} + \frac{11}{35} = \frac{105 + 154}{490} = \frac{259}{490}$$

Ex. 5 : *A, B play a game of alternate tossing a coin, one who gets head first wins the game. Find the probability of B winning the game if A has a start.*   **(Dec. 2007)**

Sol. : In following mutually exclusive run or trails, B wins the game.

$A \to T, B \to H$	Run TH
$A \to T, B \to T, A \to T, B \to H$	Run TTTH
Similarly,	TTTTTH
	....
	....

$$P\,(TH)\ =\ P\,(T)\,P\,(H)\ =\frac{1}{2}\cdot\frac{1}{2}\ =\frac{1}{4}\ =\frac{1}{2^2}$$

$$P(TTTH)\ =\ P\,(T)\,P\,(T)\,P\,(T)\,P\,(H)\ =\frac{1}{2}\cdot\frac{1}{2}\cdot\frac{1}{2}\cdot\frac{1}{2}\ =\frac{1}{2^4}$$

$$P(TTTTTH)\ =\ \frac{1}{2^6}$$

Required probability is $P\ =\ \dfrac{1}{2^2}+\dfrac{1}{2^4}+\dfrac{1}{2^6}+\ldots\ldots$

which is G.P. with common ratio $=\dfrac{1}{4}$

$$P\ =\ \frac{\dfrac{1}{4}}{1-\dfrac{1}{4}}\ =\ \frac{1}{3}$$

Ex. 6 : *A box contains 6 red balls, 4 white balls and 5 blue balls. Three balls are drawn successively from the box. Find the probability that they are drawn in the order red, white and blue if each ball is not replaced.*

Sol. : Let A be the event - red on the first draw, B be the event - white on second draw, C be the event - blue on third draw. We want to find $P\,(A \cap B \cap C)$.

By theorem on Compound probability,

$$P\,(A \cap B \cap C)\ =\ P\,(A)\cdot P\,(B|A)\cdot P\,(C|A \cap B)$$

$$P\,(A)\ =\ \frac{6}{15}\ =\frac{2}{5}$$

$$P\,(B|A)\ =\ \frac{4}{14}$$

$$P\,(C|A \cap B)\ =\ \frac{5}{13}$$

$$\therefore\qquad P\,(A \cap B \cap C)\ =\ \frac{2}{5}\cdot\frac{4}{14}\cdot\frac{5}{13}=\ \frac{4}{91}$$

Ex. 7 : *Supposing that out of 12 test matches played between India and Pakistan during last 3 years, 6 are won by India, 4 are won by Pakistan and 2 have ended in a draw. If they agree to play a test series consisting of three matches, find the probability that India wins the test series on the basis of past performance.*

Sol. : India wins test series in following mutually exclusive cases :

(1) one win for India, 2 draws   (2) two wins for India, 1 draw

(3) two wins for India, 1 win for Pakistan.   (4) three wins for India.

On the basis of past performance

$$P \text{ (Indian win)} \ = \ \frac{6}{12} = \frac{1}{2} \quad P \text{ (Pakistan win)} = \frac{4}{12} = \frac{1}{3}$$

$$P \text{ (Draw)} \ = \ \frac{2}{12} = \frac{1}{6}$$

(i) One sequence in which Indian win and 2 draws can occur is Indian win, draw, draw (WDD).

$$\therefore \qquad P \text{ (WDD)} \ = \ P \text{ (W) } P \text{ (D) } P \text{ (D)} = \frac{1}{2} \cdot \frac{1}{6} \cdot \frac{1}{6} = \frac{1}{72}$$

One Indian win and 2 draws can occur in $^3C_1$ or 3 mutually exclusive ways.

$$P \text{ (i)} \ = \ 3 \cdot \frac{1}{72} = \frac{1}{24}$$

(ii) One sequence in which two Indian wins and a draw can occur is Indian win, Indian win, draw (WWD)

$$\therefore \qquad P \text{ (WWD)} \ = \ P \text{ (W) } P \text{ (W) } P \text{ (D)} = \frac{1}{2} \cdot \frac{1}{2} \cdot \frac{1}{6} = \frac{1}{24}$$

Two Indian wins and a draw can occur in 3 mutually exclusive ways

$$\therefore \qquad P \text{ (ii)} \ = \ 3 \cdot \frac{1}{24} = \frac{1}{8}$$

(iii) One sequence in which two Indian wins and one Pakistan win can occur is Indian win, Indian win, Pakistan win.

$$P \text{ (Indian win, Indian win, Pakistan win)} = \frac{1}{2} \cdot \frac{1}{2} \cdot \frac{1}{3} = \frac{1}{12}$$

$$P \text{ (iii)} \ = \ 3 \cdot \frac{1}{12} = \frac{1}{4}$$

(iv) Three Indian wins can occur in only one way. Indian win, Indian win, Indian win.

$$P \text{ (iv)} \ = \ \frac{1}{2} \cdot \frac{1}{2} \cdot \frac{1}{2} = \frac{1}{8}$$

Required probability P of Indian winning the series is

$$P \ = \ P \text{ (i)} + P \text{ (ii)} + P \text{ (iii)} + P \text{ (iv)}$$

$$= \ \frac{1}{24} + \frac{1}{8} + \frac{1}{4} + \frac{1}{8} = \frac{1 + 3 + 6 + 3}{24} = \frac{13}{24}$$

Ex. 8 : *A six faced die is so biased that it is twice as likely to show an even number as an odd number when thrown. It is thrown twice. What is the probability that the sum of the two numbers thrown is even ?*

Sol. : Let probability of an odd number be P, so probability of an even number appearing is 2P.

Now there are 6 outcomes (1, 2, 3, 4, 5, 6)

$\therefore \qquad P(1) = P(3) = P(5) = P, \quad P(2) = P(4) = P(6) = 2P$

$P(1) + P(2) + P(3) + P(4) + P(5) + P(6) = 1$

$\therefore \quad 9P = 1 \qquad\qquad \therefore P = \dfrac{1}{9}$

When a die is thrown twice, the sample space is described as,

$$
\begin{array}{llllll}
(1, 1), & (1, 2), & (1, 3), & (1, 4), & (1, 5), & (1, 6) \\
(2, 1), & (2, 2), & (2, 3), & (2, 4), & (2, 5), & (2, 6) \\
(3, 1), & (3, 2), & (3, 3), & (3, 4), & (3, 5), & (3, 6) \\
(4, 1), & (4, 2), & (4, 3), & (4, 4), & (4, 5), & (4, 6) \\
(5, 1), & (5, 2), & (5, 3), & (5, 4), & (5, 5), & (5, 6) \\
(6, 1), & (6, 2), & (6, 3), & (6, 4), & (6, 5), & (6, 6)
\end{array}
$$

We want to find the probability of event of sum of the two numbers even.

In first row, cases (1, 1), (1, 3), (1, 5) are favourable to the event with probabilities

$$P(1, 1) = P(1, 3) = P(1, 5) = \frac{1}{9} \times \frac{1}{9} = \frac{1}{81}$$

In second row, cases (2, 2), (2, 4), (2, 6) are favourable to the event where

$$P(2, 2) = P(2, 4) = P(2, 6) = \frac{2}{9} \times \frac{2}{9} = \frac{4}{81}$$

Similarly 3rd and 5th row have cases (3, 1), (3, 3), (3, 5) and (5, 1), (5, 3), (5, 5); and 4th and 6th row have cases (4, 2), (4, 4), (4, 6) and (6, 2), (6, 4), (6, 6).

Required probability P is given by,

$$
\begin{aligned}
P = {} & P(1, 1) + P(1, 3) + P(1, 5) + P(2, 2) + P(2, 4) + P(2, 6) \\
& + P(3, 1) + P(3, 3) + P(3, 5) + P(4, 2) + P(4, 4) + P(4, 6) \\
& + P(5, 1) + P(5, 3) + P(5, 5) + P(6, 2) + P(6, 4) + P(6, 6) \\
= {} & \frac{1}{81} + \frac{1}{81} + \frac{1}{81} + \frac{4}{81} + \frac{4}{81} + \frac{4}{81} + \frac{1}{81} + \frac{1}{81} + \frac{1}{81} + \frac{4}{81} + \frac{4}{81} + \frac{4}{81} \\
& + \frac{1}{81} + \frac{1}{81} + \frac{1}{81} + \frac{4}{81} + \frac{4}{81} + \frac{4}{81} = \frac{45}{81} = \frac{5}{9}
\end{aligned}
$$

Ex. 9 : *A is one of the eight horses entered for a race and is to be ridden by one of the two jockeys B and C. It is 2 to 1 that B rides A, in which case all the horses are equally likely to win, whereas with rider C, A's chance is doubled.*

(1)　Find the probability that A wins.

(2)　What are odds against A's winning ?　　　　　　　　　　　　　**(Dec. 2008)**

Sol. : (1) A can win in the following two mutually exclusive cases.

(i)　B rides A and A wins.

(ii)　C rides A and A wins.

$$P\,(i) \; = \; \frac{2}{3} \times \frac{1}{8} = \frac{1}{12} \qquad P\,(ii) = \frac{1}{3} \times \frac{2}{8} = \frac{1}{12}$$

Probability of A winning

$$= P\,(i) + P\,(ii) \; = \; \frac{1}{12} + \frac{1}{12} = \frac{1}{6}$$

(2)　Probability of A's losing $= \; 1 - \dfrac{1}{6} = \dfrac{5}{6}$.

Hence odds against A's winning are $\dfrac{5}{6} : \dfrac{1}{6}$, i.e. 5 : 1.

EXERCISE 8.1

1.　A throw is made with two dice. Find the probability that (i) the sum is 7 or less, (ii) the sum is a perfect square.

　　　　　　　　　　　　　　　　　Ans. (i) $\dfrac{7}{12}$; (ii) $\dfrac{7}{36}$.

2.　Three coins are tossed simultaneously. Find the probability of getting at least 2 Heads.

　　　　　　　　　　　　　　　　　　　　　　Ans. $\left(\dfrac{1}{2}\right)$

3.　From a deck of 52 cards, two cards are drawn at random. Find the probability that (i) Both are Hearts, (i) Both the cards are of different suits.

　　　　　　　　　　　　　　Ans. (i) $\dfrac{39}{613}$; (ii) $\dfrac{13}{17}$.

4.　There are six married couples in a room. If two persons are chosen at random, find the probability that (i) they are of different sex, (ii) they are married to each other.

　　　　　　　　　　　　　　　　Ans. (i) $\dfrac{6}{11}$; (ii) $\dfrac{1}{11}$.

5. Find the probability that six people selected at random will have six different birth dates.

[**Hint :** Sample space $(365)^6$]   **Ans.** 0.9595.

6. A five figure number is formed by the digits 0, 1, 3, 4, (without repetition). Find the probability that the number formed is divisible by 4.

Ans. $\dfrac{3}{10}$.

7. A, B, C throw the coin alternatively in that order. One who gets Tail first wins the game. Find the probability of B winning the game if C has a start.

Ans. $\dfrac{1}{7}$.

8. A box contains 5 red and 4 white marbles. 2 marbles are drawn successively from the box without replacement and it is noted that the second one is white. What is the probability that the first is also white ?

Ans. $\dfrac{1}{6}$.

9. Box A contains 3 red and 2 blue marbles. The box B contains 2 red and 8 blue marbles. A fair coin is tossed. If the coin shows Head, a marble is chosen from box A, if it shows Tail, a marble is chosen from box B. Find the probability that a red marble is chosen.

Ans. $\dfrac{2}{5}$.

10. One shot is fired from each of the three guns. E_1, E_2, E_3 denote the events that the target is hit by the first, second and third guns respectively. If $P(E_1) = 0.5$, $P(E_2) = 0.6$, $P(E_3) = 0.7$ and E_1, E_2, E_3 are independent events, then find the probability that at least two hits are registered.

Ans. 0.65

11. A problem on computer mathematics is given to the three students A, B and C whose chances of solving it are $\dfrac{1}{2}, \dfrac{3}{4}$ and $\dfrac{1}{4}$ respectively. What is the probability that the problem will be solved ?

Ans. $\dfrac{29}{32}$.

12. Urn I contains 6 white and 4 black balls and urn II contains 4 white and 5 black balls. From urn I, two balls are transferred to urn II without noticing the colour. Sample of size 2 is then drawn without replacement from urn II. What is the probability that the sample contains exactly 1 white ball ?

Ans. $\dfrac{4}{5}$.

MULTIPLE CHOICE QUESTIONS (MCQ's)

Type : Simple Probability

1. A throw is made with two dice. The probability of getting a score of 10 points is   (1)

   (A) $\dfrac{1}{12}$ (B) $\dfrac{1}{6}$

   (C) $\dfrac{1}{5}$ (D) $\dfrac{2}{3}$

2. A throw is made with two dice. The probability of getting a score of at least 10 points is   (1)

   (A) $\dfrac{1}{12}$ (B) $\dfrac{1}{6}$

   (C) $\dfrac{1}{4}$ (D) $\dfrac{5}{6}$

3. Probability that a leap year selected at random will contain 53 Sunday is   (2)

   (A) $\dfrac{1}{7}$ (B) $\dfrac{6}{7}$

   (C) $\dfrac{3}{7}$ (D) $\dfrac{2}{7}$

4. Two cards are drawn from a well shuffled pack of 52 cards. If the first card drawn is replaced, the probability that they are both kings is   (2)

   (A) $\dfrac{1}{15}$ (B) $\dfrac{1}{221}$

   (C) $\dfrac{1}{169}$ (D) $\dfrac{2}{221}$

5. Two cards are drawn from a well shuffled pack of 52 cards. If the first card drawn is not replaced, the probability that they are both kings is   (2)

   (A) $\dfrac{1}{15}$ (B) $\dfrac{1}{17}$

   (C) $\dfrac{1}{221}$ (D) $\dfrac{2}{221}$

6. An envelope contains six tickets with numbers 1, 2, 3, 5, 6, 7. Another envelope contains four tickets with numbers 1, 3, 5, 7. An envelope is chosen at random and ticket is drawn from it. Probability that the ticket bears the numbers 2 or 7 is   (2)

   (A) $\dfrac{1}{6}$ (B) $\dfrac{7}{24}$

   (C) $\dfrac{1}{8}$ (D) $\dfrac{5}{24}$

7. Three coins are tossed simultaneously. The probability of getting at least two head is (2)

(A) $\dfrac{1}{2}$ (B) $\dfrac{3}{8}$

(C) $\dfrac{1}{4}$ (D) $\dfrac{3}{4}$

8. There are six married couples in a room. If two persons are chosen at random, the probability that they are of different sex is (2)

(A) $\dfrac{3}{11}$ (B) $\dfrac{1}{11}$

(C) $\dfrac{5}{11}$ (D) $\dfrac{6}{11}$

9. A ball is drawn from a box containing 6 red balls, 4 white balls and 5 black balls. Determine the probability that it is not red is (2)

(A) $\dfrac{4}{15}$ (B) $\dfrac{1}{3}$

(C) $\dfrac{2}{5}$ (D) $\dfrac{3}{5}$

10. A problem in statistics is given to three students A, B, C whose chance of solving it are $\dfrac{1}{2}, \dfrac{1}{3}, \dfrac{1}{4}$ respectively. The probability that all of them can solved the problems is (2)

(A) $\dfrac{1}{8}$ (B) $\dfrac{1}{24}$

(C) $\dfrac{1}{12}$ (D) $\dfrac{1}{6}$

11. The probability that A can solve a problem is $\dfrac{2}{3}$ and B can solve it is problem is $\dfrac{3}{4}$. If both attempt the problem, then the probability that the problem get solved is (2)

(A) $\dfrac{11}{12}$ (B) $\dfrac{7}{12}$

(C) $\dfrac{5}{12}$ (D) $\dfrac{9}{12}$

Answers

1. (A)	2. (B)	3. (D)	4. (C)	5. (C)	6. (B)	7. (A)	8. (D)
9. (D)	10. (B)	11. (A)					

8.6 PROBABILITY DISTRIBUTION

In Chapter 7, we have seen that statistical data can be presented in the form of frequency distribution, giving tabulated values of variate x and corresponding frequencies. Probability distribution for a variate x can be presented in a similar manner. Consider an experiment of simultaneous throw with three coins. The results of three tosses are independent of each other and all the outcomes can be given as,

HHH (all the three tosses giving Heads), HHT, HTH, HTT, THH, THT, TTH and TTT.

There are in all eight outcomes. Probability of any of these outcomes viz. the event HHH is given by $\quad$ P (HHH) $=$ P (H) P (H) P (H)

$$= \frac{1}{2} \cdot \frac{1}{2} \cdot \frac{1}{2} = \frac{1}{8}$$

All these outcomes will have the same probabilities.

Let x denote the number of Heads appearing in each case.

$\therefore \quad$ (i) $\quad$ P $(x = 0)$ $=$ P (TTT) $= \dfrac{1}{8}$

$\qquad$ (ii) $\quad$ P $(x = 1)$ $=$ P (HTT) + P (TTH) + P (THT), mutually exclusive events

$$= \frac{1}{8} + \frac{1}{8} + \frac{1}{8} = \frac{3}{8}$$

$\qquad$ (iii) $\quad$ P $(x = 2)$ $=$ P (HTH) + P (THH) + P (HHT), mututally exclusive events

$$= \frac{1}{8} + \frac{1}{8} + \frac{1}{8} = \frac{3}{8}$$

and (iv) $\quad$ P $(x = 3)$ $=$ P (HHH) $= \dfrac{1}{8}$

x	0	1	2	3
f	1	3	3	1
P (x)	$\dfrac{1}{8}$	$\dfrac{3}{8}$	$\dfrac{3}{8}$	$\dfrac{1}{8}$

Here the variate x is taking the values x = 0, 1, 2, 3 and the corresponding probabilities are $\dfrac{1}{8}, \dfrac{3}{8}, \dfrac{3}{8}, \dfrac{1}{8}$ respectively.

The frequencies are replaced by corresponding probabilities in the probability distribution table.

Here $\sum$ P (x) $= \dfrac{1}{8} + \dfrac{3}{8} + \dfrac{3}{8} + \dfrac{1}{8} = 1$ which is always the case when all possible outcomes are considered.

Corresponding to the number $\bar{x}$ which is *Arithmetic mean* in frequency distribution and is given by,

$$\boxed{\bar{x} = \frac{\sum fx}{\sum f}}$$

we have, $E(x) = \dfrac{\sum x\, P(x)}{\sum P(x)} = \sum x\, P(x)$

$E(x)$ is called Mathematical Expectation or simply the Expectation of the variable x. In above example, the expectation of x,

i.e. $E(x) = 0 \cdot \dfrac{1}{8} + 1 \cdot \dfrac{3}{8} + 2 \cdot \dfrac{3}{8} + 3 \cdot \dfrac{1}{8} = \dfrac{12}{8} = \dfrac{3}{2} = 1.5$

In an experiment of throw of a dice, which results in outcomes (1, 2, 3, 4, 5, 6) with probability $\dfrac{1}{6}$ for every outcome,

$$E(x) = \frac{1}{6} \cdot 1 + \frac{1}{6} \cdot 2 + \frac{1}{6} \cdot 3 + \frac{1}{6} \cdot 4 + \frac{1}{6} \cdot 5 + \frac{1}{6} \cdot 6$$

$$= \frac{21}{6} = \frac{7}{2} = 3.5$$

We shall now consider various types of Probability Distributions.

8.7 BINOMIAL PROBABILITY DISTRIBUTIONS

Consider the experiment or a trial which has only two outcomes, a success or failure with p as the probability of success and q as the probability of failure. Since there are only two outcomes, $p + q = 1$.

Let us consider series of n such trials each of which either results in success or failure. To find the probability of r successes in n trials, consider one run of outcomes.

$$\underbrace{SSS \ldots\ldots\ldots S}_{r} \qquad \underbrace{FFF \ldots\ldots\ldots F}_{n-r}$$

In which there are r consecutive successes and $n - r$ failures.

Probability of this event is given by

$P(SSS \ldots S\ FFF \ldots F) = P(S)\,P(S) \ldots (r\ \text{times}) \times P(F)\,P(F) \ldots \{(n-r)\ \text{times}\}$

$$= pp \ldots p\ (r\ \text{times}) \times qq \ldots q\ (n-r\ \text{times})$$

$$= p^r q^{n-r}$$

r success and $n - r$ failures can occur in ^nC_r mutually exclusive cases each of which has the probability $p^r q^{n-r}$.

$\therefore$ Probability of r success in n trials is $^nC_r \cdot p^r q^{n-r}$. This formula gives probability of $r = 0, 1, 2, 3, \ldots n$ success in n trials.

Putting it in tabular form,

r	0	1	2	3	......	n
p (r)	$^nC_0\, p^0\, q^n$	$^nC_1\, p^1\, q^{n-1}$	$^nC_2\, p^2\, q^{n-2}$	$^nC_3\, p^3\, q^{n-3}$	......	$^nC_n\, p^n\, q^{n-n}$

$$^nC_0 = 1, \quad ^nC_n = 1$$

Consider now the Binomial expansion of

$$(q + p)^n = q^n + {}^nC_1\, q^{n-1}\, p + {}^nC_2\, q^{n-2}\, p^2 + \ldots + p^n$$

Terms on R.H.S. of this expansion give probability of $r = 0, 1, 2, \ldots, n$ success. This is the reason for above probability distribution to be called Binomial probability distribution. It is denoted by B (n, p, r).

Thus, $B (n, p, r) = {}^nC_r\, p^r\, q^{n-r}$

ILLUSTRATIONS

Ex. 1 : *An unbiased coin is thrown 10 times. Find the probability of getting exactly 6 Heads, at least 6 Heads.*

Sol. : Here $p = q = \dfrac{1}{2}$ and $n = 10$. Here occurrence of Head is treated as success.

Probability of getting exactly 6 Heads is

$$P (6) = {}^{10}C_6 \left(\frac{1}{2}\right)^6 \left(\frac{1}{2}\right)^4$$

Events of at least six Heads occur when coin shows up Head 6, 7, 8, 9 or 10 times the probabilities for these events are

$$P (7) = {}^{10}C_7 \left(\frac{1}{2}\right)^7 \left(\frac{1}{2}\right)^3 \qquad P (8) = {}^{10}C_8 \left(\frac{1}{2}\right)^8 \left(\frac{1}{2}\right)^2$$

$$P (9) = {}^{10}C_9 \left(\frac{1}{2}\right)^9 \left(\frac{1}{2}\right)^1 \qquad P (10) = {}^{10}C_{10} \left(\frac{1}{2}\right)^{10} \left(\frac{1}{2}\right)^0 = \left(\frac{1}{2}\right)^{10}$$

$$p \text{ (at least 6 Heads)} = p (6) + p (7) + p (8) + p (9) + p (10)$$

[The events of 6, 7, ... etc. Heads are mutually exclusive].

Ex. 2 : *Probability of Man aged 60 years will live for 70 years is $\dfrac{1}{10}$. Find the probability of 5 mean selected at random 2 will live for 70 years.*

Sol. : Here $p = \dfrac{1}{10}, \quad q = \dfrac{9}{10}, \quad r = 2, \quad n = 5.$

$$P \text{ (2 men living for 70 years)} = {}^5C_2 \left(\frac{1}{10}\right)^2 \left(\frac{9}{10}\right)^3 = 0.0729$$

Ex. 3 : *A department in a works has 10 machines which may need adjustment from time to time during the day. Three of these machines are old, each having a probability of $\frac{1}{10}$ of needing adjustment during the day and 7 are new, having corresponding probability $\frac{1}{20}$. Assuming that no machine needs adjustment twice on the same day, determine the probabilities that on a particular day*

(i) just two old and no new machines need adjustment.

(ii) just two machines need adjustment which are of the same type.

Sol. : Out of 3 old machines, if 2 need adjustment then this combination of 2 needing adjustment and one needing cannot occur in $^3C_2$ ways.

$$p_1 = \text{Probability of old machine needing adjustment} \qquad = \frac{1}{10}$$

$$q_1 = \text{Probability of old machine not needing an adjustment} \quad = \frac{9}{10}$$

$$p_2 = \text{Probability of new machine needing an adjustment} \qquad = \frac{1}{20}$$

$$q_2 = \text{Probability of new machine not needing an adjustment} \; = \frac{19}{20}$$

We are looking for an event A where 2 old machines needing adjustment alongwith one not needing and remaining 7 new machines not needing an adjustment. Hence

$$P(A) \; = \; ^3C_2 \left(\frac{1}{10}\right)^2 \left(\frac{9}{10}\right)\left(\frac{19}{20}\right)^7 = \frac{3 \times 9 \times (19)^7}{10^3 (20)^7} = 0.0189$$

Consider the event B in which case, no old machine out of 3 need adjustment and 2 out of 7 new machines need adjustment. Proceeding in the same way

$$P(B) \; = \; \left(\frac{9}{10}\right)^3 \; ^7C_2 \left(\frac{1}{20}\right)^2 \left(\frac{19}{20}\right)^5 = \frac{7 \cdot 6}{1 \cdot 2} \left(\frac{9}{10}\right)^3 \left(\frac{1}{20}\right)^2 \left(\frac{19}{20}\right)^5$$

$$= \; 21 \left(\frac{9}{10}\right)^3 \left(\frac{1}{20}\right)^2 \left(\frac{19}{20}\right)^5 \; = \; 0.0296$$

Event, two machines needing an adjustment which are of the same type A + B.

$$\therefore \qquad P(A + B) \; = \; P(A) + P(B) \; [A, B \text{ are mutually exclusive}].$$

$$\text{Required probability} \; = \; 0.0189 + 0.0296 = 0.0485$$

If n independent trials constitute one experiment and the experiment is repeated N times then r successes would be expected to occur $N \times {}^nC_r \, p^r \, q^{n-r}$ times. This is called the expected frequency of r success in N experiments.

Ex. 4 : *On an average a box containing 10 articles is likely to have 2 defectives. If we consider a consignment of 100 boxes, how many of them are expected to have three or less defectives ?*   **(May 2009)**

$$p = \text{Probability of box containing defective articles} = \frac{2}{10} = \frac{1}{5}$$

$$q = \text{Probability of non-defective items} = \frac{4}{5}$$

Sol. : Probability of box containing three or less defective articles

$$= p\,(r \le 3) = p\,(r = 0) + p\,(r = 1) + p\,(r = 2) + p\,(r = 3)$$

[r denotes the number of defective items.]

$$p\,(r = 0) = {}^{10}C_0 \left(\frac{1}{5}\right)^0 \left(\frac{4}{5}\right)^{10} = 0.1074$$

$$p\,(r = 1) = {}^{10}C_1 \left(\frac{1}{5}\right)^1 \left(\frac{4}{5}\right)^9 = 0.2684$$

$$p\,(r = 2) = {}^{10}C_2 \left(\frac{1}{5}\right)^2 \left(\frac{4}{5}\right)^8 = 0.302$$

$$p\,(r = 3) = {}^{10}C_3 \left(\frac{1}{5}\right)^3 \left(\frac{4}{5}\right)^7 = 0.2013$$

$$p\,(r \le 3) = 0.1074 + 0.2684 + 0.302 + 0.2013 = 0.8791$$
$$= 100 \times 0.8791 = 87.91$$

88 boxes are expected to contain three or less defectives.

Ex. 5 : *In a quality control department of a rubber tube manufacturing factory, 10 rubber tubes are randomly selected from each day's production for inspection. If not more than 1 of the 10 tubes is found to be defective, the production lot is approved. Otherwise it is rejected. Find the probability of the rejection of a day's production lot if the true proportion of defectives in the lot is 0.3.*

Solution : Suppose X denotes the number of defective tubes in the 10 randomly selected tubes.

$$\therefore \qquad X \to B\,(n = 10, \ p = 0.3)$$

The production lot is accepted if not more than one tube (i.e. at the most one tube) is found defective.

$$\therefore \quad P\,(\text{Accepting the lot}) = P\,(X = 0) + P\,(X = 1)$$
$$= q^n + npq^{n-1}$$
$$= (0.7)^{10} + 10\,(0.3)\,(0.7)^9$$
$$= (0.7)^9\,[3.7] = 0.1493$$

$$\therefore \quad P\,(\text{Rejection of the lot}) = 1 - 0.1493 = 0.8507$$

Ex. 6 : *A r.v. X $\sim$ B (n = 6, p). Find p if 9 P (R = 4) = P (R = 2).*

Solution : $\quad$ P (R = r) $=$ $^nC_r\, p^r\, q^{n-r}$ $\;$ r $= 0, 1, \ldots$ n

Here, $\qquad\qquad\qquad$ n $=$ 6

$\therefore \qquad\qquad\qquad$ 9P (4) $=$ P (2)

$\Rightarrow \qquad\quad$ $9 \cdot \binom{6}{4}\, p^4 q^2$ $=$ $\binom{6}{2}\, p^2 q^4$

$\therefore \qquad\qquad\quad$ $9p^2$ $=$ q^2 $\qquad\quad \because\; \binom{6}{4} = \binom{6}{2}$

$\therefore \qquad\qquad\quad$ $9p^2$ $=$ $(1 - p)^2 = 1 - 2p + p^2$

$\therefore \qquad\quad$ $8p^2 + 2p - 1$ $=$ 0

$\therefore \qquad$ $(4p - 1)(2p + 1)$ $=$ 0

$\Rightarrow \qquad\qquad$ $p = \dfrac{1}{4}$ or $p = -\dfrac{1}{2}$

The value $p = -\dfrac{1}{2}$ is inadmissible. Hence, the answer is $p = \dfrac{1}{4}$.

Ex. 7 : *A coin is so biased that appearance of head is twice likely as that of tail. If a throw is made 6 times, find the probability that atleast 2 heads will appear.*

Sol.: Here $p(H) = \dfrac{2}{3}$, q (T) $= \dfrac{1}{3}$

A is the event of appearance of atleast two heads

$\qquad$ p(A) $=$ p(2) + p(3) + p(4) + p(5) + p(6)

$\qquad\qquad$ $=$ $1 - p(0) - p(1)$

$\qquad\qquad$ $=$ $1 - {}^6C_0 \left(\dfrac{2}{3}\right)^0 \left(\dfrac{1}{3}\right)^6 - {}^6C_1 \left(\dfrac{2}{3}\right)^1 \left(\dfrac{1}{3}\right)^5$

$\qquad\qquad$ $=$ $1 - \left\{ 1 \times \left(\dfrac{1}{3}\right)^6 + 6 \times \dfrac{2}{3}\left(\dfrac{1}{3}\right)^5 \right\}$

$\qquad\qquad$ $=$ 0.98213

Mean and Variance of Binomial Distribution : $\qquad\qquad\qquad$ **(Dec. 2005)**

We shall first obtain moments of the binomial distribution about r = 0 (about origin).

$$\mu_1' = \sum_{r=0}^{n} r \cdot {}^nC_r\, p^r\, q^{n-r}$$

$$= 0 \cdot q^n + 1 \cdot {}^nC_1\, p^1\, q^{n-1} + 2 \cdot {}^nC_2\, p^2\, q^{n-2} + 3 \cdot {}^nC_3\, p^3\, q^{n-3} \ldots np^n$$

$$= npq^{n-1} + 2 \cdot \frac{n(n-1)}{2!}\, p^2 q^{n-2} + 3 \cdot \frac{n(n-1)(n-2)}{2!}\, p^3 q^{n-3} \ldots np^n$$

$$= np \times \left[q^{n-1} + (n-1)\, pq^{n-2} + \frac{(n-1)\,(n-2)}{2!}\, p^2\, q^{n-3} \ldots p^{n-1} \right]$$

$$= np\,[(q+p)^{n-1}] \qquad \boxed{\mu' = np}$$

But $\qquad \mu_1' = \mu_1 = \text{Mean}$

Hence Mean of the Binomial distribution or which is also the expectation of variable r is np.

Now consider

$$\mu_2' = \sum_{r=0}^{n} r^2 \, {}^nC_r \, p^r \, q^{n-r}$$

$$= \sum_{r=0}^{n} \{r\,(r-1) + r\}\, {}^nC_r\, p^r\, q^{n-r} = \sum_{r=2}^{n} r\,(r-1)\, {}^nC_r\, p^r\, q^{n-r} + \sum_{r=0}^{n} r\, {}^nC_r\, p^r\, q^{n-r}$$

$$= \sum_{r=2}^{n} r\,(r-1)\, {}^nC_r\, p^r\, q^{n-r} + np$$

$$= 1.2\, {}^nC_2\, p^2\, q^{n-2} + 2.3\, {}^nC_3\, p^3\, q^{n-3} + 3.4\, {}^nC_4\, p^4\, q^{n-4} \ldots n\,(n-1)\, p^n + np$$

$$= 1.2\, \frac{n\,(n-1)}{2!}\, p^2\, q^{n-2} + 2.3\, \frac{n\,(n-1)\,(n-2)}{3!}\, p^3\, q^{n-3}$$

$$+ 3.4\, \frac{n\,(n-1)\,(n-2)\,(n-3)}{4!}\, p^4\, q^{n-4} \ldots n\,(n-1)\, p^n + np$$

$$= n\,(n-1) \times p^2 \left[q^{n-2} + (n-2)\, p\, q^{n-3} + \frac{(n-2)\,(n-3)}{2!}\, p^2\, q^{n-4} \ldots p^{n-2} \right] + np$$

$$= n\,(n-1)\, p^2\, \{q+p\}^{n-2} + np = n\,(n-1)\, p^2 + np$$

$$= n^2\, p^2 - np^2 + np = n^2\, p^2 + np\,\{1-p\} = n^2\, p^2 + npq$$

$$\mu_2 = \text{Variance} = \mu_2' - {\mu_1'}^2 = n^2\, p^2 + npq - (np)^2$$

$$\boxed{\sigma^2 = npq}$$

$$\boxed{\sigma = \text{Standard deviation} = \sqrt{npq}}$$

ILLUSTRATIONS

Ex. 1 : *Point out the fallacy of the statement 'The Mean of Binomial distribution is 3 and variance 5'.*

Sol. : Given $\qquad \text{Mean} = np = 3, \qquad \text{Variance} = npq = 5$

$$\therefore \qquad q = \frac{npq}{np} = \frac{5}{3} > 1$$

which is not possible since probability cannot exceed unity.

Ex. 2 : *The Mean and Variance of Binomial distribution are 6 and 2 respectively. Find p (r ≥ 1).*

Sol. : Here r denotes the number of successes in n trials. Given that

$$\text{Mean } = np = 6 \quad \text{and} \quad \text{Variance } = npq = 2$$

$$\therefore \quad q = \frac{npq}{np} = \frac{2}{6} = \frac{1}{3}$$

$$p = 1 - q = 1 - \frac{1}{3} = \frac{2}{3}$$

$$np = 6 \quad \therefore \quad n = \frac{6}{2/3} = 9$$

$$p\,(r \geq 1) = 1 - p\,(r = 0) = 1 - q^n = 1 - \left(\frac{1}{3}\right)^9 = 0.999949$$

8.8 HYPERGEOMETRIC DISTRIBUTION

We know that binomial distribution is applied whenever we draw a random sample *with* replacement. This is because, in sampling with replacement, the probability of getting 'success' p, remains same at every draw. Also, the successive draws remain independent. Thus, the assumptions of binomial experiment are satisfied. Now, consider the following situation.

A bag contains 4 red and 5 black balls. Suppose 3 balls are drawn at random from this bag *without* replacement and we are interested in the number of red balls drawn. Clearly at the first draw, probability of getting a red ball is $\frac{4}{9}$. Now, suppose a red ball is selected at the first draw. Because, it would be kept aside, the probability of getting a red ball at the second draw would be $\frac{3}{8}$. Thus 'p' does not remain constant. Also, the successive draws are not independent. Probability of getting red balls in the second draw is dependent on which ball you have drawn at the first draw. Thus, in case of sampling *without* replacement, the binomial distribution cannot be applied.

In such situations the hypergeometric distribution is used. Consider the following situation.

Suppose a bag contains N balls of which M are red and N – M are black. A sample of 'n' balls is drawn *without replacement* from the N balls. Let X denote the number of red balls in the *sample*. Hence, the possible values of X are 0, 1, 2, …, n (assuming n ≤ M). The p.m.f. is obtained in the following manner.

We want to get P [X = x].

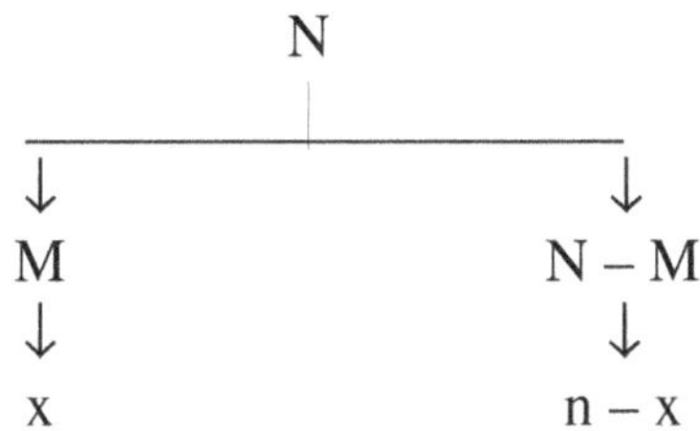

If the sample of 'n' balls contains 'x' red balls, then it will contain 'n – x' black balls. Hence, number of ways in which x red balls can be selected from M red balls is $\binom{M}{x}$ and number of ways in which n – x black balls can be selected from N – M black balls is $\binom{N-M}{n-x}$. The sample contains both red and black balls. Therefore, the total number of ways in which the above event can occur is $\binom{M}{x}\binom{N-M}{n-x}$. In all 'n' balls are selected from N balls. Therefore, the total number of possible selections is $\binom{N}{n}$. Using the definition of probability of an event, we get,

$$P(x) = P[X = x] = \frac{\binom{M}{x}\binom{N-M}{n-x}}{\binom{N}{n}} \quad ; \quad x = 0, 1, ..., n$$

$$= 0 \quad ; \quad \text{otherwise}$$

The above P (x) is called as the p.m.f. of hypergeometric distribution with parameters N, M and n.

Notation : $X \to H(N, M, n)$.

If we don't assume $n \le M$, then the range X is 0, 1, 2, ..., min (n, M). This is because at the most M red balls can be there in the sample.

Remark : Applicability of Hypergeometric Distribution

Hypergeometric distribution is applied whenever a random sample is taken _without_ replacement from a population consisting of two classes. Some situations are

(i)   In quality control department, a random sample of items is inspected from a consignment containing defective and non-defective items.

(ii)   A lake contains N fish. A sample of fish is taken from the lake, marked and released back in the lake. Next time, another sample of fish is selected and number of marked fish are counted.

(iii)   A committee of n persons is to be formed from N persons of whom M are ladies and N – M are gentlemen. The number of ladies on the committee follows hypergeometric distribution.

(iv)   In opinion surveys, where the persons have to give answers of 'yes', 'no' type.

The following conditions should be satisfied for the application of hypergeometric distribution.

1.   The population is divided into two mutually exclusive categories.

2.   The successive outcomes are dependent.

3.   The probability of 'success' changes from trial to trial.

4.   The number of draws are fixed.

ILLUSTRATIONS

Ex. 1 : *A room has 4 sockets. From a collection of 12 bulbs of which only 5 are good. A person selects 4 bulbs at random (without replacement) and puts them in the sockets. Find the probability that (i) the room is lighted, (ii) exactly one bulb in the selected bulbs is good.*

Solution : Notice that $N = 12$, $M = 5$, $n = 4$, $X =$ number of good bulbs in the sample.

$$\therefore \quad X \to H (N = 12, M = 5, n = 4)$$

$$\therefore \qquad P(x) = \frac{\binom{5}{x}\binom{7}{4-x}}{\binom{12}{4}} ; \qquad x = 0, 1, \ldots, 4$$

(i) The room is lighted even if a single bulb is good. Therefore the required probability is

$$P(X \geq 1) = 1 - P(X = 0)$$

$$= 1 - \frac{\binom{5}{0}\binom{7}{4}}{\binom{12}{4}} = 0.9292$$

(ii) $$P[X = 1] = \frac{\binom{5}{1}\binom{7}{3}}{\binom{12}{4}} = 0.707$$

Ex. 2 : *Among the 200 employees of a company, 160 are union numbers and the others are non-union. If four employees are to be chosen to serve on the staff welfare committee, find the probability that two of them will be union members and the others non-union, using hypergeometric distribution.*

Solution : Let X denote number of union members selected in the sample.

$$\therefore \quad X \to H (N = 200, M = 160, n = 4).$$

(i) The required probability is

$$P[X = 2] = \frac{\binom{160}{2}\binom{40}{2}}{\binom{200}{4}} = \frac{\dfrac{160 \times 159}{2} \times \dfrac{40 \times 39}{2}}{\dfrac{200 \times 199 \times 198 \times 197}{4 \times 3 \times 2}}$$

$$= 0.1534$$

8.9 POISSON DISTRIBUTION

When 'p' be the probability of success is very small and n the number of trials is very large and np is finite then we get another distribution called Poisson distribution. It is considered as limiting case of Binomial distribution with $n \to \infty$, $p \to 0$ and np remaining finite.

Consider the Binomial distribution

$$B(n, p, r) = {}^nC_r \, p^r \, q^{n-r}$$

$$= \frac{n(n-1)(n-2) \dots (n-(r-1))}{r!} \, p^r \, (1-p)^{n-r}$$

Let $z = np$ $\therefore$ $p = \dfrac{z}{n}$

$$B(n, p, r) = \frac{np(np-p)(np-2p) \dots (np-(r-1)p)}{r!} \times \frac{(1-p)^n}{(1-p)^r}$$

$$= \frac{z\left(z-\dfrac{z}{n}\right)\left(z-\dfrac{2z}{n}\right) \dots \left[z-(r-1)\dfrac{z}{n}\right]}{r!} \times \frac{\left(1-\dfrac{z}{n}\right)^n}{\left(1-\dfrac{z}{n}\right)^r}$$

Now taking the limit as $n \to \infty$ and $np = z$, $p \to 0$

$$\lim B(n, p, r) = \frac{z^r \, e^{-z}}{r!} \left[\lim_{n \to \infty} \left(1-\frac{z}{n}\right)^n = e^{-z} \text{ and } \lim_{n \to \infty} \left(1-\frac{z}{n}\right)^r = 1 \right]$$

This is called Poisson distribution which may be denoted by p (r).

Thus the probability of r successes in a series of large number of trials n with p the probability of success at each trial, a small number is given by,

$$p(r) = \frac{z^r \, e^{-z}}{r!}$$

Here Mean of the Poisson distribution is given by

$$\text{Mean} = \text{Lim } np = z$$

$$\text{Variance} = \text{Lim } npq = z \; [\text{Lim } q = 1 \text{ as } p \to 0]$$

$$\text{Standard deviation} = \sqrt{z}$$

ILLUSTRATIONS

Ex. 1 : *A manufacturer of cotter pins knows that 2% of his product is defective. If he sells cotter pins in boxes of 100 pins and guarantees that not more than 5 pins will be defective in a box, find the approximate probability that a box will fail to meet the guaranteed quality.*   **(Dec. 2011)**

Sol. : Here, n = 100.

p the probability of defective pins $= \dfrac{2}{100} = 0.02$

$$z \;=\; \text{mean number of defective pins in a box}$$

$$z \;=\; np = 100 \times 0.02 \;=\; 2$$

Since p is small, we can use Poisson distribution.

$$p\,(r) \;=\; \frac{e^{-z}\,z^r}{r!} \;=\; \frac{e^{-2}\,2^r}{r!}$$

Probability that a box will fail to meet the guaranteed quality is

$$p\,(r > 5) \;=\; 1 - p\,(r \le 5)$$

$$= 1 - \sum_{r=0}^{5} \frac{e^{-2}\,2^r}{r!} \;=\; 1 - e^{-2} \sum_{r=0}^{5} \frac{2^r}{r!} \;=\; 0.0165$$

Ex. 2 : *In a certain factory turning out razor blades, there is a small chance of 1/500 for any blade to be defective. The blades are supplied in a packet of 10. Use Poisson distribution to calculate the approximate number of packets containing no defective and two defective blades, in a consignment of 10,000 packets.*   **(May 2009)**

Sol. : Here $p = 0.002$, $n = 10$, $z = np = 0.02$

$$p\,(\text{no defective}) \;=\; p\,(r = 0) \;=\; \frac{e^{-0.02}\,(0.02)^0}{0\,!} \;=\; \frac{1}{e^{0.02}}$$

$$p\,(2\text{ defectives}) \;=\; p\,(r = 2) \;=\; \frac{e^{-0.02}\,(0.02)^2}{2}$$

Number of packets containing no defective blades in a consignment of 10,000 packets

$$= \; 10{,}000 \times \frac{1}{e^{0.02}} \;=\; 9802$$

Number of packets containing 2 defective blades

$$= \; 10{,}000 \times \frac{(0.02)^2}{2 \times e^{0.02}} \;=\; 2$$

Ex. 3 : *In a Poisson distribution if $p\,(r = 1) = 2p\,(r = 2)$, find $p\,(r = 3)$.*

Sol. :
$$p\,(r) \;=\; \frac{e^{-z}\,z^r}{r!}$$

$$p\,(r = 1) \;=\; \frac{e^{-z}\,z}{1}, \quad p\,(r = 2) \;=\; \frac{e^{-z}\,z^2}{2}$$

$$\therefore \qquad z e^{-z} \;=\; 2 \times \frac{e^{-z}\,z^2}{2} \quad \text{which gives } z = 1$$

$$p\,(r = 3) \;=\; \frac{e^{-1}\,(1)}{3!} \;=\; e^{-1}\,\frac{1}{6} \;=\; \frac{1}{6e} \;=\; 0.0613$$

Ex. 4 : *The accidents per shift in a factory are given by the table :* **(Dec. 08, May 12)**

Accidents x per shift	0	1	2	3	4	5
Frequency f	142	158	67	27	5	1

Fit a Poisson distribution to the above table and calculate theoretical frequencies.

Sol. :

$$z = \text{The mean number of accidents}$$

$$= \frac{0 \times 142 + 1 \times 158 + 2 \times 67 + 3 \times 27 + 4 \times 5 + 5 \times 1}{142 + 158 + 67 + 27 + 5 + 1}$$

$$= \frac{158 + 134 + 81 + 20 + 5}{400} = \frac{398}{400} = 0.995$$

$$p(r) = \frac{e^{-0.995}(0.995)^r}{r!} \qquad p(0) = e^{-0.995} = 0.3697$$

$$p(1) = 0.36785 \qquad\qquad p(2) = 0.813$$

$$p(3) = 0.0607 \qquad\qquad p(4) = 0.0151$$

$$p(5) = 0.003$$

Theoretical frequencies are

$$p(0) \times 400 = 0.3697 \times 400 = 148$$

$$p(1) \times 400 = 0.36785 \times 400 = 147$$

$$p(2) \times 400 = 0.183 \times 400 = 73$$

$$p(3) \times 400 = 0.0607 \times 400 = 24$$

$$p(4) \times 400 = 0.0151 \times 400 = 6$$

$$p(5) \times 400 = 0.003 \times 400 = 1$$

Ex. 5 : *Fit a poisson distribution to the following frequency distribution and compare the theortical frequencies with observed frequencies.*

x	0	1	2	3	4	5
f	150	154	60	35	10	1

Sol.:

$$z = np = \text{mean} = \frac{0 \times 150 + 1 \times 154 + 2 \times 60 + 3 \times 35 + 4 \times 10 + 5 \times 1}{150 + 154 + 60 + 35 + 10 + 1}$$

$$= \frac{424}{410} = 1.034$$

$$p(r) = \frac{e^{-1.034}(1.034)^r}{r!}$$

$$p(0) = e^{-1.034} = 0.356, \; p(1) = 0.368, \; p(2) = 0.190, \; p(3) = 0.0656,$$

$$p(4) = 0.017, \; p(5) = 0.0035$$

Theoretical frequencies are

$$p(0) \times 410 = 0.356 \times 410 = 145.96$$

$$p(1) \times 410 = 0.368 \times 410 = 150.88$$

$$p(2) \times 410 = 0.190 \times 410 = 77.9$$

$$p(3) \times 410 = 0.0656 \; 410 = 26.896$$

$$p(4) \times 410 = 0.017 \times 410 = 6.97$$

$$p(5) \times 410 = 0.0035 \times 410 = 1.435$$

Remark : Theoretical frequencies compare well with observed frequencies.

Ex. 6 : *Show that in a Poisson distribution with unit mean, mean deviation about mean is (2/e) times the standard deviation.*

Sol. : Here $z = 1$, $\quad p(r) = \dfrac{e^{-z} z^r}{r!} = \dfrac{e^{-1} (1)^r}{r!} = \dfrac{e^{-1}}{r!}$

Mean deviation about mean 1 is

$$\sum_{r=0}^{\infty} |r - 1| \, p(r) = \sum_{r=0}^{\infty} |r - 1| \, \frac{e^{-1}}{r!}$$

$$= e^{-1} \left[1 + \frac{1}{2!} + \frac{2}{3!} + \frac{3}{4!} + \ldots \right]$$

We have, $\qquad \dfrac{n}{(n+1)!} = \dfrac{(n+1) - 1}{(n+1)!} = \dfrac{1}{n!} - \dfrac{1}{(n+1)!}$

$\therefore \quad$ Mean deviation about mean

$$= e^{-1} \left[1 + \left(1 - \frac{1}{2!} \right) + \left(\frac{1}{2!} - \frac{1}{3!} \right) + \left(\frac{1}{3!} - \frac{1}{4!} \right) + \ldots \right]$$

$$= e^{-1} (1 + 1) = \frac{2}{e} \times 1$$

But for Poisson distribution, standard deviation $\sqrt{z} = 1$.

$\therefore \quad$ Mean deviation about mean $= \dfrac{2}{e}$ (standard deviation).

Ex. 7 : *The average number of misprints per page of a book is 1.5. Assuming the distribution of number of misprints to be Poisson, find*

(i) the probability that a particular book is free from misprints.

(ii) number of pages containing more than one misprint if the book contains 900 pages.

Sol. : Let X : Number of misprints on a page in the book.

$\qquad$ Given : $X \to P(Z = 1.5)$ $\qquad E(r) = Z = 1.5$

Here the p.m.f. is given by,

$$P(r) = \frac{e^{-z} Z^r}{r!}$$

$$P(r) = \frac{e^{-1.5} (1.5)^r}{r!}$$

(i) $\quad P(r = 0) = \dfrac{e^{-1.5} (1.5)}{0!} = e^{-1.5} = 0.223130$ (From statistical tables)

Note : The Poisson probabilities for $m = 0.1, 0.2, 0.3 \ldots 15.0$ are given in the statistical tables.

(ii)
$$P[r > 1] = 1 - P[r \leq 1]$$

$$= 1 - \{P(R = 0) + P(r = 1)\}$$

$$= 1 - \left\{ e^{-1.5} + \frac{e^{-1.5} (1.5)^1}{1!} \right\}$$

$$= 1 - \{0.223130 + 0.334695\} \quad \left[\begin{array}{l}\text{From statistical} \\ \text{tables} \end{array} \right]$$

$$= 0.442175$$

$\therefore$ Number of pages in the book containing more than one misprint.

$$= (900)\, P[r > 1] = (900)\,(0.442175)$$

$$= 397.9575 \approx 398$$

Ex. 8 : *Number of road accidents on a high way during a month follows a Poisson distribution with mean 5. Find the probability that in a certain month number of accidents on the highway will be*

(i)   Less than 3   **(May 14, Nov. 16)**

(ii) Between 3 and 5   **(May 14, Nov. 16)**

(iii) More than 3.

Sol. : Let X : number of road accidents on a highway during a month.

Given : $X \to P(Z = 5)$

$\therefore$ The p.m.f is given by,

$$P[r] = \frac{e^{-z} Z^{-r}}{r!} \;;\; r = 0, 1, 2 \ldots\ldots$$

$$P[r] = \frac{e^{-5} 5^r}{r!}$$

(i) $\quad P\,[r < 3] \;=\; P\,[r \le 2] = P\,[r = 0] + P\,[r = 1] + P\,[r = 2]$

$$= \frac{e^{-5}\,5^0}{0!} \;+\; \frac{e^{-5}\,5^1}{1!} \;+\; \frac{e^{-5}\,5^2}{2!}$$

$$= 0.006738 + 0.033690 + 0.084224$$

(From statistical tables)

$$= 0.124652$$

(ii) $\quad P\,[3 \le r \le] \;=\; P\,(3) + P\,(4) + P\,(5)$

$$= 0.140374 + 0.175467 + 0.175467 = 0.491308$$

(iii) $\quad P\,[r > 3] \;=\; 1 - P\,[r \le 3]$

$$= 1 - [P\,(0) + P\,(1) + P\,(2) + P\,(3)]$$

$$= 0.734974$$

8.10 NORMAL DISTRIBUTION

Normal distribution is obtained as a limiting form of Binomial distribution when n the number of trials is very large and neither p nor q is very small. Most of the modern statistical methods have been based on this distribution.

Normal distribution curve is given by the equation

$$y \;=\; \frac{1}{\sigma \sqrt{2\pi}}\; e^{-\,(x - \mu)^2/2\sigma^2} \qquad \dots (1)$$

Its shape is as shown in Fig. 8.9.

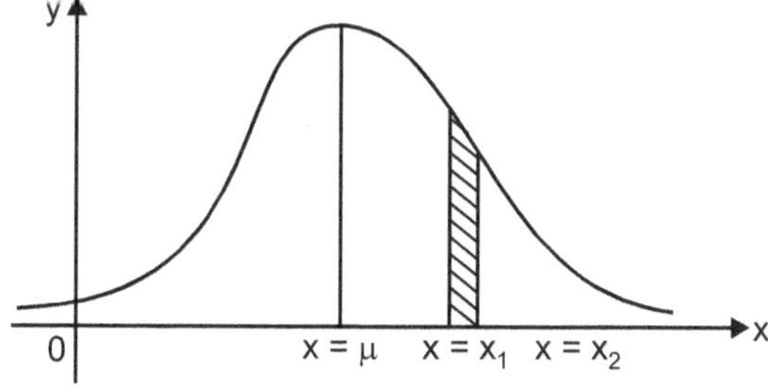

Fig. 8.9

The area under the curve from $x = x_1$ to $x = x_2$ gives the probability of the variable x lying between the values $x = x_1$ and $x = x_2$. The total area under the curve (which is symmetrical about $x = \mu$) is given by $\int\limits_{-\infty}^{\infty} y\,dx = 1$.

Numbers μ and σ occurring in equation (1) are respectively the mean and the standard deviation of the distribution.

If the origin is shifted to $(\mu, 0)$, the equation of curve becomes

$$y = \frac{1}{\sigma \sqrt{2\pi}}\ e^{-x^2/2\sigma^2} \qquad \qquad \dots (2)$$

We shall now obtain Normal distribution as a limiting case of Binomial distribution as $n \to \infty$.

The probability function of the Binomial distribution with parameters n and p is given by

$$p(x) = {}^nC_x\, p^x\, q^{n-x} = \frac{n!}{x!\,(n-x)!}\ p^x\, q^{n-x}, \ x = 0, 1, 2, \dots n \qquad \dots (3)$$

Let us now consider the standard Binomial variate.

$$z = \frac{x - np}{\sqrt{npq}}\ ; \qquad x = 0, 1, 2 \dots n \qquad \qquad \dots (4)$$

When $\qquad\qquad x = 0, \qquad\qquad z = \frac{-np}{\sqrt{npq}} = \sqrt{\frac{np}{q}}$

and when $\qquad\qquad x = n, \qquad\qquad z = \frac{n - np}{\sqrt{npq}} = \sqrt{\frac{nq}{p}}$

Thus in the limit as $n \to \infty$, z takes the values from $-\infty$ to ∞.

Hence the distribution of x will be a continuous distribution over the range $-\infty$ to ∞.

Using Stirling's approximation to $n!$ for large n i.e.

$$\lim_{n \to \infty}\ n! = \sqrt{2\pi}\ e^{-n}\, n^{n+1/2}$$

Now considering $\lim n \to \infty$ and hence $x \to \infty$

$$\lim p(x) = \lim \left[\frac{\sqrt{2\pi}\ e^{-n}\, n^{n+1/2}\, p^x\, q^{n-x}}{\sqrt{2\pi}\ e^{-x}\, x^{x+1/2} \sqrt{2\pi}\ e^{-(n-x)}\, (n-x)^{n-x+1/2}} \right]$$

$$= \lim \left[\frac{1}{\sqrt{2\pi}} \cdot \frac{1}{\sqrt{npq}}\ \frac{(np)^{x+1/2}\,(nq)^{n-x+1/2}}{x^{x+1/2}\,(n-x)^{n-x+1/2}} \right]$$

$$= \lim \left[\frac{1}{\sqrt{2\pi}} \cdot \frac{1}{\sqrt{npq}} \left(\frac{np}{x}\right)^{x+1/2} \left(\frac{nq}{n-x}\right)^{n-x+1/2} \right] \qquad \dots (5)$$

From (4), we have $\qquad x = np + z\sqrt{npq}$

$$\therefore \qquad\qquad \frac{x}{np} = 1 + z\sqrt{\frac{q}{np}}$$

Also
$$n - x \;=\; n - np - z\sqrt{npq} \;=\; nq - z\sqrt{npq}$$

$$\therefore \qquad \frac{n-x}{nq} \;=\; 1 - z\sqrt{\frac{p}{nq}}$$

Also
$$dz \;=\; \frac{1}{\sqrt{npq}}\,dx$$

Hence the probability differential of the distribution of z in the limit is given from (5) by

$$d\,G(z) \;=\; g(z)\,dz \;=\; \lim_{n \to \infty}\left[\frac{1}{\sqrt{2\pi}} \times \frac{1}{N}\right] dz \qquad \dots (6)$$

where
$$N \;=\; \left[\frac{x}{np}\right]^{x+1/2}\left[\frac{n-x}{nq}\right]^{n-x+1/2}$$

Taking log on both the sides,

$$\log N \;=\; \left(x + \frac{1}{2}\right)\log(x/np) + \left(n - x + \frac{1}{2}\right)\log\left(\frac{n-x}{nq}\right)$$

$$=\; \left(np + z\sqrt{npq} + \frac{1}{2}\right)\log\left[1 + z\sqrt{q/np}\right] + \left(nq - z\sqrt{npq}\;\frac{1}{2}\right)\log\left[1 - z\sqrt{p/nq}\right]$$

$$=\; \left(np + z\sqrt{npq} + \frac{1}{2}\right)\left[z\sqrt{\frac{q}{np}} - \frac{1}{2}z^2\left(\frac{q}{np}\right) + \frac{1}{3}z^2\left(\frac{q}{np}\right)^{3/2} \dots + \dots\right]$$

$$+\left(nq - z\sqrt{npq} + \frac{1}{2}\right)\left[-z\sqrt{\frac{p}{nq}} - \frac{1}{2}z^2\left(\frac{p}{nq}\right) - \frac{1}{3}z^3\left(\frac{p}{nq}\right)^{3/2} \dots + \dots\right]$$

$$=\; \left\{z\sqrt{npq} - \frac{1}{2}qz^2 + \frac{1}{3}z^3\frac{q^{3/2}}{\sqrt{np}} + z^2 q - \frac{1}{2}z^3\frac{q^{3/2}}{\sqrt{np}} + \frac{1}{2}z\sqrt{\frac{q}{np}}\right.$$

$$\left. - \frac{1}{4}z^2\frac{q}{np} + \frac{+1}{6}z^3\left(\frac{q}{np}\right)^{3/2} \dots\right\}$$

$$+\left[-z\sqrt{npq} - \frac{1}{2}z^2 p - \frac{1}{3}z^3\frac{p^{3/2}}{\sqrt{nq}} + z^2 p + \frac{1}{2}z^3\frac{p^{3/2}}{\sqrt{nq}} - \frac{1}{2}z\sqrt{\frac{p}{nq}} - \frac{1}{4}z^2\left(\frac{p}{nq}\right) - \frac{1}{6}z^3\left(\frac{p}{nq}\right)^{3/2} \dots\right]$$

(terms higher than fourth power of z are neglected.)

Now, we can write

$$\log N \;=\; \left[\frac{z}{2\sqrt{n}}\left\{\sqrt{\frac{q}{p}} - \sqrt{\frac{p}{q}}\right\} - \frac{1}{2}z(p+q) + z^2(p+q)\right]$$

$$+ \text{ terms containing power of } n \text{ in denominator}$$

Taking the limit as $n \to \infty$

$$\lim_{n \to \infty} \log N = \frac{z^2}{2} \text{ or } \lim_{n \to \infty} N = e^{-z^2/2}$$

Putting in (6), we get $dG(z) = g(z)\, dz = \dfrac{1}{\sqrt{2\pi}}\, e^{-z^2/2}\, dz$ for $-\infty < z < \infty$.

This is the probability density function of the normal distribution with mean 0 and unit variance.

If X is a normal variate with mean μ and s.d. σ then $Z = (X - \mu)/\sigma$ is a standard normal variate. The probability density function of a normal variate with mean μ and variance σ^2 is given by

$$p(X) = \frac{1}{\sigma\sqrt{2\pi}}\, e^{-(x-\mu)^2/2\sigma^2}, \quad -\infty < x < \infty$$

8.10.1 Mean Deviation from the Mean

$$\text{M.D.} = \int_{-\infty}^{\infty} |x - \mu|\, p(x)\, dx$$

$$= \frac{1}{\sigma\sqrt{2\pi}} \int_{-\infty}^{\infty} |x - \mu|\, e^{-(x-\mu)^2/2\sigma^2}\, dx$$

Put $\dfrac{x - \mu}{\sigma} = z$; $dx = \sigma\, dz = \dfrac{1}{\sigma\sqrt{2\pi}} \int_{-\infty}^{\infty} \sigma^2\, |z|\, e^{-z^2/2}\, dz = \dfrac{\sigma}{\sqrt{2\pi}} \int_{-\infty}^{\infty} |z|\, e^{-z^2/2}\, dz$

$$= \frac{\sigma}{\sqrt{2\pi}} \cdot 2 \int_{0}^{\infty} |z|\, e^{-z^2/2}\, dz$$

$[f(z) = |z| = e^{-z^2/2}$ is even function of $z]$

$$\text{M.D.} = \sqrt{\frac{2}{\pi}}\, \sigma \int_{0}^{\infty} z e^{-z^2/2}\, dz \quad [|z| = z \text{ for } 0 < z < \infty]$$

$$= \sqrt{\frac{2}{\pi}}\, \sigma \int_{0}^{\infty} \frac{1}{2}\, e^{-z^2/2}\, d(z^2)$$

$$= \sqrt{\frac{2}{\pi}} \cdot \frac{\sigma}{2} \left[\frac{e^{-z^2/2}}{-1.2} \right]_{0}^{\infty}$$

$$= \sqrt{\frac{2}{\pi}}\, \sigma\, [1] = \frac{4}{5}\, \sigma \text{ (approximately)}$$

8.10.2 Area Property (Normal Probability Integral)

The probability of random value x lying between $x = \mu$ and $x = x_1$ is given by

Table 8.1

Z	0.00	0.01	0.02	0.03	0.04	0.05	0.06	0.07	0.08	0.09
0.0	0.5000	0.5040	0.5080	0.5120	0.5160	0.5199	0.5239	0.5279	0.5319	0.5259
0.1	0.5398	0.5438	0.5478	0.5517	0.5557	0.5596	0.5636	0.5675	0.5714	0.5753
0.2	0.5793	0.5832	0.5871	0.5910	0.5948	0.5987	0.6026	0.6064	0.6103	0.6141
0.3	0.6179	0.6217	0.6255	0.6293	0.6331	0.6368	0.6406	0.6443	0.6480	0.6517
0.4	0.6554	0.6591	0.6628	0.6664	0.6700	0.6736	0.6772	0.6808	0.6844	0.6879
0.5	0.6915	0.6950	0.6985	0.7019	0.7054	0.7088	0.7123	0.7157	0.7190	0.7224
0.6	0.7257	0.7291	0.7324	0.7357	0.7389	0.7422	0.7454	0.7486	0.7517	0.7549
0.7	0.7580	0.7611	0.7642	0.7673	0.7703	0.7734	0.7764	0.7793	0.7823	0.7852
0.8	0.7881	0.7910	0.7939	0.7967	0.7995	0.8023	0.8051	0.8078	0.8106	0.8133
0.9	0.8159	0.8186	0.8212	0.8238	0.8264	0.8289	0.8315	0.8340	0.8365	0.8389
1.0	0.8413	0.8438	0.8461	0.8485	0.8508	0.8531	0.8554	0.8577	0.8599	0.8621
1.1	0.8643	0.8665	0.8686	0.8708	0.8729	0.8749	0.8770	0.8790	0.8810	0.8830
1.2	0.8849	0.8869	0.8888	0.8906	0.8925	0.8943	0.8962	0.8980	0.8997	0.9015
1.3	0.9032	0.9049	0.9066	0.9082	0.9099	0.9115	0.9131	0.9147	0.9162	0.9177
1.4	0.9192	0.9207	0.9222	0.9236	0.9251	0.9265	0.9279	0.9292	0.9306	0.9319
1.5	0.9332	0.9345	0.9357	0.9370	0.9382	0.9394	0.9406	0.9418	0.9429	0.9441
1.6	0.9452	0.9463	0.9474	0.9494	0.9495	0.9505	0.9515	0.9525	0.9535	0.9545
1.7	0.9554	0.9564	0.9573	0.9582	0.9591	0.9599	0.9608	0.9616	0.9625	0.9633
1.8	0.9641	0.9649	0.9656	0.9664	0.9871	0.9678	0.9686	0.9693	0.9699	0.9708
1.9	0.9713	0.9719	0.9726	0.9732	0.9738	0.9744	0.9750	0.9756	0.9761	0.9767
2.0	0.9772	0.9778	0.9783	0.9788	0.9793	0.9783	0.9803	0.9808	0.9812	0.9817
2.1	0.9821	0.9826	0.9830	0.9634	0.9838	0.9842	0.9846	0.9850	0.9854	0.9857
2.2	0.9861	0.9864	0.98686	0.9871	0.9875	0.9878	0.9881	0.9884	0.9887	0.9890
2.3	0.9893	0.9896	0.9898	0.9901	0.9904	0.9906	0.9809	0.9911	0.9913	0.9916
2.4	0.9918	0.9920	0.9922	0.9925	0.9927	0.9929	0.9931	0.9932	0.9934	0.9936
2.5	0.9938	0.9940	0.9941	0.9943	0.9945	0.9946	0.9948	0.9949	0.9951	0.9952
2.6	0.9953	0.9955	0.9956	0.9957	0.9959	0.9960	0.9961	0.9962	0.9963	0.9964
2.7	0.9965	0.9966	0.9967	0.9968	0.9969	0.9970	0.9971	0.9972	0.9973	0.9974
2.8	0.9974	0.9975	0.9976	0.977	0.9977	0.9978	0.9979	0.9979	0.9980	0.9981
2.9	0.9981	0.9982	0.9982	0.9983	0.9984	0.9984	0.9985	0.9985	0.9988	0.9986
3.0	0.9987	0.9987	0.9987	0.9988	0.9988	0.9989	0.9989	0.9989	0.9990	0.9990
3.1	0.9990	0.9991	0.9991	0.9991	0.9992	0.9992	0.9992	0.9992	0.9993	0.9993
3.2	0.9993	0.9993	0.9994	0.9994	0.9994	0.9994	0.9994	0.9995	0.9995	0.9995
3.3	0.9995	0.9995	0.9995	0.9996	0.9996	0.9996	0.9996	0.9996	0.9998	0.9997
3.4	0.9997	0.9997	0.9997	0.9997	0.9997	0.9997	0.9997	0.9997	0.9997	0.9898

In each row and each column 0.5 to be subtracted.

$$P(\mu < x < x_1) = \int_{\mu}^{x_1} P(x)\, dx = \frac{1}{\sigma \sqrt{2\pi}} \int_{\mu}^{x_1} e^{-(x-\mu)^2/2\sigma^2}\, dx$$

Put $$\frac{x-\mu}{\sigma} = z \quad \text{i.e.} \quad x - \mu = \sigma z$$

when $$x = \mu, \qquad z = 0$$

$$x = x_1, \qquad z = z_1 \text{ (say)}$$

$$P(\mu < x < x_1) = P(0 < z < z_1)$$

$$= \frac{1}{\sigma \sqrt{2\pi}} \int_{0}^{z_1} e^{-z^2/2} \cdot \sigma\, dz = \frac{1}{\sqrt{2\pi}} \int_{0}^{z_1} e^{-z^2/2} \cdot dz = \int_{0}^{z_1} f(z)\, dz$$

The definite integral $\int_{0}^{z_1} f(z)$ is known as normal probability integral and gives the area under standard normal curve between $z = 0$ and $z = z_1$.

ILLUSTRATIONS

Ex. 1 : *The mean weight of 500 students is 63 kgs and the standard deviation is 8 kgs. Assuming that the weights are normally distributed, find how many students weigh 52 kgs? The weights are recorded to the nearest kg.*

Sol. : The frequency curve for the given distribution is

$$y = \frac{500}{8\sqrt{2\pi}} \operatorname{Exp}\left(-\frac{1}{2}\left(\frac{x-63}{8}\right)^2\right) \qquad \dots (1)$$

Since the weights are recorded to the nearest kg, the students weighing 52 kgs have their actual weights between $x = 51.5$ and 52.5 kg. So the area under the curve (1) from $x = 51.5$ to $x = 52.5$ is to be obtained.

$$z = \frac{x-\mu}{\sigma} \quad \Rightarrow \quad z_1 = \frac{51.5 - 63}{8} = -1.4375 = -1.44 \text{ (appx)}$$

$$z_2 = \frac{52.5 - 63}{8} = -1.3125 = -1.31 \text{ (appx)}$$

The number of students weighing 52 kg

$$= 500 \int_{51.5}^{52.5} p(x)\, dx = \frac{500}{\sqrt{2\pi}} \int_{-1.4375}^{-1.3125} e^{-z^2/2}\, dz$$

$$= 500\,(A_1 - A_2)$$

$$= 500\,(0.4251 - 0.4049) = 10 \text{ students approximately.}$$

where, $A_1 = 0.4251$ is the area for $z_1 = 1.44$,

and $A_2 = 0.4049$ is the area for $z_2 = 1.31$.

Ex. 2 : *For a normal distribution when mean $\bar{x} = 1$, S.D. $= 3$, find the probabilities for the intervals :*

(i)　$3.43 \leq x \leq 6.19$; (ii) $-1.43 \leq x \leq 6.19$

Sol. : (i) $z_1 = \dfrac{3.43 - 1}{3} = 0.81, \quad z_2 = \dfrac{6.19 - 1}{3} = 1.73$

Required probability $= A_1 - A_2$

where,　　　A_1 is area corresponding to $z_1 = 1.73$

　　　　　A_2 is area corresponding to $z_2 = 0.81$

　　　　　$= (0.4582 - 0.2910) = 0.1672$

(ii)　$z_1 = \dfrac{-1.43 - 1}{3} = -0.81, \quad z_2 = \dfrac{6.19 - 1}{3} = 1.73$

　　　Required probability $= A_1 + A_2 = 0.2910 + 0.4582 = 0.7492$

Ex. 3 : *Assuming that the diameters of 1000 brass plugs taken consecutively from machine form a normal distribution with mean 0.7515 cm and standard deviation 0.0020 cm. How many of the plugs are likely to be approved if the acceptable diameter is 0.752 ± 0.004 cm ?*　　　　　　**(Dec. 2008, May 2009, 2016)**

Sol. :

$$\sigma = 0.0020, \quad \mu = 0.7515$$
$$x_1 = 0.752 + 0.004 = 0.756$$
$$x_2 = 0.752 - 0.004 = 0.748$$
$$z_1 = \frac{x_1 - \mu}{\sigma} = \frac{0.756 - 0.7515}{0.0020} = 2.25$$
$$z_2 = \frac{x_2 - \mu}{\sigma} = \frac{0.748 - 0.7515}{0.0020} = -1.75$$

A_1 corresponding to $z_1 = 2.25$ (Refer table 8.1)

　　　　　$= 0.4878$

A_2 corresponding to $z_2 = 1.75 = 0.4599$

$p\,(0.748 < x < 0.756) = 0.4878 + 0.4599 = 0.9477$

Number of plugs likely to be approved $= 1000 \times 0.9477 = 948$ approximately.

Ex. 4 : *In a certain examination test, 2000 students appeared in a subject of statistics. Average marks obtained were 50% with standard deviation 5%. How many students do you expect to obtain more than 60% of marks, supposing that marks are distributed normally ?*　　　　　　**(Dec. 2006)**

Sol. :

$$\mu = 0.5, \qquad \sigma = 0.05$$
$$x_1 = 0.6, \qquad z_1 = \frac{0.6 - 0.5}{0.05} = 2$$

A corresponding to $z = 2$ is 0.4772

　　　　　$p\,(x \geq 6) = 0.5 - 0.4772 = 0.0228$

Number of students expected to get more than 60% marks

　　　　　$= 0.0228 \times 200 = 46$ students approximately.

Ex. 5 : *In a certain city 4000 tube lights are installed. If the lamps have average life of 1500 burning hours. Assuming normal distribution*

(i) How many lamps will fail in first 1400 hours

(ii) How many lamps will last beyond 1600 hours

Sol.:

$$z = \frac{x - \mu}{\sigma}$$

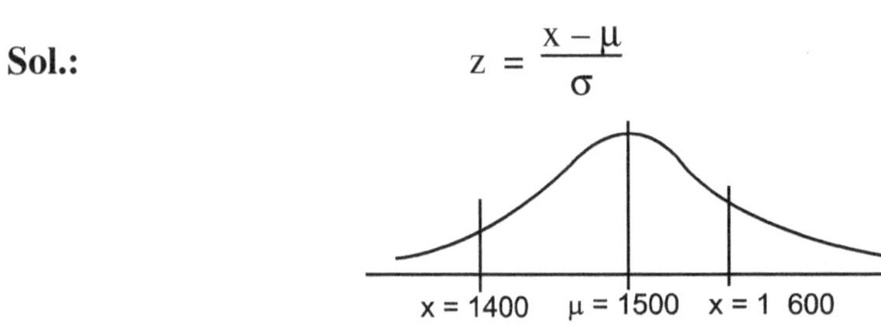

Fig. 8.10

(i) $z = \dfrac{1400 - 1500}{100} = -\dfrac{100}{100} = 1$

Corresponding to z = 1, A = 0.3413

No. of tubes failing in first 1400 hours will be

$$= 4000 \times 0.3413$$

$$= 1365.2 \text{ or } 1365$$

(ii) $z = \dfrac{1600 - 1500}{100} = 1$

Area to the right of x = 1600 = 0.5 – 0.3413 = 0.1587

No. of tubes which will continue to burn after 1600 hours will be 4000 × 0.1587 or 635.

Ex. 6 : *In a normal distribution 10% of items are under 40 and 5% are over 80. Find the mean and standard deviation of distribution.*

Sol.:

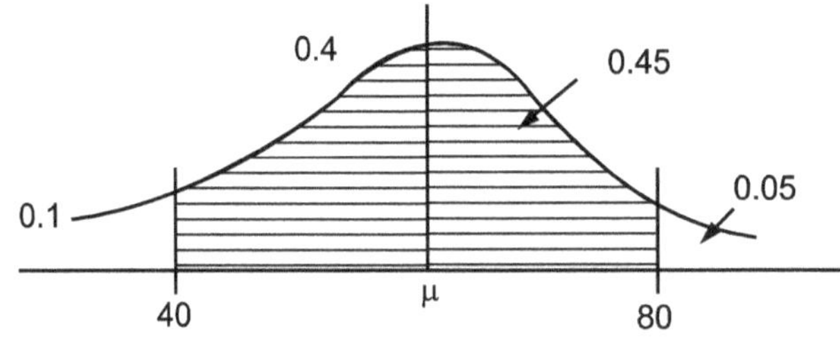

Fig. 8.11

p(x < 40) = 0.1 and p(x > 80) = 0.05

x = 40, x = 80 are located as shown in Fig.

for x = 40, $z = \dfrac{40 - \mu}{\sigma} = - z_1$ (say– ve sign because x = 40 is to the left of x = μ).

when x = 80, $z = \dfrac{80 - \mu}{\sigma} = z_2$ (+ ve sign because x = 80 is to the right of x = μ)

Corresponding to A = 0.4, Z = 1.29

Corresponding to A = 0.45, Z = 1.65

$$\frac{40 - \mu}{\sigma} = - 1.29, \quad \frac{80 - \mu}{\sigma} = 1.65$$

$$40 - \mu = - 1.29\ \sigma \ , \ 80 - \mu = 1.65\ \sigma$$

$$40 = (1.65 + 1.29)\sigma = 2.94\sigma$$

$\therefore$ $\qquad\qquad \sigma = 13.6$

$$\mu = 40 + 1.29\ \sigma = 57.54$$

Ex. 7 : *In a distribution, exactly normal, 7% of the items are under 35 and 89% are under 63. Find the mean and standard deviation of the distribution.*   **(May 2012, 2014)**

Sol. : From Fig. 8.10, it is clear that 7% of items are under 35 means area under 35 is 0.07. Similarly area for x > 63 is 0.11.

$$p\,(x < 35)\ = 0.07 \quad \text{and} \quad p\,(x > 63) = 0.11$$

$$x = 35, \quad x\ = 63 \text{ are located as shown in Fig. 8.10.}$$

When x = 35, $z = \dfrac{35 - \mu}{\sigma} = - z_1$ (say), (– ve sign because x = 35 to the left of x = μ)

When x = 63, $z = \dfrac{63 - \mu}{\sigma} = z_2$ (say), (+ve sign for x = 63 lies to the right of x = μ)

$\therefore$ From Table 8.1, we get

Area $A_1 = p\,(0 < z < z_1) = 0.43$ corresponds to $z_1 = 1.48$ (appx)

&   Area $A_2 = p\,(0 < z < z_2) = 0.39$ corresponds to $z_2 = 1.23$ (appx)

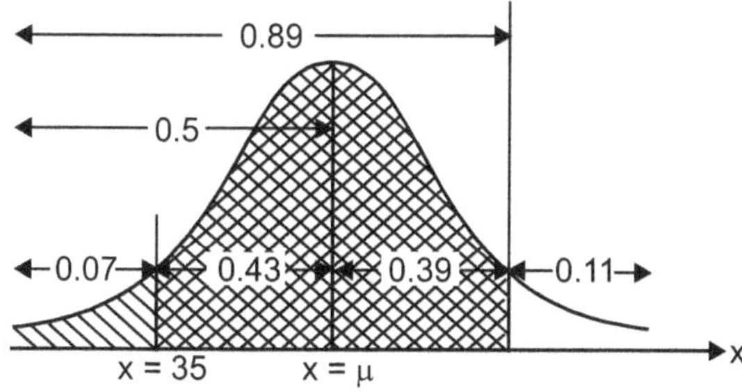

Fig. 8.12

Thus, we get two simultaneous equations

$$\frac{35 - \mu}{\sigma} = -z_1 = -1.48 \qquad \ldots (1)$$

$$\frac{63 - \mu}{\sigma} = z_2 = 1.23 \qquad \ldots (2)$$

Subtracting (1) from (2),

$$\frac{28}{\sigma} = 2.71 \quad \Rightarrow \quad \sigma = 10.33 \text{ (approximately)}$$

and (2) $\Rightarrow$

$$\mu = 63 - \sigma \times 1.23$$

$$= 63 - 10.33 \times 1.23 = 50.3 \text{ (approximately)}$$

Ex. 8 : *Let $x \to N(4, 16)$. Find (i) $P(x > 5)$, (ii) $P(x < 2)$, (iii) $P(x > 0)$, (iv) $P(6 < x < 8)$, (v) $P(|x| > 6)$.*

Sol. : Let $x \to N(4, 16) = N(\mu, \sigma^2)$, hence $\mu = 4$, and $\sigma^2 = 16 \Rightarrow \sigma = 4$.

(i)
$$P(x > 5) = P\left(z = \frac{x - \mu}{\sigma} > \frac{5 - 4}{4}\right)$$

$$= P(z > 1/4)$$

$\therefore$ From normal probability integral table we get area of shaded region as,

$$p(z > 1/4) = 0.40129$$

(ii)
$$p(x < 2) = P\left(\frac{x - \mu}{\sigma} > \frac{2 - 4}{4}\right)$$

$$= P\left(z < \frac{-2}{4}\right)$$

$$= P(z < -0.5)$$

$$= P(z > 0.5) \qquad \text{(Due to symmetry)}$$

$$= 0.30854 \qquad \text{(From the table)}$$

(iii)
$$p(x > 0) = P\left(\frac{x - \mu}{\sigma} > \frac{0 - 4}{4}\right)$$

$$= P(z > -1) = B$$

Since, only tail area is given in the table we use the fact that $A + B = 1$.

$\therefore$
$$p(z > -1) = 1 - A = 1 - p(z < -1)$$

$$= 1 - p(z > 1) \qquad \text{(Due to symmetry)}$$

$$= 1 - 0.15866$$

$$= 0.84134$$

(iv) $\qquad p\,(6 < x < 8)$

$$= P\left(\frac{6-4}{4} < \frac{x-\mu}{\sigma} < \frac{8-4}{\sigma}\right)$$

$$= P\left(\frac{2}{4} < z < 1\right)$$

$$= P\,(0.5 < z < 1) = A$$

$$= (A + B) - B$$

$$= P\,(z > 0.3) - P\,(z > 1)$$

$$= 0.30854 - 0.15866$$

$$= 0.14988$$

(v) $\qquad p\,(|x| > 6) = p\,(x > 6) + P\,(x < -6)$

$$= p\left(\frac{x-\mu}{6} > \frac{6-4}{4}\right) + P\left(\frac{x-\mu}{\sigma} > \frac{-6-4}{4}\right)$$

$$= p\,(z > 0.5) + p\,(z < -2.5)$$

$$= p\,(z > 0.5) + p\,(z > 2.5)$$

$$= 0.30854 + 0.0062097)$$

$$= 0.31475$$

Ex. 9 : _A fair coin is tossed 600 times. Using normal approximation find the probability of getting (i) number of heads less than 270. (ii) number of heads between 280 to 360._

Sol. : A fair coin tossing 600 times result into head or tail each with probability 0.5.

Let, $\qquad\qquad x$ = Number of heads in 600 tosses

$$x \to B\,(600, 0.5)$$

$$E\,(X) = np = 600 \times 0.5 = 300 \text{ and}$$

$$\text{Var}\,(X) = npq = 600 \times 0.5 \times 0.5 = 150$$

(i)   p (number of heads less than 270).

$$p\,(x < 270) = p\left(\frac{x - np}{\sqrt{npq}} < \frac{270 - 300}{\sqrt{150}}\right)$$

$$= p\,(z < -2.4495) \qquad \text{(Using normal approximate)}$$

$$= p\,(z > 2.4495) \qquad \text{(Due to symmetry)}$$

$$= 0.0071428$$

(ii) p (Number of heads are between 280 and 350)

$$= p\,(280 < x < 350)$$

$$= p\left(\frac{280 - 300}{\sqrt{150}} < z < \frac{350 - 300}{\sqrt{150}}\right)$$

Using normal approximate we get,

$$z = \frac{x - np}{\sqrt{npq}} \to N\,(0, 1)$$

$$p \approx p\,(-1.633 < z < 4.0823) \;=\; B$$
$$= 1 - A - C$$
$$= 1 - p\,(z < -1.633) - p\,(z > 4.0823) \qquad \text{(Due to symmetry)}$$
$$= 1 - p\,(z > 1.633) - p\,(z > 4.0823)$$
$$= 1 - 0.51551 - 0.000022518 \;=\; 0.4845$$

Ex. 10 : *If x is a random variable with p.d.f.*

$$f(x) \;=\; \frac{1}{3\sqrt{2\pi}}\; e^{(-1/18)}\,(x-6)^2$$

Find : (i) $p\,(x > 5)$, (ii) $p\,(2x + 3 > 10)$.

Sol. :
$$f(x) \;=\; \frac{1}{\sigma\sqrt{2\pi}}\; e^{-\dfrac{1}{2\sigma^2}\,(x-\mu)^2}$$

$$= \frac{1}{3\sqrt{2\pi}}\; e^{-\dfrac{1}{18}\,(x-\sigma)^2}$$

Comparing the p.d.f. we get,
$$\mu = 6, \quad \sigma^2 = 9$$
$$x \to\; N\,(6, 9)$$

(i)
$$p\,(x > 5) \;=\; p\!\left(\frac{x-6}{3} > \frac{5-6}{3}\right) \;=\; P\,(z > -0.3)$$

$$p\!\left(z > \frac{-1}{3} = -0.3333\right) \;=\; 0.5 + p\!\left(z < z < \frac{1}{3}\right) \;=\; 0.5 + 0.1293 \;=\; 0.6293$$

(ii)
$$2x + 3 \;\to\; N\,(\mu', \sigma^2)$$
$$\mu' \;=\; E\,(2x+3) \;=\; 2\mu + 3$$
$$= 2\,(6) + 3 \;=\; 12 + 3 = 15$$
$$\sigma'^2 \;=\; \text{Var}\,(2x+2) \;=\; 4\,\text{Var}\,(x) = 36$$
$$2x + 3 \;\to\; N\,(15, 36)$$

$$\therefore \qquad p\,(2x + 3 > 10) \;=\; p\!\left(\frac{2x + 3 - 15}{6} > \frac{10 - 15}{6}\right)$$
$$= p\,(z > -0.8333)$$
$$= 1 - p\,(z > 0.8333)$$
$$= 1 - 0.20327$$
$$= 0.79673$$

Ex. 11 : *Suppose heights of students follows normal distribution with mean 190 cm and variance 80 cm². In a school of 1000, students how many would you expect to be above 200 an tall.*

Sol. : Let, x = Height of students

$$x \to N\,(190, 80)$$

Proportion of students having height above 200 cm.

$$= p\,(x > 200)$$

$$= p\left(\frac{x - \mu}{\sigma} > \frac{200 - 190}{\sqrt{80}}\right)$$

$$= p\,(z > 1.1180)$$

$$= 0.13136$$

$$\therefore \begin{pmatrix} \text{Number of students} \\ \text{out of 1000} \\ \text{having height above} \\ \text{200 cm} \end{pmatrix} = 1000 \times \begin{pmatrix} \text{Proportion of students} \\ \text{having height above} \\ \text{200 cm} \end{pmatrix}$$

$$= 1000 \times 0.13136$$

$$= 131.36$$

$$= 131$$

Ex. 12 : *Fit a normal distribution to the following data and find expected frequencies.*

Class	*10-15*	*15-20*	*20-25*	*25-30*	*30-35*	*35-40*
Frequency	*18*	*30*	*40*	*21*	*9*	*0*

Sol. :

Class	Mid-points x_i	Freq. f_i	l_i	$z_i = \dfrac{l_i - \mu}{\sigma}$	$\phi\,(z_i)$	$p_i = \phi(z_i + 1) - \phi(z_i)$	Np
$-\infty$–10	–	–	$-\infty$	$-\infty$	0		
10-15	12.5	18	10	-0.5254	0.30153	0.30153	35.5805
15-20	17.5	30	15	-0.2941	0.38591	0.08438	9.9474
20-25	22.5	40	20	-0.0627	0.47608	0.09017	10.6401
25-30	27.5	21	25	0.1686	0.43644	-0.03964	-4.6775
30-35	32.5	9	30	0.3999	0.34827	-0.08817	-10.4041
35-40	37.5	0	35	0.6313	0.26435	-0.08392	-9.9026
40-∞	–	–	40	0.8627	0.19489	-0.06946	-8.1963
Total	–	**118**	–	–	–	–	**22.9875**

$$\bar{x} = \frac{\sum f_i x_i}{\sum f_i} = \frac{2520}{118} = 21.3559$$

$$\sigma^2 = \frac{\sum f_i x_i^2}{\sum f_i} - \bar{X} = 467.0975$$

$$\hat{\mu} = \bar{x} = 21.3559$$

$$\hat{\sigma} = 21.6124$$

8.11 SAMPLING DISTRIBUTIONS

In order to draw inference about a certain phenomenon, sampling is a well accepted tool. Entire population cannot be studied due to several reasons. In such a situation sampling is the only alternative. A properly drawn sample is much useful in drawing reliable conclusions. Here, we draw a sample from probability distribution rather than a group of objects. Using simulation technique sample is drawn.

Random Sample from a Continuous Distribution

A random sample from a continuous probability distribution $f(x, \theta)$ is nothing but the values of independent and identically distributed random variables with the common probability density function $f(x, \theta)$.

Definition : If $X_1, X_2, \dots, X_n$ are independent and identically distributed random variables, with p.d.f. $f(x, \theta)$, then we say that, they form a sample from the population with p.d.f. $f(x, \theta)$.

Note :

(1) For drawing inference, we use the numerical values of $X_1, X_2, \dots, X_n$.

(2) The joint p.d.f. of $X_1, X_2, \dots X_n$ is,

$$f(x_1, x_2, \dots, x_n) = f(x_1), f(x_2), \dots, f(x_n) = \prod_{i=1}^{n} f(x_i)$$

8.12 STATISTIC AND PARAMETER

Using the random sample $X_1, X_2, \dots, X_n$ we draw conclusion about the unknown probability distribution. However probability distribution can be studied if the parameter θ is known. In other words study of probability distribution reduces to the study of parameter θ. We use sampled observations for this purpose. There are various ways of summarizing the sampled observations. The summarized quantity is called as statistic. We define it precisely as follows.

Definition : If $X_1, X_2, \dots, X_n$ is a random sample from a probability distribution $f(x, \theta)$, then $T = T(x_1, x_2, \dots, x_n)$ a function of sample values which does not involve unknown parameter θ is called as a *statistic (or estimator)*.

Some typical statistics are given below :

(i) Sample mean : $\quad T = T(x_1, x_2, \dots, x_n) = \dfrac{\sum x_i}{n}$

$$\therefore \qquad T = \bar{X} \text{ is a statistic}$$

(ii) Sample variance :

$$T = T(x_1, x_2, \dots x_n)$$

$$= \frac{1}{n-1} \sum (x_i - \bar{x})^2 \text{ is a statistic.}$$

8.13 CHI-SQUARE DISTRIBUTION

Introduction :

The Chi-square (pronounced as Ki, sky without 's') distribution is one of the important distributions in Statistics. It is mainly applied in testing of hypothesis for testing the independence of attributes, testing the goodness of fit of a model etc.

The chi-square variable is denoted by χ_n^2. Hence n is the parameter of the distribution, also, called as the 'degrees of freedom' (d.f.). The χ_n^2 variate is defined as sum of squares of n independent standard normal [N (0, 1)] variables.

8.14 DEFINITION

Let $X_1, X_2, \dots, X_n$ be n independent N (0, 1) variables, then

$$Y = \sum_{i=1}^{n} X_i^2 \text{ follows chi-square distribution with n degrees of freedom (d.f.).}$$

Notation : $Y \to \chi_n^2$. $(\because \text{ in positive integer})$

8.15 ADDITIVE PROPERTY

Statement : If Y_1 and Y_2 are independent χ^2 variates with n_1 and n_2 d.f. respectively, then $Y_1 + Y_2$ has χ^2 distribution with $(n_1 + n_2)$ degrees of freedom.

8.16 APPLICATIONS OF CHI-SQUARE DISTRIBUTION TO TESTS OF HYPOTHESIS

Meaning of Statistical Hypothesis

We are mainly interested in testing certain claims about the population parameters such as mean, variance, proportion. For example, a particular scooter gives average of 50 km per litre, proportion of unemployed persons is same for two states etc. These claims stated in terms of population parameters or statistical distribution are called hypothesis.

Definition : Hypothesis : It is a statement or assertion about the statistical distribution or unknown parameter of statistical distribution.

In other words, hypothesis is a claim to be tested.

8.17 CONCEPTS OF NULL HYPOTHESIS AND ALTERNATIVE HYPOTHESIS

In each problem of test of significance, two hypothesis are to be set. These are set in such a way that if one is rejected, the other is to be accepted. These hypothesis are referred to as null hypothesis and alternative hypothesis.

Null Hypothesis : A hypothesis of "no difference" is called as null hypothesis according to R. A. Fisher. Null hypothesis is denoted by H_0.

For example : $H_0 : \mu = 100$. Here the hypothesis states that there is no difference in population mean and 100. $H_0 : \mu_1 = \mu_2$. This hypothesis states that there is no difference between two population means. While conducting the test, some difference will be observed in sample value and hypothesized value. Whether this difference is just due to chance element, is decided in testing procedure.

Alternative Hypothesis : It is a hypothesis to be accepted in case null hypothesis is rejected. In other words, a complementary hypothesis to null hypothesis is called as alternative hypothesis. It is denoted by H_1.

For example : If $H_0 : \mu_1 = \mu_2$ then alternative hypothesis may be $H_1 : \mu_1 \neq \mu_2$ or $H_1 : \mu_1 < \mu_2$ or $H_1 : \mu_1 > \mu_2$.

8.18 ONE AND TWO TAILED HYPOTHESIS

By considering the nature of hypothesis, these are classified as one sided or two sided.

Hypothesis of the type $H_1 : \mu > \mu_0$, $H_1 : P < 0.5$, $H_1 : \mu_1 < \mu_2$, $H_0 : \sigma_1 > \sigma_2$ etc. are called as *one sided*. On the other hand, the hypothesis of the type $H_1 : P_1 \neq 0.5$, $H_1 : \sigma_1 \neq \sigma_2$, $H_1 : \mu \neq \mu_0$ etc. are called as *two sided*.

In this text we will consider null hypothesis to be hypothesis of equality and alternative hypothesis to be two sided. Choice of one sided hypothesis as null hypothesis is beyond the scope of the book.

8.19 TYPE I AND TYPE II ERRORS

Since decision of acceptance or rejection of H_0, is based on sampling, it is subject to two kinds of errors. For instance, in the inspection of a lot of manufactured items, the inspector will choose a sample of suitable size and accordingly take decision whether to accept or reject the lot. In this process, two errors are possible viz, rejection of a good lot and acceptance of a bad lot. In testing of hypothesis these errors are called as type I and type II errors.

Type I error : Rejecting H_0 when it is true.

Type II error : Accepting H_0 when it is false.

These errors can be put in tabular form to remember easily.

Actual Situation	Decision	
	Reject H_0	**Accept H_0**
H_0 is true	Type I error	Correct decision
H_0 is false	Correct decision	Type II error

8.20 CRITICAL REGION

Let x_1, x_2, ..., x_n be a random sample taken for testing H_0. The set of values of $(x_1, x_2, ..., x_n)$ for which H_0 is rejected is called as critical region or rejection region.

Many a times, critical region is expressed with the help of test statistic e.g. $\overline{x} \geq c$, where c is constant. Critical region is denoted by W. The set of all sample observations can be partitioned into two subsets : critical region (W) and acceptance region (W^c) as shown below.

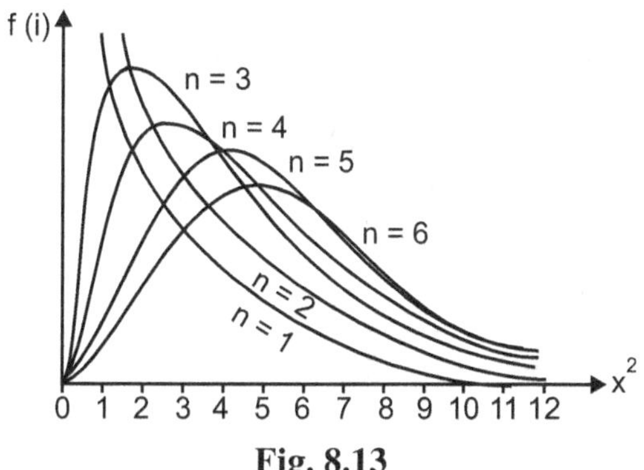

Fig. 8.13

8.21 TEST OF HYPOTHESIS

A rule which leads to the decision of acceptance of H_0 or rejection of H_0 on the basis of observations in a random sample is called test of hypothesis.

Statistical inference is that branch of statistics which concerned with using probability concept to deal with uncertainly in decision making field of statistical inference has a fruitful development since the letter half of the 19th century. It refers to the process of selecting and using a sample statistic to draw inference about a population parameter based on a sub-set of it the simple drawn from the population. Statistical inference treats two different classes of problems.

(i)   Hypothesis testing and (ii) Estimation.

Hypothesis testing begins with us assumption called as hypothesis, which is made by the population parameter. A hypothesis is a supposition made as basis for reasoning.

In article 8.14 to 8.21 we discussed the various terms like statistical hypothesis, null hypothesis and alternative hypothesis, critical region, level of significance etc.

Now we will see the method of testing population mean (μ) equal to specified value (μ_0).

Testing Population Mean (μ) equal to specified value (μ_0) : Test statistic is

$$U \;=\; \frac{\overline{X} - \mu_0}{\sigma/\sqrt{n}}$$

Under H_0, $\qquad\qquad U \;=\; \frac{\overline{X} - \mu_0}{\sigma/\sqrt{n}} \;\to\; N\,(0,\,1)$

Critical region : Value of $|U| > 1.96$ at 5% level of significance.

If calculated value of U is more than 1.96 or less than -1.96, H_0 is rejected and accepted otherwise.

8.22 ONE SIDED AND TWO SIDED TESTS

The tests used for testing null hypothesis are called as one sided or two sided tests according as the alternative hypothesis are one sided or two sided.

8.23 TEST STATISTIC

A function of sample observations which is used to test null hypothesis H_0 is called a *test statistic*. The distribution of test statistic is completely known under H_0. Hence, it can be used to test H_0.

8.24 LEVEL OF SIGNIFICANCE

Probability of rejecting H_0 when it is true is called as *level of significance*. Thus, it is probability of committing type I error. It is denoted by α.

Level of significance can be interpreted as proportion of cases in which H_0 is rejected though it is true.

If we try to minimize level of significance, the probability of type II error increases. So level of significance cannot be made zero. However, we can fix it in advance as 0.05 (i.e. 5%) or 0.01 (i.e. 1 %). In most of the cases, it is taken as 5%.

Test for Goodness of Fit of χ^2 Distribution :

For a given data (frequency distribution), we try to fit some probability distribution. Since there are several probability distributions, which distribution will fit properly may be a question of interest. In such cases, we want to test the appropriateness of the fit. Hence we desire to test H_0 : Fitting of the probability distribution to given data is proper (good). The test based on χ^2 distribution used to test this H_0 is called χ^2 test of goodness of fit.

In this case, we compare the expected and observed frequencies. Thus we can take H_0. There is no significant difference between observed and (theoretical) expected frequencies. The test is carried out as follows :

Suppose $o_1, o_2, \ldots, o_i, \ldots, o_k$ be a set of observed frequencies and $e_1, e_2, \ldots, e_i - e_k$ be corresponding expected frequencies obtained under H_0.

$$\sum_{i=1}^{k} o_i \ = \ N \ = \ \sum_{i=1}^{k} e_i$$

p = number of parameters estimated for fitting the probability distribution.

If H_0 is true, then the statistic

$$\chi^2 \ = \ \sum_{i=1}^{k} \frac{(o_i - e_i)^2}{e_i} \ = \ \sum_{i=1}^{k} \left(\frac{o_i^2}{e_i}\right) - N$$

has χ^2 distribution with $(k - p - 1)$ degrees of freedom. In this case, the critical region at *l*.o.s. α is $\qquad \chi^2_{k-p-1} \ \geq \ \chi^2_{k-p-1} \ ; \ \alpha$

It is shown by the shaded region in Fig. 8.14.

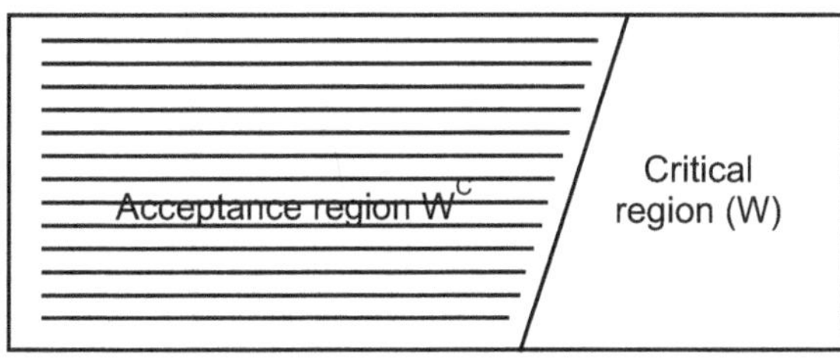

Fig. 8.14

Thus, we reject H_0 at *l*.o.s. α if,

$$\chi^2_{k-p-1} \ \geq \ \chi^2_{k-p-1;\ \alpha}$$

Note :

1. We can apply this test if expected frequencies are greater than or equal to 5 (i.e. $e_i \geq 5$) and total of cell frequencies is sufficiently large (greater than 50).

2. When expected frequency of a class is less than 5, the class is merged into neighbouring class alongwith its observed and expected frequencies until total of expected frequencies becomes ≥ 5. This procedure is called *'pooling the classes'*. In this case, k is the number of class frequencies after pooling.

3. It is obvious that if any parameters are not estimated while fitting a probability distribution or obtaining expected frequencies, the value of p is zero.

4. This test is not applicable for testing goodness of fitting of straight line or curves such as second degree curve, exponential curve etc.

Remark :

Yate's Correction : If in a 2×2 contingency table, any cell frequency is less than 5 then the test statistic χ^2 is corrected in a specific way. This correction is due to Yate's and hence is known as Yate's correction. It is beyond the scope of this book.

ILLUSTRATIONS

Ex. 1 : *A nationalized bank utilizes four teller windows to render fast service to the customers. On a particular day, 800 customers were observed. They were given service at the different windows as follows :*

Window Number	Observed Number of customers (O_i)
1	150
2	250
3	170
4	230

Test whether the customers are uniformly distributed over the windows.

Sol. : Here we want to test H_0 : Customers are uniformly distributed over the windows. i.e. H_0 : customers on all windows are equal against H_1 : They are not equal on all windows.

Under H_0, the expected frequencies are :

Window Number	Expected Number of customers (e_i)
1	200
2	200
3	200
4	200

The test statistic is

$$\chi^2_{k-p-1} = \sum_{i=1}^{k} \frac{(o_i - e_i)^2}{e_i} = \frac{(-50)^2}{200} + \frac{(50)^2}{200} + \frac{(-30)^2}{200} + \frac{(30)^2}{200}$$

Here number of parameters estimated $= p = 0$, $k = 4$.

$$\therefore \qquad \chi^2_3 = 34 \qquad \text{[Calculated value]}$$

$$\chi^2_3 = 34 > \chi^2_{3;\,0.05} = 7.815 \qquad \text{[Table value]}$$

We reject H_0 at 5 % *l.o.s.*

Conclusion : The customers in the nationalized bank may not be uniformly distributed over different windows.

Ex. 2 : *One hundred samples were drawn from a production process each after 5 hours. The number of defectives in these samples were noted. A Poisson distribution by estimating the parameter m was fitted to these data. The results obtained are as follows :*

Number of defectives	Number of samples (observed)	Expected number of samples
0	63	60.65
1	28	30.33
2	6	7.58
3	2	1.26
4	1	0.16
5 and above	0	0.02

Test the goodness of fit of Poisson distribution in above situation.

[Use 5 % level of significance]

Sol. : We want to test

H_0 : Fitting of Poisson distribution is good (proper) against

H_1 : Fitting of Poisson distribution is not proper.

Here we pool expected frequencies until their sum becomes ≥ 5 and also pool corresponding observed frequencies. Thus the frequencies can be written as :

Observed frequencies (o_i)	Expected frequencies (e_i)
63	60.65
28	30.33
9	9.02

We use the test statistic

$$\chi^2_{k-p-1} \;=\; \sum_{i=1}^{k} \left(\frac{o_i^2}{e_i} \right) - N$$

Here number of parameters estimated $= p = 1$, $N = 100$, $k = 3$.

$\therefore \qquad\qquad \chi_1^2 \;=\; 100.27009 - 100$

$\therefore \qquad\qquad \chi_1^2 \;=\; 0.27009 \qquad\qquad$ [Calculated value]

$\qquad \chi_1^2 = 0.27009 \;<\; \chi_{1;\,0.05}^2 \;=\; 3.841 \qquad$ [Table value]

Hence we accept H_0 at 5 % *l.o.s.*

Conclusion : Fitting of Poisson distribution may be good to the given data.

Ex. 3 : *Among 64 offsprings of a certain cross between guinea pigs 34 were red, 10 were black and 20 were white. According to a genetic model, these numbers should be in the ratio 9 : 3 : 4.*

Are the data consistent with the model at 5 % level ? **(May 2012)**

Sol. : Here H_0 : The offsprings red, black and white in the colour are in the ratio 9 : 3 : 4. In this problem, N = 64. Hence observed and expected frequencies are as follows :

Observed frequencies (o_i)	34	10	20
Expected frequencies (e_i)	$\frac{9}{16} \times 64 = 36$	$\frac{3}{16} \times 64 = 12$	$\frac{4}{16} \times 54 = 16$

To test H_0, the test statistic is

$$\chi^2_{k-p-1} = \sum_{i=1}^{k} \frac{(o_i - e_i)^2}{e_i} \quad \text{Here } p = 0 \text{ and } k = 3.$$

$$\therefore \qquad \chi^2_2 = 1.444444 \qquad \text{[Calculated value]}$$

$$\chi^2_{2:0.05} = 5.991 \qquad \text{[Table value]}$$

$$\chi^2_2 = 1.444444 \; < \; \chi^2_{2;0.05} = 5.99$$

We accept H_0 at 5 % _l.o.s._

Conclusion : The data are consistent with the genetic model that the offsprings red, black and white in colour are in the ratio 9 : 3 : 4.

Ex. 4 : _The table below gives number of books issued from a certain library on the various days of a week._

Days	No. of books issued	$(o_i - e_i)^2$
Mon.	120	0
Wed.	130	100
Thr.	110	100
Fri.	115	25
Sat.	135	225
Sun.	110	100

Test at 5 % l.o.s. whether issuing the book is day dependent.

Sol. : The issuing of the book is not dependent on the day of the week.

$$\chi^2_{k-p-1} = \chi^2_{6-0-1} = \chi^2_5$$

$$\therefore \qquad \chi^2_5 = \frac{\sum (o_i - e_i)^2}{e_i}$$

$$\therefore \qquad \chi^2_5 = \frac{550}{120} = 4.5833$$

$$\chi^2_{5, 0.05} = 11.07$$

$$\chi^2_5 \; < \; \chi^2_{5, 0.05}$$

Accept H_0.

i.e. issuing of book is independent of day.

Ex. 5 : *In experiment on pea breeding, the following frequencies of seeds were obtained :*

Round and green	Wrinkled and green	Round and yellow	Wrinkled and yellow	Total
222	120	32	150	524

Theory predicts that the frequencies should be in proportion 8 : 2 : 2 : 1. Examine the correspondence between theory and experiment.

Sol. : From the given data the corresponding frequencies are, i.e. expected frequencies are

Expected frequencies (e_i)	$\frac{8}{13} \times 524 = 323$	$\frac{2}{13} \times 524 = 81$	$\frac{2}{13} \times 524 = 81$	$\frac{1}{13} \times 524 = 40$

$$\chi^2_{k-p-1} = \chi^2_3 = \frac{\sum (o_i - e_i)^2}{e_i}$$

$$\chi^2_3 = \frac{(222 - 323)^2}{323} + \frac{(120 - 81)^2}{81} + \frac{(32 - 81)^2}{81} + \frac{(150 - 40)^2}{40}$$

$$\chi^2_3 = 31.5820 + 18.7778 + 29.64198 + 302.5$$

$$\chi^2_3 = 382.502$$

$$\chi^2_{3,\,0.05} = 7.815$$

The calculated value of χ^2 is much more than $\chi^2_{3,\,0.05}$, there is a very low degree of agreement between the theory and experiment.

Ex. 6 : *A set of five similar coins is tossed 210 times and the result is*

No. of heads	0	1	2	3	4	5
Frequency	2	5	20	60	100	23

Test the hypothesis that the data follow a binomial distribution.   **(Dec. 2007)**

Sol. : Here $k - p - 1 = 5$.

$$p \;:\; \text{Probability of getting a head} = \frac{1}{2}$$

$$q \;:\; \text{Probability of getting a tail} = \frac{1}{2}\;.$$

Hence the theoretical frequencies of getting 0, 1, 2, 3, 4, 5 heads are the successive terms of the binomial expansion $210\,(p + q)^5$

$$= 210\,[p^5 + 5\,p^4 q + 10\,p^3 q^2 + 10\,p^2 q^3 + 5\,pq^4 + q^5]$$

$$= 210\left[\frac{1}{32} + \frac{5}{32} + \frac{10}{32} + \frac{10}{32} + \frac{5}{32} + \frac{1}{32}\right]$$

$$= 7 + 33 + 66 + 66 + 33 + 7$$

$\therefore$ The theoretical frequencies are 7, 33, 66, 66, 33, 7.

Hence, $\chi_5^2 = \dfrac{(2-7)^2}{7} + \dfrac{(5-33)^2}{33} + \dfrac{(20-66)^2}{66} + \dfrac{(60-66)^2}{66} + \dfrac{(100-33)^2}{33} + \dfrac{(23-7)^2}{7}$

$\chi_5^2 = 3.57143 + 23.7576 + 32.06061 + 0.5455 + 136.0303 + 36.5714$

$\chi_5^2 = 232.53684$

$\therefore \quad \chi_{5,\,0.05}^2 = 11.070$

Since the calculated value of χ^2 is much greater than $\chi_{5,\,0.05}^2$, the hypothesis that the data follow the binomial distribution is rejected.

Ex. 7 : *The figures given below are (a) the theoretical frequencies of a distribution and (b) the frequencies of a normal distribution having the same mean, standard deviation and the total frequency as in (a).*

(a)	1	5	20	28	42	22	15	5	2
(b)	1	6	18	25	40	25	18	6	1

Apply the χ^2 test of goodness of fit.

Sol. : Since the observed and expected frequencies are less and 10 in the beginning and end of the series, we pull the classes and then apply the χ^2 test.

o_i	e_i	$(o_i - e_i)^2$	$(o_i - e_i)^2/E_i$
$\left.\begin{array}{r}1\\5\end{array}\right\}\,6$	$\left.\begin{array}{r}1\\6\end{array}\right\}\,7$	1	0.1429
20	18	4	0.2222
28	25	9	0.36
42	40	4	0.1
22	25	9	0.36
15	18	9	0.5
$\left.\begin{array}{r}5\\2\end{array}\right\}\,7$	$\left.\begin{array}{r}6\\1\end{array}\right\}\,7$	0	0

Now, $\qquad \chi_{6,\,0.05}^2 = \displaystyle\sum_i \dfrac{(o_i - e_i)^2}{e_i}$

We take table value of χ_6^2. Because, we have total 9 classes, 2 classes are pulled, so after pulling number of classes is 7.

$\therefore$ The degree of freedom for this experiment is 6.

$\therefore \qquad \chi_{6,\,0.05}^2 = 12.592$

Now, we have,

$$\chi_6^2 < \chi_{6,\,0.05}^2$$

$\therefore$ Accept H_0.

Conclusion : The fit is good.

Ex. 8 : *The demand for a particular spare part in a factory was found to vary from day to day. In a sample study the following information was obtained.*

Days	Mon.	Tues.	Wed.	Thurs.	Fri.	Sat.
No. of parts demanded	1124	1125	1110	1120	1126	1115

Test the hypothesis that the number of parts demanded does not depend on the day of the week.

Sol. : To test : H_0 : The number of parts demanded does not depend on the day of the week.

Vs H_1 : The number of parts demanded depend on the day of the week.

The number of parts demanded during six days = 6720.

$\therefore$ Expected no. of parts to be demanded each day of the week $= \dfrac{6720}{6} = 1120$.

Applying χ^2 test :

Days	o_i	e_i	$(o_i - e_i)^2$	$(o_i - e_i)^2/e_i$
Monday	1124	1120	16	0.01429
Tuesday	1125	1120	25	0.0223
Wednesday	1110	1120	100	0.0893
Thursday	1120	1120	0	0
Friday	1126	1120	36	0.0321
Saturday	1115	1120	25	0.0223

Now, $\chi^2_5 \ = \ \Sigma \ \dfrac{(o_i - e_i)^2}{e_i}$

The critical value at 5% l.o.s. is $\chi^2_{5,\,0.05} \ - \ 11.07$

$\therefore$ $\chi^2_5 \ < \ \chi^2_{5,\,0.05}$

$\therefore$ Accept H_0.

Conclusion : The number of parts demanded does not depend on the day of the week.

8.25 STUDENTS T-DISTRIBUTION

In number of situations such as biological experiments, clinical trials etc. in which sample sizes are small (n < 30) exact tests can be used for testing hypothesis about a population parameter.

In large sample tests, the distribution of test statistic z is taken as standard normal which seems to be reasonable.

In small sample tests the statistic follows exact sampling distribution viz. χ^2, t or F for sample of any size. Hence small sample tests are regarded as exact tests. The procedure of testing a null hypothesis H_0 in small sample tests is almost identical to that of large sample test. We discuss below the test called t-distribution or student t-distribution.

Test for Population Mean.

Let $x_1, x_2, \ldots x_i, \ldots, x_n$ be a random sample of size n from a normal population with mean μ and variance σ^2. We desire to test $H_0 : \mu = \mu_0$ against $H_1 : \mu \neq \mu_0$

where, μ_0 represents a specified value of population mean μ.

If the population variance σ^2 is known then the test statistic. Under $H_0 : \mu = \mu_0$ is,

$$\frac{\overline{X} - \mu_0}{\dfrac{\sigma}{\sqrt{n}}} \to N(0, 1) \qquad \ldots \text{(i)}$$

The difficulty in testing H_0 arises when σ^2 is unknown. We shall discuss following two cases when σ^2 is *unknown*.

(i) $H_0 : \mu = \mu_0$ against $H_1 : \mu \neq \mu_0$. (ii) $H_0 : \mu = \mu_0$ against $H_1 : \mu > \mu_0$ or $\mu < \mu_0$

Case (i) : $H_0 : \mu = \mu_0$ against $H_1 : \mu \neq \mu_0$

In order to overcome the difficulty that σ^2 is unknown, we propose the statistics U and V as follows :

$$U = \frac{\overline{x} - \mu}{\dfrac{\sigma}{\sqrt{n}}} \quad \text{and} \quad V = \frac{\Sigma\,(x_i - \overline{x})^2}{\sigma^2}$$

Then $U \to N(0, 1)$ and $V \to \chi^2$ distribution with $(n - 1)$ degrees of freedom. Moreover U and V are independent variates. Hence, we can define statistic as $t = \dfrac{U}{\sqrt{\dfrac{V}{n - 1}}}$ which has t-distribution with $(n - 1)$ degrees of freedom.

$$\therefore \quad t = \frac{U}{\sqrt{\dfrac{V}{n - 1}}} = \frac{\dfrac{\overline{x} - \mu}{\dfrac{\sigma}{\sqrt{n}}}}{\sqrt{\dfrac{\Sigma\,(x_i - \overline{x})^2}{\dfrac{\sigma^2}{n - 1}}}}$$

$$= \frac{\overline{x} - \mu}{\dfrac{s}{\sqrt{n}}} \qquad \text{where, } s^2 = \frac{\Sigma(x_i - \overline{x})^2}{n - 1} \qquad \ldots \text{(ii)}$$

$\therefore$ Under $H_0 : \mu = \mu_0$, $t = \dfrac{\overline{x} - \mu_0}{\dfrac{s}{\sqrt{n}}} \to$ t-distribution with $(n - 1)$ degrees of freedom.

Thus we obtain test statistic which is free from unknown parameter σ.

Since, the alternative hypothesis $H_1 : \mu \neq \mu_0$ is two sided, the rejection region is $|t_{n-1}| \geq t_{n-1; \frac{\alpha}{2}}$ where value $t_{n-1; \frac{\alpha}{2}}$ is such that $P\left\{|t_{n-1}| \geq t_{n-1; \frac{\alpha}{2}}\right\} = \alpha$

This value is also shown in the figure 8.15.

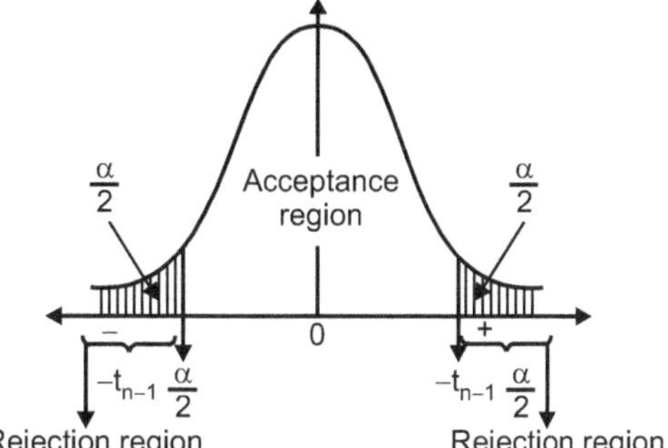

Fig. 8.15

So, the decision rule is, reject H_0 at level of significance α, if $|t_{n-1}| \geq t_{n-1; \alpha}$ and accept H_0 otherwise. Then the conclusion about the population mean can be drawn accordingly.

Remarks : (I) If σ is known, we use test statistic (i) Which follows $N(0, 1)$ distribution, where as if σ is unknown, we use test statistic (ii) Apparently we may think that the unknown σ is replaced by s but it is not so which is clear from the above discussion.

(II) For using any test based on t-distribution, one has to ensure that the observations in the parent population (population from which sample is drawn) follow normal distribution.

Case (ii) : $H_0 : \mu = \mu_0$ against $H_1 : \mu < \mu_0$ or $\mu > \mu_0$. In this case we use the same test statistic as in case (i). If $H_1 : \mu < \mu_0$, then the critical region at level of significance α is $t_{n-1} \leq - t_{n-1; \alpha}$. It is shaded region as shown in Fig. 8.16.

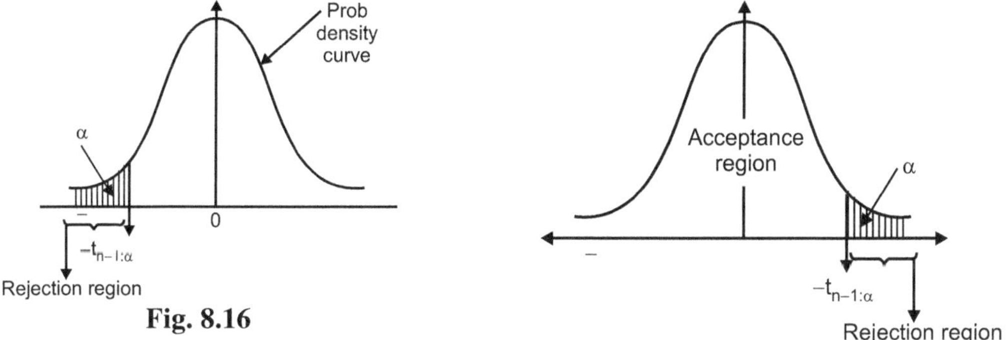

Fig. 8.16   **Fig. 8.17**

On the other hand if $H_1 : \mu > \mu_0$ then critical region at level of significance α is $t_{n-1} \geq t_{n-1; \alpha}$. It is shaded region as shown in Fig. 8.17.

ILLUSTRATIONS

Ex. 1 : *In order to start new S.T. bus to a certain remote village it is required to get the average fare of Rs. 400 daily. Reports on number of passengers for 21 days revealed that the average daily collection of fare from the passengers was Rs. 390 with standard deviation of Rs. 40. Do these data support the demand of people for starting new bus to the village ?*   *[Use 5% l.o.s.]*

Solution : Here, we want to test $H_0 : \mu = \mu_0 = 400$ against $H_1 : \mu < 400$.

$\therefore$ The test statistic is given by

$$t_{n-1} = \frac{\overline{X} - \mu_0}{\dfrac{s}{\sqrt{n}}} \qquad \text{where, } \overline{x} = \text{sample mean} = 390$$

and

$$s^2 = \frac{\Sigma (x_i - \overline{x})^2}{n-1} = \frac{n \,(\text{sample variance})}{n-1} = \frac{(21)\,(1600)}{20} = 1680$$

$\therefore \qquad s = 40.987803$

$\therefore \qquad t_{20} = \dfrac{390 - 400}{\dfrac{40.987803}{\sqrt{21}}} = \dfrac{(-10)\sqrt{21}}{40.987803}$

$\qquad\qquad = -1.1180342 \quad$ [calculated value]

$t_{20;\,0.05} = 1.725 \qquad$ [table value]

[Since H_1 is one sided see the value in statistical table corresponding to n = 20 and probability 0.1].

As $H_1 : \mu < \mu_0$ the decision rule is reject H_0 if t_{20} (calculated value) $< - t_{20;\,0.05}$ $= -1.725$ and accept H_0 otherwise. Here $t_{20} = -1.1180342 > -1.725$. Hence we accept H_0 at 5 % l.o.s.

Conclusion : These data support the demand of people for starting new bus to the village.

Ex. 2 : *Suppose that sweets are sold in packages of fixed weight of the contents. The producer of the packages is interested in testing that average weight of contents in packages in 1 kg. Hence a random sample of 12 packages is drawn and their contents found (in kg) as follows : 1.05, 1.01, 1.04, 0.98, 0.96, 1.01, 0.97, 0.99, 0.98, 0.95, 0.97, 0.95.*

Using the above data what should he conclude about the average weight of contents in the packets ?   *[Use 5 % l.o.s]*

Solution : Let μ denote the average weight of contents in packages. Producer wants to test $H_0 : \mu = \mu_0 = 1$ against $H_1 : \mu \neq 1$.

Test statistic is given by

$$t_{n-1} = \frac{\overline{x} - \mu_0}{\dfrac{s}{\sqrt{n}}}$$

where, $\qquad \overline{x} = \text{sample mean} = \dfrac{\Sigma x_i}{n} \quad$ and $\quad s^2 = \dfrac{\Sigma x_i^2 - n\,\overline{x}^2}{n-1}$

Here, $\qquad \overline{x} = 0.9883,$

$\qquad\qquad s^2 = \dfrac{11.7376 - 11.7208}{11} = 0.001164$

$\therefore \qquad s = 0.034112$

$$\therefore \quad t_{11} = \frac{(0.9883 - 1)\sqrt{12}}{0.034112} = -\frac{0.04053}{0.034112} = -1.188145$$

$\therefore \quad |t_{11}| = 1.188145$ [calculated value] $< t_{11;\,0.05} = 2.201$ [Table value]

$\therefore$ We accept H_0 at 5 % *l.o.s.*

Conclusion : The producer should conclude that the average weight of contents of package may be taken as 1 kg.

Ex. 3 : *A random sample of 17 drinks from a soft drink machine has one average constant of 7.40 ounces with a standard deviation of 0.48 ounces. Test the hypothesis that $\mu = 7.5$ ounces against the alternative hypothesis $\mu < 7.5$ ounces. Use 5% level of significance. Symbols have their own meanings. State your assumptions if any.*

Solution : Let x denote the variable under study.

Assumptions : (i) $x \sim N(\mu, \sigma^2)$, σ^2 unknown.

(ii) A r.s. of size n is drawn from distribution of x (n small).

$$\textbf{To test :} \qquad H_0 = \mu = \mu_0 = 7.5$$
$$H_1 = \mu < 7.5$$

Test statistics : $\qquad t_0 = \dfrac{\overline{x} - \mu_0}{s/\sqrt{n}} \sim t\,(n-1)$ under H_0

where, $\qquad\qquad n = 17$

$$\overline{x} = 7.40$$

$$\text{Standard deviation} = s = 0.48$$

$$s^2_{\text{unknown}} = \frac{ns^2}{n-1} = \frac{17\,(0.48)^2}{16} = \frac{17\,(0.2304)}{16} = 0.2448$$

$$s_{\text{unknown}} = 0.4948$$

Critical region : $\quad C = \{t_0 \mid t_0 < t_{2\sigma,\,n-1}\}$

i.e. H_0 is rejected if $t_0 < -t_{2\sigma,\,n-1}$ and is accepted otherwise

$$\therefore \qquad\qquad \alpha = 0.05$$

$$t_0 = \frac{\overline{x} - \mu_0}{s/\sqrt{n}} = \frac{7.40 - 7.5}{0.4948/4.1231} = \frac{-0.1}{0.1200} = -0.8333$$

$$-t_{2\alpha,\,n-1} = -t_{0.1,\,16} = -1.746$$
$$t_0 > -t_{0.1,\,16}$$

$\therefore$ Accept H_0.

Conclusion : $\qquad \mu = \mu_0 = 7.5$ ounces

Ex. 4 : *A roil order photo finishing company charges ₹ 50 per roll as handling cost. The manager suspects that handling cost has gone up. To verify this suspicion, he takes a random sample of 16 orders and finds that the average cost is ₹ 55 with a standard deviation of ₹ 8/-. Do these data confirm manager's suspension at 1% l.o.s. ?*

Solution : Let x denote the heading cost per roil.

Assumptions :

(i) $x \sim N(\mu, \sigma^2)$, σ^2 unknown.

(ii) A random sample of size n is drawn from distribution of x (n small).

To test : $\quad\quad$ $H_0 = \mu = \mu_0 = 50$ $\;$ Vs $\;$ $H_1 : \mu > 50$

Test statistics : $\quad$ $t_0 = \dfrac{\bar{x} - \mu_0}{s/\sqrt{n}} \sim t_{n-1}$ under H_0.

where, $\quad\quad\quad\quad$ $\bar{x}$ = Sample mean $x = \dfrac{\sum x_i}{n}$

$$s^2_{unknown} = \frac{ns^2}{n-1}$$

Critical region : $\quad$ $C = \{t_0 \mid t_0 > t_{2\alpha,\,n-1}\}$

i.e. H_0 is rejected if $t_0 > t_{2\alpha,\,n-1}$ and accepted otherwise.

Here, $\quad\quad\quad\quad\quad\quad$ $n = 16$

$$\bar{x} = 55$$

Standard deviation $= s = 8$

$$s^2_{unknown} = \frac{ns^2}{n-1} = \frac{16\,(64)}{15} = 68.2667$$

$$s_{unknown} = 8.2624$$

$$t_0 = \frac{\bar{x} - \mu_0}{s/\sqrt{n}} = \frac{55 - 50}{8.2624/4} = \frac{5}{2.0656} = 2.4206$$

$$t_{2\alpha,\,n-1} = t_{2\,(0.01),\,15} = 2.602$$

$$t_0 < t_{0.02,\,15} \quad \therefore \text{ Accept } H_0.$$

Conclusion : The data do not confirm the manager's suspension.

EXERCISE 8.2

1. 10 coins are thrown simultaneously. Find the probability that
   (i) Exactly 3 Heads will appear. (ii) Three or less Heads will appear.

   Ans. (i) 0.1172; (ii) 0.1718.

2. Probability of man now aged 60 years will live upto 70 years of age is 0.65. Find the probability of out of 10 men sixty years old 6 or more will live upto the age of 70 years.

   Ans. 0.2377

3. In sampling the large numbers of parts manufactured by a machine, the mean number of defectives in a sample of 20 is 2 out of 1000 such samples. How many would be expected to contain at least 3 defective parts ?

   Ans. 323.

4. According to past record of one day internationals between India and Pakistan, India has won 15 matches and lost 10. If they decide to play a series of 6 matches now, what is the probability of India winning the series ? (Draw is ruled out).

   Ans. 0.5443

5. Two dice are thrown 100 times and the number of nines recorded. What is the probability that 'r' nines occur ? Find the probability that at least 3 nines occur.

   Ans. 0.00045

6. Fit a Poisson distribution to the following frequency distribution and compare the theoretical frequencies with observed frequencies.

x	0	1	2	3	4	5
f	158	160	60	25	10	2

7. A source of liquid is known to contain bacteria with the mean number of bacteria per cubic centimetre equal to 2. Five 1 c.c. test tubes are filled with the liquid, assuming that Poisson distribution is applicable, calculate the probability that all test tubes show growth.

Ans. 0.036

8. Between 2 p.m. and 3 p.m. the average number of phone calls per minute coming into the company are 2. Find the probability that during one particular minute, there will be
(i) No phone calls at all.
(ii) 2 or less calls.   **(Dec. 2014, May 2015)**

Ans. (i) 0.1353; 6/65

9. In a Telephone exchange, the probability that any one call is wrongly connected is 0.02. What is the minimum number of calls required to ensure a probability 0.1 that at least one call is wrongly connected ?

Ans. 6 calls approximately

10. A manufacturer of electronic goods has 4 % of his product defective. He sells the articles in packets of 300 and guarantees 90 % good quality. Determine the probability that a particular packet will violate the guarantee.

$$\textbf{Ans. } \quad 1 - \sum_{r=1}^{r} \frac{e^{-12} (12)^r}{r!}$$

11. Obtain the equation of normal curve that may be fitted to the following distribution.

x	50	60	70	80	90	100
f	5	20	120	250	240	5

Also obtain expected normal frequencies.

12. X is normally distributed and the mean of X is 15 and standard deviation 3. Determine the probability of
(i) $0 < X < 10$; (ii) $X \geq 18$

Ans. (i) 0.10483; (ii) 0.1587

13. In a certain examination, the percentage of passes and distinction were 48 and 10 respectively. Estimate the average marks obtained by the candidates, the minimum pass and distinction marks being 40 and 75 respectively.

Ans. 38.5772

14. 5000 candidates appeared in a certain paper carrying a maximum of 100 marks. It was found that marks were normally distributed with mean 39.5 and standard deviation 12.5. Determine approximately the number of candidates who secured a first class for which a minimum of 60 marks is necessary.

Ans. 253

15. In a normal distribution, 31 % of the items are under 45 and 8 % are over 64. Find the mean and standard deviation of distribution.

Ans. $\sigma = 10.0529$; $\mu = 49.9259$

16. A random sample of 200 screws is drawn from a population which represents the size of screws. If a sample is distributed normally with a mean 3.15 cm and standard deviation 0.025 cm, find expected number of screws whose size falls between 3.12 cm and 3.2 cm.   **(Nov. 2015)**

Area corresponding to $1.2 \to 0.3849$; Area corresponding to $2.0 \to 0.4772$

[**Note :** $p(-1.2 < z < 2) = p(0 < z < 1.2) + p(0 < z < 2)$].

Ans. 172 Approximately.

17. Fit a Binomial distribution to the following data.

x	0	1	2	3	4	5
f	2	22	63	76	96	56

Ans. $[315\,(0.34 + 0.66)^5]$

18. For a normal distribution, $N = 300$, $\mu = 75$ and $\sigma = 15$. How many values lie between $x = 60$ and $x = 70$?

The area under the normal curve for various values of Z is given as,

Z	Area
0.33	0.12930
0.34	0.13307
1.0	0.34134

Ans. 63 approximately.

19. Prove that the following data represents Poisson distribution.

x	0	1	2	3	4
y	109	65	22	3	1

Ans. Mean = Variance = 0.61

20. In a certain city, 2000 electric lamps are installed. If the lamps have average life of 1000 burning hours with standard deviation of 200 hours,

(i) What number of lamps might be expected to fail in first 700 burning hours ?

(ii) After what period of burning hours, 10% of lamps would still be burning ?

Given that if
$$F(z) = \frac{1}{\sqrt{2\pi}} \int_{-\infty}^{z} e^{-\frac{1}{2}z^2}\, dz$$

then $F(1.5) = 0.933$
and $F(1.28) = 0.900$

Ans. (i) 866, (ii) 1256

21. Explain the test procedure for testing the independence of two attributes in an $r \times s$ contingency table.

22. Describe χ^2 test for goodness of fit. State the assumptions we make while applying the test.

23. The table below gives the number of accidents that occurred in the certain factory on the various days of a particular week.

Days of week	Sun.	Mon.	Tues.	Wed.	Thurs.	Fri.	Sat.
No. of accidents	6	4	9	7	8	10	12

Test at 5% level whether accidents are uniformly distributed over the different days

$\chi_6^2 = 5.25$; χ_6^2; $0.05 = 15.592$ Accept 40.

Ans. $\chi_6^2 = 5.25$ $\chi_{6;\,0.05}^6 = 15.592$ Accept H_0

24. The following is a 2×2 contingency table :

Eye colour in father	Eye colour in son	
	Not light	Light
Not light	23	15
Light	15	47

Test whether the eye colour in son is associated with the eye colour in father.

Ans. $\chi_1^2 = 13.2$ $\chi_{1;\,0.05}^2 = 3.841$ Reject H_0

25. A die when tossed 300 times gave the following results :

Score	1	2	3	4	5	6
Frequency	43	49	56	45	66	41

Are the data consistent at 5 % level of significance with the hypothesis that the die is true ?

Ans. $\chi_5^2 = 8.56$ $\chi_{5;\,0.05}^2 = 11.07$ Accept H_0

26. The table below gives the number of books issued from a certain library on the various days of a week.

Days	Mon.	Tues.	Wed.	Thurs.	Fri.	Sat.
No. of books issued	120	130	110	115	135	110

Test at 5% *l.o.s.* whether the issuing of books is independent of a day.

Ans. $\chi_5^2 = 4.583333$ $\chi_{5;\,0.05}^2 = 11.07$ Accept H_0

27. In a locality, 100 persons were randomly selected and asked for their educational achievements. The results are given as under.

Sex	Education		
	Primary school	**High school**	**College**
Male	10	15	25
Female	25	10	15

Test whether education depends on sex at 1% level of significance.

Ans. $\chi_2^2 = 9.929$ $\chi_{2;\,0.05}^2 = 5.991$ Reject H_0

28. In an experiment on pea breeding, a scientist obtained the following frequencies of seeds : 316 round and yellow, 102 wrinkled and yellow, 109 round and green and 33 wrinkled and green. Theory predicts that the frequencies of seeds should be in the proportion 9 : 3 : 3 : 1 respectively. Set a proper hypothesis and test it at 5 % *l.o.s.*

Ans. $\chi_3^2 = 0.3555554$, $\chi_{3;\,0.5}^2 = 7.815$ Accept H_0

29. A newspaper publisher is interested in testing whether newspaper readership in the society is associated with readers' educational achievement. A related survey showed the followed results :

Level of Education			
Type of readership	**Post graduate**	**Graduate**	**Passed S.S.C**	**Not passed S.S.C.**
Never	09	12	30	60
Sometimes	25	20	15	20
Daily	68	48	40	10

Test whether type of newspaper readership depends on level of education.

[Take $\alpha = 0.05$]

Ans. $\chi_6^2 = 97.651$, $\chi_{6;\,0.05}^2 = 12.592$ Reject H_0

30. From the information given below, test whether the type of occupation and attitude towards the social laws are independent. [Use 1 % *l.o.s.*]

Attitude towards Social Laws			
Occupation	Favourable	Neutral	Opposite
Blue-collar	29	26	37
White-collar	25	32	56
Professional	34	21	42

Ans. $\chi_4^2 = 5.415$ $\chi_{4;\,0.01}^2 = 9.488$ Accept H_0

31. Ten individuals are chosen at random from a population whose heights are found to be (in cms) 159, 162, 164, 170, 169, 171, 172, 168, 171, 175 cms. Can this sample be regarded as drawn from a population with mean height more than 170 cms at 5% level of significance ?

Ans. $|t| = 1.833$, Accept H_0.

32. The height of 8 persons in a office is found to be 68, 64, 67, 70, 62, 64, 66, 70 inches. Is it reasonable to believe that average height is 64 inches ? Test at 5% level of significance.

Ans. $|t| = 3$, Reject H_0

Degree of freedom	Distribution of χ^2		Degree of freedom	Distribution of χ^2	
	5 %	1 %		5 %	1 %
1	3.841	6.635	6	15.592	16.812
2	5.991	9.210	7	15.067	18.475
3	7.815	11.345	8	15.507	20.090
4	9.488	13.277	9	16.919	21.666
5	11.070	15.086	10	18.307	23.209
11	19.675	24.725	16	26.296	32.000
12	21.026	26.217	17	27.587	33.409
13	22.362	27.668	18	28.869	34.191
14	23.685	29.141	19	30.144	36.191
15	24.996	30.578	20	31.410	37.566
21	32.671	38.932	26	38.885	45.642
22	33.924	40.289	27	40.113	46.963
23	35.172	41.638	28	41.337	48.278
24	36.415	42.980	29	42.557	49.588
25	37.652	44.314	30	43.773	50.892
40	55.759	63.691			
60	79.082	88.379			
∞	–	–			

MULTIPLE CHOICE QUESTIONS (MCQ's)

Type : Probability Distributions.

1. In binomial probability distribution, probability of r successes in n trials is (where p probability of successes and q probability of failure in a single trial) (1)

   (A) $p^r q^{n-r}$

   (B) $^nC_r p^r q^{n+r}$

   (C) $^nC_r p^r q^{n-r}$

   (D) $^rC_n p^n q^{n-r}$

2. Mean of binomial probability distribution is (1)

   (A) nq

   (B) n^2p

   (C) npq

   (D) np

3. Variance of binomial probability distribution is (1)

   (A) npq

   (B) np

   (C) np^2q

   (D) npq^2

4. Standard deviation of binomial probability distribution is (1)

   (A) $\sqrt{pq}$

   (B) $\sqrt{npq}$

   (C) $\sqrt{np}$

   (D) np

5. An unbiased coin is thrown five times. Probability of getting three heads is (2)

   (A) $\dfrac{1}{16}$

   (B) $\dfrac{3}{16}$

   (C) $\dfrac{5}{16}$

   (D) $\dfrac{5}{8}$

6. 20% of bolts produced by machine are defective. The probability that out of three bolts chosen at random 1 is defective is (2)

   (A) 0.384

   (B) 0.9728

   (C) 0.5069

   (D) 0.6325

7. Probability of man now aged 60 years will live upto 70 years of age is 0.65. The probability that out of 10 men 60 years old 2 men will live upto 70 is (2)

   (A) 0.5

   (B) 0.002281

   (C) 0.003281

   (D) 0.004281

8. The probability that a person hit a target in shooting practice is 0.3. If the shoots 10 times, the probability that he hits the target is (2)

   (A) 1

   (B) $1 - (0.7)^{10}$

   (C) $(0.7)^{10}$

   (D) $(0.3)^{10}$

9. An unbiased coin is tossed five times. The probability of getting at least one head is   (2)

(A) $\dfrac{1}{32}$

(B) $\dfrac{31}{32}$

(C) $\dfrac{16}{32}$

(D) $\dfrac{13}{32}$

10. A box contains 100 bulbs out of which 10 are defective. A sample of 5 bulbs is drawn. The probability that none is defective is   (2)

(A) $\left(\dfrac{1}{10}\right)^5$

(B) $\left(\dfrac{1}{2}\right)^5$

(C) $\left(\dfrac{9}{10}\right)^5$

(D) $\dfrac{9}{10}$

11. On an average a packet containing 10 blades is likely to have two defective blades. In a box containing 100 packets, number of packets expected to contain less than two defective blades is   (2)

(A) 38

(B) 52

(C) 26

(D) 47

12. Out of 2000 families with 4 children each, the number of families you would expect to have no girls is

p = probability of having a boy $= \dfrac{1}{2}$, q = probability of having a girl $= 1 - \dfrac{1}{2} = \dfrac{1}{2}$ (2)

(A) 300

(B) 150

(C) 200

(D) 125

13. In 100 set of 10 tosses of a coin, the number of cases you expect 7 head and 3 tail is   (2)

(A) 8

(B) 12

(C) 15

(D) 17

14. 20% of bolts produced by machine are defective. The mean and standard deviation of defective bolts in total of 900 bolts are respectively   (2)

(A) 180 and 12

(B) 12 and 180

(C) 90 and 12

(D) 9 and 81

15. The mean and variance of binomial probability distribution are $\frac{5}{4}$ and $\frac{15}{16}$ respectively. Probability of success in a single trial p is equal to   (2)

(A) $\frac{1}{2}$ (B) $\frac{15}{16}$

(C) $\frac{1}{4}$ (D) $\frac{3}{4}$

16. The mean and variance of binomial probability distribution are 6 and 4 respectively. Number of trials n is given by   (2)

(A) 14   (B) 10

(C) 12   (D) 18

17. The mean and standard derivation of binomial probability distribution are 36 and 3 respectively. Number of trials n is given by   (2)

(A) 42   (B) 36

(C) 48   (D) 24

18. The mean and variance of binomial probability distribution are 6 and 2 respectively. $p\,(r \geq 2)$ is   (2)

(A) 0.66   (B) 0.88

(C) 0.77   (D) 0.99

19. If X follows the binomial distribution with parameter n = 6 and p and $9P\,(X = 4) = P(X = 2)$, then p is equal to   (2)

(A) $\frac{1}{4}$ (B) $\frac{1}{3}$

(C) $\frac{3}{4}$ (D) $\frac{2}{3}$

20. If X follows the binomial distribution with parameter n and $p = \frac{1}{2}$ and $P(X = 6) = P(X = 8)$, then n is equal to   (2)

(A) 10   (B) 14

(C) 12   (D) 7

21. If X follows the binomial distribution with parameter n and $p = \frac{1}{2}$ and $P(X = 4) = P(X = 5)$, then $P(X = 2)$ is equal to   (2)

(A) $^{7}C_2 \left(\frac{1}{2}\right)^{7}$ (B) $^{11}C_2 \left(\frac{1}{2}\right)^{11}$

(C) $^{10}C_2 \left(\frac{1}{2}\right)^{10}$ (D) $^{9}C_2 \left(\frac{1}{2}\right)^{9}$

22. If $z = np$ where n the number of trials is very large and p the probability of success at each trial, then in Poisson's probability distribution p(r) the probability of r successes is given by   (1)

(A) $\dfrac{e^z z}{r!}$

(B) $\dfrac{e^{-z} z^r}{r}$

(C) $\dfrac{e^{-z} z^r}{r!}$

(D) $\dfrac{e^z z^r}{r!}$

23. In a Poisson's probability distribution if $n = 100$, $p = 0.01$, $p(r = 0)$ is given by   (2)

(A) $\dfrac{1}{e}$

(B) $\dfrac{2}{e}$

(C) $\dfrac{3}{e}$

(D) $\dfrac{4}{e}$

24. In a Poisson's probability distribution if $n = 100$, $p = 0.02$, $p(r = 1)$ is given by   (2)

(A) $\dfrac{1}{e^2}$

(B) $\dfrac{2}{e^2}$

(C) $\dfrac{2}{e}$

(D) $\dfrac{1}{e}$

25. For a tabular data   (2)

x	0	1	2	3
F	2	4	6	8

Poisson's fit p(r) is given by

(A) $\dfrac{e^{-1} 2^r}{r!}$

(B) $\dfrac{e^{-2} 2^r}{r!}$

(C) $\dfrac{e^{-2} 2^3}{r!}$

(D) $\dfrac{e^{-3} 3^r}{r!}$

26. For a tabulated data :   (2)

x	0	1	2	3
f	1	4	15	24

Poisson's fit p(r) is given by

(A) $\dfrac{e^{-4.609} (4.609)^r}{r!}$

(B) $\dfrac{e^{-6.709} (6.709)^r}{r!}$

(C) $\dfrac{e^{-3.509} (3.509)^r}{r!}$

(D) $\dfrac{e^{-2.409} (2.409)^r}{r!}$

27. In a Poisson's probability distribution if $p (r = 1) = 2p (r = 2)$ and $p (r = 3)$ is given by   (2)

(A) $\dfrac{1}{6e}$

(B) $\dfrac{2}{3e}$

(C) $\dfrac{1}{8e}$

(D) $\dfrac{1}{9e}$

28. In a Poisson's probability distribution if $3p\,(r = 4) = p\,(r = 5)$ and $p\,(r = 6)$ is given by (2)

(A) $\dfrac{e^{-12}\,(12)^6}{6!}$

(B) $\dfrac{e^{-18}\,(18)^6}{6!}$

(C) $\dfrac{e^{-15}\,(15)^6}{6!}$

(D) $\dfrac{e^{-10}\,(10)^6}{6!}$

29. In a Poisson's probability distribution if $p\,(r = 2) = 9p\,(r = 4) + 90p\,(r = 6)$ then mean of the distribution is (2)

(A) ± 1

(B) ± 2

(C) ± 3

(D) ± 4

30. Number of road accidents on a highway during a month follows a Poisson distribution with mean 2. Probability that in a certain month number of accidents on the highway will be equal to 2 is (2)

(A) 0354

(B) 0.2707

(C) 0.435

(D) 0.521

31. Between 2 P.M. and 3 P.M. the average number of phone calls per minute coming into company are 2. Using Poisson's probability distribution, the probability that during one particular minute there will be no phone call at all, is given by (2)

(A) 0.354

(B) 0.356

(C) 0.135

(D) 0.457

32. Average number of phone calls per minute coming into company are 3, during certain period. These calls follows Poisson's probability distribution. Probability that during one particular minute there will be less than two calls, is given by (2)

(A) 0.299

(B) 0.333

(C) 0.444

(D) 0.199

33. In a certain factory turning out razor blades, there is a small chance of $\dfrac{1}{500}$ for any blade to be defective. The blades are supplied in a packets of 10. Using Poisson distribution, the probability that a packet contain one defective blade is (2)

(A) 0.0196

(B) 0.0396

(C) 0.0596

(D) 0.0496

34. The average number of misprints per page of a book is 1.5. Assuming the distribution of number of misprints to be Poisson. The probability that a particular book is free from misprints, is   (2)

(A) 0.329   (B) 0.435   (C) 0.549   (D) 0.2231

35. Normal distribution curve is given by the equation $y = \dfrac{1}{\sigma\sqrt{2\pi}}\, e^{-\frac{(x-\mu)^2}{2\sigma^2}}$. Integral

$\displaystyle\int_{\mu}^{\infty} y\, dx$ has the value.   (1)

(A) 0.025   (B) 1   (C) 0.5   (D) 0.75

36. Normal distribution curve is given by the equation $y = \dfrac{1}{\sigma\sqrt{2\pi}}\, e^{-\frac{(x-\mu)^2}{2\sigma^2}}$. Integral

$\displaystyle\int_{-\infty}^{\infty} y\, dx$ has the value   (1)

(A) 0.025   (B) 1   (C) 0.5   (D) 0.75

37. X is normally distributed. The mean of X is 15 and standard deviation 3. Given that for $z = 1$, $A = 0.3413$, $p\,(X \geq 18)$ is given by   (2)

(A) 0.1587   (B) 0.4231   (C) 0.2231   (D) 0.3413

38. X is normally distributed. The mean of X is 15 and standard deviation 3. Given that for $z = 1$, $A = 0.3413$, $p\,(X \geq 12)$ is given by   (2)

(A) 0.6587   (B) 0.8413

(C) 0.9413   (D) 0.7083

39. X is normally distributed. The mean of X is 15 and standard deviation 3. Given that for $z = 1.666$, $A = 0.4515$, $p\,(x \leq 10)$ is given by   (2)

(A) 0.0585   (B) 0.0673   (C) 0.0485   (D) 0.1235

40. X is normally distributed. The mean of X is 30 and variance 25. The probability $p\,(26 \leq x \leq 40)$ is (Given : Area corresponding to $z = 0.8$ is 0.2881 and Area corresponding to $z = 2$ is 0.4772).   (2)

(A) 0.8562   (B) 0.6574   (C) 0.3745   (D) 0.7653

41. In a sample of 1000 candidates, the mean of certain test is 14 and standard deviation is 2.5. Assuming Normal distribution, the probability of candidates getting less than eight marks i.e. $p\,(x \leq 8)$ is

(Given : Area corresponding to $z = 2.4$ is 0.4918)   (2)

(A) 0.0054   (B) 0.0075

(C) 0.0082   (D) 0.0035

42. In a normally distributed group of 450 students with mean 42 and standard deviation 8, the number of students scoring less than 48 marks is   (2)
(Given : Area corresponding to z = 0.75 is 0.2734).

(A) 348   (B) 102   (C) 127   (D) 250

43. In a certain examination test 10000 students appeared in a subject of mathematics. Average marks obtained were 50% with standard deviation 5%. Marks are normally distributed. Number of students expected to get more than 60% marks is equal to (2)
(z = 2, A = 0.4772)

(A) 200   (B) 300   (C) 325   (D) 228

44. The probability density function of normal variable x with mean μ and variance σ^2 is (2)

(A) $f(x) = \dfrac{1}{\sigma\sqrt{2\pi}}\, e^{\dfrac{(x-\mu)^2}{2\sigma^2}}$ (B) $f(x) = \dfrac{1}{\sqrt{2\pi}}\, e^{\dfrac{(x-\mu)^2}{2\sigma^2}}$

(C) $f(x) = \dfrac{1}{\sigma\sqrt{2\pi}}\, e^{-\dfrac{(x-\mu)^2}{2\sigma^2}}$ (D) $f(x) = e^{-\dfrac{(x-\mu)^2}{2\sigma^2}}$

45. For normal variable x with probability density function $f(x) = \dfrac{1}{3\sqrt{2\pi}}\, e^{-\frac{1}{18}(x-6)^2}$ the mean μ and standard deviation σ are   (2)

(A) 3, 9   (B) 9, 6   (C) 6, 3   (D) 18, 6

Answers

1. (C)	2. (D)	3. (A)	4. (B)	5. (C)	6. (A)	7. (D)	8. (B)
9. (B)	10. (C)	11. (A)	12. (D)	13. (B)	14. (A)	15. (C)	16. (D)
17. (C)	18. (D)	19. (A)	20. (B)	21. (D)	22. (C)	23. (A)	24. (B)
25. (B)	26. (D)	27. (A)	28. (C)	29. (A)	30. (B)	31. (C)	32.(D)
33. (A)	34. (D)	35. (C)	36. (B)	37. (A)	38. (B)	39. (C)	40. (D)
41. (C)	42. (A)	43. (D)	44. (C)	45. (C)			

Type II : Chi-square Distribution :

1. A bank utilizes three teller windows to render service to the customer. On a particular day 600 customer were served. If the customers are uniformly distributed over the counters. Expected numbers of customer served on each counter is   (2)

(A) 100   (B) 200   (C) 300   (D) 150

2. 200 digits are chosen at random from a set of tables. The frequencies of the digits are as follows :

Digit	0	1	2	3	4	5	6	7	8	9
Frequency	18	19	23	21	16	25	22	20	21	15

The expected frequency and degree of freedom for uniform distribution is
(A) 20 and 10 (B) 21 and 9
(C) 20 and 9 (D) 15 and 8

3. In experiment on pea breeding, the observed frequencies are 222, 120, 32, 150 and expected frequencies are 323, 81, 81, 40, then χ_3^2 has the value   (2)
(A) 382.502 (B) 380.50
(C) 429.59 (D) 303.82

4. If observed frequencies O_1, O_2, O_3 are 5, 10, 15 and expected frequencies e_1, e_2, e_3 are each equal to 10, then χ_2^2 has the value   (2)
(A) 20 (B) 10 (C) 15 (D) 5

5. Number of books issued on six days of the week, excluding Sunday which is holiday are given as 120, 130, 110, 115, 135, 110 and expectation is 120 books on each day, then χ_5^2 is   (2)
(A) 2.58 (B) 3.56 (C) 6.56 (D) 4.58

6. A coin is tossed 160 times and following are expected and observed frequencies for number of heads   (2)

No. of heads	0	1	2	3	4
Observed frequency	17	52	54	31	6
Expected Frequency	10	40	60	40	10

Then χ_4^2 is
(A) 12.72 (B) 9.49 (C) 12.8 (D) 9.00

7. Among 64 offspring's of a certain cross between guinea pig 34 were red, 10 were black and 20 were white. Acceding to genetic model, these number should in the ratio 9 :3 : 4. Expected frequencies in the order   (2)
(A) 36, 12, 16 (B) 12, 36, 16 (C) 20, 12, 16 (D) 36, 12, 25

8. A sample analysis of examination results of 500 students was made. The observed frequencies are 220, 170, 90 and 20 and the numbers are in the ratio 4 : 3 : 2 : 1 for the various categories. Then the expected frequencies are
(A) 150, 150, 50, 25 (B) 200, 100, 50, 10
(C) 200, 150, 100, 50 (D) 400, 300, 200, 100

9. In experiment on pea breeding, the observed frequencies are 222, 120, 32, 150 and the theory predicts that the frequencies should be in proportion 8 : 2 : 2 : 1. Then the expected frequencies are   (2)
(A) 323, 81, 40, 81 (B) 81, 323, 40, 81
(C) 323, 81, 81, 40 (D) 433, 81, 81, 35

Answers

1. (B)	2. (C)	3. (A)	4. (D)	5. (D)	6. (A)	7. (A)	8. (C)
9. (C)							

CHAPTER NINE

VECTOR ALGEBRA

9.1 INTRODUCTION

Subject of vector analysis had its development since nineteenth century. It has helped engineers, mathematicians and physicists in presenting mathematical formulations of physical phenomena in a very compact manner. Equations which take different shapes in different co-ordinate systems can be combined into a single equation and dealt in a precise manner. Whenever required, this single equation in vector form or its solution can be readily expressed in desired coordinate system. Besides this, vector analysis helps in understanding the physical nature of the problem and in correlating mathematical ideas and physical aspects of a problem.

Aim of this work is to acquaint the readers with the subject of vector calculus. Before we take-up the subject of vector calculus, we shall briefly discuss the elementary aspects of vector algebra.

9.2 VECTOR ALGEBRA

A quantity which has got both *magnitude* and *direction* is termed as a *vector quantity*. Physical quantities like displacement, velocity, acceleration, force, current etc. come under this category.

A quantity which has *magnitude alone but not direction* is termed as a *scalar quantity*. Some examples of scalar quantity are mass, length, time, temperature, speed, etc.

Formally a vector is defined as a *directed line segment* and is graphically represented by an arrow AB (See Fig. 9.1) defining the direction. The magnitude of the vector is given by length of the line segment AB, and we write

vector AB as $\overrightarrow{AB}$ or $\overline{AB}$ or by Bold faced type **AB**. The magnitude of the vector, that is the length AB is simply

expressed as AB = $|\overrightarrow{AB}|$. The tail end A of the arrow is called the initial point of the *vector* and the other end B is called the *terminal point*.

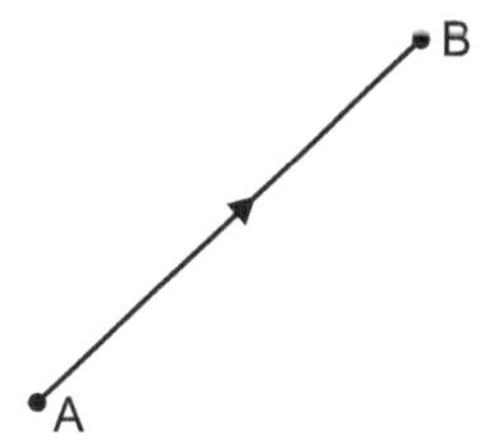

Fig. 9.1

Position Vector : A point A in space can be associated with a vector by joining the point A with some point 'O' in space called origin of reference. Thus, $\overrightarrow{OA} = \overline{a}$, is associated with point A and is called position vector (p.v.) of the point A. (See Fig. 9.2)

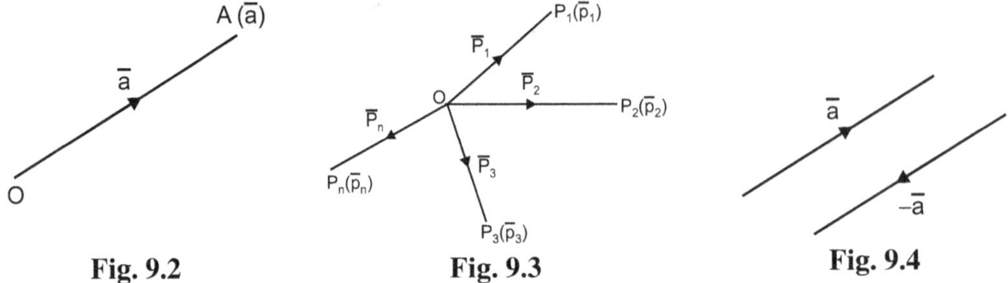

Fig. 9.2   **Fig. 9.3**   **Fig. 9.4**

Various points P_1, P_2, P_3, …… P_n can be associated with vectors

$$\overrightarrow{OP}_1 = \bar{p}_1, \quad \overrightarrow{OP}_2 = \bar{p}_2$$

$$\overrightarrow{OP}_3 = \bar{p}_3, \quad \overrightarrow{OP}_n = \bar{p}_n$$

and are called position vectors of P_1, P_2, … P_n respectively (See Fig. 9.3).

Many times, vectors are graphically represented without specifying initial and/or terminal points. A vector having direction opposite to that of vector $\bar{a}$ but having the same magnitude is denoted by $-\bar{a}$. (Refer to Fig. 9.4)

Equality of Vectors : Two vectors $\overrightarrow{AB}$ and $\overrightarrow{CD}$ are said to be equal if they are of the same magnitude and direction. Graphically, they are represented along parallel lines (See Fig. 9.5) or could be represented on the same line with different initial points, an arrow indicating the same direction.

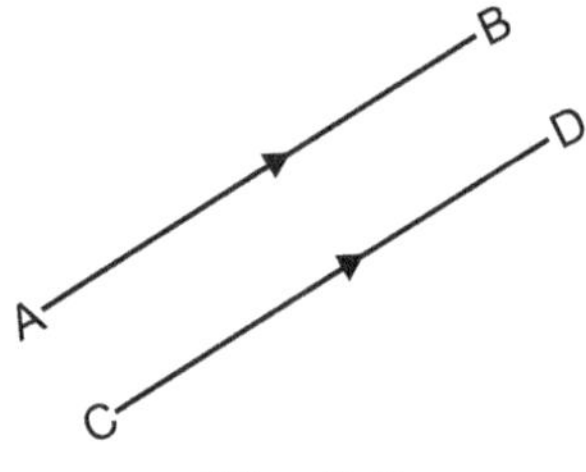

Fig. 9.5

We shall now define the basic operations of addition, subtraction, multiplication of vector quantities.

1. Addition of Vectors : The sum of vectors $\bar{a}$ and $\bar{b}$ is the vector $\bar{c}$ formed by placing the initial point of $\bar{b}$ on the terminal point of $\bar{a}$ and then joining the initial point of $\bar{a}$ to the terminal point of $\bar{b}$.

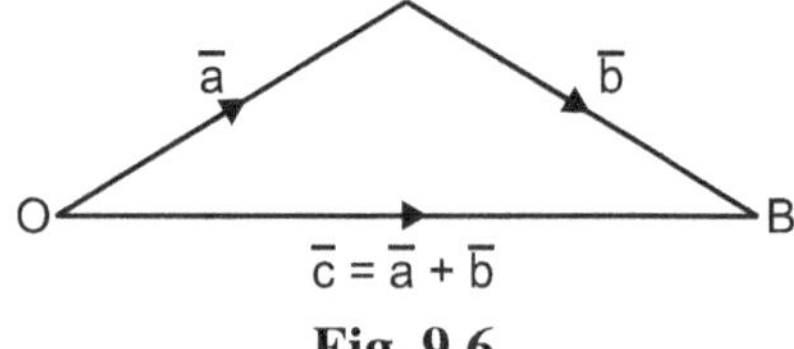

Fig. 9.6

$$\therefore \quad \bar{c} = \bar{a} + \bar{b} = \overrightarrow{OA} + \overrightarrow{AB} = \overrightarrow{OB}$$

The definition here is equivalent to the parallelogram law for vector addition. The vector $\bar{c}$ is called the resultant of $\bar{a}$ and $\bar{b}$. The definition of vector addition can be easily extended to cover the addition of more than two vectors.

Now, $\overrightarrow{OA} + \overrightarrow{AB} = \overrightarrow{OB} \Rightarrow \overrightarrow{OA} + \overrightarrow{AB} - \overrightarrow{OB} = \bar{0} \Rightarrow \overrightarrow{OA} + \overrightarrow{AB} + \overrightarrow{BO} = \bar{0}$ which is the triangle law of vectors.

2. The Difference of Vectors : The difference of vectors $\bar{a}$ and $\bar{b}$ represented by $\bar{a} - \bar{b}$ is defined as the sum $\bar{a} + (-\bar{b})$. If $\bar{a} = \bar{b}$, then $\bar{a} - \bar{b}$ is zero vector $\bar{0}$ or simply 0, it has zero magnitude and can have any direction.

3. Multiplication of Vector by a Scalar : The multiplication of vector $\bar{a}$ by a scalar m is a vector $m\bar{a}$, its magnitude is |m| times the magnitude of $\bar{a}$. If $\hat{a}$ denote a unit vector along $\bar{a}$ then we can write $\bar{a} = a\,\hat{a}$, where a is the magnitude of $\bar{a}$ i.e. a = | $\bar{a}$ |.

4. Laws of Vector Algebra : For any vectors $\bar{a}$, $\bar{b}$, $\bar{c}$ and scalars m and n, following laws can be easily established. They are stated here without proof.

(a) $\bar{a} + \bar{b} = \bar{b} + \bar{a}$ (Commutative law for addition)

(b) $\bar{a} + (\bar{b} + \bar{c}) = (\bar{a} + \bar{b}) + \bar{c}$ (Associative law for addition)

(c) $m\bar{a} = \bar{a}\, m$ (Commutative law for multiplication)

(d) $m (n\, \bar{a}) = (m\, n)\, \bar{a}$ (Associative law for multiplication)

(e) $(m + n)\, \bar{a} = m\, \bar{a} + n\, \bar{a}$ (Distributive law)

(f) $m (\bar{a} + \bar{b}) = m\, \bar{a} + m\, \bar{b}$ (Distributive law)

5. Product of Vectors : The two vectors $\bar{a}$ and $\bar{b}$ do not multiply like scalars m and n. In respect of vectors $\bar{a}$ and $\bar{b}$, two types of product are defined.

(a) Scalar or Dot Product of Vectors : If $\bar{a}$ and $\bar{b}$ are two vectors inclined at an angle 'θ' with respect to each other then the dot product of vectors $\bar{a}$ and $\bar{b}$ is denoted by $\bar{a} \cdot \bar{b}$ or $\bar{a} \circ \bar{b}$ (read as $\bar{a}$ dot $\bar{b}$) and is given by

$$\bar{a} \circ \bar{b} = \bar{a} \cdot \bar{b} = |\bar{a}||\bar{b}| \cos \theta = ab \cos \theta$$

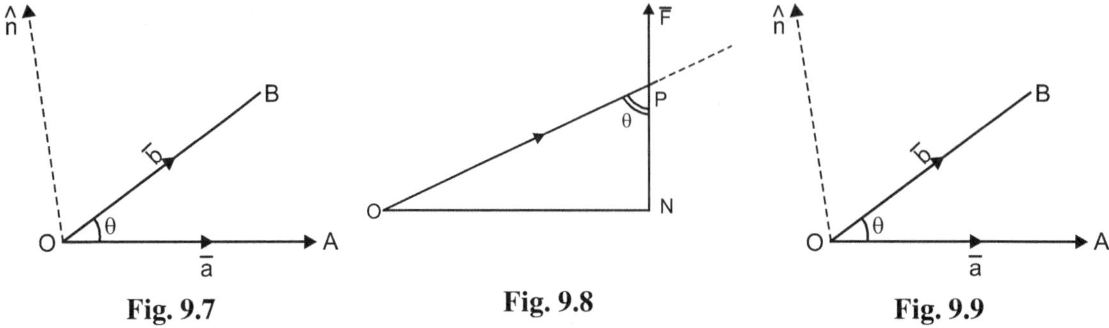

Fig. 9.7   **Fig. 9.8**   **Fig. 9.9**

This product gives a scalar quantity and hence the product $\bar{a} \cdot \bar{b}$ is also called scalar product. If $\theta = 90°$, $\cos \theta = 0$ and $\bar{a} \cdot \bar{b} = 0$. To interpret physically, consider force vector $\bar{F}$ and the displacement vector $\bar{d}$ (See Fig. 9.8). $\bar{F} \cdot \bar{d} = Fd \cos \theta$ gives the work done by the force $\bar{F}$ in causing a displacement $\bar{d}$.

(b) Vector or Cross Product of Vectors : Another type of product that exists between the two vectors $\bar{a}$ and $\bar{b}$ is the vector product or cross product. Unlike (a), it gives a vector quantity. Consider the vectors $\bar{a}$, $\bar{b}$ (See Fig. 9.9), inclined at an angle θ. The vector product or cross product of $\bar{a}$ and $\bar{b}$ is denoted by $\bar{a} \times \bar{b}$ (read as $\bar{a}$ cross $\bar{b}$) and is given by

$$\bar{a} \times \bar{b} = |\bar{a}||\bar{b}| \sin \theta \, \hat{n} = ab \sin \theta \, \hat{n}$$

where, $\hat{n}$ is a unit vector perpendicular to the plane of $\bar{a}$ and $\bar{b}$ such that $\bar{a}$, $\bar{b}$ and $\hat{n}$ form a right handed system. (If a screw is rotated from the first vector $\bar{a}$ to the second vector $\bar{b}$ i.e. in an anticlockwise sense then it will come out, indicating the direction of $\hat{n}$). It is obvious from the definition that $\bar{b} \times \bar{a}$ will have opposite direction of $\bar{a} \times \bar{b}$ and $\bar{a} \times \bar{b} = -(\bar{b} \times \bar{a})$. Thus, in taking the cross product of two vectors, the order in which they occur is of importance.

$$|\bar{a} \times \bar{b}| = ab \sin \theta$$

If $\bar{a}$ and $\bar{b}$ are parallel vectors i.e., if the angle $\theta = 0$ or π, then $\sin \theta = 0$ and $\bar{a} \times \bar{b} = 0$.

Similarly, $\bar{a} \times \bar{a} = 0$ as $\theta = 0$

To interpret vector product physically, we shall consider two examples.

(i) Moment of a Force : In statics, Moment of Force about a point is given by the product of the magnitude of the force and the perpendicular distance of the point from the line of action of the force. With reference to Fig. 9.10, moment of the force F about the point 'O' is given by F multiplied by ON or OP $\sin \theta$ i.e. F $\times$ OP $\sin \theta$. The sense of the moment is anticlockwise as shown in Fig. 9.10. Since, the moment has got both the magnitude and direction, it can be represented in vector form by the cross product $\bar{r} \times \bar{F}$, where $\bar{r} = \overrightarrow{OP}$ (the position vector of P, any point on the line of action $\bar{F}$).

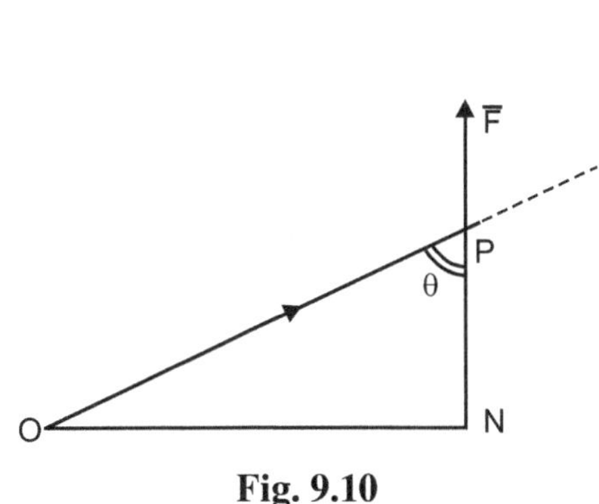

Fig. 9.10

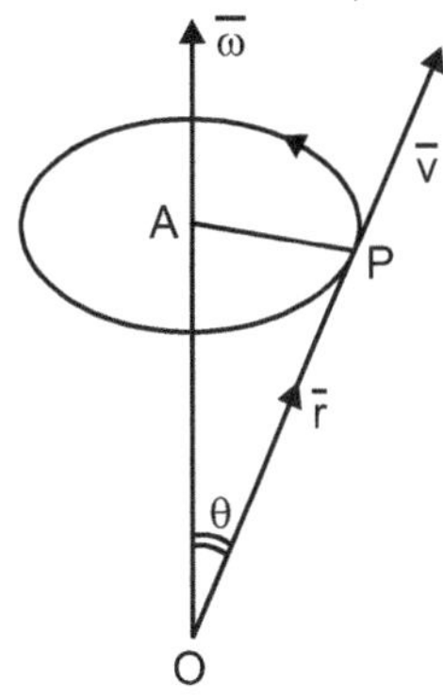

Fig. 9.11

By definition, $\bar{r} \times \bar{F} = rF \sin\theta \,\hat{n}$,	($\bar{r}$, $\bar{F}$, $\hat{n}$ forming a right handed system)

$\therefore$	$|\bar{r} \times \bar{F}| = rF \sin\theta$	or	$F\,r \sin\theta$

which is same as the moment of $\bar{F}$ about O. The direction of the moment is associated with $\hat{n}$. Thus, $\bar{r} \times \bar{F}$ represents the moment vector $\bar{M}$ which represents the moment of the force $\bar{F}$ about the point 'O'.

(ii) Rigid Body Rotation about an Axis : Consider a rigid body rotating with angular velocity $\bar{\omega}$ about an axis OA. Vector $\bar{\omega}$ has magnitude ω and direction parallel to the axis OA (See Fig. 9.11). If P ($\bar{r}$) is any point on the body, the linear velocity $\bar{v}$ of the point has magnitude AP ω i.e. $r \sin\theta \,\omega$ (AP = $r \sin\theta$) and the direction along the tangent to the circle at P as shown in Fig. 9.11. $\overrightarrow{OP} = \bar{r}$ is the position vector of the point P with respect to 'O' as the origin of the reference. From Fig. 9.11, it is clear that $\bar{\omega}$, $\bar{r}$, $\bar{v}$ constitute a right handed system and we can express $\bar{v}$ as

$$\bar{v} = \bar{\omega} \times \bar{r} \quad \text{or} \quad \bar{r} \times \bar{v} = \bar{\omega}$$

[Note that $|\bar{v}| = |\bar{\omega} \times \bar{r}| = \omega r \sin\theta$]

6. Scalar Triple Product or Box Product : Between three vectors $\bar{a}$, $\bar{b}$, $\bar{c}$ there exists scalar triple product or mixed product $\bar{a} \times \bar{b} \cdot \bar{c}$ which can also be written as $[\bar{a}\ \bar{b}\ \bar{c}]$. Here dot and cross are interchangeable and $\bar{a} \times \bar{b} \cdot \bar{c} = \bar{a} \cdot \bar{b} \times \bar{c}$. Hence the positions of '·' and 'x' are immaterial which leads to the notation $[\bar{a}\ \bar{b}\ \bar{c}]$ read as Box

Product. This product of three vectors is a scalar quantity hence the name Scalar Triple Product. It can be easily established that $[\bar{a}\ \bar{b}\ \bar{c}] = [\bar{b}\ \bar{c}\ \bar{a}] = [\bar{c}\ \bar{a}\ \bar{b}]$ i.e. cyclic change between $\bar{a}$, $\bar{b}$, $\bar{c}$ does not alter the value of the scalar triple product. To interpret it physically, consider a rectangular parallelopiped (See Fig. 9.12) with edges OA, OB, OC of lengths a, b, c respectively. Consider the vectors $\bar{a}$, $\bar{b}$, $\bar{c}$ along OA, OB, OC as shown. 'p' is the length of the perpendicular from 'C' on the base OADB. 'θ' is the angle between OA and OB, α is the angle between OC and OM.

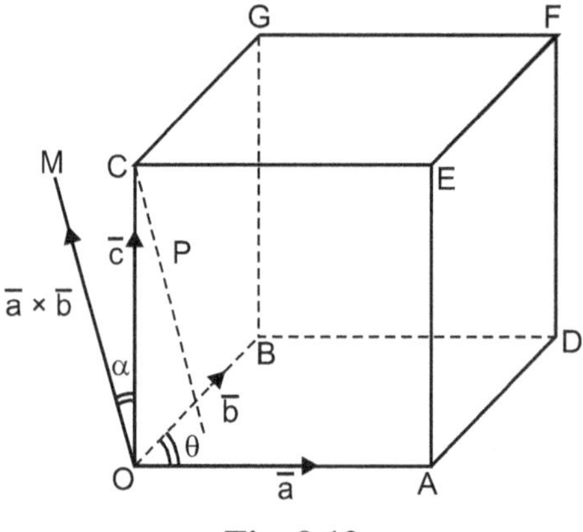

Fig. 9.12

$\bar{a} \times \bar{b}$ is a vector perpendicular to the plane of $\bar{a}$ and $\bar{b}$; $\bar{a}$, $\bar{b}$ and $\bar{a} \times \bar{b}$ forming a right handed system. $|\bar{a} \times \bar{b}| = ab \sin \theta$ which is equal to the area of the parallelogram OADB, direction of $\bar{a} \times \bar{b}$ is along OM.

By definition,
$$\bar{a} \times \bar{b} \cdot \bar{c} = |\bar{a} \times \bar{b}||\bar{c}| \cos \alpha = ab \sin \theta\, c \cos \alpha$$
$$= ab \sin \theta p \qquad\qquad [\because p = c \cos \alpha]$$

Or
$$\bar{a} \times \bar{b} \cdot \bar{c} = \text{Area of parallelogram} \times \text{Altitude}$$
$$= \text{Volume of parallelopiped}$$

Thus $\bar{a} \times \bar{b} \cdot \bar{c}$ represents volume of a parallelopiped with coterminus edges of lengths a, b, c.

Obviously $\bar{a} \times \bar{b} \cdot \bar{c} = \bar{a} \cdot \bar{b} \times \bar{c}$ = volume of the parallelopiped which shows that dot and cross are interchangeable in scalar triple product. It can also be seen that out of $\bar{a}, \bar{b}, \bar{c}$ if any two vectors are equal or parallel then $\bar{a} \times \bar{b} \cdot \bar{c} = 0$.

7. Vector Triple Product : Between three vectors, we can consider another type of product $\bar{a} \times (\bar{b} \times \bar{c})$ which is called *vector triple product*. It can be proved that,

$$\bar{a} \times (\bar{b} \times \bar{c}) = (\bar{a} \cdot \bar{c})\,\bar{b} - (\bar{a} \cdot \bar{b})\,\bar{c}.$$

This follows from the fact that $\bar{a} \times (\bar{b} \times \bar{c})$ is a vector which lies in the plane of $\bar{b}$ and $\bar{c}$ and can be expressed as a linear combination of $\bar{b}, \bar{c}$. The proof is left to the students as an exercise.

To obtain $(\bar{a} \times \bar{b}) \times \bar{c}$, we write it as

$$(\bar{a} \times \bar{b}) \times \bar{c} = -\bar{c} \times (\bar{a} \times \bar{b}), \quad [\because \bar{a} \times \bar{b} = -\bar{b} \times \bar{a}]$$

$$= -[(\bar{c} \cdot \bar{b})\,\bar{a} - (\bar{c} \cdot \bar{a})\,\bar{b}] = (\bar{c} \cdot \bar{a})\,\bar{b} - (\bar{c} \cdot \bar{b})\,\bar{a}$$

Expression for $\bar{a} \times (\bar{b} \times \bar{c})$ is of great importance and students are advised to memorise it.

8. Quadruple Products :

(a) Consider the product $(\bar{a} \times \bar{b}) \cdot (\bar{c} \times \bar{d})$ involving four vectors $\bar{a}, \bar{b}, \bar{c}$ and $\bar{d}$.

$$(\bar{a} \times \bar{b}) \cdot (\bar{c} \times \bar{d}) = (\bar{a} \times \bar{b}) \cdot \bar{p} = \bar{a} \cdot \bar{b} \times \bar{p}, \quad [\text{where } \bar{p} = \bar{c} \times \bar{d}]$$

$$= \bar{a} \cdot [\bar{b} \times (\bar{c} \times \bar{d})] = \bar{a} \cdot [(\bar{b} \cdot \bar{d})\,\bar{c} - (\bar{b} \cdot \bar{c})\,\bar{d}]$$

$$= (\bar{a} \cdot \bar{c})(\bar{b} \cdot \bar{d}) - (\bar{a} \cdot \bar{d})(\bar{b} \cdot \bar{c}) \to \text{a scalar.}$$

This product is known as scalar quadruple product.

(b) We can also consider the product $(\bar{a} \times \bar{b}) \times (\bar{c} \times \bar{d})$.

$$(\bar{a} \times \bar{b}) \times (\bar{c} \times \bar{d}) = (\bar{a} \times \bar{b}) \times \bar{p} = -\bar{p} \times (\bar{a} \times \bar{b})$$

$$= -[(\bar{p} \cdot \bar{b})\,\bar{a} - (\bar{p} \cdot \bar{a})\,\bar{b}], \quad [\bar{p} = \bar{c} \times \bar{d}]$$

$$= (\bar{p} \cdot \bar{a})\,\bar{b} - (\bar{p} \cdot \bar{b})\,\bar{a} = [(\bar{c} \times \bar{d}) \cdot \bar{a}]\,\bar{b} - [(\bar{c} \times \bar{d}) \cdot \bar{b}]\,\bar{a}$$

$$= [\bar{c}\ \bar{d}\ \bar{a}]\,\bar{b} - [\bar{c}\ \bar{d}\ \bar{b}]\,\bar{a}$$

Similarly, if $\bar{a} \times \bar{b} = \bar{p}$

$$(\bar{a} \times \bar{b}) \times (\bar{c} \times \bar{d}) = \bar{p} \times (\bar{c} \times \bar{d}) = (\bar{p} \cdot \bar{d})\,\bar{c} - (\bar{p} \cdot \bar{c})\,\bar{d}$$

$$= [\bar{a} \times \bar{b} \cdot \bar{d}]\,\bar{c} - [\bar{a} \times \bar{b} \cdot \bar{c}]\,\bar{d} = [\bar{a}\ \bar{b}\ \bar{d}]\,\bar{c} - [\bar{a}\ \bar{b}\ \bar{c}]\,\bar{d}$$

$$\to \text{ a vector}$$

Thus it is seen that $(\bar{a} \times \bar{b}) \times (\bar{c} \times \bar{d})$ can be expressed as linear combination of $\bar{a}$ and $\bar{b}$ or that of $\bar{c}$ and $\bar{d}$ i.e. it lies in the plane of $(\bar{a}, \bar{b})$ and $(\bar{c}, \bar{d})$ both or along the common section of the planes of $\bar{a}, \bar{b}$ and $\bar{c}, \bar{d}$. This product is known as vector quadruple product.

9.3 ORTHOGONAL VECTOR TRIAD

It is quite useful to consider a set of three mutually perpendicular unit vectors $\bar{i}$, $\bar{j}$, $\bar{k}$ taken along x, y, z axes (which are mutually perpendicular) as shown in Fig. 9.13. If $\bar{a}$ is any vector in space, it can always be expressed as a linear combination of any three non-coplaner vectors. $\bar{i}, \bar{j}, \bar{k}$ being three non-coplaner vectors, $\bar{a}$ can be expressed as $\bar{a} = a_1 \bar{i} + a_2 \bar{j} + a_3 \bar{k}$, where a_1, a_2, a_3 are the scalar components of $\bar{a}$ along x, y and z axes. If P (x, y, z) is any point in space then vector $\overline{OP}$ is generally denoted by $\bar{r}$ and can be expressed as $\bar{r} = x \bar{i} + y \bar{j} + z \bar{k}$.

From the definitions of the dot and the cross product, it can be easily seen that

$$\bar{i} \cdot \bar{i} = |\bar{i}||\bar{i}| \cos 0 = 1 \ [\text{as} \ |\bar{i}| = 1, \cos 0 = 1]$$

$$\bar{j} \cdot \bar{j} = 1, \ \bar{k} \cdot \bar{k} = 1$$

$$\bar{i} \cdot \bar{j} = \bar{j} \cdot \bar{k} = \bar{k} \cdot \bar{i} = 0$$

$\because \bar{i}, \bar{j}, \bar{k}$ are mutually perpendicular and $\cos \left(\dfrac{\pi}{2}\right) = 0$.

Also $\bar{i} \times \bar{i} = 0, \ \bar{j} \times \bar{j} = 0, \ \bar{k} \times \bar{k} = 0$

$$\bar{i} \times \bar{j} = \bar{k}, \ \bar{j} \times \bar{k} = \bar{i}, \ \bar{k} \times \bar{i} = \bar{j}$$

$[\bar{i}, \bar{j}, \bar{k}$ constitute a right handed system].

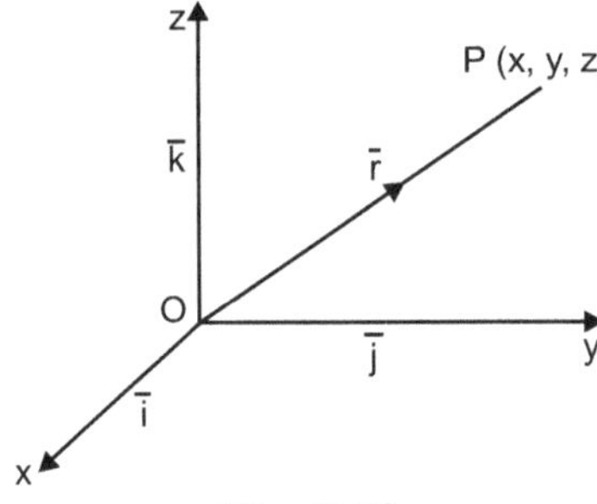

Fig. 9.13

If $\quad \bar{a} = a_1 \bar{i} + a_2 \bar{j} + a_3 \bar{k}, \quad \bar{b} = b_1 \bar{i} + b_2 \bar{j} + b_3 \bar{k}$

$$\bar{a} \cdot \bar{b} = (a_1 \bar{i} + a_2 \bar{j} + a_3 \bar{k}) \cdot (b_1 \bar{i} + b_2 \bar{j} + b_3 \bar{k})$$

$$= a_1 \bar{i} \cdot (b_1 \bar{i} + b_2 \bar{j} + b_3 \bar{k}) + a_2 \bar{j} \cdot (b_1 \bar{i} + b_2 \bar{j} + b_3 \bar{k}) +$$

$$a_3 \bar{k} \cdot (b_1 \bar{i} + b_2 \bar{j} + b_3 \bar{k})$$

$$= a_1 b_1 + a_2 b_2 + a_3 b_3 \qquad\qquad (\because \bar{i} \cdot \bar{i} = 1, \ \bar{i} \cdot \bar{j} = 0 \text{ etc.})$$

If θ is the angle between $\bar{a}$ and $\bar{b}$,

$$\bar{a} \cdot \bar{b} = |\bar{a}||\bar{b}|\cos\theta = a_1b_1 + a_2b_2 + a_3b_3$$

$$\therefore \qquad \cos\theta = \frac{a_1b_1 + a_2b_2 + a_3b_3}{|\bar{a}||\bar{b}|}$$

To determine $|\bar{a}|$, $|\bar{b}|$ consider

$$\bar{a} \cdot \bar{a} = (a_1\bar{i} + a_2\bar{j} + a_3\bar{k}) \cdot (a_1\bar{i} + a_2\bar{j} + a_3\bar{k}) = a_1^2 + a_2^2 + a_3^2$$

But $\qquad \bar{a} \cdot \bar{a} = |\bar{a}||\bar{a}|\cos 0 = |\bar{a}|^2$

$$\therefore \qquad |\bar{a}| = \sqrt{\bar{a} \cdot \bar{a}} = \sqrt{a_1^2 + a_2^2 + a_3^2} \quad \text{Similarly, } |\bar{b}| = \sqrt{b_1^2 + b_2^2 + b_3^2}$$

The angle θ between vectors $\bar{a}$, $\bar{b}$ can now be calculated from the formula,

$$\cos\theta = \frac{a_1b_1 + a_2b_2 + a_3b_3}{\sqrt{a_1^2 + a_2^2 + a_3^2}\,\sqrt{b_1^2 + b_2^2 + b_3^2}}$$

To obtain $\hat{a}$ [the unit vector along $\bar{a}$] $\quad \bar{a} = a\hat{a} \quad \therefore \quad \hat{a} = \frac{\bar{a}}{a} = \frac{a_1\bar{i} + a_2\bar{j} + a_3\bar{k}}{\sqrt{a_1^2 + a_2^2 + a_3^2}}$

To obtain cross product $\bar{a} \times \bar{b}$

$$\bar{a} \times \bar{b} = (a_1\bar{i} + a_2\bar{j} + a_3\bar{k}) \times (b_1\bar{i} + b_2\bar{j} + b_3\bar{k})$$

$$= a_1\bar{i} \times (b_1\bar{i} + b_2\bar{j} + b_3\bar{k}) + a_2\bar{j} \times (b_1\bar{i} + b_2\bar{j} + b_3\bar{k})$$

$$+ a_3\bar{k} \times (b_1\bar{i} + b_2\bar{j} + b_3\bar{k})$$

$$= a_1b_2\bar{k} - a_1b_3\bar{j} - a_2b_1\bar{k} + a_2b_3\bar{i} + a_3b_1\bar{j} - a_3b_2\bar{i}$$

$$[\,\bar{i} \times \bar{i} = 0,\ \bar{i} \times \bar{j} = \bar{k},\ \bar{i} \times \bar{k} = -\bar{j}\ \text{etc.}]$$

$$= (a_2b_3 - a_3b_2)\bar{i} + (a_3b_1 - a_1b_3)\bar{j} + (a_1b_2 - a_2b_1)\bar{k}$$

This result can be expressed in a more convenient determinant form as

$$\bar{a} \times \bar{b} = \begin{vmatrix} \bar{i} & \bar{j} & \bar{k} \\ a_1 & a_2 & a_3 \\ b_1 & b_2 & b_3 \end{vmatrix}$$

To compute mixed product

$$\bar{a} \times \bar{b} \cdot \bar{c} \qquad \text{where,} \quad \bar{c} = c_1\,\bar{i} + c_2\,\bar{j} + c_3\,\bar{k}$$

$$\bar{a} \times \bar{b} \cdot \bar{c} = [(a_2 b_3 - a_3 b_2)\,\bar{i} + (a_3 b_1 - a_1 b_3)\,\bar{j}$$

$$+ (a_1 b_2 - a_2 b_1)\,\bar{k}] \cdot [c_1\,\bar{i} + c_2\,\bar{j} + c_3\,\bar{k}]$$

$$= (a_2 b_3 - a_3 b_2)\,c_1 + (a_3 b_1 - a_1 b_3)\,c_2 + (a_1 b_2 - a_2 b_1)\,c_3$$

$$\text{which can also be expressed as} = \begin{vmatrix} a_1 & a_2 & a_3 \\ b_1 & b_2 & b_3 \\ c_1 & c_2 & c_3 \end{vmatrix}$$

ILLUSTRATION

Ex. 1 : *If*　$\bar{a} = 2\bar{i} + 2\bar{j} + \bar{k};\ \bar{b} = \bar{i} - \bar{j} + 2\bar{k};\ \bar{c} = \bar{i} + \bar{j} - \bar{k}$

　　find　(i)　*the angle between* $\bar{a}$ *and* $\bar{b}$　　　(ii)　$\hat{a}$

　　　　(iii)　$\bar{a} \times \bar{b}$　　　　　　　　(iv)　$\bar{a} \times \bar{b} \cdot \bar{c}$

Sol. :　(i)　If θ is the angle between $\bar{a}$, $\bar{b}$

$$\cos\theta = \frac{\bar{a} \cdot \bar{b}}{|\bar{a}|\,|\bar{b}|} = \frac{2 - 2 + 2}{\sqrt{4 + 4 + 1}\,\sqrt{1 + 1 + 4}} = \frac{2}{3\sqrt{6}}$$

$$\theta = \cos^{-1}\left(\frac{2}{3\sqrt{6}}\right)$$

(ii)　　　　$\hat{a} = \dfrac{\bar{a}}{|\bar{a}|} = \dfrac{2\bar{i} + 2\bar{j} + \bar{k}}{\sqrt{4 + 4 + 1}} = \dfrac{2\bar{i} + 2\bar{j} + \bar{k}}{3}$

(iii)　　　　$\bar{a} \times \bar{b} = \begin{vmatrix} \bar{i} & \bar{j} & \bar{k} \\ 2 & 2 & 1 \\ 1 & -1 & 2 \end{vmatrix}$

$$= \bar{i}\,(4 + 1) + \bar{j}\,(1 - 4) + \bar{k}\,(-2 - 2) = 5\bar{i} - 3\bar{j} - 4\bar{k}$$

(iv)　　$\bar{a} \times \bar{b} \cdot \bar{c} = \begin{vmatrix} 2 & 2 & 1 \\ 1 & -1 & 2 \\ 1 & 1 & -1 \end{vmatrix}$

$$= 2\,(1 - 2) + 2\,(2 + 1) + 1\,(1 + 1)$$

$$= -2 + 6 + 2 = 6$$

□□□

CHAPTER TEN

VECTOR DIFFERENTIATION

10.1 DEFINITION AND ELEMENTARY RULES

In ordinary differentiation (not involving vectors), the derivative $\dfrac{dy}{dx}$ [where y = f (x)] is defined as

$$\frac{dy}{dx} = \lim_{h \to 0} \left[\frac{f(x+h) - f(x)}{h} \right]$$

Consider vector $\bar{r}$, which may depend for its value on scalar variable t, the functional relationship being $\qquad \bar{r} = \bar{F}(t)$

Here we have vector function $\bar{r} = \bar{F}(t)$ depending upon scalar variable t. Corresponding to a change δt in t, let there be a change $\delta\bar{r}$ in $\bar{r}$ i.e.

$$\delta\bar{r} = \bar{F}(t + \delta t) - \bar{F}(t)$$

The vector derivative can now be defined as

$$\frac{d\bar{r}}{dt} = \lim_{\delta t \to 0} \left[\frac{\bar{F}(t + \delta t) - \bar{F}(t)}{\delta t} \right]$$

This limit when exists is denoted by $\bar{F}'(t)$ or $\dfrac{d\bar{r}}{dt}$ and is called *rate of change of*

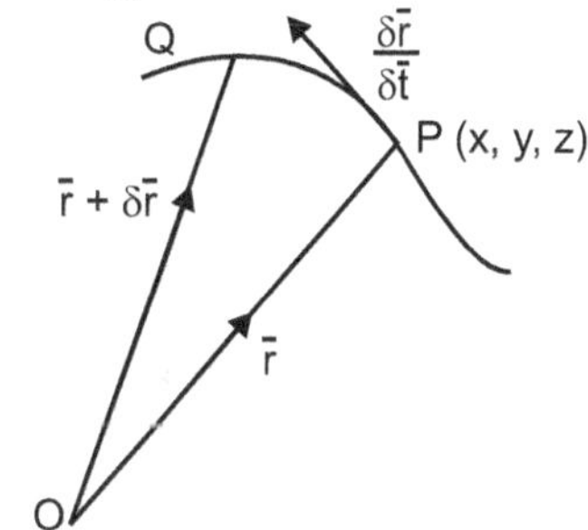

Fig. 10.1

r with respect to t. Thus, the vector derivative is defined in the same way as the scalar derivative and all the laws of scalar differentiation can be suitably extended to cover vector differentiation.

To interpret physically, consider a point P on the curve whose position vector is $\bar{r}(t)$. Corresponding to different values of t, we get different points on the curve. Let t change by an amount δt and the point P move to Q. Let $\bar{r} + \delta\bar{r}$ be the position vector of Q.

$$\overrightarrow{PQ} = \overrightarrow{OQ} - \overrightarrow{OP} = \bar{r} + \delta\bar{r} - \bar{r} = \delta\bar{r}$$

Consider the vector $\qquad \dfrac{\overrightarrow{PQ}}{\delta t} = \dfrac{\delta\bar{r}}{\delta t}$

Now taking the limit as $\delta t \to 0$, i.e. $Q \to P$, $\displaystyle \lim_{\delta t \to 0} \frac{\overrightarrow{PQ}}{\delta t} = \lim_{\delta t \to 0} \frac{\delta \overline{r}}{\delta t} = \frac{d\overline{r}}{dt}$

In the limiting case when $Q \to P$, the vector $\overrightarrow{PQ}$ assumes the position of tangent vector at P. Thus $\dfrac{d\overline{r}}{dt}$ represents the tangent vector $\overline{T}$ at P (See Fig. 10.1).

In particular, if t is the time variable, $\overrightarrow{PQ}$ represents displacement vector then $\dfrac{d\overline{r}}{dt}$ represents the velocity vector $\overline{V}$.

Thus, in general, $\dfrac{d\overline{r}}{dt}$ will represent tangent vector denoted by $\overline{T}$ and in particular when t is the time variable, $\dfrac{d\overline{r}}{dt}$ represents velocity vector denoted by $\overline{V}$. The second and higher order derivatives can be defined in the same way as first order derivative. $\dfrac{d\overline{V}}{dt} = \dfrac{d^2\overline{r}}{dt^2}$ represents acceleration vector denoted by $\overline{a}$.

In another particular case, if the arc $PQ = \delta s$ and P, Q are very close to each other, chord PQ is approximately equal to arc PQ i.e. δs and from the distance formula,

$$\delta s^2 = \delta x^2 + \delta y^2 + \delta z^2 \text{ (See Fig. 10.1)}$$

Dividing by δs^2 and taking the limit as $Q \to P$ or $\delta s \to 0$

$$1 = \left(\frac{dx}{ds}\right)^2 + \left(\frac{dy}{ds}\right)^2 + \left(\frac{dz}{ds}\right)^2$$

just as $\lim \dfrac{\overrightarrow{PQ}}{\delta t}$ represents tangent vector.

$$\lim \frac{\overrightarrow{PQ}}{\delta s} = \lim \frac{\delta \overline{r}}{\delta s} = \frac{d\overline{r}}{ds} \text{ also represents a tangent vector}$$

Now,

$$\overline{r} = x\overline{i} + y\overline{j} + z\overline{k}$$

$$d\overline{r} = \overline{i}\, dx + \overline{j}\, dy + \overline{k}\, dz$$

$$\therefore \qquad \frac{d\bar{r}}{ds} = \bar{i}\,\frac{dx}{ds} + \bar{j}\,\frac{dy}{ds} + \bar{k}\,\frac{dz}{ds}$$

$$\left|\frac{d\bar{r}}{ds}\right| = \sqrt{\left(\frac{dx}{ds}\right)^2 + \left(\frac{dy}{ds}\right)^2 + \left(\frac{dz}{ds}\right)^2} = 1$$

Thus, $\dfrac{d\bar{r}}{ds}$ represents a tangent vector at P with unit magnitude denoted by $\hat{T}$.

From the definition of vector derivative, following results can be easily established.

For vectors $\bar{u}(t),\ \ \bar{v}(t),\ \bar{w}(t)$

(i) $\dfrac{d}{dt}(\bar{u}+\bar{v}) = \dfrac{d\bar{u}}{dt} + \dfrac{d\bar{v}}{dt}$ $\qquad$ (ii) $\dfrac{d}{dt}(\bar{u}-\bar{v}) = \dfrac{d\bar{u}}{dt} - \dfrac{d\bar{v}}{dt}$

(iii) $\dfrac{d}{dt}(\bar{u}\cdot\bar{v}) = \bar{v}\cdot\dfrac{d\bar{u}}{dt} + \bar{u}\cdot\dfrac{d\bar{v}}{dt}$ (iv) $\dfrac{d}{dt}(\bar{u}\times\bar{v}) = \dfrac{d\bar{u}}{dt}\times\bar{v} + \bar{u}\times\dfrac{d\bar{v}}{dt}$

[The order in which $\bar{u}, \bar{v}$ occur is maintained]

(v) $\dfrac{d}{dt}[\bar{u}\times\bar{v}\cdot\bar{w}] = \dfrac{d\bar{u}}{dt}\times\bar{v}\cdot\bar{w} + \bar{u}\times\dfrac{d\bar{v}}{dt}\cdot\bar{w} + \bar{u}\times\bar{v}\cdot\dfrac{d\bar{w}}{dt}$

(vi) $\dfrac{d}{dt}[\bar{u}\times(\bar{v}\times\bar{w})] = \dfrac{d\bar{u}}{dt}\times(\bar{v}\times\bar{w}) + \bar{u}\times\left(\dfrac{d\bar{v}}{dt}\times\bar{w}\right) + \bar{u}\times\left(\bar{v}\times\dfrac{d\bar{w}}{dt}\right)$

[In (iv), (v) and (vi) order in which $\bar{u}, \bar{v}, \bar{w}$ occur is maintained]

(vii) If s is any scalar depending upon t,

$$\frac{d}{dt}(s\,\bar{u}) = \frac{ds}{dt}\bar{u} + s\frac{d\bar{u}}{dt}$$

(viii) $\dfrac{d}{dt}\left(\dfrac{\bar{u}}{s}\right) = \dfrac{s\,\dfrac{d\bar{u}}{dt} - \bar{u}\,\dfrac{ds}{dt}}{s^2}$

(ix) If s is constant, $\dfrac{d}{dt}(s\,\bar{u}) = s\dfrac{d\bar{u}}{dt}$

Since $\dfrac{\bar{u}}{\bar{v}}$ is not defined, hence $\dfrac{d}{dt}\left(\dfrac{\bar{u}}{\bar{v}}\right)$ is also not defined or has no meaning.

If $\bar{u}(x, y)$, $\bar{v}(x, y)$ are vector functions of scalars x, y; the partial derivatives $\dfrac{\partial \bar{u}}{\partial x}, \dfrac{\partial \bar{u}}{\partial y}$ are defined as

$$\frac{\partial \bar{u}}{\partial x} = \lim_{\delta x \to 0} \left[\frac{\bar{u}(x + \delta x, y) - \bar{u}(x, y)}{\delta x} \right], \quad \frac{\partial \bar{u}}{\partial y} = \lim_{\delta y \to 0} \left[\frac{\bar{u}(x, y + \delta y) - \bar{u}(x, y)}{\delta y} \right]$$

if the limits exist.

The mixed derivatives $\dfrac{\partial^2 \bar{u}}{\partial x\, \partial y}$ and higher order partial derivatives $\dfrac{\partial^2 \bar{u}}{\partial x^2}, \dfrac{\partial^2 \bar{u}}{\partial y^2}, \dfrac{\partial^2 \bar{v}}{\partial x^2},$ $\dfrac{\partial^3 \bar{u}}{\partial x^3}$ can be similarly defined and can be computed.

Rules for partial differentiation of vectors are similar to those used in calculus for scalar functions. Following results can be easily established :

$$\frac{\partial}{\partial x}(\bar{u} \pm \bar{v}) = \frac{\partial \bar{u}}{\partial x} \pm \frac{\partial \bar{v}}{\partial x}$$

$$\frac{\partial}{\partial x}(\bar{u} \cdot \bar{v}) = \frac{\partial \bar{u}}{\partial x} \cdot \bar{v} + \bar{u} \cdot \frac{\partial \bar{v}}{\partial x}$$

$$\frac{\partial}{\partial x}(\bar{u} \times \bar{v}) = \frac{\partial \bar{u}}{\partial x} \times \bar{v} + \bar{u} \times \frac{\partial \bar{v}}{\partial x}$$

10.2 APPLICATIONS OF MECHANICS

This includes a study of the motion of particles along curves. Newton's second law of motion states that $\bar{F} = \dfrac{d}{dt}(m\bar{V})$, where $m\bar{V}$ is the momentum of the object. If m is constant, then this becomes $\bar{F} = m\dfrac{d\bar{V}}{dt} = m\,\bar{a}$, where $\bar{a}$ is the acceleration of the object. This law is quite useful in the study of dynamics.

(A) **Plane motion of a particle along a circle :** Consider a particle P moving along a circle of radius r with constant angular speed ω.

$$\omega = \frac{d\theta}{dt}$$

$$\bar{r} = \overline{OP} = x\bar{i} + y\bar{j} = r\cos\theta\,\bar{i} + r\sin\theta\,\bar{j}$$

Differentiating w.r.t. t

$$\overline{V} = \frac{d\overline{r}}{dt} = -r\sin\theta\,\overline{i}\,\frac{d\theta}{dt} + r\cos\theta\,\overline{j}\,\frac{d\theta}{dt} = (-r\sin\theta\,\overline{i} + r\cos\theta\,\overline{j}\,)\,\omega$$

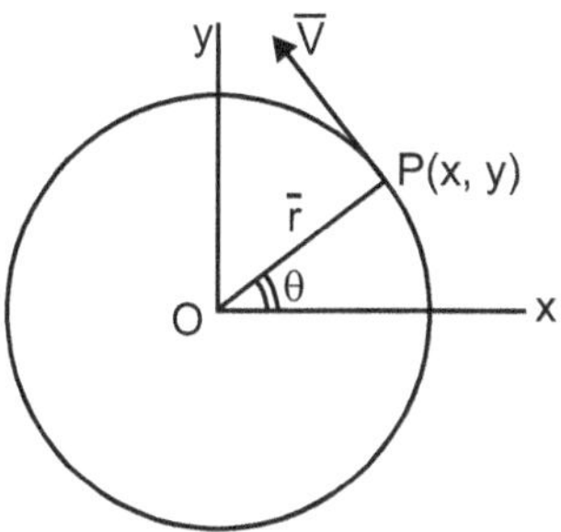

Fig. 10.2

Differentiating again w.r.t. t,

$$\frac{d\overline{V}}{dt} = \overline{a} = \left(-r\cos\theta\,\frac{d\theta}{dt}\,\overline{i} - r\sin\theta\,\frac{d\theta}{dt}\,\overline{j}\right)\omega = (-r\cos\theta\,\overline{i} - r\sin\theta\,\overline{j})\,\omega^2 = -\overline{r}\,\omega^2$$

Hence the acceleration is directed towards the centre.

(B) Radial and Transverse Components of Velocity and Acceleration : Consider a particle moving along a curve C (See Fig. 10.3).

Let $\overrightarrow{OP} = \overline{r}$ be the position vector of point P, $\hat{r}$ and $\hat{s}$ be unit vectors along the radius vector $\overline{r}$ (radial direction) and perpendicular to $\overline{r}$ (transverse direction).

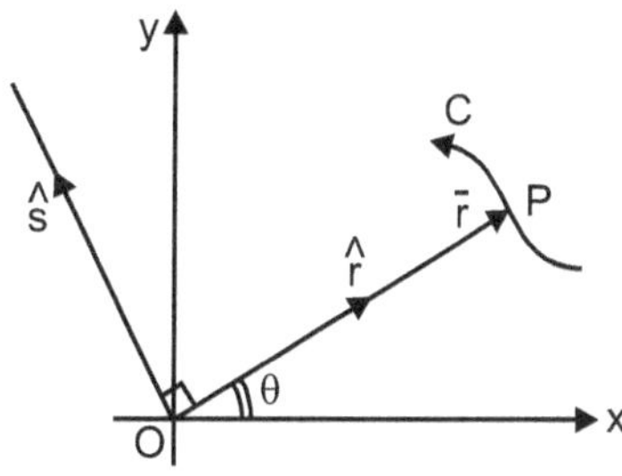

$$\hat{r} = \cos\theta\,\overline{i} + \sin\theta\,\overline{j}$$

$$\hat{s} = \cos\left(\frac{\pi}{2}+\theta\right)\overline{i} + \sin\left(\frac{\pi}{2}+\theta\right)\overline{j}$$

$$= -\sin\theta\,\overline{i} + \cos\theta\,\overline{j}$$

Fig. 10.3

Differentiating both w.r.t. t, we get

$$\frac{d\hat{r}}{dt} = -\sin\theta\,\frac{d\theta}{dt}\,\overline{i} + \cos\theta\,\frac{d\theta}{dt}\,\overline{j} = (-\sin\theta\,\overline{i} + \cos\theta\,\overline{j})\frac{d\theta}{dt} = \hat{s}\,\frac{d\theta}{dt}$$

Similarly,
$$\frac{d\hat{s}}{dt} = -\hat{r}\,\frac{d\theta}{dt}$$

Now
$$\overline{r} = r\,\hat{r}$$

and $\bar{V}$ the velocity of the point P is

$$\bar{V} = \frac{d\bar{r}}{dt} = \frac{d}{dt}(r\,\hat{r}) = \frac{dr}{dt}\,\hat{r} + r\frac{d\hat{r}}{dt}$$

$$\boxed{\bar{V} = \frac{dr}{dt}\,\hat{r} + \left(r\frac{d\theta}{dt}\right)\hat{s}} \qquad \dots (1)$$

Thus the radial and transverse components of velocity are $\dfrac{dr}{dt}$ (or $\dot{r}$) and $r\,\dfrac{d\theta}{dt}$ (or $r\,\dot{\theta}$) respectively.

To obtain radial and transverse components of acceleration,

$$\bar{a} = \frac{d\bar{v}}{dt} = \frac{d}{dt}\left[\frac{dr}{dt}\,\hat{r} + \left(r\frac{d\theta}{dt}\right)\hat{s}\right] = \frac{d^2r}{dt^2}\,\hat{r} + \frac{dr}{dt}\frac{d\hat{r}}{dt} + \left(\frac{dr}{dt}\frac{d\theta}{dt} + r\frac{d^2\theta}{dt^2}\right)\hat{s} + \left(r\frac{d\theta}{dt}\right)\frac{d\hat{s}}{dt}$$

but $\qquad \dfrac{d\hat{r}}{dt} = \hat{s}\,\dfrac{d\theta}{dt} \quad$ and $\quad \dfrac{d\hat{s}}{dt} = -\hat{r}\,\dfrac{d\theta}{dt}$

$$\therefore \qquad \bar{a} = \frac{d\bar{v}}{dt} = \frac{d^2r}{dt^2}\,\hat{r} + \frac{dr}{dt}\left(\hat{s}\,\frac{d\theta}{dt}\right) + \frac{dr}{dt}\frac{d\theta}{dt}\,\hat{s} + r\frac{d^2\theta}{dt^2}\,\hat{s} + r\frac{d\theta}{dt}\left(-\hat{r}\,\frac{d\theta}{dt}\right)$$

$$= \left[\frac{d^2r}{dt^2} - r\left(\frac{d\theta}{dt}\right)^2\right]\hat{r} + \left[2\frac{dr}{dt}\frac{d\theta}{dt} + r\frac{d^2\theta}{dt^2}\right]\hat{s}$$

$$\therefore \qquad \boxed{\bar{a} = [\ddot{r} - r\,(\dot{\theta})^2]\,\hat{r} + [2\,\dot{r}\,\dot{\theta} + r\,\ddot{\theta}]\,\hat{s}} \qquad \dots (2)$$

Thus $\ddot{r} - r\,\dot{\theta}^2$ is radial and $2\,\dot{r}\,\dot{\theta} + r\,\ddot{\theta}$ is transverse component of acceleration.

(C) Tangential and Normal Components of Acceleration :

$$\bar{V} = \frac{d\bar{r}}{dt} = \frac{d\bar{r}}{ds}\frac{ds}{dt}$$

but $\qquad \dfrac{d\bar{r}}{ds} = \hat{T}$ [unit tangent vector] and $\dfrac{ds}{dt} = v = |\bar{V}|$ [speed]

$$\therefore \qquad \bar{V} = \frac{ds}{dt}\,\hat{T} = v\,\hat{T}$$

and $\qquad \bar{a} = \dfrac{d\bar{V}}{dt} = \dfrac{dv}{dt}\,\hat{T} + v\,\dfrac{d\hat{T}}{dt}$

$$= \frac{d^2s}{dt^2}\,\hat{T} + \frac{ds}{dt}\left(\frac{d\hat{T}}{ds}\frac{ds}{dt}\right) = \frac{d^2s}{dt^2}\,\hat{T} + \left(\frac{ds}{dt}\right)^2\frac{d\hat{T}}{ds}$$

From Serret-Frenet formulae,

$$\frac{d\hat{T}}{ds} = k\,\hat{N}, \qquad\qquad [\hat{N} \text{ is unit principal normal vector}]$$

$$\bar{a} = \frac{d^2s}{dt^2}\,\hat{T} + \left(\frac{ds}{dt}\right)^2 k\,\hat{N}, \qquad\qquad [k \text{ is curvature}]$$

$$= \frac{d^2s}{dt^2}\,\hat{T} + \frac{1}{\rho}\left(\frac{ds}{dt}\right)^2 \hat{N}, \quad \left[k = \frac{1}{\rho}, \text{ where } \rho \text{ is radius of curvature}\right]$$

$$\boxed{\;\bar{a} = \frac{dv}{dt}\,\hat{T} + \frac{v^2}{\rho}\,\hat{N} = a_T\,\hat{T} + a_N\,\hat{N}\;}$$

where $\qquad a_T = \dfrac{dv}{dt} = \dfrac{d^2s}{dt^2} = \dfrac{\bar{r}\cdot\bar{r}}{|\bar{r}|}$, $\qquad$ is tangential component of $\bar{a}$,

and $\qquad a_N = \dfrac{v^2}{\rho} = \dfrac{1}{\rho}\left(\dfrac{ds}{dt}\right)^2 = \dfrac{|\bar{r}\times\bar{r}|}{|\bar{r}|}$, $\qquad$ is normal component of $\bar{a}$.

(D) Law of central orbits (orbital motion) : Consider a particle P, describing the curve C under the action of a force F always directed towards the centre 'O'. From equation (2) of (b),

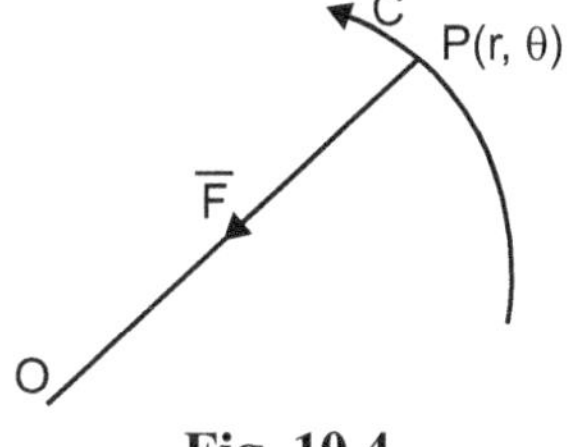

Fig. 10.4

$$F = -\left[\frac{d^2r}{dt^2} - r\left(\frac{d\theta}{dt}\right)^2\right] \qquad\qquad \dots (1)$$

As the force or acceleration is directed towards the centre and since there is no transverse component of acceleration,

$$2\,\dot{r}\,\dot{\theta} + r\,\ddot{\theta} = 0 \qquad\qquad \therefore \qquad \frac{1}{r}(2\,r\,\dot{r}\,\dot{\theta} + r^2\,\ddot{\theta}) = 0$$

i.e. $\qquad \dfrac{1}{r}\dfrac{d}{dt}\left[r^2\dfrac{d\theta}{dt}\right] = 0$

which implies $r^2\dfrac{d\theta}{dt} = h$ (constant), taking $u = \dfrac{1}{r}$, we get

$$\therefore \qquad \frac{d\theta}{dt} = \frac{h}{r^2} = hu^2 \qquad \Rightarrow \qquad \frac{dr}{dt} = \frac{dr}{d\theta}\frac{d\theta}{dt} = hu^2\frac{dr}{d\theta}$$

$$\text{but} \qquad r = \frac{1}{u} \qquad \Rightarrow \qquad \frac{dr}{d\theta} = -\frac{1}{u^2}\frac{du}{d\theta}$$

$$\therefore \quad \frac{dr}{dt} = hu^2\left(-\frac{1}{u^2}\frac{du}{d\theta}\right) = -h\frac{du}{d\theta}$$

$$\frac{d^2r}{dt^2} = -h\frac{d^2u}{d\theta^2}\frac{d\theta}{dt} = -h\frac{d^2u}{d\theta^2}hu^2 = -h^2u^2\frac{d^2u}{d\theta^2}$$

Putting in (1) for $\dfrac{d\theta}{dt}$, $\dfrac{d^2r}{dt^2}$

$$F = -\left[-h^2u^2\frac{d^2u}{d\theta^2} - \frac{1}{u}(h^2u^4)\right] = h^2u^2\left(\frac{d^2u}{d\theta^2} + u\right)$$

$$\therefore \quad \boxed{F = h^2u^2\left(\frac{d^2u}{d\theta^2} + u\right)}$$

Which gives the law of force or acceleration which is always directed towards the centre (pole) when the particle describes the given orbit. In above discussion, $r^2\dfrac{d\theta}{dt}$ = constant, represents moment of velocity of the particle about the centre, which remains constant throughout the motion of the particle.

ILLUSTRATIONS

Ex. 1 : *A curve is given by the equations* $x = t^2 + 1$, $y = 4t - 3$, $z = 2t^2 - 6t$. *Find the angle between tangents at* $t = 1$ *and at* $t = 2$.

Sol. :
$$\bar{r} = x\bar{i} + y\bar{j} + z\bar{k}, \quad \text{where } x = t^2 + 1, \quad y = 4t - 3, \quad z = 2t^2 - 6t$$

$$\therefore \quad \bar{T} = \frac{d\bar{r}}{dt} = \bar{i}\frac{dx}{dt} + \bar{j}\frac{dy}{dt} + \bar{k}\frac{dz}{dt} = 2t\bar{i} + 4\bar{j} + (4t - 6)\bar{k}$$

$$\therefore \quad \bar{T}_1 = \{\bar{T}\}_{t=1} = 2\bar{i} + 4\bar{j} - 2\bar{k} \text{ and } \bar{T}_2 = \{\bar{T}\}_{t=2} = 4\bar{i} + 4\bar{j} + 2\bar{k}$$

$$\therefore \quad \hat{T}_1 = \frac{2\bar{i} + 4\bar{j} - 2\bar{k}}{\sqrt{4 + 16 + 4}} = \frac{2\bar{i} + 4\bar{j} - 2\bar{k}}{2\sqrt{6}} = \frac{\bar{i} + 2\bar{j} - \bar{k}}{\sqrt{6}}$$

$$\text{and} \quad \hat{T}_2 = \frac{4\bar{i} + 4\bar{j} + 2\bar{k}}{\sqrt{16 + 16 + 4}} = \frac{4\bar{i} + 4\bar{j} + 2\bar{k}}{6} = \frac{2\bar{i} + 2\bar{j} + \bar{k}}{3}$$

Now, $\hat{T}_1 \cdot \hat{T}_2 = |\hat{T}_1||\hat{T}_2|\cos\theta$ [θ is the angle between the tangents]

$$\cos\theta = \hat{T}_1 \cdot \hat{T}_2 = \frac{2 + 4 - 1}{3\sqrt{6}} = \frac{5}{3\sqrt{6}}$$

$$\therefore \quad \theta = \cos^{-1}\left\{\frac{5}{3\sqrt{6}}\right\}$$

Ex. 2 : *For the curve* $x = e^t \cos t$, $y = e^t \sin t$, $z = e^t$ *find the velocity and acceleration of the particle moving on the curve at* $t = 0$.

Sol. :

$$\bar{V} = \bar{i}\,\frac{dx}{dt} + \bar{j}\,\frac{dy}{dt} + \bar{k}\,\frac{dz}{dt}$$

$$= \bar{i}\,\{e^t \cos t - e^t \sin t\} + \bar{j}\,\{e^t \sin t + e^t \cos t\} + \bar{k}\,\{e^t\}$$

$$\bar{a} = \frac{d\bar{V}}{dt} = \bar{i}\,\{e^t \cos t - e^t \sin t - e^t \sin t - e^t \cos t\}$$

$$+ \bar{j}\,\{e^t \sin t + e^t \cos t + e^t \cos t - e^t \sin t\} + \bar{k}\,\{e^t\}$$

$$= \bar{i}\,\{-2\,e^t \sin t\} + \bar{j}\,\{2 e^t \cos t\} + \bar{k}\,\{e^t\}$$

$$\bar{V}\big|_{t\,=\,0} = \bar{i} + \bar{j} + \bar{k}$$

$$\bar{a}\big|_{t\,=\,0} = 2\,\bar{j} + \bar{k}$$

Ex. 3 : *If* $\bar{r}$ *is the position vector of a particle of mass m w.r.t. 'O' as origin and* $\bar{F}$ *is the external force on the particle, then show that the moment of* $\bar{F}$ *about O is given by* $\bar{M} = \dfrac{d\bar{H}}{dt}$ *, where* $\bar{H} = \bar{r} \times m\bar{V}$ *and* $\bar{V}$ *is the velocity of the particle.*

Sol. :

$$\bar{M} = \bar{r} \times \bar{F} = \bar{r} \times \frac{d}{dt}(m\bar{V})$$

$$\frac{d\bar{H}}{dt} = \frac{d}{dt}\,(\bar{r} \times m\bar{V}) = \frac{d\bar{r}}{dt} \times m\bar{V} + \bar{r} \times \frac{d}{dt}(m\bar{V})$$

$$= \bar{V} \times m\bar{V} + \bar{r} \times \frac{d}{dt}(m\bar{V}) = 0 + \bar{r} \times \frac{d}{dt}(m\bar{V})$$

Thus,

$$\bar{M} = \bar{r} \times \frac{d}{dt}(m\bar{V}) = \frac{d\bar{H}}{dt}$$

Ex. 4 : *For the curve* $x = t^3 + 1$, $y = t^2$, $z = t$, *find the magnitude of tangential and normal components of acceleration for a particle moving on the curve at* $t = 1$.

Sol. : Let

$$\bar{a} = a_T\,\hat{T} + a_N\,\hat{N} \qquad\qquad \text{... (i)}$$

where a_T, a_N are tangential and normal components of acceleration, respectively.

$$\bar{V} = \frac{d\bar{r}}{dt} = \bar{i}\,\frac{dx}{dt} + \bar{j}\,\frac{dy}{dt} + \bar{k}\,\frac{dz}{dt}$$

$$= \bar{i}(3t^2) + 2t\,\bar{j} + \bar{k} = 3\,\bar{i} + 2\,\bar{j} + \bar{k} \ \text{ at } t = 1$$

$$\bar{a} = \frac{d^2\bar{r}}{dt^2} = 6t\,\bar{i} + 2\,\bar{j} = 6\,\bar{i} + 2\,\bar{j} \ \text{ at } t = 1$$

From (i), $\quad \bar{a} \cdot \hat{T} = a_T \hat{T} \cdot \hat{T} + a_N \hat{N} \cdot \hat{T} = a_T$ as $\hat{N} \cdot \hat{T} = 0$

$$\hat{T} = \frac{d\bar{r}/dt}{\left|\dfrac{d\bar{r}}{dt}\right|} = \frac{3\bar{i} + 2\bar{j} + \bar{k}}{\sqrt{9 + 4 + 1}} = \frac{1}{\sqrt{14}} (3\bar{i} + 2\bar{j} + \bar{k})$$

$$\bar{a} \cdot \hat{T} = (6\bar{i} + 2\bar{j}) \cdot \frac{1}{\sqrt{14}} (3\bar{i} + 2\bar{j} + \bar{k}) = \frac{1}{\sqrt{14}} (18 + 4) = \frac{22}{\sqrt{14}}$$

Thus $\quad a_T = \dfrac{22}{\sqrt{14}}$ (Magnitude of tangential component of acceleration).

To obtain normal component, consider

$$a_N \hat{N} = \bar{a} - a_T \hat{T}$$

Taking the dot product with itself

$$a_N \hat{N} \cdot a_N \hat{N} = (\bar{a} - a_T \hat{T}) \cdot (\bar{a} - a_T \hat{T})$$

$$a_N^2 = \left((6\bar{i} + 2\bar{j}) - \frac{22}{\sqrt{14}} \frac{(3\bar{i} + 2\bar{j} + \bar{k})}{\sqrt{14}}\right) \cdot \left((6\bar{i} + 2\bar{j}) - \frac{22}{\sqrt{14}} \frac{(3\bar{i} + 2\bar{j} + \bar{k})}{\sqrt{14}}\right)$$

$$\therefore \quad a_N^2 = \left[\left(\frac{84\bar{i} - 66\bar{i} + 28\bar{j} - 44\bar{j} - 22\bar{k}}{14}\right) \cdot \left(\frac{84\bar{i} - 66\bar{i} + 28\bar{j} - 44\bar{j} - 22\bar{k}}{14}\right)\right]$$

$$= \left[\left(\frac{18\bar{i} - 16\bar{j} - 22\bar{k}}{14}\right) \cdot \left(\frac{18\bar{i} - 16\bar{j} - 22\bar{k}}{14}\right)\right]$$

$$= \left(\frac{9\bar{i} - 8\bar{j} - 11\bar{k}}{7}\right) \cdot \left(\frac{9\bar{i} - 8\bar{j} - 11\bar{k}}{7}\right)$$

$$= \frac{1}{49} [81 + 64 + 121] = \frac{266}{49} = \frac{38}{7}$$

$$\therefore \quad a_N = \sqrt{\frac{38}{7}} \qquad \text{[Magnitude of normal component of acceleration]}$$

Ex. 5 : *For the curve $x = \cos t + t \sin t$, $y = \sin t - t \cos t$, find the tangential and normal components of acceleration at any time t.*

Sol. : $\quad \dfrac{dx}{dt} = -\sin t + \sin t + t \cos t = t \cos t$

$\dfrac{d^2x}{dt^2} = \cos t - t \sin t$

$\dfrac{dy}{dt} = \cos t - \cos t + t \sin t = t \sin t$

$$\frac{d^2y}{dt^2} = \sin t + t \cos t$$

$$\overline{r} = x\,\overline{i} + y\,\overline{j}$$

$$\overline{T} = \overline{i}\,\frac{dx}{dt} + \overline{j}\,\frac{dy}{dt} = \overline{i}\,(t \cos t) + \overline{j}\,(t \sin t)$$

$$\overline{a} = \overline{i}\,\frac{d^2x}{dt^2} + \overline{j}\,\frac{d^2y}{dt^2} = \overline{i}\,(\cos t - t \sin t) + \overline{j}\,(\sin t + t \cos t)$$

Let $\qquad \overline{a} = a_T\,\hat{T} + a_N\,\hat{N}$

$$\overline{a} \cdot \hat{T} = a_T$$

$$\hat{T} = \frac{\overline{i}\,(t \cos t) + \overline{j}\,(t \sin t)}{\sqrt{t^2 \cos^2 t + t^2 \sin^2 t}} = \overline{i}\,(\cos t) + \overline{j}\,(\sin t)$$

$$\overline{a} \cdot \hat{T} = [\,\overline{i}\,(\cos t - t \sin t) + \overline{j}\,(\sin t + t \cos t)\,] \cdot [\,\overline{i}\,(\cos t) + \overline{j}\,(\sin t)\,]$$

$$= \cos^2 t - t \sin t \cos t + \sin^2 t + t \cos t \sin t = 1$$

Thus $\qquad a_T = \overline{a} \cdot \hat{T} = 1 \qquad\qquad\qquad$ (tangential component)

$$a_N\,\hat{N} = \overline{a} - a_T\,\hat{T}$$

$$\therefore \quad (a_N\,\hat{N}) \cdot (a_N\,\hat{N}) = (\overline{a} - a_T\,\hat{T}) \cdot (\overline{a} - a_T\,\hat{T})$$

$$a_N^2 = (\overline{a} - a_T\,\hat{T}) \cdot (\overline{a} - a_T\,\hat{T})$$

$$\overline{a} - a_T\,\hat{T} = \overline{i}\,(\cos t - t \sin t) + \overline{j}\,(\sin t + t \cos t) - \overline{i}\,(\cos t) - \overline{j}\,(\sin t)$$

$$= (-t \sin t)\,\overline{i} + (t \cos t)\,\overline{j}$$

$$a_N^2 = [(-t \sin t)\,\overline{i} + (t \cos t)\,\overline{j}\,] \cdot [(-t \sin t)\,\overline{i} + (t \cos t)\,\overline{j}\,]$$

$$= t^2 \sin^2 t + t^2 \cos^2 t = t^2$$

$$a_N = t \qquad\qquad\qquad \text{(Normal component of acceleration)}$$

Ex. 6 : *A particle describes the cardioide r = a (1 + cos θ) under the attraction of a force directed towards the pole. Find the law of force.*

Sol. : From article 10.2 (d), law of force is given by

$$F = h^2 u^2 \left(\frac{d^2u}{d\theta^2} + u \right)$$

where $\quad u = \dfrac{1}{r}$ $\qquad\qquad u = \dfrac{1}{a}\,\dfrac{1}{(1 + \cos\theta)}$

$$\frac{du}{d\theta} = \frac{1}{a}\left[\frac{1\,(\sin\theta)}{(1 + \cos\theta)^2}\right] = \frac{\sin\theta}{a\,(1 + \cos\theta)^2}$$

$$\frac{d^2u}{d\theta^2} = \frac{1}{a}\left[\frac{\cos\theta\,(1 + \cos\theta)^2 + 2\,(1 + \cos\theta)\,\sin^2\theta}{(1 + \cos\theta)^4}\right]$$

$$= \frac{1}{a}\left[\frac{\cos\theta\,(1 + \cos\theta) + 2\,\sin^2\theta}{(1 + \cos\theta)^3}\right] = \frac{1}{a}\left[\frac{\cos\theta + 1 + \sin^2\theta}{(1 + \cos\theta)^3}\right]$$

$$\frac{d^2u}{d\theta^2} + u = \frac{1}{a}\left[\frac{\cos\theta + 1 + \sin^2\theta}{(1 + \cos\theta)^3} + \frac{1}{(1 + \cos\theta)}\right]$$

$$= \frac{1}{a}\left[\frac{\cos\theta + 1 + \sin^2\theta + 1 + 2\cos\theta + \cos^2\theta}{(1 + \cos\theta)^3}\right]$$

$$= \frac{1}{a}\left[\frac{3\,(1 + \cos\theta)}{(1 + \cos\theta)^3}\right] = \frac{1}{a}\,\frac{3}{(1 + \cos\theta)^2}$$

$$F = h^2u^2\left(\frac{d^2u}{d\theta^2} + u\right) = h^2\,\frac{1}{a^2\,(1 + \cos\theta)^2}\cdot\frac{3}{a}\cdot\frac{1}{(1 + \cos\theta)^2}$$

$$= \frac{3h^2\,a}{a^4\,(1 + \cos\theta)^4} = \frac{3h^2\,a}{r^4}$$

Or force is proportional to r^{-4}.

Ex. 7 : *A particle describes the curve r = 2a cos θ with constant angular speed ω. Find the radial and transverse components of velocity and acceleration.*   **(May 2009)**

Sol. : From article 10.2 (b),

$$\overline{V} = \frac{dr}{dt}\,\hat{r} + \left(r\,\frac{d\theta}{dt}\right)\hat{s}$$

$$\overline{a} = \left[\frac{d^2r}{dt^2} - r\left(\frac{d\theta}{dt}\right)^2\right]\hat{r} + \left[2\,\frac{dr}{dt}\,\frac{d\theta}{dt} + r\,\frac{d^2\theta}{dt^2}\right]\hat{s}$$

Consider $\qquad\qquad r = 2a\cos\theta$

$$\frac{dr}{dt} = -2a\sin\theta\,\frac{d\theta}{dt} = -2a\,\omega\sin\theta \qquad\qquad r\,\frac{d\theta}{dt} = 2a\cos\theta\,\omega$$

Thus, the radial and transverse components of velocity are $-2a\,\omega\sin\theta$ and $2a\,\omega\cos\theta$ respectively.

$$\frac{d^2r}{dt^2} = -2a\,\omega\cos\theta\,\frac{d\theta}{dt} = -2a\,\omega^2\cos\theta$$

Radial component of acceleration is

$$\frac{d^2r}{dt^2} - r\left(\frac{d\theta}{dt}\right)^2 = -2a\,\omega^2\cos\theta - 2a\cos\theta\,\omega^2 = -4a\,\omega^2\cos\theta$$

Transverse component of acceleration is

$$2\frac{dr}{dt}\frac{d\theta}{dt} + r\frac{d^2\theta}{dt^2} = 2\frac{dr}{dt}\,\omega\quad\left[\text{as }\frac{d^2\theta}{dt^2} = 0\right]$$

i.e. $\;2\,(-2a\,\omega\sin\theta)\,\omega = -4a\,\omega^2\sin\theta$

Ex. 8 : *A particle P moves in a plane with constant angular velocity ω about O. If the rate of increase of acceleration is parallel to PO, prove that*

$$\frac{d^2r}{dt^2} = \frac{1}{3}\,r\omega^2$$

Sol. : From result (2) of article 10.2 (b),

$$\bar{a} = \left[\frac{d^2r}{dt^2} - r\left(\frac{d\theta}{dt}\right)^2\right]\hat{r} + \left[2\frac{dr}{dt}\frac{d\theta}{dt} + r\frac{d^2\theta}{dt}\right]\hat{s}$$

In proving this result, we had also seen that

$$\frac{d\hat{r}}{dt} = \hat{s}\,\frac{d\theta}{dt} \qquad\qquad \frac{d\hat{s}}{dt} = -\hat{r}\,\frac{d\theta}{dt}$$

$$\because\qquad \frac{d\theta}{dt} = \omega = \text{constant}$$

$$\bar{a} = \left[\frac{d^2r}{dt^2} - r\omega^2\right]\hat{r} + \left[2\omega\,\frac{dr}{dt}\right]\hat{s} \qquad\qquad \left[\text{as }\frac{d^2\theta}{dt^2} = 0\right]$$

Differentiating w.r.t. t

$$\frac{d\bar{a}}{dt} = \left[\frac{d^3r}{dt^3} - \frac{dr}{dt}\,\omega^2\right]\hat{r} + \left[\frac{d^2r}{dt^2} - r\omega^2\right]\frac{d\hat{r}}{dt} + 2\omega\frac{d^2r}{dt^2}\,\hat{s} + 2\omega\frac{dr}{dt}\frac{d\hat{s}}{dt}$$

Putting $\quad\dfrac{d\hat{r}}{dt} = \hat{s}\,\dfrac{d\theta}{dt},\quad \dfrac{d\hat{s}}{dt} = -\hat{r}\,\dfrac{d\theta}{dt}$

$$\frac{d\bar{a}}{dt} = \left[\frac{d^3r}{dt^3} - \frac{dr}{dt}\,\omega^2\right]\hat{r} + \left[\frac{d^2r}{dt^2} - r\omega^2\right]\hat{s}\,\frac{d\theta}{dt} + 2\omega\frac{d^2r}{dt^2}\,\hat{s} + 2\omega\frac{dr}{dt}\left(-\hat{r}\,\frac{d\theta}{dt}\right)$$

Putting ω for $\dfrac{d\theta}{dt}$ and rearranging,

$$\frac{d\bar{a}}{dt} = \left[\frac{d^3r}{dt^3} - \frac{dr}{dt}\,\omega^2 - 2\omega^2\frac{dr}{dt}\right]\hat{r} + \left[\omega\frac{d^2r}{dt^2} - r\omega^3 + 2\omega\frac{d^2r}{dt^2}\right]\hat{s}$$

Since $\dfrac{d\bar{a}}{dt}$ is parallel to PO i.e. along $\hat{r}$, coefficient of $\hat{s}$ must be zero.

i.e. $\quad 3\omega\dfrac{d^2r}{dt^2} - r\omega^3 = 0 \qquad\qquad\text{Or}\qquad\qquad \dfrac{d^2r}{dt^2} = \dfrac{1}{3}\,r\omega^2$

Ex. 9 : *If* $\bar{r} \times \dfrac{d\bar{r}}{dt} = 0$, *show that* $\bar{r}$ *has a constant direction.*　**(Dec. 05, 07, 08, 11)**

Sol. : Let $\bar{r} = r\,\hat{r}$, where $\hat{r}$ is a unit vector in the direction of $\bar{r}$ and $r = |\bar{r}|$.

$$\frac{d\bar{r}}{dt} = r\,\frac{d\hat{r}}{dt} + \hat{r}\,\frac{dr}{dt}$$

$$\bar{r} \times \frac{d\bar{r}}{dt} = r\,\hat{r} \times \left(r\frac{d\hat{r}}{dt} + \hat{r}\,\frac{dr}{dt} \right) = r^2\hat{r} \times \frac{d\hat{r}}{dt} + r\,\frac{dr}{dt}\,(\hat{r} \times \hat{r})$$

$$= r^2\,\hat{r} \times \frac{d\hat{r}}{dt}\ [\hat{r} \times \hat{r} = 0]$$

Now, $\qquad \bar{r} \times \dfrac{d\bar{r}}{dt} = 0$ (given) $\qquad \therefore \qquad r^2\hat{r} \times \dfrac{d\hat{r}}{dt} = 0$

i.e. $\qquad \hat{r} \times \dfrac{d\hat{r}}{dt} = 0\ \ [\text{as } r \neq 0]$ $\qquad\qquad\qquad\qquad\qquad$ ...(i)

Again $\qquad \hat{r} \cdot \hat{r} = 1$ $\qquad\qquad \therefore \qquad \hat{r} \cdot \dfrac{d\hat{r}}{dt} = 0$ $\qquad$ ... (ii)

(i) implies $\dfrac{d\hat{r}}{dt}$ is parallel to $\hat{r}$ $\qquad$ (ii) implies $\dfrac{d\hat{r}}{dt}$ is perpendicular to $\hat{r}$

both cannot be true simultaneously $\qquad \therefore \qquad \dfrac{d\hat{r}}{dt} = 0$

which means $\hat{r}$ has constant direction.

Ex. 10 : *Show that tangential and normal components of acceleration are given by*

$$\frac{\bar{V} \cdot \bar{a}}{V} \quad and \quad \frac{|\bar{V} \times \bar{a}|}{|\bar{V}|}$$

Also show that $\qquad \rho = \dfrac{V^3}{|\bar{V} \times \bar{a}|}$

Sol. : Let $\qquad \bar{a} = a_T\,\hat{T} + a_N\,\hat{N}, \quad \bar{V} = V\,\hat{T}$

$\therefore \qquad \bar{V} \cdot \bar{a} = V\hat{T} \cdot (a_T\,\hat{T} + a_N\,\hat{N}) = V\,a_T\hat{T} \cdot \hat{T} + V\,a_N\,\hat{T} \cdot \hat{N}$

but $\qquad \hat{T} \cdot \hat{T} = 1, \quad \hat{T} \cdot \hat{N} = 0$

$\therefore \qquad a_T = \dfrac{\bar{V} \cdot \bar{a}}{V}$ $\qquad\qquad\qquad\qquad\qquad\qquad\qquad$ ... (1)

$$\bar{V} \times \bar{a} = V\hat{T} \times (a_T \hat{T} + a_N \hat{N}) = V a_t \hat{T} \times \hat{T} + V a_N \hat{T} \times \hat{N}$$

but $\qquad \hat{T} \times \hat{T} = 0$

$\therefore \qquad |\bar{V} \times \bar{a}| = V a_N |\hat{T} \times \hat{N}| = V a_N \quad \text{as } |\hat{T} \times \hat{N}| = 1$

$$\therefore \qquad a_N = \frac{|\bar{V} \times \bar{a}|}{V} \quad \text{or} \quad \frac{|\bar{V} \times \bar{a}|}{|\bar{V}|} \qquad \qquad \ldots (2)$$

From article 10.2 (c), we know that

$$\bar{a} = \frac{dV}{dt}\hat{T} + \frac{V^2}{\rho}\hat{N}$$

$$\bar{V} \times \bar{a} = V\hat{T} \times \left(\frac{dV}{dt}\hat{T} + \frac{V^2}{\rho}\hat{N}\right) = \frac{V^3}{\rho}\hat{T} \times \hat{N} \qquad [\because \hat{T} \times \hat{T} = 0]$$

$$\therefore \qquad |\bar{V} \times \bar{a}| = \frac{V^3}{\rho}|\hat{T} \times \hat{N}| = \frac{V^3}{\rho}$$

$$\therefore \qquad \rho = \frac{V^3}{|\bar{V} \times \bar{a}|} \qquad \qquad \ldots (3)$$

(1), (2), (3) are the required results.

Ex. 11 : *If a particle moves along the cardioide* $r = a(1 + \cos\theta)$ *with constant velocity, show that* $\dfrac{d\theta}{dt}$ *is proportional to* $\dfrac{1}{\sqrt{r}}$. **(May 2008, Dec. 2008)**

Sol. : From article 10.2 (b), we know that

$$\bar{V} = \frac{d\bar{r}}{dt} = \frac{dr}{dt}\hat{r} + \left(r\frac{d\theta}{dt}\right)\hat{s} = \frac{dr}{d\theta}\frac{d\theta}{dt}\hat{r} + \left(r\frac{d\theta}{dt}\right)\hat{s} = \frac{d\theta}{dt}\left(\frac{dr}{d\theta}\hat{r} + r\hat{s}\right)$$

$$\therefore \qquad |\bar{V}| = \frac{d\theta}{dt}\left|\frac{dr}{d\theta}\hat{r} + r\hat{s}\right| = \frac{d\theta}{dt}\sqrt{\left(\frac{dr}{d\theta}\right)^2 + r^2}$$

$$= \frac{d\theta}{dt}\sqrt{a^2 \sin^2\theta + a^2(1 + \cos\theta)^2}$$

$$= a\frac{d\theta}{dt}\sqrt{\sin^2\theta + 1 + 2\cos\theta + \cos^2\theta} = \frac{d\theta}{dt}\sqrt{2}\, a\sqrt{1 + \cos\theta}$$

but $\qquad |\bar{V}| = \text{constant (given)} \quad \text{and} \quad \sqrt{1 + \cos\theta} = \dfrac{\sqrt{r}}{\sqrt{a}}$

$$\therefore \qquad \frac{d\theta}{dt} = \frac{c\sqrt{a}}{\sqrt{2}\, a\sqrt{r}} = \frac{c}{\sqrt{2}\, a}\frac{1}{\sqrt{r}}$$

$\therefore \quad \dfrac{d\theta}{dt}$ is proportional to $\dfrac{1}{\sqrt{r}}$.

Ex. 12 : *A particle moves along the curve s = a log (sec ψ + tan ψ), where ψ is the angle made by the tangent with x-axis. If the motion is such that the tangent to the curve rotates uniformly, then show that the resultant acceleration of the particle varies as the square of radius of curvature.*

Sol. : Since the tangent rotates uniformly, $\dfrac{d\psi}{dt} = \omega = $ constant.

$$\rho = \frac{ds}{d\psi} = a \cdot \frac{(\sec \psi \tan \psi + \sec^2 \psi)}{\sec \psi + \tan \psi} = a \cdot \frac{\sec \psi (\tan \psi + \sec \psi)}{(\sec \psi + \tan \psi)}$$

$$\rho = a \sec \psi$$

$$\frac{ds}{dt} = \frac{ds}{d\psi} \frac{d\psi}{dt} = a\,\omega \sec \psi$$

From article 10.2 (c),

$$\bar{a} = \frac{d^2 s}{dt^2} \hat{T} + \frac{1}{\rho} \left(\frac{ds}{dt}\right)^2 \hat{N} = a_T\,\hat{T} + a_N\,\hat{N}$$

$$|\bar{a}| = \sqrt{a_T^2 + a_N^2}$$

$$a_T = \frac{d^2 s}{dt^2} = a\,\omega \sec \psi \tan \psi \frac{d\psi}{dt} = a\,\omega^2 \sec \psi\,\tan \psi$$

$$a_N = \frac{1}{\rho} \left(\frac{ds}{dt}\right)^2 = \frac{1}{a \sec \psi}\, a^2\,\omega^2 \sec^2 \psi = a\,\omega^2 \sec \psi$$

$$|\bar{a}|^2 = a^2\,\omega^4 \sec^2 \psi\,\tan^2 \psi + a^2\,\omega^4 \sec^2 \psi$$

$$= a^2\,\omega^4 \sec^2 \psi\,(\tan^2 \psi + 1) = a^2\,\omega^4 \sec^4 \psi$$

$\therefore \qquad |\bar{a}| = a\,\omega^2 \sec^2 \psi$

but $\qquad \rho = a \sec \psi \qquad \therefore \ \sec \psi = \dfrac{\rho}{a}$

$\therefore \qquad |\bar{a}| = a\,\omega^2 \cdot \dfrac{\rho^2}{a^2} = \dfrac{\omega^2}{a} \cdot \rho^2 \quad \therefore \ \ |\bar{a}| = k\,\rho^2$

as ω, a are constants.

$\therefore$ Acceleration varies as the square of radius of curvature.

Ex. 13 : *A particle moves along a curve $x = 2t^2$, $y = t^2 - 4t$, $z = 2t - 5$. Find components of velocity and acceleration at t = 1 in the direction $\bar{i} - 3\bar{j} + 2\bar{k}$.*

Sol. :
$$\bar{r} = x\bar{i} + y\bar{j} + z\bar{k}$$

$$= 2t^2\,\bar{i} + (t^2 - 4t)\,\bar{j} + (2t - 5)\,\bar{k}$$

$$\bar{v} = \frac{d\bar{r}}{dt} = 4t\,\bar{i} + (2t - 4)\,\bar{j} + 2\bar{k}$$

$$\bar{v}|_{t=1} = 4\bar{i} - 2\bar{j} + 2\bar{k}$$

$$\bar{a} = \frac{d^2\bar{r}}{dt^2} = 4\bar{i} + 2\bar{j}, \quad \bar{a}]_{t=1} = 4\bar{i} + 2\bar{j}$$

$$\bar{b} = \bar{i} - 3\bar{j} + 2\bar{k}$$

$$\hat{b} = \frac{\bar{i} - 3\bar{j} + 2\bar{k}}{\sqrt{1+9+4}} = \frac{1}{\sqrt{14}} (\bar{i} - 3\bar{j} + 2\bar{k})$$

Velocity component along

$$\hat{b} = \bar{v} \cdot \hat{b} = (4\bar{i} - 2\bar{j} + 2\bar{k}) \cdot \frac{1}{\sqrt{14}} (\bar{i} - 3\bar{j} + 2\bar{k})$$

$$= \frac{1}{\sqrt{14}} (4 + 6 + 4) = \frac{14}{\sqrt{14}} = \sqrt{14}$$

Acceleration component along

$$\hat{b} = \bar{a} \cdot \hat{b} = (4\bar{i} + 2\bar{j}) \cdot \frac{1}{\sqrt{14}} (\bar{i} - 3\bar{j} + 2\bar{k})$$

$$= \frac{1}{\sqrt{14}} (4 - 6) = -\frac{2}{\sqrt{14}}$$

EXERCISE 10.1

1. Find the angle between tangents to the curve :

$$\bar{r} = (t^3 + 2)\bar{i} + (4t - 5)\bar{j} + (2t^2 - 6t)\bar{k} \text{ at } t = 0 \text{ and } t = 2.$$

$$\left(\textbf{Ans. } \frac{1}{\sqrt{13}\,\sqrt{14}}\right)$$

2. For the curve $\bar{r} = e^{-t}\bar{i} + \log(t^2 + 1)\bar{j} - \tan t\,\bar{k}$, find velocity and acceleration at $t = 0$.

$$(\textbf{Ans. } -\bar{i} - \bar{k}, \ \bar{i} + 2\bar{j})$$

3. If $\bar{r} = \bar{a}\,e^{2t} + \bar{b}\,e^{3t}$, where $\bar{a}, \bar{b}$ are constant vectors, then show that

$$\frac{d^2\bar{r}}{dt^2} - 5\frac{d\bar{r}}{dt} + 6\bar{r} = 0.$$

4. If $\bar{r} = \bar{a}\cos nt + \bar{b}\sin nt$, where $\bar{a} = 2\bar{i} + 2\bar{j} - \bar{k}, \bar{b} = 3\bar{i} - 2\bar{j} + 2\bar{k}$ then

show that (i) $\dfrac{d^2\bar{r}}{dt^2} + n^2\bar{r} = 0$; (ii) Find $\bar{r} \cdot \bar{v}$; (iii) $\bar{r} \times \bar{v}$.

$$(\textbf{Ans. } (ii) \ 4n\sin 2nt, \ (iii) \ n(2\bar{i} + 7\bar{j} - 10\bar{k}))$$

5. A particle describes the straight line $r = a \sec \theta$ with constant angular velocity ω. Find the radial and transverse components of velocity and acceleration.

(**Ans.** (i) $a\omega \sec \theta \tan \theta$, $a\omega \sec \theta$,   (ii) $2\, a\omega^2 \sec \theta \tan^2 \theta$, $2\, a\omega^2 \sec \theta \tan \theta$)

6. A particle describes the following curves : (i) $\dfrac{l}{r} = 1 + e \cos \theta$,   (ii) $r^2 = a^2 \cos 2\theta$

under the action of a force directed towards the pole. Find the law of force in each case.

(**Ans.** (i) $F \propto r^{-2}$,   (ii) $F \propto r^{-7}$)

7. Find the tangential and normal components of acceleration at any time t for the curve

$$\bar{r} = at \cos t \ \bar{i} + at \sin t \ \bar{j}.$$

$$\left(\textbf{Ans. } \frac{at}{\sqrt{1 + t^2}}, \ \frac{a\,(t^2 + 2)}{\sqrt{1 + t^2}}\right)$$

8. The vector $\bar{r}$ satisfies the equation

$$m \frac{d^2 \bar{r}}{dt^2} = e \bar{E} + \frac{e}{c} \frac{d\bar{r}}{dt} \times \bar{H}, \text{ where } \bar{E} = E\bar{j}, \bar{H} = H \bar{k}. \text{ Find the solution satisfying the}$$

conditions $\bar{r} = \dfrac{d\bar{r}}{dt} = 0$ at $t = 0$, where e, m, c, E and H are constants.

9. If $\bar{r} \cdot \dfrac{d\bar{r}}{dt} = 0$, then show that $\bar{r}$ has constant magnitude.

10. A particle moves along the curve $x = a \cos t$, $y = a \sin t$, $z = bt$ with constant angular velocity ω. Find the radial and transverse components of its linear velocity and acceleration at any time t.

$$\left(\textbf{Ans. } \frac{b^2 t}{\sqrt{a^2 + b^2\ t^2}}, \ \omega \sqrt{a^2 + b^2 t^2} \ ; \ \frac{a^2 b^2}{(a^2 + b^2 t^2)^{3/2}} - \omega^2 \sqrt{a^2 + b^2 t^2}, \ \frac{2b^2 t\ \omega}{\sqrt{a^2 + b^2 t^2}}\right)$$

11. An electron moves such that its velocity is always perpendicular to its radius vector. Show that its path is a circle.

12. A particle describes an ellipse $\dfrac{l}{r} = 1 + e \cos \theta$ with uniform angular velocity ω. Show that when the particle is at one end of latus rectum through the pole, the component of acceleration towards the pole is $(1 - 2e^2)\, \omega^2 l$.

13. Prove that $\dfrac{d}{dt}\left(\bar{v} \cdot \dfrac{d\bar{v}}{dt} \times \dfrac{d^2 \bar{v}}{dt^2}\right) = \bar{v} \cdot \dfrac{d\bar{v}}{dt} \times \dfrac{d^3 \bar{v}}{dt^3}.$ (**May 2005**)

14. If $\bar{r} = \bar{a}\, e^{mt} + \bar{b}\, e^{nt}$, where $\bar{a},\ \bar{b}$ are constant vectors, show that $\bar{r}$ satisfies the differential equation $\dfrac{d^2\bar{r}}{dt^2} - (m + n)\dfrac{d\bar{r}}{dt} + mn\,\bar{r} = 0$.

15. Show that tangent at any point on the curve $x = e^t \cos t,\ \ y = e^t \sin t,\ z = e^t$ makes constant angle with z-axis.   **(Dec. 2007, May 2012)**

$$\textbf{(Ans. } \phi = \cos^{-1}\tfrac{1}{\sqrt{3}})$$

16. If $\bar{r}(t) = t^2\,\bar{i} + t\,\bar{j} - 2t^3\,\bar{k}$, then evaluate $\displaystyle\int_1^2 \bar{r} \times \dfrac{d^2\bar{r}}{dt^2}\, dt$.

$$\textbf{(Ans. } -28\,\bar{i} + 30\,\bar{j} - 3\,\bar{k})$$

17. If $\bar{r} = \bar{a}\, \sinh t + \bar{b}\, \cosh t$, then prove that   **(May 2007)**

(i) $\dfrac{d^2\bar{r}}{dt^2} = \bar{r}$ (ii) $\dfrac{d\bar{r}}{dt} \times \dfrac{d^2\bar{r}}{dt^2} = $ constant   (iii) $\bar{r} \cdot \dfrac{d\bar{r}}{dt} \times \dfrac{d^2\bar{r}}{dt^2} = 0$

18. The position vector of a particle at time t is

$$\bar{r} = \cos(t - 1)\,\bar{i} + \sinh(t - 1)\,\bar{j} + mt^3\,\bar{k}$$

Find the condition imposed on m by requiring that at time $t = 1$, the acceleration is normal to the position vector.   **(May 2008, Dec. 2011)**

$$\textbf{(Ans. } m = \tfrac{1}{\sqrt{6}})$$

19. Prove that if a particle moves always on the surface of the sphere

(i) $\bar{r} \cdot \bar{a} + \bar{V} \cdot \bar{V} = 0$ (ii) $\bar{r} \cdot \bar{a} \le 0$

20. If a particle P moves along the curve $r = ae^\theta$ with constant angular velocity ω, then show that the radial and transverse components of its velocity are equal and its acceleration is always perpendicular to radius vector and is equal to $2\,r\,\omega^2$.

MULTIPLE CHOICE QUESTIONS (MCQ's)

Type : Vector Differentiation

1. If $\bar{r}(t)$ is position vector of a point on the curve C where t is a scalar variable then $\dfrac{d\bar{r}}{dt}$ represents   (1)

     (A) Tangent vector   (B) Normal vector

     (C) Radius vector   (D) Orthogonal vector

2. If $\bar{r}(t) = x(t)\,\bar{i} + y(t)\,\bar{j} + z(t)\,\bar{k}$ be the position vector of a particle moving along the curve at time t then $\dfrac{d\bar{r}}{dt}$ represents (1)

   (A) Acceleration vector   (B) Velocity vector

   (C) Radius vector   (D) Normal vector

3. If $\bar{r}(t) = x(t)\,\bar{i} + y(t)\,\bar{j} + z(t)\,\bar{k}$ be the position vector of a particle moving along the curve at time t then $\dfrac{d^2\bar{r}}{dt^2}$ represents (1)

   (A) Radius vector   (B) Velocity vector

   (C) Acceleration vector   (D) Orthogonal vector

4. For vector function $\bar{u}(t)$ and $\bar{v}(t)$, $\dfrac{d}{dt}(\bar{u}\cdot\bar{v}) =$ (1)

   (A) $\bar{u}\cdot\dfrac{d\bar{v}}{dt} - \dfrac{d\bar{u}}{dt}\cdot\bar{v}$ (B) $\bar{u}\times\dfrac{d\bar{v}}{dt} + \dfrac{d\bar{u}}{dt}\times\bar{v}$

   (C) $\bar{u}\cdot\dfrac{d\bar{u}}{dt} + \dfrac{d\bar{v}}{dt}\cdot\bar{v}$ (D) $\bar{u}\cdot\dfrac{d\bar{v}}{dt} + \dfrac{d\bar{u}}{dt}\cdot\bar{v}$

5. For vector functiosn $\bar{u}(t)$ and $\bar{v}(t)$, $\dfrac{d}{dt}(\bar{u}\times\bar{v}) =$ (1)

   (A) $\bar{v}\times\dfrac{d\bar{u}}{dt} + \dfrac{d\bar{v}}{dt}\times\bar{u}$ (B) $\dfrac{d\bar{u}}{dt}\times\bar{v} + \bar{u}\times\dfrac{d\bar{v}}{dt}$

   (C) $\dfrac{d\bar{v}}{dt}\times\bar{v} - \bar{u}\times\dfrac{d\bar{v}}{dt}$ (D) $\bar{u}\cdot\dfrac{d\bar{v}}{dt} + \dfrac{d\bar{u}}{dt}\cdot\bar{v}$

6. For vector functions $\bar{u}(t)$, $\bar{v}(t)$ and $\bar{w}(t)$, $\dfrac{d}{dt}[\bar{u}\cdot(\bar{v}\times\bar{w})] =$ (1)

   (A) $\dfrac{d\bar{u}}{dt}\cdot(\bar{v}\times\bar{w}) - \bar{u}\cdot\left(\dfrac{d\bar{v}}{dt}\times\bar{w}\right) - \bar{u}\cdot\left(\bar{v}\times\dfrac{d\bar{w}}{dt}\right)$

   (B) $\dfrac{d\bar{u}}{dt}\times(\bar{v}\times\bar{w}) + \bar{u}\times\left(\dfrac{d\bar{v}}{dt}\times\bar{w}\right) + \bar{u}\times\left(\bar{v}\times\dfrac{d\bar{w}}{dt}\right)$

   (C) $\dfrac{d\bar{u}}{dt}\cdot(\bar{v}\times\bar{w}) + \bar{u}\cdot\left(\dfrac{d\bar{v}}{dt}\times\bar{w}\right) + \bar{u}\cdot\left(\bar{v}\times\dfrac{d\bar{w}}{dt}\right)$

   (D) $\dfrac{d\bar{u}}{dt}\cdot(\bar{w}\times\bar{v}) + \bar{u}\cdot\left(\dfrac{d\bar{v}}{dt}\times\bar{w}\right) + \bar{u}\cdot\left(\dfrac{d\bar{w}}{dt}\times\bar{v}\right)$

7. For vector functions $\bar{u}(t)$, $\bar{v}(t)$ and $\bar{w}(t)$, $\dfrac{d}{dt}\left[\bar{u}\times(\bar{v}\times\bar{w})\right] =$ (1)

(A) $\dfrac{d\bar{u}}{dt}\times(\bar{v}\times\bar{w}) + \bar{u}\times\left(\dfrac{d\bar{v}}{dt}\times\bar{w}\right) + \bar{u}\times\left(\bar{v}\times\dfrac{d\bar{w}}{dt}\right)$

(B) $\dfrac{d\bar{u}}{dt}\cdot(\bar{v}\times\bar{w}) + \bar{u}\cdot\left(\dfrac{d\bar{v}}{dt}\times\bar{w}\right) + \bar{u}\cdot\left(\bar{v}\times\dfrac{d\bar{w}}{dt}\right)$

(C) $\dfrac{d\bar{u}}{dt}\times(\bar{w}\times\bar{v}) + \bar{u}\times\left(\bar{w}\times\dfrac{d\bar{v}}{dt}\right) + \bar{u}\times\left(\dfrac{d\bar{w}}{dt}\times\bar{v}\right)$

(D) $\dfrac{d\bar{u}}{dt}\times(\bar{w}\times\bar{v}) + \left(\dfrac{d\bar{v}}{dt}\times\bar{w}\right)\times\bar{u} + \left(\dfrac{d\bar{w}}{dt}\times\bar{v}\right)\times\bar{u}$

8. For scalar function $s(t)$ and vector functions $\bar{u}(t)$, $\dfrac{d}{dt}\left[s(t)\,\bar{u}(t)\right] =$ (1)

(A) $\dfrac{ds}{dt}\cdot\bar{u} + s\cdot\dfrac{d\bar{u}}{dt}$ (B) $\dfrac{ds}{dt}\bar{u} - s\dfrac{d\bar{u}}{dt}$

(C) $\dfrac{\dfrac{ds}{dt}\bar{u} - s\dfrac{d\bar{u}}{dt}}{s^2}$ (D) $\dfrac{ds}{dt}\bar{u} + s\dfrac{d\bar{u}}{dt}$

9. If $\bar{r} = r\cos\theta\,\bar{i} + r\sin\theta\,\bar{j}$, then $\hat{r}$ is given by   (1)

(A) $\cos\theta\,\bar{i} + \sin\theta\,\bar{j}$ (B) $\sin\theta\,\bar{i} + \sec\theta\,\bar{j}$

(C) $\cos\theta\,\bar{i} + \operatorname{cosec}\theta\,\bar{j}$ (D) $\tan\theta\,\bar{i} + \cos\theta\,\bar{j}$

10. A curve is given by $x = t^2 + 1$, $y = 4t - 3$, $z = 2t^2 - 6t$. Tangent vectors to the curve at $t = 1$ and $t = 2$ are   (2)

(A) $2\bar{i} + 4\bar{j} + 2\bar{k},\ 2\bar{i} + 4\bar{j} + \bar{k}$ (B) $2\bar{i} + 4\bar{j} - 2\bar{k},\ 4\bar{i} + 4\bar{j} + 2\bar{k}$

(C) $2\bar{i} + 4\bar{j} - 2\bar{k},\ 2\bar{i} + 4\bar{j} - 2\bar{k}$ (D) $3\bar{i} + 4\bar{j} + 2\bar{k},\ 5\bar{i} + 4\bar{j} - 2\bar{k}$

11. A curve is given by $\bar{r} = (t^3 + 2)\,\bar{i} + (4t - 5)\,\bar{j} + (2t^2 - 6t)\,\bar{k}$. Tangent vectors to the curve at $t = 0$ and $t = 2$ are   (2)

(A) $3\bar{i} + 4\bar{j} - 6\bar{k},\ 6\bar{i} + 4\bar{j} + 2\bar{k}$ (B) $3\bar{i} - 6\bar{k},\ 12\bar{i} + 4\bar{j} + 2\bar{k}$

(C) $4\bar{j} - 6\bar{k},\ 12\bar{i} + 4\bar{j} + 2\bar{k}$ (D) $4\bar{j} - 6\bar{k},\ 12\bar{i} + 2\bar{k}$

12. A curve is given by $\bar{r} = 2t^2\,\bar{i} + (t^2 - 4t)\,\bar{j} + (2t - 5)\,\bar{k}$. Tangent vectors to the curve at $t = 1$ and $t = 3$ are   (1)

(A) $2\bar{i} - 2\bar{j} + 2\bar{k},\ 3\bar{i} + 2\bar{j} + 2\bar{k}$

(B) $4\bar{i} + 2\bar{j} + 2\bar{k},\ 12\bar{i} - 2\bar{j} + 2\bar{k}$

(C) $4\bar{i} - 2\bar{j},\ 12\bar{i} + 2\bar{j}$

(D) $4\bar{i} - 2\bar{j} + 2\bar{k},\ 12\bar{i} + 2\bar{j} + 2\bar{k}$

13. The tangent vector to the curve $x = a \cos t$, $y = a \sin t$, $z = at \tan \alpha$ at $t = \dfrac{\pi}{4}$, where a and α are constants is   (2)

(A) $-\dfrac{a}{\sqrt{2}}\,\bar{i} + \dfrac{a}{\sqrt{2}}\,\bar{j} + a \tan \alpha\,\bar{k}$

(B) $\dfrac{a}{\sqrt{2}}\,\bar{i} - \dfrac{a}{\sqrt{2}}\,\bar{j} + a \tan \alpha\,\bar{k}$

(C) $-\dfrac{a}{2}\,\bar{i} + \dfrac{a}{2}\,\bar{j} + a \tan \alpha\,\bar{k}$

(D) $-\dfrac{a}{\sqrt{2}}\,\bar{i} + \dfrac{a}{\sqrt{2}}\,\bar{j} + \alpha\,\bar{k}$

14. A curve is given by $\bar{r} = (e^t \cos t)\,\bar{i} + (e^t \sin t)\,\bar{j} + (e^t)\,\bar{k}$. Tangent vector to the curve at $t = 0$ is   (2)

(A) $-\bar{i} - \bar{j} - \bar{k}$

(B) $\bar{j} + \bar{k}$

(C) $2\bar{i} + 2\bar{j} + \bar{k}$

(D) $\bar{i} + \bar{j} + \bar{k}$

15. For the curve $\bar{r} = e^{-t}\,\bar{i} + \log(t^2 + 1)\,\bar{j} - \tan t\,\bar{k}$, velocity and acceleration vectors at $t = 0$ are   (2)

(A) $\bar{i} + 2\bar{j} - \bar{k},\ \bar{i} + 2\bar{j}$

(B) $\bar{i} + \bar{k},\ \bar{i} + 2\bar{j}$

(C) $-\bar{i} - \bar{k},\ \bar{i} + 2\bar{j}$

(D) $-\bar{i} - \bar{k},\ \bar{i} - 2\bar{k}$

16. For the curve $x = t^3 + 1$, $y = t^2$, $z = t$, velocity and acceleration vectors at $t = 1$ are   (2)

(A) $4\bar{i} + 2\bar{j},\ 6\bar{i} + 2\bar{j}$

(B) $3\bar{i} + 2\bar{j} + \bar{k},\ 6\bar{i} + 2\bar{j}$

(C) $2\bar{i} + 2\bar{j} + \bar{k},\ 3\bar{i} + 2\bar{j}$

(D) $3\bar{i} + 2\bar{j},\ 6\bar{i} + \bar{j}$

17. For the curve $x = t$, $y = t^2$, $z = t^3$, angle between tangents at $t = 0$ and $t = 1$ is given by   (1)

(A) $\dfrac{\pi}{2}$

(B) $\cos^{-1}\dfrac{1}{\sqrt{5}}$

(C) $\cos^{-1}\dfrac{1}{3}$

(D) $\cos^{-1}\left(\dfrac{1}{\sqrt{14}}\right)$

18. Angle between tangents $\overline{T}_1 = 2\overline{i} + 4\overline{j} - 2\overline{k}$, $\overline{T}_2 = 4\overline{i} + 4\overline{j} + 2\overline{k}$ to the curve $x = t^2 + 1$, $y = 4t - 3$, $z = 2t^2 - 6t$ at $t = 1$ and $t = 2$ is   (2)

(A) $\cos^{-1}\left(\dfrac{5}{\sqrt{6}}\right)$ (B) $\cos^{-1}\left(\dfrac{1}{3\sqrt{6}}\right)$

(C) $\cos^{-1}\left(\dfrac{5}{3\sqrt{6}}\right)$ (D) $\tan^{-1}\left(\dfrac{5}{3\sqrt{6}}\right)$

19. Angle between tangents to the curve $x = 2t^2$, $y = t^2 - 4t$, $z = 2t - 5$ at $t = 0$ and $t = 1$ is   (2)

(A) $\cos^{-1}\left(\dfrac{12}{\sqrt{6}\,\sqrt{5}}\right)$ (B) $\cos^{-1}\left(\dfrac{3}{\sqrt{6}\,\sqrt{5}}\right)$

(C) $\cos^{-1}\left(\dfrac{3}{\sqrt{5}}\right)$ (D) $\tan^{-1}\left(\dfrac{3}{\sqrt{6}\,\sqrt{5}}\right)$

20. Angle between tangent to the curve $\overline{r} = (e^t \cos t)\,\overline{i} + (e^t \sin t)\,\overline{j} + (e^t)\,\overline{k}$ at $t = 0$ and z axis is given by   (2)

(A) $\cos^{-1}\left(\dfrac{1}{\sqrt{3}}\right)$ (B) $\cos^{-1}\left(\dfrac{2}{\sqrt{3}}\right)$

(C) $\cos^{-1}\left(\sqrt{3}\right)$ (D) $\dfrac{\pi}{2}$

21. If $\overline{r} = \overline{a}\,e^{5t} + \overline{b}\,e^{-5t}$ where $\overline{a}$ and $\overline{b}$ are constant vectors then $\dfrac{d^2\overline{r}}{dt^2} - 25\overline{r}$ is equal to   (2)

(A) 1   (B) 2

(C) zero   (D) 5

22. If $\overline{r} = \overline{a}\cos 2t + \overline{b}\sin 2t$ where $\overline{a}$ and $\overline{b}$ are constant vectors then $\dfrac{d^2\overline{r}}{dt^2}$ is equal to   (2)

(A) $-4\overline{r}$ (B) $4\overline{r}$

(C) $-\overline{r}$ (D) $\overline{r}$

23. If $\overline{r} = at\cos t\,\overline{i} + bt\sin t\,\overline{j}$ where a and b are constants then $\dfrac{d^2\overline{r}}{dt^2}$ at $t = 0$ is equal to   (2)

(A) $2b\overline{j}$ (B) $-2a\overline{i}$

(C) $a\overline{i} + b\overline{j}$ (D) $\overline{0}$

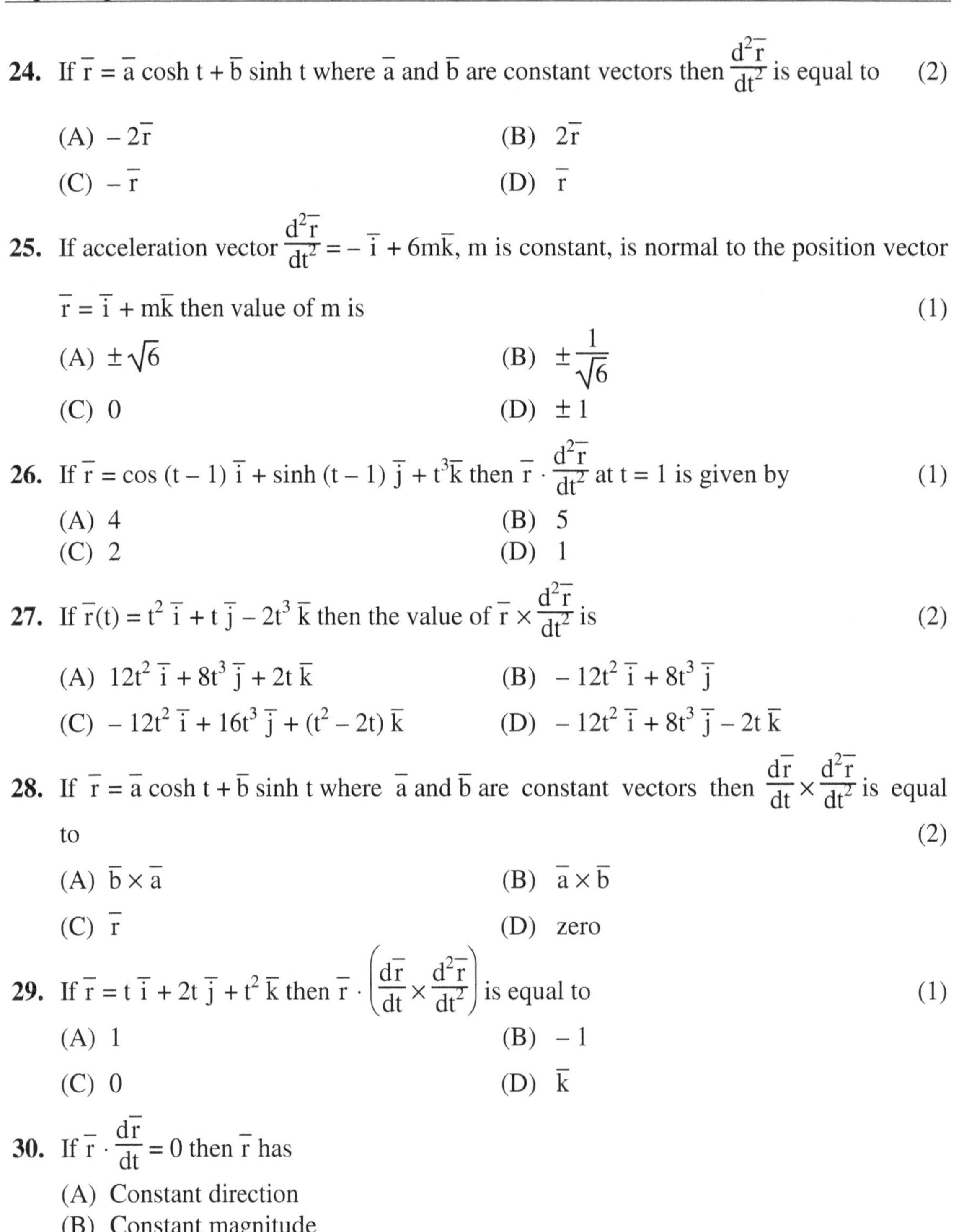

24. If $\bar{r} = \bar{a}\cosh t + \bar{b}\sinh t$ where $\bar{a}$ and $\bar{b}$ are constant vectors then $\dfrac{d^2\bar{r}}{dt^2}$ is equal to   (2)

    (A) $-2\bar{r}$ (B) $2\bar{r}$

    (C) $-\bar{r}$ (D) $\bar{r}$

25. If acceleration vector $\dfrac{d^2\bar{r}}{dt^2} = -\,\bar{i} + 6m\bar{k}$, m is constant, is normal to the position vector

$\bar{r} = \bar{i} + m\bar{k}$ then value of m is   (1)

    (A) $\pm\sqrt{6}$ (B) $\pm\dfrac{1}{\sqrt{6}}$

    (C) 0 (D) ± 1

26. If $\bar{r} = \cos(t-1)\,\bar{i} + \sinh(t-1)\,\bar{j} + t^3\bar{k}$ then $\bar{r}\cdot\dfrac{d^2\bar{r}}{dt^2}$ at $t = 1$ is given by   (1)

    (A) 4   (B) 5

    (C) 2   (D) 1

27. If $\bar{r}(t) = t^2\,\bar{i} + t\,\bar{j} - 2t^3\,\bar{k}$ then the value of $\bar{r}\times\dfrac{d^2\bar{r}}{dt^2}$ is   (2)

    (A) $12t^2\,\bar{i} + 8t^3\,\bar{j} + 2t\,\bar{k}$ (B) $-12t^2\,\bar{i} + 8t^3\,\bar{j}$

    (C) $-12t^2\,\bar{i} + 16t^3\,\bar{j} + (t^2 - 2t)\,\bar{k}$ (D) $-12t^2\,\bar{i} + 8t^3\,\bar{j} - 2t\,\bar{k}$

28. If $\bar{r} = \bar{a}\cosh t + \bar{b}\sinh t$ where $\bar{a}$ and $\bar{b}$ are constant vectors then $\dfrac{d\bar{r}}{dt}\times\dfrac{d^2\bar{r}}{dt^2}$ is equal to   (2)

    (A) $\bar{b}\times\bar{a}$ (B) $\bar{a}\times\bar{b}$

    (C) $\bar{r}$ (D) zero

29. If $\bar{r} = t\,\bar{i} + 2t\,\bar{j} + t^2\,\bar{k}$ then $\bar{r}\cdot\left(\dfrac{d\bar{r}}{dt}\times\dfrac{d^2\bar{r}}{dt^2}\right)$ is equal to   (1)

    (A) 1   (B) -1

    (C) 0   (D) $\bar{k}$

30. If $\bar{r}\cdot\dfrac{d\bar{r}}{dt} = 0$ then $\bar{r}$ has

    (A) Constant direction
    (B) Constant magnitude
    (C) Both constant magnitude and direction
    (D) None of these

31. An electron moves such that its velocity is always perpendicular to its radius vector then its path is   (2)

(A) Ellipse

(B) Hyperbola

(C) Straight line

(D) Circle

32. $\dfrac{d}{dt}\left[\bar{r}\cdot\left(\dfrac{d\bar{r}}{dt}\times\dfrac{d^2\bar{r}}{dt^2}\right)\right] =$ (2)

(A) $\left(\dfrac{d\bar{r}}{dt}\times\dfrac{d^2\bar{r}}{dt^3}\right)$

(B) $\bar{r}\cdot\left(\dfrac{d^2\bar{r}}{dt^2}\times\dfrac{d^3\bar{r}}{dt^3}\right)$

(C) $\bar{r}\cdot\left(\dfrac{d\bar{r}}{dt}\times\dfrac{d^3\bar{r}}{dt^3}\right)$

(D) 0

33. If $\dfrac{d\bar{u}}{dt} = \bar{w}\times\bar{u}$ and $\dfrac{d\bar{v}}{dt} = \bar{w}\times\bar{v}$ then $\dfrac{d}{dt}(\bar{u}\times\bar{v}) =$ (2)

(A) $(\bar{v}\cdot\bar{w})\,\bar{u} - (\bar{u}\cdot\bar{w})\,\bar{v}$

(B) $(\bar{v}\cdot\bar{w})\,\bar{u} + (\bar{v}\cdot\bar{w})\,\bar{u}$

(C) $(\bar{u}\cdot\bar{w})\,\bar{v} - (\bar{u}\cdot\bar{v})\,\bar{w}$

(D) $(\bar{v}\cdot\bar{w})\,\bar{u} + (\bar{u}\cdot\bar{v})\,\bar{w}$

34. If $\bar{a}$ is a constant vector then $\dfrac{d}{dt}\left[r^3\bar{r} + \bar{a}\times\dfrac{d^2\bar{r}}{dt^2}\right] =$ (2)

(A) $r^3\dfrac{d\bar{r}}{dt} + \bar{a}\times\dfrac{d^2\bar{r}}{dt^2}$

(B) $3r^2\dfrac{dr}{dt}\,\bar{r} + r^3\dfrac{d\bar{r}}{dt} + \bar{a}\times\dfrac{d^3\bar{r}}{dt^3}$

(C) $3r^2\,\bar{r} + r^3\dfrac{d\bar{r}}{dt}$

(D) $r^2\,\bar{r} + r^2\dfrac{d\bar{r}}{dt} + \bar{a}\times\dfrac{d^2\bar{r}}{dt^2}$

35. If $\bar{v} = t^2\,\bar{i} + 2t\,\bar{j} + (4t-5)\,\bar{k}$ then the value of $\bar{v}\cdot\left(\dfrac{d\bar{v}}{dt}\times\dfrac{d^2\bar{v}}{dt^2}\right)$ is   (2)

(A) $t^2 - 4t + 5$

(B) 10

(C) $16t + 10$

(D) 20

36. If $\bar{r} = t^2\,\bar{i} + t\,\bar{j}$, value of $\displaystyle\int_0^1\left(\bar{r}\times\dfrac{d\bar{r}}{dt}\right)dt$ is given by   (1)

(A) $\bar{i} + \bar{j}$

(B) $-\dfrac{1}{3}\bar{k}$

(C) $\dfrac{2}{3}(\bar{i} + \bar{k})$

(D) $(\bar{i} - \bar{k})$

Answers

1. (A)	2. (B)	3. (C)	4. (D)	5. (B)	6. (C)	7. (A)	8. (D)
9. (A)	10. (B)	11. (C)	12. (D)	13. (A)	14. (D)	15. (C)	16. (B)
17. (D)	18. (C)	19. (B)	20. (A)	21. (C)	22. (A)	23. (A)	24. (D)
25. (B)	26.(B)	27. (D)	28. (A)	29. (C)	30. (B)	31. (D)	32. (C)
33. (A)	34. (B)	35. (D)	36. (B)				

10.3 GRADIENT, DIVERGENCE AND CURL

Before we define these quantities which are so often encountered in vector analysis, we shall introduce certain terms.

(i) Scalar point function : If a scalar quantity ϕ depends for its value on its position say (x, y, z) in space, then ϕ (x, y, z) is called scalar point function. Pressure in a fluid usually varies according to its depth, hence p (x, y, z) is a scalar point function. Temperature, density, potential etc. are other examples of a scalar point functions, as these quantities usually take different values at different points.

(ii) Vector point function : If a vector quantity $\overline{F}$ depends for its value on its position (x, y, z) in space, then $\overline{F}$ (x, y, z) is called vector point function. Velocity, Force, Electric Intensity etc. are examples of vector point functions.

In dealing with scalar point function ϕ (x, y, z) and vector point function $\overline{F}$ (x, y, z), following operations of differential calculus are found quite useful.

$$d\phi = \frac{\partial \phi}{\partial x} dx + \frac{\partial \phi}{\partial y} dy + \frac{\partial \phi}{\partial z} dz \qquad\qquad \frac{\partial \phi}{\partial s} = \frac{\partial \phi}{\partial x} \frac{\partial x}{\partial s} + \frac{\partial \phi}{\partial y} \frac{\partial y}{\partial s} + \frac{\partial \phi}{\partial z} \frac{\partial z}{\partial s}$$

$$d\overline{F} = \frac{\partial \overline{F}}{\partial x} dx + \frac{\partial \overline{F}}{\partial y} dy + \frac{\partial \overline{F}}{\partial z} dz \qquad\qquad \frac{\partial \overline{F}}{\partial s} = \frac{\partial \overline{F}}{\partial x} \frac{\partial x}{\partial s} + \frac{\partial \overline{F}}{\partial y} \frac{\partial y}{\partial s} + \frac{\partial \overline{F}}{\partial z} \frac{\partial z}{\partial s}$$

If required these results can be converted into spherical polar or cylindrical co-ordinate system.

(iii) Level surface : Let scalar point function ϕ (x, y, z) be continuous and is defined in a certain region of space. *The surface drawn in space containing all those points where ϕ (x, y, z) has same value is called a level surface.* Equipotential or isothermal surfaces are examples of level surface.

(iv) Operator 'Del' or 'Nabla' (∇) : The vector differential operator $\overline{i} \dfrac{\partial}{\partial x} + \overline{j} \dfrac{\partial}{\partial y} + \overline{k} \dfrac{\partial}{\partial z}$ is denoted by the symbol ∇ called **Del** or **Nabla**. When it operates on a scalar point function ϕ (x, y, z), we get a vector quantity $\nabla \phi = \overline{i} \dfrac{\partial \phi}{\partial x} + \overline{j} \dfrac{\partial \phi}{\partial y} + \overline{k} \dfrac{\partial \phi}{\partial z}$, called Gradient of the scalar point function ϕ (x, y, z). This is also written as Gradient ϕ or simply Grad ϕ.

$$\therefore \qquad \text{Grad } \phi = \nabla \phi = \overline{i} \frac{\partial \phi}{\partial x} + \overline{j} \frac{\partial \phi}{\partial y} + \overline{k} \frac{\partial \phi}{\partial z}$$

Consider
$$\overline{r} = x\,\overline{i} + y\,\overline{j} + z\,\overline{k}$$

$$\therefore \qquad d\overline{r} \equiv \overline{i}\, dx + \overline{j}\, dy + \overline{k}\, dz$$

$$\nabla \phi \cdot d\overline{r} \equiv \left(\overline{i} \frac{\partial \phi}{\partial x} + \overline{j} \frac{\partial \phi}{\partial y} + \overline{k} \frac{\partial \phi}{\partial z} \right) \cdot (\overline{i}\, dx + \overline{j}\, dy + \overline{k}\, dz)$$

$$\equiv \frac{\partial \phi}{\partial x} dx + \frac{\partial \phi}{\partial y} dy + \frac{\partial \phi}{\partial z} dz \equiv d\phi$$

This result has many useful applications. To interpret Gradient or $\nabla\phi$ physically, consider the level surfaces through $P(\bar{r})$ and $Q\,(\bar{r} + \delta\bar{r})$ where scalar function has values ϕ and $\phi + \delta\phi$ respectively (See Fig. 10.5).

$$\overrightarrow{PQ} = \bar{r} + \delta\bar{r} - \bar{r} = \delta\bar{r}$$

$$\left|\overrightarrow{PQ}\right| = \delta r.$$

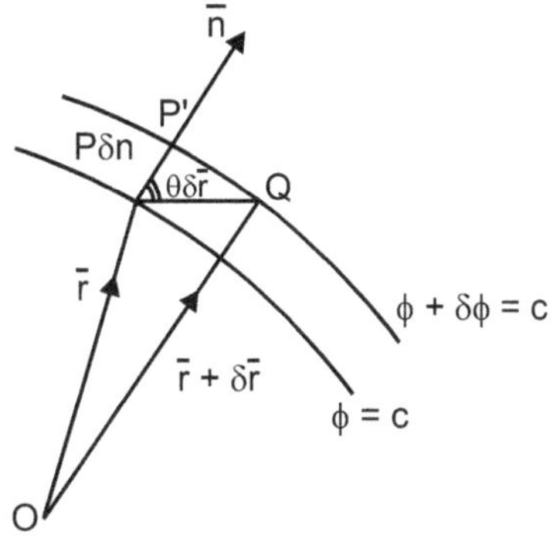

Fig. 10.5

Let $\bar{n}$ be a vector normal to the level surface $\phi = c$ at P, $\hat{n}$ be a unit vector in the same direction.

Let θ be the angle between vectors $\delta\bar{r}$ and $\hat{n}$ and let PP' $= \delta n$, then $\dfrac{\partial\phi}{\partial r}$ represents the rate of change of ϕ along the direction $\overrightarrow{PQ}$ and $\dfrac{\partial\phi}{\partial n}$ the rate of change of ϕ along the direction of normal $\hat{n}$.

We can easily see that rate of change of ϕ is maximum along the normal direction.

For
$$\frac{\delta\phi}{\delta r} = \frac{\delta\phi}{\delta n} \cdot \frac{\delta n}{\delta r} = \frac{\delta\phi}{\delta n} \cos\theta$$

$$\lim \frac{\delta\phi}{\delta r} = \frac{\partial\phi}{\partial r} \text{ and } \lim \frac{\delta\phi}{\delta n} = \frac{\partial\phi}{\partial n}$$

Above relation clearly shows that

$$\frac{\partial\phi}{\partial r} \leq \frac{\partial\phi}{\partial n}, \text{ as } \cos\theta \leq 1$$

Since PP' $= \delta n =$ projection of PQ along the normal

We have
$$dn \equiv \hat{n} \cdot d\bar{r}$$

Writing
$$d\phi \equiv \frac{\partial\phi}{\partial n}\, dn \equiv \frac{\partial\phi}{\partial n}\,(\hat{n} \cdot d\bar{r})$$

But
$$d\phi \equiv \nabla\phi \cdot d\bar{r}$$

$\therefore$
$$\nabla\phi \cdot d\bar{r} \equiv \frac{\partial\phi}{\partial n}\,\hat{n} \cdot d\bar{r}$$

Thus
$$\nabla\phi = \frac{\partial\phi}{\partial n}\,\hat{n}$$

Which shows that $\nabla\phi$ (grad ϕ) represents maximum rate of change of ϕ, which is along the outward drawn normal to the level surface, $\phi = $ constant.

$\dfrac{\partial\phi}{\partial r}$ represents rate of change of ϕ in any other direction and is termed as **directional derivative**. Among all the directional derivatives, $|\nabla\phi| = \dfrac{\partial\phi}{\partial n}$ has the maximum value.

It is also clear that the directional derivative of ϕ along $\overrightarrow{PQ}$ is the scalar resolute of $\nabla\phi$ in that direction. The directional derivative of ϕ along certain direction $\bar{a}$ is given by $\nabla\phi \cdot \hat{a}$.

By virtue of its definition, the vector differential operator ∇ behaves like ordinary differential operator $D = \dfrac{d}{dx}$.

Following deductions follow from the definition :

For any scalars u and v

(i) $\nabla (u + v) = \nabla u + \nabla v$ (ii) $\nabla (u - v) = \nabla u - \nabla v$

(iii) $\nabla (uv) = u\nabla v + v\nabla u$ (iv) $\nabla \left(\dfrac{u}{v}\right) = \dfrac{v\nabla u - u\nabla v}{v^2}$

(v) $\nabla [f(u)] = f'(u)\, \nabla u$ (vi) $\nabla (au) = a\nabla u.$

ILLUSTRATIONS

Ex. 1 : *Find $\nabla\phi$ for (i) $\phi = x^2 + y^2 + z^2$ at (1, 1, 1).*

(ii) $\phi = r^m$, where $\bar{r} = x\,\bar{i} + y\,\bar{j} + z\,\bar{k}$

(iii) $\phi = e^{-r}\, r^3$,   (iv) $\nabla f(r) = \dfrac{f'(r)}{r}\,\bar{r}$, where $\bar{r} = x\,\bar{i} + y\,\bar{j} + z\,\bar{k}$.   **(Dec. 2006)**

Sol. : (i) $\phi = x^2 + y^2 + z^2$

$$\frac{\partial\phi}{\partial x} = 2x,\ \frac{\partial\phi}{\partial y} = 2y,\ \frac{\partial\phi}{\partial z} = 2z.$$

$$\nabla\phi = \bar{i}\,\frac{\partial\phi}{\partial x} + \bar{j}\,\frac{\partial\phi}{\partial y} + \bar{k}\,\frac{\partial\phi}{\partial z} = (2x\,\bar{i} + 2y\,\bar{j} + 2z\,\bar{k})$$

$\therefore$ $\{\nabla\phi\}_{(1,1,1)} = 2\,\bar{i} + 2\,\bar{j} + 2\,\bar{k},$ [putting $x = y = z = 1$]

(ii) $\phi = r^m$, $\bar{r} = x\,\bar{i} + y\,\bar{j} + z\,\bar{k}$,

$$r = \sqrt{x^2 + y^2 + z^2} \qquad\qquad \frac{\partial\phi}{\partial x} = mr^{m-1}\frac{\partial r}{\partial x}$$

$$\frac{\partial r}{\partial x} = \frac{1.2x}{2\sqrt{x^2 + y^2 + z^2}} = \frac{x}{r} \qquad \therefore \ \frac{\partial \phi}{\partial x} = mr^{m-1} \cdot \frac{x}{r} = mr^{m-2} \cdot x$$

Similarly,
$$\frac{\partial \phi}{\partial y} = mr^{m-2}\, y, \quad \frac{\partial \phi}{\partial z} = mr^{m-2}\, z$$

$$\nabla \phi = \bar{i}\,\frac{\partial \phi}{\partial x} + \bar{j}\,\frac{\partial \phi}{\partial y} + \bar{k}\,\frac{\partial \phi}{\partial z}$$

$$= \bar{i}\ mr^{m-2}\, x + \bar{j}\ mr^{m-2}\, y + \bar{k}\ mr^{m-2}\, z$$

$$= mr^{m-2}\,(x\,\bar{i} + y\,\bar{j} + z\,\bar{k})$$

$$\nabla \phi = mr^{m-2}\,\bar{r}$$

This is taken as a standard result.

(iii) $\phi = e^{-r}\, r^3$

$$\nabla \phi = \nabla\,(e^{-r}\, r^3)$$

$$= r^3\,\nabla\,(e^{-r}) + e^{-r}\,\nabla\,(r^3) = r^3\,(-e^{-r})\,\nabla\,(r) + e^{-r}\,3r\,\bar{r}$$

$$= -r^3\, e^{-r}\,\frac{1}{r}\,\bar{r} + 3r\, e^{-r}\,\bar{r} = e^{-r}\,\bar{r}\,(-r^2 + 3r)$$

(iv)
$$\nabla f(r) = f\,'(r)\,\nabla r \qquad\qquad \left(\because \nabla\, f(u) = f'(u)\,\nabla u \right)$$

$$= f\,'(r)\,\left(\bar{i}\,\frac{\partial r}{\partial x} + \bar{j}\,\frac{\partial r}{\partial y} + \bar{k}\,\frac{\partial r}{\partial z} \right)$$

$$= f\,'(r)\,\left(\bar{i}\,\frac{x}{r} + \bar{j}\,\frac{y}{r} + \bar{k}\,\frac{z}{r} \right)$$

$$\boxed{\nabla f(r) = \frac{f\,'(r)}{r}\,\bar{r}}\ .\ \text{This is also taken as a standard result.}$$

Ex. 2 : *Find the directional derivative of $\phi = xy^2 + yz^3$ at (1, –1, 1),* **(May 06, 2015)**

(i)   along the vector $\bar{i} + 2\,\bar{j} + 2\,\bar{k}$

(ii)   towards the point (2, 1, –1)

(iii)   along the direction normal to the surface $x^2 + y^2 + z^2 = 9$ at (1, 2, 2).

Sol. : (i) $\dfrac{\partial \phi}{\partial x} = y^2, \quad \dfrac{\partial \phi}{\partial y} = 2xy + z^3, \quad \dfrac{\partial \phi}{\partial z} = 3yz^2$

$$\nabla \phi = y^2\,\bar{i} + (2xy + z^3)\,\bar{j} + 3yz^2\,\bar{k}$$

$$[\nabla \phi]_{(1,\,-1,\,1)} = \bar{i} - \bar{j} - 3\,\bar{k}$$

$$\bar{a} = \bar{i} + 2\bar{j} + 2\bar{k}, \hat{a} = \frac{\bar{i} + 2\bar{j} + 2\bar{k}}{\sqrt{1+4+4}} = \frac{1}{3}(\bar{i} + 2\bar{j} + 2\bar{k})$$

∴ Directional derivative $= \nabla\phi \cdot \hat{a} = (\bar{i} - \bar{j} - 3\bar{k}) \cdot \frac{1}{3}(\bar{i} + 2\bar{j} + 2\bar{k})$

$$= \frac{1}{3}[1 - 2 - 6] = \frac{-7}{3}$$

(ii) $\bar{a}$ is along the line joining $(1, -1, 1)$ and $(2, 1, -1)$.

∴
$$\bar{a} = (2-1)\bar{i} + (1+1)\bar{j} + (-1-1)\bar{k} = \bar{i} + 2\bar{j} - 2\bar{k}$$

$$\hat{a} = \frac{\bar{i} + 2\bar{j} - 2\bar{k}}{\sqrt{1+4+4}} = \frac{1}{3}(\bar{i} + 2\bar{j} - 2\bar{k})$$

∴ Directional derivative $= \nabla\phi \cdot \hat{a} = (\bar{i} - \bar{j} - 3\bar{k}) \cdot \frac{1}{3}(\bar{i} + 2\bar{j} - 2\bar{k})$

$$= \frac{1}{3}(1 - 2 + 6) = \frac{5}{3}$$

(iii) $\qquad \phi_1 = x^2 + y^2 + z^2 - 9 \qquad\qquad \nabla\phi_1 = 2x\,\bar{i} + 2y\,\bar{j} + 2z\,\bar{k}$

∴ $\qquad [\nabla\phi_1]_{(1, 2, 2)} = 2\bar{i} + 4\bar{j} + 4\bar{k} \qquad\qquad \bar{a} = 2\bar{i} + 4\bar{j} + 4\bar{k}$

$$\hat{a} = \frac{2\bar{i} + 4\bar{j} + 4\bar{k}}{\sqrt{4+16+16}} = \frac{2\bar{i} + 4\bar{j} + 4\bar{k}}{6}$$

∴ Directional derivative $= \nabla\phi \cdot \hat{a} = (\bar{i} - \bar{j} - 3\bar{k}) \cdot \left(\frac{2\bar{i} + 4\bar{j} + 4\bar{k}}{6}\right)$

$$= \frac{1}{6}(2 - 4 - 12) = \frac{-14}{6} = \frac{-7}{3}$$

Ex. 3 : *If the directional derivative of $\phi = axy + byz + czx$ at $(1, 1, 1)$ has maximum magnitude 4 in a direction parallel to x-axis, find the values of a, b, c.*

(Dec. 2005, 2008, May 2008, Dec. 2011, 2014)

Sol. : $\qquad \dfrac{\partial\phi}{\partial x} = ay + cz, \quad \dfrac{\partial\phi}{\partial y} = ax + bz, \quad \dfrac{\partial\phi}{\partial z} = by + cz$

∴ $\qquad \nabla\phi = \bar{i}(ay + cz) + \bar{j}(ax + bz) + \bar{k}(by + cx)$

and $\qquad [\nabla\phi]_{(1, 1, 1)} = (a + c)\bar{i} + (a + b)\bar{j} + (b + c)\bar{k}$

Now $\quad (a + c)\bar{i} + (a + b)\bar{j} + (b + c)\bar{k} = 4\bar{i}$ (given)

$$\therefore \quad a + c = 4, \quad a + b = 0, \quad b + c = 0$$

which gives on solving $a = 2, b = -2, c = 2$.

Ex. 4 : *The directional derivative of $\phi(x, y)$ at the point A (3, 2) towards the point B (2, 3) is $3\sqrt{2}$ and towards the point C (1, 0) is $\sqrt{8}$. Find the directional derivative at the point A towards the point D (2, 4).*

Sol. : For function $\phi(x, y)$, $\nabla\phi = \bar{i}\dfrac{\partial\phi}{\partial x} + \bar{j}\dfrac{\partial\phi}{\partial y}$

$$\overrightarrow{AB} = (2-3)\,\bar{i} + (3-2)\,\bar{j} = -\bar{i} + \bar{j}$$

Directional derivative of $\phi(x, y)$ towards $\overrightarrow{AB}$ is

$$\nabla\phi \cdot \hat{AB} = \left(\bar{i}\frac{\partial\phi}{\partial x} + \bar{j}\frac{\partial\phi}{\partial y}\right) \cdot \left(\frac{-\bar{i} + \bar{j}}{\sqrt{2}}\right) = 3\sqrt{2}$$

$$\therefore \quad -\frac{\partial\phi}{\partial x} + \frac{\partial\phi}{\partial y} = 6 \qquad\qquad \dots (1)$$

Directional derivative at A (3, 2) towards C (1, 0) is

$$\nabla\phi \cdot \hat{AC} = \left(\bar{i}\frac{\partial\phi}{\partial x} + \bar{j}\frac{\partial\phi}{\partial y}\right) \cdot \frac{(-2\,\bar{i} - 2\,\bar{j})}{\sqrt{8}} = \sqrt{8}$$

$$\therefore \quad -2\frac{\partial\phi}{\partial x} - 2\frac{\partial\phi}{\partial y} = 8 \quad \text{or} \quad \frac{\partial\phi}{\partial x} + \frac{\partial\phi}{\partial y} = -4 \qquad\qquad \dots (2)$$

From (1) and (2), $\quad \dfrac{\partial\phi}{\partial y} = 1, \quad \dfrac{\partial\phi}{\partial x} = -5$

$$\therefore \quad \nabla\phi = -5\,\bar{i} + \bar{j}$$

Hence, directional derivative at A (3, 2) towards D (2, 4) is

$$\nabla\phi \cdot \hat{AD} = (-5\,\bar{i} + \bar{j}) \cdot \left(\frac{-\bar{i} + 2\,\bar{j}}{\sqrt{5}}\right) = \frac{7}{\sqrt{5}}$$

Ex. 5 : *For the function $f = x^2 y + 2y^2 x$, find the following at the point P (1, 3) :*

(i)   the direction of the greatest increase in f.

(ii)   the direction of the greatest decrease in f.

(iii) the directional derivative of f in the direction of the greatest increase in f.

(iv)   the directions in which the directional derivative is zero.

Sol. : (i) Direction of greatest increase in f is along ∇f

and
$$\nabla f = \bar{i}\frac{\partial f}{\partial x} + \bar{j}\frac{\partial f}{\partial y} = \bar{i}\,(2xy + 2y^2) + \bar{j}\,(x^2 + 4yx)$$

i.e.
$$[\nabla f]_{(1,\,3)} = 24\,\bar{i} + 13\,\bar{j}$$

(ii)   Direction of greatest decrease in f is along

$$[-\nabla f]_{(1,\,3)} = -24\,\bar{i} - 13\,\bar{j}$$

(iii)   Directional derivative of f along the direction of greatest increase in f

$$= [\nabla f]_{(1,\,3)} \cdot \frac{(24\,\bar{i} + 13\,\bar{j})}{\sqrt{(24)^2 + (13)^2}} = (24\,\bar{i} + 13\,\bar{j}) \cdot \frac{(24\,\bar{i} + 13\,\bar{j})}{\sqrt{(24)^2 + (13)^2}}$$

$$= \sqrt{(24)^2 + (13)^2} = 27.294$$

(iv)   If directional derivative is zero along $a_1\,\bar{i} + a_2\,\bar{j}$

then
$$[\nabla f]_{(1,\,3)} \cdot (a_1\,\bar{i} + a_2\,\bar{j}) = 0$$

$$(24\,\bar{i} + 13\,\bar{j}) \cdot (a_1\,\bar{i} + a_2\,\bar{j}) = 0$$

$$24\,a_1 + 13\,a_2 = 0 \qquad \therefore \ \frac{a_1}{13} = \frac{-a_2}{24}$$

$\therefore$ Directions are $\bar{u}_1 = 13\,\bar{i} - 24\,\bar{j},\ \bar{u}_2 = -13\,\bar{i} + 24\,\bar{j}$.

Ex. 6 : *In what direction from the point (2, 1, –1) is the directional derivative of* $\phi = x^2\,yz^3$ *a maximum ? What is the magnitude of this maximum ?* **(Nov. 16)**

Sol. :
$$\phi = x^2\,y\,z^3$$

$$\nabla\phi = (2xyz^3)\,\bar{i} + (x^2\,z^3)\,\bar{j} + (3x^2\,yz^2)\,\bar{k}$$

$$(\nabla\phi)_{(2,\,1,\,-1)} = -4\,\bar{i} - 4\,\bar{j} + 12\,\bar{k}$$

$\therefore$ Directional derivative of ϕ is maximum in the direction of $\nabla\phi$ i.e. in the direction of $-4\,\bar{i} - 4\,\bar{j} + 12\,\bar{k}$.

The maximum magnitude $= |\nabla\phi| = \sqrt{16 + 16 + 144} = 4\sqrt{11}$.

Ex. 7 : *Find the directional derivative of $\phi = e^{2x} \cdot \cos yz$ at (0, 0, 0) in the direction of tangent to the curve $x = a\sin t;\ y = a\cos t;\ z = at,\ at\ t = \dfrac{\pi}{4}$.* **(May 2007)**

Sol. : $\phi = e^{2x} \cos yz$

$$\nabla\phi = (2e^{2x} \cos yz)\,\bar{i} - (e^{2x} z \cdot \sin yz)\,\bar{j} - (e^{2x} y \sin yz)\,\bar{k}$$

$\therefore \quad (\nabla\phi)_{(0,\,0,\,0)} = 2\,\bar{i}$

Also, for $\quad \bar{r} = x\,\bar{i} + y\,\bar{j} + z\,\bar{k} = (a \sin t)\,\bar{i} + (a \cos t)\,\bar{j} + (at)\,\bar{k}$

tangent to the curve $= \dfrac{d\bar{r}}{dt} = (a \cos t)\,\bar{i} - a \sin t\,\bar{j} + a\,\bar{k}$

$\therefore$ At $t = \dfrac{\pi}{4}$, $\quad \dfrac{d\bar{r}}{dt} = \dfrac{a}{\sqrt{2}}\,\bar{i} - \dfrac{a}{\sqrt{2}}\,\bar{j} + a\,\bar{k} = \bar{u}$ (say)

$\therefore$ Directional derivative $= \nabla\phi \cdot \hat{u}$

$$= (2\bar{i}) \cdot \left(\frac{\dfrac{a}{\sqrt{2}}\,\bar{i} - \dfrac{a}{\sqrt{2}}\,\bar{j} + a\,\bar{k}}{\sqrt{\dfrac{a^2}{2} + \dfrac{a^2}{2} + a^2}} \right) = \frac{\sqrt{2}\,a}{\sqrt{2}\,a} = 1$$

Ex. 8 : *If directional derivative of $\phi = ax^2 y + by^2 z + cz^2 x$ at $(1, 1, 1)$ has maximum magnitude 15 in the direction parallel to $\dfrac{x-1}{2} = \dfrac{y-3}{-2} = \dfrac{z}{1}$, hence find the values of a, b, c.*   **(May 2006, 2016)**

Sol. : $\phi = ax^2 y + by^2 z + cz^2 x$

$$\nabla\phi = (2axy + cz^2)\,\bar{i} + (ax^2 + 2byz)\,\bar{j} + (by^2 + 2czx)\,\bar{k}$$

$$(\nabla\phi)_{(1,\,1,\,1)} = (2a + c)\,\bar{i} + (a + 2b)\,\bar{j} + (b + 2c)\,\bar{k}$$

Given direction is $2\,\bar{i} - 2\,\bar{j} + \bar{k}$.

$\therefore \quad \dfrac{2a + c}{2} = \dfrac{a + 2b}{2} = \dfrac{b + 2c}{1}$

Solving first two $\quad 3a + 2b + c = 0$

Solving last two $\quad a + 4b + 4c = 0$

$\therefore \quad \dfrac{a}{4} = \dfrac{b}{-11} = \dfrac{c}{10} = \lambda$ (say)

$a = 4\lambda, \quad b = -11\lambda, \quad c = 10\lambda$

$\therefore \quad 15 = |\nabla\phi| = \sqrt{(2a + c)^2 + (a + 2b)^2 + (b + 2c)^2}$

$$= \sqrt{(18\lambda)^2 + (-18\lambda)^2 + (9\lambda)^2}$$

$$15 = \pm 27 \lambda \qquad \therefore \lambda = \pm \frac{5}{9}$$

$$a = \pm \frac{20}{9}, \quad b = \pm \frac{55}{9}, \quad c = \pm \frac{50}{9}$$

Ex. 9 : *If T be the temperature at a point (x, y, z) then find the directional derivative of T at (1, 1, 1) in the direction of the vector $\bar{i} - \bar{j} + 2\bar{k}$ assuming that ∇T at (1, 1, 1) is $2\bar{i} + 3\bar{j} + 4\bar{k}$ and further estimate the change in the temperature as we move from the point to a distance 0.2 units in the direction of the vector $\bar{i} - \bar{j} + 2\bar{k}$. Also find two unit vectors such that the directional derivative of T is zero at (1, 1, 1).*

Sol. :
$$(\nabla T)_{(1, 1, 1)} = 2\bar{i} + 3\bar{j} + 4\bar{k}$$

$$\bar{a} = \bar{i} - \bar{j} + 2\bar{k} \qquad \therefore \hat{a} = \frac{\bar{i} - \bar{j} + 2\bar{k}}{\sqrt{6}}$$

$\therefore$ Directional derivative $= (\nabla T) \cdot \hat{a}$

$$= (2\bar{i} + 3\bar{j} + 4\bar{k}) \cdot \frac{\bar{i} - \bar{j} + 2\bar{k}}{\sqrt{6}} = \frac{7}{\sqrt{6}}$$

The change in T that results from moving away $\Delta s = 0.2$ units from (1, 1, 1) in the direction of $\hat{a}$ is $(\nabla T \cdot \hat{a}) \Delta s = \frac{7}{\sqrt{6}} (0.2) = \frac{7}{5\sqrt{6}}$

Let $\hat{a} = \dfrac{a_1 \bar{i} + a_2 \bar{j} + a_3 \bar{k}}{\sqrt{a_1^2 + a_2^2 + a_3^2}}$ be the unit vector such that directional derivative of T is zero at (1, 1, 1).

$\therefore \qquad (\nabla T) \cdot \hat{a} = 0 \Rightarrow (2\bar{i} + 3\bar{j} + 4\bar{k}) \cdot (a_1 \bar{i} + a_2 \bar{j} + a_3 \bar{k}) = 0$

$$2a_1 + 3a_2 + 4a_3 = 0$$

Let $a_3 = 0$

$\therefore \qquad 2a_1 + 3a_2 = 0$

$$\frac{a_1}{3} = -\frac{a_2}{2} \qquad \therefore \hat{a} = \frac{3\bar{i} - 2\bar{j}}{\sqrt{13}}$$

Similarly, $\qquad \hat{b} = \dfrac{-3\bar{i} + 2\bar{j}}{\sqrt{13}}$

Ex. 10 : *If $\nabla \phi = (y^2 + 2y + z)\bar{i} + (2xy + 2x)\bar{j} + x\bar{k}$, find ϕ if $\phi(1, 1, 0) = 5$.*

Sol. :
$$\frac{\partial \phi}{\partial x} = y^2 + 2y + z \qquad \qquad \dots (1)$$

$$\frac{\partial \phi}{\partial y} = 2xy + 2x \qquad \ldots(2)$$

$$\frac{\partial \phi}{\partial z} = x \qquad \ldots(3)$$

Integrating (1) partially w.r.t. x,

$$\phi(x, y, z) = xy^2 + 2xy + zx + c_1(y, z)$$

$$\frac{\partial \phi}{\partial y} = 2xy + 2x + \frac{\partial c_1}{\partial y} = 2xy + 2x$$

$$\therefore \qquad \frac{\partial c_1}{\partial y} = 0$$

Integrating,

$$c_1 = c_2(z)$$

$$\phi = xy^2 + 2xy + zx + c_2(z)$$

$$\frac{\partial \phi}{\partial z} = x + 2\frac{dc_2}{dz} = x$$

$$\therefore \qquad \frac{dc_2}{dz} = 0 \qquad \text{or} \quad c_2 = c$$

$$\therefore \qquad \phi(x, y, z) = xy^2 + 2xy + zx + c$$

$$\phi(1, 1, 0) = 1 + 2 + c = 5$$

$$\therefore \qquad c = 2$$

$$\therefore \qquad \phi(x, y, z) = xy^2 + 2xy + zx + 2$$

V. DIVERGENCE OF A VECTOR

When a vector differential operator ∇ operates scalarly on vector point function $\overline{F}$, it gives a scalar quantity $\nabla \cdot \overline{F}$, called **Divergence of $\overline{F}$** or **Div $\overline{F}$**.

As an illustration, consider $\overline{r} = x\,\overline{i} + y\,\overline{j} + z\,\overline{k}$

$$\therefore \qquad \nabla \cdot \overline{r} = \left(\overline{i}\,\frac{\partial}{\partial x} + \overline{j}\,\frac{\partial}{\partial y} + \overline{k}\,\frac{\partial}{\partial z} \right) \cdot (x\,\overline{i} + y\,\overline{j} + z\,\overline{k})$$

$$= \frac{\partial}{\partial x}(x) + \frac{\partial}{\partial y}(y) + \frac{\partial}{\partial z}(z) = 1 + 1 + 1 = 3$$

This is taken as a standard result.

In general, if

$$\overline{F} = F_1\,\overline{i} + F_2\,\overline{j} + F_3\,\overline{k}$$

$$\nabla \cdot \overline{F} = \frac{\partial F_1}{\partial x} + \frac{\partial F_2}{\partial y} + \frac{\partial F_3}{\partial z}$$

it is also written as div $\overline{F}$.

In particular, if $\nabla \cdot \overline{F} = 0$, the vector field $\overline{F}$ is called solenoidal.

It may also be noted here that, while $\nabla \cdot \bar{F}$ gives divergence of a vector field

$$\bar{F} \cdot \nabla = (F_1 \bar{i} + F_2 \bar{j} + F_3 \bar{k}) \cdot \left(\bar{i} \frac{\partial}{\partial x} + \bar{j} \frac{\partial}{\partial y} + \bar{k} \frac{\partial}{\partial z} \right)$$

$$= F_1 \frac{\partial}{\partial x} + F_2 \frac{\partial}{\partial y} + F_3 \frac{\partial}{\partial z}$$

gives a scalar differential operator.

Note : $\qquad\qquad \nabla \cdot \bar{F} \neq \bar{F} \cdot \nabla$

If $\bar{a} = a_1 \bar{i} + a_2 \bar{j} + a_3 \bar{k}$ is a constant vector and $\bar{r} = x \bar{i} + y \bar{j} + z \bar{k}$

$$(\bar{a} \cdot \nabla) \bar{r} = \left(a_1 \frac{\partial}{\partial x} + a_2 \frac{\partial}{\partial y} + a_3 \frac{\partial}{\partial z} \right) \bar{r} = a_1 \frac{\partial \bar{r}}{\partial x} + a_2 \frac{\partial \bar{r}}{\partial y} + a_3 \frac{\partial \bar{r}}{\partial z}$$

$$= a_1 \bar{i} + a_2 \bar{j} + a_3 \bar{k} \left[\because \ \frac{\partial \bar{r}}{\partial x} = \bar{i} \text{ etc.} \right]$$

$\therefore \qquad\qquad (\bar{a} \cdot \nabla) \ \bar{r} = \bar{a}$

This is also taken as a standard result.

To interpret divergence of a vector field physically, consider the motion of fluid with velocity $\bar{v} = V_1 \bar{i} + V_2 \bar{j} + V_3 \bar{k}$ at a point A (x, y, z). Consider a small parallelopiped with edges δx, δy, δz parallel to the axes in the mass of fluid with one of its corners at the point A. (See Fig. 10.6).

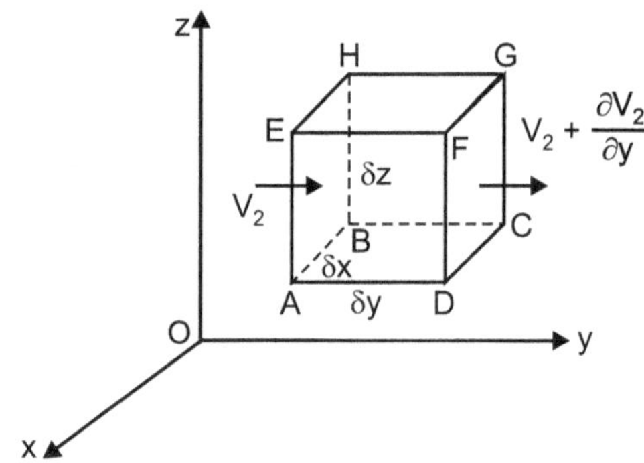

Fig. 10.6

Consider the flow parallel to y-axis that is across the faces ABEH and DCFG. Flow per unit time across the face ABEH $= V_2 \cdot \delta x \, \delta z$
where, V_2 is y component of velocity at the face ABEH.

Now, the y component of velocity at the face DCFG is $V_2 + \dfrac{\partial V_2}{\partial y} \delta y$

$\therefore \quad$ Flow per unit time across the face DCFG is $\left(V_2 + \dfrac{\partial V_2}{\partial y} \delta y \right) \delta x \, \delta z$.

Thus the rate at which fluid flows out from the elementary volume along the y direction is $\left(V_2 + \dfrac{\partial V_2}{\partial y}\, \delta y\right) \delta x\, \delta z - V_2\, \delta x\, \delta z = \dfrac{\partial V_2}{\partial y}\, \delta x\, \delta y\, \delta z.$

Similarly, the rate of outward flow along x and z directions will be given by

$$\frac{\partial V_1}{\partial x}\, \delta x\, \delta y\, \delta z, \quad \frac{\partial V_3}{\partial z}\, \delta x\, \delta y\, \delta z \text{ respectively.}$$

Thus the rate at which fluid flows out of the volume

$$= \left(\frac{\partial V_1}{\partial x} + \frac{\partial V_2}{\partial y} + \frac{\partial V_3}{\partial z}\right) \delta x\, \delta y\, \delta z$$

The rate of outward flow per unit volume

$$= \frac{\partial V_1}{\partial x} + \frac{\partial V_2}{\partial y} + \frac{\partial V_3}{\partial z} = \nabla \cdot \bar{v}$$

Thus the divergence of $\bar{v}$ represents the rate of outward flow through unit volume. Similarly, if $\bar{V}$ represents an electric flux, div $\bar{V}$ is the amount of flux which diverges per unit volume. Various other examples can be quoted to interpret the divergence of $\bar{F}$ in a similar manner.

VI. CURL OF A VECTOR

When a vector differential operator ∇ operates vertorially on vector point function $\bar{F}$, it gives a vector quantity $\nabla \times \bar{F}$, called **curl of $\bar{F}$** or simply **curl $\bar{F}$**.

If
$$\bar{F} = F_1\, \bar{i} + F_2\, \bar{j} + F_3\, \bar{k}$$

$$\text{curl } \bar{F} = \nabla \times \bar{F} = \left(\bar{i}\, \frac{\partial}{\partial x} + \bar{j}\, \frac{\partial}{\partial y} + \bar{k}\, \frac{\partial}{\partial z}\right) \times (F_1\, i + F_2\, \bar{j} + F_3\, \bar{k})$$

$$= \bar{k}\, \frac{\partial F_2}{\partial x} - \bar{j}\, \frac{\partial F_3}{\partial x} - \bar{k}\, \frac{\partial F_1}{\partial y} + \bar{i}\, \frac{\partial F_3}{\partial y} + \bar{j}\, \frac{\partial F_1}{\partial z} - \bar{i}\, \frac{\partial F_2}{\partial z}$$

$$= \bar{i}\left(\frac{\partial F_3}{\partial y} - \frac{\partial F_2}{\partial z}\right) + \bar{j}\left(\frac{\partial F_1}{\partial z} - \frac{\partial F_3}{\partial x}\right) + \bar{k}\left(\frac{\partial F_2}{\partial x} - \frac{\partial F_1}{\partial y}\right)$$

Conveniently, this can also be expressed in the determinant form as

$$\text{curl } \bar{F} = \nabla \times \bar{F} = \begin{vmatrix} \bar{i} & \bar{j} & \bar{k} \\[4pt] \dfrac{\partial}{\partial x} & \dfrac{\partial}{\partial y} & \dfrac{\partial}{\partial z} \\[4pt] F_1 & F_2 & F_3 \end{vmatrix}$$

For
$$\bar{r} = x\,\bar{i} + y\,\bar{j} + z\,\bar{k}$$

$$\nabla \times \bar{r} = \begin{vmatrix} \bar{i} & \bar{j} & \bar{k} \\ \dfrac{\partial}{\partial x} & \dfrac{\partial}{\partial y} & \dfrac{\partial}{\partial z} \\ x & y & z \end{vmatrix} = \bar{i}\left(\dfrac{\partial z}{\partial y} - \dfrac{\partial y}{\partial z}\right) + \bar{j}\left(\dfrac{\partial x}{\partial z} - \dfrac{\partial z}{\partial x}\right) + \bar{k}\left(\dfrac{\partial y}{\partial x} - \dfrac{\partial x}{\partial y}\right)$$

$$\therefore \qquad \nabla \times \bar{r} = 0$$

This result is taken as a standard result and can be used in the solution of problems.

Vector field $\bar{F}$ is called irrotational if $\nabla \times \bar{F} = 0$

To interprete curl of a vector field physically, consider the motion of a rigid body about a fixed axis passing through O [Refer article 10.2 (b) (ii)]. If $\bar{\omega}$ is the angular velocity of the rigid body, $\bar{v}$ the linear velocity of a point P $(\bar{r})$, then

$$\bar{v} = \bar{\omega} \times \bar{r}$$

$$\text{Curl } \bar{v} = \nabla \times (\bar{\omega} \times \bar{r})$$

Let
$$\bar{\omega} = \omega_1\,\bar{i} + \omega_2\,\bar{j} + \omega_3\,\bar{k}$$

$$\therefore \qquad \bar{\omega} \times \bar{r} = \begin{vmatrix} \bar{i} & \bar{j} & \bar{k} \\ \omega_1 & \omega_2 & \omega_3 \\ x & y & z \end{vmatrix}$$

$$= \bar{i}\,(\omega_2 z - \omega_3 y) + \bar{j}\,(\omega_3 x - \omega_1 z) + \bar{k}\,(\omega_1 y - \omega_2 x)$$

$$\therefore \quad \nabla \times (\bar{\omega} \times \bar{r}) = \begin{vmatrix} \bar{i} & \bar{j} & \bar{k} \\ \dfrac{\partial}{\partial x} & \dfrac{\partial}{\partial y} & \dfrac{\partial}{\partial z} \\ \omega_2 z - \omega_3 y & \omega_3 x - \omega_1 z & \omega_1 y - \omega_2 x \end{vmatrix}$$

$$= \bar{i}\left\{\dfrac{\partial}{\partial y}(\omega_1 y - \omega_2 x) - \dfrac{\partial}{\partial z}(\omega_3 x - \omega_1 z)\right\} + \bar{j}\left\{\dfrac{\partial}{\partial z}(\omega_2 z - \omega_3 y) - \dfrac{\partial}{\partial x}(\omega_1 y - \omega_2 x)\right\}$$

$$+ \bar{k}\left\{\dfrac{\partial}{\partial x}(\omega_3 x - \omega_1 z) - \dfrac{\partial}{\partial y}(\omega_2 z - \omega_3 y)\right\}$$

$$= \bar{i}\,(\omega_1 + \omega_1) + \bar{j}\,(\omega_2 + \omega_2) + \bar{k}\,(\omega_3 + \omega_3) = 2\,(\omega_1\,\bar{i} + \omega_2\,\bar{j} + \omega_3\,\bar{k})$$

$$\text{curl } \bar{v} = 2\,\bar{\omega}$$

$$\text{or} \qquad \bar{\omega} = \frac{1}{2}\,\text{curl } \bar{v}$$

Thus the angular velocity of rotation at any point is equal to half the curl of the velocity vector. **The curl of vector thus signifies rotation**.

10.4 VECTOR IDENTITIES

Given scalar function ϕ and vector functions $\bar{u}, \bar{v}$. Following results involving operation of ∇ are quite useful.

(1) $\qquad \nabla \cdot (\phi\,\bar{u}) = \nabla\phi \cdot \bar{u} + \phi\,(\nabla \cdot \bar{u})$

or $\qquad \text{Div}\,(\phi\,\bar{u}) = \bar{u} \cdot \text{Grad }\phi + \phi\,\text{Div }\bar{u}$

Let $\qquad \bar{u} = u_1\,\bar{i} + u_2\,\bar{j} + u_3\,\bar{k}$

$\therefore \qquad \phi\,\bar{u} = \phi\,u_1\,\bar{i} + \phi\,u_2\,\bar{j} + \phi\,u_3\,\bar{k}$

$$\text{L.H.S.} = \nabla \cdot (\phi\,\bar{u}) = \frac{\partial}{\partial x}\,(\phi\,u_1) + \frac{\partial}{\partial y}\,(\phi\,u_2) + \frac{\partial}{\partial z}\,(\phi\,u_3)$$

$$= \phi\frac{\partial u_1}{\partial x} + u_1\frac{\partial \phi}{\partial x} + \phi\frac{\partial u_2}{\partial y} + u_2\frac{\partial \phi}{\partial y} + \phi\frac{\partial u_3}{\partial z} + u_3\frac{\partial \phi}{\partial z}$$

$$= \phi\left(\frac{\partial u_1}{\partial x} + \frac{\partial u_2}{\partial y} + \frac{\partial u_3}{\partial z}\right) + u_1\frac{\partial \phi}{\partial x} + u_2\frac{\partial \phi}{\partial y} + u_3\frac{\partial \phi}{\partial z}$$

$$= \phi\,(\nabla \cdot \bar{u}) + (u_1\,\bar{i} + u_2\,\bar{j} + u_3\,\bar{k}) \cdot \left(\bar{i}\frac{\partial \phi}{\partial x} + \bar{j}\frac{\partial \phi}{\partial y} + \bar{k}\frac{\partial \phi}{\partial z}\right)$$

$$= \phi\,(\nabla \cdot \bar{u}) + \bar{u} \cdot \nabla\phi = \text{R.H.S.}$$

Alternatively, the result can be proved by symbolic procedure.

∇ being vector differential operator, it behaves like an operator $D = \dfrac{d}{dx}$ just as

$$D\,(uv) = uDv + vDu = D_u\,(uv) + D_v\,(uv)$$

We can write $\quad \nabla \cdot (\phi\,\bar{u}) = \nabla_\phi \cdot (\phi\,\bar{u}) + \nabla\,\bar{u} \cdot (\phi\,\bar{u})$

(the suffix of ∇ is to be treated as constant in each expression.)

$$= \phi\,(\nabla_\phi \cdot \bar{u}) + \bar{u} \cdot \nabla_{\bar{u}}\,\phi$$

Omitting the suffix now $= \phi\,(\nabla \cdot \bar{u}) + \bar{u} \cdot \nabla_\phi$

Symbolic procedure is not rigorous way of presenting the proof of vector identities, but is quite useful in solution of problems.

(2) $\nabla \times (\phi\,\bar{u}) = \nabla\phi \times \bar{u} + \phi\,(\nabla \times \bar{u})$

or $\qquad\qquad \text{curl}\,(\phi\,\bar{u}) = \text{Grad}\,\phi \times \bar{u} + \phi\,\text{curl}\,\bar{u}$

As before, let $\qquad\qquad \bar{u} = u_1\,\bar{i} + u_2\,\bar{j} + u_3\,\bar{k}$

$\text{L.H.S.} = \nabla \times (\phi\,\bar{u})$

$$= \begin{vmatrix} \bar{i} & \bar{j} & \bar{k} \\[6pt] \dfrac{\partial}{\partial x} & \dfrac{\partial}{\partial y} & \dfrac{\partial}{\partial z} \\[10pt] \phi\,u_1 & \phi\,u_2 & \phi\,u_3 \end{vmatrix}$$

$$= \bar{i}\left\{\frac{\partial}{\partial y}(\phi u_3) - \frac{\partial}{\partial z}(\phi u_2)\right\} + \bar{j}\left\{\frac{\partial}{\partial z}(\phi u_1) - \frac{\partial}{\partial x}(\phi u_3)\right\} + \bar{k}\left\{\frac{\partial}{\partial x}(\phi u_2) - \frac{\partial}{\partial y}(\phi u_1)\right\}$$

$$= \bar{i}\left\{\phi\frac{\partial u_3}{\partial y} + u_3\frac{\partial \phi}{\partial y} - \phi\frac{\partial u_2}{\partial z} - u_2\frac{\partial \phi}{\partial z}\right\} + \bar{j}\left\{\phi\frac{\partial u_1}{\partial z} + u_1\frac{\partial \phi}{\partial z} - \phi\frac{\partial u_3}{\partial x} - u_3\frac{\partial \phi}{\partial x}\right\}$$

$$+ \bar{k}\left\{u_2\frac{\partial \phi}{\partial x} + \phi\frac{\partial u_2}{\partial x} - \phi\frac{\partial u_1}{\partial y} - u_1\frac{\partial \phi}{\partial y}\right\}$$

$$= \phi\left[\bar{i}\left(\frac{\partial u_3}{\partial y} - \frac{\partial u_2}{\partial z}\right) + \bar{j}\left(\frac{\partial u_1}{\partial z} - \frac{\partial u_3}{\partial x}\right) + \bar{k}\left(\frac{\partial u_2}{\partial x} - \frac{\partial u_1}{\partial y}\right)\right]$$

$$+ \bar{i}\left(u_3\frac{\partial \phi}{\partial y} - u_2\frac{\partial \phi}{\partial z}\right) + \bar{j}\left(u_1\frac{\partial \phi}{\partial z} - u_3\frac{\partial \phi}{\partial x}\right) + \bar{k}\left(u_2\frac{\partial \phi}{\partial x} - u_1\frac{\partial \phi}{\partial y}\right)$$

$$= \phi\,(\nabla \times \bar{u}) + \nabla\phi \times \bar{u}$$

$\text{For} \quad \nabla\phi \times \bar{u} = \begin{vmatrix} \bar{i} & \bar{j} & \bar{k} \\[6pt] \dfrac{\partial \phi}{\partial x} & \dfrac{\partial \phi}{\partial y} & \dfrac{\partial \phi}{\partial z} \\[10pt] u_1 & u_2 & u_3 \end{vmatrix}$

$$= \bar{i}\left(u_3\frac{\partial \phi}{\partial y} - u_2\frac{\partial \phi}{\partial z}\right) + \bar{j}\left(u_1\frac{\partial \phi}{\partial z} - u_3\frac{\partial \phi}{\partial x}\right) + \bar{k}\left(u_2\frac{\partial \phi}{\partial x} - u_1\frac{\partial \phi}{\partial y}\right)$$

which proves the result.

Alternatively, $\nabla \times (\phi\,\bar{u}) = \nabla_\phi \times (\phi\,\bar{u}) + \nabla\bar{u} \times (\phi\,\bar{u})$

$$= \phi\,(\nabla_\phi \times \bar{u}) + \nabla_{\bar{u}} \times (\phi\,\bar{u})$$

$$= \phi\,(\nabla \times \bar{u}) + \nabla\phi \times \bar{u} \qquad\qquad \text{(Dropping the suffixes)}$$

(3) $\nabla \cdot (\bar{u} \times \bar{v}) = \bar{v} \cdot (\nabla \times \bar{u}) - \bar{u} \cdot (\nabla \times \bar{v})$

or $\qquad \text{Div} (\bar{u} \times \bar{v}) = \bar{v} \cdot \text{curl } \bar{u} - \bar{u} \cdot \text{curl } \bar{v}$

Using symbolic procedure,

$$\nabla \cdot (\bar{u} \times \bar{v}) = \nabla_{\bar{u}} \cdot (\bar{u} \times \bar{v}) + \nabla_{\bar{v}} \cdot (\bar{u} \times \bar{v})$$

Using the property of scalar triple product and remembering that $\nabla_{\bar{u}}$ must immediately precede $\bar{v}$ as $\bar{u}$ is to be treated as constant and $\nabla_{\bar{v}}$ must precede $\bar{u}$ as $\bar{v}$ is to be treated as constant, we write

$$\nabla \cdot (\bar{u} \times \bar{v}) = -\bar{u} \cdot (\nabla_{\bar{u}} \times \bar{v}) + \bar{v} \cdot (\nabla_{\bar{v}} \times \bar{u})$$

$$[\bar{a} \cdot \bar{b} \times \bar{c}] = -\bar{b} \cdot (\bar{a} \times \bar{c}) = \bar{c} \cdot (\bar{a} \times \bar{b})$$

$\qquad$ Dropping the suffixes $= -\bar{u} \cdot (\nabla \times \bar{v}) + \bar{v} \cdot (\nabla \times \bar{u})$

which establishes the result.

$\qquad$ Students are advised to establish the result by components method i.e. taking

$$\bar{u} = u_1 \bar{i} + u_2 \bar{j} + u_3 \bar{k} \text{ etc. and proving}$$
$$\text{L.H.S.} = \text{R.H.S. by actually obtaining dot and cross products.}$$

(4) $\nabla \times (\bar{u} \times \bar{v}) = \bar{u} (\nabla \cdot \bar{v}) - (\bar{u} \cdot \nabla) \bar{v} + (\bar{v} \cdot \nabla) \bar{u} - \bar{v} (\nabla \cdot \bar{u})$

$$\nabla \times (\bar{u} \times \bar{v}) = \nabla_{\bar{u}} \times (\bar{u} \times \bar{v}) + \nabla_{\bar{v}} \times (\bar{u} \times \bar{v}) \qquad \ldots (1)$$

Using $\bar{a} \times (\bar{b} \times \bar{c}) = (\bar{a} \cdot \bar{c}) \bar{b} - (\bar{a} \cdot \bar{b}) \bar{c}$ and remembering that when $\bar{u}$ is to be treated as constant $\bar{u} \cdot \nabla$ is meaningful rather than $\nabla \cdot \bar{u}$ and $\nabla_{\bar{u}}$ must precede $\bar{v}$ etc.

$$\nabla_{\bar{u}} \times (\bar{u} \times \bar{v}) = (\nabla_{\bar{u}} \cdot \bar{v}) \bar{u} - (\bar{u} \cdot \nabla_{\bar{u}}) \bar{v},$$

$$\nabla_{\bar{v}} \times (\bar{u} \times \bar{v}) = (\bar{v} \cdot \nabla_{\bar{v}}) \bar{u} - (\nabla_{\bar{v}} \cdot \bar{u}) \bar{v}$$

Dropping the suffixes and putting the values of $\nabla_{\bar{u}} (\bar{u} \times \bar{v})$ and $\nabla_{\bar{v}} \times (\bar{u} \times \bar{v})$ in (1),

we get $\qquad \nabla \times (\bar{u} \times \bar{v}) = (\nabla \cdot \bar{v}) \bar{u} - (\bar{u} \cdot \nabla) \bar{v} + (\bar{v} \cdot \nabla) \bar{u} - (\nabla \cdot \bar{u}) \bar{v}$

which establishes the result.

(5) $\nabla (\bar{u} \cdot \bar{v}) = \bar{u} \times (\nabla \times \bar{v}) + (\bar{u} \cdot \nabla) \bar{v} + \bar{v} \times (\nabla \times \bar{u}) + (\bar{v} \cdot \nabla) \bar{u}$

$$\nabla (\bar{u} \cdot \bar{v}) = \nabla_{\bar{u}} (\bar{u} \cdot \bar{v}) + \nabla_{\bar{v}} (\bar{u} \cdot \bar{v}) \qquad \ldots (1)$$

Consider $\bar{u} \times (\nabla_{\bar{u}} \times \bar{v}) = \nabla_{\bar{u}} (\bar{u} \cdot \bar{v}) - (\bar{u} \cdot \nabla_{\bar{u}}) \bar{v}$

$\therefore \qquad \nabla_{\bar{u}} (\bar{u} \cdot \bar{v}) = \bar{u} \times (\nabla_{\bar{u}} \times \bar{v}) + (\bar{u} \cdot \nabla_{\bar{u}}) \bar{v}$

$\qquad\qquad\qquad = \bar{u} \times (\nabla \times \bar{v}) + (\bar{u} \cdot \nabla) \bar{v}$ (Dropping the suffixes)

Similarly, $\bar{v} \times (\nabla_{\bar{v}} \times \bar{u}) = \nabla_{\bar{v}} (\bar{u} \cdot \bar{v}) - (\bar{v} \cdot \nabla_{\bar{v}}) \bar{u}$

$\therefore \qquad \nabla_{\bar{v}} (\bar{u} \cdot \bar{v}) = \bar{v} \times (\nabla_{\bar{v}} \times \bar{u}) + (\bar{v} \cdot \nabla_{\bar{v}}) \bar{u}$

$\qquad\qquad\qquad = \bar{v} \times (\nabla \times \bar{u}) + (\bar{v} \cdot \nabla) \bar{u}$ (Dropping the suffixes)

Putting the values of $\nabla_{\bar{u}} (\bar{u} \cdot \bar{v})$ and $\nabla_{\bar{v}} (\bar{u} \cdot \bar{v})$ in (1), the required result is established.

Results (iv) and (v) can also be established by component method.

Using component method, the expressions involving second order differential operators can also be obtained.

Let us find equivalent expressions for

(1) $\nabla \cdot \nabla\phi$ or divergence Grade ϕ

$$\nabla \cdot \nabla\phi = \nabla \cdot \left\{ \bar{i} \frac{\partial\phi}{\partial x} + \bar{j} \frac{\partial\phi}{\partial y} + \bar{k} \frac{\partial\phi}{\partial z} \right\}$$

$$= \frac{\partial}{\partial x} \left(\frac{\partial\phi}{\partial x} \right) + \frac{\partial}{\partial y} \left(\frac{\partial\phi}{\partial y} \right) + \frac{\partial}{\partial z} \left(\frac{\partial\phi}{\partial z} \right)$$

$$= \frac{\partial^2\phi}{\partial x^2} + \frac{\partial^2\phi}{\partial y^2} + \frac{\partial^2\phi}{\partial z^2}$$

We can write $\quad \nabla \cdot \nabla\phi = (\nabla \cdot \nabla) \phi = \nabla^2\phi$

Thus $\qquad\qquad \nabla^2\phi = \frac{\partial^2\phi}{\partial x^2} + \frac{\partial^2\phi}{\partial y^2} + \frac{\partial^2\phi}{\partial z^2}$

Operator $\qquad\qquad \nabla^2 \equiv \frac{\partial^2}{\partial x^2} + \frac{\partial^2}{\partial y^2} + \frac{\partial^2}{\partial z^2}$

which is a second order differential operator and is known as Laplacian operator and the equation $\nabla^2\phi = 0$ is called Laplace equation, frequently encountered in engineering problems.

(2) $\nabla \times (\nabla\phi)$ or curl Grad ϕ

$$\nabla \times (\nabla\phi) = \nabla \times \left\{ \bar{i} \frac{\partial\phi}{\partial x} + \bar{j} \frac{\partial\phi}{\partial y} + \bar{k} \frac{\partial\phi}{\partial z} \right\}$$

$$= \begin{vmatrix} \bar{i} & \bar{j} & \bar{k} \\ \dfrac{\partial}{\partial x} & \dfrac{\partial}{\partial y} & \dfrac{\partial}{\partial z} \\ \dfrac{\partial \phi}{\partial x} & \dfrac{\partial \phi}{\partial y} & \dfrac{\partial \phi}{\partial z} \end{vmatrix}$$

$$= \bar{i}\left\{\frac{\partial^2 \phi}{\partial y \partial z} - \frac{\partial^2 \phi}{\partial y \partial z}\right\} + \bar{j}\left\{\frac{\partial^2 \phi}{\partial x \partial z} - \frac{\partial^2 \phi}{\partial x \partial z}\right\} + \bar{k}\left\{\frac{\partial^2 \phi}{\partial x \partial y} - \frac{\partial^2 \phi}{\partial x \partial y}\right\}$$

$$= 0$$

We can write $\quad \nabla \times (\nabla \phi) = (\nabla \times \nabla)\,\phi = 0$

Thus curl Grad $\phi = 0$

(3) $\nabla\,(\nabla \cdot \bar{u}) = $ Grad Div $\bar{u}$

Let $\qquad \bar{u} = u_1\,\bar{i} + u_2\,\bar{j} + u_3\,\bar{k}$

$$\nabla \cdot \bar{u} = \frac{\partial u_1}{\partial x} + \frac{\partial u_2}{\partial y} + \frac{\partial u_3}{\partial z}$$

$$\nabla\,(\nabla \cdot \bar{u}) = \bar{i}\,\frac{\partial}{\partial x}\left\{\frac{\partial u_1}{\partial x} + \frac{\partial u_2}{\partial y} + \frac{\partial u_3}{\partial z}\right\} + \bar{j}\,\frac{\partial}{\partial y}\left\{\frac{\partial u_1}{\partial x} + \frac{\partial u_2}{\partial y} + \frac{\partial u_3}{\partial z}\right\}$$

$$+ \bar{k}\,\frac{\partial}{\partial z}\left\{\frac{\partial u_1}{\partial x} + \frac{\partial u_2}{\partial y} + \frac{\partial u_3}{\partial z}\right\}$$

$$= \bar{i}\left[\frac{\partial^2 u_1}{\partial x^2} + \frac{\partial^2 u_2}{\partial x\,\partial y} + \frac{\partial^2 u_3}{\partial x\,\partial z}\right] + \bar{j}\left[\frac{\partial^2 u_1}{\partial x\,\partial y} + \frac{\partial^2 u_2}{\partial y^2} + \frac{\partial^2 u_3}{\partial y\,\partial z}\right]$$

$$+ \bar{k}\left[\frac{\partial^2 u_1}{\partial x\,\partial z} + \frac{\partial^2 u_2}{\partial y\,\partial z} + \frac{\partial^2 u_3}{\partial z^2}\right]$$

(4) $\nabla \cdot (\nabla \times \bar{u})$ or Div curl $\bar{u}$

$$\nabla \times \bar{u} = \begin{vmatrix} \bar{i} & \bar{j} & \bar{k} \\ \dfrac{\partial}{\partial x} & \dfrac{\partial}{\partial y} & \dfrac{\partial}{\partial z} \\ u_1 & u_2 & u_3 \end{vmatrix} = \bar{i}\left(\frac{\partial u_3}{\partial y} - \frac{\partial u_2}{\partial z}\right) + \bar{j}\left(\frac{\partial u_1}{\partial z} - \frac{\partial u_3}{\partial x}\right) + \bar{k}\left(\frac{\partial u_2}{\partial x} - \frac{\partial u_1}{\partial y}\right)$$

$$\nabla \cdot (\nabla \times \bar{u}) = \frac{\partial}{\partial x}\left\{\frac{\partial u_3}{\partial y} - \frac{\partial u_2}{\partial z}\right\} + \frac{\partial}{\partial y}\left\{\frac{\partial u_1}{\partial z} - \frac{\partial u_3}{\partial x}\right\} + \frac{\partial}{\partial z}\left\{\frac{\partial u_2}{\partial x} - \frac{\partial u_1}{\partial y}\right\}$$

$$= \frac{\partial^2 u_3}{\partial x\,\partial y} - \frac{\partial^2 u_2}{\partial x\,\partial z} + \frac{\partial^2 u_1}{\partial y\,\partial z} - \frac{\partial^2 u_3}{\partial x\,\partial y} + \frac{\partial^2 u_2}{\partial x\,\partial z} - \frac{\partial^2 u_1}{\partial y\,\partial z} = 0$$

Thus Divergence curl $\bar{u} = 0$. (Note that scalar triple product with two identical vectors is zero.)

(5) $\nabla \times (\nabla \times \overline{u})$ or curl curl $\overline{u}$

Instead of taking $\overline{u} = u_1 \overline{i} + u_2 \overline{j} + u_3 \overline{k}$, etc., we find the equivalent expression by using the property $\overline{a} \times (\overline{b} \times \overline{c}) = (\overline{a} \cdot \overline{c}) \overline{b} - (\overline{a} \cdot \overline{b}) \overline{c}$.

$$\nabla \times (\nabla \times \overline{u}) = \nabla (\nabla \cdot \overline{u}) - (\nabla \cdot \nabla) \overline{u} = \nabla (\nabla \cdot \overline{u}) - \nabla^2 \overline{u}$$

LIST OF FORMULAE

$\nabla = \overline{i} \dfrac{\partial}{\partial x} + \overline{j} \dfrac{\partial}{\partial y} + \overline{k} \dfrac{\partial}{\partial z}$	$\nabla \phi = \overline{i} \dfrac{\partial \phi}{\partial x} + \overline{j} \dfrac{\partial \phi}{\partial y} + \overline{k} \dfrac{\partial \phi}{\partial z}$
$\nabla (u \pm v) = \nabla u \pm \nabla v$	$\nabla (uv) = u \nabla v + v \nabla u$
$\nabla \left(\dfrac{u}{v} \right) = \dfrac{v \nabla u - u \nabla v}{v^2}$	$\nabla (au) = a \nabla u$
$\nabla (f(u)) = f'(u) (\nabla u)$	$\nabla f(r) = \left(\dfrac{f'(r)}{r} \right) \overline{r}$
$d\phi \equiv \nabla \phi \cdot d\overline{r}$	D.D. of $\phi = \nabla \phi \cdot \hat{a}$
$\text{div } \overline{F} = \nabla \cdot \overline{F} = \dfrac{\partial F_1}{\partial x} + \dfrac{\partial F_2}{\partial y} + \dfrac{\partial F_3}{\partial z}$	$\nabla \cdot \overline{F} = 0 \Rightarrow \overline{F}$ is solenoidal
$\text{rot } \overline{F} = \text{curl } \overline{F} = \nabla \times \overline{F} = \begin{vmatrix} \overline{i} & \overline{j} & \overline{k} \\ \dfrac{\partial}{\partial x} & \dfrac{\partial}{\partial y} & \dfrac{\partial}{\partial z} \\ F_1 & F_2 & F_3 \end{vmatrix}$	$\nabla \times \overline{F} = 0 \Rightarrow \overline{F}$ is irrotational.
$\nabla (\overline{a} \cdot \overline{r}) = \overline{a}$	$\nabla (\overline{a} \cdot \overline{b}) = 0$
$\nabla \cdot \overline{a} = 0, \ \nabla \times \overline{a} = 0$	$\nabla \cdot \overline{r} = 3, \nabla \times \overline{r} = 0$
$\nabla \cdot (\phi \overline{u}) = \phi (\nabla \cdot \overline{u}) + \nabla \phi \cdot \overline{u}$	$\nabla \times (\phi \overline{u}) = \phi (\nabla \times \overline{u}) + \nabla \phi \times \overline{u}$
$\nabla \cdot (\overline{u} \times \overline{v}) = \overline{v} \cdot (\nabla \times \overline{u}) - \overline{u} \cdot (\nabla \times \overline{v})$	$\nabla \times (\overline{u} \times \overline{v}) = \overline{u} (\nabla \cdot \overline{v}) - (\overline{u} \cdot \nabla) \overline{v}$ $+ (\overline{v} \cdot \nabla) \overline{u} - \overline{v} (\nabla \cdot \overline{u})$
$\nabla (\overline{u} \cdot \overline{v}) = \overline{u} \times (\nabla \times \overline{v}) + (\overline{u} \cdot \nabla) \overline{v} + \overline{v} \times (\nabla \times \overline{u}) + (\overline{v} \cdot \nabla) \overline{u}$	
$\nabla \cdot (r^n \overline{r}) = (n + 3) r^n$	$\nabla \times (r^n \overline{r}) = 0$
$\nabla \cdot (\nabla \phi) = (\nabla \cdot \nabla) \phi$ $\nabla^2 \phi = \dfrac{\partial^2 \phi}{\partial x^2} + \dfrac{\partial^2 \phi}{\partial y^2} + \dfrac{\partial^2 \phi}{\partial z^2}$	$\nabla^2 \equiv \dfrac{\partial^2}{\partial x^2} + \dfrac{\partial^2}{\partial y^2} + \dfrac{\partial^2}{\partial z^2};$ $\nabla^2 \phi = 0$ is Laplace equation
$\nabla \times (\nabla \phi) = 0; \ \nabla \cdot (\nabla \times \overline{u}) = 0$	Curl curl $\overline{u} = \nabla \times (\nabla \times \overline{u}) = \nabla (\nabla \cdot \overline{u}) - \nabla^2 \overline{u}$

• $\quad \nabla\,(\nabla \cdot \bar{u}) = \nabla \times (\nabla \times \bar{u}) + \nabla^2\,\bar{u}$	• $\quad$ Group operator $\quad \equiv \bar{a} \cdot \nabla \equiv a_1 \dfrac{\partial}{\partial x} + a_2 \dfrac{\partial}{\partial y} + a_3 \dfrac{\partial}{\partial z}$ $\quad (\bar{a} \cdot \nabla)\,\bar{r} = \bar{a}$

ILLUSTRATIONS

Ex. 1 : *Given* $\qquad \bar{u} \;=\; xyz\,\bar{i} \;+\; (2x^2z - y^2x)\,\bar{j} \;+\; xz^3\,\bar{k}$

$$\bar{v} \;=\; x^2\,\bar{i} \;+\; 2yz\,\bar{j} \;+\; (1 + 2z)\,\bar{k}$$

$$\phi \;=\; xy + yz + z^2$$

Find *(i)* $\nabla \cdot \bar{u}$ *(ii)* $\nabla \times \bar{v}$ *(iii)* $\nabla \cdot (\phi\bar{u})$ *(iv)* $\nabla \times (\phi\bar{v})$ *at* *(1, 0, –1).*

Sol. :

(i) $\quad \nabla \cdot \bar{u} = \dfrac{\partial}{\partial x}\,(xyz) + \dfrac{\partial}{\partial y}\,(2x^2z - y^2x) + \dfrac{\partial}{\partial z}\,(xz^3) = yz - 2xy + 3xz^2$

$\therefore \qquad [\nabla \cdot \bar{u}\,]_{(1,\,0,\,-1)} \;=\; 3$

(ii) $\qquad [\nabla \times \bar{v}\,] \;=\; \begin{vmatrix} \bar{i} & \bar{j} & \bar{k} \\[4pt] \dfrac{\partial}{\partial x} & \dfrac{\partial}{\partial y} & \dfrac{\partial}{\partial z} \\[8pt] x^2 & 2yz & (1+2z) \end{vmatrix}$

$$= \bar{i}\,(0 - 2y) + \bar{j}\,(0 - 0) + \bar{k}\,(0 - 0) = -\,2y\,\bar{i}$$

$\therefore \qquad [\nabla \times \bar{v}\,]_{(1,\,0,\,-1)} \;=\; 0$

(iii) $\qquad \nabla \cdot (\phi\bar{u}) \;=\; \nabla\phi \cdot \bar{u} + \phi\nabla \cdot \bar{u}$

$$\nabla\phi \;=\; \bar{i}\,\dfrac{\partial\phi}{\partial x} + \bar{j}\,\dfrac{\partial\phi}{\partial y} + \bar{k}\,\dfrac{\partial\phi}{\partial z} = y\,\bar{i} + (x + z)\,\bar{j} + (y + 2z)\,\bar{k}$$

$$\nabla\phi\,|_{(1,\,0,\,-1)} \;=\; 0 + 0 - 2\,\bar{k} = -\,2\,\bar{k}$$

$$\phi\,|_{(1,\,0,\,-1)} \;=\; 1, \quad \nabla \cdot \bar{u} = 3$$

$\therefore \qquad \nabla \cdot (\phi\bar{u}) \;=\; -\,2\,\bar{k} \cdot (-\,2\,\bar{j} - \bar{k}) + 1\,(3) = 2 + 3 = 5$

(iv) $\qquad \nabla \times (\phi\,\bar{v}) \;=\; \nabla\phi \times \bar{v} + \phi\nabla \times \bar{v}$

$$= \nabla\phi \times \bar{v} \quad \text{as } \nabla \times \bar{v} = 0$$

$$\bar{v}\,|_{(1,\,0,\,-1)} \;=\; \bar{i} - \bar{k}, \quad \nabla\phi = -\,2\,\bar{k}$$

$\therefore \qquad \nabla \times (\phi\,\bar{v}) \;=\; \nabla\phi \times \bar{v} = -\,2\,\bar{k} \times (\bar{i} - \bar{k}) = -\,2\,\bar{j}$

Ex. 2 : *For scalar functions ϕ and ψ, show that*

(i) $\nabla \cdot (\phi \nabla \psi - \psi \nabla \phi) = \phi \nabla^2 \psi - \psi \nabla^2 \phi.$ **(Dec. 2007)**

(ii) $\nabla^2 (\phi \psi) = \phi \nabla^2 \psi + 2 \nabla \phi \cdot \nabla \psi + \psi \nabla^2 \phi$ **(Dec. 2007, May 2009)**

Sol. : (i) $\nabla \cdot (\phi \nabla \psi) = \nabla \phi \cdot \nabla \psi + \phi (\nabla \cdot (\nabla \psi)) = \nabla \phi \cdot \nabla \psi + \phi \nabla^2 \psi$

$\nabla \cdot (\psi \nabla \phi) = \nabla \psi \cdot \nabla \phi + \psi \nabla^2 \phi$

$\therefore \quad \nabla \cdot (\phi \nabla \psi - \psi \nabla \phi) = \nabla \cdot (\phi \nabla \psi) - \nabla \cdot (\psi \nabla \phi)$

$$= \nabla \phi \cdot \nabla \psi + \phi \nabla^2 \psi - \nabla \psi \cdot \nabla \phi - \psi \nabla^2 \phi$$

$$= \phi \nabla^2 \psi - \psi \nabla^2 \phi$$

(ii) $\nabla^2 (\phi \psi) = \nabla \cdot \nabla (\phi \psi) = \nabla \cdot (\phi \nabla \psi + \psi \nabla \phi)$

$$= \nabla \cdot (\phi \nabla \psi) + \nabla \cdot (\psi \nabla \phi)$$

$$= \nabla \phi \cdot \nabla \psi + \phi \nabla^2 \psi + \nabla \psi \cdot \nabla \phi + \psi \nabla^2 \phi$$

$$= \phi \nabla^2 \psi + 2 \nabla \phi \cdot \nabla \psi + \psi \nabla^2 \phi$$

Ex. 3 : *For constant vector $\bar{a}$, show that,*

(i) $\nabla(\bar{a} \cdot \bar{r}) = \bar{a}$ (ii) $\nabla \times (\bar{a} \times \bar{r}) = 2 \bar{a}$ **(May 2016)**

(iii) $\nabla \left(\dfrac{\bar{a} \cdot \bar{r}}{r^n} \right) = \dfrac{\bar{a}}{r^n} - \dfrac{n(\bar{a} \cdot \bar{r})}{r^{n+2}} \bar{r}$ **(May 2015)**

where, $\bar{r} = x\bar{i} + y\bar{j} + z\bar{k}$, $r = \sqrt{x^2 + y^2 + z^2}$

Sol. : (i) Let $\bar{a} = a_1 \bar{i} + a_2 \bar{j} + a_3 \bar{k}$

$\therefore \qquad \bar{a} \cdot \bar{r} = a_1 x + a_2 y + a_3 z$

$$\nabla (\bar{a} \cdot \bar{r}) = \bar{i} \frac{\partial}{\partial x} (a_1 x + a_2 y + a_3 z) + \bar{j} \frac{\partial}{\partial y} (a_1 x + a_2 y + a_3 z)$$

$$+ \bar{k} \frac{\partial}{\partial z} (a_1 x + a_2 y + a_3 z)$$

$$= \bar{i} a_1 + \bar{j} a_2 + \bar{k} a_3$$

$\therefore \qquad \nabla (\bar{a} \cdot \bar{r}) = \bar{a}$

(ii) $\nabla \times (\bar{a} \times \bar{r}) = (\nabla \cdot \bar{r}) \bar{a} - (\bar{a} \cdot \nabla) \bar{r}$

$$= 3\bar{a} - \bar{a} \qquad\qquad [(\bar{a} \cdot \nabla) \bar{r} = \bar{a}]$$

$$= 2\bar{a}$$

(iii)
$$\nabla\left(\frac{\bar{a}\cdot\bar{r}}{r^n}\right) = \frac{1}{r^n}\,\nabla(\bar{a}\cdot\bar{r}) + (\bar{a}\cdot\bar{r})\,\nabla\left(\frac{1}{r^n}\right)$$

$$= \frac{\bar{a}}{r^n} + (\bar{a}\cdot\bar{r})(-n)\,r^{-n-2}\,\bar{r}$$

$$= \frac{\bar{a}}{r^n} - \frac{n\,(\bar{a}\cdot\bar{r})}{r^{n+2}}\,\bar{r}$$

Ex. 4 : *With usual notations, show that*

(i) $\quad \nabla\times[\bar{a}\times(\bar{b}\times\bar{r})] = \bar{a}\times\bar{b}$ **(May 2012)**

(ii) $\nabla[(\bar{r}\times\bar{a})\cdot(\bar{r}\times\bar{b})] = \bar{b}\times(\bar{r}\times\bar{a}) + \bar{a}\times(\bar{r}\times\bar{b})$ **(May 2005, 2008)**

Sol. : (i) $\quad \bar{a}\times(\bar{b}\times\bar{r}) = (\bar{a}\cdot\bar{r})\bar{b} - (\bar{a}\cdot\bar{b})\bar{r}$

$$\nabla\times[\bar{a}\times(\bar{b}\times\bar{r})] = \nabla\times[(\bar{a}\cdot\bar{r})\bar{b} - (\bar{a}\cdot\bar{b})\bar{r}\,]$$

$$= \nabla\times[(\bar{a}\cdot\bar{r})\bar{b}] - \nabla\times[(\bar{a}\cdot\bar{b})\bar{r}]$$

$$= \nabla(\bar{a}\cdot\bar{r})\times\bar{b} + (\bar{a}\cdot\bar{r})\,\nabla\times\bar{b}$$

$$- \nabla(\bar{a}\cdot\bar{b})\times\bar{r} - (\bar{a}\cdot\bar{b})\,(\nabla\times\bar{r})$$

$$= \bar{a}\times\bar{b}\ [\bar{a},\bar{b}\ \text{being constant vectors}]$$

$$\nabla\times\bar{b} = 0,\ \ \nabla(\bar{a}\cdot\bar{b}) = 0\ \text{ and } \nabla\times\bar{r} = 0$$

(ii) $\quad$ L.H.S. $= \nabla[(\bar{r}\times\bar{a})\cdot(\bar{r}\times\bar{b})]$

Let $\quad \bar{p} = \bar{r}\times\bar{a}$

$\therefore \quad (\bar{r}\times\bar{a})\cdot(\bar{r}\times\bar{b}) = \bar{p}\cdot(\bar{r}\times\bar{b}) = (\bar{p}\times\bar{r})\cdot\bar{b}$ [by interchanging dot and cross]

$$= \{(\bar{r}\times\bar{a})\times\bar{r}\}\cdot\bar{b} = -\{\bar{r}\times(\bar{r}\times\bar{a})\}\cdot\bar{b}$$

$$= -\{(\bar{r}\cdot\bar{a})\bar{r} - (\bar{r}\cdot\bar{r})\bar{a}\}\cdot\bar{b}$$

$$= -(\bar{r}\cdot\bar{a})(\bar{r}\cdot\bar{b}) + (\bar{r}\cdot\bar{r})(\bar{a}\cdot\bar{b})$$

$\therefore \quad$ L.H.S. $= \nabla[(\bar{r}\cdot\bar{r})(\bar{a}\cdot\bar{b}) - (\bar{r}\cdot\bar{a})(\bar{r}\cdot\bar{b})]$

$$= \nabla\{(\bar{r}\cdot\bar{r})(\bar{a}\cdot\bar{b})\} - \nabla\{(\bar{r}\cdot\bar{a})(\bar{r}\cdot\bar{b})\}$$

$$= (\bar{a}\cdot\bar{b})\,\nabla(r^2) - (\bar{r}\cdot\bar{r})\,\nabla(\bar{a}\cdot\bar{b}) - (\bar{r}\cdot\bar{b})\,\nabla(\bar{r}\cdot\bar{a})$$

$$- (\bar{r}\cdot\bar{a})\,\nabla(\bar{r}\cdot\bar{b})$$

Now,
$$\nabla (r^2) = 2\bar{r}, \quad \nabla (\bar{a} \cdot \bar{b}) = 0, \quad \nabla (\bar{r} \cdot \bar{a}) = \bar{a}, \quad \nabla (\bar{r} \cdot \bar{b}) = \bar{b}$$

$$\text{L.H.S.} = 2 (\bar{a} \cdot \bar{b}) \bar{r} - (\bar{r} \cdot \bar{b}) \bar{a} - (\bar{r} \cdot \bar{a}) \bar{b} \quad [\nabla (\bar{a} \cdot \bar{b}) = 0]$$

$$\text{R.H.S.} = b \times (\bar{r} \times \bar{a}) + \bar{a} \times (\bar{r} \times \bar{b})$$

$$= (\bar{b} \cdot \bar{a}) \bar{r} - (\bar{b} \cdot \bar{r}) \bar{a} + (\bar{a} \cdot \bar{b}) \bar{r} - (\bar{a} \cdot \bar{r}) \bar{b}$$

$$= 2 (\bar{a} \cdot \bar{b}) \bar{r} - (\bar{r} \cdot \bar{b}) \bar{a} - (\bar{r} \cdot \bar{a}) \bar{b}$$

$$\text{L.H.S.} = \text{R.H.S.} \quad \text{which proves the result.}$$

Ex. 5 : *Show that*

(i) 　　　$\nabla^2 [\nabla \cdot (\bar{r}/r^2)] = \dfrac{2}{r^4}$ 　　　　　　**(Dec. 2005, May 2009, Dec. 2011)**

(ii) 　　　$\nabla \times \left(\dfrac{\bar{a} \times \bar{r}}{r^3} \right) = -\dfrac{\bar{a}}{r^3} + \dfrac{3 (\bar{a} \cdot \bar{r})}{r^5} \bar{r}$ 　**(May 05, May 07, Dec. 08, May 12)**

Sol. : (i) 　　　$\nabla \cdot (\bar{r}/r^2) = \nabla \cdot (\bar{r} \; r^{-2}) = \nabla (r^{-2}) \cdot \bar{r} + r^{-2} \nabla \cdot \bar{r}$

$$= - 2r^{-4} \bar{r} \cdot \bar{r} + 3r^{-2} \qquad\qquad [\because \nabla \cdot \bar{r} = 3]$$

$$= -\frac{2}{r^2} + \frac{3}{r^2} = \frac{1}{r^2}$$

$$\nabla^2 [\nabla \cdot (\bar{r}/r^2)] = \nabla^2 \left(\frac{1}{r^2} \right) = \nabla \cdot \nabla \left(\frac{1}{r^2} \right)$$

$$= \nabla \cdot \{ - 2r^{-4} \bar{r} \} = - 2 [\nabla (r^{-4}) \cdot \bar{r} + r^{-4} (\nabla \cdot \bar{r})]$$

$$= - 2 [-4r^{-6} \bar{r} \cdot \bar{r} + 3r^{-4}] = - 2 [- 4r^{-6} r^2 + 3r^{-4}] = \frac{2}{r^4}$$

(ii) 　　　$\nabla \times \left(\dfrac{\bar{a} \times \bar{r}}{r^3} \right) = \nabla \times (\bar{a} \times \bar{r} \; r^{-3})$

$$= \{ \nabla \cdot (\bar{r} \; r^{-3}) \} \bar{a} - (\bar{a} \cdot \nabla) \bar{r} \; r^{-3}$$

$$\nabla \cdot (\bar{r} \; r^{-3}) = \nabla (r^{-3}) \cdot \bar{r} + r^{-3} \nabla \cdot \bar{r}$$

$$= - 3r^{-5} \bar{r} \cdot \bar{r} + 3r^{-3} = - 3r^{-3} + 3r^{-3} = 0$$

Treating operator $\bar{a} \cdot \nabla$ like operator D,

$$(\bar{a} \cdot \nabla) \bar{r} \; r^{-3} = r^{-3} (\bar{a} \cdot \nabla) \bar{r} + \bar{r} (\bar{a} \cdot \nabla) \; r^{-3}$$

But 　　　$(\bar{a} \cdot \nabla) \bar{r} = \bar{a}$

and 　　　$(\bar{a} \cdot \nabla) r^{-3} = \bar{a} \cdot \nabla r^{-3} = \bar{a} \cdot (-3) r^{-5} \bar{r} = \dfrac{-3 (\bar{a} \cdot \bar{r})}{r^5}$

$$\therefore \qquad (\bar{a} \cdot \nabla)\,\bar{r}\ r^{-3} \;=\; \frac{\bar{a}}{r^3} - \frac{3\,(\bar{a} \cdot \bar{r})}{r^5}\,\bar{r}$$

$$\therefore \qquad \nabla \times \left(\frac{\bar{a} \times \bar{r}}{r^3}\right) \;=\; \frac{-\,\bar{a}}{r^3} + \frac{3\,(\bar{a} \cdot \bar{r})}{r^5}\,\bar{r}$$

Ex. 6 : *Show that*

(i) $\nabla^2 f(r) = \dfrac{d^2 f}{dr^2} + \dfrac{2}{r}\,\dfrac{df}{dr}$ **(May 2005, , 2017, Dec. 2011)**

(ii) $\nabla^4 e^r = e^r + \dfrac{4}{r}\,e^r$ **(Dec. 2005, 2008, Nov. 2013, Dec. 2014)**

Sol. : (i) $\nabla^2 f(r) \;=\; \nabla \cdot (\nabla f(r)) \;=\; \nabla \cdot \left\{\dfrac{f'(r)}{r}\,\bar{r}\right\} = \dfrac{f'(r)}{r}\,(\nabla \cdot \bar{r}) + \nabla\left(\dfrac{f'(r)}{r}\right)\cdot \bar{r}$

$$= \frac{f'(r)}{r}\,(3) + \left(\frac{r f''(r) - f'(r)}{r^2}\right)\frac{\bar{r}}{r}\cdot\bar{r}$$

$$= \frac{3\,f'(r)}{r} + \left(\frac{r\,f''(r) - f'(r)}{r^3}\right)(\bar{r} \cdot \bar{r})$$

$$= \frac{3\,f'(r)}{r} + \left(\frac{r\,f''(r) - f'(r)}{r}\right) = \frac{3\,f'(r)}{r} + f''(r) - \frac{f'(r)}{r}$$

$$\therefore \qquad \nabla^2 f(r) = f''(r) + \frac{2}{r}\,f'(r) \qquad\qquad\qquad \ldots\text{(i)}$$

(ii) $\nabla^4 e^r \;=\; \nabla^2 \nabla^2 (e^r)$

Let $f(r) = e^r \;\Rightarrow\; f'(r) = e^r, \quad f''(r) = e^r$

$$\therefore \qquad \nabla^2 (e^r) = \frac{2}{r}\,e^r + e^r = \left(\frac{2}{r} + 1\right)e^r \qquad\qquad \ldots\text{ by result (i)}$$

Let $F(r) = e^r\left(\dfrac{2}{r} + 1\right) \;\Rightarrow\; F'(r) = e^r\left(\dfrac{2}{r} + 1\right) + e^r\left(-\dfrac{2}{r^2}\right)$

$$\therefore \qquad F''(r) = e^r\left(\frac{2}{r} + 1\right) + e^r\left(-\frac{2}{r^2}\right) + \frac{4}{r^3}\,e^r - \frac{2}{r^2}\,e^r$$

$$= e^r\left(\frac{2}{r} + 1 - \frac{4}{r^2} + \frac{4}{r^3}\right)$$

$$\therefore \qquad \frac{2}{r}\,F'(r) = \frac{4}{r^2}\,e^r + \frac{2}{r}\,e^r - \frac{4}{r^3}\,e^r$$

and $\nabla^4 e^r \;=\; \nabla^2(\nabla^2 e^r) \;=\; \nabla^2\left\{e^r\left(\dfrac{2}{r} + 1\right)\right\}$

$$= e^r\left\{\frac{2}{r} + 1 - \frac{4}{r^2} + \frac{4}{r^3} + \frac{4}{r^2} + \frac{2}{r} - \frac{4}{r^3}\right\} \qquad \ldots\text{ by result (i)}$$

$$= \frac{4}{r}\,e^r + e^r.$$

Ex. 7 : *If $\rho\,\bar{E} = \nabla\phi$, prove that $\bar{E} \cdot curl\,\bar{E} = 0$.* **(May 2007)**

Sol. :

$$\bar{E} = \frac{1}{\rho}\nabla\phi$$

$\therefore$

$$curl\,\bar{E} = \nabla \times \left(\frac{1}{\rho}\nabla\phi\right) = \nabla\left(\frac{1}{\rho}\right) \times \nabla\phi + \frac{1}{\rho}\,\nabla \times (\nabla\phi)$$

$$= \nabla\left(\frac{1}{\rho}\right) \times \nabla\phi \qquad [\text{as } \nabla \times \nabla\phi = 0]$$

$$\bar{E} \cdot curl\,\bar{E} = \bar{E} \cdot \left[\nabla\left(\frac{1}{\rho}\right) \times \nabla\phi\right]$$

$$= \nabla\left(\frac{1}{\rho}\right) \cdot [\nabla\phi \times \bar{E}] \qquad [\text{By } \bar{a} \cdot (\bar{b} \times \bar{c}) = \bar{b} \cdot (\bar{c} \times \bar{a})]$$

$$= \nabla\left(\frac{1}{\rho}\right) \cdot [\rho\bar{E} \times \bar{E}] = 0 \qquad [\text{as } \bar{E} \times \bar{E} = 0]$$

Ex. 8 : *For a solenoidal vector field $\bar{E}$, show that $curl\,curl\,curl\,curl\,\bar{E} = \nabla^4\bar{E}$.*

(Dec. 04, 06, Nov. 2015, May 09, 12,)

Sol. : $\bar{E}$ being solenoidal,

$$\nabla \cdot \bar{E} = 0$$

$$curl\,\,curl\,\bar{E} = \nabla \times (\nabla \times \bar{E})$$

$$= \nabla(\nabla \cdot \bar{E}) - (\nabla \cdot \nabla)\,\bar{E}$$

$$= -\nabla^2\bar{E} \qquad [\text{as } \nabla \cdot \bar{E} = 0]$$

Let

$$\bar{F} = -\nabla^2\bar{F}$$

$\therefore$

$$curl\,curl\,curl\,curl\,\bar{E} = curl\,curl\,\bar{F}$$

$$= \nabla \times (\nabla \times \bar{F}) = \nabla(\nabla \cdot \bar{F}) - (\nabla \cdot \nabla)\,\bar{F}$$

$$= \nabla[\nabla \cdot (-\nabla^2\bar{E})] - \nabla^2\bar{F}$$

$$= \nabla[-\nabla^2(\nabla \cdot \bar{E})] - \nabla^2(-\nabla^2\bar{E})$$

$$[\text{By commutative property of partial derivatives}]$$

$$= \nabla^4\bar{E} \qquad [\text{as } \nabla \cdot \bar{E} = 0]$$

Ex. 9 : *Show that* $\overline{F} = (6xy + z^3)\,\overline{i} + (3x^2 - z)\,\overline{j} + (3xz^2 - y)\,\overline{k}$ *is irrotational. Find scalar* ϕ *such that* $\overline{F} = \nabla\phi.$ **(Dec. 2008, May 2015, 2016)**

Sol. :
$$
\nabla \times \overline{F} = \begin{vmatrix} \overline{i} & \overline{j} & \overline{k} \\ \dfrac{\partial}{\partial x} & \dfrac{\partial}{\partial y} & \dfrac{\partial}{\partial z} \\ 6xy + z^3 & 3x^2 - z & 3xz^2 - y \end{vmatrix}
$$

$$
= \overline{i}\left\{\frac{\partial}{\partial y}(3xz^2 - y) - \frac{\partial}{\partial z}(3x^2 - z)\right\} + \overline{j}\left\{\frac{\partial}{\partial z}(6xy + z^3) - \frac{\partial}{\partial x}(3xz^2 - y)\right\}
$$

$$
+ \overline{k}\left\{\frac{\partial}{\partial x}(3x^2 - z) - \frac{\partial}{\partial y}(6xy + z^3)\right\}
$$

$$
= \overline{i}\,\{-1 + 1\} + \overline{j}\,\{3z^2 - 3z^2\} + \overline{k}\,\{6x - 6x\} = 0
$$

which shows that $\overline{F}$ is irrotational. To find corresponding scalar ϕ, consider the relation

$$
d\phi \equiv \nabla\phi \cdot d\overline{r}
$$

but
$$
\overline{F} \equiv \nabla\phi
$$

$\therefore$
$$
d\phi \equiv \overline{F} \cdot d\overline{r}
$$

$$
\equiv [(6xy + z^3)\,\overline{i} + (3x^2 - z)\,\overline{j} + (3xz^2 - y)\,\overline{k}] \cdot [\overline{i}\,dx + \overline{j}\,dy + \overline{k}\,dz]
$$

$$
\equiv (6xy + z^3)\,dx + (3x^2 - z)\,dy + (3xz^2 - y)\,dz
$$

$$
\equiv (6xy\,dx + 3x^2\,dy) + (z^3\,dx + 3xz^2\,dz) - (z\,dy + y\,dz)
$$

$$
\equiv d\,(3x^2 y) + d\,(z^3 x) - d\,(yz)
$$

Integrating, we get

$$
\phi = 3x^2\,y + z^3\,x - yz + c
$$

Ex. 10 : *Show that the vector field* $f(r)\,\overline{r}$ *is always irrotational and determine* $f(r)$ *such that the field is solenoidal also. Also find* $f(r)$ *such that* $\nabla^2 f(r) = 0.$
                    (Dec. 2004, 2005, 2008, 2010; May 2007, 2009, May 2011)

Sol. : Consider
$$
\nabla \times f(r)\,\overline{r} = [\nabla f(r)] \times \overline{r} + f(r)\,[\nabla \times \overline{r}]
$$

$$
= \frac{f'(r)}{r}\,\overline{r} \times r + \overline{0} \qquad\qquad (\because \nabla \times \overline{r} = 0)
$$

$$
= \overline{0} \qquad\qquad (\because \overline{r} \times \overline{r} = \overline{0})
$$

Hence the vector field $f(r)\,\bar{r}$ is irrotational. Now, for vector field $f(r)\,\bar{r}$ to be solenoidal, we must have

$$\nabla \cdot [f(r)\,\bar{r}] = 0$$

$$\nabla \cdot [f(r)\,\bar{r}] = \nabla f(r) \cdot \bar{r} + f(r)\,[\nabla \cdot \bar{r}\,]$$

$$= \frac{f'(r)}{r}\,\bar{r} \cdot \bar{r} + 3\,f(r) = f'(r)\,r + 3\,f(r)$$

$$\therefore \qquad f'(r)\,r + 3\,f(r) = 0 \qquad \text{or} \qquad \frac{f'(r)}{f(r)} + \frac{3}{r} = 0$$

On integrating,

$$\log f(r) + 3 \log r = \log C \qquad \text{or} \qquad \log f(r)\,r^3 = \log C$$

$$\text{or} \qquad f(r)\,r^3 = C \qquad \text{or} \qquad f(r) = \frac{C}{r^3}$$

Now, to find $f(r)$ such that $\nabla^2 f(r) = 0$, we have

$$\nabla^2 f(r) = f''(r) + \frac{2}{r}\,f'(r)$$

$$\therefore \qquad f''(r) + \frac{2}{r}\,f'(r) = 0$$

$$\frac{f''(r)}{f'(r)} + \frac{2}{r} = 0$$

On integrating,

$$\log f'(r) + 2 \log r = \log C_1$$

$$\text{or} \qquad \log f'(r)\,r^2 = \log C_1$$

$$\text{or} \qquad f'(r) = \frac{C_1}{r^2}$$

Again integrating, we have

$$f(r) = \int \frac{C_1}{r^2}\,dr + C_2$$

$$f(r) = -\frac{C_1}{r} + C_2$$

Ex. 11 : *Prove that* $\nabla \times \left(\bar{a} \times \nabla \dfrac{1}{r} \right) + \nabla \left(\bar{a} \cdot \nabla \dfrac{1}{r} \right) = 0$

Sol. : $\qquad \nabla \times \left(\bar{a} \times \nabla \dfrac{1}{r} \right) = \nabla \times \left(\bar{a} \times -\dfrac{1}{r^3}\,\bar{r} \right)$

$$= -\nabla \times (\bar{a} \times \bar{r}\ r^{-3})$$

$$= -\left\{ [\nabla \cdot (r^{-3}\,\bar{r})]\,\bar{a} - (\bar{a} \cdot \nabla)\,(\bar{r}\ r^{-3}) \right\}$$

$$= -\left\{ 0 - [(\bar{a} \cdot \nabla)\,\bar{r}\,]\,r^{-3} - \bar{r}\,[(\bar{a} \cdot \nabla)\,r^{-3}] \right\}$$

$$= (\bar{a})\, r^{-3} + \bar{r}\,[\bar{a} \cdot \nabla (r^{-3})]$$

$$= \frac{\bar{a}}{r^3} + \bar{r}\left[\bar{a} \cdot \left(\frac{-3}{r^5}\right)\bar{r}\right]$$

$$\nabla \times \left(\bar{a} \times \nabla \frac{1}{r}\right) = \frac{\bar{a}}{r^3} - \frac{3\,(\bar{a}\cdot\bar{r})\,\bar{r}}{r^5} \qquad \dots (1)$$

$$\nabla\left(\bar{a} \cdot \nabla \frac{1}{r}\right) = \nabla\left[\bar{a} \cdot -\frac{1}{r^3}\bar{r}\right]$$

$$= -(\bar{a} \cdot \bar{r})\,\nabla(r^{-3}) - r^{-3}\,\nabla(\bar{a}\cdot\bar{r})$$

$$= -(\bar{a} \cdot \bar{r})\left(-\frac{3}{r^5}\right)\bar{r} - r^{-3}\,\bar{a}$$

$$\nabla\left(\bar{a} \cdot \nabla \frac{1}{r}\right) = \frac{3\,(\bar{a}\cdot\bar{r})\,\bar{r}}{r^5} - \frac{\bar{a}}{r^3} \qquad \dots (2)$$

By adding (1) and (2), $\nabla \times \left(\bar{a} \times \nabla \dfrac{1}{r}\right) + \nabla\left(\bar{a} \cdot \nabla \dfrac{1}{r}\right) = 0$

Ex. 12 : *Prove that*

(i) $\nabla(\bar{r} \cdot \bar{u}) = \bar{r} \times (\nabla \times \bar{u}) + (\bar{r} \cdot \nabla)\bar{u} + \bar{u}$ 　　　　　**(Dec. 2005, May 2007)**

(ii) $\nabla \times (\bar{r} \times \bar{u}) = \bar{r}(\nabla \cdot \bar{u}) - (\bar{r} \cdot \nabla)\bar{u} - 2\bar{u}$ 　　　　　**(Dec. 2005)**

Sol. : (i) We have,

$$\nabla(\bar{u} \cdot \bar{v}) = \bar{u} \times (\nabla \times \bar{v}) + (\bar{u} \cdot \nabla)\bar{v} + \bar{v} \times (\nabla \times \bar{u}) + (\bar{v} \cdot \nabla)\bar{u}$$

$$\therefore \quad \nabla(\bar{r} \cdot \bar{u}) = \bar{r} \times (\nabla \times \bar{u}) + (\bar{r} \cdot \nabla)\bar{u} + \bar{u} \times (\nabla \times \bar{r}) + (\bar{u} \cdot \nabla)\bar{r}$$

$$\nabla(\bar{r} \cdot \bar{u}) = \bar{r} \times (\nabla \times \bar{u}) + (\bar{r} \cdot \nabla)\bar{u} + \bar{u}$$

$$(\because \nabla \times \bar{r} = 0,\ (\bar{u} \cdot \nabla)\bar{r} = \bar{u})$$

(ii) We have, $\nabla \times (\bar{u} \times \bar{v}) = \bar{u}(\nabla \cdot \bar{v}) - (\bar{u} \cdot \nabla)\bar{v} + (\bar{v} \cdot \nabla)\bar{u} - \bar{v}(\nabla \cdot \bar{u})$

$$\therefore \quad \nabla \times (\bar{r} \times \bar{u}) = \bar{r}(\nabla \cdot \bar{u}) - (\bar{r} \cdot \nabla)\bar{u} + (\bar{u} \cdot \nabla)\bar{r} - \bar{u}(\nabla \cdot \bar{r})$$

$$= \bar{r}(\nabla \cdot \bar{u}) - (\bar{r} \cdot \nabla)\bar{u} + \bar{u} - 3\bar{u}$$

$$(\because \nabla \cdot \bar{r} = 3,\ (\bar{u} \cdot \nabla)\bar{r} = \bar{u})$$

$$= \bar{r}(\nabla \cdot \bar{u}) - (\bar{r} \cdot \nabla)\bar{u} - 2\bar{u}$$

Ex. 13 : *Show that* $\bar{F} = \dfrac{1}{r} [r^2\, \bar{a} + (\bar{a} \cdot \bar{r})\, \bar{r}]$ *is irrotational. Hence find scalar potential* ϕ. **(Dec. 2006)**

Sol. :

$$\bar{F} = r\,\bar{a} + (\bar{a} \cdot \bar{r})\,\frac{\bar{r}}{r}$$

$$\nabla \times \bar{F} = \nabla \times (r\,\bar{a}) + \nabla \times \left[(\bar{a} \cdot \bar{r})\,\frac{\bar{r}}{r}\right]$$

$$= r\,(\nabla \times \bar{a}) + \nabla r \times \bar{a} + (\bar{a} \cdot \bar{r})\left(\nabla \times \frac{\bar{r}}{r}\right) + \nabla\,(\bar{a} \cdot \bar{r}) \times \frac{\bar{r}}{r}$$

$$= \frac{\bar{r}}{r} \times \bar{a} + \bar{a} \times \frac{\bar{r}}{r} = 0$$

$$\therefore \quad \nabla \times \bar{F} = 0 \Rightarrow \bar{F} \text{ is irrotational.}$$

We have $\quad d\phi \equiv \nabla\phi \cdot d\bar{r}$

Since $\bar{F}$ is irrotational, therefore $\bar{F} = \nabla\phi$

$$\therefore \qquad d\phi \equiv \bar{F} \cdot d\bar{r} \equiv \left[r\,\bar{a} + (\bar{a} \cdot \bar{r})\,\frac{\bar{r}}{r}\right] \cdot d\bar{r}$$

$$\equiv r\,(\bar{a} \cdot d\bar{r}) + (\bar{a} \cdot \bar{r})\,\frac{\bar{r} \cdot d\bar{r}}{r}$$

$$\equiv r\,d\,(\bar{a} \cdot \bar{r}) + (\bar{a} \cdot \bar{r})\left(\frac{r\,dr}{r}\right) \qquad (\because \bar{r} \cdot d\bar{r} = r\,dr)$$

$$\therefore \qquad \equiv r\,d\,(\bar{a} \cdot \bar{r}) + (\bar{a} \cdot \bar{r})\,dr$$

$$\equiv d\,[r\,(\bar{a} \cdot \bar{r})]$$

$$\therefore \qquad \phi = r\,(\bar{a} \cdot \bar{r}) + c$$

Ex. 14 : *Find curl curl* $\bar{F}$ *at the point (0, 1, 2) where* **(May 2014)**

$$\bar{F} = x^2 y\,\bar{i} + xyz\,\bar{j} + z^2 y\,\bar{k}$$

Sol.

$$(\nabla \times \bar{F}) = \begin{vmatrix} \bar{i} & \bar{j} & \bar{k} \\ \dfrac{\partial}{\partial x} & \dfrac{\partial}{\partial y} & \dfrac{\partial}{\partial z} \\ x^2 y & xyz & z^2 y \end{vmatrix}$$

$$= \bar{i}\,(z^2 - xy) + \bar{j}\,(0 - 0) + \bar{k}\,(yz - x^2)$$

$$\nabla \times (\nabla \times \overline{F}) = \begin{vmatrix} \overline{i} & \overline{j} & \overline{k} \\ \dfrac{\partial}{\partial x} & \dfrac{\partial}{\partial y} & \dfrac{\partial}{\partial z} \\ z^2 - xy & 0 & yz - x^2 \end{vmatrix}$$

$$= \overline{i}(z) + \overline{j}\,(2z + 2x) + \overline{k}\,(x)$$

$\therefore$ curl curl $\overline{F}$ at $(0, 1, 2) = 2\overline{i} + 4\overline{j}$

Ex. 15 : *Show that $\overline{F} = r^2\,\overline{r}$ is conservative and obtain the scalar potential associated with it.*

Sol. : $\nabla \times \overline{F} = \nabla \times (r^2\,\overline{r}) = \nabla r^2 \times \overline{r} + r^2\,\nabla \times \overline{r}$

$$= 2r^{2-2}\,\overline{r} \times \overline{r} + r^2\,\nabla \times \overline{r}$$

$$= 0 + 0$$

$\therefore$ $\overline{F}$ is conservative.

$$d\phi = \overline{F} \cdot d\overline{r}$$

$$= r^2\,\overline{r} \cdot d\overline{r} = \frac{1}{2}\,r^2\,d\,(\overline{r} \cdot \overline{r}) = \frac{1}{2}\,r^2\,d\,(r^2)$$

$$= \frac{1}{2}\,r^2 \cdot 2r\,dr = r^3\,dr$$

$$\phi = \frac{r^4}{4} + c$$

Ex. 16 : *Show that $\overline{F} = (ye^{xy}\cos z)\,\overline{i} + (xe^{xy}\cos z)\,\overline{j} - e^{xy}\sin z\,\overline{k}$ is irrotational. Find corresponding scalar ϕ, such that $\overline{F} = \nabla\phi$.*

Sol. : $\nabla \times \overline{F} = \begin{vmatrix} \overline{i} & \overline{j} & \overline{k} \\ \dfrac{\partial}{\partial x} & \dfrac{\partial}{\partial y} & \dfrac{\partial}{\partial z} \\ ye^{xy}\cos z & x\,e^{xy}\cos z & -e^{xy}\sin z \end{vmatrix}$

$$= \overline{i}\,(-x\,e^{xy}\sin z + x\,e^{xy}\sin z) + \overline{j}\,(-y\,e^{xy}\sin z + y\,e^{xy}\sin z)$$

$$+ \overline{k}\,(e^{xy}\cos z + xy\,e^{xy}\cos z - e^{xy}\cos z - xy\,e^{xy}\cos z)$$

$$= 0$$

$$d\phi = \nabla\phi \cdot d\bar{r} = \bar{F} \cdot d\bar{r}$$

$$= F_1\, dx + F_2\, dy + F_3\, dz$$

$$= y\, e^{xy} \cos z\, dx + x\, e^{xy} \cos z\, dy - e^{xy} \sin z\, dz$$

$$= \cos z\, (y\, e^{xy}\, dx + x\, e^{xy}\, dy) - e^{xy} \sin z\, dz$$

$$= \cos z\, d\,(e^{xy}) + e^{xy}\, d\,(\cos z)$$

$$= d\,(e^{xy} \cos z)$$

$$\therefore \qquad \phi = e^{xy} \cos z + c$$

Ex. 17 : *Evaluate* $\displaystyle\int_C \frac{x\,dx + y\,dy}{(x^2 + y^2)^{3/2}}$ *along the curve* $\bar{r}(t) = e^t \cos t\, \bar{i} + e^t \sin t\, \bar{j}$ *from (1, 0) to (2π, 0).*

Sol. :

$$x = e^t \cos t, \quad y = e^t \sin t$$

$$dx = (e^t \cos t - e^t \sin t)\, dt, \quad dy = (e^t \sin t + e^t \cos t)\, dt$$

$$x^2 + y^2 = e^{2t}(\cos^2 t + \sin^2 t) = e^{2t}$$

$$I = \int \frac{e^{2t}(\cos^2 t - \sin t \cos t + \sin^2 t + \sin t \cos t)\, dt}{e^{2t}}$$

$x = 1, y = 0$ correspond to $t = 0$.

$x = 2\pi, y = 0$ correspond to $t = \log 2\pi$.

$$\therefore \qquad I = \int_0^{\log 2\pi} dt = [t]_0^{\log 2\pi} = \log 2\pi$$

EXERCISE 10.2

1. Find $\nabla\phi$ for

   (i) $\phi = \log(x^2 + y^2 + z^2)$ (ii) $\phi = 2x\, z^4 - x^2 y;$ at $(2, -2, 1)$

   $$\textbf{(Ans. (i) } \frac{2}{(x^2 + y^2 + z^2)}(x\,\bar{i} + y\,\bar{j} + z\,\bar{k}), \text{ (ii) } 10\,\bar{i} - 4\,\bar{j} + 6\,\bar{k})$$

2. For $\bar{u} = 3xyz^2\,\bar{i} + 2xy^3\,\bar{j} - x^2yz\,\bar{k}$, $\bar{v} = x^3 yz\,\bar{i} + 2xy\,\bar{j} + z^2\bar{k}$, $\phi = 3x^2 - yz$

   find (i) $\nabla \cdot \bar{u}$, (ii) $\bar{u} \cdot \nabla\phi$, (iii) $\nabla \cdot (\phi\,\bar{u})$, (iv) $\nabla \times \bar{v}$, (v) $\nabla \times (\phi\,\bar{u})$,

   (vi) $\bar{u} \times \nabla\phi$ at $(1, 2, -1)$.

   $$\textbf{(Ans. (i) } 28, \text{ (ii) } 48, \text{ (iii) } 188, \text{ (iv) } 2\bar{i} + 3\,\bar{k}, \text{ (v) } \bar{i} - 72\,\bar{j} + 129\,\bar{k}, \text{ (vi) } 6)$$

3. If $\bar{v}_1$, $\bar{v}_2$ are the vectors which join the fixed points P (x_1, y_1, z_1), Q (x_2, y_2, z_2) to the variable point R (x, y, z) then, show that **(May 2008)**

(i) $\nabla (\bar{v}_1 \cdot \bar{v}_2) = \bar{v}_2 + \bar{v}_1$, (ii) $\nabla \times (\bar{v}_1 \times \bar{v}_2) = 2 (\bar{v}_1 - \bar{v}_2)$, (iii) $\nabla \cdot (\bar{v}_1 \times \bar{v}_2) = 0$.

(**Ans.** (i) Irrotational, xy sin z + cos x + y²z, (ii) Irrotational log r,

(iii) Irrotational, $\dfrac{1}{2}$ (a · r)²)

4. Show that $\nabla \int f(u)\, du = f(u)\, \nabla u$.

5. If $\bar{F} = (x^2 - y^2 + 2xz)\, \bar{i} + (xz - xy + yz)\, \bar{j} + (z^2 + x^2)\, \bar{k}$

then show that curl $\bar{F}$ at $(1, 2, -3)$ and $(2, 3, 12)$ are orthogonal.

6. If $u = x + y$, $v = x - y + z$, $w = (2x + z)^2 + (2y - z)^2$ then show that $\nabla u, \nabla v, \nabla w$ are coplanar vectors.

7. If $\bar{F} = 2x^3\, \bar{i} - 3yz\, \bar{j} + xz\, \bar{k}$ and $\phi = 2x - z^3 y$, find

(i) $\bar{F} \cdot \nabla\phi$, (ii) $\bar{F} \times \nabla\phi$ at the point $(1, 2, 1)$.

(**Ans.** (i) 4, (ii) 37 $\bar{i}$ + 14 $\bar{j}$ + 10 $\bar{k}$)

8. Find the directional derivative of $\phi = 4xz^3 - 3x^2 y^2 z$ at $(2, -1, 2)$ **(May 2009)**

(i) In the direction $2\, \bar{i} - 3\, \bar{j} + 6\, \bar{k}$. (ii) Towards the point $\bar{i} + \bar{j} - \bar{k}$.

(iii) Along a line equally inclined with co-ordinate axes,

(iv) Along tangent to the curve $x = e^t \cos t$, $y = e^t \sin t$, $z = e^t$ at $t = 0$. **(May 2005)**

(**Ans.** (i) $\dfrac{664}{7}$, (ii) $\dfrac{64}{\sqrt{14}}$, (iii) $\dfrac{140}{\sqrt{3}}$, (iv) $\dfrac{140}{\sqrt{3}}$)

9. Find directional derivative of $xy^2 + yz^3$ at $(2, -1, 1)$ along the line $2 (x - 2) = (y + 1) = (z - 1)$. **(Dec. 2007, May 2017)**

10. Find the directional derivative of the function $\phi = e^{2x - y - z}$ at $(1, 1, 1)$ in the direction of the tangent to the curve $x = e^{-t}$, $y = 2 \sin t + 1$, $z = t - \cos t$ at $t = 0$.

(Dec. 09, Nov. 2015) (**Ans.** $- 5/\sqrt{6}$)

11. Find the directional derivative of f at $(1, 2, -1)$ where $f(x, y, z) = x^2 y + xyz + z^3$ along normal to the surface $x^2 y^3 = 4xy + y^2 z$ at the point $(1, 2, 0)$. **(Dec. 2009)**

(**Ans.** $- \dfrac{1}{3}$)

12. If the directional derivative of $\phi = a (x + y) + b (y + z) + c (x + z)$ has maximum value 12 in the direction parallel to the line $\dfrac{x - 1}{1} = \dfrac{y - 2}{2} = \dfrac{z - 1}{3}$, find the values of a, b, c.

13. Find the values of the constants a, b, c so that the directional derivative of $\phi = axy^2 + byz + cz^2x^2$ at (2, 1, 1) has a maximum magnitude 12 in a direction parallel to x-axis.   (**Ans.** a = 4, b = – 16, c = 2)

14. The directional derivative of a given function f(x, y) at a point P(2, 3) in a direction towards Q(1, –1) is $\sqrt{17}$ and in a direction towards R(–2, 1) is $\sqrt{20}$. Find the directional derivative of f(x, y) at P(2, 3) towards the point S(6, 2).   (**Ans.** $\dfrac{-68}{7\sqrt{17}}$)

15. Find the constants a and b, so that the surface $ax^2 - byz = (a + 2)\,x$ will be orthogonal to the surface $4x^2 y + z^3 = 4$ at the point (1, –1, 2).

(Dec. 2006, May 2012, May 2005, 2014)

(**Ans.** a $= \dfrac{5}{2}$, b = 1)

16. Evaluate (i) $\nabla \cdot (r^3 \, \bar{r})$, (**Dec. 2007**) (ii) $\nabla \cdot [r\nabla (1/r^3)]$ (**Ans.** (i) $3r^3 + 3r$, (ii) $\dfrac{3}{r^4}$)

17. Show that

(i) $\nabla \cdot \left(\dfrac{\bar{a} \times \bar{r}}{r} \right) = 0$ **(Dec. 2011, May 2014)**

(ii) $\nabla \times \left(\dfrac{\bar{a} \times \bar{r}}{r^n} \right) = \dfrac{(2-n)}{r^n}\,\bar{a} + \dfrac{n}{r^{n+2}}\,(\bar{a} \cdot \bar{r})\,\bar{r}$.   **(Dec. 2006, May 2011)**

18. $\bar{a} \cdot \nabla \left[\bar{b} \cdot \nabla \left(\dfrac{1}{r} \right) \right] = \dfrac{3\,(\bar{a} \cdot \bar{r})\,(\bar{b} \cdot \bar{r})}{r^5} - \dfrac{\bar{a} \cdot \bar{b}}{r^3}$ **(Dec. 15, 16, 08, May 12, 14, 16)**

19. Prove that $\bar{b} \times \nabla\,[\bar{a} \cdot \nabla \log r] = \dfrac{\bar{b} \times \bar{a}}{r^2} - \dfrac{2\,(\bar{a} \cdot \bar{r})}{r^4}\,(\bar{b} \times \bar{r})$ **(May 12, Nov. 15)**

20. Show that

(i) $\nabla^4 \, (r^2 \log r) = \dfrac{6}{r^2}$ **(May 06, 09, 15, 17)**

(ii) $\nabla \cdot \left[r \nabla \left(\dfrac{1}{r^n} \right) \right] = \dfrac{n\,(n-2)}{r^{n+1}}$ **(May 05, 06, 17; Dec. 09, 10, 14)**

(iii) $\nabla^2 \left(\dfrac{\bar{a} \cdot \bar{b}}{r} \right) = 0.$ **(May 2006)**

21. If $\bar{r}$ be a position vector such that $r = |\bar{r}|$ and $\bar{u}$ be a differentiable vector function, then using vector identities, prove that,

(i) $\nabla \int r^n \, dr = r^{n-1}\,\bar{r}$

(ii) $\nabla^2 \, (r^n \log r) = [n\,(n+1)\log r + 2n + 1]\,r^{n-2}$ **(Dec. 06, 08, 09; May 2011)**

22. For scalars ϕ and ψ, show that $\nabla \times (\phi \nabla \psi) = \nabla \phi \times \nabla \psi = - \nabla \times (\psi \nabla \phi)$.

23. If $\bar{F} = (y + z)\,\bar{i} + (z + x)\,\bar{j} + (x + y)\,\bar{k}$ then show that

curl curl curl curl $\bar{F} = \nabla^4\,[(y + z)\,\bar{i} + (z + x)\,\bar{j} + (x + y)\,\bar{k}]$　　　**(Dec. 2007)**

24. If $\bar{w}$ is constant vector and $\bar{v} = \bar{w} \times \bar{r}$, prove that div $\bar{v} = 0$.

25. (i)　Prove that $\bar{F} = \dfrac{1}{(x^2 + y^2)}\,(x\,\bar{i} + y\,\bar{j})$ is solenoidal.　　　**(May 2006)**

(ii)　Find the function f(r) so that f(r) $\bar{r}$ is solenoidal.　　　**(Dec. 2004)**

26. If $\bar{u}$ and $\bar{v}$ are irrotational vectors then prove that $\bar{u} \times \bar{v}$ is solenoidal vector.

(May 2008)

27. If ϕ, ψ satisfy Laplace equation, then prove that the vector $(\phi\nabla\psi - \psi\nabla\phi)$ is solenoidal.

28. Show that $\bar{F} = \dfrac{\bar{a} \times \bar{r}}{r^n}$ is solenoidal field.

29. If $\bar{F}_1 = yz\,\bar{i} + zx\,\bar{j} + xy\,\bar{k}$, $\bar{F}_2 = (\bar{a} \cdot \bar{r})\,\bar{a}$ then show that $\bar{F}_1 \times \bar{F}_2$ is solenoidal.

30. Verify whether following fields are irrotational and if so, find corresponding potential ϕ.

(i)　$(y \sin z - \sin x)\,\bar{i} + (x \sin z + 2\,yz)\,\bar{j} + (xy \cos z + y^2)\,\bar{k}$.　　　**(May 2009)**

(ii)　$\dfrac{\bar{r}}{r^2}$ **(May 2007)** (iii) $(\bar{a} \cdot \bar{r})\,\bar{a}$.

31. Show that the vector field given by $\bar{F} = (y^2 \cos x + z^2)\,\bar{i} + (2y \sin x)\,\bar{j} + 2xz\,\bar{k}$ is conservative and find scalar field such that $\bar{F} = \nabla\phi$. **(Dec. 06, 07, Nov. 15; May 06, 13)**

32. If the vector field $\bar{F} = (x + 2y + az)\,\bar{i} + (bx - 3y - z)\,\bar{j} + (4x + cy + 2z)\,\bar{k}$ is irrotational, find a, b, c and determine ϕ such that $\bar{F} = \nabla\phi$.

(May 05, Dec. 07, May 11, 12, 17)

33. Show that $\bar{F} = r^2\bar{r}$ is conservative and obtain the scalar potential associated with it.

34. Show that $\bar{F} = (2xz^3 + 6y)\,\bar{i} + (6x - 2yz)\,\bar{j} + (3x^2z^2 - y^2)\,\bar{k}$ is irrotational. Find scalar potential ϕ such that $\bar{F} = \nabla\phi$.**(Ans.** $\phi = 6xy + x^2z^3 - y^2z$**) (May 2008, Dec. 14)**

35. Show that vector field $\bar{F} = (x^2 - yz)\,\bar{i} + (y^2 - zx)\,\bar{j} + (z^2 - xy)\,\bar{k}$ is irrotational. Find scalar potential ϕ such that $\bar{F} = \nabla\phi$.　　**(Nov. 16) (Ans.** $\phi = x^3/3 + y^3/3 + z^3/3 - xyz + c$**)**

MULTIPLE CHOICE QUESTIONS (MCQ's)

Type : Gradient, Divergence, Curl and Directional Derivative

1. Vector differential oprator ∇ is defined by   (1)

  (A) $\bar{i}\dfrac{\partial}{\partial x} + \bar{j}\dfrac{\partial}{\partial y} + \bar{k}\dfrac{\partial}{\partial z}$ (B) $\dfrac{\partial}{\partial x} + \dfrac{\partial}{\partial y} + \dfrac{\partial}{\partial z}$

  (C) $\dfrac{\partial^2}{\partial x^2} + \dfrac{\partial^2}{\partial y^2} + \dfrac{\partial^2}{\partial z^2}$ (D) $\bar{i}\dfrac{\partial^2}{\partial x^2} + \bar{j}\dfrac{\partial^2}{\partial y^2} + \bar{k} + \dfrac{\partial^2}{\partial z^2}$

2. Gradient of scalar point function $\phi(x, y, z)$ is   (1)

  (A) $\dfrac{\partial^2\phi}{\partial x^2} + \dfrac{\partial^2\phi}{\partial y^2} + \dfrac{\partial^2\phi}{\partial z^2}$ (B) $\dfrac{\partial\phi}{\partial x} + \dfrac{\partial\phi}{\partial y} + \dfrac{\partial\phi}{\partial z}$

  (C) $\dfrac{\partial\phi}{\partial x} \dfrac{\partial\phi}{\partial y} \dfrac{\partial\phi}{\partial z}$ (D) $\dfrac{\partial\phi}{\partial x}\bar{i} + \dfrac{\partial\phi}{\partial y}\bar{j} + \dfrac{\partial\phi}{\partial z}\bar{k}$

3. For the level surface $\phi(x, y, z) = c$, gradient of ϕ represents   (1)

  (A) unive vector   (B) tangent vector

  (C) normal vector   (D) radius vector

4. For the scalar point functions ϕ and ψ, $\nabla(\phi\psi) =$ (1)

  (A) $\phi\nabla\psi - \psi\nabla\phi$ (B) $\phi\nabla\psi + \psi\nabla\phi$

  (C) $\phi(\nabla^2\psi) + \psi(\nabla^2\phi)$ (D) $\dfrac{\phi\nabla\psi - \psi\nabla\phi}{\psi^2}$

5. For the scalar point function ϕ and ψ, $\nabla\left(\dfrac{\phi}{\psi}\right) =$ (1)

  (A) $\phi\nabla\psi + \psi\nabla\phi$ (B) $\dfrac{\phi\nabla\psi - \psi\nabla\phi}{\psi^2}$

  (C) $\dfrac{\psi\nabla\phi + \phi\nabla\psi}{\psi^2}$ (D) $\dfrac{\psi\nabla\phi - \phi\nabla\psi}{\psi^2}$

6. If $\bar{F} = F_1(x, y, z)\,\bar{i} + F_2(x, y, z)\,\bar{j} + F_3(x, y, z)\,\bar{k}$ is a vector field then divergence of $\bar{F}$ is   (1)

  (A) $\dfrac{\partial F_1}{\partial x} + \dfrac{\partial F_2}{\partial y} + \dfrac{\partial F_3}{\partial z}$

  (B) $\dfrac{\partial F_1}{\partial x}\bar{i} + \dfrac{\partial F_2}{\partial y}\bar{j} + \dfrac{\partial F_3}{\partial z}\bar{k}$

  (C) $\dfrac{\partial F_1}{\partial x} \dfrac{\partial F_2}{\partial y} \dfrac{\partial F_3}{\partial z}$

  (D) $\left(\bar{i}\dfrac{\partial}{\partial x} + \bar{j}\dfrac{\partial}{\partial y} + \bar{k}\dfrac{\partial}{\partial z}\right) \times (F_1\bar{i} + F_2\bar{j} + F_3\bar{k})$

7. If $\bar{F} = F_1(x, y, z)\,\bar{i} + F_2(x, y, z)\,\bar{j} + F_3(x, y, z)\,\bar{k}$ is a vector field then curl of $\bar{F}$ is　(1)

(A) $\dfrac{\partial F_1}{\partial x}\,\bar{i} + \dfrac{\partial F_2}{\partial y}\,\bar{j} + \dfrac{\partial F_3}{\partial z}\,\bar{k}$

(B) $\dfrac{\partial F_1}{\partial x} + \dfrac{\partial F_2}{\partial y} + \dfrac{\partial F_3}{\partial z}$

(C) $\left(\bar{i}\,\dfrac{\partial}{\partial x} + \bar{j}\,\dfrac{\partial}{\partial y} + \bar{k}\,\dfrac{\partial}{\partial z}\right) \times (F_1\bar{i} + F_2\bar{j} + F_3\bar{k})$

(D) $\dfrac{\partial F_1}{\partial x}\ \dfrac{\partial F_2}{\partial y}\ \dfrac{\partial F_3}{\partial z}$

8. A rigid body rotating with costant angular velocity $\bar{\omega}$ about a fixed axis, if $\bar{v}$ is the linear velocity of a point of the body then curl $\bar{v}$ is　(1)

(A) $\bar{\omega}$ 　　　　　　　　　　　　　　(B) $2\bar{\omega}$

(C) $\dfrac{\bar{\omega}}{2}$ 　　　　　　　　　　　　(D) $3\bar{\omega}$

9. Vector field $\bar{F}$ is solenoidal if　(1)

(A) $\nabla \times \bar{F} = 0$ 　　　　　　　　　　(B) $\nabla \cdot \bar{F} = 0$

(C) $\nabla^2 \bar{F} = 0$ 　　　　　　　　　　(D) $\bar{F} \cdot \nabla = 0$

10. Vector field $\bar{F}$ is irrotational if　(1)

(A) $\nabla \cdot \bar{F} = 0$ 　　　　　　　　　　(B) $\bar{F} \times \nabla = 0$

(C) $\nabla^2 \bar{F} = 0$ 　　　　　　　　　　(D) $\nabla \times \bar{F} = \bar{0}$

11. Directional derivative of scalar point function $\phi(x, y, z)$ at a point $P(x_1, x_2, x_3)$ in the direction of vector $\bar{u}$ is　(1)

(A) $\nabla \cdot (\phi\,\hat{u})_{(x_1,\, x_2,\, x_3)}$ 　　　　　　(B) $(\nabla \phi)_{(x_1,\, x_2,\, x_3)} \times \hat{u}$

(C) $(\nabla \phi)_{(x_1,\, x_2,\, x_3)} \cdot \hat{u}$ 　　　　　(D) $(\nabla^2 \phi)_{(x_1,\, x_2,\, x_3)} \cdot \hat{u}$

12. Magnitude of maximum directional derivative of scalar point function $\phi(x, y, z)$ in the given direction is　(1)

(A) $|\nabla \phi|$ 　　　　　　　　　　　　(B) $|\nabla^2 \phi|$

(C) $|\phi \nabla \phi|$ 　　　　　　　　　　(D) zero

13. Maximum directional derivative of scalar point function $\phi(x, y, z)$ is in the direction of　　　　(1)

(A) tangent vector

(B) $\bar{i} + \bar{j} + \bar{k}$

(C) radius vector

(D) normal vector

14. If $\phi = xy^2 + yz^2$ and $(\nabla\phi)_{(1, -1, 1)} = \bar{i} - \bar{j} - 3\bar{k}$ then the value of maximum directional derivative is　　　　(1)

(A) $\dfrac{\bar{i} - \bar{j} - 3\bar{k}}{\sqrt{11}}$

(B) $\dfrac{1}{\sqrt{11}}$

(C) $\sqrt{4}$

(D) $\sqrt{11}$

15. If $\bar{r} = x\bar{i} + y\bar{j} + z\bar{k}$ and $r = \sqrt{x^2 + y^2 + z^2}$ then ∇r is given by　　　　(2)

(A) $\dfrac{\bar{r}}{r}$

(B) $\bar{r}$

(C) $\dfrac{\bar{r}}{r^2}$

(D) $\dfrac{1}{r^3}$

16. If $\phi = x + y + z$, $\bar{a} = \bar{i} + \bar{j} + \bar{k}$ then $\nabla\phi \cdot \hat{a}$ is equal to　　　　(2)

(A) $\dfrac{3}{2}$

(B) $\sqrt{3}$

(C) 0

(D) $-\dfrac{5}{2}$

17. If $\phi = mx^2 + y + z$, $\bar{b} = 2\bar{i} - 3\bar{j} + \bar{k}$ and $\nabla\phi$ at the point $(1, 0, 1)$ is perpendicular to $\bar{b}$ then m is equal to　　　　(2)

(A) 0

(B) $\dfrac{3}{2}$

(C) $\dfrac{1}{2}$

(D) $-\dfrac{5}{2}$

18. The divergence of vector field $\bar{F} = 3xz\,\bar{i} + 2xy\,\bar{j} - yz^2\,\bar{k}$ at a point $(1, 1, 1)$ is　　　　(2)

(A) 3

(B) 4

(C) 7

(D) 0

19. The divergence of vector field $\bar{F} = x^2y\,\bar{i} + y^2\,\bar{j} + z^2x\,\bar{k}$ at a point $(1, 2, 1)$ is　　　　(2)

(A) 5

(B) 8

(C) 10

(D) 12

20. If vector field $\bar{v} = (x + 3y)\,\bar{i} + (y - 2z)\,\bar{j} + (x + az)\,\bar{k}$ is solenoidal then value of a is　(2)

  (A) 0　　　　　　　　　　　　(B) 3

  (C) 2　　　　　　　　　　　　(D) – 2

21. The value of λ so that the vector field $\bar{u} = (2x + 3y)\,\bar{i} + (4y - 2z)\,\bar{j} + (3x - \lambda 6z)\,\bar{k}$ is solenoidal is　(2)

  (A) – 6　　　　　　　　　　　　(B) 1

  (C) 0　　　　　　　　　　　　(D) – 1

22. The curl of vector field $\bar{\bar{F}} = x^2 y\,\bar{i} + xyz\,\bar{j} + z^2 y\,\bar{k}$ at the point $(0, 1, 2)$ is　(2)

  (A) $4\bar{i} - 2\bar{j} + 2\bar{k}$　　　　　　　　　　(B) $4\bar{i} + 2\bar{j} + 2\bar{k}$

  (C) $4\bar{i} + 2\bar{k}$　　　　　　　　　　　(D) $2\bar{i} + 4\bar{k}$

23. If the vector field $\bar{\bar{F}} = (x + 2y + az)\,\bar{i} + (2x - 3y - z)\,\bar{j} + (4x - y + 2z)\,\bar{k}$ is irrotational then the value of a is　(2)

  (A) – 4　　　　　　　　　　　　(B) 3

  (C) – 3　　　　　　　　　　　　(D) 4

24. If $\bar{u} = x^2 y\,\bar{i} + y^2 x^3\,\bar{j} - 3x^2 z^2\,\bar{k}$ and $\phi = x^2 yz$, then $(\bar{u} \cdot \nabla)\,\phi$ at the point $(1, 2, 1)$ is　(2)

  (A) 6　　　　　　　　　　　　(B) 9

  (C) 18　　　　　　　　　　　(D) 5

25. If $u = x + y + z$, $v = x + y$, $w = -2xz - 2yz - z^2$ then $\nabla u \cdot (\nabla v \times \nabla w)$ is　(2)

  (A) $-2y - 2z$　　　　　　　　　　(B) 0

  (C) $-4x - 4y - 4z$　　　　　　　(D) $-2x - 2y - 2z$

26. Unit vector in the direction normal to the surface $x^2 + y^2 + z^2 = 9$ at $(1, 2, 2)$ is　(2)

  (A) $\dfrac{1}{3}(\bar{i} + 2\bar{j} + 2\bar{k})$　　　　　　　(B) $\dfrac{1}{3}(\bar{i} - 2\bar{j} - 2\bar{k})$

  (C) $\dfrac{1}{3}(\bar{i} + \bar{j} + \bar{k})$　　　　　　　　(D) $\dfrac{1}{9}(\bar{i} + 2\bar{j} + 2\bar{k})$

27. Unit vector in the direction normal to the surface $xy = z^2$ at $(1, 1, 1)$ is　(2)

  (A) $\dfrac{1}{\sqrt{6}}(2\bar{i} + \bar{j} + 2\bar{k})$　　　　　　(B) $\dfrac{1}{\sqrt{6}}(\bar{i} - \bar{j} + 2\bar{k})$

  (C) $\dfrac{1}{6}(\bar{i} - \bar{j} - 2\bar{k})$　　　　　　　(D) $\dfrac{1}{\sqrt{6}}(\bar{i} + \bar{j} - 2\bar{k})$

28. Unit vector in the direction normal to the surfae $2x + 3y + 4z = 7$ at $(1, -1, 2)$ is   (2)

(A) $\dfrac{1}{\sqrt{29}} (2\bar{i} + \bar{j} - 4\bar{k})$

(B) $\dfrac{1}{\sqrt{29}} (2\bar{i} + 3\bar{j} + 4\bar{k})$

(C) $\dfrac{1}{29} (2\bar{i} - 3\bar{j} + 4\bar{k})$

(D) $\dfrac{1}{\sqrt{29}} (8\bar{i} + 6\bar{j} + 48\bar{k})$

29. Unit vector in the direction of tangent to the curve $x = \sin t$, $y = \cos t$, $z = t$ at $t = \dfrac{\pi}{4}$ is   (2)

(A) $\dfrac{1}{2} (\bar{i} - \bar{j} + \bar{k})$

(B) $-\dfrac{1}{2}\bar{i} + \dfrac{1}{2}\bar{j} + \dfrac{1}{\sqrt{2}}\bar{k}$

(C) $\dfrac{1}{2}\bar{i} - \dfrac{1}{2}\bar{j} + \dfrac{1}{\sqrt{2}}\bar{k}$

(D) $\dfrac{1}{4}\bar{i} - \dfrac{1}{4}\bar{j} + \dfrac{1}{\sqrt{2}}\bar{k}$

30. Unit vector in the direction of tangent to the curve $x = e^{-t}$, $y = 2 \sin t + 1$, $z = t - \cos t$ at $t = 0$ is   (2)

(A) $\dfrac{1}{\sqrt{6}} (-\bar{i} + 2\bar{j} + \bar{k})$

(B) $\dfrac{1}{6} (-\bar{i} + 2\bar{j} + \bar{k})$

(C) $\dfrac{1}{\sqrt{6}} (-2\bar{i} + \bar{j} + \bar{k})$

(D) $\dfrac{1}{\sqrt{6}} (-\bar{i} + \bar{j} - \bar{k})$

31. Unit vector in the direction of tangent to the curve $x = t^3 - 1$, $y = 3t - 1$, $z = t^2 - 1$ at $t = 1$ is   (2)

(A) $\dfrac{1}{22} (3\bar{i} + 3\bar{j} + \bar{k})$

(B) $\dfrac{1}{\sqrt{22}} (3\bar{i} + \bar{j} + \bar{k})$

(C) $\dfrac{1}{\sqrt{22}} (\bar{i} - 3\bar{j} + 2\bar{k})$

(D) $\dfrac{1}{\sqrt{22}} (3\bar{i} + 3\bar{j} + 2\bar{k})$

32. Unit vector along the line equal inclined with co-ordinate axes is   (2)

(A) $\dfrac{1}{\sqrt{3}} (\bar{i} + \bar{j} + \bar{k})$

(B) $\dfrac{1}{\sqrt{3}} (\bar{i} - \bar{j} - \bar{k})$

(C) $\dfrac{1}{3} (\bar{i} + \bar{j} + \bar{k})$

(D) $\dfrac{1}{\sqrt{3}} (-\bar{i} + \bar{j} - \bar{k})$

33. Unit vector along the direction of line $2 (x - 2) = (y + 1) = (z - 1)$ is   (2)

(A) $\dfrac{1}{\sqrt{3}} (\bar{i} + 2\bar{j} - 2\bar{k})$

(B) $\dfrac{1}{3} (\bar{i} + 2\bar{j} + 2\bar{k})$

(C) $\dfrac{1}{3} (\bar{i} - 2\bar{j} + 2\bar{k})$

(D) $\dfrac{1}{3} (2\bar{i} + \bar{j} + 2\bar{k})$

34. Unit vector along the direction of line $\dfrac{x-1}{2} = \dfrac{y+2}{1} = \dfrac{z-3}{5}$ is	(2)

(A) $\dfrac{1}{\sqrt{14}}(\bar{i} - 2\bar{j} - 3\bar{k})$

(B) $\dfrac{1}{\sqrt{30}}(\bar{i} + 2\bar{j} + 5\bar{k})$

(C) $\dfrac{1}{30}(2\bar{i} + \bar{j} - 5\bar{k})$

(D) $\dfrac{1}{\sqrt{30}}(2\bar{i} + \bar{j} + 5\bar{k})$

35. The directional derivative of $\phi = 2x^2 + 3y^2 + z^2$ at the point $(2, 1, 3)$ in the direction of vector $\bar{u} = \bar{i} - 2\bar{j} + 2\bar{k}$ is	(2)

(A) $\dfrac{8}{3}$

(B) 8

(C) $\dfrac{4}{3}$

(D) $\dfrac{16}{3}$

36. The directional derivative of $\phi = xy^2 + yz^3$ at the point $(1, -1, 1)$ in the direction of vector $\bar{u} = 2\bar{i} + 4\bar{j} + 4\bar{k}$ is	(2)

(A) $\dfrac{7}{3}$

(B) $-\dfrac{7}{3}$

(C) -7

(D) $-\dfrac{7}{6}$

37. The directional derivative of $\phi = xy + yz + xz$ at the point $(1, 2, 0)$ in the direction of vector $\bar{u} = 2\bar{i} + \bar{j} + 3\bar{k}$ is	(2)

(A) $\dfrac{14}{\sqrt{6}}$

(B) $\dfrac{10}{\sqrt{14}}$

(C) $\sqrt{14}$

(D) $\dfrac{8}{\sqrt{14}}$

38. The directional derivative of $\phi = e^{2x - y - z}$ at the point $(1, 1, 1)$ in the direction of vector $\bar{u} = -\bar{i} + 2\bar{j} + \bar{k}$ is	(2)

(A) $-\dfrac{5}{2}$

(B) $-\dfrac{1}{\sqrt{6}}$

(C) $-\dfrac{5}{\sqrt{6}}$

(D) $\dfrac{5}{\sqrt{6}}$

39. The directional derivative of $\phi = e^{2x}\cos(yz)$ at origin in the direction of vector $\bar{u} = \bar{i} + \bar{j} + \bar{k}$ is	(2)

(A) $\dfrac{4}{\sqrt{3}}$

(B) $\dfrac{2}{\sqrt{3}}$

(C) 0

(D) $\dfrac{5}{\sqrt{3}}$

40. The directional derivative of $\phi = xy^2 + yz^3$ at $(1, -1, 1)$ in the direction towards the point $(2, 1, -1)$ is [Given : $(\nabla\phi)_{(1, -1, 1)} = \bar{i} - \bar{j} - 3\bar{k}$] (2)

(A) $\dfrac{5}{3}$　　　　　　　　　　　　(B) 5

(C) 3　　　　　　　　　　　　(D) $\dfrac{5}{\sqrt{3}}$

41. If the partial derivatives of certain function $\phi(x, y)$ are given by the equations $-\dfrac{\partial\phi}{\partial x} + \dfrac{\partial\phi}{\partial y} = 6$, $\dfrac{\partial\phi}{\partial x} + \dfrac{\partial\phi}{\partial y} = -4$ then the directional derivative of $\phi(x, y)$, along the direction of the vector $\bar{i} + \bar{j}$ is given by (2)

(A) $2\sqrt{2}$　　　　　　　　　　　　(B) $3\sqrt{2}$

(C) $\sqrt{2}$　　　　　　　　　　　　(D) $-2\sqrt{2}$

42. For what values of a, b, c the directional derivative of $\phi = axy + byz + czx$ at $(1, 1, 1)$ has maximum magnitude 4 in a direction paralllel to x-axis (2)

[Given : $(\nabla\phi)_{(1, 1, 1)} = (a + c)\,\bar{i} + (a + b)\,\bar{j} + (b + c)\,\bar{k}$]

(A) $a = -2, b = 2, c = -2$　　　　　　(B) $a = 1, b = -1, c = 1$

(C) $a = 2, b = -2, c = 2$　　　　　　(D) $a = 2, b = 2, c = 2$

43. For what values of a, b, c the directional derivative of $\phi = axy^2 + byz + cz^2x^3$ at $(1, 2, -1)$ has maximum magnitude 64 in a direction parallel to z-axis (2)

[Given : $(\nabla\phi)_{1, 2, -1} = (4a + 3c)\,\bar{i} + (4a - b)\,\bar{j} + (2b - 2c)\,\bar{k}$]

(A) $a = 24, b = 6, c = -8$　　　　　　(B) $a = -6, b = -24, c = 8$

(C) $a = 4, b = 16, c = 16$　　　　　　(D) $a = 6, b = 24, c = -8$

44. The directional derivative of $\phi = x^2yz^3$ at $(2, 1, -1)$ has maximum value in the direction of vector (2)

(A) $-4\bar{i} - 4\bar{j} - 2\bar{k}$　　　　　　(B) $-4\bar{i} - 4\bar{j} + 12\bar{k}$

(C) $-\bar{i} + 4\bar{j} + 12\bar{k}$　　　　　　(D) $4\bar{i} - 4\bar{j} - 12\bar{k}$

45. The dierctional derivative of $\phi = xy + yz + xz$ at $(1, 2, 0)$ has maximum value in the direction of vector (2)

(A) $2\bar{i} + \bar{j} + 3\bar{k}$　　　　　　(B) $\bar{i} + 2\bar{j} + 3\bar{k}$

(C) $2\bar{i} + 3\bar{j}$　　　　　　(D) $2\bar{j} + 3\bar{j} + \bar{k}$

46. The directional derivative of $f = x^2y + 2y^2x$ at $(1, 3)$ has maximum value in the direction of vector $\hspace{2cm}$ (2)

(A) $42\bar{i} + 13\bar{j}$ (B) $24\bar{i} + 31\bar{j}$

(C) $13\bar{i} + 24\bar{j}$ (D) $24\bar{i} + 13\bar{j}$

47. If the directional derivatived of $\phi = ax + by$ has maximum magnitude 2 along x-axis, then a, b are respectively given by $\hspace{2cm}$ (2)

(A) $1, 0$ (B) $0, 1$

(C) $2, 0$ (D) $1, 1$

48. Maximum value of directional derivative of $\phi = 4xy^2 - 16yz + 2z^2x^2$ at $(2, 1, 1)$ is (2)

(A) 12   (B) 8

(C) 16   (D) 4

49. Maximum value of directional derivative of $\phi = xyz^2$ at $(1, 0, 3)$ is $\hspace{2cm}$ (2)

(A) 12   (B) 9

(C) 3   (D) 17

50. Maximum value of directional derivative of $\phi = 2xy - 2yz + 2xz$ at $(1, 1, 1)$ is $\hspace{1cm}$ (2)

(A) 2   (B) 13

(C) 4   (D) 11

51. The angle between the surfaces $\phi = x \log z - y^2 - 1 = 0$ and $\psi = x^2y + z + 2 = 0$ at $(1, 1, 1)$ is [Given : $\nabla\phi = \log z\,\bar{i} + (-2y)\,\bar{j} + \dfrac{x}{z}\bar{k}$ and $\nabla\psi = 2xy\,\bar{i} + x^2\,\bar{j} + \bar{k}$] $\hspace{1cm}$ (2)

(A) $\cos^{-1}\left(-\dfrac{3}{\sqrt{10}}\right)$ (B) $\cos^{-1}\left(-\dfrac{1}{\sqrt{30}}\right)$

(C) $\cos^{-1}\left(-\dfrac{1}{2\sqrt{3}}\right)$ (D) $\cos^{-1}-\left(\dfrac{2}{\sqrt{30}}\right)$

52. The angle between the surfaces $\phi = \dfrac{5}{2}x^2 - yz - \dfrac{9}{2}x = 0$ and $\psi = 4x^2y + z^3 - 4 = 0$ at $(1, 1, 1)$ is $\hspace{2cm}$ (2)

[Given : $\nabla\phi = \left(5x - \dfrac{9}{2}\right)\bar{i} + (-z)\,\bar{j} + (-y)\,\bar{k}$ and $\nabla\psi = 8xy\,\bar{i} + 4x^2\,\bar{j} + 3z^2\,\bar{k}$]

(A) $\cos^{-1}\left(-\dfrac{2}{\sqrt{89}}\right)$ (B) $\cos^{-1}\left(-\dfrac{9}{2\sqrt{89}}\right)$

(C) $\cos^{-1}\left(\dfrac{2}{\sqrt{89}}\right)$ (D) $\cos^{-}\left(-\dfrac{10}{3\sqrt{89}}\right)$

53. If the surfaces $\phi_1 = xyz - 1 = 0$ and $\phi_2 = x^2 + ay^2 + z^2 = 0$ are orthogonal at $(1, 1, 1)$ then a is equal to　　　(2)

(A) -1　　　　　　　　　　(B) 2

(C) 1　　　　　　　　　　(D) -2

Answers

1. (A)	2. (D)	3. (C)	4. (B)	5. (D)	6. (A)	7. (C)	8. (B)
9. (B)	10. (D)	11.(C)	12. (A)	13. (D)	14. (D)	15. (A)	16. (B)
17. (C)	18. (A)	19. (C)	20. (D)	21. (B)	22. (C)	23. (D)	24.(A)
25. (B)	26. (A)	27. (D)	28. (B)	29. (C)	30. (A)	31. (D)	32. (A)
33. (B)	34. (D)	35. (A)	36. (B)	37. (C)	38. (C)	39. (B)	40. (A)
41. (D)	42. (C)	43. (D)	44. (B)	45. (A)	46. (D)	47. (C)	48. (A)
49. (B)	50. (C)	51. (B)	52. (A)	53. (D)			

Type : Vector Identities.

1. $\nabla f(r)$ is equal to　　　(1)

(A) $\dfrac{f(r)}{r}\,\bar{r}$　　　　　　　　(B) $\dfrac{f\,'(r)}{r}\,\bar{r}$

(C) $\dfrac{r}{f\,'(r)}\,\bar{r}$　　　　　　　　(D) $f\,'(r)\,\bar{r}$

2. For a constant vector $\bar{a}$, $\nabla\,(\bar{a}\cdot\bar{r})$ is equal to　　　(1)

(A) $\bar{a}$　　　　　　　　　　(B) $3\bar{a}$

(C) $\bar{r}$　　　　　　　　　　(D) 0

3. For constant vectors $\bar{a}$ and $\bar{b}$, $\nabla\,(\bar{a}\cdot\bar{b})$ is equal to　　　(1)

(A) $\bar{a}\cdot\bar{b}$　　　　　　　　　(B) $\bar{a}$

(C) $\bar{b}$　　　　　　　　　　(D) 0

4. $\nabla\cdot\bar{r}$ is equal to　　　(1)

(A) 0　　　　　　　　　　(B) $\dfrac{1}{r}\,\bar{r}$

(C) 3　　　　　　　　　　(D) 1

5. $\nabla\times\bar{r} =$　　　(1)

(A) $\bar{r}$　　　　　　　　　　(B) 3

(C) $\dfrac{1}{r}\,\bar{r}$　　　　　　　　　(D) $\bar{0}$

6. For a constant vector $\bar{a}$, $(\bar{a} \cdot \nabla)\,\bar{r}$ is equal to   (1)

(A) $\bar{a}$ (B) $\bar{a} \cdot \bar{r}$

(C) $\bar{a} \cdot \dfrac{1}{r}\,\bar{r}$ (D) 3

7. For scalar function ϕ and vector function $\bar{u}$, $\nabla \cdot (\phi\bar{u})$ is equal to   (1)

(A) $\phi(\nabla \times \bar{u}) + \nabla\phi \times \bar{u}$ (B) $\phi(\nabla \cdot \bar{u}) + \nabla\phi \cdot \bar{u}$

(C) $\phi(\nabla \cdot \bar{u}) - \nabla\phi \cdot \bar{u}$ (D) $\phi(\bar{u} \cdot \nabla) + \bar{u} \cdot \nabla\phi$

8. For scalar function ϕ and vector function $\bar{u}$, $\nabla \times (\phi\bar{u})$ is equal to   (1)

(A) $\phi(\nabla \times \bar{u}) + \bar{u} \times \nabla\phi$ (B) $\phi(\nabla \cdot \bar{u}) - \nabla\phi \cdot \bar{u}$

(C) $\phi(\nabla \times \bar{u}) + \nabla\phi \times \bar{u}$ (D) $\phi(\nabla \cdot \bar{u}) + \nabla\phi \cdot \bar{u}$

9. For the vector function $\bar{u}$ and $\bar{v}$, $\nabla \cdot (\bar{u} \times \bar{v})$ is equal to   (1)

(A) $\bar{v} \cdot (\nabla \times \bar{u}) - \bar{u} \cdot (\nabla \times \bar{v})$ (B) $\bar{v} \times (\nabla \cdot \bar{u}) - \bar{u} \times (\nabla \cdot \bar{v})$

(C) $\bar{u} \cdot (\nabla \times \bar{v}) - \bar{v} \cdot (\nabla \times \bar{u})$ (D) $\bar{v} \cdot (\bar{u} \times \nabla) + \bar{u} \cdot (\bar{v} \times \nabla)$

10. For the scalar function ϕ, div (grad ϕ) is equal to   (1)

(A) 1 (B) $\dfrac{\partial\phi}{\partial x}\,\bar{i} + \dfrac{\partial\phi}{\partial y}\,\bar{j} + \dfrac{\partial\phi}{\partial z}\,\bar{k}$

(C) $\dfrac{\partial^2\phi}{\partial x^2} + \dfrac{\partial^2\phi}{\partial y^2} + \dfrac{\partial^2\phi}{\partial z^2}$ (D) 0

11. For the scalar function ϕ, curl (grad ϕ) is equal to   (1)

(A) $\dfrac{\partial^2\phi}{\partial x^2}\,\bar{i} + \dfrac{\partial^2\phi}{\partial y^2}\,\bar{j} + \dfrac{\partial^2\phi}{\partial z^2}\,\bar{k}$ (B) $\dfrac{\partial\phi}{\partial x}\,\bar{i} + \dfrac{\partial\phi}{\partial y}\,\bar{j} + \dfrac{\partial\phi}{\partial z}\,\bar{k}$

(C) $\dfrac{\partial^2\phi}{\partial x^2} + \dfrac{\partial^2\phi}{\partial y^2} + \dfrac{\partial^2\phi}{\partial z}$ (D) $\bar{0}$

12. For vector function $\bar{u}$, div (curl $\bar{u}$) is equal to   (1)

(A) $(\nabla \cdot \bar{u}) - \nabla^2\bar{u}$ (B) 0

(C) $\nabla\,(\nabla \cdot \bar{u}) - \nabla^2\bar{u}$ (D) $\nabla\,(\nabla \cdot \bar{u}) + \nabla^2\bar{u}$

13. For vector function $\bar{u}$, curl (curl $\bar{u}$) is equal to   (1)

(A) $\nabla\,(\nabla \cdot \bar{u}) - \nabla^2\bar{u}$ (B) $\nabla\,(\nabla \cdot \bar{u}) + \nabla^2\bar{u}$

(C) $\nabla\,(\nabla \times \bar{u}) - \nabla \cdot \bar{u}$ (D) $\nabla \cdot (\nabla \times \bar{u}) + \nabla^2\bar{u}$

14. $\nabla^2 f(r)$ is equal to $\hspace{2cm}$ (1)

(A) $\dfrac{f'(r)}{r}\,\bar{r}$

(B) $\dfrac{d^2f}{dr^2} + \dfrac{df}{dr}$

(C) $\dfrac{d^2f}{dr^2} - \dfrac{2}{r}\dfrac{df}{dr}$

(D) $\dfrac{d^2f}{dr^2} + \dfrac{2}{r}\dfrac{df}{dr}$

15. If $\bar{F}$ is irrotational vector field then there exits scalar potential ϕ such that $\hspace{1cm}$ (1)

(A) $\bar{F} = \nabla^2\phi$

(B) $\bar{F} = \nabla\phi$

(C) $\phi = \nabla \cdot \bar{F}$

(D) $\nabla \times \bar{F} = \nabla\phi$

16. ∇e^r is equal to $\hspace{2cm}$ (1)

(A) $e^r\,\bar{r}$

(B) $\dfrac{e^r}{r}$

(C) $\dfrac{e^r}{r}\,\bar{r}$

(D) $\dfrac{r}{e^r}\,\bar{r}$

17. $\nabla \log r$ is equal to $\hspace{2cm}$ (1)

(A) $\dfrac{\log r}{r}\,\bar{r}$

(B) $\dfrac{1}{r^2}\,\bar{r}$

(C) $\bar{r}$

(D) $\dfrac{1}{r}\,\bar{r}$

18. ∇r^n is equal to $\hspace{2cm}$ (1)

(A) $n\,r^{n-1}$

(B) $\dfrac{r^{n+1}}{n+1}\,\bar{r}$

(C) $\dfrac{3r^{n-2}}{r}$

(D) $n\,r^{n-2}\,\bar{r}$

19. $\nabla(r^2 e^{-r})$ is given by $\hspace{2cm}$ (2)

(A) $(2-r)\,\bar{r}\,e^{-r}$

(B) $(2+r^2)\,\bar{r}\,e^{-r}$

(C) $(2-r)\,e^{-r}$

(D) $\bar{r}\,e^{-r}$

20. $\nabla(r^2 \log r)$ is equal to $\hspace{2cm}$ (2)

(A) $(2\log r + 1)\,r\,\bar{r}$

(B) $(2r + 1)\log r\,\bar{r}$

(C) $(2\log r + 1)\,\bar{r}$

(D) $(2\log r + 1)$

21. For constant vector $\bar{a}$, $\nabla\left(\dfrac{\bar{a}\cdot\bar{r}}{r^n}\right)$ is equal to $\hspace{1cm}$ (2)

(A) $\dfrac{\bar{a}\cdot\bar{r}}{r^n} - \dfrac{1}{r^{n+2}}\,\bar{r}$

(B) $\dfrac{\bar{a}}{r^n} - \dfrac{n\,(\bar{a}\cdot\bar{r})}{r^{n+2}}\,\bar{r}$

(C) $\dfrac{\bar{a}}{r^n} + \dfrac{(\bar{a}\cdot\bar{r})}{r^{n+2}}\,\bar{r}$

(D) $\dfrac{\bar{a}}{r^n} - \dfrac{n(\bar{a}\cdot\bar{r})}{r^{n+1}}$

22. $\nabla \cdot (r^n \, \bar{r})$ is equal to (2)

    (A) $(n + 3)\, r^n$ (B) $3r^n + \dfrac{n}{r^{-n-2}}$

    (C) $(n - 3)\, r^n$ (D) $(n + 3)\, r^{-n}$

23. For constant vector $\bar{a}$, $\nabla \cdot [(\bar{a} \cdot \bar{r})\, \bar{a}]$ is equal to (2)

    (A) $\bar{a} \cdot \bar{r}$ (B) 0

    (C) $\bar{a} \cdot \bar{a}$ (D) $|\bar{a}|$

24. $\nabla \cdot [(\log r)\, \bar{r}]$ is equal to (2)

    (A) $3 \log r + \dfrac{1}{r}$ (B) $3 \log r + \dfrac{1}{r^2}\, \bar{r}$

    (C) $5 + 6 \log r$ (D) $1 + 3 \log r$

25. $\nabla \cdot \left[r\nabla \left(\dfrac{1}{r^3} \right) \right]$ is equal to (2)

    (A) $\dfrac{3}{r^4}$ (B) $\dfrac{3}{r^2}$

    (C) $\dfrac{1}{r^4}$ (D) $3r^4$

26. If $\nabla^2 \phi = 0$ and $\nabla^2 \psi = 0$ then $\nabla \cdot [\phi \nabla \psi - \psi \nabla \phi]$ is equal to (2)

    (A) 0 (B) $2\nabla \phi \cdot \nabla \psi$

    (C) $\nabla \phi + \nabla \psi$ (D) $[\phi \nabla \psi - \psi \nabla \phi]$

27. $\nabla \left[\bar{b} \cdot \nabla \left(\dfrac{1}{r} \right) \right] =$ (2)

    (A) $\dfrac{\bar{b}}{r^3} - \dfrac{3}{r^4}\, (\bar{b} \cdot \bar{r})\, \bar{r}$ (B) $-\dfrac{\bar{b}}{r^3} + \dfrac{3}{r^5}\, \bar{r}$

    (C) $\dfrac{\bar{b}}{r^3} - \dfrac{3}{r^5}\, (\bar{b} \cdot \bar{r})$ (D) $-\dfrac{\bar{b}}{r^3} + \dfrac{3}{r^5}\, (\bar{b} \cdot \bar{r})\, \bar{r}$

28. $\nabla [\bar{a} \cdot \nabla \log r] =$ (2)

    (A) $\dfrac{\bar{a}}{r^2} + \dfrac{2}{r^4}\, \bar{r}$ (B) $\dfrac{\bar{a}}{r} + \dfrac{1}{r^3}\, (\bar{a} \cdot \bar{r})\, \bar{r}$

    (C) $\dfrac{\bar{a}}{r^2} - \dfrac{2}{r^4}\, (\bar{a} \cdot \bar{r})\, \bar{r}$ (D) $\dfrac{\bar{a}}{r^2} - \dfrac{2}{r^3}\, (\bar{a} \cdot \bar{r})$

29. $\nabla \times \left(\dfrac{\bar{r}}{r^3} \right)$ is equal to (2)

    (A) $\dfrac{3}{r^2}$ (B) $\bar{0}$

    (C) $-\dfrac{2}{r^2}$ (D) $\dfrac{1}{r^2}\,\bar{r}$

30. $\nabla \times \left(\dfrac{\bar{a} \times \bar{r}}{r^n} \right) =$ (2)

    (A) $\dfrac{2+n}{r^n}\,\bar{a} + \dfrac{1}{r^{n+2}}\,(\bar{a} \cdot \bar{r})\,\bar{r}$ (B) $\dfrac{2-n}{r^n} + \dfrac{n}{r^n}\,(\bar{a} \cdot \bar{r})\,\bar{r}$

    (C) $\dfrac{2-n}{r^n}\,\bar{a} + \dfrac{n}{r^{n+2}}\,(\bar{a} \cdot \bar{r})\,\bar{r}$ (D) $\dfrac{2-n}{r^n}\,\bar{a} + \dfrac{n}{r^{-n-2}}\,(\bar{a} \cdot \bar{r})$

31. $\nabla \times \left((\bar{a} \cdot \bar{r})\,\dfrac{\bar{r}}{r} \right) =$ (2)

    (A) $\bar{a} \times \dfrac{\bar{r}}{r}$ (B) $\dfrac{\bar{r}}{r} \times \bar{a}$

    (C) $\bar{a} \times \bar{r}$ (D) $\dfrac{\bar{r}}{r} + \dfrac{1}{r^2}\,(\bar{a} \cdot \bar{r})$

32. Given $\bar{v} = 2y^2 z\,\bar{i} + (3xy - yz^4)\,\bar{j} + 2x^3 z\,\bar{k}$, the value of $\nabla\,(\nabla \cdot \bar{v})$ at $(1, 1, 2)$ is (2)

    (A) $7\bar{i} + 8\bar{j} - 32\bar{k}$ (B) $2\bar{i} + 3\bar{j} + 2\bar{k}$

    (C) $9\bar{i} + 32\bar{k}$ (D) $9\bar{i} - 32\bar{k}$

33. $\nabla^2 \left(\dfrac{1}{r^2} \right)$ is equal to (2)

    (A) $\dfrac{1}{r^3}$ (B) $\dfrac{2}{r^4}$

    (C) $-\dfrac{2}{r^4}\,\bar{r}$ (D) $\dfrac{6}{r^4}$

34. $\nabla^2 e^r$ is equal to (2)

    (A) $e^r + \dfrac{2}{r}\,e^r$ (B) $e^r + \dfrac{1}{r}\,e^r$

    (C) $\dfrac{e^r}{r}\,\bar{r}$ (D) $e^r - \dfrac{2}{r}\,e^r$

35. $\nabla^2 (r^2 \log r)$ is equal to　　　　(2)

(A) $\dfrac{(1 + \log r)}{r} \bar{r}$

(B) $(3 + 2 \log r)$

(C) $(5 + 6 \log r)$

(D) $(5 + 6 \log r) r$

36. $\nabla^2 \left(\dfrac{\bar{a} \cdot \bar{b}}{r} \right)$ is equal to　　　　(2)

(A) $- (\bar{a} \cdot \bar{b}) \dfrac{1}{r^2} \bar{r}$

(B) $\dfrac{4}{r^3} (\bar{a} \cdot \bar{b})$

(C) $(\bar{a} \cdot \bar{b}) \left(\dfrac{2}{r^3} - \dfrac{1}{r^2} \right)$

(D) 0

37. If $\nabla^2 (r^2 \log r) = 5 + 6 \log r$ then $\nabla^4 (r^2 \log r) =$　　　　(2)

(A) $\dfrac{18}{r^2}$

(B) $\dfrac{6}{r^2}$

(C) $-\dfrac{6}{r^2}$

(D) $-\dfrac{6}{r^2} + \dfrac{6}{r}$

38. If $\phi = 2xz + 2yz + z^2$ then $\nabla^2 \phi$ is　　　　(2)

(A) $2 (x + y + z)$

(B) 2

(C) 0

(D) $6z$

39. For constant vector $\bar{a}$, $\nabla \times (\bar{a} \times \bar{r}) =$　　　　(2)

(A) $3\bar{a}$

(B) $\bar{a}$

(C) 0

(D) $2\bar{a}$

40. div $(\text{grad } r^3) = \nabla \cdot (\nabla r^3) =$　　　　(2)

(A) $12r$

(B) $8r$

(C) $2r$

(D) $4r$

41. If $\phi = 2x^2 - 3y^2 + 4z^2$ then curl $(\text{grad } \phi)$ is　　　　(2)

(A) 3

(B) $4x \,\bar{i} - 6y \,\bar{j} + 8z \,\bar{k}$

(C) 0

(D) $4x - 6y + 2z$

42. If $\bar{F}$ is a solenoidal vector field then curl curl $\bar{F}$ is (2)

(A) $\nabla^2 \bar{\bar{F}}$ (B) $-\nabla^2 \bar{\bar{F}}$

(C) $\nabla^4 \bar{\bar{F}}$ (D) $\nabla (\nabla \cdot \bar{F})$

43. If $\bar{F}$ is a solenoidal vector field and curl curl $\bar{F} = -\nabla^2 \bar{F}$ then curl curl curl curl $\bar{F}$ is (2)

(A) $\nabla^2 \bar{\bar{F}}$ (B) $\nabla^4 \bar{\bar{F}}$

(C) $-\nabla^4 \bar{F}$ (D) $\bar{0}$

44. For the vector field $\bar{F} = (6xy + z^3)\,\bar{i} + (3x^2 - z)\,\bar{j} + (3xz^2 - y)\,\bar{k}$, $\nabla \times \bar{F}$ is (2)

(A) $6y\,\bar{i} + 6xz\,\bar{k}$ (B) $-2\bar{i} + 6z^2\,\bar{j} + 12x\,\bar{k}$

(C) $\bar{0}$ (D) $6y + 6xz$

45. For the vector field $\bar{F} = (2xz^3 + 6y)\,\bar{i} + (6x - 2yz)\,\bar{j} + (3x^2z^2 - y^2)\,\bar{k}$, $\nabla \times \bar{F}$ is (2)

(A) $2z^3\bar{i} - 2z\bar{j} + 6xz^2\,\bar{k}$ (b) $4y\,\bar{i} - 12xz^2\,\bar{j} + 12\bar{k}$

(C) $2z^3 - 2z + 6xz^2$ (D) $\bar{0}$

46. If for the vector field $\bar{u}$ and $\bar{v}$ are irrotational vectors then the value of $\nabla \cdot (\bar{u} \times \bar{v})$ is (2)

(A) 2 (B) 1

(C) 3 (D) 0

47. The vector field $\bar{F} = (6xy + z^3)\,\bar{i} + (3x^2 - z)\,\bar{j} + (3xz^2 - y)\,\bar{k}$ is irrotational. Corresponding scalar function ϕ satisfying $\bar{F} = \nabla\phi$ is (2)

(A) $3x^2y + z^3x - yz + c$ (B) $3x^2y + z^2x + c$

(C) $6x^2y + x^3 + xy - yz + c$ (D) $x^2y + z^3x - y^3 + c$

48. For irrotational vector field $\bar{F} = (x + 2y + 4z)\,\bar{i} + (2x - 3y - z)\,\bar{j} + (4x - y + 2z)\,\bar{k}$, scalar function ϕ such that $\bar{F} = \nabla\phi$ is (2)

(A) $\dfrac{x^2}{2} + 2xy + 4xz - \dfrac{3}{2}y^2 - yz + z^2 + c$ (B) $x^2 + xy + xz - y^2 - yz + z^2 + c$

(C) $\dfrac{x^2}{2} + 2xy + 4xz - \dfrac{1}{2}y^2 - yz + c$ (D) $\dfrac{x^2}{2} + y^2 + 4xz - yz + 2z^2 + c$

49. For irrotational vector field $\overline{F} = (2xz^3 + 6y)\,\overline{i} + (6x - 2yz)\,\overline{j} + (3x^2z^2 - y^2)\,\overline{k}$, scalar function ϕ such that $\overline{F} = \nabla\phi$ is   (2)

(A) $x^2z^3 + 3y^2 + 3x^2 - \dfrac{y^3}{3} + c$

(B) $x^2z^3 + 6xy + 3x^2 - 2y^2z + x^2z^3 + c$

(C) $xz^3 + 6xy + y^2z + \dfrac{y^3}{3} + c$

(D) $x^2z^3 + 6xy - y^2z + c$

50. For irrotational vector field $\overline{F} = (y^2\cos x + z^2)\,\overline{i} + (2y\sin x - 4)\,\overline{j} + (2xz + 2)\,\overline{k}$, scalar function ϕ such that $\overline{F} = \nabla\phi$ is   (2)

(A) $-y^2\sin x + z^2x + y^2\sin x + xz^2 + c$

(B) $y^2\sin x + z^2x - 4y + 2z + c$

(C) $y^2\cos x + z^2x + y^2\sin x - 4y + xz^3 + c$

(D) $\dfrac{y^2}{3}\sin x + z^3y + 2y\cos x - 4x + c$

51. If $\overline{F} = yz\,\overline{i} + zx\,\overline{j} + xy\,\overline{k}$ and $\overline{F} = \nabla\phi$, then ϕ is given by   (2)

(A) $x + y + z + c$

(B) $x^2 + y^2 + z^2 + c$

(C) $xyz + c$

(D) $x^2 + y + z + c$

52. If $\nabla\phi = (y^2 + 2y + z)\,\overline{i} + (2xy + 2x)\,\overline{j} + x\,\overline{k}$ and $\phi\,(1, 1, 0) = 5$ then ϕ is   (2)

(A) $xy^2 + 4xy + 2zx + xy^2 - 5$

(B) $xy^2 + 2xy + zx + 2$

(C) $xy^2 + xy + zx + 2$

(D) $xy^2 + 2xy + 2zx + y^2 - 2$

53. If $\overline{F} = r^2\,\overline{r}$ is conservative, then scalar ϕ associated with it is given by   (2)

(A) $\dfrac{r^4}{4} + c$

(B) $\dfrac{r^2}{2} + c$

(C) $\dfrac{r^3}{3} + c$

(D) $r + c$

54. If $\nabla \cdot \{f(r)\,\overline{r}\} = 0$, then $f(r)$ is given by (c is constant)   (2)

(A) $\dfrac{c}{r^2}$

(B) $\dfrac{c}{r}$

(C) $\dfrac{c}{r^4}$

(D) $\dfrac{c}{r^3}$

Answers

1. (B)	2. (A)	3. (D)	4. (C)	5. (D)	6. (A)	7. (B)	8. (C)
9. (A)	10. (C)	11. (D)	12. (B)	13. (A)	14. (D)	15. (B)	16. (C)
17. (B)	18. (D)	19. (A)	20. (C)	21. (B)	22. (A)	23. (C)	24. (D)
25. (A)	26. (A)	27. (D)	28. (C)	29. (B)	30. (C)	31. (A)	32. (D)
33. (B)	34. (A)	35. (C)	36. (D)	37. (B)	38. (B)	39. (D)	40. (A)
41. (C)	42. (B)	43. (B)	44. (C)	45. (D)	46. (D)	47. (A)	48. (A)
49. (D)	50. (B)	51. (C)	52. (B)	53. (A)	54. (D)		

CHAPTER ELEVEN

VECTOR INTEGRATION

11.1 LINE INTEGRAL

Uptil now we have discussed various aspects of vector differentiation. We shall now consider integration of vector point functions. Let $\overline{F}(x, y, z)$ be a vector point function defined in certain region of the space. 'C' is some smooth continuous curve in this region. Let $P(\overline{r})$ be certain point on the curve 'C' at which $\overline{F}$ acts in a direction shown (See Fig. 11.1).

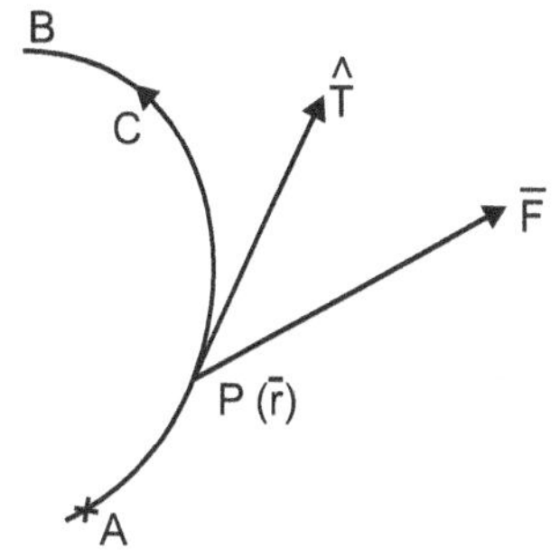

Fig. 11.1

$\hat{T}$ is unit tangent vector at P. Integral of tangential component of $\overline{F}$ along the curve 'C' between some fixed points A and B is denoted by $\int_{C:A}^{B} \overline{F} \cdot \hat{T}\, ds$ [δs is an arc element] and is called line integral of $\overline{F}$ along the curve C between points A and B. In general, line integral along the curve 'C' is written as $\int_{C} \overline{F} \cdot \hat{T}\, ds$, if the curve 'C' is closed one, it is written as $\oint_{C} \overline{F} \cdot \hat{T}\, ds$.

$\overline{F} \cdot \hat{T}\, \delta s$ represents work done in the force field $\overline{F}$ in displacing the particle of unit mass through distance δs along the curve 'C'. Integration being summation process. $\int_{C:A}^{B} \overline{F} \cdot \hat{T}\, ds$ will represent work done in moving a particle of unit mass along the curve 'C' from A to B in the force field $\overline{F}$. This is the physical interpretation of Line integration.

For evaluation of line integral,

$$\hat{T} = \frac{d\overline{r}}{ds} \quad \text{hence} \quad \int_{C} \overline{F} \cdot \hat{T}\, ds = \int_{C} \overline{F} \cdot \frac{d\overline{r}}{ds}\, ds = \int_{C} \overline{F} \cdot d\overline{r}$$

$\therefore$
$$\boxed{\text{A line integral} = \int_{C} \overline{F} \cdot d\overline{r}}$$

(11.1)

This form is quite convenient for calculating the value of the integral.

Let
$$\overline{F} = F_1\,\overline{i} + F_2\,\overline{j} + F_3\,\overline{k}$$

$$d\overline{r} = \overline{i}\,dx + \overline{j}\,dy + \overline{k}\,dz$$

$$\therefore \quad \int_C \overline{F}\cdot d\overline{r} = \int_C (F_1\,\overline{i} + F_2\,\overline{j} + F_3\,\overline{k})\cdot(\overline{i}\,dx + \overline{j}\,dy + \overline{k}\,dz)$$

$$= \int_C F_1\,dx + F_2\,dy + F_3\,dz$$

$$\therefore \quad \boxed{\textbf{A line integral} = \int_C \overline{F}\cdot d\overline{r} = \int_C F_1\,dx + F_2\,dy + F_3\,dz}$$

As an illustration, consider $\overline{F} = x^2\,\overline{i} + xy\,\overline{j}$, we shall obtain $\int_C \overline{F}\cdot d\overline{r}$ for the two cases (i) C is the curve $y^2 = x$ joining $(0, 0)$ and $(1, 1)$. (ii) C is the curve $y = x$ joining the same points. **(Nov. 2016)**

$$\int_C \overline{F}\cdot d\overline{r} = \int_C (x^2\,\overline{i} + xy\,\overline{j})\cdot(\overline{i}\,dx + \overline{j}\,dy) = \int_C x^2\,dx + xy\,dy$$

(i) Consider the parabolic path OP joining $(0, 0)$ and $(1, 1)$.

Equation of parabola is $y^2 = x$

$$\therefore \quad 2y\,dy = dx$$

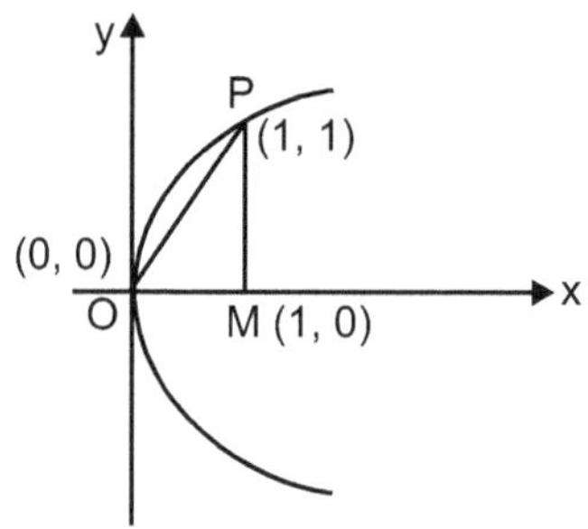

Fig. 11.2

$$\therefore \quad \int_C x^2\,dx + xy\,dy = \int_0^1 y^4 \cdot 2y\,dy + y^2 \cdot y\,dy$$

$$= \int_0^1 (2y^5 + y^3)\,dy$$

$$= \left[2\frac{y^6}{6} + \frac{y^4}{4}\right]_0^1$$

$$= \frac{1}{3} + \frac{1}{4} = \frac{7}{12}$$

(ii) Consider the straight line path $y = x$ joining $(0, 0)$ and $(1, 1)$.

$$y = x \qquad \therefore \quad dy = dx$$

$$\therefore \quad \int_C x^2\,dx + xy\,dy = \int_0^1 x^2\,dx + x \cdot x\,dx = \int_0^1 (x^2 + x^2)\,dx = 2\frac{x^3}{3}\Big]_0^1 = \frac{2}{3}$$

Thus we get different values for different paths.

Normally the value of line integral $\int\limits_{C:A}^{B} \overline{F} \cdot d\overline{r}$ depends upon the curve C joining the points A and B i.e. we get different values of line integrals along the different curves joining the same points. But if $\overline{F}$ is expressible as gradient of scalar point function ϕ.

i.e. $\overline{F} = (\nabla\phi$ then $\int\limits_{C:A}^{B} \overline{F} \cdot d\overline{r} = \int\limits_{C:A}^{B} \nabla\phi \cdot d\overline{r} = \int\limits_{C:A}^{B} d\phi = \phi)\Big|_{A}^{B} = \phi_B - \phi_A$

Thus in this case, the value of the line integral depends upon the value that ϕ takes at A and B irrespective of the curve joining A and B. Such field $\overline{F} = \nabla\phi$ is called **conservative field**.

In particular for a closed path integration in a conservative field,

$$\oint\limits_{C} \overline{F} \cdot d\overline{r} = \oint\limits_{C} \nabla\phi \cdot dr = \oint\limits_{C} d\phi = \phi\Big|_{A}^{A} = \phi_A - \phi_A = 0$$

[For a closed curve, starting point and end point are the same.]

$\oint\limits_{C} \overline{F} \cdot d\overline{r}$ for a closed curve 'C' is called **circulation**, which is zero in a conservative field. Physically it means, work done in carrying a particle of unit mass along a closed curve in a conservative force field is zero.

It may also be noted that conservative force field $\overline{F} = \nabla\phi$ is also irrotational, for $\nabla \times \overline{F} = \nabla \times \nabla\phi = 0$.

As an illustration, consider the conservative (irrotational) field $\overline{F} = x^2\,\overline{i} + y^2\,\overline{j}$ (This field can be easily seen to be an irrotational field) and let us find $\int\limits_{C} \overline{F} \cdot d\overline{r}$ along the same two paths considered in earlier problem.

(i) Consider the path $y^2 = x$ joining $(0, 0)$ and $(1, 1)$.

$$\int\limits_{C} \overline{F} \cdot d\overline{r} = \int\limits_{C} x^2\,dx + y^2\,dy$$

Now $2y\,dy = dx$ $\therefore$ $\int\limits_{C} \overline{F} \cdot d\overline{r} = \int\limits_{0}^{1} y^4 \cdot 2y\,dy + y^2\,dy = \int\limits_{0}^{1} (2y^5 + y^2)\,dy$

$$= \left[2\frac{y^6}{6} + \frac{y^3}{3}\right]_{0}^{1} = \frac{2}{6} + \frac{1}{3} = \frac{2}{3}$$

(ii) Consider the path $y = x$ (straight line).

$$\int\limits_{C} \overline{F} \cdot d\overline{r} = \int\limits_{C} x^2\,dx + y^2\,dy, \qquad\qquad [x = y \Rightarrow dx = dy]$$

$$= \int\limits_{0}^{1} y^2\,dy + y^2\,dy = \int\limits_{0}^{1} 2y^2\,dy = 2 \cdot \frac{y^3}{3}\Big|_{0}^{1} = \frac{2}{3}$$

To illustrate the point further, consider the path OMP (See Fig. 11.2).

(iii)
$$\int_C \bar{F} \cdot d\bar{r} = \int_{OM} \bar{F} \cdot d\bar{r} + \int_{MP} \bar{F} \cdot d\bar{r}$$

$$= \int_{OM} x^2\,dx + y^2\,dy + \int_{MP} x^2\,dx + y^2\,dy$$

along OM, $y = 0$, $dy = 0$

along MP, $x = 1$, $dx = 0$

$$\int_C \bar{F} \cdot d\bar{r} = \int_0^1 x^2\,dx + \int_0^1 y^2\,dy = \frac{x^3}{3}\Big]_0^1 + \frac{y^3}{3}\Big]_0^1 = \frac{1}{3} + \frac{1}{3} = \frac{2}{3}$$

Values of $\int_C \bar{F} \cdot d\bar{r}$ come out to be the same for all the three paths joining $(0, 0)$ and $(1, 1)$ because $\bar{\bar{F}}$ is conservative.

11.2 GREEN'S LEMMA

Consider the closed curve C enclosing an area A. Let $u\,(x, y)$, $v\,(x, y)$ and their first partials $\dfrac{\partial u}{\partial x}$, $\dfrac{\partial u}{\partial y}$, $\dfrac{\partial v}{\partial x}$, $\dfrac{\partial v}{\partial y}$ be continuous and single valued over the region bounded by the curve C, then

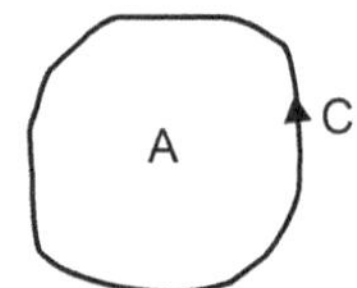

Fig. 11.3

$$\oint_C u\,dx + v\,dy = \iint_A \left(\frac{\partial v}{\partial x} - \frac{\partial u}{\partial y}\right) dx\,dy$$

To express it in vector form

let $\bar{F} = u\,\bar{i} + v\,\bar{j}$ [a vector function in xy plane]

$$\nabla \times \bar{F} = \begin{vmatrix} \bar{i} & \bar{j} & \bar{k} \\ \dfrac{\partial}{\partial x} & \dfrac{\partial}{\partial y} & \dfrac{\partial}{\partial z} \\ u & v & 0 \end{vmatrix}$$

$$= \bar{i}\left(0 - \frac{\partial v}{\partial z}\right) + \bar{j}\left(\frac{\partial u}{\partial z} - 0\right) + \bar{k}\left(\frac{\partial v}{\partial x} - \frac{\partial u}{\partial y}\right)$$

as the vector function is in xy plane

$$\therefore \quad z = 0 \qquad \therefore \quad \frac{\partial v}{\partial z} = \frac{\partial u}{\partial z} = 0$$

$$\therefore \qquad \nabla \times \bar{F} = \bar{k}\left(\frac{\partial v}{\partial x} - \frac{\partial u}{\partial y}\right)$$

$$\bar{k} \cdot (\nabla \times \bar{F}) = \bar{k} \cdot \bar{k}\left(\frac{\partial v}{\partial x} - \frac{\partial u}{\partial y}\right) = \frac{\partial v}{\partial x} - \frac{\partial u}{\partial y}$$

dx dy = dS is an area element in xy plane.

$$\therefore \quad \iint_A \left(\frac{\partial v}{\partial x} - \frac{\partial u}{\partial y}\right) dx\, dy \text{ can be expressed as } \iint \bar{k} \cdot (\nabla \times \bar{F})\, dS$$

$$\oint_C u\, dx + v\, dy = \oint_C \bar{F} \cdot d\bar{r}$$

Thus the Green's Lemma can be expressed in vector form as

$$\oint_C \bar{F} \cdot d\bar{r} = \iint_A \bar{k} \cdot (\nabla \times \bar{F})\, dS.$$

To illustrate the use of Green's Lemma in evaluation of line integral, consider the following example.

Evaluate $\oint_C (\cos y\, \bar{i} + x\,(1 - \sin y)\, \bar{j}) \cdot d\bar{r}$ for a closed curve which is given by $x^2 + y^2 = 1,\ z = 0$.

Given integral is written as

$$I = \oint_C \cos y\, dx + \{x\,(1 - \sin y)\}\, dy.$$

Here $\qquad u = \cos y, \quad v = x\,(1 - \sin y)$

$$\frac{\partial v}{\partial x} = 1 - \sin y, \quad \frac{\partial u}{\partial y} = -\sin y$$

$$I = \iint_A \left(\frac{\partial v}{\partial x} - \frac{\partial u}{\partial y}\right) dy\, dx \quad [A \text{ is the area of circle } x^2 + y^2 = 1]$$

$$I = \iint_A (1 - \sin y + \sin y)\, dx\, dy$$

$$= \iint_A dx\, dy$$

$$= \pi \cdot (1)^2 = \pi, \qquad \left[\text{The area of the circle is given by } \iint_A dx\, dy\right]$$

Consider some more illustrations on the line integration.

ILLUSTRATIONS

Ex. 1 : *Evaluate $\int_C \overline{F} \cdot d\overline{r}$ for $\overline{F} = 3x^2\,\overline{i} + (2xz - y)\,\overline{j} + z\,\overline{k}$ along the following paths :*   **(May 2012, 2015, Dec. 2014)**

(i)   *The straight line joining (0, 0, 0) and (2, 1, 3).*

(ii)   *The curve $x = 2t^2$, $y = t$, $z = 4t^2 - t$ from $t = 0$ to $t = 1$.*

(iii) *Along the curve defined by $x^2 = 4y$, $3x^3 = 8z$ from $x = 0$ to $x = 2$.*

Sol. :   (i) $\int_C \overline{F} \cdot d\overline{r} = \int_C 3x^2\,dx + (2xz - y)\,dy + z\,dz$

Along the straight line joining (0, 0, 0) and (2, 1, 3) which is given by $\dfrac{x}{2} = \dfrac{y}{1} = \dfrac{z}{3} = t$ i.e. $x = 2t$, $y = t$, $z = 3t$ and $dx = 2\,dt$, $dy = dt$, $dz = 3\,dt$ and t varies from 0 to 1 along the path.

$$\int_C \overline{F} \cdot d\overline{r} = \int_0^1 3\,(4t^2)\,2\,dt + (12t^2 - t)\,dt + 3t \cdot 3\,dt$$

$$= \int_0^1 (24t^2 + 12t^2 - t + 9t)\,dt = \int_0^1 (36t^2 + 8t)\,dt$$

$$= \left[36\,\frac{t^3}{3} + 8\,\frac{t^2}{2}\right]_0^1 = \frac{36}{3} + \frac{8}{2} = 12 + 4 = 16$$

(ii)   Along the curve $x = 2t^2$, $y = t$, $z = 4t^2 - t$

$$dx = 4t\,dt, \quad dy = dt, \quad dz = (8t - 1)\,dt$$

$$\int_C \overline{F} \cdot d\overline{r} = \int_0^1 3\,(4t^4)\,4t\,dt + (16t^4 - 4t^3 - t)\,dt + (4t^2 - t)\,(8t - 1)\,dt$$

$$= \int_0^1 (48t^5 + 16t^4 - 4t^3 - t + 32t^3 - 12t^2 + t)\,dt$$

$$= \int_0^1 (48t^5 + 16t^4 + 28t^3 - 12t^2)\,dt$$

$$= \left[48\,\frac{t^6}{6} + 16\,\frac{t^5}{5} + 28\,\frac{t^4}{4} - 12\,\frac{t^3}{3}\right]_0^1 = 8 + \frac{16}{5} + 7 - 4 = 11 + \frac{16}{5} = \frac{71}{5}$$

(iii) Along the curve $x^2 = 4y$, $3x^3 = 8z$ from $x = 0$ to $x = 2$.

The parametric equations may be taken as

$$x = 2t, \qquad y = t^2, \qquad\qquad z = 3t^3 \text{ (from } t = 0 \text{ to } t = 1)$$

$$dx = 2\,dt, \qquad dy = 2t\,dt, \qquad\qquad dz = 9t^2\,dt$$

$$\int_C \overline{F} \cdot d\overline{r} \;=\; \int_0^1 3\,(4t^2)\,2dt + (12t^4 - t^2)\,2t\,dt + 3t^3 \cdot 9t^2\,dt$$

$$=\; \int_0^1 (24t^2 + 24t^5 - 2t^3 + 27t^5)\,dt = \int_0^1 (51\,t^5 - 2t^3 + 24\,t^2)\,dt$$

$$=\; 51\,\frac{t^6}{6} - 2\,\frac{t^4}{4} + 24\,\frac{t^3}{3}\Bigg]_0^1$$

$$=\; \frac{51}{6} - \frac{1}{2} + 8 \;=\; \frac{51 - 3 + 48}{6} \;=\; \frac{96}{6} = 16$$

Ex. 2 : *Find the work done in moving a particle once round the ellipse* $\dfrac{x^2}{25} + \dfrac{y^2}{16} = 1,$
z = 0 under the field of force given by

$$\overline{F} \;=\; (2x - y + z)\,\overline{i} + (x + y - z^2)\,\overline{j} + (3x - 2y + 4z)\,\overline{k}$$

Is the field conservative ?   **(Dec. 2004, 2008; May 2008)**

Sol. : Work done, $W \;=\; \oint_C (2x - y + z)\,dx + (x + y - z^2)\,dy + (3x - 2y + 4z)\,dz$

where, C is the arc of the ellipse.

Since $z \;=\; 0$ $\therefore$ $dz = 0$

$\therefore$ $W \;=\; \oint_C (2x - y)\,dx + (x + y)\,dy$

Taking the parametric equations of the ellipse

$$x \;=\; 5\cos\theta, \; y = 4\sin\theta$$

$$dx \;=\; -5\sin\theta\,d\theta, \; dy = 4\cos\theta\,d\theta$$

$$W \;=\; \int_0^{2\pi} (10\cos\theta - 4\sin\theta)\,(-5\sin\theta)\,d\theta + (5\cos\theta + 4\sin\theta)\,(4\cos\theta)\,d\theta$$

$$=\; \int_0^{2\pi} \{-50\sin\theta\cos\theta + 20\sin^2\theta + 20\cos^2\theta + 16\sin\theta\cos\theta\}\,d\theta$$

$$=\; \int_0^{2\pi} 20\,(\sin^2\theta + \cos^2\theta)\,d\theta - 34\int_0^{2\pi}\sin\theta\cos\theta\,d\theta$$

$$=\; 20\,[\theta]_0^{2\pi} \;=\; 40\,\pi \qquad\qquad \left[\because \int_0^{2\pi}\sin\theta\cos\theta\,d\theta = 0\right]$$

Since the work done is not zero, the vector field is not conservative.

Ex. 3 : *Verify Green's theorem for the field $\overline{F} = x^2\,\overline{i} + xy\,\overline{j}$ over the region R enclosed by $y = x^2$ and then line $y = x$.*   **(May 2005, 2014, 2017; Nov. 2015)**

Sol. : By Green's theorem

$$\oint_C u\,dx + v\,dy = \iint_R \left(\frac{\partial v}{\partial x} - \frac{\partial u}{\partial y}\right) dx\,dy$$

$$\text{L.H.S.} = \oint_C x^2\,dx + xy\,dy = \int_{OP} x^2\,dx + xy\,dy + \int_{PAO} x^2\,dx + xy\,dy$$

$$= I_1 + I_2$$

For
$$I_1 = \int_{OP} x^2\,dx + xy\,dy$$

$$y = x, \quad \therefore \quad dy = dx$$

$\therefore$
$$I_1 = \int_0^1 x^2\,dx + x^2\,dx = 2\left[\frac{x^3}{3}\right]_0^1 = \frac{2}{3}$$

For
$$I_2 = \int_{PAO} x^2\,dx + xy\,dy$$

$$y = x^2, \quad \therefore \quad dy = 2x\,dx$$

$$= \int x^2\,dx + x \cdot x^2 \cdot 2x\,dx$$

$$= \int_1^0 (x^2 + 2x^4)\,dx$$

$$= \left[\frac{x^3}{3} + 2\frac{x^5}{5}\right]_1^0 = -\frac{1}{3} - \frac{2}{5} = \frac{-11}{15}$$

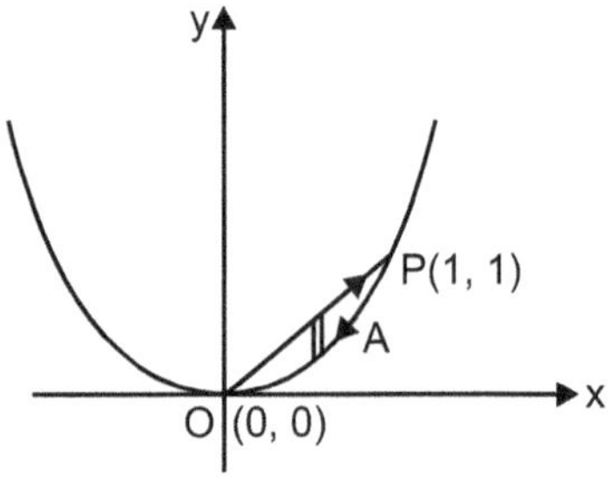

Fig. 11.4

$\therefore$
$$\text{L.H.S.} = I_1 + I_2 = \frac{2}{3} - \frac{11}{15} = \frac{10 - 11}{15} = -\frac{1}{15}$$

Now,
$$\text{R.H.S.} = \iint_R \left(\frac{\partial v}{\partial x} - \frac{\partial u}{\partial y}\right) dx\,dy$$

Put $v = xy$, $u = x^2$
$$= \int_0^1 \int_{x^2}^{x} (y - 0)\,dx\,dy = \int_0^1 \left[\frac{y^2}{2}\right]_{x^2}^{x} dx$$

$$= \frac{1}{2} \int_0^1 (x^2 - x^4)\,dx = \frac{1}{2}\left[\frac{x^3}{3} - \frac{x^5}{5}\right]_0^1$$

$\therefore$
$$\text{R.H.S.} = \frac{1}{2}\left[\frac{1}{3} - \frac{1}{5}\right] = \frac{1}{15} \quad \text{and} \quad \text{L.H.S.} = -\frac{1}{15}$$

L.H.S. value is with –ve sign ($\because$ the path is considered clockwise.)

Hence the theorem is verified.

Ex. 4 : *Verify Green's theorem for* $\bar{F} = x\bar{i} + y^2\bar{j}$ *over the first quadrant of the circle* $x^2 + y^2 = a^2$.

Sol. :

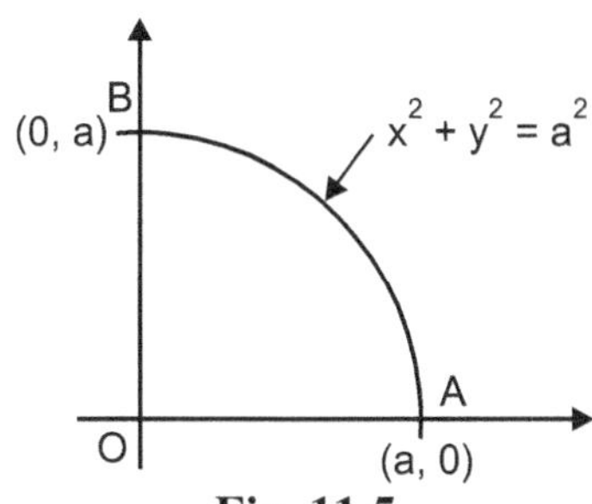

Fig. 11.5

$$I = \int F \cdot d\bar{r} = \int_{OABO} x\, dx + y^2\, dy$$

By Green's theorem,

$$I = \int_C P\, dx + Q\, dy = \iint_A \left(\frac{\partial Q}{\partial x} - \frac{\partial P}{\partial y}\right) dx\, dy$$

$$Q = y^2, \frac{\partial Q}{\partial x} = 0, \quad P = x, \frac{\partial P}{\partial y} = 0$$

$$\therefore \quad \iint_A \left(\frac{\partial Q}{\partial x} - \frac{\partial P}{\partial y}\right) dx\, dy = 0$$

$$\int_C x\, dx + y^2\, dy \quad \text{where, C is the path OABO}$$

Along OA, $y = 0, \quad dy = 0, \quad I_1 = \int_0^a x\, dx = \left[\frac{x^2}{2}\right]_0^a = \frac{a^2}{2}$

Along arc AB, $x = a\cos\theta, \qquad y = a\sin\theta$

$$dx = -a\sin\theta\, d\theta, \quad dy = a\cos\theta\, d\theta$$

$$I_2 = \int_{AB} x\, dx + y^2\, dy = \int_0^{\pi/2} (-a^2\sin\theta\cos\theta + a^2\sin^2\theta\cos\theta)\, d\theta$$

$$= a^2\left[-\frac{1.1}{2} + \frac{1.1}{3.1}a\right] = \frac{-a^2}{2} + \frac{a^3}{3}$$

$$I_3 = \int_{BO} y^2\, dy \quad \text{as} \quad dx = 0$$

$$= \left[\frac{y^3}{3}\right]_a^0 = -\frac{a^3}{3}$$

$$\therefore \quad I = \frac{a^2}{2} - \frac{a^2}{2} + \frac{a^3}{3} - \frac{a^3}{3} = 0 \qquad \text{[Adding } I_1, I_2, I_3]$$

$$\text{L.H.S.} = \text{R.H.S.}$$

$\therefore$ Green's theorem is verified.

Ex. 5 : *Using Green's theorem, show that the area bounded by a simple closed curve C is given by $\frac{1}{2} \int x\,dy - y\,dx$. Hence find the area of the ellipse $x = a \cos\theta, y = b \sin\theta$.*

(Dec. 2014)

Sol. : By Green's theorem,

$$\oint_C P\,dx + Q\,dy = \iint_A \left(\frac{\partial Q}{\partial x} - \frac{\partial P}{\partial y}\right) dx\,dy$$

Comparing $\oint_C P\,dx + Q\,dy$ with $\frac{1}{2} \int x\,dy - y\,dx$

we get $\qquad P = -\frac{y}{2}, \quad Q = \frac{x}{2}$

$$\therefore \qquad \frac{\partial Q}{\partial x} = \frac{1}{2}, \quad \frac{\partial P}{\partial y} = -\frac{1}{2}$$

$$\therefore \quad \frac{1}{2} \oint_C x\,dy - y\,dx = \iint_A \left(\frac{1}{2} + \frac{1}{2}\right) dx\,dy = \iint_A dx\,dy$$

i.e. the area bounded by closed curve.

In case of ellipse $\quad x = a \cos\theta, \quad y = b \sin\theta$

$$\frac{1}{2} \oint_C x\,dy - y\,dx = \frac{1}{2} \int (a \cos\theta\, b \cos\theta + b \sin\theta\, a \sin\theta)\,d\theta$$

$$= \frac{1}{2} \int_0^{2\pi} ab\,(\cos^2\theta + \sin^2\theta)\,d\theta = \frac{1}{2}\,ab\,[\theta]_0^{2\pi}$$

$$= \frac{1}{2}\,ab \cdot 2\pi = \pi ab \quad \text{which is the area of the ellipse.}$$

EXERCISE 11.1

1. Show that $\int_C \phi \nabla\phi \cdot d\overline{r} = 0$ for any closed curve C.

2. Evaluate $\int_C \overline{F} \cdot d\overline{r}$ for $\overline{F} = (2x + y)\,\overline{i} + (3y - x)\,\overline{j}$ and C is the curve

    (i)   Straight line joining $(0, 0)$ and $(3, 2)$

    (ii)   Along the path joining $(0, 0)$ and $(2, 0)$ and then from $(2, 0)$ to $(0, 3)$.   **(Nov. 2015)**

                                                     Ans. (i)   15,   (ii) $\frac{15}{2}$

3. If $\overline{F} = (2x + y^2)\,\overline{i} + (3y - 4x)\,\overline{j}$ then evaluate $\int_C \overline{F} \cdot d\overline{r}$ around the following paths :

    (i)   Triangle ABC where A, B, C have the co-ordinates $(0, 0)$, $(2, 0)$, $(2, 1)$ respectively.

(ii)   The parabolic arc $y = x^2$ joining $(0, 0)$ and $(1, 1)$.

(iii) The parabolic arc $y^2 = x$ joining $(0, 0)$ and $(1, 1)$.   **Ans.** (i) $-\dfrac{14}{3}$, (ii) $\dfrac{1}{30}$, (iii) $\dfrac{5}{3}$

4. Evaluate $\int_C \overline{F} \cdot d\overline{r}$ for $\overline{F} = (2y + 3)\, \overline{i} + xz\, \overline{j} + (yz - x)\, \overline{k}$ along the following paths :

(i) $x^2 = 2t^2,\ y = t,\ z = t^3$ from $t = 0$ to $t = 1$.   **(May 2014)**

(ii) The straight lines from $(0, 0, 0)$ to $(0, 0, 1)$, then to $(0, 1, 1)$ and then to $(2, 1, 1)$.

(iii) The straight line joining $(0, 0, 0)$ and $(3, 1, 1)$.

$$\textbf{Ans. (i) }\ \frac{483\sqrt{2} + 60}{140}\ ,\ \text{(ii) } 10,\ \ \text{(iii) }\ \frac{71}{6}$$

5. If $\overline{F} = (2xy + 3z^2)\, \overline{i} + (x^2 + 4yz)\, \overline{j} + (2y^2 + 6xz)\, \overline{k}$, evaluate $\int_C \overline{F} \cdot d\overline{r}$ where C is

the curve $x = t,\ y = t^2,\ z = t^3$ joining the points $(0, 0, 0)$ and $(1, 1, 1)$.   **Ans.** 6

6. A vector field is given by

$$\overline{F} = \sin y\, \overline{i} + x\,(1 + \cos y)\, \overline{j},\ \text{ evaluate the integral } \int_C \overline{F} \cdot d\overline{r}$$

where, C is the ellipse $\dfrac{x^2}{a^2} + \dfrac{y^2}{b^2} = 1,\ z = 0$.   **Ans.** π ab **(May 2005)**

7. Evaluate $\int_C \overline{F} \cdot d\overline{r}$ where $\overline{F} = (2xy + z^3)\, \overline{i} + x^2\overline{j} + 3xz^2\, \overline{k}$ along the straight line

joining the points $(1, -2, 1)$ and $(3, 1, 4)$.

$$\left[\textbf{Hint : Equation of straight line } \frac{x - 1}{2} = \frac{y + 2}{3} = \frac{z - 1}{3} = t\right]\ \textbf{Ans. } 202.$$

8. Evaluate $\oint_C \overline{F} \cdot d\overline{r}$ where $\overline{F} = \sin z\, \overline{i} + \cos x\, \overline{j} + \sin y\, \overline{k}$ and C is the boundary of

the rectangle $0 \le x \le \pi$ and $0 \le y \le 1$ and $z = 3$.

[**Hint :** Consider paths : OA $(y = 0)$, AB $(x = \pi)$, BC $(y = 1)$ and CO $(x = 0)$] **Ans.** $- 2$

9. If $\overline{F} = \dfrac{(-y\,\overline{i} + x\,\overline{j})}{x^2 + y^2}$ then show that $\oint_C \overline{F} \cdot d\overline{r} = 2\pi$, where, C is a circle with centre

at the origin.   **(May 2006)**

10. Evaluate $\int \dfrac{x\,dx + y\,dy}{(x^2 + y^2)^{3/2}}$ along the curve $\overline{r} = e^t \cos t\, \overline{i} + e^t \sin t\, \overline{j}$ joining $(1, 0)$ to

$(e^{2\pi}, 0)$.   [**Hint :** $x^2 + y^2 = e^{2t}$, $x\,dx + y\,dy = e^{2t}\,dt$ and $t = 0$ to $t = 2\pi$] **Ans.** $1 - e^{-2\pi}$

11. Find the work done in moving a particle from $(0, 1, -1)$ to $\left(\dfrac{\pi}{2}, -1, 2\right)$ in a force field

$\overline{F} = (y^2 \cos x + z^3)\, \overline{i} + (2y \sin x - 4)\, \overline{j} + (3xz^2 + 2)\, \overline{k}$. Is the field conservative ?

Ans. $15 + 4\pi$ **(Dec. 2007)**

12. Find the work done in moving a particle along $x = a \cos \theta$, $y = a \sin \theta$, $z = b\theta$ from

$\theta = \dfrac{\pi}{4}$ to $\theta = \dfrac{\pi}{2}$ under a field of force given by **(Dec. 05; May 07, 2011)**

$\overline{F} = -3a \sin^2 \theta \cos \theta\, \overline{i} + a\, (2 \sin \theta - 3 \sin^3 \theta)\, \overline{j} + b \sin 2\theta\, \overline{k}$.

$$\left[\textbf{Hint :} \int_{\pi/4}^{\pi/2} \overline{F} \cdot d\overline{r} = \int_{\pi/4}^{\pi/2} (a^2 + b^2) \sin 2\theta\, d\theta = \frac{a^2 + b^2}{2}\right] \textbf{Ans.}\ \frac{a^2 + b^2}{2}$$

13. Find work done by the force $(x^2 - yz)\, \overline{i} + (y^2 - zx)\, \overline{j} + (z^2 - xy)\, \overline{k}$ in taking a particle

from $(1, 1, 1)$ to $(3, -5, 7)$ along straight line. **Ans.** $\left(\dfrac{560}{3}\right)$ **(May 2007)**

14. Find the work-done in moving a particle once round the ellipse $\dfrac{x^2}{16} + \dfrac{y^2}{9} = 1$ in the

plane $z = 0$, under the filed of force given by $\overline{F} = (3x - 2y)\, \overline{i} + (2x + 8y)\, \overline{j} + y^2 \overline{k}$

Is the field conservative ?

$$\left[\textbf{Hint :} \int_0^{2\pi} \overline{F} \cdot d\overline{r} = 24 \int_0^{2\pi} d\theta + \int_0^{2\pi} 24 \sin \theta \cos \theta\, d\theta\right] \textbf{Ans.}\ 48\pi, \text{ field is not conservative}$$

15. Find the work-done in moving a particle from $(1, -2, 1)$ to $(3, 1, 4)$ in the force field

$\overline{F} = 3x^2 y\, \overline{i} + (x^3 + 2yz)\, \overline{j}$ **Ans.** 29

16. Verify green's theorem for $\overline{F} = x\overline{i} + y^2 \overline{j}$ over the first quadrant of the circle $x^2 + y^2 = 1$.

17. Verify Green's theorem in the plane $z = 0$ for $\oint_C (3x^2 - 8y^2)\, dx + (4y - 6xy)\, dy$

where C is the boundary of the region defined by $y = \sqrt{x}$ and $y = x^2$.

Ans. Common value $= \dfrac{3}{2}$

18. Using Green's theorem evaluate $\oint_C (xy - y^2)\, dx + x^2 y\, dy$ along the closed curve

formed by $y = 0$, $x = 1$ and $y = x$. **Ans.** $-\dfrac{1}{12}$

ANSWERS

11.3 SURFACE INTEGRAL

The surface integral of a vector point function $\overline{F}$ over a surface S is defined as the integral of the normal component of $\overline{F}$ taken over the surface S.

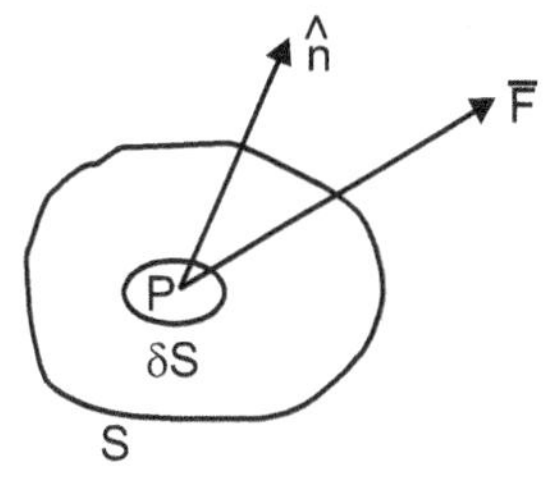

Consider a surface S (Fig. 11.6). Let $\overline{F}$ act at P enclosed by an element of area δS, $\hat{n}$ is a unit vector normal to the surface at P. Normal component of $\overline{F}$ is given by $\overline{F} \cdot \hat{n}$. The surface integral can be expressed as

Fig. 11.6

$$\int_S \overline{F} \cdot \hat{n}\ dS \quad \text{or} \quad \iint_S (\overline{F} \cdot \hat{n})\ dS$$

If we write $d\overline{S} = \hat{n}\ dS$, the above integral can also be written as

$$\int_S \overline{F} \cdot d\overline{S} \quad \text{or} \quad \iint_S \overline{F} \cdot d\overline{S}$$

Physically the surface integral of a vector function $\overline{F}$ expresses the normal flux through a surface. If $\overline{F}$ represents velocity vector $\overline{q}$ of a fluid, the surface integral of $\overline{q}$ over a closed surface, represents the rate of flow of fluid through the surface.

We shall now consider an important theorem known as Gauss-Divergence theorem, which connects a surface integral with volume integral.

11.4 GAUSS-DIVERGENCE THEOREM

Statement : Gauss-Divergence theorem states that **the surface integral of the normal component of a vector point function $\overline{F}$ over a closed surface S is equal to the volume integral of the Divergence of $\overline{F}$ taken throughout the volume V enclosed by the surface S.**

It is written as

$$\boxed{\iint_S \overline{F} \cdot \hat{n}\ dS = \iiint_V \nabla \cdot \overline{F}\ dV} \qquad \qquad \dots (1)$$

Here $\hat{n}$ is a unit vector at a point P enclosed by an element of area δS, along an outward drawn normal to the surface at P.

Equation (1) sometimes, could also be expressed in the form

$$\int_S \bar{F} \cdot d\bar{S} \;=\; \int_V \nabla \cdot \bar{F} \; dV$$

where $\qquad d\bar{S} \;=\; \hat{n} \; dS$

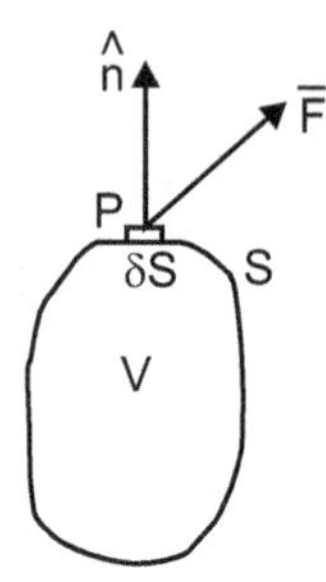

Fig. 11.7

Proof : Let S be a closed surface which is such that any line parallel to the co-ordinate axes cuts S in atmost two points. Let the equations of the upper and lower portions be $z = f(x, y)$ and $z = \phi(x, y)$ respectively. Let the projection on the xy plane be R.

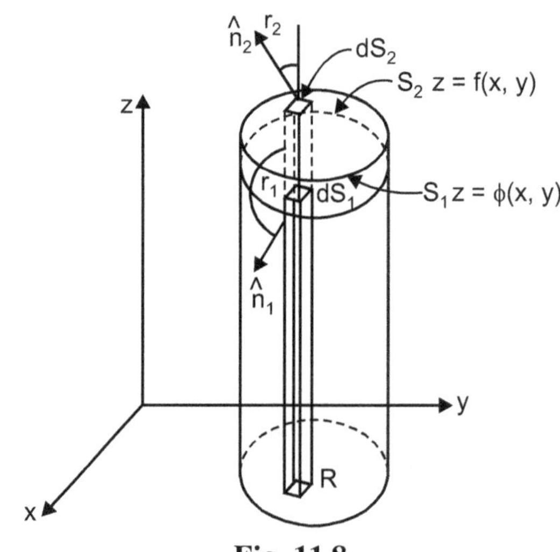

Fig. 11.8

Let, $\qquad\qquad \bar{F} \;=\; F_1 \bar{i} + F_2 \bar{j} + F_3 \bar{k}$

Consider $\qquad \iiint_V \dfrac{\partial F_3}{\partial z} \; dV \;=\; \iiint_V \dfrac{\partial F_3}{\partial z} \; dx \; dy \; dz$

Integrating $\qquad\qquad = \iint_R \left[\int_{\phi(x,y)}^{f(x,y)} \dfrac{\partial F_3}{\partial z} \; dz \right] dx \; dy$

$\qquad\qquad\qquad = \iint_R F_3(x, y, z) \; \Big\}_{z=\phi(x,y)}^{z=f(x,y)} \; dx \; dy$

$\qquad\qquad\qquad = \iint_R \{ F_3(x, y, f) - F_3(x, y, \phi) \} \; dx \; dy$

For the upper portion S_2, $\quad dx\,dy = \cos\gamma_2,\quad dS_2 = \overline{k}\cdot\hat{n}_2\,dS_2$.

For the lower portion S_1, $dx\,dy = -\cos\gamma_1,\ dS_1 = -\overline{k}\cdot\hat{n}_1\,dS_1$

(Since the normal $\hat{n}_1$ to S_1 makes an obtuse angle γ_1 with $\overline{k}$)

$$\text{Now}\qquad \iint_R F_3(x, y, f)\,dx\,dy = \iint_{S_2} F_3\,\overline{k}\cdot\hat{n}_2\,dS_2$$

$$\iint_R F_3(x, y, \phi)\,dx\,dy = -\iint_{S_1} F_3\,\overline{k}\cdot\hat{n}_1\,dS_1$$

$$\therefore\qquad \iint_R F_3(x, y, f)\,dx\,dy = -\iint_R F_3(x, y, \phi)\,dx\,dy$$

$$= \iint_{S_2} F_3\,\overline{k}\cdot\hat{n}_2\,dS_1 + \iint_{S_1} F_3\,\overline{k}\cdot\hat{n}_1\,dS_1$$

$$= \iint_S F_3\overline{k}\cdot\hat{n}\,dS$$

$$\text{Thus}\qquad \iiint_V \frac{\partial F_3}{\partial z}\,dV = \iint_S F_3\overline{k}\cdot\hat{n}\,dS$$

Similarly by projecting S on the other co-ordinate planes, we can establish that

$$\iiint_V \frac{\partial F_2}{\partial z}\,dV = \iint_S F_2\,\overline{j}\cdot\hat{n}\,dS$$

$$\iiint_V \frac{\partial F_1}{\partial z}\,dV = \iint_S F_1\,\overline{i}\cdot\hat{n}\,dS$$

$\therefore\qquad$ Summation gives

$$\iiint_V \left(\frac{\partial F_1}{\partial x} + \frac{\partial F_2}{\partial y} + \frac{\partial F_3}{\partial z}\right)dV = \iint_S (F_1\,\overline{i} + F_2\,\overline{j} + F_3\,\overline{k})\cdot\hat{n}\,ds$$

$$\text{or}\qquad \iiint_V \nabla\cdot\overline{F}\,dV = \iint_S \overline{F}\cdot\hat{n}\,dS$$

which proves the theorem.

ILLUSTRATIONS

Ex. 1 : *Verify Divergence theorem for* $\overline{F} = 4xz\,\overline{i} - y^2\overline{j} + yz\,\overline{k}$ *and S, the surface of the cube bounded by the planes* $x = 0$, $x = 2$, $y = 0$, $y = 2$, $z = 0$, $z = 2$.

Sol. : Taking the co-ordinate axes as shown in Fig. 11.9, we proceed to evaluate volume and surface integrals.

$$\nabla \cdot \overline{F} = \frac{\partial}{\partial x}(4xz) + \frac{\partial}{\partial y}(-y^2) + \frac{\partial}{\partial z}(yz) = 4z - 2y + y = 4z - y$$

$$\iiint \nabla \cdot \overline{F}\ dV = \int\limits_{x=0}^{2} \int\limits_{y=0}^{2} \int\limits_{z=0}^{2} (4z - y)\ dx\ dy\ dz$$

$$= \int\limits_{0}^{2} \int\limits_{0}^{2} \left(\frac{4z^2}{2} - yz\right)_{0}^{2} dx\ dy = \int\limits_{0}^{2} \int\limits_{0}^{2} (8 - 2y)\ dx\ dy$$

$$= \int\limits_{0}^{2} \left(8y - \frac{2y^2}{2}\right)_{0}^{2} dx = \int\limits_{0}^{2} (16 - 4)\ dx = 12\ [x]_{0}^{2} = 24$$

Thus $\quad \iiint\limits_{V} \nabla \cdot \overline{F}\ dV = 24$

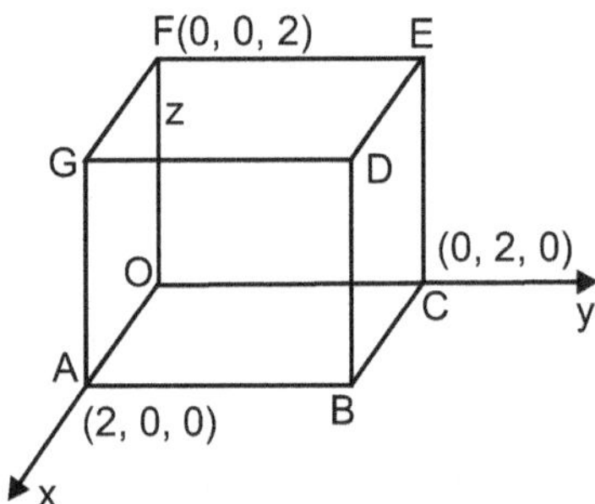

Fig. 11.9

Now to evaluate surface integrals, consider the surfaces $S_1 = OABC$, $S_2 = GDEF$, $S_3 = OAGF$, $S_4 = BCED$, $S_5 = OCEF$, $S_6 = ABDG$.

$$I_1 = \iint\limits_{S_1} \overline{F} \cdot \hat{n}\ dS$$

For S_1, $\qquad \hat{n} = -\overline{k}, \quad dS = dx\ dy$

$$\overline{F} \cdot \hat{n} = \overline{F} \cdot (-\overline{k}) = (4xz\ \overline{i} - y^2 \overline{j} + yz\ \overline{k}) \cdot (-\overline{k}) = -yz$$

$$I_1 = \iint -yz\ dx\ dy. \text{ But } z = 0 \text{ in the plane OABC}$$

$$I_1 = 0$$

For S_2, $\qquad \hat{n} = \overline{k}, \quad dS = dx\ dy, \quad \overline{F} \cdot \hat{n} = yz$

$$I_2 = \iint yz\ dx\ dy. \qquad\qquad \text{Here } z = 2$$

$$= 2 \int\limits_{0}^{2} \int\limits_{0}^{2} y\ dx\ dy = 2 \int\limits_{0}^{2} \left[\frac{y^2}{2}\right]_{0}^{2} dx = 4\ [x]_{0}^{2} = 8$$

For S_3, i.e. surface OAGF,

$$\hat{n} = -\bar{j}$$

$$dS = dx\,dz, \quad \bar{F} \cdot \hat{n} = \bar{F} \cdot (-\bar{j}) = y^2$$

$$I_3 = \iint y^2\,dx\,dz. \text{ But } y = 0 \text{ in the plane } S_3$$

$$\therefore \qquad I_3 = 0$$

For S_4, i.e. surface BCED, $\hat{n} = \bar{j}, \quad dS = dx\,dz$

$$\bar{F} \cdot \hat{n} = -y^2$$

$$I_4 = \int_0^2 \int_0^2 -y^2\,dx\,dz$$

but $y = 2$

$$= -4 \int_0^2 [z]_0^2\,dx = -4 \int_0^2 2\,dx = -8\,[x]_0^2 = -16$$

For S_5, i.e. surface OCEF, $\hat{n} = -\bar{i}$

$$dS = dy\,dz, \quad \bar{F} \cdot \hat{n} = \bar{F} \cdot (-\bar{i}) = -4xz$$

$$I_5 = \int_0^2 \int_0^2 -4xz\,dy\,dz. \text{ But } x = 0 \text{ in this plane}$$

$$\therefore \qquad I_5 = 0$$

Lastly for the surface S_6 i.e. ABDG, $\hat{n} = \bar{i}$

$$\bar{F} \cdot \hat{n} = \bar{F} \cdot \bar{i} = 4xz, \quad dS = dy\,dz, \quad x = 2,$$

$$\therefore \qquad I_6 = \int_0^2 \int_0^2 4xz\,dy\,dz = \int_0^2 \int_0^2 8z\,dy\,dz$$

$$= 8 \int_0^2 \left[\frac{z^2}{2}\right]_0^2 dy = 16\,[y]_0^2 = 32$$

Thus the surface integral which is the sum of all these integrals

$$= I_1 + I_2 + I_3 + I_4 + I_5 + I_6$$

$$= 0 + 8 + 0 - 16 + 0 + 32 = 24$$

i.e. $\qquad \iint_S \bar{F} \cdot \hat{n}\,dS = 24 = \iiint_V \nabla \cdot \bar{F}\,dV$

which verifies the divergence theorem.

Ex. 2 : *Verify the divergence theorem for*

$$\overline{F} = (x + y^2)\,\overline{i} - 2x\,\overline{j} + 2yz\,\overline{k}$$

and the volume of a tetrahedron bounded by co-ordinate planes and the plane $2x + y + 2z = 6.$ **(Dec. 2014)**

Sol. : Let us first evaluate the volume integral.

Given plane cuts-off intercepts 3, 6, 3 on x, y and z axes respectively.

$$\nabla \cdot \overline{F} = \frac{\partial}{\partial x}(x + y^2) + \frac{\partial}{\partial y}(-2x) + \frac{\partial}{\partial z}(2yz)$$

$$= 1 + 0 + 2y = (1 + 2y)$$

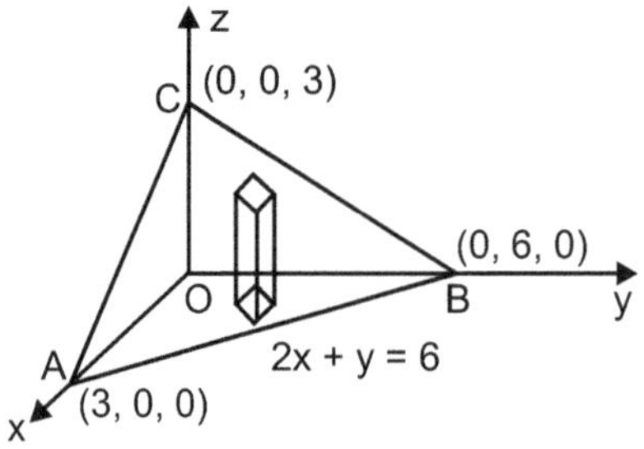

Fig. 11.10

$$\iiint\limits_{V} \nabla \cdot \overline{F}\ dV = \int_0^3 \int_0^{6-2x} \int_0^{(6-2x-y)/2} (1 + 2y)\ dx\ dy\ dz$$

$$= \int_0^3 \int_0^{6-2x} (1 + 2y)\ [z]_0^{(6-2x-y)/2}\ dx\ dy$$

$$= \int_0^3 \int_0^{6-2x} (1 + 2y)\ \frac{(6 - 2x - y)}{2}\ dx\ dy$$

$$= \frac{1}{2} \int_0^3 \left\{ (6 - 2x)\left(y + 2\frac{y^2}{2}\right) - \frac{y^2}{2} - 2\frac{y^3}{3} \right\}_0^{6-2x} dx$$

$$= \frac{1}{2} \int_0^3 \left[(6 - 2x)\{6 - 2x + (6 - 2x)^2\} - \frac{(6 - 2x)^2}{2} - \frac{2}{3}(6 - 2x)^3 \right] dx$$

$$\therefore \quad \text{Volume integral} = \frac{1}{2}\left[\frac{(6 - 2x)^3}{-6} + \frac{(6 - 2x)^4}{-8} + \frac{(6 - 2x)^3}{12} + \frac{(6 - 2x)^4}{12} \right]_0^3$$

$$= \frac{1}{2}[36 + 162 - 18 - 108] = 36$$

To evaluate the surface integrals, consider the four surfaces S_1 [plane ABC (S_2) plane z = 0], S_3 (plane y = 0), S_4 (plane x = 0). First consider the surface S_1 whose equation is $2x + y + 2z - 6 = 0$

Let,

$$\phi = 2x + y + 2z - 6$$

$$\frac{\partial \phi}{\partial x} = 2, \quad \frac{\partial \phi}{\partial y} = 1, \quad \frac{\partial \phi}{\partial z} = 2$$

$$\nabla \phi = 2\bar{i} + \bar{j} + 2\bar{k}$$

$$\hat{n} = \frac{2\bar{i} + \bar{j} + 2\bar{k}}{\sqrt{4+1+4}} = \frac{2\bar{i} + \bar{j} + 2\bar{k}}{3}$$

$$\bar{F} \cdot \hat{n} = \left\{ (x + y^2)\bar{i} - 2x\,\bar{j} + 2yz\,\bar{k} \right\} \cdot \left\{ \frac{2\bar{i} + \bar{j} + 2\bar{k}}{3} \right\}$$

$$= \frac{1}{3} \{ 2(x + y^2) - 2x + 4yz \}$$

Let dS be an element of area in plane ABC.

Taking its projection in xoy plane, we get dS $\cos \theta$ = dx dy, where θ is angle between

normals to the surfaces S_1 and xoy plane respectively. Unit normal to the xoy plane is $\bar{k}$.

$$\therefore \qquad \cos\theta = \hat{n} \cdot \bar{k} \qquad \text{or} \qquad dS = \frac{dx\,dy}{\left| \hat{n} \cdot \bar{k} \right|}$$

In the problem, $\qquad \hat{n} = \dfrac{2\bar{i} + \bar{j} + 2\bar{k}}{3}$

$$\hat{n} \cdot \bar{k} = \frac{(2\bar{i} + \bar{j} + 2\bar{k})}{3} \cdot \bar{k} = \frac{2}{3}$$

$$dS = \frac{dx\,dy}{2/3} = \frac{3}{2}\,dx\,dy$$

$$I_1 = \iint\limits_{S_1} \bar{F} \cdot \hat{n}\, dS = \iint\limits_{S_1} \frac{1}{3} \{ 2(x + y^2) - 2x + 4yz \} \cdot \frac{3}{2}\,dx\,dy$$

Putting $\qquad z = \dfrac{6 - 2x - y}{2}$

$$I_1 = \frac{1}{2} \int\limits_0^3 \int\limits_0^{6-2x} \left\{ 2(x + y^2) - 2x + 4y\left(\frac{6 - 2x - y}{2} \right) \right\} dx\,dy$$

$$= \frac{1}{2} \int\limits_0^3 \left\{ 2\frac{y^3}{3} + (6 - 2x)\, 2\frac{y^2}{2} - 2\frac{y^3}{3} \right\}_0^{6-2x} dx$$

$$= \frac{1}{2} \int\limits_0^3 (6 - 2x)^3\, dx = \frac{1}{2}\, \frac{(6 - 2x)^4}{-8} \Big|_0^3 = 81$$

Next consider the surface S_2, (plane $z = 0$)

$$\hat{n} = -\bar{k}, \qquad \bar{F} \cdot \hat{n} = \bar{F} \cdot (-\bar{k}) = -2yz, \quad dS = dx\, dy$$

$$I_2 = \int \int -2yz\, dx\, dy = 0 \quad \text{as} \quad z = 0$$

Now consider the surface S_3, (plane $y = 0$)

$$\hat{n} = -\bar{j} \qquad\qquad \bar{F} \cdot (-\bar{j}) = 2x$$

$$I_3 = \int_0^3 \int_0^{3-x} 2x\, dx\, dz = \int_0^3 2x\, [z]_0^{3-x}\, dx$$

$$= \int_0^3 2x\, (3-x)\, dx = \left\{ 6\frac{x^2}{2} - 2\frac{x^3}{3} \right\}_0^3 = 27 - 18 = 9$$

Lastly consider the surface S_4 (plane $x = 0$)

$$\hat{n} = -\bar{i}, \ \bar{F} \cdot (-\bar{i}) = -(x + y^2)$$

$$I_4 = \iint_{S_4} -(x + y^2)\, dy\, dz$$

$$= \int_0^6 \int_0^{(6-y)/2} -y^2\, dz = -\int_0^6 y^2\, [z]_0^{(6-y)/2}\, dy$$

$$= -\frac{1}{2} \int_0^6 y^2\, (6-y)\, dy = -\frac{1}{2} \left[\frac{6y^3}{3} - \frac{y^4}{4} \right]_0^6$$

$$= -\frac{1}{2}\, [2 \times 216 - 324] = -\frac{108}{2} = -54$$

$$\text{Surface integral} = I_1 + I_2 + I_3 + I_4$$

$$= 81 + 0 + 9 - 54 = 36 = \text{Volume integral.}$$

Hence the divergence theorem is verified.

Ex. 3 : *Verify divergence theorem for $\bar{F} = 4xz\,\bar{i} + xyz^2\,\bar{j} + 3z\,\bar{k}$ over the region above the xoy plane bounded by the cone $z^2 = x^2 + y^2$ and the plane $z = 4$.*   **(May 12, 15)**

Sol. : Region is the interior of the cone bounded by the plane $z = 4$. (See Fig. 11.11).

To verify divergence theorem, let us first evaluate volume integral.

$$\nabla \cdot \bar{F} = \frac{\partial}{\partial x}\, (4xz) + \frac{\partial}{\partial y}\, (xyz^2) + \frac{\partial}{\partial z}\, (3z) = 4z + xz^2 + 3$$

Volume integral $= \iiint\limits_{V} \nabla \cdot \overline{F}\ dV,$ where V is the volume of the cone.

$$I = \iiint (4z + xz^2 + 3)\ dx\ dy\ dz$$

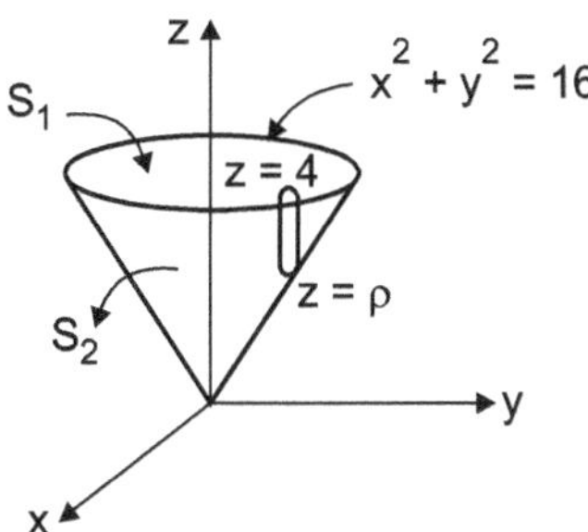

Fig. 11.11

To evaluate the integral, let us transform to cylindrical system

$$x = \rho \cos \phi, \ y = \rho \sin \phi, \ z = z$$

$$dx\ dy\ dz = \rho\ d\rho\ d\phi\ dz$$

$$I = \int\limits_{\phi=0}^{2\pi} \int\limits_{\rho=0}^{4} \int\limits_{z=\rho}^{4} (4z + \rho \cos \phi\ z^2 + 3)\ \rho\ d\rho\ d\phi\ dz$$

[Limits of z are obtained by considering a rectangular block which touches the cone $z^2 = \rho^2$ i.e. $z = \rho$ and the plane $z = 4$. Limits of ρ and ϕ are obtained from the circle $x^2 + y^2 = 16$ i.e. $\rho = 4$]

$$I = \int\limits_{0}^{2\pi} \int\limits_{0}^{4} \left\{ \frac{4z^2}{2} \rho \cos \phi \frac{z^3}{3} + 3z \right\}_{\rho}^{4} \rho\ d\rho\ d\phi$$

$$= \int\limits_{0}^{2\pi} \int\limits_{0}^{4} \left\{ 2 \times 16 - 2\rho^2 + \frac{\rho \cos \phi}{3} \times 64 - \frac{\rho^4 \cos \phi}{3} + 12 - 3\rho \right\} \rho\ d\rho\ d\phi$$

$$= \int\limits_{0}^{2\pi} \left\{ 32 \frac{\rho^2}{2} - 2 \frac{\rho^4}{4} + \frac{64}{3} \frac{\rho^3}{3} \cos \phi - \frac{\cos \phi}{3} \frac{\rho^6}{6} + \frac{12 \rho^2}{2} - \frac{3\rho^3}{3} \right\}_{0}^{4} d\phi$$

$$I = \int\limits_{0}^{2\pi} \left\{ 256 - 128 + \frac{64 \times 64}{9} \cos \phi - \frac{1}{18} (16 \times 256) \cos \phi + 96 - 64 \right\} d\phi$$

Integrals of terms containing $\cos \phi$ vanish as the limits are from 0 to 2π.

$$\therefore \quad I = \int\limits_{0}^{2\pi} 160\ d\phi = 160\ [\phi]_{0}^{2\pi} = 160 \times 2\pi = 320\ \pi$$

To obtain surface integrals, we have to consider two surfaces S_1, S_2 where S_1 is the plane surface of the circle $x^2 + y^2 = 16$ in the plane $z = 4$ and surface S_2 which is curved surface of the cone.

For surface S_1, $\hat{n} = \overline{k}$, $dS = dx\, dy$

$$\overline{F} \cdot \hat{n} = \overline{F} \cdot \overline{k} = 3z$$

$$I_1 = \iint_{S_1} 3z\, dx\, dy, \qquad\qquad \text{where } z = 4$$

$$= 12 \iint_{S_1} dx\, dy = 12 \times \text{Area of circle} = 12 \times \pi\,(4)^2 = 192\,\pi$$

For surface S_2, $\hat{n} = \dfrac{\nabla\phi}{|\nabla\phi|}$,   where $\phi = x^2 + y^2 - z^2$

$$\nabla\phi = 2x\,\overline{i} + 2y\,\overline{j} - 2z\,\overline{k}$$

$$\hat{n} = \frac{2x\,\overline{i} + 2y\,\overline{j} - 2z\,\overline{k}}{\sqrt{4x^2 + 4y^2 + 4z^2}} = \frac{x\,\overline{i} + y\,\overline{j} - z\,\overline{k}}{\sqrt{x^2 + y^2 + z^2}}$$

$$\overline{F} \cdot \hat{n} = (4xz\,\overline{i} + xyz^2\,\overline{j} + 3z\overline{k}) \cdot \left(\frac{x\,\overline{i} + y\,\overline{j} + z\,\overline{k}}{\sqrt{x^2 + y^2 + z^2}}\right) = \frac{4x^2 z + xy^2 z^2 - 3z^2}{\sqrt{x^2 + y^2 + z^2}}$$

Let dS be an element of area on the curved surface of the cone.

Taking its projection in xoy plane,

$$dS \cos\theta = dx\, dy$$

or $$dS = \frac{dx\, dy}{\left|\hat{n} \cdot \overline{k}\right|}$$

$$\hat{n} \cdot \overline{k} = \frac{x\,\overline{i} + y\,\overline{j} - z\,\overline{k}}{\sqrt{x^2 + y^2 + z^2}} \cdot \overline{k} = \frac{-z}{\sqrt{x^2 + y^2 + z^2}}$$

$$dS = \frac{\sqrt{x^2 + y^2 + z^2}}{z}\, dx\, dy$$

$$I_2 = \iint \overline{F} \cdot \hat{n}\, dS = \iint \frac{4x^2 z + xy^2 z^2 - 3z^2}{\sqrt{x^2 + y^2 + z^2}} \cdot \frac{\sqrt{x^2 + y^2 + z^2}}{z}\, dx\, dy$$

$$= \iint (4x^2 + xy^2 z - 3z)\, dx\, dy$$

where, the integration is to be carried over the circle $x^2 + y^2 = 16$ in xoy plane after replacing z by $\sqrt{x^2 + y^2}$.

$$I_2 = \iint \left\{ 4x^2 + xy^2\sqrt{x^2 + y^2} - 3\sqrt{x^2 + y^2} \right\} dx\, dy$$

For evaluation of the integral over the plane of the circle, transforming to polars.

i.e. $x = r \cos \theta$ and $y = r \sin \theta$

$\therefore \qquad dx\, dy = r\, dr\, d\theta$

$$I_2 = \int_{\theta=0}^{2\pi} \int_{r=0}^{4} \{4r^2 \cos^2\theta + r\cos\theta\, r^2 \sin^2\theta \cdot r - 3r\}\, r\, d\theta\, dr$$

$$= \int_0^{2\pi} \left\{4\cos^2\theta \frac{r^4}{4} + \frac{r^6}{6}\sin^2\theta\cos\theta - \frac{3r^3}{3}\right\}_0^4 d\theta$$

$$= \int_0^{2\pi} \left\{4\cos^2\theta \times 64 + \frac{64 \times 64}{6}\sin^2\theta\cos\theta - 64\right\} d\theta$$

Integral of the second term is zero as the limits are from 0 to 2π.

$$I_2 = \int_0^{2\pi} (256\cos^2\theta - 64)\, d\theta = 4\int_0^{\pi/2} (256\cos^2\theta - 64)\, d\theta$$

$$= 4\left\{256 \frac{1}{2}\frac{\pi}{2} - 64\,[\theta]_0^{\pi/2}\right\} = 4\,[64\pi - 32\pi] = 128\pi$$

Surface integral $= I_1 + I_2 = 192\pi + 128\pi = 320\pi =$ Volume integral.

Hence the divergence theorem is verified.

Ex. 4 : *Use the divergence theorem to evaluate* $\iint\limits_{S} (y^2 z^2\, \bar{i} + z^2 x^2\, \bar{j} + x^2 y^2\, \bar{k}) \cdot d\bar{S},$ *where, S is the upper part of the sphere* $x^2 + y^2 + z^2 = 9$ *above the xoy plane.*

(May 2005, Dec. 2005, Dec. 2011)

Sol. : To apply the divergence theorem, consider the closed surface S bounded by plane surface S_1 (plane of the circle $x^2 + y^2 = 9$).

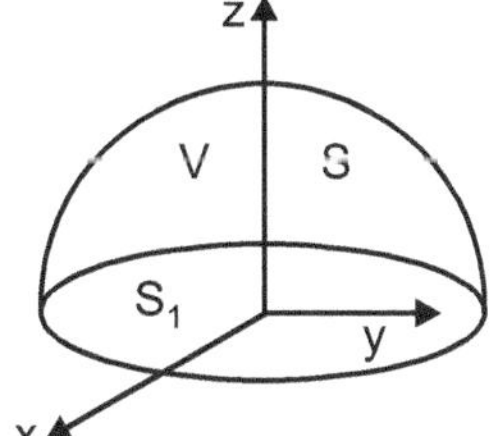

Fig. 11.12

$$\bar{F} = y^2 z^2\, \bar{i} + z^2 x^2\, \bar{j} + x^2 y^2\, \bar{k}$$

$$\nabla \cdot \bar{F} = \frac{\partial}{\partial x}(y^2 z^2) + \frac{\partial}{\partial y}(z^2 x^2) + \frac{\partial}{\partial z}(x^2 y^2) = 0$$

By the divergence theorem,

$$\iiint\limits_{V} \nabla \cdot \bar{F}\, dV = \iint\limits_{S} \bar{F} \cdot d\bar{S} + \iint\limits_{S_1} \bar{F} \cdot d\bar{S}$$

where, V is the volume enclosed between S and S_1.

Now, $\iiint\limits_{V} \nabla \cdot \overline{F} \; dV = 0$ as $\nabla \cdot \overline{F} = 0$

$\therefore$ $\iint\limits_{S} \overline{F} \cdot d\overline{S} = -\iint\limits_{S_1} \overline{F} \cdot d\overline{S}$

For surface S_1, $\hat{n} = -\overline{k}$

$$\overline{F} \cdot \hat{n} = \overline{F} \cdot (-\overline{k}) = (y^2 z^2 \, \overline{i} + z^2 x^2 \, \overline{j} + x^2 y^2 \overline{k}) \cdot (-\overline{k})$$
$$= -x^2 y^2$$
$$dS = dx \, dy$$

$$\iint\limits_{S_1} \overline{F} \cdot d\overline{S} = \iint\limits_{S_1} \overline{F} \cdot \hat{n} \, dx \, dy = -\iint\limits_{S_1} x^2 y^2 \, dx \, dy$$

S_1 is the plane of the circle $x^2 + y^2 = 9$.

Converting to polars $x = r \cos\theta$, $y = r \sin\theta$, $x^2 + y^2 = 9$

$$dx \, dy = r \, d\theta \, dr$$

$$\iint\limits_{S_1} x^2 y^2 \, dx \, dy = \int\limits_{0}^{2\pi} \int\limits_{r=0}^{3} r^4 \cos^2\theta \, \sin^2\theta \; r \, d\theta \, dr$$

$$= \int\limits_{0}^{2\pi} \left[\frac{r^6}{6}\right]_0^3 \cos^2\theta \, \sin^2\theta \, d\theta = \int\limits_{0}^{2\pi} \frac{27 \times 27}{6} \cos^2\theta \, \sin^2\theta \, d\theta$$

$$= 4 \int\limits_{0}^{2\pi} \frac{243}{2} \cos^2\theta \, \sin^2\theta \, d\theta$$

$$= 2 \times 243 \; \frac{1 \cdot 1}{4 \cdot 2} \frac{\pi}{2} \qquad \text{[Applying reduction formula]}$$

$$= \frac{243 \, \pi}{8}$$

$$\iint\limits_{S_1} \overline{F} \cdot d\overline{S} = -\frac{243 \, \pi}{8}$$

$$\iint\limits_{S} \overline{F} \cdot d\overline{S} = -\left(-\frac{243 \, \pi}{8}\right) = \frac{243 \, \pi}{8}$$

Ex. 5 : *Evaluate* $\iint\limits_{S} (x^3\,\bar{i} + y^3\,\bar{j} + z^3\,\bar{k}) \cdot d\bar{S}$ *, where S is the surface of the sphere*

$x^2 + y^2 + z^2 = 16.$ **(Dec. 07, 08, 2014, 2016; May 06, 09, 16)**

Sol. :

$$\bar{F} = x^3\,\bar{i} + y^3\,\bar{j} + z^3\,\bar{k}$$

$$\nabla \cdot \bar{F} = \frac{\partial}{\partial x}(x^3) + \frac{\partial}{\partial y}(y^3) + \frac{\partial}{\partial z}(z^3) = 3x^2 + 3y^2 + 3z^2$$

Applying the divergence theorem,

$$\iint\limits_{S} (x^3\,\bar{i} + y^3\,\bar{j} + z^3\,\bar{k}) \cdot d\bar{S} = \iiint\limits_{V} \nabla \cdot \bar{F}\ dV$$

$$I = \iiint 3\,(x^2 + y^2 + z^2)\ dx\ dy\ dz$$

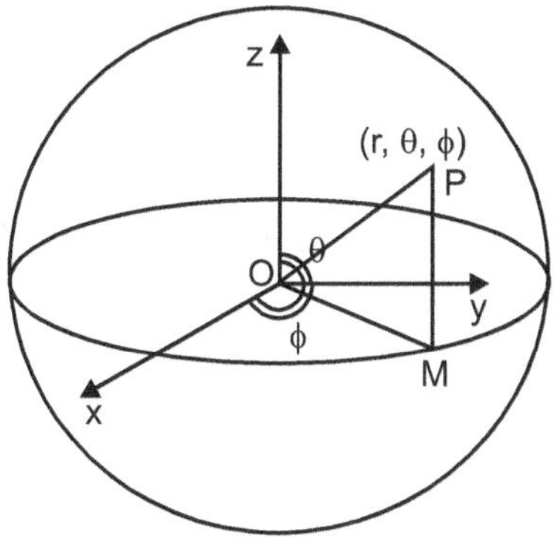

Fig. 11.13

Transforming to spherical polars

$$x = r \sin\theta \cos\phi, \quad y = r \sin\theta \sin\phi, \quad z = r \cos\theta$$

$$x^2 + y^2 + z^2 = r^2, \qquad dx\ dy\ dz = r^2 \sin\theta\ dr\ d\theta\ d\phi$$

For the entire sphere, r will vary from r = 0 to r = 4, θ from 0 to π, φ from 0 to 2π.
Substituting the limits for I

$$I = \int\limits_{\phi=0}^{2\pi} \int\limits_{\theta=0}^{\pi} \int\limits_{r=0}^{4} 3\,r^2\,r^2 \sin\theta\ dr\ d\theta\ d\phi$$

$$= 3 \int\limits_{0}^{2\pi} \int\limits_{0}^{\pi} \left[\frac{r^5}{5}\right]_{0}^{4} \sin\theta\ d\theta\ d\phi = 3 \cdot \frac{(4)^5}{5} \int\limits_{0}^{2\pi} [-\cos\theta]_{0}^{\pi}\ d\phi$$

$$= \frac{3}{5} \times 4 \times 256 \int\limits_{0}^{2\pi} (1 + 1)\ d\phi$$

$$= \frac{6}{5} \times 4 \times 256\ [\phi]_{0}^{2\pi} = \frac{48 \times 256\ \pi}{5} = \frac{12288\ \pi}{5}$$

Ex. 6 : *Evaluate* $\iint_S 2x^2 y \, dy \, dz - y^2 \, dz \, dx + 4xz^2 \, dx \, dy$ *over the curved surface of the cylinder* $y^2 + z^2 = 9$, *bounded by* $x = 0$ *and* $x = 2$.   **(Dec. 2005, 2008; May 2009)**

Sol. : Let dS be the element of the area on the curved surface of the cylinder.

Expressing $d\overline{S}$ in terms of its projections on co-ordinate planes, we can write

$$d\overline{S} = \overline{i} \, dy \, dz + \overline{j} \, dz \, dx + \overline{k} \, dx \, dy$$

Taking
$$\overline{F} = 2x^2 y \, \overline{i} - y^2 \overline{j} + 4xz^2 \, \overline{k}$$

the given integral can be written as

$$\iint_S \overline{F} \cdot d\overline{S} , \qquad \text{where S is the curved surface of the cylinder.}$$

$$d\overline{S} = \hat{n} \, dS, \text{ where } \hat{n} \text{ is unit outward drawn normal vector to the cylinder}$$

Let
$$\phi = y^2 + z^2 - 9$$

$$\frac{\partial \phi}{\partial x} = 0, \qquad \frac{\partial \phi}{\partial y} = 2y, \qquad \frac{\partial \phi}{\partial z} = 2z$$

$$\nabla \phi = 2y \, \overline{j} + 2z \, \overline{k} , \qquad \hat{n} = \frac{\nabla \phi}{|\nabla \phi|}$$

$$\hat{n} = \frac{2y \, \overline{j} + 2z \, \overline{k}}{\sqrt{4y^2 + 4z^2}} = \frac{y \, \overline{j} + z \, \overline{k}}{\sqrt{y^2 + z^2}} = \frac{1}{3} \, (y \, \overline{j} + z \, \overline{k})$$

$$\overline{F} \cdot \hat{n} = (2x^2 y \, \overline{i} - y^2 \overline{j}) + 4xz^2 \overline{k} \cdot \frac{1}{3} \, (y \, \overline{j} + z \, \overline{k}) = \frac{1}{3} \, (- y^3 + 4xz^3)$$

$$I = \iint_S \overline{F} \cdot d\overline{S} = \frac{1}{3} \iint (- y^3 + 4xz^3) \, dS$$

Transforming to cylindrical co-ordinate system

$$y = \rho \cos \phi, \quad z = \rho \sin \phi, \qquad x = x$$
$$dS = \rho \, dx \, d\phi$$

but
$$\rho = 3$$

$$I = \frac{1}{3} \int_{\phi=0}^{2\pi} \int_{x=0}^{2} (- 27 \cos^3 \phi + 4x \cdot 27 \sin^3 \phi) \, 3 \, dx \, d\phi$$

$$= \int_{0}^{2\pi} \left\{ - 27 \cos^3 \phi \, x + 108 \sin^3 \phi \, \frac{x^2}{2} \right\}_0^2 d\phi$$

$$= \int_{0}^{2\pi} \{ - 54 \cos^3 \phi + 216 \sin^3 \phi \} \, d\phi = 0$$

[Integrals of odd powers of sine and cosine vanish for limits 0 to 2π]

Ex. 7 : *Show that* $\iiint\limits_{V} \dfrac{dV}{r^2} = \iint\limits_{S} \dfrac{\overline{r} \cdot \hat{n}}{r^2}\ dS.$　　　　**(Nov. 2015, May 2016)**

Sol. : By divergence theorem,

$$\iint\limits_{S} \frac{\overline{r} \cdot \hat{n}\ dS}{r^2} = \iiint\limits_{V} \nabla \cdot \left(\frac{\overline{r}}{r^2}\right) dV$$

Now,　　　　$\nabla \cdot \left(\dfrac{\overline{r}}{r^2}\right) = \nabla \cdot (\overline{r}\ r^{-2}) = (\nabla \cdot \overline{r})\, r^{-2} + \nabla\, (r^{-2}) \cdot \overline{r}$

$$= \frac{3}{r^2} - 2r^{-4}\,\overline{r} \cdot \overline{r} = \frac{3}{r^2} - \frac{2}{r^4}\,r^2 = \frac{1}{r^2}$$

$\therefore$　　　　$\iint\limits_{S} \dfrac{\overline{r} \cdot \hat{n}\ dS}{r^2} = \iiint\limits_{V} \dfrac{dV}{r^2}$ which is the required result.

Ex. 8 : *Prove that :* $\iint\limits_{S} (\phi\nabla\psi - \psi\nabla\phi) \cdot d\overline{S} = \iiint\limits_{V} (\phi\nabla^2\psi - \psi\nabla^2\phi)\ dV.$**(May 08, 14, 17)**

Sol. : Let　　　　$\overline{F} = \phi\nabla\psi - \psi\nabla\phi$

$$\nabla \cdot \overline{F} = \nabla \cdot [\phi\nabla\psi - \psi\nabla\phi]$$
$$\nabla \cdot (\phi\nabla\psi) = \nabla\phi \cdot \nabla\psi + \phi\nabla \cdot \nabla\psi$$
$$= \nabla\phi \cdot \nabla\psi + \phi\nabla^2\psi$$
$$\nabla \cdot (\psi\nabla\phi) = \nabla\psi \cdot \nabla\phi + \psi\nabla \cdot \nabla\phi$$
$$= \nabla\psi \cdot \nabla\phi + \psi\nabla^2\phi$$
$$\nabla \cdot \overline{F} = \nabla\phi \cdot \nabla\psi + \phi\nabla^2\psi - \nabla\psi \cdot \nabla\phi - \psi\nabla^2\phi$$
$$= \phi\nabla^2\psi - \psi\nabla^2\phi$$

By divergence theorem,

$$\iint\limits_{S} (\phi\nabla\psi - \psi\nabla\phi) \cdot d\overline{S} = \iiint\limits_{V} \nabla \cdot \{\phi\nabla\psi - \psi\nabla\phi\}\, dV = \iiint \{\phi\nabla^2\psi - \psi\nabla^2\phi\}\, dV$$

which is the required result.

Ex. 9 : *If* $\overline{u} \cdot \overline{v}$ *are two vector point functions, show that for a closed surface S,*

$$\iiint\limits_{V} [\overline{v} \cdot (\nabla \times \nabla \times \overline{u}) - \overline{u} \cdot (\nabla \times \nabla \times \overline{v})]\ dV = \iint\limits_{S} [\overline{u} \times (\nabla \times \overline{v}) - \overline{v} \times (\nabla \times \overline{u})] \cdot d\overline{S}$$

Sol. : By the divergence theorem,

$$\iint\limits_{S} [\overline{u} \times (\nabla \times \overline{v}) - \overline{v} \times (\nabla \times \overline{u})] \cdot d\overline{S} = \iiint\limits_{V} \nabla \cdot [\overline{u} \times (\nabla \times \overline{v}) - \overline{v} \times (\nabla \times \overline{u})]\, dV$$

$$= \iiint\limits_{V} \{\nabla \cdot [\overline{u} \times (\nabla \times \overline{v})] - \nabla \cdot [\overline{v} \times (\nabla \times \overline{u})]\}\, dV$$

$$\dots (1)$$

Now
$$\nabla \cdot [\bar{u} \times (\nabla \times \bar{v})] = (\nabla \times \bar{v}) \cdot (\nabla \times \bar{u}) - \bar{u} \cdot (\nabla \times \nabla \times \bar{v})$$

Similarly
$$\nabla \cdot [\bar{v} \times (\nabla \times \bar{u})] = (\nabla \times \bar{u}) \cdot (\nabla \times \bar{v}) - \bar{v} \cdot (\nabla \times \nabla \times \bar{u})$$

$$\therefore \quad \nabla \cdot [\bar{u} \times (\nabla \times \bar{v})] - \nabla \cdot [\bar{v} \times (\nabla \times \bar{u})] = (\nabla \times \bar{v}) \cdot (\nabla \times \bar{u}) - \bar{u} \cdot (\nabla \times \nabla \times \bar{v})$$

$$- (\nabla \times \bar{u}) \cdot (\nabla \times \bar{v}) + \bar{v} \cdot (\nabla \times \nabla \times \bar{u})$$

$$= \bar{v} \cdot (\nabla \times \nabla \times \bar{u}) - \bar{u} \cdot (\nabla \times \nabla \times \bar{v})$$

Substituting in (1), required result follows.

Ex. 10 : *Show that the value of $\displaystyle \int \int p \left(\frac{x^4}{a^2} + \frac{y^4}{b^2} + \frac{z^4}{c^2} \right) dS$ taken over the surface of the ellipsoid $\dfrac{x^2}{a^2} + \dfrac{y^2}{b^2} + \dfrac{z^2}{c^2} = 1$, where p is the length of the perpendicular from origin to the tangent plane at (x, y, z) is : $\dfrac{4\pi}{5} abc (a^2 + b^2 + c^2)$.*

Sol. : Tangent plane of the ellipsoid at (x, y, z) is

$$\frac{X \cdot x}{a^2} + \frac{Y \cdot y}{b^2} + \frac{Z \cdot z}{c^2} = 1$$

$$p = \frac{1}{\sqrt{\dfrac{x^2}{a^4} + \dfrac{y^2}{b^4} + \dfrac{z^2}{c^4}}}$$

$$I = \iint \frac{1}{\sqrt{\dfrac{x^2}{a^4} + \dfrac{y^2}{b^4} + \dfrac{z^2}{c^4}}} \left(\frac{x^4}{a^2} + \frac{y^4}{b^2} + \frac{z^4}{c^2} \right) dS$$

$$\Phi = \frac{x^2}{a^2} + \frac{y^2}{b^2} + \frac{z^2}{c^2} - 1$$

$$\nabla \phi = \frac{2x\,\bar{i}}{a^2} + \frac{2y\,\bar{j}}{b^2} + \frac{2z\,\bar{k}}{c^2}$$

$$\hat{n} = \frac{\nabla \phi}{|\nabla \phi|} = \frac{\dfrac{x}{a^2}\bar{i} + \dfrac{y}{b^2}\bar{j} + \dfrac{z}{c^2}\bar{k}}{\sqrt{\dfrac{x^2}{a^4} + \dfrac{y^2}{b^4} + \dfrac{z^2}{c^4}}}$$

If
$$\bar{F} = x^3\,\bar{i} + y^3\,\bar{j} + z^3\,\bar{k}$$

$$I = \iint \bar{F} \cdot \hat{n}\, dS$$

$$I = \iiint \nabla \cdot \bar{F}\, dV \qquad \text{(by divergence theorem)}$$

$$= 3 \iiint_V (x^2 + y^2 + z^2)\, dx\, dy\, dz$$

where, V is the volume of the ellipsoid

$$\frac{x^2}{a^2} + \frac{y^2}{b^2} + \frac{z^2}{c^2} = 1$$

Put
$$x = aX, \quad y = bY, \quad z = cZ$$

$$I = 3 \iiint_V (a^2X^2 + b^2Y^2 + c^2Z^2) \ abc \ dX \ dY \ dZ$$

where, V is the volume of the sphere

$$X^2 + Y^2 + Z^2 = 1$$

Put
$$X = r \sin\theta \cos\phi, \quad Y = r \sin\theta \sin\phi, \quad Z = r \cos\theta$$

$$dX \ dY \ dZ = r^2 \sin\theta \ dr \ d\theta \ d\phi$$

$$I = 3 \int_0^{2\pi} \int_{\theta=0}^{\pi} \int_{r=0}^{1} \{a^2 r^2 \sin^2\theta \cos^2\phi + b^2 r^2 \sin^2\theta \sin^2\phi + c^2 r^2 \cos^2\theta\}$$
$$\times \ abc \ r^2 \sin\theta \ dr \ d\theta \ d\phi$$

$$= 4 \times 3 \times 2 \int_0^{\pi/2} \int_0^{\pi/2} \int_0^{1} \{r^4 a^2 \sin^3\theta \cos^2\phi + r^4 b^2 \sin^3\theta \sin^2\phi$$
$$+ \ r^4 c^2 \cos^2\theta \sin\theta\} \ dr \ d\theta \ d\phi \ abc$$

$$= 24 \left[\frac{r^5}{5}\right]_0^1 \int_0^{\pi/2} \int_0^{\pi/2} \{a^2 \sin^3\theta \cos^2\phi + b^2 \sin^3\theta \sin^2\phi + c^2 \cos^2\theta \sin\theta\} \ d\theta \ d\phi \ abc$$

$$= \frac{24}{5} \int_0^{\pi/2} \left\{a^2 \cos^2\phi \frac{2}{3} + b^2 \sin^2\phi \frac{2}{3} + c^2 \frac{1.1}{3}\right\} d\phi \ abc$$

$$= \frac{24}{5} \left[a^2 \frac{1}{2} \frac{\pi}{2} \cdot \frac{2}{3} + b^2 \frac{1}{2} \frac{\pi}{2} \cdot \frac{2}{3} + c^2 \cdot \frac{1}{3} \frac{\pi}{2}\right] abc$$

$$= \frac{24}{5} \left[\frac{\pi}{6} a^2 + \frac{\pi}{6} b^2 + \frac{\pi}{6} c^2\right] abc = \frac{4}{5} \pi \ abc \ (a^2 + b^2 + c^2)$$

Ex. 11 : *Evaluate* $\iint_S (x\bar{i} + y\bar{j} + z^2\bar{k}) \cdot d\bar{s}$ *where S is the curved surface of the cylinder* $x^2 + y^2 = 4$, *bounded by the planes* $z = 0$ *and* $z = 2$.　　　　**(May 2014)**

Sol. : S_1 is the plane surface of the circle $z = 0$, $x^2 + y^2 = 4$ and S_2 is the plane surface of the circle $z = 2$, $x^2 + y^2 = 4$. S_1, S_2 and S together enclose the volume bounded by the cylinder.

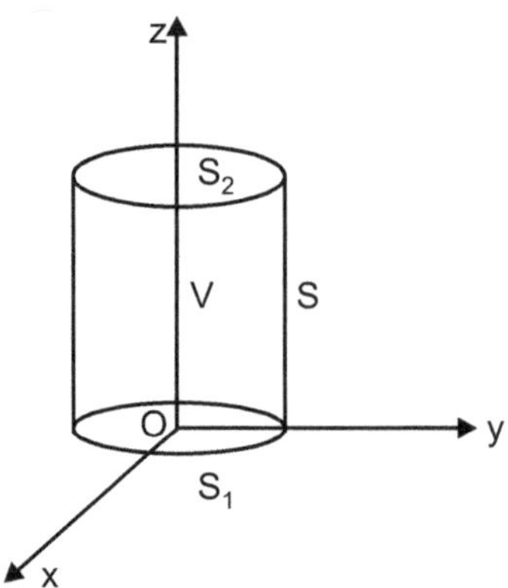

Fig. 11.14

By divergence theorem,

$$\iint_S \overline{F} \cdot d\overline{s} + \iint_{s_1} \overline{F} \cdot d\overline{s} + \iint_{s_2} \overline{F} \cdot d\overline{s} = \iiint_V \nabla \cdot \overline{F} \cdot dv$$

where,

$$\overline{F} = x\overline{i} + y\overline{j} + z^2 \overline{k}$$

$$\nabla \cdot \overline{F} = 1 + 1 + 2z$$

$$\text{R.H.S.} = \iiint (2 + 2z)\ dx\ dy\ dz = 2\iint \int_{z=0}^{2} (1 + z)\ dx\ dy\ dz$$

$$= 2\iint \left\{ z + \frac{z^2}{2} \right\}_0^2 dx\ dy = 2\iint_{s_1} \left(2 + \frac{4}{2} \right) dx\ dy$$

$$= 8\iint_{s_1} dx\ dy = 8 \cdot \pi \times 4 = 32\pi$$

For S_1, $\hat{n} = -\overline{k}$, $\overline{F} \cdot d\overline{s} = \overline{F} \cdot (-\overline{k})\ ds = -z^2\ dx\ dy$

$$\iint_{s_1} -z^2\ dx\ dy = 0 \quad \text{as the plane is } z = 0.$$

For S_2, $\hat{n} = \overline{k}$, $\overline{F} \cdot \hat{n}\ ds = z^2\ dx\ dy$

$$\iint_{s_2} \overline{F} \cdot d\overline{s} = \iint_{s_2} \overline{F} \cdot \hat{n}\ ds = \iint_{s_2} z^3\ dx\ dy \quad \text{where } z = 2$$

$$\therefore \quad \iint_{s_2} \overline{F} \cdot d\overline{s} = \iint_{s_2} 4\ dx\ dy = 4 \cdot \pi 4 = 16\pi$$

$$\therefore \quad \iint_S \overline{F} \cdot d\overline{s} = \iiint_V \nabla \cdot \overline{F}\ dv - \iint_{s_1} \overline{F} \cdot d\overline{s} - \iint_{s_2} \overline{F} \cdot d\overline{s}$$

$$= 32\pi - 0 - 16\pi$$

$$= 16\pi$$

EXERCISE 11.2

1. Verify divergence theorem for $\bar{F} = 2y^2x\,\bar{i} + (xz^2 - y^3)\,\bar{j} + z^3\,\bar{k}$ over the volume of a cube with edges of length unity parallel to the co-ordinate axes.

Ans. Common value $= -\dfrac{2}{3}$

2. Verify divergence theorem for $\bar{F} = 2xy\,\bar{i} - y\,\bar{j} + z^2\,\bar{k}$ over the volume bounded by $2x + y + 2z = 4$ and the co-ordinate planes. **Ans.** Common value $= \dfrac{16}{3}$

3. Verify Gauss divergence theorem for $\bar{F} = (x + y^2)\,\bar{i} - 2x\,\bar{j} + 2z\,\bar{k}$ over the volume of the tetrahedron bounded by co-ordinate planes and the plane $x + y + z = 1$.

Ans. Common value $= \dfrac{1}{2}$

4. Verify the divergence theorem for $\bar{F} = x\,\bar{i} + y\,\bar{j} + z^2\,\bar{k}$ over the cylindrical region bounded by $x^2 + y^2 = 4$, $z = 0$, $z = 2$. **(May 2011)**
[**Hint :** Refer solved example 11.. For the surface S, $\phi = x^2 + y^2 - 4$,

$$\hat{n} = \frac{\nabla\phi}{|\nabla\phi|} = \frac{x\bar{i} + y\bar{j}}{2} \quad\text{and}\quad \iint_S \bar{F}\cdot\hat{n}\,ds = 16\,\pi \qquad \textbf{Ans.}\ \text{Common value} = 32\pi$$

5. Evaluate $\iint_S \bar{F}\cdot d\bar{S}$ where $\bar{F} = yz\,\bar{i} + zx\,\bar{j} + xy\,\bar{k}$ and S is the part of the surface of

the sphere $x^2 + y^2 + z^2 = 1$ which lies in the first octant. **Ans.** $\dfrac{3}{8}$ **(May 08, 17, Nov. 15)**

6. Evaluate the surface integral $\iint_S (y^2z^2\,\bar{i} + z^2x^2\,\bar{j} + x^2y^2\,\bar{k})\cdot d\bar{S}$, where S is the surface

of the sphere $x^2 + y^2 + z^2 = a^2$ in the positive octant. **Ans.** $\dfrac{\pi\,a^6}{32}$

7. Evaluate $\iint_S \bar{F}\cdot d\bar{S}$ over the surface of the parabolic cylinder $y^2 = 8x$ in the first

octant bounded by the planes $y = 4$ and $z = 6$ where $\bar{F} = 2y\,\bar{i} - z\,\bar{j} + x^2\,\bar{k}$. **(Ans.** 132)

8. Evaluate $\iint_S xz^2\,dy\,dz + (x^2y - z^2)\,dz\,dx + (2xy + y^2z)\,dx\,dy$, where S is the surface

enclosing a region bounded by hemisphere $x^2 + y^2 + z^2 = 4$ above the xoy plane.

$\left[\textbf{Hint :}\ \bar{F} = xz^2\,\bar{i} + (x^2y - z^2)\,\bar{j} + (2xy + y^2z)\,\bar{k}\ \ \nabla\cdot\bar{F} = z^2 + x^2 + y^2;\right.$

$d\bar{S} = dy\,dz\,\bar{i} + dz\,dx\,\bar{j} + dx\,dy\,\bar{k}\,\Big]$ **Ans.** $\dfrac{64\,\pi}{5}$ **(Dec. 2009, Dec. 2011)**

9. Evaluate $\iint\limits_{S} (x^2 y^3\, \bar{i} + z^2 x^3\, \bar{j} + x^2 y^3\, \bar{i}) \cdot d\bar{s}$, where S is the curved surface of sphere

$x^2 + y^2 + z^2 = a^2$ above the plane z = 0.   **Ans.** $\dfrac{\pi a^8}{64}$

10. Evaluate $\iint\limits_{S} (yz\, \bar{i} + zx\, \bar{j} + xy\, \bar{k}) \cdot d\bar{S}$ where S is the curved surface of the cone

$x^2 + y^2 = z^2,\ \ z = 4.$ **Ans.** 0

11. Evaluate $\iint\limits_{S} \dfrac{dS}{\sqrt{a^2 x^2 + b^2 y^2 + c^2 z^2}}$ over the closed surface of the ellipsoid

$ax^2 + by^2 + cz^2 = 1,$ by applying Gauss Divergence theorem.

$\left[\textbf{Hint : Given } \bar{F} \cdot \hat{n} = \dfrac{1}{\sqrt{a^2 x^2 + b^2 y^2 + c^2 z^2}} \text{ for } \phi = ax^2 + by^2 + cz^2 - 1, \right.$

$\left. \hat{n} = \dfrac{\nabla\phi}{|\nabla\phi|} = \dfrac{ax\,\bar{i} + by\,\bar{j} + cz\,\bar{k}}{\sqrt{a^2 x^2 + b^2 y^2 + c^2 z^2}} \ \therefore\ \bar{F} = x\,\bar{i} + y\,\bar{j} + z\,\bar{k} \text{ and } \nabla \cdot \bar{F} = 3 \right]$ **Ans.** $\left(\dfrac{4\pi}{\sqrt{abc}}\right)$

12. Evaluate $\iint\limits_{S} (lx^2 + my^2 + nz^2)\, dS$, where S is the surface of the sphere

$(x - a)^2 + (y - b)^2 + (z - c)^2 = R^2;\ l,\ m,\ n$ being the direction cosines of the outward
normal to the surface.   **(May 2006)**

$\left[\textbf{Hint : Given } \hat{n} = l\,\bar{i} + m\,\bar{j} + j\,\bar{k} \text{ and } \bar{F} = x^2\bar{i} + y2\bar{j} + z^2\bar{k} \ \therefore\ \nabla \cdot \bar{F} = 2x + 2y + 2z \right.$

$\left. \therefore \iint\limits_{S} \bar{F} \cdot \hat{n}\, ds = 2 \iiint\limits_{v} (x + y + z)\, dx\, dy\, dz \right]$ **Ans.** $\dfrac{8}{3}\pi\,(a + b + c)\,R^3$

13. Evaluate $\iint\limits_{S} (2xy\,\bar{i} + yz^2\,\bar{j} + xz\,\bar{k}) \cdot d\bar{S}$ over the surface of the region bounded by

$x = 0,\, y = 0,\, y = 3,\, z = 0$ and $x + 2z = 6.$ **(Dec. 2010)**

$\left[\textbf{Hint : } \iint\limits_{S} \bar{F} \cdot d\bar{S} = \iiint\limits_{v} (2y + z^2 + x)\, dx\, dy\, dz \right]$ **Ans.** $\dfrac{351}{2}$

14. Calculate the rate at which volume of a fluid into a cube of edges of length 2a, if the

velocity field is given by $\bar{q} = -x^3 y^2\,\bar{i} + y^2 z\,\bar{j} + z^2 x\,\bar{k}$
where origin is at the centre of the cube and axes parallel to the edges of the cube.

     Ans. $\left[\dfrac{8}{3}a^7\right]$

15. Evaluate $\iint\limits_{S} \overline{F} \cdot d\overline{S}$ over a closed surface of a triangular prism of unit length in the

x-direction whose base is bounded by the positive y and z axes and the line $y + z = 1$,

$x = 0$, where $\overline{F} = 2y^2 z\,\overline{j} + yz^2\,\overline{k}$.   **Ans.** $\dfrac{1}{3}$

16. Evaluate the surface integral $\iint\limits_{S} \overline{r} \cdot \overline{n}\; dS$, $\overline{r} = x\,\overline{i} + y\,\overline{j} + z\,\overline{k}$ over the part of the

spherical surface S of the sphere $x^2 + y^2 + z^2 = a^2$ that lies within the vertical
cylinder $x^2 + y^2 = ax$.   **Ans.** $2\pi a^3$

17. Show that for closed surface S $\iint\limits_{S} \dfrac{\overline{r}}{r^3} \cdot \hat{n}\; dS = 0.$ **(May 2015)**

$$\left[\textbf{Hint :} \text{ Use } \iint\limits_{S} \frac{\overline{r}}{r^3}\, d\overline{s} = \iiint\limits_{S} \left[\nabla \left(\frac{\overline{r}}{r^3} \right) \right] dv = 0 \right]$$

18. Evaluate $\iint\limits_{S} \overline{r} \cdot \hat{n}\; dS$ over the surface of a sphere of radius 1 with centre at origin.

$$\left[\textbf{Hint :} \iint\limits_{S} \overline{r} \cdot \hat{n}\; ds = \iiint\limits_{v} (\nabla \cdot \overline{v})\, dv = 3 \iiint\limits_{v} dv = 3 \left(\frac{4}{3}\pi 1^3 \right) \right] \textbf{Ans.} \; 4\pi$$

19. If $\overline{w} = \dfrac{1}{2}\, \nabla \times \overline{v}$ and $\overline{v} = \nabla \times \overline{u}$, then show that

$$\frac{1}{2} \iiint\limits_{V} (\overline{v} \cdot \overline{v})\, dV = \frac{1}{2} \iint\limits_{S} \overline{u} \times \overline{v}\; d\overline{S} + \iiint\limits_{V} (\overline{u} \cdot \overline{w})\, dV.$$

20. Prove that $\iiint\limits_{V} \dfrac{1}{r^2}\, dV = \iint\limits_{S} \dfrac{1}{r^2}\, \overline{r} \cdot d\overline{S}$ where S is closed surface enclosing the

volume V. Hence evaluate $\iint\limits_{S} \dfrac{x\,\overline{i} + y\,\overline{j} + z\,\overline{k}}{r^2} \cdot d\overline{S}$ where S is the surface of the

sphere $x^2 + y^2 + z^2 = a^2$.   **Ans.** $4\pi a$

11.5 STOKE'S THEOREM AND RELATED PROBLEMS

We shall now consider Stoke's theorem which connects a surface integral with a line integral.

Statement : *The surface integral of the normal component of the curl of the vector point function $\overline{F}$ taken over an open surface S bounded by closed curve C is equal to the line integral of the tangential component of $\overline{F}$ taken around the curve C.*

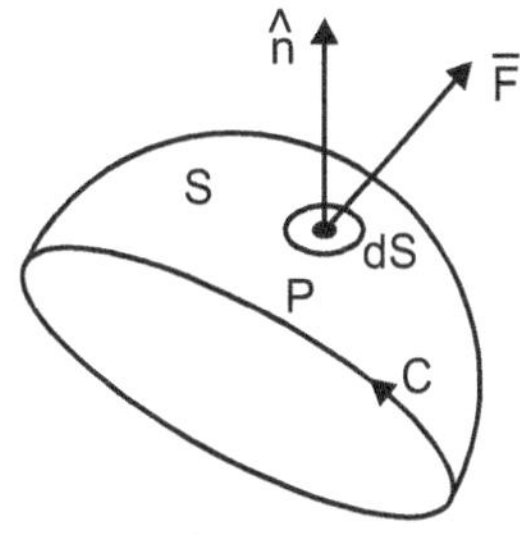

Fig. 11.15

In Fig. 11.15, S is the open surface to which $\hat{n}$ is unit outward drawn normal vector. $\overline{F}$ is acting at P enclosed by element dS. Curve 'C' is the boundary of the surface.

The Stoke's theorem can be expressed as

$$\iint_S \hat{n} \cdot \text{curl } \overline{F} \, dS = \oint_C \overline{F} \cdot d\overline{r} \quad \text{or} \quad \int_S \hat{n} \cdot \text{curl } \overline{F} \, dS = \oint_C \overline{F} \cdot d\overline{r}$$

or sometimes written as
$$\boxed{\oint_C \overline{\mathbf{F}} \cdot d\overline{\mathbf{r}} = \iint_S (\nabla \times \overline{\mathbf{F}}) \cdot d\overline{\mathbf{S}}}$$

Proof : Let $\overline{F} = F_1 \overline{i} + F_2 \overline{j} + F_3 \overline{k}$

Consider the surface S bounded by the curve C.

$$\int_C \overline{F} \cdot d\overline{r} = \int_C F_1 \, dx + F_2 \, dy + F_3 \, dz$$

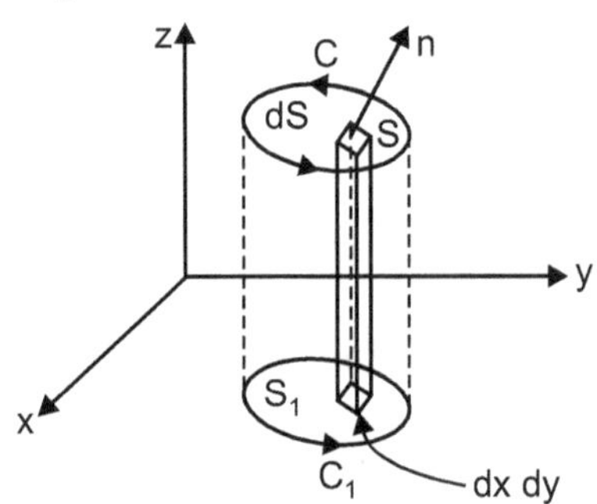

Fig. 11.16

We want to prove that $\iint_S \hat{n} \cdot \text{curl } \overline{F} \, dS$ equals the line integral. Let the equation of the surface S be z = f (x, y), [It could also be x = g (y, z) or y = h (x, z)] which is single valued and differentiable.

$$\iint_S \hat{n} \cdot \text{curl } \overline{F} \, dS = \iint_S \text{curl } \overline{F} \cdot \hat{n} \, dS = \iint_S (\nabla \times \overline{F}) \cdot \hat{n} \, dS$$

$$= \iint_S \nabla \times (F_1 \overline{i} + F_2 \overline{j} + F_3 \overline{k}) \cdot \hat{n} \, dS$$

$$= \iint_S \{\nabla \times (F_1 \overline{i})\} \cdot \hat{n} \, dS + \iint_S \{\nabla \times (F_2 \overline{j})\} \cdot \hat{n} \, dS$$

$$+ \iint_S \{\nabla \times (F_3 \overline{k})\} \cdot \hat{n} \, dS$$

Let us consider $\iint\limits_{S} \{\nabla \times (F_1\,\overline{i}\,)\} \cdot \hat{n}\ dS$

Now,
$$\nabla \times F_1\,\overline{i} \;=\; \begin{vmatrix} \overline{i} & \overline{j} & \overline{k} \\[4pt] \dfrac{\partial}{\partial x} & \dfrac{\partial}{\partial y} & \dfrac{\partial}{\partial z} \\[8pt] F_1 & 0 & 0 \end{vmatrix} \;=\; \overline{j}\,\frac{\partial F_1}{\partial z} - \overline{k}\,\frac{\partial F_1}{\partial y}$$

$$[\nabla \times (F_1\,\overline{i}\,)] \cdot \hat{n}\ dS \;=\; \left(\frac{\partial F}{\partial z}\,\overline{j} \cdot \hat{n} - \frac{\partial F_1}{\partial y}\,\overline{k} \cdot \hat{n} \right)\ ds \qquad \ldots (1)$$

Let $\qquad\qquad \overline{r} \;=\; x\,\overline{i} + y\,\overline{j} + z\,\overline{k}\ $ be the position vector of any point on S.

But $\qquad\qquad z \;=\; f\,(x,\,y)$ on S.

$\therefore \qquad\qquad \overline{r} \;=\; x\,\overline{i} + y\,\overline{j} + f\,(x,\,y)\,\overline{k}$

$$\frac{\partial \overline{r}}{\partial y} \;=\; \overline{j} + \frac{\partial f}{\partial y}\,\overline{k}\,,$$

which is a tangent vector to S and hence perpendicular to $\hat{n}$.

$\therefore \qquad\qquad \hat{n} \cdot \dfrac{\partial \overline{r}}{\partial y} \;=\; 0 \;=\; \hat{n} \cdot \overline{j} + \dfrac{\partial f}{\partial y}\,\hat{n} \cdot \overline{k}$

Or $\qquad\qquad \hat{n} \cdot \overline{j} \;=\; -\dfrac{\partial f}{\partial y}\,\hat{n} \cdot \overline{k}$

i.e. $\qquad\qquad \hat{n} \cdot \overline{j} \;=\; -\dfrac{\partial z}{\partial y}\,\hat{n} \cdot \overline{k}$

Putting in (1),

$$[\nabla \times (F_1\,\overline{i}\,)] \cdot \hat{n}\ dS \;=\; -\left(\frac{\partial F_1}{\partial z} \cdot \frac{\partial z}{\partial y} + \frac{\partial F_1}{\partial y} \right) \hat{n} \cdot \overline{k}\ dS$$

On S, $\qquad F_1\,(x,\,y,\,z) \;=\; F_1\,[x,\,y,\,f\,(x,\,y)] \;=\; \phi\,(x,\,y)$ say

Differentiating w.r.t. y,

$$\frac{\partial F_1}{\partial y} + \frac{\partial F_1}{\partial z} \cdot \frac{\partial F_1}{\partial y} \;=\; \frac{\partial \phi}{\partial y}$$

If dx dy is the projection of dS in xoy plane, $dS\cos\theta = dx\ dy$ or $(\hat{n} \cdot \overline{k}\,)\ dS = dx\ dy$

$$[\nabla \times (F_1\,\overline{i}\,)] \cdot \hat{n}\ dS \;=\; -\frac{\partial \phi}{\partial y}\ dx\ dy$$

$$\therefore \qquad \iint\limits_{S} [\nabla \times (F_1 \bar{i})] \cdot n \, dS = \iint\limits_{S_1} -\frac{\partial \phi}{\partial y} \, dx \, dy$$

where, S_1 is the projection of S in xoy plane.

By Green's Lemma, $\displaystyle\int\limits_{C} u \, dx + v \, dy = \iint\limits_{A} \left(\frac{\partial v}{\partial x} - \frac{\partial u}{\partial y}\right) dx \, dy$

Taking $u = \phi, \quad v = 0$

$$\iint\limits_{S_1} -\frac{\partial \phi}{\partial y} \, dx \, dy = \int\limits_{C_1} \phi \, dx \quad [C_1 \text{ is the boundary of } S_1]$$

At each point (x, y) of C_1 the value of ϕ is the same as that of F_1 at each point (x, y, z) of C and dx is the same for both curves, we have

$$\int\limits_{C_1} \phi \, dx = \int\limits_{C} F_1 \, dx$$

Thus it is established that

$$\iint\limits_{S} [\nabla \times (F_1 \bar{i})] \cdot \hat{n} \, dS = \int\limits_{C} F_1 \, dx$$

Similarly by considering projections of S on the other co-ordinate planes

$$\iint\limits_{S} [\nabla \times (F_2 \bar{j})] \cdot \hat{n} \, dS = \int\limits_{C} F_2 \, dy$$

and $\qquad \displaystyle\iint\limits_{S} [\nabla \times (F_3 \bar{k})] \cdot \hat{n} \, dS = \int\limits_{C} F_3 \, dz$

$$\iint\limits_{S} [\nabla \times (F_1 \bar{i} + F_2 \bar{j} + F_3 \bar{k})] \cdot \hat{n} \, dS = \int\limits_{C} F_1 \, dx + F_2 \, dy + F_3 \, dz$$

which proves the Stoke's theorem.

ILLUSTRATIONS

Ex. 1 : *Verify Stoke's theorem for*

$$\bar{F} = xy^2 \, \bar{i} + y \, \bar{j} + z^2 x \, \bar{k}$$

for the surface of rectangular lamina bounded by x = 0, y = 0, x = 1, y = 2, z = 0.

(May 2005, 2012, 2017, Nov. 2015, 2016)

Sol. :
$$\overline{F} = xy^2\,\overline{i} + y\,\overline{j} \text{ as } z = 0$$

$$\int_C \overline{F}\cdot d\overline{r} = \int_C xy^2\,dx + y\,dy$$

where C is the path OABCO as shown in Fig. 11.17.

Along OA, $y = 0$, $dy = 0$,

Along AB, $x = 1$, $dx = 0$,

Along BC, $y = 2$, $dy = 0$,

Along CO, $x = 0$, $dx = 0$.

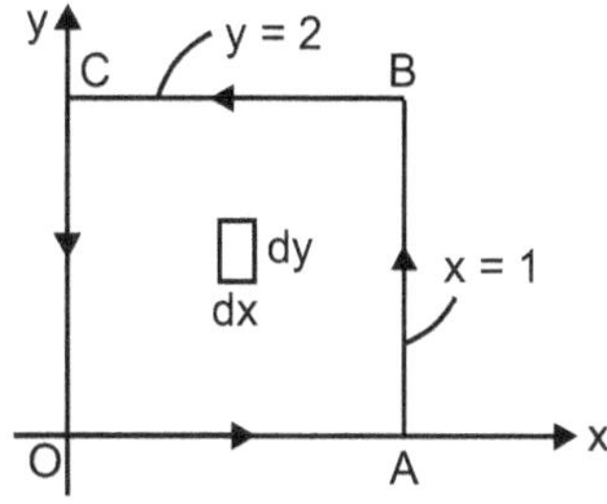

Fig. 11.17

$$\int_C \overline{F}\cdot d\overline{r} = \int_{OA} xy^2\,dx + \int_{AB} y\,dy + \int_{BC} xy^2\,dx + \int_{CO} y\,dy$$

$$= 0 + \int_0^2 y\,dy + \int_1^0 4x\,dx + \int_2^0 y\,dy = \int_0^2 y\,dy + \left[4\frac{x^2}{2}\right]_1^0 - \int_0^2 y\,dy$$

$$= 2\,[x^2]_1^0 = -2$$

To obtain surface integral

$$\nabla \times \overline{F} = \begin{vmatrix} \overline{i} & \overline{j} & \overline{k} \\ \dfrac{\partial}{\partial x} & \dfrac{\partial}{\partial y} & \dfrac{\partial}{\partial z} \\ xy^2 & y & 0 \end{vmatrix} = \overline{i}\,(0) + \overline{j}\,(0) + \overline{k}\,(-2xy)$$

normal to the surface $\hat{n} = \overline{k}$, $dS = dx\,dy$ is the surface element in S

$$\iint_S (\nabla \times \overline{F})\cdot \hat{n}\,dS = \iint_S (-2xy)\,\overline{k}\cdot\overline{k}\,dx\,dy$$

$$= -2\int_{x=0}^1 \int_0^2 xy\,dx\,dy = -2\int_0^1 x\left[\frac{y^2}{2}\right]_0^2 dx$$

$$= -2\int_0^1 x\left[\frac{4}{2}\right] dx = -4\left[\frac{x^2}{2}\right]_0^1 = -2$$

Thus
$$\int_C \overline{F}\cdot d\overline{r} = \iint_S (\nabla \times \overline{F})\cdot \hat{n}\,ds = -2$$

which verifies the Stoke's theorem.

Ex. 2 : *Verify Stoke's theorem for* $\overline{F} = (y - z + 2)\,\overline{i} + (yz + 4)\,\overline{j} - xz\,\overline{k}$ *over the surface of a cube* $x = 0,\ y = 0,\ z = 0,\ x = 2,\ z = 2$ *above the xoy plane (open at the bottom).*

Sol. : Consider the surface of the cube as shown in Fig. 11.18. Bounding path is OABCO shown by arrows

$$\oint_C \overline{F} \cdot d\overline{r} \;=\; \int_C F_1\, dx + F_2\, dy \quad [\text{as } z = 0]$$

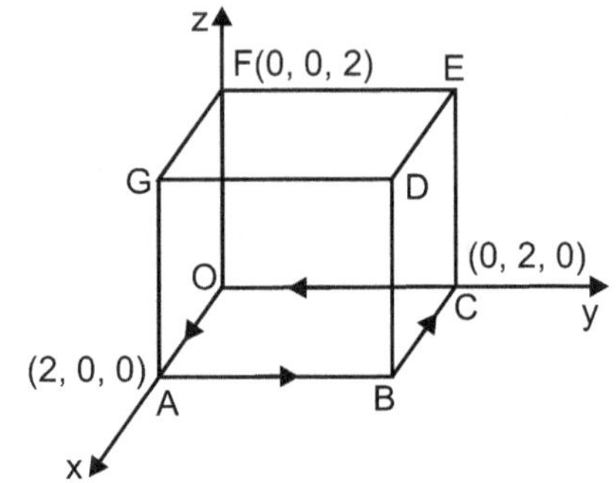

Fig. 11.18

$$\oint_C \overline{F} \cdot d\overline{r} \;=\; \int (y + 2)\, dx + 4\, dy \qquad [\text{Putting } z = 0 \text{ in } F_1 \text{ and } F_2]$$

$$= \int_{OA} (y + 2)\, dx + 4\, dy + \int_{AB} (y + 2)\, dx + 4\, dy$$

$$+ \int_{BC} (y + 2)\ dx + 4\, dy + \int_{CO} (y + 2)\, dx + 4\, dy$$

Along OA, $y = 0,\ z = 0$ $\therefore$ dy $= 0$

$$\int_{OA} (y + 2)\ dx + 4\, dy \;=\; \int_0^2 2\, dx = 2\,[x]_0^2 = 4$$

Along AB, $x = 2,\ $ dx $= 0$

$$\int_{AB} (y + 2)\, dx + 4\, dy \;=\; \int_0^2 4\,d = 4\,[y]_0^2 = 8$$

Along BC, $y = 2,\ $ dy $= 0$

$$\int_{BC} (y + 2)\ dx + 4\, dy \;=\; \int_2^0 4\, dx = 4\,[x]_2^0 = -8$$

Along CO, $x = 0,\ $ dx $= 0$

$$\int_{CO} (y + 2)\, dx + 4\, dy \;=\; \int_2^0 4\, dy = 4\,[y]_2^0 = -8$$

$$\therefore \qquad \oint_C \overline{F} \cdot d\overline{r} \;=\; 4 + 8 - 8 - 8 = -4$$

To evaluate surface integral,

consider

$$\nabla \times \overline{F} = \begin{vmatrix} \overline{i} & \overline{j} & \overline{k} \\ \dfrac{\partial}{\partial x} & \dfrac{\partial}{\partial y} & \dfrac{\partial}{\partial z} \\ y - z + 2 & yz + 4 & -xz \end{vmatrix}$$

$$= \overline{i}\,(0 - y) + \overline{j}\,(-1 + z) + \overline{k}\,(0 - 1)$$

$$= -y\,\overline{i} + (z - 1)\,\overline{j} - \overline{k}$$

Over the surface GDEF, $\hat{n} = \overline{k}$, $dS = dx\,dy$

$$\nabla \times \overline{F} \cdot \hat{n} = [-y\,\overline{i} + (z - 1)\,\overline{j} - \overline{k}] \cdot \overline{k} = -1$$

$$I_1 = \int_{x=0}^{2} \int_{y=0}^{2} (-1)\,dx\,dy = (-1) \int_0^2 \int_0^2 dx\,dy = -4$$

Over the surface OCEF, $(x = 0)$, $\hat{n} = -\overline{i}$

$$\text{Curl }\overline{F} \cdot \hat{n} = (-y\,\overline{i} + (z - 1)\,\overline{j} - \overline{k}) \cdot (-\overline{i}) = y$$

$$I_2 = \int_{y=0}^{2} \int_{z=0}^{2} y\,dy\,dz = \int_0^2 y\,[z]_0^2\,dy = 2\left[\frac{y^2}{2}\right]_0^2 = 4$$

Over the surface GABD, $\hat{n} = \overline{i}$ $(x = 2)$

$$\text{Curl }\overline{F} \cdot \hat{n} = -y$$

$$I_3 = \int_0^2 \int_0^2 -y\,dy\,dz = -4$$

Over the surface OAGF, $(y = 0)$, $\hat{n} = -\overline{j}$

$$\text{Curl }\overline{F} \cdot \hat{n} = [-y\,\overline{i} + (z - 1)\,\overline{j} - \overline{k}] \cdot (-\overline{j}) = 1 - z$$

$$I_4 = \int_{x=0}^{2} \int_{z=0}^{2} (1 - z)\,dx\,dz = \int_0^2 \left(z - \frac{z^2}{2}\right)_0^2 dx$$

$$= \int_0^2 (2 - 2)\,dx = 0$$

Over the surface BDEC, $(y = 2)$, $\hat{n} = \overline{j}$

$$\text{Curl } \overline{F} \cdot \hat{n} = (z - 1)$$

$$I_5 = \int_0^2 \int_0^2 (z - 1)\, dx\, dz = 0$$

$$\text{Surface integral} = I_1 + I_2 + I_3 + I_4 + I_5$$

$$= -4 + 4 - 4 + 0 + 0 = -4$$

Thus $$\iint_S \text{Curl } \overline{F} \cdot \hat{n}\, dS = \int_C \overline{F} \cdot d\overline{r} = -4$$

which verifies Stoke's theorem.

Ex. 3 : *Verify Stoke's theorem for* $\overline{F} = (x^2 + y - 4)\,\overline{i} + 3xy\,\overline{j} + (2xz + z^2)\,\overline{k}$ *over the surface of hemisphere* $x^2 + y^2 + z^2 = 16$ *above the xoy plane. Evaluate* $\iint_S \text{curl } \overline{F} \cdot \hat{n}\, ds$ *for the surface of the paraboloid* $z = 9 - (x^2 + y^2)$. **(May 06, Nov. 15, 16, May 12)**

Sol. : For verification of Stoke's theorem, consider $\int_C \overline{F} \cdot d\overline{r}$, where C is the bounding circle $x^2 + y^2 = 16$ (bounding the hemispherical surface).

$$= \int_C \overline{F} \cdot d\overline{r} = \int_C (x^2 + y - 4)\, dx + 3\, xy\, dy + (2xz + z^2)\, dz$$

As z = 0 $$= \int_C (x^2 + y - 4)\, dx + 3\, xy\, dy$$

Put $x = 4 \cos \theta$, $y = 4 \sin \theta$

$$dx = -4 \sin \theta\, d\theta, \quad dy = 4 \cos \theta\, d\theta$$

$$= \int_0^{2\pi} (16 \cos^2 \theta + 4 \sin \theta - 4)(-4 \sin \theta)\, d\theta + 48 \sin \theta \cos \theta\, (4 \cos \theta)\, d\theta$$

$$= \int_0^{2\pi} -16 \sin^2 \theta\, d\theta$$

[other integrals containing odd powers of sine and cosine vanish for the limits 0 to 2π]

$$= -16 \times 4 \int_0^{\pi/2} \sin^2 \theta\, d\theta = -64\, \frac{1}{2}\, \frac{\pi}{2} = -16\pi$$

To evaluate the surface integral,

$$\text{Curl } \overline{F} = \begin{vmatrix} \overline{i} & \overline{j} & \overline{k} \\ \dfrac{\partial}{\partial x} & \dfrac{\partial}{\partial y} & \dfrac{\partial}{\partial z} \\ x^2 + y - 4 & 3xy & 2xz + z^2 \end{vmatrix}$$

$$= \overline{i}\,(0 - 0) + \overline{j}\,(0 - 2z) + \overline{k}\,(3y - 1)$$

$$\hat{n} = \frac{\nabla \phi}{|\nabla \phi|} \quad \text{where} \quad \phi = x^2 + y^2 + z^2 - 16$$

$$\frac{\partial \phi}{\partial x} = 2x, \qquad \frac{\partial \phi}{\partial y} = 2y, \qquad \frac{\partial \phi}{\partial z} = 2z$$

$$\hat{n} = \frac{2x\,\overline{i} + 2y\,\overline{j} + 2z\,\overline{k}}{\sqrt{4x^2 + 4y^2 + 4z^2}} = \frac{x\,\overline{i} + y\,\overline{j} + z\,\overline{k}}{4}$$

$$\text{Curl } \overline{F} \cdot \hat{n} = \{-2z\,\overline{j} + (3y - 1)\,\overline{k}\} \cdot \left\{ \frac{x\,\overline{i} + y\,\overline{j} + z\,\overline{k}}{4} \right\}$$

$$= \frac{-2yz + (3y - 1)\,z}{4}$$

The surface element dS on hemisphere in spherical polar system is given by

$$dS = r^2 \sin \theta \, d\theta \, d\phi = 16 \sin \theta \, d\theta \, d\phi$$

For hemispherical surface, θ varies from 0 to $\pi/2$ and ϕ varies from 0 to 2π.

$$I = \iint_S \text{curl } \overline{F} \cdot \hat{n} \, dS = \frac{1}{4} \iint_S \{-2yz + (3y - 1)\,z\} \, dS$$

Putting, $\quad y = r \sin \theta \sin \phi = 4 \sin \theta \sin \phi$

$$z = r \cos \theta = 4 \cos \theta$$

$$I = \frac{1}{4} \int_{\phi = 0}^{2\pi} \int_{\theta = 0}^{\pi/2} \{-32 \sin \theta \cos \theta \sin \phi + (12 \sin \theta \sin \phi - 1) \times 4 \cos \theta\}\, 16 \sin \theta \, d\theta \, d\phi$$

$$= \frac{1}{4} \int_{0}^{2\pi} \int_{0}^{\pi/2} \{-512 \sin^2 \theta \cos \theta \sin \phi + 768 \sin^2 \theta \cos \theta \sin \phi - 64 \sin \theta \cos \theta\} \, d\theta \, d\phi$$

Applying reduction formula,

$$I = \frac{1}{4} \int_{0}^{2\pi} \left\{ -512 \frac{1.1}{3.1} \sin \phi + 768 \frac{1.1}{3.1} \sin \phi - 64 \frac{1.1}{2} \right\} d\phi$$

Integrals of first two terms are zero between the limits 0 to 2π.

$$\therefore \quad I = \frac{1}{4} \int\limits_{0}^{2\pi} -32 \, d\phi = -8 \, [\phi]_0^{2\pi} = -16\pi$$

The line integral is equal to the surface integral, hence Stoke's theorem is verified.

To obtain $\iint\limits_{S} \text{curl} \, \overline{F} \cdot \hat{n} \, dS$ for the surface of paraboloid, we apply alternative method based on Stoke's theorem. Taking the section of the paraboloid by the plane $z = 0$, it gives a circle $x^2 + y^2 = 9$, $z = 0$. The perimeter of circle thus bounds the surface of paraboloid as well as plane surface of the circle.

By Stoke's theorem,

$$\iint\limits_{S} \text{curl} \, \overline{F} \cdot \hat{n} \, dS = \int\limits_{C} \overline{F} \cdot d\overline{r} = \iint\limits_{S_1} \text{curl} \, \overline{F} \cdot \hat{n} \, dS$$

where, S is the surface of the paraboloid, C is the perimeter of the circle and S_1 is the plane surface of the circle.

For S_1, $\hat{n} = \overline{k}$, $\text{curl} \, \overline{F} \cdot \hat{n} = \{-2z \, \overline{j} + (3y - 1) \, \overline{k}\} \cdot \overline{k} = (3y - 1)$

$$dS = dx \, dy$$

$$\iint\limits_{S} \text{curl} \, \overline{F} \cdot \hat{n} \, dS = \iint\limits_{S_1} \text{curl} \, \overline{F} \cdot \hat{n} \, dS = \iint\limits_{S_1} (3y - 1) \, dx \, dy$$

where, S_1 is the plane of the circle $x^2 + y^2 = 9$.

Putting $x = r \cos \theta$, $y = r \sin \theta$, $dx \, dy = r \, d\theta \, dr$

$$\iint\limits_{S_1} (3y - 1) \, dx \, dy = \int\limits_{\theta = 0}^{2\pi} \int\limits_{r = 0}^{3} (3r \sin \theta - 1) \, r \, d\theta \, dr$$

$$= \int\limits_{0}^{2\pi} \left\{ \frac{3r^3}{3} \sin \theta - \frac{r^2}{2} \right\}_0^3 d\theta = \int\limits_{0}^{2\pi} \left(27 \sin \theta - \frac{9}{2} \right) d\theta$$

$$= -\frac{9}{2} \int\limits_{0}^{2\pi} d\theta = -\frac{9}{2} [\theta]_0^{2\pi} \qquad \left[\because \int\limits_{0}^{2\pi} 27 \sin \theta \, d\theta = 0 \right]$$

$$= -\frac{9}{2} \times 2\pi = -9\pi$$

Ex. 4 : *Apply Stoke's theorem to calculate* $\int\limits_{C} 4y \, dx + 2z \, dy + 6y \, dz$, *where C is the curve of intersection of* $x^2 + y^2 + z^2 = 6z$ *and* $z = x + 3$.　　　　**(Dec. 2004, 2011, May 2015)**

Sol. : Taking $\overline{F} = 4y \, \overline{i} + 2z \, \overline{j} + 6y \, \overline{k}$ and applying Stoke's theorem,

$$\int\limits_{C} 4y \, dx + 2z \, dy + 6y \, dz = \iint\limits_{S} (\nabla \times F) \cdot \hat{n} \, dS \quad \text{where, S is the surface of the circle}$$

$x^2 + y^2 + z^2 = 6z$, $z = x + 3$, $\hat{n}$ is normal to the plane $x - z + 3 = 0$

Let,　　　$\theta = x - z + 3, \quad \dfrac{\partial \phi}{\partial x} = 1, \quad \dfrac{\partial \phi}{\partial y} = 0, \quad \dfrac{\partial \phi}{\partial z} = 1$

$$\hat{n} = \frac{\nabla \phi}{|\nabla \phi|} = \frac{\bar{i} - \bar{k}}{\sqrt{2}}$$

$$\nabla \times \bar{F} = \begin{vmatrix} \bar{i} & \bar{j} & \bar{k} \\ \dfrac{\partial}{\partial x} & \dfrac{\partial}{\partial y} & \dfrac{\partial}{\partial z} \\ 4y & 2z & 6y \end{vmatrix} = \bar{i}\,(6 - 2) + \bar{j}\,(0 - 0) + \bar{k}\,(0 - 4)$$

$$= 4\,\bar{i} - 4\,\bar{k}$$

$$(\nabla \times \bar{F}) \cdot \hat{n} = (4\,\bar{i} - 4\,\bar{k}) \cdot \left(\frac{\bar{i} - \bar{k}}{\sqrt{2}} \right) = \frac{1}{\sqrt{2}}(4 + 4) = \frac{8}{\sqrt{2}} = 4\sqrt{2}$$

$$\iint_S (\nabla \times \bar{F}) \cdot \hat{n}\, dS = \iint_S 4\sqrt{2}\, dS = 4\sqrt{2} \times \text{area of circle.}$$

Centre of the sphere $x^2 + y^2 + (z - 3)^2 = 9$, $(0, 0, 3)$ lies on plane $z = x + 3$, that means given circle is a great circle of the sphere, where radius is same as that of the sphere.

∴　　　　Radius of circle $= 3$,　　　　Area $= \pi\,(3)^2 = 9\pi$

∴　　　$\iint_S (\nabla \times \bar{F}) \cdot \hat{n}\, dS = 4\sqrt{2} \times 9\pi = 36\pi\sqrt{2}$.

Ex. 5 : *Evaluate* $\iint_S (\nabla \times \bar{F}) \cdot d\bar{S}$, *where* $\bar{F} = (x^3 - y^3)\,\bar{i} - xyz\,\bar{j} + y^3\,\bar{k}$ *and S is the surface* $x^2 + 4y^2 + z^2 - 2x = 4$ *above the plane* $x = 0$.　　　　**(May 2007, Dec. 2008)**

Sol. : $\iint_S (\nabla \times \bar{F}) \cdot dS = \int_C \bar{F} \cdot d\bar{r}$ [by Stoke's theorem], where C is the bounding curve.

$$4y^2 + z^2 = 4 \qquad\qquad \text{[Putting } x = 0 \text{ in the equation of surface]}$$

i.e.　the ellipse　$\dfrac{y^2}{1} + \dfrac{z^2}{4} = 1$

whose parametric equations are $y = \cos\theta, \ z = 2\sin\theta$.

$$\int_C \bar{F} \cdot d\bar{r} = \int_C (x^3 - y^3)\, dx - xy\,z\, dy + y^3\, dz$$

Putting $x = 0, dx = 0$

$$= \int_C y^3\, dz = \int_0^{2\pi} \cos^3\theta \cdot 2\cos\theta\, d\theta$$

$$= 8 \int_0^{\pi/2} \cos^4\theta\, d\theta = 8\,\frac{3}{4}\,\frac{1}{2}\,\frac{\pi}{2} = \frac{3\pi}{2}$$

Ex. 6 : *Evaluate* $\iint_S (\nabla \times \overline{F}) \cdot \hat{n}\, ds$ *where 'S' is the curved surface of the paraboloid*

$x^2 + y^2 = 2z$ *bounded by the plane* $z = 2$, *where* $\overline{F} = 3(x-y)\,\overline{i} + 2xz\,\overline{j} + xy\,\overline{k}$.

(May 2014)

Sol. :

$$\nabla \times \overline{F} = \begin{vmatrix} \overline{i} & \overline{j} & \overline{k} \\ \dfrac{\partial}{\partial x} & \dfrac{\partial}{\partial y} & \dfrac{\partial}{\partial z} \\ 3(x-y) & 2xz & xy \end{vmatrix}$$

$$= \overline{i}(x - 2x) + \overline{j}(0 - y) + \overline{k}(2z + 3) = -x\overline{i} - 7\overline{j} + (2z + 3)\overline{k}$$

Curved surface of the paraboloid is bounded by the arc of the circle $x^2 + y^2 = 4$

[$\because z = 2$] which is also the boundary of the plane of the circle $x^2 + y^2 = 4$ for which $\hat{n} = \overline{k}$

$$\therefore \quad \text{curl}\,\overline{F} \cdot \hat{n}\, ds = \text{curl}\,\overline{F} \cdot \hat{k}\, ds = (2z + 3)\, dx\, dy$$

$$\therefore \quad \iint_S (\nabla \times \overline{F}) \cdot \hat{n}\, ds = \iint_{S_1} (2z + 3)\, dx\, dy \quad \text{where} \quad z = 2 \quad \text{and} \quad S_1 \text{ is the plane of}$$

the circle $x^2 + y^2 = 4$.

$$\therefore \qquad I = \iint 7dx\, dy = 7 \times \text{Area of circle} = 7 \times 4\pi = 28\pi$$

Ex. 7 : *Evaluate* $\iint_S \nabla \times \overline{F} \cdot d\overline{s}$ *for* $\overline{F} = y\overline{i} + z\overline{j} + x\overline{k}$.　　　**(Dec. 2007, Nov. 2013)**

where S is the surface of the paraboloid $z = 1 - x^2 - y^2$, $z \geq 0$.

Sol. : $\nabla \times \overline{F} = \begin{vmatrix} \overline{i} & \overline{j} & \overline{k} \\ \dfrac{\partial}{\partial x} & \dfrac{\partial}{\partial y} & \dfrac{\partial}{\partial z} \\ y & z & x \end{vmatrix} = \overline{i}(0 - 1) + \overline{j}(0 - 1) + \overline{k}(0 - 1) = -\overline{i} - \overline{j} - \overline{k}$

Surface of paraboloid has boundary, the circle, which is also the boundary of plane surface S_1 of the circle $x^2 + y^2 = 1$.

$$\iint_S (\nabla \times \overline{F}) \cdot d\overline{s} = \iint_{S_1} (\nabla \times \overline{F}) \cdot \hat{n}\, ds$$

$$\hat{n} = \overline{k} \text{ for } S_1$$

$$(\nabla \times \overline{F}) \cdot \overline{k} = -1$$

$$\therefore \quad \iint_{S_1} (-1)\, dx\, dy = -\pi$$

EXERCISE 11.3

1. Verify Stoke's theorem for $\bar{F} = x^2\,\bar{i} + xy\,\bar{j}$ for the surface of a square lamina bounded by $x = -1$, $x = 1$, $y = -1$, $y = 1$.   **Ans.** Common value 0 **(May 2009)**

2. Verify Stoke's theorem for $\bar{F} = xz\,\bar{i} - y\,\bar{j} + x^2 y\,\bar{k}$, where S is the surface of the region bounded by $y = 0$, $z = 0$, $3x + y + 3z = 6$ which is not included in the yz plane.

$$\textbf{Ans. Common value } \frac{4}{3}$$

3. Verify Stoke's theorem for the vector field $\bar{F} = (2y + z)\,\bar{i} + (x - z)\,\bar{j} + (y - x)\,\bar{k}$ over the portion of the plane $x + y + z = 1$ cut off by the co-ordinate planes.

$$\textbf{Ans. Common value } \frac{3}{2}$$

4. Verify Stoke's theorem when $\bar{F} = (2x - y)\,\bar{i} - yz^2\,\bar{j} - y^2 z\,\bar{k}$, where S is the upper half surface of the sphere $x^2 + y^2 + z^2 = 1$ and C is the boundary.   **Ans.** Common value π **(Dec. 2009)**

5. Verify Stoke's theorem for $\bar{F} = -y^3\,\bar{i} + x^3\,\bar{j}$ and the closed curve C is the boundary of the ellipse $\dfrac{x^2}{a^2} + \dfrac{y^2}{b^2} = 1$.   **(Dec. 2006, May 2008, Dec. 2011)**

$$\textbf{Ans. Common value } \frac{3\pi\,ab}{16}\,(a^2 + b^2)$$

6. Evaluate using Stoke's theorem $\displaystyle\int_C (y\,dx + z\,dy + x\,dz)$, C being intersection of $x^2 + y^2 + z^2 = a^2$, $x + z = a$.   **(Dec. 2010, May 2014, 2015)**

$$\left[\textbf{Hint : } \nabla \times \bar{F} = -\bar{i} - \bar{j} - \bar{k},\ \hat{n} = \frac{\nabla\phi}{|\nabla\phi|} = \frac{\bar{i} + \bar{k}}{\sqrt{2}} \ \therefore\ (\nabla \times \bar{F}) \cdot \hat{n} = -\sqrt{2}\right] \textbf{Ans. } -\frac{\pi a^2}{\sqrt{2}}$$

7. Verify Stoke's theorem for $\bar{F} = yz\,\bar{i} + zx\,\bar{j} + xy\,\bar{k}$ and C is the curve of intersection of $x^2 + y^2 = 1$ and $y = z^2$. $\left[\textbf{Hint : } \nabla \times \bar{F} = \bar{0}\right]$ **Ans.** Common value 0

8. Evaluate $\displaystyle\iint_S \nabla \times \bar{F} \cdot \hat{n}\ dS$ for the surface of the paraboloid $z = 4 - x^2 - y^2$ $(z \geq 0)$ and $\bar{F} = y^2\,\bar{i} + z\,\bar{j} + xy\,\bar{k}$.   **Ans.** 0

9. Evaluate $\displaystyle\iint_S \nabla \times \bar{F} \cdot \hat{n}\ dS$ where, $\bar{F} = (x - y)\,\bar{i} + (x^2 + yz)\,\bar{j} - 3xy^2\,\bar{k}$ and S is the surface of the cone $z = 4 - \sqrt{x^2 + y^2}$ above xoy plane.   **Ans.** -16π **(Dec. 2005, 2014)**

10. Use Stoke's theorem to evaluate $\int_C (4y\,\bar{i} + 2z\,\bar{j} + 6y\,\bar{k}) \cdot d\bar{r}$, where, C is the curve of intersection of $x^2 + y^2 + z^2 = 2z$ and $x = z - 1$.

$$\left[\textbf{Hint :} \ \nabla \times \bar{F} = 4\bar{i} - 4\bar{k}, \ \hat{n} = \frac{\nabla \phi}{|\nabla \phi|} = \frac{\bar{i} - \bar{k}}{\sqrt{2}}, \ (\nabla \times \bar{F}) \cdot \hat{n} = 4\sqrt{2} \right] \textbf{Ans. } 4\pi\sqrt{2}$$

11. Apply Stoke's theorem to prove that $\int_C (y\,\bar{i} + z\,\bar{j} + x\,\bar{k}) \cdot d\bar{r} = -2\sqrt{2}\,\pi a^2$, where C is the curve given by $x^2 + y^2 + z^2 - 2ax - 2ay = 0$, $x + y = 2a$.

$$\left[\textbf{Hint :} \ \nabla \times \bar{F} = -\bar{i} - \bar{j} - \bar{k}, \ \hat{n} = \frac{\nabla \phi}{|\nabla \phi|} = \frac{\bar{i} + \bar{j}}{\sqrt{2}}, \ (\nabla \times \bar{F}) \cdot \hat{n} = -\sqrt{2} \right] \textbf{Ans. } -2\sqrt{2}\,\pi a^2$$

12. Evaluate $\int_C (xy\,dx + xy^2\,dy)$ by Stoke's theorem, where C is the square in x-y plane with vertices $(1, 0), (-1, 0), (0, 1), (0, -1)$. $\qquad$ **Ans.** $-\dfrac{1}{3}$

13. Using Stoke's theorem, deduce that the surface integral of curl $\bar{F}$ taken over a closed surface is zero.

14. Using Stoke's and Gauss's theorem, prove that Curl grad $\phi = 0$, Div curl $\bar{F} = 0$ respectively.

15. Prove that $\int_C (\bar{a} \times \bar{r}) \cdot d\bar{r} = 2\bar{a} \cdot \iint_S d\bar{S}$ $\qquad\qquad$ **(Dec. 2004, 2006, 2007)**

$$[\textbf{Hint :} \ \nabla \times (\bar{a} \times \bar{r}) = 2\bar{a}]$$

16. Show that $\int_C [\bar{u} \times (\bar{r} \times \bar{v})] \cdot d\bar{r} = -(\bar{u} \times \bar{v}) \cdot \iint_S d\bar{S}$

where S is the open surface bounded by closed curve C and $\bar{u}$ and $\bar{v}$ are constant vectors.

$$\left[\textbf{Hint :} \ \nabla \times [(\bar{u} \cdot \bar{v})\,\bar{r} - (\bar{u} \cdot \bar{r})\,\bar{v}] = -(\bar{u} \times \bar{v}) \right]$$

CHAPTER TWELVE

APPLICATION OF VECTORS TO FLUID MECHANICS

12.1 LINE INTEGRAL

Vector Calculus has enormous applications in Fluid Mechanics. Complicated equations can be represented in compact vector form. In discussing applications, we shall restrict to ideal fluids, that is the effects of viscosity will be neglected. In view of limited scope of the text, we shall consider only fundamental aspects of the subject.

12.2 STREAM LINES AND PATH LINES

Definition : An imaginary curve drawn in the fluid such that at any instant of time, the tangent at any point of it is along the velocity vector at the point is called *stream line.*

Stream lines indicate the direction of motion at each point (See Fig. 12.1). From the definition it is clear that there can be no flow across a stream line.

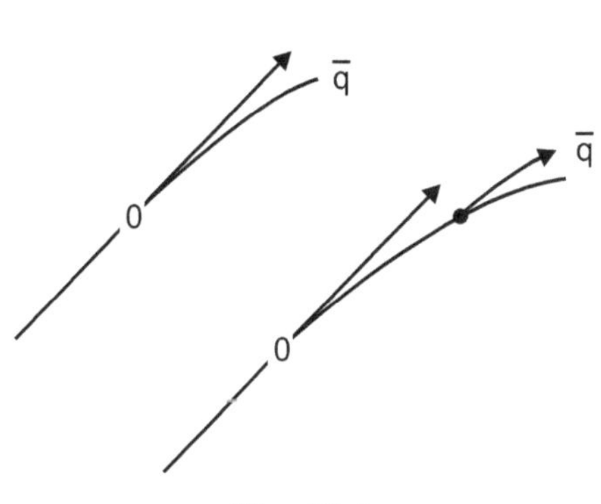

Fig. 12.1

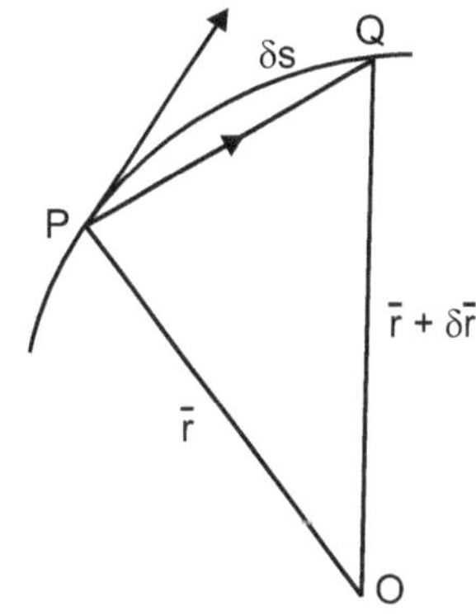

Fig. 12.2

To find the equation of stream line, consider two points P $(\bar{r})$ and Q $(\bar{r} + \delta\bar{r})$ on the stream line.

$$\therefore \qquad \overrightarrow{PQ} = \bar{r} + \delta\bar{r} - \bar{r} = \delta\bar{r}$$

$$\therefore \qquad \lim_{Q \to P} \frac{\overrightarrow{PQ}}{\delta s} = \lim_{Q \to P} \frac{\delta\bar{r}}{\delta s} = \frac{d\bar{r}}{ds}$$

represents unit tangent vector $\hat{T}$ at P or $\dfrac{d\bar{r}}{ds} = \hat{T}$

Let $\bar{q} = u\bar{i} + v\bar{j} + w\bar{k}$ be velocity vector at P.

From the definition, $\qquad \bar{q} = K\dfrac{d\bar{r}}{ds}$ $\qquad$ [K is some constant]

$\therefore \qquad u\bar{i} + v\bar{j} + w\bar{k} = K\left(\dfrac{dx}{ds}\bar{i} + \dfrac{dy}{ds}\bar{j} + \dfrac{dz}{ds}\bar{k}\right)$

Equating $\bar{i}$, $\bar{j}$, $\bar{k}$ components, we get

$$u = K\dfrac{dx}{ds}, \qquad v = K\dfrac{dy}{ds}, \qquad w = K\dfrac{dz}{ds}$$

$\therefore \qquad \dfrac{dx}{u} = \dfrac{dy}{v} = \dfrac{dz}{w} = \dfrac{ds}{K}$

or $\qquad \dfrac{dx}{u} = \dfrac{dy}{v} = \dfrac{dz}{w}$ $\qquad\qquad$ ... (1)

represents the differential equations of the stream line.

Definition : A path line is a curve traced by a single fluid particle during its motion.

Fig. 12.3 shows the path line which indicates the position occupied by the fluid particle A at times t_1, t_2 and t_3.

When the motion is steady so that the pattern of flow does not vary with time, the paths of the fluid particles coincide with the stream lines. In unsteady motion, however, the flow pattern varies with time and the paths of the particles do not coincide with the stream lines, though the stream line through any point P does touch the path line through P.

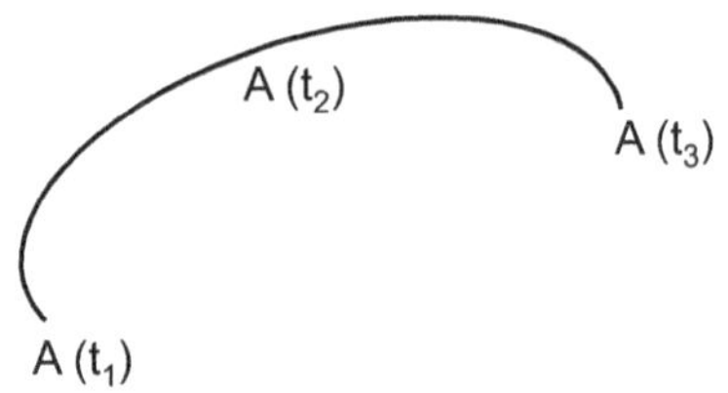

Fig. 12.3

The path lines are the solutions of the differential equations :

$$\dfrac{dx}{dt} = u; \qquad \dfrac{dy}{dt} = v; \qquad \dfrac{dz}{dt} = w$$

12.3 THE VELOCITY POTENTIAL

If $\bar{q} = u\bar{i} + v\bar{j} + w\bar{k}$, we have already seen that, equations of stream lines are

$$\dfrac{dx}{u} = \dfrac{dy}{v} = \dfrac{dz}{w} \qquad\qquad ... (1)$$

These lines cut the surfaces,

$$u\,dx + v\,dy + w\,dz = 0 \qquad\qquad ... (2)$$

orthogonally. Find scalar function ϕ (x, y, z, t) uniform throughout the entire field of flow at some instant such that,

$$- d\phi \equiv u\,dx + v\,dy + w\,dz \qquad \text{... (3)}$$

But
$$d\phi \equiv \frac{\partial \phi}{\partial x}\,dx + \frac{\partial \phi}{\partial y}\,dy + \frac{\partial \phi}{\partial z}\,dz \qquad \text{... (4)}$$

Comparison of (3) and (4) shows that

$$u = -\frac{\partial \phi}{\partial x}, \quad v = -\frac{\partial \phi}{\partial y}, \quad w = -\frac{\partial \phi}{\partial z} \qquad \text{... (5)}$$

$\therefore$
$$\bar{q} = u\bar{i} + v\bar{j} + w\bar{k}$$

$$= -\bar{i}\frac{\partial \phi}{\partial x} - \bar{j}\frac{\partial \phi}{\partial y} - \bar{k}\frac{\partial \phi}{\partial z}$$

$$= -\nabla\phi$$

Here this ϕ is called as velocity potential.

The necessary and sufficient condition for (5) to hold is $\nabla \times \bar{q} = 0$ $\qquad$ ... (6)

The surfaces ϕ (x, y, z, t) = constant, are called equipotentials. From (1) and (2), it follows that at all points of the field of flow, the equipotentials are cut orthogonally by the stream lines. The negative sign in $\bar{q} = -\nabla\phi$ is a matter of convention. It ensures that flow takes place from the higher to the lower potentials. Some authors also use $\bar{q} = \nabla\phi$.

12.4 VORTICITY VECTOR

In flows where $\nabla \times \bar{q} \neq 0$, the vector,

$$\bar{\zeta} = \nabla \times \bar{q}$$

is called a vorticity vector. The necessary and sufficient condition for potential flow is $\bar{\zeta} = 0$. A vortex line is a curve drawn in the fluid, such that the tangent to it at every point is in the direction of vorticity vector $\bar{\zeta}$.

If
$$\bar{\zeta} = \zeta_1\,\bar{i} + \zeta_2\,\bar{j} + \zeta_3\,\bar{k}$$

the equations of vortex lines are given by

$$\frac{dx}{\zeta_1} = \frac{dy}{\zeta_2} = \frac{dz}{\zeta_3}$$

In general, these do not coincide with the stream lines.

12.5 LOCAL AND PARTICLE RATES OF CHANGE

Suppose a particle of fluid moves from P (x, y, z) at time t to P$'$ $(x + \delta x, y + \delta y, z + \delta z)$ at time $t + \delta t$. Let $f(x, y, z, t)$ be some scalar function associated with fluid property. In the motion of the particle from P to P$'$ the total change of f is given by

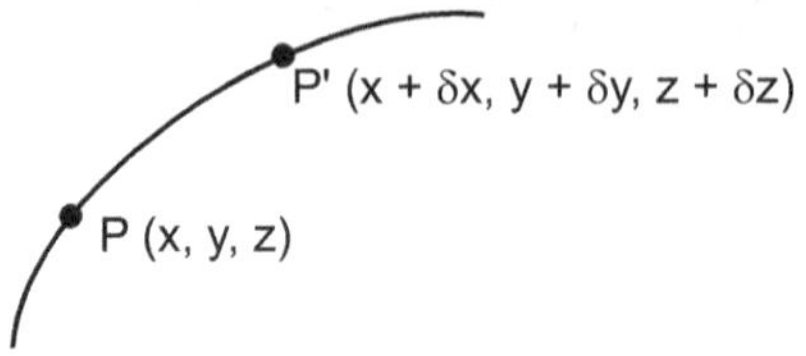

$$\delta f = \frac{\partial f}{\partial x}\,\delta x + \frac{\partial f}{\partial y}\,\delta y + \frac{\partial f}{\partial z}\,\delta z + \frac{\partial f}{\partial t}\,\delta t$$

Fig. 12.4

Thus the total rate of change of f at the point P at time t in the motion of the particle is,

$$\frac{df}{dt} = \lim_{\delta t \to 0}\left(\frac{\delta f}{\delta t}\right) = \frac{\partial f}{\partial x}\frac{dx}{dt} + \frac{\partial f}{\partial y}\frac{dy}{dt} + \frac{\partial f}{\partial z}\frac{dz}{dt} + \frac{\partial f}{\partial t}$$

But

$$\bar{q} = u\bar{i} + v\bar{j} + w\bar{k}$$

where

$$u = \frac{dx}{dt}, \quad v = \frac{dy}{dt} \quad \text{and} \quad w = \frac{dz}{dt}$$

$$\therefore \quad \frac{df}{dt} = u\frac{\partial f}{\partial x} + v\frac{\partial f}{\partial y} + w\frac{\partial f}{\partial z} + \frac{\partial f}{\partial t}$$

Now,

$$\nabla f = \bar{i}\frac{\partial f}{\partial x} + \bar{j}\frac{\partial f}{\partial y} + \bar{k}\frac{\partial f}{\partial z} \quad \text{and} \quad \bar{q} = u\bar{i} + v\bar{j} + w\bar{k}$$

$$\therefore \quad \bar{q} \cdot \nabla f = u\frac{\partial f}{\partial x} + v\frac{\partial f}{\partial y} + w\frac{\partial f}{\partial z}$$

$$\therefore \quad \frac{df}{dt} = \bar{q} \cdot \nabla f + \frac{\partial f}{\partial t} \qquad \qquad \dots (1)$$

Similarly, for a vector function $\bar{F}(x, y, z, t)$ associated with some property of the fluid, we can prove that,

$$\frac{d\bar{F}}{dt} = (\bar{q} \cdot \nabla)\bar{F} + \frac{\partial \bar{F}}{\partial t} \qquad \qquad \dots (2)$$

Thus for scalar and vector functions, there is an operational equivalence.

$$\frac{d}{dt} \equiv \bar{q} \cdot \nabla + \frac{\partial}{\partial t} \qquad \qquad \dots (3)$$

In particular, if $\overline{F} = \overline{q}$ (the velocity vector), $\dfrac{d\overline{q}}{dt}$ represents acceleration vector $\overline{a}$ and

it is expressed as $\qquad \overline{a} = \dfrac{d\overline{q}}{dt} = (\overline{q} \cdot \nabla)\,\overline{q} + \dfrac{\partial \overline{q}}{\partial t}$ $\qquad\qquad$ ... (4)

Let $\qquad\qquad\qquad \overline{a} = a_x\,\overline{i} + a_y\,\overline{j} + a_z\,\overline{k}$

Substituting in (4),

$$a_x\,\overline{i} + a_y\,\overline{j} + a_z\,\overline{k} = \left(u\dfrac{\partial}{\partial x} + v\dfrac{\partial}{\partial y} + w\dfrac{\partial}{\partial z}\right)(u\overline{i} + v\overline{j} + w\overline{k}) + \overline{i}\dfrac{\partial u}{\partial t} + \overline{j}\dfrac{\partial v}{\partial t} + \overline{k}\dfrac{\partial w}{\partial t}$$

$$\qquad\qquad ... (5)$$

Equating $\overline{i}$, $\overline{j}$, $\overline{k}$ components, we get

$$\left. \begin{aligned}
a_x &= u\dfrac{\partial u}{\partial x} + v\dfrac{\partial u}{\partial y} + w\dfrac{\partial u}{\partial z} + \dfrac{\partial u}{\partial t} \\[2mm]
a_y &= u\dfrac{\partial v}{\partial x} + v\dfrac{\partial v}{\partial y} + w\dfrac{\partial v}{\partial z} + \dfrac{\partial v}{\partial t} \\[2mm]
a_z &= u\dfrac{\partial w}{\partial x} + v\dfrac{\partial w}{\partial y} + w\dfrac{\partial w}{\partial z} + \dfrac{\partial w}{\partial t}
\end{aligned} \right\} \qquad ... (6)$$

This gives components of acceleration in scalar form.

12.6 EQUATION OF CONTINUITY

Equation of continuity is the expression of the law of conservation of matter. When a region of fluid contains neither sources nor sinks, that is there are no inlets or outlets through which fluid can enter or leave the region, then the amount of fluid within the region is conserved according to the principle of conservation of matter. We will now obtain mathematical expression of this principle. Let S be a closed surface drawn in the fluid and taken fixed in space. Suppose it encloses a volume V of the fluid. Let ρ (x, y, z, t) be the fluid density i.e. mass per unit volume at any point (x, y, z) of the fluid at time t.

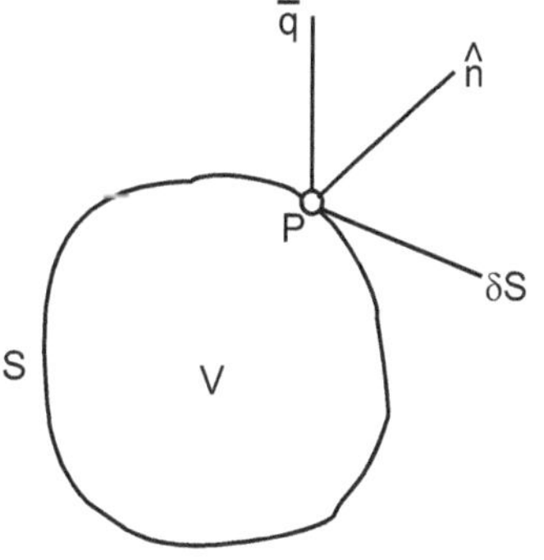

Fig. 12.5

Let δS be the surface element and $\hat{n}$ be the unit outward drawn normal to δS. $\overline{q}$ is the fluid velocity at the element δS.

Rate of normal flux of fluid mass per unit time across $\delta S = \rho\,\hat{n}\,(q)\ \delta S$.

Total rate of mass flow out of V across S $= \int_S \rho \, \hat{n} \cdot \bar{q} \; \delta S$

Total rate of mass flow into V to $- \int_V \nabla \cdot (\rho \bar{q}) \, dV$

or using Gauss divergence theorem, it is equal to $- \int_V \nabla \cdot (\rho \bar{q}) \, dV$

At time t, the mass of fluid within the element is $\int_V \rho \, dV$

Rate of increase of mass within V $= \dfrac{\partial}{\partial t} \int_V \rho \, dV = \int_V \dfrac{\partial \rho}{\partial t} \, dV$

Since the matter is neither created nor destroyed in the region (in the absence of sources and sinks), we must have

$$\int_V \frac{\partial \rho}{\partial t} \, dV = - \int_V \nabla \cdot (\rho \bar{q}) \, dV$$

or $\qquad \int_V \left[\dfrac{\partial \rho}{\partial t} + \nabla \cdot (\rho \bar{q}) \right] dV = 0$

Since this is true for all volumes V,

$$\frac{\partial \rho}{\partial t} + \nabla \cdot (\rho \bar{q}) = 0 \qquad\qquad \text{... (1)}$$

which is called the equation of continuity.

Since $\qquad\qquad \nabla \cdot (\rho \bar{q}) = \nabla \rho \cdot \bar{q} + \rho \, \nabla \cdot \bar{q}$

(1) can be written as $\dfrac{\partial \rho}{\partial t} + \nabla \rho \cdot \bar{q} + \rho \nabla \cdot \bar{q} = 0 \qquad\qquad \text{... (2)}$

If the motion is steady, $\dfrac{\partial \rho}{\partial t} = 0$ (density does not change w.r.t. t) and if the fluid is incompressible $\nabla \rho = 0$, equation of continuity takes the form

$$\rho \, \nabla \cdot \bar{q} = 0 \qquad\qquad \text{or} \qquad\qquad \nabla \cdot \bar{q} = 0 \qquad\qquad \text{... (3)}$$

$$\text{If } \bar{q} = u\bar{i} + v\bar{j} + w\bar{k} \qquad \nabla \cdot \bar{q} = \frac{\partial u}{\partial x} + \frac{\partial v}{\partial y} + \frac{\partial w}{\partial z}$$

Hence equation of continuity, in cartesian form, is

$$\frac{\partial u}{\partial x} + \frac{\partial v}{\partial y} + \frac{\partial w}{\partial z} = 0 \qquad\qquad \text{... (4)}$$

Equation of continuity in spherical polar system and in cylindrical system can also be obtained by similar considerations.

If fluid flow is potential $\overline{q} = -\nabla\phi$ then from (3),

$$\nabla \cdot (-\nabla\phi) = 0 \qquad \text{or} \qquad \nabla^2 \phi = 0 \qquad \qquad \text{... (5)}$$

which is called *Laplace equation.* Velocity potential ϕ thus satisfies Laplace equation.

12.7 EULER'S EQUATION OF MOTION

Consider an infinitesimal volume element ABCDEFGH whose edges are of lengths δx, δy, δz. Mass element of the fluid $= \rho \cdot \delta x\, \delta y\, \delta z$.

The element of mass is acted by

(i)   Normal pressure thrusts on the surface of the element due to surrounding fluid.

(ii)   External force $\overline{F}$ per unit mass.

Let $p = p(x, y, z)$ be the pressure at the point A.

Force due to pressure p on the face ADHE perpendicular to y-axis

$$= p(x, y, z)\, \delta x\, \delta z\, \overline{j}$$

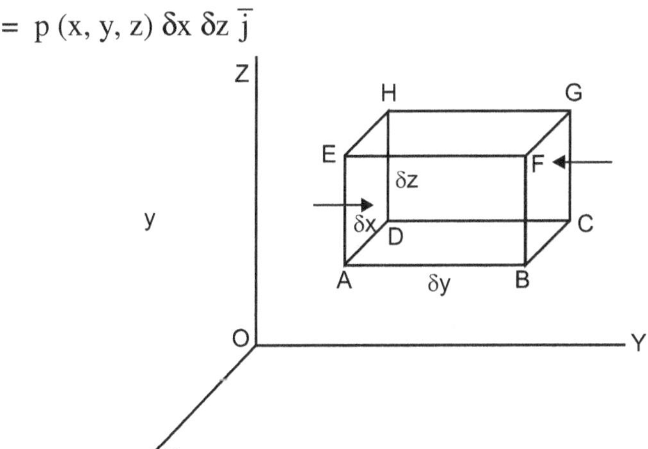

Fig. 12.6

Force on the face BCGF $= p(x, y + \delta y, z)\, \delta x\, \delta z\, \overline{j} = \left\{ p(x, y, z) + \dfrac{\partial p}{\partial y}\, \delta y \right\} \delta x\, \delta z\, \overline{j}$

Net force due to pressure on the faces perpendicular to y-axis

$$= \left\{ p\, \delta x\, \delta z - p\, \delta x\, \delta z - \frac{\partial p}{\partial y}\, \delta x\, \delta y\, \delta z \right\} \overline{j} = \left\{ -\frac{\partial p}{\partial y}\, \delta x\, \delta y\, \delta z \right\} \overline{j}$$

Similarly, there will be pressure forces acting on faces perpendicular to x and z-axes, which will be,

$$\left\{ -\frac{\partial p}{\partial x}\, \delta x\, \delta y\, \delta z \right\} \overline{i} \quad \text{and} \quad \left\{ -\frac{\partial p}{\partial z}\, \delta x\, \delta y\, \delta z \right\} \overline{k}$$

Resultant pressure force is the sum of these forces that is

$$= \left\{ -\bar{i}\frac{\partial p}{\partial x} - \bar{j}\frac{\partial p}{\partial y} - \bar{k}\frac{\partial p}{\partial z} \right\} \delta x \, \delta y \, \delta z$$

$$= - \nabla p \, \delta x \, \delta y \, \delta z$$

Total external force on the element of mass $= \rho \, \bar{F} \, \delta x \, \delta y \, \delta z$

From Newton's second law of motion which gives,

$$\text{Force} = \text{Mass} \times \text{Acceleration}$$

and if $\bar{a}$ is the acceleration vector,

$$(\rho \, \delta x \, \delta y \, \delta z) \, \bar{a} = \rho \bar{F} \, \delta x \, \delta y \, \delta z - (\nabla p) \, \delta x \, \delta y \, \delta z$$

i.e. $$\bar{a} = \bar{F} - \frac{1}{\rho} \, \nabla p$$

From equation (4) of article (12.5),

$$\bar{a} = \frac{d\bar{q}}{dt} = (\bar{q} \cdot \nabla) \, \bar{q} + \frac{\partial \bar{q}}{\partial t}$$

$$\therefore \qquad (\bar{q} \cdot \nabla) \, \bar{q} + \frac{\partial \bar{q}}{\partial t} = \bar{F} - \frac{1}{\rho} \, \nabla p \qquad \qquad \dots (1)$$

which is the Euler's equation of fluid motion.

$$\because \qquad \qquad \bar{q} = u\bar{i} + v\bar{j} + w\bar{k}$$

and $$\bar{F} = F_x \, \bar{i} + F_y \, \bar{j} + F_z \, \bar{k}$$

(1) can be written as

$$\left(u\frac{\partial}{\partial x} + v\frac{\partial}{\partial y} + w\frac{\partial}{\partial z} \right)(u\bar{i} + v\bar{j} + w\bar{k}) + \frac{\partial}{\partial t}(u\bar{i} + v\bar{j} + w\bar{k})$$

$$= F_x \, \bar{i} + F_y \, \bar{j} + F_z \, \bar{k} - \frac{1}{\rho}\left(\bar{i}\frac{\partial p}{\partial x} + \bar{j}\frac{\partial p}{\partial y} + \bar{k}\frac{\partial p}{\partial z} \right)$$

Equating $\bar{i}$, $\bar{j}$, $\bar{k}$ components we get the equations of motion in cartesian form as,

$$u\frac{\partial u}{\partial x} + v\frac{\partial u}{\partial y} + w\frac{\partial u}{\partial z} + \frac{\partial u}{\partial t} = F_x - \frac{1}{\rho}\frac{\partial p}{\partial x}$$

$$u\frac{\partial v}{\partial x} + v\frac{\partial v}{\partial y} + w\frac{\partial v}{\partial z} + \frac{\partial v}{\partial t} = F_y - \frac{1}{\rho}\frac{\partial p}{\partial y} \qquad \dots (2)$$

$$u\frac{\partial w}{\partial x} + v\frac{\partial w}{\partial y} + w\frac{\partial w}{\partial z} + \frac{\partial w}{\partial t} = F_z - \frac{1}{\rho}\frac{\partial p}{\partial z}$$

If $\dfrac{D}{Dt} \equiv \dfrac{\partial}{\partial t} + u\,\dfrac{\partial}{\partial x} + v\,\dfrac{\partial}{\partial y} + w\,\dfrac{\partial}{\partial z}$ (a conventional standard notation), above equations can be expressed as

$$\frac{Du}{Dt} = F_x - \frac{1}{\rho}\frac{\partial p}{\partial x}$$

$$\frac{Dv}{Dt} = F_y - \frac{1}{\rho}\frac{\partial p}{\partial y} \qquad \dots (3)$$

$$\frac{Dw}{Dt} = F_z - \frac{1}{\rho}\frac{\partial p}{\partial z}$$

12.8 INTEGRATION OF EULER'S EQUATION OF MOTION

To integrate Euler's equations of motion (1) of previous section, namely

$$(\bar{q} \cdot \nabla)\,\bar{q} + \frac{\partial \bar{q}}{\partial t} = \bar{F} - \frac{1}{\rho}\,\nabla p$$

Let us consider following conditions :

(i)   Fluid motion is steady so that $\dfrac{\partial \bar{q}}{\partial t} = 0$

(ii)   Motion is irrotational giving $\nabla \times \bar{q} = 0$

(iii)   External force $\bar{F}$ is conservative such that

$$\bar{F} = -\nabla v \quad [v \text{ is force potential}]$$

Using vector identity result, we can write,

$$\nabla (q^2) = \nabla (\bar{q} \cdot \bar{q}) = 2\bar{q} \times (\nabla \times q) + 2\,(\bar{q} \cdot \nabla)\,\bar{q}$$

$$\therefore \qquad (\bar{q} \cdot \nabla)\,\bar{q} = \frac{1}{2}\nabla (q)^2 - \bar{q} \times (\nabla \times \bar{q})$$

But $\qquad\qquad \nabla \times \bar{q} = 0 \quad [\text{motion is irrotational}]$

$$\therefore \qquad (\bar{q} \cdot \nabla)\,\bar{q} = \frac{1}{2}\nabla (q^2)$$

Euler's equation of motion now takes the form,

$$\frac{1}{2}\,\nabla (q^2) = -\nabla v - \frac{1}{\rho}\nabla p$$

Taking dot product with $d\bar{r}$, above equation can be written as,

$$\frac{1}{2}\,\nabla (q^2) \cdot d\bar{r} = -\nabla v \cdot d\bar{r} - \frac{1}{\rho}\,\nabla p \cdot d\bar{r}$$

But $dv = \nabla v \cdot \overline{dr}$, $dp = \nabla p \cdot \overline{dr}$ and $\nabla (q^2) \cdot \overline{dr} = d (q^2)$

$\therefore \qquad \dfrac{1}{2} d (q^2) = - dv - \dfrac{1}{\rho} dp$

Integrating above equation along a stream line,

$$\dfrac{1}{2} q^2 = - v - \int \dfrac{dp}{\rho} + C$$

or $\qquad \boxed{\dfrac{1}{2} q^2 + v + \int \dfrac{dp}{\rho} = C}$ $\qquad$ ...(1)

where C is constant of integration, depending upon stream line.

Equation (1) is of great importance and is called Bernoulli's equation.

ILLUSTRATIONS

Ex. 1 : *Velocity distribution for a fluid flow is given by $u = - x$, $v = 2y$ and $w = 3 - z$. Find the equation of stream line passing through the point (1, 1, 2).* **(Dec. 07)**

Sol. : The differential equations of stream line are given by

$$\dfrac{dx}{u} = \dfrac{dy}{v} = \dfrac{dz}{w}$$

Putting for u, v, w, we get

$$\dfrac{dx}{-x} = \dfrac{dy}{2y} = \dfrac{dz}{3 - z}$$

There are two independent equations, consider

$$\dfrac{dx}{-x} = \dfrac{dy}{2y}$$

Integrating, $\qquad - \log x = \dfrac{1}{2} \log y + C_1$ $\qquad$ ... (1)

as stream line passes through (1, 1, 2), put $x = 1$, $y = 1$ in (1)

$\therefore \qquad\qquad C_1 = 0$

$\therefore \qquad\qquad \log (x^{-1}) = \log (y)^{1/2}$

or $\qquad\qquad x^{-1} = y^{1/2}$ $\qquad$ i.e. $\quad \sqrt{y} = \dfrac{1}{x}$ $\qquad$ ... (2)

Consider now, $\qquad \dfrac{dy}{2y} = \dfrac{dz}{3 - z}$

Integration gives, $\dfrac{1}{2} \log y = - \log (3 - z) + C_2$ $\qquad$ ... (3)

Putting $y = 1$, $z = 2$, we get $C_2 = 0$

$\therefore \qquad \log (y)^{1/2} = \log (3 - z)^{-1} \qquad$ or $\qquad \sqrt{y} = \dfrac{1}{3 - z} \qquad$ ... (4)

(2) and (4) together represent curve of intersection of surfaces.

$$\sqrt{y} = \frac{1}{x} \quad \text{and} \quad \sqrt{y} = \frac{1}{3 - z}$$

which represents the stream line.

Ex. 2 : *Test whether the motion specified by*

$$\bar{q} = \frac{K^2 (x\bar{j} - y\bar{i})}{x^2 + y^2} \quad (K = constant)$$

is possible motion for an incompressible fluid. If so, determine the equations of the stream lines. Test whether the flow is potential and if so determine the velocity potential. Find equipotentials.

Sol. : For motion to be possible, equation of continuity $\nabla \cdot \bar{q} = 0$ must be satisfied.

$$\nabla \cdot \bar{q} = K^2 \left\{ \frac{\partial}{\partial x} \left(\frac{-y}{x^2 + y^2} \right) + \frac{\partial}{\partial y} \left(\frac{x}{x^2 + y^2} \right) \right\}$$

$$= K^2 \left\{ \frac{2xy}{(x^2 + y^2)^2} - \frac{2xy}{(x^2 + y^2)^2} \right\} = 0$$

Equation of continuity for an incompressible fluid is satisfied, hence motion is possible.

$$u = -\frac{K^2 y}{x^2 + y^2}, \qquad v = \frac{K^2 x}{x^2 + y^2}, \qquad w = 0$$

Equations of stream lines are

$$\frac{dx}{\dfrac{-K^2 y}{(x^2 + y^2)}} = \frac{dy}{\dfrac{K^2 x}{(x^2 + y^2)}} = \frac{dz}{0}$$

$\therefore \qquad \dfrac{dx}{-y} = \dfrac{dy}{x}$

or $\qquad x \, dx + y \, dy = 0$

which on integration gives $x^2 + y^2 = C_1$

Similarly, $dz = 0$ gives $z = C_2$

Stream lines are given by

$$x^2 + y^2 = C_1 \quad \text{and} \quad z = C_2$$

Thus the stream lines are circles, whose centres are on the z-axis, their planes being perpendicular to this axis.

$$\nabla \times \bar{q} = \begin{vmatrix} \bar{i} & \bar{j} & \bar{k} \\ \dfrac{\partial}{\partial x} & \dfrac{\partial}{\partial y} & \dfrac{\partial}{\partial z} \\ \dfrac{-K^2 y}{x^2 + y^2} & \dfrac{K^2 x}{x^2 + y^2} & 0 \end{vmatrix}$$

$$= \bar{i}\,(0 - 0) + \bar{j}\,(0 - 0) + \bar{k}\left\{ K^2 \left[\frac{y^2 - x^2}{(x^2 + y^2)^2} + \frac{x^2 - y^2}{(x^2 + y^2)^2} \right] \right\} = 0$$

Thus the motion is irrotational and the flow is potential such that,

$$\bar{q} = -\nabla\phi, \text{ we have,} \qquad \frac{\partial \phi}{\partial x} = -u = \frac{K^2 y}{x^2 + y^2}$$

$$\frac{\partial \phi}{\partial y} = -v = -\frac{K^2 x}{x^2 + y^2} \qquad \frac{\partial \phi}{\partial z} = -w = 0$$

Since $\quad \dfrac{\partial \phi}{\partial z} = 0, \quad \phi$ is independent of z.

$$\therefore \qquad \phi = \phi\,(x, y) \qquad\qquad \frac{\partial \phi}{\partial x} = \frac{K^2 y}{x^2 + y^2}$$

Integrating w.r.t. x, treating y as constant,

$$\phi = K^2 y \cdot \frac{1}{y}\, \tan^{-1}\left(\frac{x}{y}\right) + f\,(y)$$

$$= K^2 \tan^{-1}\left(\frac{x}{y}\right) + f\,(y)$$

Here constant of integration is taken as function of y i.e. f (y) because y is treated as constant of integration.

$$\frac{\partial \phi}{\partial y} = K^2 \left\{ \frac{1}{1 + \dfrac{x^2}{y^2}} \left(-\frac{x}{y^2} \right) \right\} + f'(y) = \frac{-K^2 x}{x^2 + y^2} + f'(y)$$

But $\qquad \dfrac{\partial \phi}{\partial y} = -\dfrac{K^2 x}{x^2 + y^2}$

$$\therefore \quad \frac{-K^2 x}{x^2 + y^2} + f'(y) = \frac{-K^2 x}{x^2 + y^2}$$

$$\therefore \qquad f'(y) = 0 \quad \text{or} \quad f\,(y) = \text{Constant of integration}$$

$$\therefore \qquad \phi = K^2 \tan^{-1}\left(\frac{x}{y}\right) + \text{constant}$$

As the constant is immaterial, we may take velocity potential as,

$$\phi = K^2 \tan^{-1}\left(\frac{x}{y}\right)$$

The surfaces $\quad \phi = C$ are equipotentials, whose equations are

$$K^2 \tan^{-1}\left(\frac{x}{y}\right) = C \quad \text{or} \quad \tan^{-1}\left(\frac{x}{y}\right) = C_1$$

or $$\frac{x}{y} = \tan C_1 = C_2$$

$\therefore \qquad x = C_2\, y$ are equipotentials

Ex. 3 : *Given the velocity field*

$$\bar{q} = (6 + 2xy + t^2)\,\bar{i} - (xy^2 + 10\,t)\,\bar{j} + 25\,\bar{k}$$

What is the acceleration of a particle at (3, 0, 2) at time t = 1 ?

Sol. : We have, $u = 6 + 2xy + t^2, \quad v = -(xy^2 + 10\,t), \quad w = 25$

The acceleration components are given by

$$a_x = \frac{du}{dt} = \frac{\partial u}{\partial t} + u\frac{\partial u}{\partial x} + v\frac{\partial u}{\partial y} + w\frac{\partial u}{\partial z}$$

$$a_y = \frac{dv}{dt} = \frac{\partial v}{\partial t} + u\frac{\partial v}{\partial x} + v\frac{\partial v}{\partial y} + w\frac{\partial v}{\partial z}$$

$$a_z = \frac{dw}{dt} = \frac{\partial w}{\partial t} + u\frac{\partial w}{\partial x} + v\frac{\partial w}{\partial y} + w\frac{\partial w}{\partial z}$$

$$\frac{\partial u}{\partial x} = 2y, \quad \frac{\partial u}{\partial y} = 2x, \quad \frac{\partial u}{\partial z} = 0, \quad \frac{\partial u}{\partial t} = 2t$$

$$\frac{\partial v}{\partial x} = -y^2, \quad \frac{\partial v}{\partial y} = -2xy, \quad \frac{\partial v}{\partial z} = 0, \quad \frac{\partial v}{\partial t} = -10$$

$$\frac{\partial w}{\partial x} = 0, \quad \frac{\partial w}{\partial y} = 0, \quad \frac{\partial w}{\partial z} = 0, \quad \frac{\partial w}{\partial t} = 0$$

$\therefore \qquad a_x = 2t + (6 + 2xy + t^2) \cdot 2y + [-(xy^2 + 10t)] + 2x + 25 \times 0$

$\qquad\qquad a_y = -10 + (6 + 2xy + t^2)(-y^2) + (xy^2 + 10t)(2xy) + 25 \times 0$

$\qquad\qquad a_z = 0$

Substituting $\qquad x = 3, \quad y = 0, \quad z = 2, \quad t = 1$

$\qquad\qquad a_x = 2 - 10 \times 6 = -58$

$\qquad\qquad a_y = -10, \quad a_z = 20$

$\therefore \qquad |\bar{a}| = \sqrt{a_x^2 + a_y^2 + a_z^2} = \sqrt{(58)^2 + 100 + 0} = 58.86$ units

Ex. 4 : *A long pipe is of length l and has slowly tapering cross-section. It is inclined at angle α to the horizontal and water flows steadily through it from the upper to the lower end. The section at the upper end, has twice the radius of lower end. At the lower end, the water is delivered at atmospheric pressure. If the pressure at the upper end is twice the atmospheric pressure, find the velocity of delivery.*

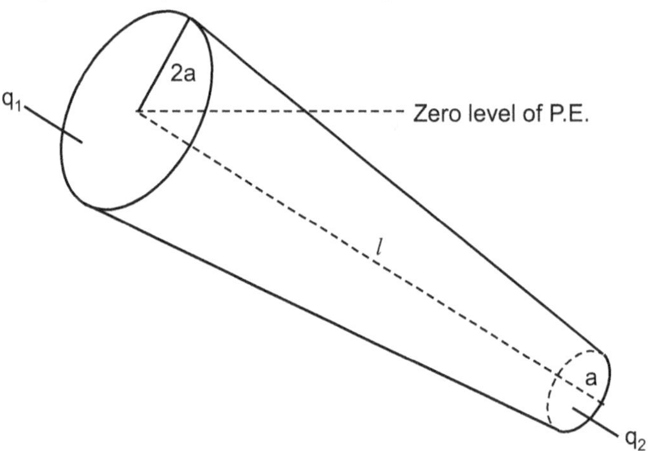

Fig. 12.7

Sol. : In equation (1) of art. 9.8 if ρ is constant,

Bernoulli's equation takes the form

$$\frac{1}{2}\, q^2 + v^2 + \frac{p}{\rho} \;=\; \text{constant} \qquad\qquad \text{[v is force potential]}$$

Let q_1, q_2 be the entry and exit velocities; $2a$, a the radii of the entry and exit sections. Take the horizontal through the centre of the entry section as zero level of potential energy [See Fig. 12.7]. When the flow is steady, taking π as the pressure at exit and 2π that at entry, Bernoulli's equation gives

$$\frac{2\pi}{\rho} + \frac{1}{2}\, q_1^2 + 0 \;=\; \frac{\pi}{\rho} + \frac{1}{2}\, q_2^2 - gl \sin \alpha \qquad\qquad \text{... (1)}$$

Since $- gl \sin \alpha$ is the P.E. per unit mass of the gravitational force at the lower end.

From the equation of continuity, the mass of fluid that enters at entry section must leave at exit section.

$$\therefore \qquad q_1 \times 4\pi a^2 \;=\; q_2 \times \pi a^2 \qquad\qquad \therefore \quad q_1 \;=\; \frac{q_2}{4}$$

Putting in (1),

$$\frac{2\pi}{\rho} + \frac{1}{2} \cdot \frac{q_2^2}{16} \;=\; \frac{\pi}{\rho} + \frac{1}{2}\, q_2^2 - gl \sin \alpha$$

$$\therefore \qquad \frac{q_2^2}{2} - \frac{q_2^2}{32} = \frac{\pi}{\rho} + gl \sin \alpha \qquad\qquad \frac{15}{32} q_2^2 = \frac{\pi}{\rho} + gl \sin \alpha$$

$$\therefore \qquad q_2^2 = \frac{32}{15}\left(\frac{\pi}{\rho} + gl \sin \alpha\right) \quad \text{or} \quad q_2 = \sqrt{\frac{32}{15}\left(\frac{\pi}{\rho} + gl \sin \alpha\right)}$$

which is the required exit velocity.

Ex. 5 : *Determine the condition that* $\bar{q} = (ax + by)\,\bar{i} + (cx + dy)\bar{j}$ *may give the velocity of an incompressible fluid. Show that the stream lines of this motion are rectangular hyperbolas when the motion is irrotational.*

Sol. : For an incompressible fluid motion,

$$\nabla \cdot \bar{q} = 0$$

i.e. $\quad \dfrac{\partial}{\partial x}(ax + by) + \dfrac{\partial}{\partial y}(cx + dy) = 0$

$$a + d = 0 \qquad\qquad \therefore \quad d = -a$$

Stream lines are given by

$$\frac{dx}{ax + by} = \frac{dy}{cx + dy}$$

$$\therefore \qquad (cx + dy)\,dx - (ax + by)\,dy = 0$$

Here $\qquad\qquad\qquad M = cx + dy, \qquad\qquad N = -(ax + by)$

$$\therefore \qquad\qquad \frac{\partial M}{\partial y} = d, \qquad\qquad \frac{\partial N}{\partial x} = -a$$

Condition of exactness is satisfied.

$\therefore$ Solution is given by

$$\int_{\substack{\\ y\ \text{const.}}} (cx + dy)\,dx - \int by\,dy = 0$$

$$\therefore \qquad c\frac{x^2}{2} + dxy - b\frac{y^2}{2} = k \qquad\qquad\qquad \dots (1)$$

When the motion is irrotational,

$$\nabla \times \bar{q} = 0$$

i.e.
$$\begin{vmatrix} \bar{i} & \bar{j} & \bar{k} \\ \dfrac{\partial}{\partial x} & \dfrac{\partial}{\partial y} & \dfrac{\partial}{\partial z} \\ ax + by & cx + dy & 0 \end{vmatrix} = 0$$

$$\bar{i}\,(0-0) + \bar{j}\,(0-0) + \bar{k}\,(c-b) = 0$$

$$\therefore \qquad\qquad b = c$$

Putting in (1), stream lines are given by

$$cx^2 + 2dxy - cy^2 = A$$

which represents rectangular hyperbola.

Ex. 6 : *If the velocity of an incompressible fluid at (x, y, z) is given by*

$$\bar{q} = \frac{3xz}{r^5}\,\bar{i} + \frac{3yz}{r^5}\,\bar{j} + \frac{3z^2 - r^2}{r^5}\,\bar{k}$$

where $\qquad\qquad r = \sqrt{x^2 + y^2 + z^2}$

then determine the stream lines of motion.   **(Dec. 2004, 2008; May 2009)**

Sol. : Equations of stream lines are given by

$$\frac{dx}{3xz/r^5} = \frac{dy}{3yz/r^5} = \frac{dz}{3z^2 - r^2/r^5}$$

or $\qquad\qquad \dfrac{r^5\,dx}{3xz} = \dfrac{r^5\,dy}{3yz} = \dfrac{r^5\,dz}{3z^2 - r^2}$

$\therefore \qquad\qquad \dfrac{dx}{3xz} = \dfrac{dy}{3yz} = \dfrac{dz}{3z^2 - r^2}$

$$\frac{dx}{3xz} = \frac{dy}{3yz} \quad\Rightarrow\quad \log x = \log y + \log c \quad \text{or} \quad x = cy \qquad \text{... (1)}$$

Similarly, $\qquad \dfrac{dx}{3xz} = \dfrac{x\,dx + y\,dy + z\,dz}{3x^2z + 3y^2z + 3z^3 - zr^2} = \dfrac{x\,dx + y\,dy + z\,dz}{z\,(3x^2 + 3y^2 + 3z^2 - x^2 - y^2 - z^2)}$

$\therefore \qquad\qquad \dfrac{dx}{3x} = \dfrac{x\,dx + y\,dy + z\,dz}{2\,(x^2 + y^2 + z^2)}$

Integrating, $\qquad \dfrac{1}{3} \log x = \dfrac{1}{4} \log (x^2 + y^2 + z^2) + \log c$

or $\qquad\qquad 4 \log x = 3 \log (x^2 + y^2 + z^2) + \log k$

or $\qquad\qquad x^4 = k\,(x^2 + y^2 + z^2)^3 \qquad\qquad \text{... (2)}$

(1) and (2) together represent stream lines.

Ex. 7 : *Show that the velocity potential* $\phi = \dfrac{1}{2}\,a\,(x^2 + y^2 - 2z^2)$ *satisfies the Laplace's equation. Also determine the stream lines.*   **(May 2005, 12; Dec. 11)**

Sol. : $\qquad\qquad \nabla\phi = \dfrac{1}{2}\,a\,\left\{ 2x\,\bar{i} + 2y\,\bar{j} - 4z\,\bar{k} \right\} \qquad\qquad \text{... (1)}$

$$\nabla^2\phi \ = \ \nabla \cdot \nabla\phi \ = \ \frac{a}{2}\left[\frac{\partial}{\partial x}\,(2x) + \frac{\partial}{\partial y}\,(2y) + \frac{\partial}{\partial z}\,(-4z)\right]$$

$$= \ \frac{a}{2}\,[2 + 2 - 4] \ = \ 0$$

which shows that ϕ satisfies Laplace's equation.

$$\bar{q} \ = \ \nabla\phi \ = \ ax\,\bar{i} \ + ay\,\bar{j} \ - 2az\,\bar{k}$$

$\therefore$ Stream lines are given by

$$\frac{dx}{ax} \ = \ \frac{dy}{ay} \ = \ \frac{dz}{-2az}$$

Consider, $\dfrac{dx}{x} \ = \ \dfrac{dy}{y}$

$\therefore$ $\log x \ = \ \log y + \log c_1$ $\therefore \ x = c_1\,y$ ... (2)

Next consider, $\dfrac{dy}{y} \ = \ \dfrac{dz}{-2z}$

$\therefore$ $\log y \ = \ -\dfrac{1}{2}\,\log z + \log c_2$ $\therefore \ y = \dfrac{c_2}{\sqrt{z}}$ ... (3)

(2) and (3) together represent stream lines.

Ex. 8 : *A liquid is in equilibrium under the action of field $\bar{F}$ per unit mass given by*

$$\bar{F} \ = \ \lambda\left[(y + z)\,\bar{i} \ + (z + x)\,\bar{j} \ + (x + y)\,\bar{k}\right]$$

Find the pressure at any point of the field.

Sol. : Let v be the force potential.

$$\bar{F} \ = \ \nabla v$$

$\therefore$ $dv \ = \ \nabla v \cdot d\bar{r} \ = \ \bar{F} \cdot d\bar{r} \ = \ \lambda\,[(y + z)\,dx + (z + x)\,dy + (x + y)\,dz]$

$$= \ \lambda\,[(y\,dx + x\,dy) + (z\,dx + x\,dz) + (z\,dy + y\,dz)]$$

$$= \ \lambda\,[d\,(xy) + d\,(xz) + d\,(zy)]$$

$$v \ = \ \lambda\,[xy + xz + yz]$$

From the Bernoulli's equation

$$\frac{p}{\rho} + v \ = \ c$$

or $\dfrac{p}{\rho} + \lambda\,(xy + xz + yz) \ = \ c$

which gives pressure at any point.

Ex. 9 : *Find the surfaces of equipressure in the case of steady motion of a liquid which has velocity potential $\phi = \log x + \log y + \log z$ and is under the action of force*

$$\overline{F} = yz\,\overline{i} + zx\,\overline{j} + xy\,\overline{k}.$$

Sol. :

$$\overline{q} = \nabla\phi = \frac{1}{x}\,\overline{i} + \frac{1}{y}\,\overline{j} + \frac{1}{z}\,\overline{k}$$

If v is force potential, $dv = \overline{F} \cdot d\overline{r} = yz\,dx + zx\,dy + xy\,dz = d\,(xyz)$

$$\therefore \qquad v = xyz$$

$$q^2 = \frac{1}{x^2} + \frac{1}{y^2} + \frac{1}{z^2}$$

From Bernoulli's equation

$$\frac{p}{\rho} + \frac{1}{2}\,q^2 + v = c$$

$$\frac{p}{\rho} + \frac{1}{2}\left(\frac{1}{x^2} + \frac{1}{y^2} + \frac{1}{z^2}\right) + xyz = c$$

which is the surface of equipressure.

Note : When the conditions : (i) steady motion, (ii) an irrotational motion and (iii) conservative field (as $\overline{F} = \nabla\phi$) are satisfied, we can apply directly the Bernoulli's equation.

Ex. 10 : *A liquid mass is rotating with a constant angular velocity ω about a vertical axis under the action of gravity. Find the pressure at any point of the liquid if the motion is steady.*

Sol. : Let the vertical axis be taken along positive direction of z-axis.

If $\overline{q}$ is linear velocity,

$$\overline{q} = \overline{\omega} \times \overline{r} = \omega\overline{k} \times [x\overline{i} + y\overline{j} + z\overline{k}] = \omega x\,\overline{j} - \omega y\,\overline{i}$$

$$(\overline{q} \cdot \nabla)\,\overline{q} = \left(-\omega y\frac{\partial}{\partial x} + \omega x\frac{\partial}{\partial y}\right)(-\omega y\,\overline{i} + \omega x\,\overline{j}) = -\omega^2\,[x\overline{i} + y\overline{j}\,]$$

$\therefore$ The equation of motion is

$$\frac{\partial\overline{q}}{\partial t} + (\overline{q} \cdot \nabla)\,\overline{q} = \overline{F} - \frac{1}{\rho}\,\nabla p$$

But,

$$\frac{\partial\overline{q}}{\partial t} = 0, \qquad \overline{F} = -g\overline{k}$$

$\therefore$

$$-\omega^2\,[x\overline{i} + y\overline{j}\,] = -g\overline{k} - \frac{1}{\rho}\,\nabla p$$

$$\therefore \qquad -\omega^2\,[x\,\overline{i}+y\,\overline{j}\,]\cdot d\overline{r} \;=\; -g\overline{k}\cdot d\overline{r}-\frac{1}{\rho}\,\nabla p\cdot d\overline{r}$$

$$-\omega^2\,[x\,dx+y\,dy] \;=\; -g\,dz-\frac{1}{\rho}\,dp$$

Integrating, $\qquad \dfrac{-\omega^2}{2}\,[x^2+y^2] \;=\; -gz-\dfrac{p}{\rho}+c$

$$\therefore \qquad \frac{p}{\rho}-\frac{\omega^2}{2}\,(x^2+y^2)+gz \;=\; c$$

which gives pressure at any point.

EXERCISE 12.1

1. Show that $u = 3x + y$, $v = 2x - 3y$, $w = 0$ are the velocity components of a possible fluid motion. Determine whether flow is irrotational.

    Ans. : Possible motion, not irrotational

2. Show that $u = -\dfrac{2xyz}{(x^2+y^2)^2}$; $v = \dfrac{(x^2-y^2)\,z}{(x^2+y^2)^2}$; $w = \dfrac{y}{(x^2+y^2)}$ are the velocity components of a possible fluid motion. Verify whether the motion is irrotational.

3. Obtain the equation of stream lines in case of steady motion of fluid defined by

    $$\overline{q} \;=\; (y-xz)\,\overline{i}+(yz+x)\,\overline{j}+(x^2+y^2)\,\overline{k} \qquad \textbf{(May 2010, Dec. 2010)}$$

    Ans. : $xy = z + c_1$, $\quad x^2 - y^2 + z^2 = c_2$

4. Is the motion represented by $(x^2-yz)\,\overline{i}+(y^2-zx)\,\overline{j}+(z^2-xy)\,\overline{k}$

    is irrotational ? If so, find corresponding velocity potential.

    Ans. : Irrotational, $\phi = \dfrac{1}{3}\,(x^3+y^3+z^3)-xyz$

5. Find the surface of equipressure in case of steady motion of a liquid which has velocity potential $\phi = xy + yz + zx$ and is under the action of force

    $$\overline{F} \;=\; (mz+ny)\,\overline{i}+(nx+lz)\,\overline{j}+(ly+mx)\,\overline{k}$$

    Ans. : $\dfrac{p}{\rho}+x^2+y^2+z^2\,(l+1)\,yz+(m+1)\,zx+(n+1)\,xy = c$

6. If the velocity potential of a fluid motion is given by $\phi = \log(xyz)$, find the equation of stream line.

    Ans. : $x^2 - y^2 = c_1,\; y^2 - z^2 = c$

7. Show that the motion of an incompressible perfect fluid is a possible motion when the velocity $\bar{q}$ is given by

$$\bar{q} = x(y^2 - z^2)\,\bar{i} + y(z^2 - x^2)\,\bar{j} + z(x^2 - y^2)\,\bar{k}$$

Find whether the motion is irrotational or not.

8. In the steady motion of an incompressible homogeneous fluid under no force, the velocity at any point is $ax\,\bar{i} + ay\,\bar{j} - 2az\,\bar{k}$. Find surface of equal pressure.

$$\textbf{Ans. } x^2 + y^2 + 4z^2 = c.$$

9. Show that the motion of incompressible perfect fluid is a possible motion when the velocity $\bar{q}$ is given by

(i) $\quad \bar{q} = \dfrac{1}{(x^2 + y^2)^2}\,\{-2xy\,\bar{i} + (x^2 - y^2)\,z\,\bar{j} + y(x^2 + y^2)\,\bar{k}\}$

(ii) $\quad \bar{q} = x(y - z)\,\bar{i} + y(z - x)\,\bar{j} + z(x - y)\,\bar{k}.$

Find in each case whether the motion is irrotational or not.

10. The fluid motion is given by $\bar{q} = (y + z)\,\bar{i} + (z + x)\,\bar{j} + (x + y)\,\bar{k}.$

(i) Is this motion irrotational and if so find the velocity potential ?

(ii) Is the motion possible for an incompressible fluid ?

Hint :

(i) Here $\nabla \times \bar{q} = \bar{0}$, hence the motion is irrotational

and $d\phi = \nabla\phi \cdot d\bar{r}$ gives $\phi = (xy + yz + zx) + c.$

(ii) Also, $\nabla \cdot \bar{q} = 0$, hence the fluid motion defined by $\bar{q}$ is a possible motion.

APPLICATIONS OF PARTIAL DIFFERENTIAL EQUATIONS

13.1 INTRODUCTION

Partial differential equations arise in connection with various physical and geometrical problems when the functions involved depend on two or more independent variables. Most problems in fluid and solid mechanics (dynamics, elasticity), heat transfer, electromagnetic theory, quantum mechanics and other areas of physics lead to *partial differential equations*. The independent variables involved may be time and one or several co-ordinates in space. The present chapter is devoted to some of the most important partial differential equations occurring in engineering applications. We derive these equations as models of physical systems and consider methods for obtaining solutions of those equations corresponding to the given physical situations.

Since the general solution of a partial differential equation in a region R contains arbitrary constants or arbitrary functions, the unique solution of a partial differential equation corresponding to a physical problem will satisfy certain other conditions at the boundary of the region R. These are known as *boundary conditions*. When these conditions are specified for the time t = 0, they are known as *initial conditions*. A partial differential equation together with boundary conditions constitutes a *boundary value problem.*

In the applications of ordinary linear differential equations, we first find the general solution and then determine the arbitrary constants from the initial values. But the same method is not applicable to problems involving partial differential equations. Most of the boundary value problems involving linear partial differential equations can be solved by the method of separation of variables. In this method, right from the beginning, we try to find the particular solutions of the partial differential equation which satisfy all or some of the boundary conditions and then adjust them till the remaining conditions are also satisfied. A combination of these particular solutions gives the solution of the problem. Fourier series is a powerful aid in determining the arbitrary functions.

13.2 PRELIMINARIES

Differential equations in which partial derivatives are involved, are called *partial differential equations* (PDE). The order of the PDE is the highest order of partial derivatives present in it. It is obvious that the number of independent variables must be two or more than two.

Formation of Partial Differential Equations

A. By eliminating arbitrary constants :

(i)
$$z = ax + by$$

$\therefore$
$$\frac{\partial z}{\partial x} = a \qquad \text{and} \qquad \frac{\partial z}{\partial y} = b$$

$\therefore$
$$z = x\,\frac{\partial z}{\partial x} + y\,\frac{\partial z}{\partial y}$$

i.e. a partial differential equation of order one obtained by eliminating two arbitrary constants a and b.

(ii) $(x - a)^2 + (y - b)^2 + (z - c)^2 = d^2$, where z is a function of x and y.

Differentiating partially w.r.t. x and y respectively, we get

$$2(x - a) + 2(z - c)\,\frac{\partial z}{\partial x} = 0$$

$$\text{and } 2(y - b) + 2(z - c)\,\frac{\partial z}{\partial y} = 0$$

Differentiating first equation partially w.r.t. x and second equation partially w.r.t. y, we get

$$1 + \left(\frac{\partial z}{\partial x}\right)^2 = -(z - c)\,\frac{\partial^2 z}{\partial x^2}$$

$$\text{and} \qquad 1 + \left(\frac{\partial z}{\partial y}\right)^2 = -(z - c)\,\frac{\partial^2 z}{\partial y^2}$$

$\therefore$
$$\frac{\partial^2 z}{\partial y^2}\left[1 + \left(\frac{\partial z}{\partial x}\right)^2\right] = \frac{\partial^2 z}{\partial x^2}\left[1 + \left(\frac{\partial z}{\partial y}\right)^2\right]$$

i.e. a partial differential equation of order two obtained by eliminating four arbitrary constants a, b, c and d.

B. By eliminating arbitrary functions :

(iii)
$$z = x\,f\left(\frac{y}{x}\right)$$

$$\frac{\partial z}{\partial x} = f\left(\frac{y}{x}\right) + x\,f'\left(\frac{y}{x}\right)\left(-\frac{y}{x^2}\right)$$

$$\text{and} \qquad \frac{\partial z}{\partial y} = x\,f'\left(\frac{y}{x}\right)\cdot\frac{1}{x}$$

$\therefore$
$$x\,\frac{\partial z}{\partial x} + y\,\frac{\partial z}{\partial y} = x\,f\left(\frac{y}{x}\right) = z$$

i.e. a partial differential equation of order one obtained by eliminating one arbitrary function f. Note that it is same as obtained in (i).

(iv) $\qquad z = f(y + ax) + \phi(y - ax)$

$\therefore \qquad \dfrac{\partial z}{\partial x} = a\,f'(y + ax) - a\,\phi'(y - ax)$

and $\qquad \dfrac{\partial z}{\partial y} = f'(y + ax) + \phi'(y - ax)$

$\qquad \dfrac{\partial^2 z}{\partial x^2} = a^2\,f''(y + ax) + a^2\,\phi''(y - ax)$

and $\qquad \dfrac{\partial^2 z}{dy^2} = f''(y + ax) + \phi''(y - ax)$

$\therefore \qquad \dfrac{\partial^2 z}{\partial x^2} = a^2\,\dfrac{\partial^2 z}{\partial y^2}$

i.e. a partial differential equation of order two obtained by eliminating two arbitrary functions f and ϕ.

(v) $\qquad z = ax + by + f\left(\dfrac{y}{x}\right)$

$\therefore \qquad \dfrac{\partial z}{\partial x} = a + f'\left(\dfrac{y}{x}\right) \cdot \left(-\dfrac{y}{x^2}\right)$

and $\qquad \dfrac{\partial z}{\partial y} = b + f'\left(\dfrac{y}{x}\right) \cdot \dfrac{1}{x}$

$\therefore \quad x\dfrac{\partial z}{\partial x} + y\dfrac{\partial z}{\partial y} = ax + by$

Differentiating partially w.r.t. x and y respectively, we get

$$x\dfrac{\partial^2 z}{\partial x^2} + \dfrac{\partial z}{\partial x} + y\dfrac{\partial^2 z}{\partial x\,\partial y} = a$$

and $$x\dfrac{\partial^2 z}{\partial y\,\partial x} + \dfrac{\partial z}{\partial y} + y\dfrac{\partial^2 z}{\partial y^2} = b$$

Multiplying first by x and second by y and adding, we get

$$x^2\dfrac{\partial^2 z}{\partial x^2} + xy\left(\dfrac{\partial^2 z}{\partial x\,\partial y} + \dfrac{\partial^2 z}{\partial y\,\partial x}\right) + y^2\dfrac{\partial^2 z}{\partial y^2} = 0$$

i.e. a PDE of order two obtained by eliminating two arbitrary constants a and b and arbitrary function f.

Note : We observe that there is some relationship between the order of PDE and the arbitrary constants or arbitrary functions involved in the most general solutions. The general solution must involve either arbitrary constants equal to twice the order of PDE or arbitrary functions equal to the order of PDE. In case both are involved then the sum of arbitrary constants divided by two and number of arbitrary functions must be equal to the order of PDE.

Some of the important partial differential equations involving two independent variables and one dependent variable which occur in the study of Engineering and Physical problems are :

I. The Wave Equation :

$$\frac{\partial^2 y}{\partial t^2} = c^2 \frac{\partial^2 y}{\partial x^2}$$

which occurs in the problems involving *vibrations of a stretched string*. It is also called as *one-dimensional wave equation.*

II. Diffusion Equation in One Dimension (One-dimensional heat flow equation) :

$$\frac{\partial u}{\partial t} = a^2 \frac{\partial^2 u}{\partial x^2}$$

which occurs in the conduction of heat flow along a bar.

III. Laplace's Equation in Two dimensions (Two-dimensional heat flow equation) :

(a) $$\frac{\partial^2 u}{\partial x^2} + \frac{\partial^2 u}{\partial y^2} = 0 \quad \text{(Cartesian form)}$$

which occurs in the conduction of heat in a plate in steady state. The equation is also satisfied by electrostatic potential (ϕ).

(b) $$r^2 \frac{\partial^2 u}{\partial r^2} + r \frac{\partial u}{\partial r} + \frac{\partial^2 u}{\partial \theta^2} = 0 \quad \text{(Polar form)}$$

There are various methods of solving PDEs. However, in what follows, we shall consider solution of linear PDE by the method of separation of variables. This method in general is used to reduce the PDE to the solutions of a set of ordinary differential equations each of which involves only one of the variables.

Note : We know that if an ordinary differential equation is linear and homogeneous then from known solutions, we can obtain further solutions by superposition. For a homogeneous linear partial differential equation, the situation is quite similar.

If y_1 and y_2 are any solutions of a linear homogeneous partial differential equation in some region R, then $\boxed{y = c_1 y_1 + c_2 y_2}$ where c_1 and c_2 are any constants, is also a solution of that equation in R.

13.3 MODELING OF VIBRATIONS OF A STRETCHED STRING (ONE-DIMENSIONAL WAVE EQUATION)

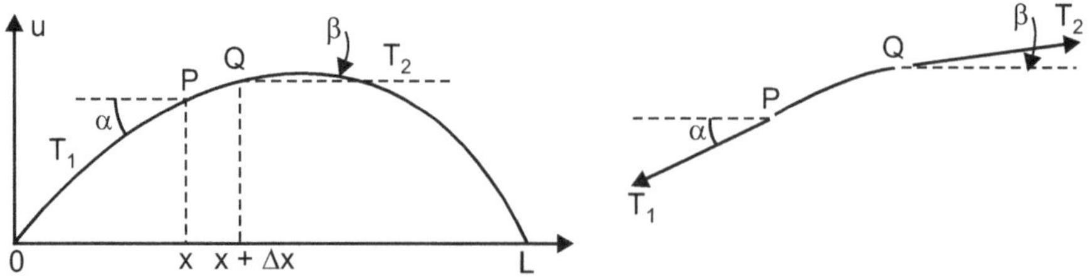

Fig. 13.1 : Deflected String at Fixed Time t

Let us derive the equation governing small transverse vibrations of an elastic string (such as a violin string). We stretch the string to length _l_ and fix it at the ends. We then distort it and at some instant, say, t = 0, we release it and allow it to vibrate. The problem is to determine the vibrations of the string, that is, to find its deflection u (x, t) at any point x and at any time t > 0.

While deriving a differential equation corresponding to a given physical problem, we usually have to make simplifying assumptions to ensure that the resulting equation does not become too complicated.

We assume the following _physical assumptions_ :
- (a) The string is perfectly elastic and does not offer any resistance to bending.
- (b) The mass of the string per unit length is constant.
- (c) The tension caused by stretching the string before fixing it at the ends is so large that the action of the gravitational force on the string can be neglected.
- (d) The string performs small transverse motions in a vertical plane; that is, every particle of the string moves strictly vertically and so that the deflection and the slope at every point of the string always remain small in absolute value.

Under these assumptions, we may expect that the solution u(x, t) of the differential equation to be obtained will reasonably well describe small vibrations of the physical non-idealized string of small homogeneous mass under large tension.

Consider the forces acting on a small portion of the string. Since the string does not offer resistance to bending, the tension is tangential to the curve of the string at each point. Let T_1 and T_2 be the tensions at the end points P and Q of that portion. Since there is no motion in horizontal direction, the horizontal components of the tension must be constant.

$$\therefore \qquad T_1 \cos \alpha = T_2 \cos \beta = T = \text{constant} \qquad\qquad \dots (1)$$

In vertical direction, we have two forces, the vertical components $- T_1 \sin \alpha$ and $T_2 \sin \beta$ of T_1 and T_2 (minus sign appears because that component at P is directed downward.).

By Newton's second law, the resultant of these two forces is equal to the mass "m δx" of the portion times the acceleration $\dfrac{\partial^2 u}{\partial t^2}$, evaluated at some point between x and x + δx, where, m = mass of the undeflected string per unit length, δx = the length of the portion of the undeflected string.

$$\therefore \qquad T_2 \sin \beta - T_1 \sin \alpha = m\, \delta x . \dfrac{\partial^2 u}{\partial t^2}$$

By using equation (1), we can divide this by $T_2 \cos \beta = T_1 \cos \alpha = T,$

$$\dfrac{T_2 \sin \beta}{T_2 \cos \beta} - \dfrac{T_1 \sin \alpha}{T_1 \cos \alpha} = \left(\dfrac{m\, \delta x}{T}\right) \dfrac{\partial^2 u}{\partial t^2}$$

$$\dfrac{T}{m} \dfrac{(\tan \beta - \tan \alpha)}{\delta x} = \dfrac{\partial^2 u}{\partial t^2}$$

Now $\tan \alpha$ and $\tan \beta$ are the slopes of the string at x and x + δx.

$$\therefore \quad \tan \alpha = \left(\frac{\partial u}{\partial x}\right)_x \quad \text{and} \quad \tan \beta = \left(\frac{\partial u}{\partial x}\right)_{x + \delta x}$$

Note : Here we write partial derivatives because u also depends on t.

$$\therefore \quad \frac{T}{m} \left[\frac{\left(\frac{\partial u}{\partial x}\right)_{x + \delta x} - \left(\frac{\partial u}{\partial x}\right)_x}{\delta x} \right] = \frac{\partial^2 u}{\partial t^2}$$

As $\delta x \to 0$,

$$\frac{T}{m} \cdot \frac{\partial^2 u}{\partial x^2} = \frac{\partial^2 u}{\partial t^2}$$

Let

$$c^2 = \frac{T}{m}$$

$$\therefore \quad \boxed{\frac{\partial^2 u}{\partial t^2} = c^2 \frac{\partial^2 u}{\partial x^2}}$$

This is called one-dimensional wave equation. One-dimensional indicates that the equation involves only one space variable, x.

The notation c^2 (instead of c) for the physical constant $\frac{T}{m}$ has been chosen to indicate that this constant is positive.

Note : Vibration in membrane or drumhead, oscillations induced in a guitar or violin string is governed by wave equation.

13.4 SOLUTION OF WAVE EQUATION BY METHOD OF SEPARATION OF VARIABLES

The vibrations of an elastic string are governed by the one-dimensional wave equation :

$$\boxed{\frac{\partial^2 u}{\partial t^2} = c^2 \frac{\partial^2 u}{\partial x^2}} \qquad \qquad \dots (1)$$

where, u (x, t) is the deflection of the string.

To find out how the string moves, we determine a solution u (x, t) of (1) that also satisfies the conditions imposed by the physical system.

Since the string is fixed at the ends x = 0 and x = *l*, we have two **boundary conditions.**

$$\boxed{\textbf{B.C. : u (0, t) = 0, u (}\textit{l}\textbf{, t) = 0 \; for all t}} \qquad \dots (2)$$

The form of the motion of the string will depend on the initial deflection, say f(x) (deflection at t = 0) and on the initial velocity, say g(x) (velocity at t = 0).

∴ We obtain the two **initial conditions.**

$$\text{I.C. : } u(x, 0) = f(x), \quad \left(\frac{\partial u}{\partial t}\right)_{t=0} = g(x) \qquad \ldots (3)$$

Our problem is now to find a solution of (1) satisfying the conditions (2) and (3).

We take the following important steps :

Step 1 : By applying the so-called method of separation of variables (or product method), we shall obtain two ordinary differential equations.

Step 2 : We shall determine solutions of those two equations that satisfy the boundary conditions.

Step 3 : Using Fourier series, we shall compose those solutions, in order to get a solution of the wave equation (1) that also satisfies the given initial conditions.

Let us consider these steps one by one.

Step 1 : Two ordinary differential equations : In the method of separating variables (or product method), we determine solution of the wave equation (1) of the form :

$$u(x, t) = F(x) \cdot G(t) \qquad \ldots (4)$$

where, F (x) is a function of x alone and G (t) is a function of t alone.

$$\frac{\partial u}{\partial t} = F(x)\frac{dG}{dt} \quad \therefore \quad \frac{\partial^2 u}{\partial t^2} = F(x) \cdot \frac{d^2 G}{dt^2}$$

$$\frac{\partial u}{\partial x} = \frac{dF}{dx} \cdot G(t) \quad \therefore \quad \frac{\partial^2 u}{\partial x^2} = \frac{d^2 F}{dx^2} \cdot G(t)$$

But
$$\frac{\partial^2 u}{\partial t^2} = c^2 \frac{\partial^2 u}{\partial x^2}$$

∴
$$F(x) \cdot \frac{d^2 G}{dt^2} = c^2 \frac{d^2 F}{dx^2} \cdot G(t)$$

Or
$$F\,G'' = c^2\,F''\,G$$

$$\frac{G''}{c^2\,G} = \frac{F''}{F}$$

i.e.
$$\frac{F''}{F} = \frac{G''}{c^2\,G}$$

Here L.H.S. is a function of x alone and R.H.S. is a function of t alone, hence above two expressions are independent of each other. Therefore we can equate to any constant, say k.

∴
$$\frac{F''}{F} = \frac{G''}{c^2\,G} = k$$

This yields immediately two ordinary linear differential equations :

$$\frac{F''}{F} = k \implies F'' - kF = 0 \implies \frac{d^2F}{dx^2} - kF(x) = 0$$

Also,
$$\frac{G''}{c^2 G} = k \implies G'' - c^2 kG = 0 \implies \frac{d^2G}{dt^2} - c^2 kG(t) = 0$$

Step 2 : Satisfying the boundary conditions : The boundary conditions are :

$$u(0, t) = 0 , u(l, t) = 0 \quad \text{for all } t.$$

But
$$u(x, t) = F(x) \cdot G(t)$$

$\therefore$
$$u(0, t) = 0 \implies F(0) \cdot G(t) = 0$$

$$u(l, t) = 0 \implies F(l) \cdot G(t) = 0$$

If $G(t) = 0$ then $u = 0$ is a trivial solution. Thus $G(t) \neq 0$, and hence $F(0) = F(l) = 0$

Case (i) : Let $\quad k = 0$

$\therefore$
$$F'' = 0 \implies \frac{d^2F}{dx^2} = 0$$

whose solution is $F(x) = c_1 x + c_2.$

$$F(0) = 0 \implies c_2 = 0 ; \quad F(l) = 0 \implies c_1 = 0$$

$\therefore$
$$F(x) = 0 \text{ which is of no interest because then } u = 0.$$

Hence we reject the case $k = 0$.

Case (ii) : Let $k > 0 \quad$ i.e. $\ k = m^2$ (say)

$$\frac{F''}{F} = \frac{G''}{c^2 G} = m^2$$

$$\frac{F''}{F} = m^2 \implies F'' - m^2 F = 0$$

$$\frac{d^2F}{dx^2} - m^2 F = 0 \qquad \left(\text{let } D \equiv \frac{d}{dx}\right)$$

$$D^2 F - m^2 F = 0, \quad (D^2 - m^2) F = 0$$

$$\text{A.E. : } D^2 - m^2 = 0 \implies D = \pm m$$

$\therefore$
$$F(x) = c_1 e^{mx} + c_2 e^{-mx}$$

Now
$$F(0) = 0 \implies c_1 + c_2 = 0$$

$$F(l) = 0 \implies c_1 e^{ml} + c_2 e^{-ml} = 0$$

Solving we get $c_1 = 0, \ c_2 = 0 \implies f(x) = 0 \ \therefore \ u = 0$

Hence we reject the case $k > 0$ too.

Case (iii) (Important) : Let $k < 0$ i.e. $k = -m^2$ (say).

$$\frac{F''}{F} = \frac{G''}{c^2 G} = -m^2$$

$$\frac{F''}{F} = -m^2 \implies F'' + m^2 F = 0$$

$$\frac{d^2F}{dx^2} + m^2 F = 0 \qquad\qquad \left(\text{let } D \equiv \frac{d}{dx} \right)$$

$$D^2 F + m^2 F = 0, \ (D^2 + m^2)\, F = 0$$

$$\text{A.E. : } D^2 + m^2 = 0 \implies D = \pm\, im$$

$\therefore$ $F(x) = c_1 \cos mx + c_2 \sin mx.$

Now $F(0) = 0 \implies c_1 = 0$

$\therefore$ $F(x) = c_2 \sin mx,$

and $F(l) = 0 \implies 0 = c_2 \sin ml.$

Now, $c_2 \neq 0$ since otherwise $F = 0,$ and hence $u = 0.$

$\therefore$ $\sin ml = 0 \implies ml = n\pi, \ n = 1, 2, 3, 4 \ldots$ [Since $\sin n\pi = 0$ for all n]

$\therefore$ $m = \dfrac{n\pi}{l}$

We thus obtain infinitely many solutions $F(x) = F_n(x),$ where

$$F_n(x) = c_2 \sin \frac{n\pi x}{l}, \ n = 1, 2, 3, \ldots\ldots$$

Also, $\dfrac{G''}{c^2 G} = -m^2 \qquad\qquad \left(\text{where } m = \dfrac{n\pi}{l} \right)$

$$G'' + c^2 m^2 G = 0 \qquad\qquad \implies \frac{d^2G}{dt^2} + c^2 m^2 G = 0$$

Let $D \equiv \dfrac{d}{dt}$ $\therefore\ D^2 G + c^2 m^2 G = 0 \implies (D^2 + c^2 m^2)\, G = 0$

$$\text{A.E. : } D^2 + c^2 m^2 = 0 \implies D = \pm\, i\,(cm)$$

$\therefore$ $G(t) = c_3 \cos cmt + c_4 \sin cmt$

Or $G(t) = G_n(t) = c_3 \cos \dfrac{n\pi ct}{l} + c_4 \sin \dfrac{n\pi ct}{l} \qquad\qquad \left(\because m = \dfrac{n\pi}{l} \right)$

Now, $u(x, t) = F(x) \cdot G(t) = F_n(x) \cdot G_n(t) = u_n(x, t) \ \ldots$ (say)

$\therefore$ $u_n(x, t) = \left(c_2 \sin \dfrac{n\pi x}{l} \right) \left[c_3 \cos \dfrac{n\pi ct}{l} + c_4 \sin \dfrac{n\pi ct}{l} \right]$

$$u_n(x, t) = \left[A_n \cos \frac{n\pi ct}{l} + B_n \sin \frac{n\pi ct}{l} \right] \sin \frac{n\pi x}{l}$$

where, $A_n = c_2\, c_3, \ B_n = c_2\, c_4\ , \ n = 1, 2, 3, \ldots\ldots\ldots$

Step 3 : Solution of the entire problem : It is evident that no single solution of $u_n(x, t)$ can satisfy the initial conditions. However, the given P.D.E. is linear, principle of superimposition is valid meaning thereby that if, *we have several solutions then their sum is also a solution.*

Hence we take, $u(x, t) = \displaystyle\sum_{n=1}^{\infty} u_n(x, t)$

$$\boxed{u(x, t) = \sum_{n=1}^{\infty} \left(A_n \cos \frac{n\pi ct}{l} + B_n \sin \frac{n\pi ct}{l} \right) \sin \frac{n\pi x}{l}} \qquad \ldots (5)$$

as a *most general solution* which may yield a solution satisfying the initial conditions.

From (3) : $u(x, 0) = f(x)$, (5) becomes $u(x, 0) = f(x) = \displaystyle\sum_{n=1}^{\infty} (A_n) \cdot \sin \frac{n\pi x}{l}, \ 0 < x < l.$

We must choose A_n so that $u(x, 0)$ becomes the half range Fourier sine series of $f(x)$.

$$\therefore \qquad \boxed{A_n = \frac{2}{l} \int_0^l f(x) \sin \frac{n\pi x}{l} \, dx}$$

To determine B_n, we have

$$\frac{\partial u}{\partial t} = \sum_{n=1}^{\infty} \left(-\frac{n\pi c}{l} A_n \sin \frac{n\pi ct}{l} + \frac{n\pi c}{l} B_n \cos \frac{n\pi ct}{l} \right) \sin \frac{n\pi x}{l}$$

From (3), $\left(\dfrac{\partial u}{\partial t} \right)_{t=0} = g(x).$

$$g(x) = \sum_{n=1}^{\infty} \left(\frac{n\pi c}{l} B_n \right) \sin \frac{n\pi x}{l}$$

We must choose B_n so that $\left(\dfrac{\partial u}{\partial t} \right)_{t=0}$ becomes the half range Fourier sine series of $g(x)$.

$$\therefore \qquad \frac{n\pi c}{l} B_n = \frac{2}{l} \int_0^l g(x) \cdot \sin \frac{n\pi x}{l} \, dx$$

$$\therefore \qquad \boxed{B_n = \frac{2}{n\pi c} \int_0^l g(x) \cdot \sin \frac{n\pi x}{l} \, dx}$$

Substituting values of A_n and B_n in (5), we get the required solution.

Result : Our discussion shows that u (x, t) given by (5) with coefficients A_n and B_n is a solution of (1) that satisfies all the conditions (2) and (3) of our problem, provided the series (5) converges.

Summary : To solve the one-dimensional wave equation,

$$\frac{\partial^2 u}{\partial t^2} = c^2 \frac{\partial^2 u}{\partial x^2} \quad \text{subject to the conditions}$$

1. $u\,(0, t) = 0$ $\Big\}$
2. $u\,(l, t) = 0$ Boundary conditions

3. $u\,(x, 0) = f\,(x)$ $\Big\}$
4. $\left(\dfrac{\partial u}{\partial t}\right)_{t\,=\,0} = g\,(x)$ Initial conditions

The most general solution is given by

$$\boxed{u\,(x, t) = (c_1 \cos mx + c_2 \sin mx)\,(c_3 \cos cmt + c_4 \sin cmt)} \qquad \ldots(6)$$

In obtaining solutions of the problems on vibration of tightly stretched string, we should directly assume the solution given in (6).

ILLUSTRATIONS

Ex. 1 : *If* $\dfrac{\partial^2 y}{\partial t^2} = c^2 \dfrac{\partial^2 y}{\partial x^2}$ *represents the vibrations of a string of length l fixed at both ends, find the solution with boundary conditions,*

(i) $y\,(0, t) = 0$,

(ii) $y\,(l, t) = 0$

and initial conditions,

(iii) $\left(\dfrac{\partial y}{\partial t}\right)_{t\,=\,0} = 0$

(iv) $y\,(x, 0) = k\,(l\,x - x^2)\,,\ 0 \le x \le l.$ **(Dec. 08, 14, May 12, 15, 16)**

Sol. : Given $\dfrac{\partial^2 y}{\partial t^2} = c^2 \dfrac{\partial^2 y}{\partial x^2}$. The most general solution is given by

$$y\,(x, t) = (c_1 \cos mx + c_2 \sin mx)\,(c_3 \cos cmt + c_4 \sin cmt)$$

Applying condition (i), $y\,(0, t) = 0,$

$$0 = [c_1\,(1) + c_2\,(0)]\,[c_3 \cos cmt + c_4 \sin cmt] \qquad \therefore \boxed{c_1 = 0}$$

$\therefore$ $y\,(x, t) = (c_2 \sin mx)\,[c_3 \cos cmt + c_4 \sin cmt]$

To apply condition (iii), $\left(\dfrac{\partial y}{\partial t}\right)_{t\,=\,0} = 0$, we first obtain $\dfrac{\partial y}{\partial t}$.

$$\therefore \qquad \frac{\partial y}{\partial t} = (c_2 \sin mx) \quad [-\,cm\,c_3 \sin cmt + cm\,c_4 \cos cmt]$$

$$0 = (c_2 \ \sin mx) \quad [0 + cm\,c_4]$$

Here, $\qquad c_2 \neq 0, \quad \sin mx \neq 0 \qquad \therefore \boxed{c_4 = 0}$

The most general solution will be

$$y\,(x,\,t) = (c_2 \sin mx)\,(c_3 \ \cos cmt)$$

$$y\,(x,\,t) = c_5 \ \sin mx \ \cos cmt \qquad\qquad \dots (1)$$

Applying condition (ii), $y\,(l,\,t) = 0$

$$0 = c_5 \ \sin ml \,.\, \cos cmt$$

Now, $\qquad c_5 \neq 0 \qquad$ (otherwise $y\,(x,\,t) = 0$ will become trivial solution.)

$$\cos cmt \neq 0$$

$$\therefore \qquad \sin ml = 0 \;\Rightarrow\; ml = n\,\pi, \qquad \therefore \ m = \frac{n\pi}{l}, \ n = 1, 2, 3 \ \dots\dots\dots\dots$$

$\therefore \quad$ Solution (1) becomes

$$y\,(x,\,t) = c_5 \ \sin \frac{n\pi x}{l} \ \cos \frac{n\pi ct}{l}, \ n = 1, 2, \dots\dots$$

Combining all these solutions, we get

$$\boxed{\,y\,(x,\,t) = \sum_{n=1}^{\infty} b_n \ \sin \frac{n\pi x}{l} \ \cos \frac{n\pi ct}{l}\,} \qquad\qquad \dots (2)$$

Applying condition (iv),

$$y\,(x,\,0) = k\,(lx - x^2),\ 0 \leq x \leq l$$

$$k\,(lx - x^2) = \sum_{n=1}^{\infty} b_n \ \sin \frac{n\pi x}{l}, \ 0 \leq x \leq l$$

This is Fourier's half range sine series for $f(x) = k(lx - x^2)$ in $0 \leq x \leq l$.

$$b_n = \frac{2}{l} \int_0^l f\,(x) \ \sin \frac{n\pi x}{l} \ dx = \frac{2}{l} \int_0^l k\,(lx - x^2) \ \sin \frac{n\pi x}{l} \ dx$$

$$= \frac{2\,k}{l} \left\{ (lx - x^2)\left(-\frac{l}{n\pi} \cos \frac{n\pi x}{l}\right) - (l - 2x)\left(-\frac{l^2}{n^2\,\pi^2} \sin \frac{n\pi x}{l}\right) \right.$$

$$\left. + (-2)\left(\frac{l^3}{n^3\,\pi^3} \cos \frac{n\pi x}{l}\right) \right\}_0^l$$

$$= \frac{2\,k}{l} \left(-\frac{2\,l^3}{n^3\,\pi^3}\right) \left[\cos \frac{n\pi x}{l}\right]_0^l$$

$$b_n = \frac{4 k l^2}{\pi^3} \left(\frac{1 - (-1)^n}{n^3} \right)$$

Substituting in (2), we get the required most general solution.

$$y(x, t) = \frac{4 k l^2}{\pi^3} \sum_{n=1}^{\infty} \left(\frac{1 - (-1)^n}{n^3} \right) \sin \frac{n\pi x}{l} \cos \frac{n\pi ct}{l} \qquad \text{... Ans.}$$

Note : $\quad 1 - (-1)^n = 2 \ ; \ $ if n is odd

$$= 0 \ ; \ \text{if n is even}$$

∴ The above solution can be written as

$$y(x, t) = \frac{4 k l^2}{\pi^3} \left\{ \frac{2}{1^3} \sin \frac{\pi x}{l} \cos \frac{\pi ct}{l} + 0 + \frac{2}{3^3} \sin \frac{3\pi x}{l} \cos \frac{3\pi ct}{l} + 0 + \right.$$
$$\left. + \frac{2}{5^3} \sin \frac{5\pi x}{l} \cos \frac{5\pi ct}{l} + \ldots\ldots \right\}$$

$$y(x, t) = \frac{4 k l^2}{\pi^3} \sum_{n=1}^{\infty} \frac{2}{(2n-1)^3} \sin \frac{(2n-1)\pi x}{l} \cos \frac{(2n-1)\pi ct}{l}$$

$$\boxed{y(x, t) = \frac{8 k l^2}{\pi^3} \sum_{n=1}^{\infty} \frac{1}{(2n-1)^3} \sin \frac{(2n-1)\pi x}{l} \cos \frac{(2n-1)\pi ct}{l}}$$

Ex. 2 : *A string is stretched and fastened to two points l apart. Motion is started by displacing the string in the form $u = a \sin \dfrac{\pi x}{l}$ from which it is released at time t = 0. Find the displacement u (x, t) from one end. $\left(\text{Use wave equation } \dfrac{\partial^2 u}{\partial t^2} = c^2 \cdot \dfrac{\partial^2 u}{\partial x^2} \right).$*

(Dec. 2004, 2017; May 2006, 2014, 2017)

Sol. : Given $\dfrac{\partial^2 u}{\partial t^2} = c^2 \dfrac{\partial^2 u}{\partial x^2}$

Subject to the conditions

(i) $\quad u(0, t) = 0, \ \forall \ t$

(ii) $\quad u(l, t) = 0, \ \forall \ t$

(iii) $\quad \left(\dfrac{\partial u}{\partial t} \right)_{t=0} = 0$

(iv) $\quad u(x, 0) = a \sin \dfrac{\pi x}{l}$

The general solution is

$$u(x, t) = (c_1 \cos mx + c_2 \sin mx)(c_3 \cos cmt + c_4 \sin cmt)$$

Condition (i) $\Rightarrow c_1 = 0$

Condition (iii) $\Rightarrow c_4 = 0.$

$\therefore$ Solution becomes

$$u(x, t) = (c_2 \sin mx)(c_3 \cos cmt)$$

$$u(x, t) = c_5 \sin mx \cos cmt \qquad \qquad \dots (1)$$

Applying condition (ii), we get,

$$0 = c_5 \sin ml \cos cmt$$

$$c_5 \neq 0, \quad \cos cmt \neq 0 \qquad \qquad \therefore \ \sin ml = 0$$

$$ml = n\pi \qquad \qquad \therefore \ m = \frac{n\pi}{l}, \ n = 1, 2, 3, \dots\dots$$

$\therefore$ Substituting in (1), we get

$$u(x, t) = c_5 \sin \frac{n\pi x}{l} \cos \frac{n\pi ct}{l}, \ n = 1, 2, 3 \dots\dots\dots$$

Combining these solutions, we get,

$$\boxed{u(x, t) = \sum_{n=1}^{\infty} b_n \sin \frac{n\pi x}{l} \cos \frac{n\pi ct}{l}} \qquad \qquad \dots (2)$$

Applying condition (iv), we get

$$u(x, 0) = a \sin \frac{\pi x}{l}$$

$$a \sin \frac{\pi x}{l} = \sum_{n=1}^{\infty} b_n \sin \frac{n\pi x}{l}$$

$$a \sin \frac{\pi x}{l} = b_1 \sin \frac{\pi x}{l} + b_2 \sin \frac{2\pi x}{l} + \dots\dots$$

$\therefore$ $b_1 = a$, $b_2 = 0 = b_3 = \dots\dots = b_n = \dots\dots\dots$

$\therefore$ (2) will become

$$u(x, t) = b_1 \sin \frac{\pi x}{l} \cos \frac{\pi ct}{l} + b_2 \sin \frac{2\pi x}{l} \cos \frac{2\pi ct}{l} + \dots\dots$$

$$\boxed{u(x, t) = a \sin \frac{\pi x}{l} \cos \frac{\pi ct}{l}}$$

which is the required general solution.

Ex. 3 : *A string is stretched tightly between $x = 0$, $x = l$ and both ends are given displacement $y = a \sin pt$ perpendicular to the string. If the string satisfies the differential equation $\dfrac{\partial^2 y}{\partial x^2} = \dfrac{1}{c^2} \dfrac{\partial^2 y}{\partial t^2}$, prove that the oscillations of the string are given by*

$$y = a \ \sec \frac{pl}{2c} \ \cos\left(\frac{px}{c} - \frac{pl}{2c}\right) \sin pt.$$

(May 2005)

Sol. : We have the G.S.,

$$y = (c_1 \cos mx + c_2 \sin mx)(c_3 \cos cmt + c_4 \sin cmt) \qquad \dots \text{(i)}$$

The condition $y = a \sin pt$ for $x = 0$ gives

$$a \sin pt = c_1(c_3 \cos cmt + c_4 \sin cmt)$$

This implies that $c_1 c_3 = 0 \qquad \dots \text{(ii)}$

$$c_1 c_4 = a \qquad \dots \text{(iii)}$$

$$\text{and} \quad cm = p \qquad \dots \text{(iv)}$$

From (ii), (iii), $c_3 = 0$ and from (iv), $m = \dfrac{p}{c}$

Substituting in (i), we get

$$y = \left(c_1 \cos \frac{px}{c} + c_2 \sin \frac{px}{c}\right) \cdot c_4 \sin pt$$

$$= \left(c_1 c_4 \cos \frac{px}{c} + c_2 c_4 \sin \frac{px}{c}\right) \sin pt$$

$$\Rightarrow \qquad y = \left(a \cos \frac{px}{c} + c_2 c_4 \sin \frac{px}{c}\right) \sin pt \qquad \dots \text{(v)}$$

The condition $\qquad y = a \sin pt$ for $x = l$ gives

$$\boxed{a \sin pt = \left(a \cos \frac{pl}{c} + c_2 c_4 \sin \frac{pl}{c}\right) \sin pt}$$

$$\Rightarrow a\left(1 - \cos \frac{pl}{c}\right) = c_2 c_4 \sin \frac{pl}{c}$$

$$\Rightarrow \qquad c_2 c_4 = a \cdot \frac{2 \sin^2 \dfrac{pl}{2c}}{2 \sin \dfrac{pl}{2c} \cos \dfrac{pl}{2c}} = a \cdot \frac{\sin \dfrac{pl}{2c}}{\cos \dfrac{pl}{2c}}$$

Substituting in (v), we get

$$y = \left(a \cos \frac{px}{c} + a \frac{\sin \dfrac{pl}{2c}}{\cos \dfrac{pl}{2c}} \sin \frac{px}{c}\right) \sin pt$$

$$= a \cdot \frac{\cos \dfrac{px}{c} \cos \dfrac{pl}{2c} + \sin \dfrac{px}{c} \sin \dfrac{pl}{2c}}{\cos \dfrac{pl}{2c}} \sin pt$$

$$\Rightarrow \qquad \boxed{y = a \sec \frac{pl}{2c} \cos \left(\frac{px}{c} - \frac{pl}{2c}\right) \sin pt.}$$

Ex. 4 : *A tightly stretched string with fixed end points $x = 0$ and $x = l$ is initially in a position given by $y(x, 0) = y_o \sin^3\left(\dfrac{\pi x}{l}\right)$. If it is released from rest from this position, find the displacement y at any distance x from one end and at any time t.*

(Dec. 06, Nov. 15 May 07, 11)

Sol. : The differential equation satisfied by y is $\dfrac{\partial^2 y}{\partial t^2} = c^2 \dfrac{\partial^2 y}{\partial x^2}$. The initial and boundary conditions are given by :

(i) $y(0, t) = 0$,   (ii) $y(l, t) = 0$,   (iii) $\left(\dfrac{\partial y}{\partial t}\right)_{t=0} = 0$,

(iv) $y(x, 0) = y_o \sin^3\left(\dfrac{\pi x}{l}\right)$

The most general solution is given by :
$$y(x, t) = (c_1 \cos mx + c_2 \sin mx)(c_3 \cos cmt + c_4 \sin cmt)$$

Condition (i) $\Rightarrow$ $c_1 = 0$

Condition (iii) $\Rightarrow$ $c_4 = 0$

$\therefore$ The most general solution will become

$$\boxed{y(x, t) = c_5 \sin mx \cdot \cos cmt} \qquad \dots \text{(I)}$$

Condition (ii) $\Rightarrow$ $0 = c_5 \sin ml \cdot \cos cmt$

$\therefore$ $\sin ml = 0$, $ml = n\pi$

$\therefore$ $m = \dfrac{n\pi}{l}$, $n = 1, 2, \dots\dots$

$\therefore$ Solution (I) becomes :

$$y(x, t) = c_5 \sin \dfrac{n\pi x}{l} \cos \dfrac{n\pi ct}{l}, \quad n = 1, 2, \dots\dots$$

Combining all these solutions, we get

$$\boxed{y(x, t) = \sum_{n=1}^{\infty} b_n \sin \dfrac{n\pi x}{l} \cos \dfrac{n\pi ct}{l}} \qquad \dots \text{(II)}$$

Applying condition (iv),

$$y(x, 0) = y_o \sin^3 \dfrac{\pi x}{l} = \dfrac{3y_o}{4} \sin \dfrac{\pi x}{l} - \dfrac{y_o}{4} \sin \dfrac{3\pi x}{l}$$

$$\left(\text{by using} \quad \sin^3 \theta = \dfrac{3}{4} \sin \theta - \dfrac{1}{4} \sin 3\theta\right)$$

$\therefore$ $y_o \sin^3 \dfrac{\pi x}{l} = \displaystyle\sum_{n=1}^{\infty} b_n \sin \dfrac{n\pi x}{l}$

$$\frac{3\,y_o}{4}\sin\frac{\pi x}{l} - \frac{y_o}{4}\sin\frac{3\pi x}{l} = b_1 \sin\frac{\pi x}{l} + b_2 \sin\frac{2\pi x}{l} + b_3 \sin\frac{3\pi x}{l} + \ldots$$

Comparing we get, $b_1 = \dfrac{3\,y_o}{4}$; $b_2 = 0$; $b_3 = -\dfrac{y_o}{4}$; $b_4 = 0 = b_5 = b_6 = \ldots = b_n = \ldots$

Substituting in (II), we get,

$$y\,(x,\,t) = b_1 \sin\frac{\pi x}{l}\cos\frac{\pi ct}{l} + b_2 \sin\frac{2\pi x}{l}\cos\frac{2\pi ct}{l} + b_3 \sin\frac{3\pi x}{l}\cos\frac{3\pi ct}{l} + \ldots\ldots$$

$$\boxed{y\,(x,\,t) = \frac{3\,y_o}{4}\sin\frac{\pi x}{l}\cos\frac{\pi ct}{l} - \frac{y_o}{4}\sin\frac{3\pi x}{l}\cos\frac{3\pi ct}{l}}$$

Ex. 5 : *An elastic string is stretched between two fixed points at a distance l apart, one end is taken at the origin and at a distance $\dfrac{2l}{3}$ from this end the string is displaced a distance "a" transversely and is released from rest when in this position. Find y (x, t), if y satisfies the equation $\dfrac{\partial^2 y}{\partial t^2} = c^2\,\dfrac{\partial^2 y}{\partial x^2}$.*

Sol. : Slope of OB $= \dfrac{a}{2\,l\,/\,3} = \dfrac{3a}{2l}$

Equation of OB is $y = \dfrac{3a}{2l}\ x$

Slope of BA $= \dfrac{a-0}{\dfrac{2l}{3} - l} = -\dfrac{3a}{l}$

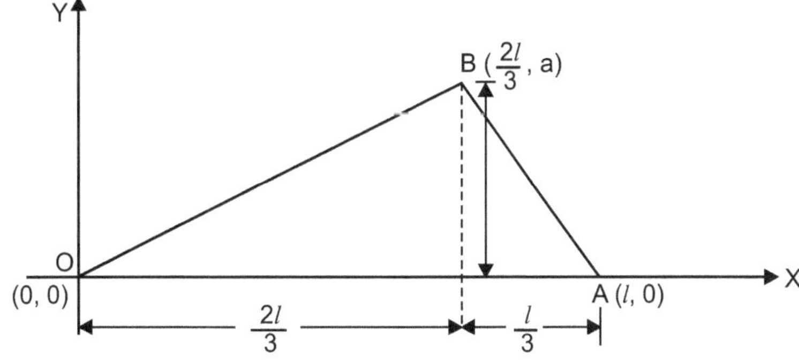

Fig. 13.2

Equation of BA is $y - 0 = -\dfrac{3a}{l}(x - l)$

$\therefore \qquad\qquad y = \dfrac{3a}{l}(l - x)$

We have to solve $\qquad\qquad \dfrac{\partial^2 y}{\partial t^2} = c^2\,\dfrac{\partial^2 y}{\partial x^2}$

The boundary conditions are

(i) $y(0, t) = 0$

(ii) $y(l, t) = 0$

Initial conditions are

(iii) $\left(\dfrac{\partial y}{\partial t}\right)_{t=0} = 0$

(iv) $y(x, 0) = \dfrac{3a}{2l}\, x, \qquad 0 \le x \le \dfrac{2l}{3}$

$\qquad\qquad = \dfrac{3a}{l}\,(l - x), \qquad \dfrac{2l}{3} \le x \le l$

The most general solution is

$$y(x, t) = (c_1 \cos mx + c_2 \sin mx)(c_3 \cos cmt + c_4 \sin cmt)$$

Condition (i) $\Rightarrow \quad c_1 = 0$

Condition (iii) $\Rightarrow \quad c_4 = 0$

$\therefore \qquad \boxed{y(x, t) = c_5\ \sin mx\ \cos cmt} \qquad\qquad \text{... (I)}$

Condition (ii) $\Rightarrow \quad 0 = c_5\ \sin ml\ \cos cmt$

$\sin ml = 0,\ ml = n\pi \quad \therefore \quad m = \dfrac{n\pi}{l},\ n = 1, 2, \ldots\ldots$

$$y(x, t) = c_5\ \sin\frac{n\pi x}{l}\ \cos\frac{n\pi ct}{l},\ n = 1, 2, \ldots\ldots$$

Combining all these solutions, we get

$$\boxed{y(x, t) = \sum_{n=1}^{\infty} b_n\ \sin\frac{n\pi x}{l}\ \cos\frac{n\pi ct}{l}} \qquad\qquad \text{... (II)}$$

Applying condition (iv), we have

$$y(x, 0) = \sum_{n=1}^{\infty} b_n\ \sin\frac{n\pi x}{l}\ ,\ \text{where}$$

$f(x) = y(x, 0) = \dfrac{3a}{2l}\, x, \qquad 0 \le x \le \dfrac{2l}{3}$

$\qquad\qquad\quad = \dfrac{3a}{l}\,(l - x), \qquad \dfrac{2l}{3} \le x \le l$

$\therefore \qquad b_n = \dfrac{2}{l} \displaystyle\int_{0}^{l} f(x)\ \sin\frac{n\pi x}{l}\ dx$

$\qquad\quad = \dfrac{2}{l}\left\{ \displaystyle\int_{0}^{\frac{2l}{3}} \frac{3ax}{2l}\ \sin\frac{n\pi x}{l}\ dx + \int_{\frac{2l}{3}}^{l} \frac{3a}{l}\,(l - x)\ \sin\frac{n\pi x}{l}\ dx \right\}$

$$= \frac{6\,a}{l^2} \left\{ \left[\left(\frac{x}{2}\right)\left(-\frac{l}{n\pi}\cos\frac{n\pi x}{l}\right) - \left(\frac{1}{2}\right)\left(-\frac{l^2}{n^2\,\pi^2}\sin\frac{n\pi x}{l}\right) \right]_0^{\frac{2l}{3}} \right.$$

$$\left. + \left[(l-x)\left(-\frac{l}{n\pi}\cos\frac{n\pi x}{l}\right) - (-1)\left(-\frac{l^2}{n^2\,\pi^2}\sin\frac{n\pi x}{l}\right) \right]_{\frac{2l}{3}}^{l} \right\}$$

$$= \frac{6a}{l^2}\left\{ -\frac{l^2}{3n\pi}\cos\frac{2n\pi}{3} + \frac{l^2}{2n^2\pi^2}\sin\frac{2n\pi}{3} + \frac{l^2}{3n\pi}\cos\frac{2n\pi}{3} + \frac{l^2}{n^2\,\pi^2}\sin\frac{2n\pi}{3} \right\}$$

$$= \frac{6a}{l^2}\left(\frac{3}{2}\,\frac{l^2}{n^2\,\pi^2}\sin\frac{2n\pi}{3} \right) = \frac{9\,a}{\pi^2}\,\frac{1}{n^2}\sin\frac{2n\pi}{3}$$

∴   Substituting in (II), we get,

$$\boxed{\;y\,(x,\,t) \;=\; \frac{9a}{\pi^2}\,\sum_{n=1}^{\infty}\,\frac{1}{n^2}\,\sin\frac{2n\pi}{3}\,\sin\frac{n\pi x}{l}\,\cos\frac{n\pi ct}{l}\;}$$

EXERCISE 13.1

1. A taut string of a length $2l$ is fastened at both ends. The mid point of the string is taken to a height b and then released from rest in that position. Obtain the displacement.

Hint : B.C. : (i) $\left(\dfrac{\partial y}{\partial t}\right)_{t=0} = 0$, (ii) $y\,(2l,\,t) = 0$,   Use $\dfrac{\partial^2 y}{\partial t^2} = c^2\,\dfrac{\partial^2 y}{\partial x^2}$

I.C. : (iii) $y\,(0,\,t) = 0$;   (iv) $y\,(x,\,0) = \begin{cases} \dfrac{bx}{l},\ 0 \le x \le l \\[2mm] \dfrac{b}{l}\,(2x - x),\ l \le x \le 2l \end{cases}$

The most GS is $y(x,\,t) = (c_1\cos mx + c_2\sin mx)(c_3\cos cmt + c_4\sin cmt)$

and use formula for $\;b_n = \dfrac{2}{2l}\displaystyle\int_0^{2l} f(x)\sin\frac{n\pi x}{2l}\,dx = \dfrac{8b}{n^2\,\pi^2}\sin\dfrac{n\pi}{2}$.

$$\textbf{Ans. :}\ \ y\,(x,\,t) = \frac{8b}{\pi^2}\,\sum_{n=1}^{\infty}\,\frac{1}{n^2}\,\sin\frac{n\pi}{2}\,\sin\frac{n\pi x}{2l}\,\cos\left(\frac{n\pi ct}{2l}\right)$$

2. If a string of length l is initially at rest in its equilibrium position and each of its point is given a velocity v (x) such that

$$v\,(x) = \begin{cases} cx, & 0 < x \le \dfrac{l}{2} \\[3mm] c\,(l-x), & \dfrac{l}{2} \le x \le l \end{cases}$$

Obtain the displacement y (x, t) at any time t.   **(Nov. 2013)**

Hint : B.C. : (i) $y(0, t) = 0$, (ii) $y(l, t) = 0$, Use $\dfrac{\partial^2 y}{\partial t^2} = a^2 \dfrac{\partial^2 y}{\partial x^2}$

(iii) I.C. : $\left(\dfrac{\partial y}{\partial t}\right)_{t=0} = \begin{cases} cx, & 0 \le x \le \dfrac{l}{2} \\[2mm] c\,(l-x), & \dfrac{l}{2} \le x \le l \end{cases}$, (iv) $y(x, 0) = 0$

and use $b_n = \dfrac{2}{l} \displaystyle\int_0^l f(x) \sin \dfrac{n\pi x}{l}\, dx = \dfrac{4cl}{n^2 \pi^2} \sin \dfrac{n\pi}{2}$.

Ans. : $y(x, t) = \dfrac{4\,c\,l^2}{a\,\pi^3} \displaystyle\sum_{n=1}^{\infty} \dfrac{1}{n^3} \sin \dfrac{n\pi}{2} \sin \dfrac{n\pi x}{l} \sin \dfrac{n\pi at}{l}$

3. A tightly stretched string with fixed ends $x = 0$ and $x = l$ is initially at rest in its equilibrium position. If it is set vibrating giving each point a velocity $3x\,(l - x)$ for $0 < x < l$, find the displacement.

Hint : BC. : (i) $y(0, t) = 0$, (ii) $y(l, t) = 0$;

I.C. : (iii) $\left(\dfrac{\partial y}{\partial t}\right)_{t=0} = 3x\,(l - x)$, (iv) $y(x, 0) = 0$.

and use $b_n = \dfrac{2}{l} \displaystyle\int_0^l f(x) \sin \dfrac{n\pi x}{l}\, dx = \dfrac{12 l^2}{n^3 \pi^3} (1 - \cos n\pi)$

Ans. : $y(x, t) = \dfrac{24\,l^3}{\pi^4 c} \displaystyle\sum_{n=1}^{\infty} \dfrac{1}{(2n-1)^4} \sin \dfrac{(2n-1)\,\pi x}{l} \sin \dfrac{(2n-1)\,\pi ct}{l}$

4. Work exercise 3, given that velocity is $v_o \sin^3 \dfrac{\pi x}{l}$, $0 \le x \le l$

Ans. : $y(x, t) = \dfrac{3 v_o\, l}{4\pi c} \left[\sin \dfrac{\pi x}{l} \sin \dfrac{\pi ct}{l} - \dfrac{1}{9} \sin \dfrac{3\pi x}{l} \sin \dfrac{3\pi ct}{l} \right]$

5. A string is stretched and fastened to two points distance l apart is displaced into the form $y(x, 0) = 3\,(lx - x^2)$ from which it is released at $t = 0$. Find the displacement of the string at a distance x from one end.

Hint : B.C. : (i) $y(0, t) = 0$, (ii) $y(l, t) = 0$,

I.C. : (iii) $\left(\dfrac{\partial y}{\partial t}\right)_{t=0} = 0$, (iv) $y(x, 0) = 3\,(lx - x^2)$

and $b_n = \dfrac{2}{l} \displaystyle\int_0^l f(x) \sin \dfrac{n\pi x}{l}\, dx = \dfrac{18 l^2}{n^3 \pi^3} (1 - \cos n\pi)$

Ans. : $\dfrac{24 l^2}{\pi^3} \displaystyle\sum_{n=1}^{\infty} \dfrac{1}{(2n-1)^3} \sin \dfrac{(2n-1)\,\pi x}{l} \cos \dfrac{(2n-1)\,\pi ct}{l}$

6. Work exercise 5, given that $l = 40$ and $y(x, 0) = 40x - x^2$, $0 \leq x \leq 40$.

$$\textbf{Ans. :} \quad y(x, t) = \frac{12800}{\pi^3} \sum_{n=1}^{\infty} \frac{1}{(2n-1)^3} \sin \frac{(2n-1)\,\pi x}{40} \cos \frac{(2n-1)\,\pi ct}{40}$$

7. An elastic string is stretched between two points at a distance l apart. One end is taken as origin and point $x = \dfrac{2l}{3}$ is displaced through distance "d" perpendicular to x-axis and released from rest from this position. Obtain the displacement.

Hint : B.C. : (i) $y(0, t) = 0$, (ii) $y(l, t) = 0$,

I.C. : (iii) $\left(\dfrac{\partial y}{\partial t}\right)_{t=0} = 0$,

$$\text{(iv) } y(x, 0) = \begin{cases} \dfrac{3d}{2l}\,x, & 0 \leq x \leq \dfrac{2l}{3} \\[3mm] \dfrac{3d}{l}\,(l - x), & \dfrac{2l}{3} \leq x \leq l \end{cases}$$

$$\textbf{Ans. :} \quad \frac{9d}{\pi^2} \sum_{n=1}^{\infty} \frac{1}{n^2} \sin \frac{2n\pi}{3} \sin \frac{n\pi x}{l} \cos \frac{n\pi ct}{l}$$

8. Work exercise 5, given that $y(x, 0) = y_o \sin \dfrac{\pi x}{l}$

Hint : $b_1 = y_0$, $b_2 = b_3 = \ldots = 0$.

$$\textbf{Ans. :} \quad y(x, t) = y_o \sin \frac{\pi x}{l} \cos \frac{\pi at}{l}$$

9. The points of trisection of a tightly stretched string of length l with fixed ends are pulled aside through a distance d on opposite sides of the position of equilibrium and the string is released from rest. Obtain the displacement of the string and show that mid-point always remains at rest.

$$\textbf{Ans. :} \quad y(x, t) = \frac{9d}{\pi^2} \sum_{n=1}^{\infty} \frac{1}{n^2} \sin \frac{2n\pi}{3} \sin \frac{2n\pi x}{l} \cos \frac{2n\pi at}{l}$$

$$\text{when } x = \frac{l}{2}, \; y\left(\frac{l}{2}, t\right) = 0 \text{ for all t.}$$

10. Work exercise 7, given that $x = \dfrac{3}{4}\, l$.

Hint : B.C. : (i) $y\,(0, t) = 0$, (ii) $y\,(l, t) = 0$,

I.C. : (iii) $\left(\dfrac{\partial y}{\partial t}\right)_{t=0} = 0$,

(iv) $y\,(x, 0) = \begin{cases} \dfrac{4d}{3l}\, x, & 0 \le x \le \dfrac{3l}{4} \\[3mm] \dfrac{4d}{l}\,(l - x), & \dfrac{3l}{4} \le x \le l \end{cases}$

$$\textbf{Ans. :}\ \ y\,(x, t) = \frac{32\,d}{3\pi^2} \sum_{n=1}^{\infty} \frac{1}{n^2} \sin\frac{3n\pi}{4}\ \sin\frac{n\pi x}{l}\ \cos\frac{n\pi a t}{l}$$

11. A uniform string stretched between the points $x = 0$ and $x = l$ is given the initial displacement $y\,(x, 0) = \sin\dfrac{\pi x}{l}$, $0 < x < l$ and initial velocity,

$$v\,(x) = \begin{cases} 0, & 0 < x < \dfrac{l}{4} \\[3mm] a, & \dfrac{l}{4} < x < \dfrac{3l}{4} \\[3mm] 0, & \dfrac{3l}{4} < x < l \end{cases}$$

Find subsequent displacement.

$$\textbf{Ans. :}\ \ y\,(x, t) = \sin\frac{\pi x}{l}\ \cos\frac{\pi a t}{l} + \frac{4l}{\pi^2} \sum_{n=1}^{\infty} \frac{1}{n^2} \sin\frac{n\pi}{2}\ \sin\frac{n\pi}{4}\ \sin\frac{n\pi x}{l}\ \sin\frac{n\pi a t}{l}$$

12. A string of length l fixed at its ends satisfies the wave equation $\dfrac{\partial^2 y}{\partial t^2} = c^2\ \dfrac{\partial^2 y}{\partial x^2}$. Find the solution if the string has initial triangular deflection given by :

$$y\,(x, 0) = \begin{cases} \dfrac{2k}{l}\, x, & 0 \le x \le \dfrac{l}{2} \\[3mm] \dfrac{2k}{l}\,(l - x), & \dfrac{l}{2} \le x \le l \end{cases}$$

and initial velocity zero. **(Dec. 2007)**

$$\textbf{Ans. :}\ y\,(x, t) = \frac{8k}{\pi^2} \sum_{1}^{\infty} \frac{(-1)^{n+1}}{(2n-1)^2}\ \sin\frac{(2n-1)\,\pi x}{l}\ \cos\frac{(2n-1)\,\pi c t}{l}$$

13. Find the deflection u (x, t) of a vibrating string $\left(\text{length } l = \pi, \text{ ends fixed and } c^2 = \dfrac{T}{\rho} = 1\right)$ corresponding to zero velocity and initial deflection $0.01\,(\pi - x)$.

$$\textbf{Ans. :}\ u\,(x, t) = 0.02 \sum_{1}^{\infty} \frac{1}{n}\ \sin nx \cos nt.$$

14. A flexible string of length π is tightly stretched between $x = 0$, $x = \pi$, on x-axis, its ends being fixed at these points. When set into small transverse vibration, the displacement $y\,(x, t)$ from x–axis of any point x at time t is given by

$$\frac{\partial^2 y}{\partial t^2} = 4 \frac{\partial^2 y}{\partial x^2}.$$

Find the solution of the equation which satisfies (i) $y\,(0, t) = 0$, (ii) $y\,(\pi, t) = 0$, (iii) $\left(\dfrac{\partial y}{\partial t}\right)_{t=0} = 0$ and (iv) $y\,(x, 0) = 0.1\,\sin x + 0.01\,\sin 4x$ for $0 \le x \le \pi$.

(May 2008)

Hint : $c^2 = 4$ $\therefore$ $c = 2$, $b_1 = 0.1$, $b_2 = 0$, $b_3 = 0$, $b_4 = 0.01$, $b_5 = b_6 = \ldots = 0$.

Ans. : $y\,(x, t) = 0.1\,\sin x\,\cos 2t + 0.01\,\sin 4x\,\cos 8t$

13.5 MODELING OF ONE-DIMENSIONAL HEAT FLOW

Derivation of Equation :

We make use of following experimental facts or empirical laws :

(i) Heat flows from higher temperature to lower temperature.

(ii) The rate of flow of heat through an area is proportional to the area and to the temperature gradient in degrees per unit distance $\left(\dfrac{\partial u}{\partial t}\right)$, where $u(x, t)$ is temperature distribution normal to the area. Constant of proportionality is called the *thermal conductivity* of the material and denoted generally by k.

(iii) The amount of heat required to change the temperature through a given range is proportional to the mass of the body and the change of temperature. The constant of proportionality is termed as specific heat and generally denoted by S.

Consider a homogeneous bar of uniform cross-section, sides coated with insulating material. It is assumed that the loss of heat from the sides by conduction or radiation is negligible. One end of the bar is treated as the origin and the direction of heat flow as positive X-axis. Let ρ be the density (gm/cm³), 'S' the specific heat (cal/gm deg) and 'k' the thermal conductivity (cal/cm-deg.sec). The temperature at any point of the bar depends on the distance x of the point from one end and time 't' and is denoted by $u(x, t)$ or u. Also the temperature distribution through a cross-section is same.

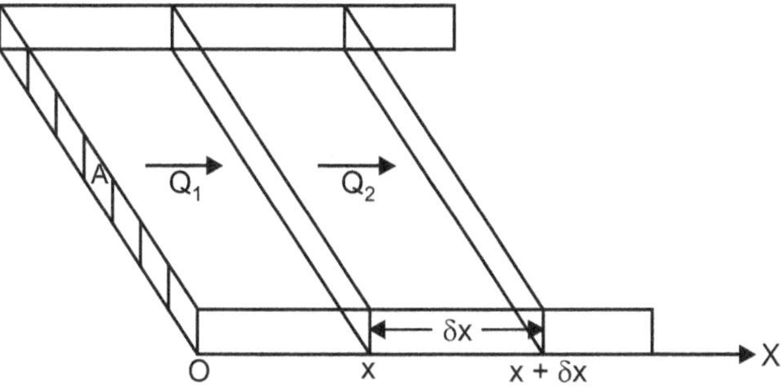

Fig. 13.3

Now, as the quantity of heat crossing any section of the bar is proportional to the area and the temperature gradient normal to the area, the quantity 'Q_1' flowing into the section at a distance x is,

$$Q_1 \;=\; -\,kA\left(\frac{\partial u}{\partial x}\right)_x$$

The quantity 'Q_2' flowing out of the section at a distance $x + \delta x$ is,

$$Q_2 \;=\; -\,kA\left(\frac{\partial u}{\partial x}\right)_{x+\delta x}$$

$\therefore$ Quantity of heat retained by the slab with thickness δx is,

$$Q_1 - Q_2 \;=\; kA\left[\left(\frac{\partial u}{\partial x}\right)_{x+\delta x} - \left(\frac{\partial u}{\partial x}\right)_x\right] \qquad \text{... (1)}$$

But the rate of increase of heat in the slab

$$=\; S\,\rho\,A\,\delta x\,\frac{\partial u}{\partial t} \qquad \text{... (2)}$$

$\therefore$ From equations (1) and (2),

$$S\,\rho\,A\,\delta x\,\frac{\partial u}{\partial t} \;=\; kA\left[\left(\frac{\partial u}{\partial x}\right)_{x+\delta x} - \left(\frac{\partial u}{\partial x}\right)_x\right]$$

$$\therefore \qquad S\,\rho\,\frac{\partial u}{\partial t} \;=\; k\left[\frac{\left(\frac{\partial u}{\partial x}\right)_{x+\delta x} - \left(\frac{\partial u}{\partial x}\right)_x}{\delta x}\right]$$

Taking limit as $\delta x \to 0$

$$S\,\rho\,\frac{\partial u}{\partial t} \;=\; k\;\lim_{\delta x \to 0}\left[\frac{\left(\frac{\partial u}{\partial x}\right)_{x+\delta x} - \left(\frac{\partial u}{\partial x}\right)_x}{\delta x}\right]$$

Or

$$\frac{\partial u}{\partial t} \;=\; \frac{k}{S\,\rho}\,\frac{\partial^2 u}{\partial x^2}$$

For $\dfrac{k}{S\,\rho} = c^2$, it reduces to $\dfrac{\partial u}{\partial t} = c^2\,\dfrac{\partial^2 u}{\partial x^2}$ and is called *one-dimensional heat flow equation*. The constant $c^2 = \dfrac{k}{S\,\rho}$ is known as diffusivity of the material of the bar.

13.6 SOLUTION OF THE HEAT EQUATION BY METHOD OF SEPARATION OF VARIABLES

We have to obtain solution of the P.D.E.

$$\boxed{\frac{\partial u}{\partial t} \;=\; c^2\,\frac{\partial^2 u}{\partial x^2}} \qquad \text{... (1)}$$

Let $u(x, t) = F(x) \cdot G(t)$ be the solution.   ... (2)

$$\therefore \qquad \frac{\partial u}{\partial t} = F(x) \cdot G'(t) \quad \text{and} \quad \frac{\partial^2 u}{\partial x^2} = F''(x) \cdot G(t)$$

Substituting in (1), we get

$$F(x) \cdot G'(t) = c^2 \, F''(x) \cdot G(t)$$

$$\frac{G'(t)}{c^2 \cdot G(t)} = \frac{F''(x)}{F(x)}$$

Since L.H.S. is a function of 't' alone and R.H.S. is a function of x alone, therefore both sides are independent of each other, hence can be equated to any arbitrary constant, say k.

$$\frac{G'(t)}{c^2 \cdot G(t)} = \frac{F''(x)}{F(x)} = k$$

Case (i) : Let $\quad k = 0 \Rightarrow G'(t) = 0 \quad \Rightarrow \quad G(t) = c_1$

and $\qquad F''(x) = 0 \Rightarrow F(x) = c_2 x + c_3$

$\therefore$ Complete solution is

$$u(x, t) = (c_2 x + c_3) \cdot c_1$$

Or $\qquad \boxed{u(x, t) = c_4 x + c_5}$ ... (3)

Case (ii) : Let $\quad k > 0 \qquad (\text{say } k = m^2)$

$$\frac{F''(x)}{F(x)} = m^2 \quad \Rightarrow \quad F''(x) - m^2 \, F(x) = 0$$

$$\frac{d^2 F}{dx^2} - m^2 F = 0 \qquad \left(\text{Let } D \equiv \frac{d}{dx}\right)$$

$$(D^2 - m^2) F = 0 \Rightarrow F(x) = c_1 e^{mx} + c_2 e^{-mx}$$

Also, $\qquad \dfrac{G'(t)}{c^2 \cdot G(t)} = m^2$

$$\frac{G'(t)}{G(t)} = c^2 m^2 \quad \Rightarrow \quad \log G(t) = c^2 m^2 \, t + A$$

$$\therefore \qquad G(t) = c_3 \, e^{c^2 m^2 t}$$

Complete solution is

$$u(x, t) = (c_1 e^{mx} + c_2 e^{-mx}) \; c_3 \cdot e^{c^2 m^2 t}$$

Or $\qquad \boxed{u(x, t) = (c_4 e^{mx} + c_5 e^{-mx}) \, e^{c^2 m^2 t}}$ ... (4)

Case (iii) : Let $k < 0$ (say $(k = -m^2)$

$$\frac{F''(x)}{F(x)} = -m^2 \quad \Rightarrow \quad F''(x) + m^2\, F(x) = 0$$

$$\frac{d^2F}{dx^2} + m^2\, F = 0 \qquad \left(\text{Let } D \equiv \frac{d}{dx}\right)$$

$$(D^2 + m^2)\ F = 0 \qquad \Rightarrow \quad F(x) = c_1 \cos mx + c_2 \sin mx$$

Also, $$\frac{G'(t)}{c^2 \cdot G(t)} = -m^2 \quad \Rightarrow \quad \frac{G'(t)}{G(t)} = -c^2 m^2$$

$$\log G(t) = -c^2 m^2 t + A$$

$$G(t) = c_3\ e^{-c^2 m^2 t}$$

$\therefore$ Complete solution is

$$u(x, t) = (c_1 \cos mx + c_2 \sin mx)\ c_3\ e^{-c^2 m^2 t}$$

Or $$\boxed{u(x, t) = (c_4 \cos mx + c_5 \sin mx)\ e^{-c^2 m^2 t}} \qquad \ldots (5)$$

Again the question arises which solution we must adopt. In present case, we are concerned with conduction of heat from a source which has finite temperature. Naturally, the temperature $u(x, t)$ cannot become unbounded as t increases. Naturally the solution given by (4) is therefore to be rejected and solution given by (5) is suitable in present case. Solution corresponding to $k = 0$ does not involve any t, hence it can be considered as steady-state solution i.e. solution when temperature no longer varies with time t.

Hence in obtaining solution of the problems of one-dimensional heat flow, we will always begin with solution given in (5) and consider solution (3) under steady-state conditions.

Note : Insulated boundary or end means no heat is flowing from it, meaning thereby $\frac{\partial u}{\partial x} = 0$ at that boundary or end.

ILLUSTRATIONS

Ex. 1 : *Solve* $\dfrac{\partial u}{\partial t} = \dfrac{\partial^2 u}{\partial x^2}$ *if (i) u is finite* $\forall\, t$, *(ii) u = 0 when x = 0,* $\pi \,\forall t$, *(iii) u = $\pi x - x^2$*

when t = 0 and $0 \le x \le \pi$.

Sol. : Given equation is $\dfrac{\partial u}{\partial t} = \dfrac{\partial^2 u}{\partial x^2}$. The boundary conditions are given as :

(i) $u(x, t)$ is bounded $\forall\, t$

(ii) $u(0, t) = 0,\ \ \forall\, t$

(iii) $u(\pi, t) = 0,\ \ \forall\, t$

(iv) $u(x, 0) = \pi x - x^2\ ,\ \ 0 \le x \le \pi$ **(Dec. 2006, 2016)**

The most general solution is

$\therefore \qquad u(x, t) = (c_4 \cos mx + c_5 \sin mx)\ e^{-m^2 t}$ $\qquad \ldots (1)$

Applying the second condition :

$$u(0, t) = 0 \Rightarrow c_4 = 0$$

$$\therefore \qquad u(x, t) = c_5 \sin mx \; e^{-m^2 t}$$

Applying the third condition $u(\pi, t) = 0$

$$\Rightarrow \qquad 0 = c_5 \sin m\pi \; e^{-m^2 t}$$

Now since $c_5 \neq 0$

$$\text{and} \quad e^{-m^2 t} \neq 0 \qquad \therefore \sin m\pi = 0 \Rightarrow m\pi = n\pi$$

$$\therefore \quad m = n \text{ for } n = 1, 2, 3, 4 \ldots\ldots$$

$$\therefore \quad \text{Solution becomes } u(x, t) = c_5 \sin nx \; e^{-n^2 t} \quad \text{for } n = 1, 2, 3 \ldots\ldots\ldots$$

Taking $n = 1, 2, 3 \ldots\ldots\ldots$ and varying the constant c_5 for each n, we see that the general solution is

$$u(x, t) = \sum_{n=1}^{\infty} b_n \sin nx \; e^{-n^2 t} \qquad\qquad \ldots (2)$$

Using aforesaid condition (iv) in (2), we get

$$\pi x - x^2 = u(x, 0) = \sum_{n=1}^{\infty} b_n \sin(nx); \qquad 0 \leq x \leq \pi$$

In order to treat this as half range Fourier sine series of $(\pi x - x^2)$ in $0 \leq x \leq \pi$, b_n should be chosen as

$$b_n = \frac{2}{\pi} \int_0^{\pi} (\pi x - x^2) \sin nx \; dx$$

$$= \frac{2}{\pi} \left\{ (\pi x - x^2) \left(-\frac{\cos nx}{n} \right) - (\pi - 2x) \left(-\frac{\sin nx}{n^2} \right) + (-2) \left(\frac{\cos nx}{n^3} \right) \right\}_0^{\pi}$$

$$= \frac{4}{\pi n^3} (1 - \cos n\pi) = \begin{cases} 0, & \text{for n even} \\ 8/\pi n^3, & \text{for n odd} \end{cases}$$

$\therefore$ Solution (2) becomes

$$u(x, t) = \frac{4}{\pi} \sum_{n=1}^{\infty} \frac{1 - (-1)^n}{n^3} \sin(nx) \cdot e^{-n^2 t}$$

$$\text{Or } u(x, t) = \frac{8}{\pi} \sum_{r=0}^{\infty} \frac{1}{(2r+1)^3} \sin[(2r+1)x] \cdot e^{-(2r+1)^2 t} \text{ which is the required}$$

solution.

Ex. 2 : *Solve* $\dfrac{\partial V}{\partial t} = k \dfrac{\partial^2 V}{\partial x^2}$ *if*   **(May 2011)**

(i) $V \neq \infty$ *as* $t \to \infty$ *(ii)* $\left(\dfrac{\partial V}{\partial x}\right)_{x = 0} = 0, \ \forall t$

(iii) $V(l, t) = 0, \ \forall t$ *(iv)* $V(x, 0) = v_o,$ *for* $0 < x < l.$ **(Dec. 2004)**

Sol. : The most general solution is

$$V(x, t) = (c_4 \cos mx + c_5 \sin mx) \ e^{-m^2 k t}$$

$$\frac{\partial V}{\partial x} = (-m c_4 \sin mx + m c_5 \cos mx) \ e^{-m^2 k t}$$

Condition (ii) $\Rightarrow$ $c_5 = 0$

$\therefore$ $V(x, t) = c_4 \cdot \cos mx \cdot e^{-m^2 k t}$

Condition (iii) $\Rightarrow$ $0 = c_4 \cos ml \ e^{-m^2 k t}$

$\therefore$ $\cos ml = 0 \Rightarrow ml = \dfrac{n\pi}{2},$ (n is odd)

or $m = \dfrac{n\,\pi/2}{l},$ (n is odd) Or $m = \dfrac{(2n + 1)\,\pi/2}{l}, \ n = 0, 1, 2, \ldots\ldots$

$$V(x, t) = c_4 \cos \frac{[(2n + 1)\,\pi/2]\,x}{l} \ e^{-\dfrac{[(2n + 1)^2\,\pi^2/4]\,kt}{l^2}} , \ n = 0, 1, 2, \ldots$$

Taking $n = 0, 1, 2, \ldots$ and combining all these solutions, we have the general solution

as $V(x, t) = \displaystyle\sum_{n = 0}^{\infty} a_{2n+1} \cos \frac{[(2n + 1)\,\pi/2]\,x}{l} \ e^{-\dfrac{[(2n + 1)^2\,\pi^2/4]\,kt}{l^2}}$

Note : Notation $a_{2n + 1}, n = 0, 1, 2, \ldots$ is used instead a_n because n is odd.

Applying condition (iv), we have

$$v_o = \sum_{n = 0}^{\infty} a_{2n+1} \cos \frac{[(2n + 1)\,\pi/2]\,x}{l}$$

which is nothing but half range Fourier cosine series for $f(x) = v_o$ in $(0, l)$ with $a_0 = 0$.

$\therefore$ $a_{2n+1} = \dfrac{2}{l} \displaystyle\int_0^l v_o \cos \frac{[(2n + 1)\,\pi/2]\,x}{l} \ dx = \dfrac{2\,v_o}{l} \left[\frac{2l}{(2n + 1)\,\pi} \sin \frac{(2n + 1)\,\pi x}{2l} \right]_0^l$

$$a_{2n+1} = \frac{4\,v_o}{\pi} \frac{1}{(2n + 1)} \sin (2n + 1) \frac{\pi}{2} = \frac{4\,v_o}{\pi} \frac{(-1)^n}{2n + 1}$$

$\therefore$ $V(x, t) = \dfrac{4\,v_o}{\pi} \displaystyle\sum_{n = 0}^{\infty} \frac{(-1)^n}{2n + 1} \cos \frac{(2n + 1)\,\pi x}{2l} \ e^{-\dfrac{(2n + 1)^2\,\pi^2\,kt}{4l^2}}$

Ex. 3 : *The equation for the conduction of heat along a bar of length l is* $\dfrac{\partial \theta}{\partial t} = k\,\dfrac{\partial^2 \theta}{\partial x^2},$

neglecting radiation. Find an expression for θ *if the ends of the bar are maintained at zero temperature and if initially the temperature is T at the centre of the bar and falls uniformly to zero at its ends.* **(May 2012)**

Sol. :

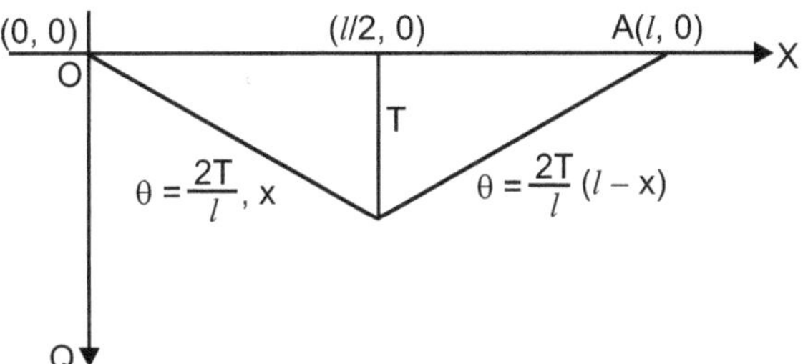

Fig. 13.4

Given equation is $\dfrac{\partial \theta}{\partial t} = k \dfrac{\partial^2 \theta}{\partial x^2}$ and the boundary condition is given as :

(i)　　　$\theta(0, t) = 0$

(ii)　　　$\theta(l, t) = 0$

(iii)　　　$\theta(x, 0) = \dfrac{2T}{l} x$ for $0 \le x \le \dfrac{l}{2}$

$$= \dfrac{2T}{l}(l - x) \text{ for } \dfrac{l}{2} \le x \le l$$

The most general solution is

$$\theta(x, t) = (c_4 \cos mx + c_5 \sin mx)\, e^{-k m^2 t} \qquad \ldots (1)$$

Applying condition (i), $\theta(0, t) = 0 \quad \Rightarrow \quad c_4 = 0$

$\therefore$ $\qquad \theta(x, t) = c_5 \sin mx\, e^{-k m^2 t}$

Applying second condition, $\theta(l, t) = 0$

$$\Rightarrow \qquad \sin ml = 0 \quad \Rightarrow \quad ml = n\pi$$

i.e.　　　　　$m = \dfrac{n\pi}{l}$　for　$n = 1, 2, 3, \ldots\ldots\ldots$

$\therefore$　Solution becomes

$$\theta(x, t) = c_5 \sin \dfrac{n\pi x}{l}\, e^{-\frac{k n^2 \pi^2 t}{l^2}}$$

Putting $n = 1, 2, 3 \ldots\ldots\ldots$ and varying constant c_5 for each n, we have the general solution as

$$\theta(x, t) = \sum_{n=1}^{\infty} b_n \sin \dfrac{n\pi x}{l}\, e^{-\frac{k n^2 \pi^2 t}{l^2}} \qquad \ldots (2)$$

Applying the last condition, at $t = 0$

$$\theta = \sum_{n=1}^{\infty} b_n \sin \frac{n\pi x}{l}$$

where $b_n = \dfrac{2}{l} \displaystyle\int_0^l \theta \cdot \sin \frac{n\pi x}{l} \, dx$

$$= \frac{2}{l} \left[\int_0^{l/2} \frac{2T}{l} \, x \, \sin \frac{n\pi x}{l} \, dx + \int_{l/2}^l \frac{2T}{l} (l-x) \sin \frac{n\pi x}{l} \, dx \right]$$

$$= \frac{4T}{l^2} \left[\left\{ (x) \left(-\frac{l}{n\pi} \cos \frac{n\pi x}{l} \right) + \frac{l^2}{n^2 \pi^2} \sin \frac{n\pi x}{l} \right\}_0^{l/2} \right.$$

$$\left. + \left\{ (l-x) \left(-\frac{l}{n\pi} \cos \frac{n\pi x}{l} \right) - \frac{l^2}{n^2\pi^2} \sin \frac{n\pi x}{l} \right\}_{l/2}^l \right]$$

$$\therefore \quad b_n = \frac{4T}{l^2} \left[-\frac{l^2}{2n\pi} \cos \frac{n\pi}{2} + \frac{l^2}{n^2 \pi^2} \sin \frac{n\pi}{2} + \frac{l^2}{2n\pi} \cos \frac{n\pi}{2} + \frac{l^2}{n^2\pi^2} \sin \frac{n\pi}{2} \right]$$

$$= \frac{8T}{n^2 \pi^2} \sin \frac{n\pi}{2}$$

Substituting in (2), we get

$$\theta(x, t) = \frac{8T}{\pi^2} \sum_{n=1}^{\infty} \frac{1}{n^2} \sin \frac{n\pi}{2} \cdot \sin \frac{n\pi x}{l} \, e^{-\frac{k n^2 \pi^2 t}{l^2}}$$

$$\theta(x, t) = \frac{8T}{\pi^2} \left[\sin \frac{\pi x}{l} \, e^{-\frac{k \pi^2 t}{l^2}} - \frac{1}{3^2} \sin \frac{3\pi x}{l} \, e^{-\frac{9k \pi^2 t}{l^2}} + \cdots \cdots \right]$$

Ex. 4 : *Solve* $\dfrac{\partial u}{\partial t} = k \dfrac{\partial^2 u}{\partial^2 x}$ *for the conduction of heat along a rod without radiation, subject to the following conditions :*

(i)   u is not infinite as $t \to \infty$

(ii) $\dfrac{\partial u}{\partial x} = 0$ *for* $x = 0$, $x = l$ *(i.e. ends are insulated i.e. no heat flows through the ends) and (iii)* $u = lx - x^2$ *for* $t = 0$ *between* $x = 0$, $x = l$.

Sol. : We have

$$u(x, t) = (c_4 \cos mx + c_5 \sin mx) \, e^{-k m^2 t} \qquad \cdots (1)$$

Now applying the second condition,

$$\frac{\partial u}{\partial x} = 0 \quad \text{for } x = 0$$

$$\frac{\partial u}{\partial x} = (-m\, c_4 \sin mx + m\, c_5 \cos mx)\, e^{-k m^2 t}$$

$$\therefore \quad \frac{\partial u}{\partial x} = 0,\ x = 0 \ \Rightarrow\ c_5 = 0$$

$\therefore$ Solution becomes

$$u = c_4 \cos mx\, e^{-k m^2 t}$$

Also,
$$\frac{\partial u}{\partial x} = -m\, c_4 \sin mx\, e^{-k m^2 t}$$

$$\frac{\partial u}{\partial x} = 0,\ x = l \ \Rightarrow\ 0 = -m\, c_4 \sin ml\, e^{-k m^2 t}$$

$$c_4 \neq 0 \qquad \therefore\ \sin ml = 0 \ \Rightarrow\ ml = n\pi$$

$$\therefore \qquad m = \frac{n\pi}{l}$$

$\therefore$ Solution is $u\,(x,\,t) = c_4 \cos \dfrac{n\pi x}{l}\, e^{\frac{-k\, n^2 \pi^2 t}{l^2}}$ for $n = 1, 2, 3, \ldots\ldots\ldots$

i.e.
$$u\,(x,\,t) = \sum_{n=1}^{\infty} a_n \cos \frac{n\pi x}{l}\, e^{\frac{-k\, n^2 \pi^2 t}{l^2}} \qquad \ldots (2)$$

Applying the third condition $u = lx - x^2$ for $t = 0$ between $x = 0$, $x = l$.
By putting $t = 0$,

$$\therefore \qquad u = \sum_{n=1}^{\infty} a_n \cos \frac{n\pi x}{l}$$

which is represented by Fourier half range cosine series for $lx - x^2$ in $(0,\, l)$ where

$$a_o = \frac{1}{l} \int_0^l (lx - x^2)\, dx = \frac{l^2}{6}$$

$$a_n = \frac{2}{l} \int_0^l (lx - x^2) \cos \frac{n\pi x}{l}\, dx$$

$$= \frac{2}{l} \left[(lx - x^2)\left(\frac{l}{n\pi} \sin \frac{n\pi x}{l}\right) - (l - 2x)\left(-\frac{l^2}{n^2 \pi^2} \cos \frac{n\pi x}{l}\right) + (-2)\left(-\frac{l^3}{n^3 \pi^3} \sin \frac{n\pi x}{l}\right) \right]_0^l$$

$$= \frac{2}{l} \left[-\frac{l^3}{n^2 \pi^2} \cos n\pi - \frac{l^3}{n^2 \pi^2} \right]$$

$$= -\frac{2l^2}{n^2 \pi^2}\,(1 + \cos n\pi) = \begin{cases} 0 & \text{for } n \text{ odd} \\[2mm] -\dfrac{4l^2}{n^2 \pi^2} & \text{for } n \text{ even} \end{cases}$$

Let $\qquad n = 2p$

$$a_{2p} = -\frac{4\,l^2}{4\,p^2\,\pi^2} = -\frac{l^2}{p^2\,\pi^2} \quad \text{for } p = 1, 2, 3, \ldots\ldots$$

Solution (2) becomes

$$u = a_0 + \sum_{p=1}^{\infty} a_{2p}\ \cos\frac{2p\pi x}{l}\ e^{\frac{-k\,4\,p^2\,\pi^2\,t}{l^2}}$$

i.e.

$$u = \frac{l^2}{6} - \frac{l^2}{\pi^2} \sum_{p=1}^{\infty} \frac{1}{p^2}\ \cos\frac{2\,p\,\pi\,x}{l}\ e^{\frac{-4k\,p^2\,\pi^2\,t}{l^2}}$$

which is the required solution.

Ex. 5 : *Solve* $\dfrac{\partial u}{\partial t} = k\,\dfrac{\partial^2 u}{\partial x^2}$ *if*

(i) $u\,(0, t) = 0$

(ii) $u_x\,(l, t) = 0$

(iii) $u\,(x, t)$ *is bounded and*

(iv) $u\,(x, 0) = \dfrac{u_o\,x}{l}$ *for* $0 \le x \le l.$ **(Nov. 2013, May 2005)**

Sol. : The most general solution is

$$u\,(x, t) = (c_4 \cos mx + c_5\ \sin mx)\ e^{-k\,m^2\,t}$$

Applying condition (i) $\Rightarrow\ c_4 = 0$

$$u\,(x, t) = c_5\ \sin mx\ e^{-k\,m^2\,t}$$

$$u_x\,(l, t) = 0 \quad \Rightarrow \quad \left(\frac{\partial u}{\partial x}\right)_{x = l} = 0$$

$$\frac{\partial u}{\partial x} = m\,.\,c_5\ \cos mx\ e^{-k\,m^2\,t}$$

$$0 = m\,.\,c_5\,.\,\cos ml\ e^{-k\,m^2\,t}$$

$$\cos ml = 0, \quad ml = \frac{n\pi}{2}\ (n = \text{odd})$$

$$m = \frac{n\pi}{2l} \quad \text{or}\quad m = \frac{(2n+1)\,\pi}{2l}, \quad n = 0, 1, 2, \ldots\ldots$$

$$u\,(x, t) = c_5\ \sin\frac{(2n+1)\,\pi\,x}{2l}\ e^{\frac{-k\,(2n+1)^2\,\pi^2\,t}{4\,l^2}}$$

Or

$$u\,(x, t) = \sum_{n=0}^{\infty} b_n \sin\frac{(2n+1)\,\pi\,x}{2\,l}\ \cdot\ e^{\frac{-k\,(2n+1)^2\,\pi^2\,t}{4\,l^2}}$$

Applying condition (iv), we get

$$\frac{u_o \cdot x}{l} = \sum_{n=0}^{\infty} b_n \sin \frac{(2n+1)\,\pi x}{2l}$$

where
$$b_n = \frac{2}{l} \int_0^l \frac{u_o \cdot x}{l} \sin \frac{(2n+1)\,\pi x}{2l}\, dx$$

$$b_n = \frac{2u_o}{l^2} \left\{ (x)\left(-\frac{2l}{(2n+1)\pi} \cos \frac{(2n+1)\,\pi x}{2l}\right) - (1)\left(-\frac{4\,l^2}{(2n+1)^2\,\pi^2} \sin \frac{(2n+1)\,\pi x}{2l}\right) \right\}_0^l$$

$$= \frac{8\,u_o}{\pi^2}\,\frac{1}{(2n+1)^2}\,\sin\,(2n+1)\,\frac{\pi}{2}$$

$$= \frac{8\,u_o}{\pi^2}\,\frac{1}{(2n+1)^2}\,\sin\left(n\pi + \frac{\pi}{2}\right)$$

$$b_n = \frac{8\,u_o}{\pi^2}\,\frac{1}{(2n+1)^2}\cdot(-1)^n$$

$\therefore$ The complete solution is

$$u\,(x,\,t) = \frac{8\,u_o}{\pi^2} \sum_{n=0}^{\infty} \frac{(-1)^n}{(2n+1)^2}\,\sin \frac{(2n+1)\,\pi x}{2\,l}\cdot e^{\frac{-(2n+1)^2\,\pi^2\,k\,t}{4\,l^2}}$$

Ex. 6 : *A homogeneous rod of conducting material of length 100 cm has its ends kept at zero temperature and the temperature initially is*

$$u\,(x,\,0) = x \qquad , \qquad 0 \le x \le 50$$
$$= 100 - x\,, \qquad 50 \le x \le 100$$

Find the temperature u (x, t) at any time.   **(Dec. 2008, 2010, 2011, 2014)**

Sol. : We have to solve $\dfrac{\partial u}{\partial t} = c^2 \dfrac{\partial^2 u}{\partial x^2}$, subject to conditions

(i) $u\,(0,\,t) = 0$

(ii) $u\,(100,\,t) = 0$

(iii) $u\,(x,\,0) = x \qquad , \; 0 \le x \le 50$

$\qquad\qquad = 100 - x,\; 50 \le x \le 100$

(iv) $u\,(x,\,t)$ is finite $\forall\, t$

The most general solution is

$$u\,(x,\,t) = (c_4 \cos mx + c_5 \sin mx)\, e^{-c^2 m^2\, t}$$

Condition (i) $\Rightarrow$ $c_4 = 0$

$$u\,(x,\,t) = c_5 \sin mx\; e^{-c^2 m^2\, t} \qquad\qquad \ldots (1)$$

Condition (ii) $\Rightarrow$ $0 = c_5 \sin 100\, m\; e^{-c^2 m^2\, t}$

$$\sin (100 \, m) = 0 \quad \Rightarrow \quad 100 \, m = n\pi$$

$$m = \frac{n\pi}{100}, \quad n = 1, \, 2, \, 3, \, \ldots\ldots\ldots$$

Solution (1) becomes

$$u \, (x, \, t) = c_5 \, \sin \frac{n\pi x}{100} \, e^{-\frac{n^2 \pi^2 c^2 \, t}{1000,00}}, \quad n = 1, \, 2, \, \ldots\ldots\ldots\ldots$$

Combining all these solutions

$$u \, (x, \, t) = \sum_{n=1}^{\infty} \, b_n \, \sin \frac{n\pi x}{100} \, e^{-\frac{n^2 \pi^2 c^2 \, t}{100,00}} \qquad \ldots \, (2)$$

Applying condition (iii), we have

$$u \, (x, \, 0) = \sum_{n=1}^{\infty} \, b_n \, \sin \frac{n\pi x}{100}$$

and is half range sine series for $u \, (x, \, 0)$.

$$\therefore \quad b_n = \frac{2}{100} \int_0^{100} u \, (x, \, 0) \, \sin \frac{n\pi x}{100} \, dx$$

$$= \frac{1}{50} \left[\int_0^{50} u \, (x, \, 0) \, \sin \frac{n\pi x}{100} \, dx + \int_{50}^{100} u \, (x, \, 0) \, \sin \frac{n\pi x}{100} \, dx \right]$$

$$= \frac{1}{50} \left[\int_0^{50} x \, \sin \frac{n\pi x}{100} \, dx + \int_{50}^{100} (100 - x) \, \sin \frac{n\pi x}{100} \, dx \right]$$

$$= \frac{1}{50} \left[\left\{ (x) \times \left(\frac{-100}{n\pi} \cos \frac{n\pi x}{100} \right) - (1) \left(-\frac{100^2}{n^2 \, \pi^2} \sin \frac{n\pi x}{100} \right) \right\}_0^{50} \right.$$

$$\left. + \left\{ (100 - x) \left(-\frac{100}{n\pi} \cos \frac{n\pi x}{100} \right) - (-1) \left(\frac{-100^2}{n^2 \, \pi^2} \sin \frac{n\pi x}{100} \right) \right\}_{50}^{100} \right]$$

$$= \frac{1}{50} \left[-\frac{100}{n\pi} \left(50 \cos \frac{n\pi}{2} - 0 \right) + \frac{100^2}{n^2 \pi^2} \left(\sin \frac{n\pi}{2} - \sin 0 \right) - \frac{100}{n\pi} \left(0 - 50 \cos \frac{n\pi}{2} \right) \right.$$

$$\left. - \frac{100^2}{n^2 \pi^2} \left(\sin n\pi - \sin \frac{n\pi}{2} \right) \right]$$

$$\therefore \quad b_n = \frac{1}{50} \left(\frac{100^2}{n^2 \pi^2} \right) 2 \sin \frac{n\pi}{2} = \frac{400}{n^2 \pi^2} \, \sin \frac{n\pi}{2} = \begin{cases} 0, & \text{if } n \text{ is even} \\[2mm] (-1)^n \, \dfrac{400}{n^2 \pi^2}, & \text{if } n \text{ is is odd} \end{cases}$$

Replace $n \rightarrow 2n + 1$

$$\therefore \qquad b_n = (-1)^n \cdot \frac{400}{(2n+1)^2 \pi^2}$$

$\therefore$ Required solution is

$$u(x, t) = \sum_{n=0}^{\infty} \frac{(-1)^n \times 400}{(2n+1)^2 \pi^2} \sin \frac{(2n+1)\pi x}{100} \cdot e^{\frac{-(2n+1)^2 \pi^2 c^2 t}{100^2}}$$

Ex. 7 : *A bar with insulated sides is initially at temperature $0°C$ throughout. The end $x = 0$ is kept at $0°C$ for all time and the heat is suddenly applied so that $\dfrac{\partial u}{\partial x} = 10$ at $x = l$ for all time. Find the temperature function $u(x, t)$.*

Sol. : We have to solve the P.D.E.

$$\frac{\partial u}{\partial t} = a^2 \frac{\partial^2 u}{\partial x^2}$$

Let
$$u(x, t) = F(x) \cdot G(t)$$
$$FG' = a^2 \, F'' G$$
$$\frac{F''}{F} = \frac{G'}{a^2 G} = -m^2 \text{ (say)}$$

then the solution is

$$u(x, t) = (c_1 \cos mx + c_2 \sin mx) \, e^{-a^2 m^2 t} \qquad \qquad \dots \text{(I)}$$

Also,
$$\frac{F''}{F} = \frac{G'}{a^2 G} = 0$$

then the solution is

$$u(x, t) = c_6 + c_7 \cdot x \qquad \qquad \dots \text{(II)}$$

Conditions are

    (i) $u(x, 0) = 0$

    (ii) $u(0, t) = 0$

    (iii) $\left(\dfrac{\partial u}{\partial x}\right)_{x = l} = 10$, for all t.

Since the above conditions of the problem are such that any one of the above solutions (i.e. (I) and (II)) does not satisfy them. We use the combinations of the solutions to satisfy the given conditions i.e. sum of (I) and (II).

$$\therefore \qquad u(x, t) = c_6 + c_7 x + (c_1 \cos mx + c_2 \sin mx) \, e^{-m^2 a^2 t}$$

Now (ii) $\Rightarrow$ $c_6 = 0, \quad c_1 = 0$

$$u(x, t) = c_7 x + c_2 \sin mx \cdot e^{-m^2 a^2 t}$$

Now (iii) $\Rightarrow$ $\dfrac{\partial u}{\partial x} = c_7 + m c_2 \cos mx \ e^{-m^2 a^2 t}$

$$10 = c_7 + m c_2 \cos ml \ e^{-m^2 a^2 t}$$

$$\Rightarrow \quad c_7 = 10$$

$$\cos ml = 0 \qquad ml = \frac{(2n+1)\pi}{2}$$

$$u(x,t) = 10x + \sum_{n=0}^{\infty} c_{2n+1} \cdot \sin \frac{(2n+1)\pi x}{2l} \cdot e^{\frac{-a^2(2n+1)^2 \pi^2 t}{4l^2}}$$

Now (i) $\Rightarrow$ t = 0, u = 0

$$-10x = \sum_{n=0}^{\infty} c_{2n+1} \sin \frac{(2n+1)\pi x}{2l}$$

$$c_{2n+1} = \frac{2}{l} \int_0^l (-10x) \sin \frac{(2n+1)\pi x}{2l} \cdot dx$$

$$= -\frac{20}{l} \left[(x)\left(-\frac{2l}{(2n+1)\pi} \cos \frac{(2n+1)\pi x}{2l}\right) + \frac{4l^2}{(2n+1)^2 \pi^2} \sin \frac{(2n+1)\pi x}{2l} \right]_0^l$$

$$c_{2n+1} = -\frac{80\, l}{(2n+1)^2 \pi^2} \sin \frac{(2n+1)\pi}{2}$$

$\therefore$ The complete solution is

$$u(x,t) = 10x - \frac{80\, l}{\pi^2} \sum_{n=0}^{\infty} \frac{1}{(2n+1)^2} \sin \frac{(2n+1)\pi}{2} \cdot \sin \frac{(2n+1)\pi x}{2l}\; e^{\frac{-a^2(2n+1)^2 \pi^2 t}{4l^2}}$$

Ex. 8 : *A rod of length l has its ends A and B maintained at 20°C and 40°C respectively until steady-state conditions prevail. The temperature at A is suddenly raised to 50°C while that at B is lowered to 10°C and maintained thereafter. Find the subsequent temperature distribution of the rod.*

Sol. : Here initial conditions of temperature distribution are not explicitly given. We will first obtain the same. Initially steady-state conditions prevail, the temperature depends on x only, let it be $u_{s_1}(x) = Ax + B$.

$$x = 0, \;\; u_{s_1}(0) = 20°\,C, \;\; x = l, \;\; u_{s_1}(l) = 40°C, \;\; 20 = B, \;\; 40 = Al + 20, \;\; A = \frac{20}{l}$$

$$u_{s_1}(x) = \frac{20x}{l} + 20$$

Hence, we have to solve the P.D.E.

$$\frac{\partial u}{\partial t} = c^2 \frac{\partial^2 u}{\partial x^2}, \text{ subject to the boundary conditions}$$

(i)　$u(0,t) = 50°\,C$

(ii)　$u(l,t) = 10°\,C$ and initial condition

$$u(x,0) = u_{s_1}(x) = \frac{20x}{l} + 20$$

Since the boundary conditions are not zero, we cannot proceed directly.

Note that after certain time, the temperature distribution of the rod has to reach steady state which implies that the solution has two parts :

(i)   Steady state part and

(ii) Transient part which ultimately becomes zero.

We denote these as u_s (x) and u_t (x, t).

$\therefore \qquad u(x, t) = u_s(x) + u_t(x, t)$

where, u_s (x) satisfies the P.D.E. under steady-state conditions i.e.

$$u_s(x) = cx + d$$

where, $\quad u_s(0) = 50°C \quad$ and $\quad u_s(l) = 10°C$

$$50 = 0 + d \qquad \therefore d = 50$$

$$10 = lc + 50 \quad \therefore \quad c = -\frac{40}{l}$$

$\therefore \qquad u_s(x) = -\frac{40\,x}{l} + 50$

$\therefore \qquad u(x, t) = -\frac{40\,x}{l} + 50 + u_t(x, t).$

Our problem reduces to obtain u_t (x, t)

where $\qquad u_t(x, t) = u(x, t) + \frac{40\,x}{l} - 50$

Substituting u_t (x, t) in the P.D.E.

$$\frac{\partial u_t}{\partial t} = c^2 \frac{\partial^2 u_t}{\partial x^2}$$

For obtaining boundary and initial conditions

$$u_t(0, t) = u(0, t) + 0 - 50$$

$$= 50 - 50 \qquad\qquad\qquad (\because u(0, t) = 50)$$

$$\boxed{u_t(0, t) = 0}$$

$$u_t(l, t) = u(l, t) + 40 - 50$$

$$= 10 + 40 - 50 \qquad\qquad\qquad (\because u(l, t) = 10)$$

$$\boxed{u_t(l, t) = 0}$$

$$u_t(x, 0) = u(x, 0) + \frac{40\,x}{l} - 50$$

$$= \frac{20\,x}{l} + 20 + \frac{40\,x}{l} - 50$$

$$\boxed{u_t\,(x,\,0)\; =\; \frac{60\,x}{l}\; -\; 30}$$

Solution is $\quad u_t\,(x,\,t)\; =\; (c_1\,\cos\,mx + c_2\,\sin\,mx)\; e^{-c^2 m^2 t}$

$$u_t\,(0,\,t)\; =\; 0\;\Rightarrow\;\; c_1 = 0$$

$$u_t\,(x,\,t)\; =\; c_2\,\sin\,mx\;\, e^{-c^2 m^2 t}$$

$$u_t\,(l,\,t)\; =\;\, 0 \Rightarrow 0\; =\; c_2\,\sin\,ml\;\, e^{-c^2 m^2 t}$$

$$\sin\,ml\; =\; 0\;\;\Rightarrow\;\; m\; =\; \frac{n\pi}{l},\;\; n\; =\; 1,\, 2,\, \ldots\ldots\ldots$$

$$u_t\,(x,\,t)\; =\; \sum_{n=1}^{\infty}\; b_n\,\sin\,\frac{n\pi x}{l}\;\, e^{-\frac{c^2 n^2 \pi^2 t}{l^2}}$$

$$u_t\,(x,\,0)\; =\; \sum_{1}^{\infty}\; b_n\,\sin\,\frac{n\pi x}{l}$$

$$b_n\; =\; \frac{2}{l}\;\int_0^l\;\left(\frac{60\,x}{l}\; -\; 30\right)\,\sin\,\frac{n\pi x}{l}\;\, dx$$

$$=\; \frac{2}{l}\;\left\{\left(\frac{60\,x}{l} - 30\right)\left(-\frac{l}{n\pi}\,\cos\,\frac{n\pi x}{l}\right) - \left(\frac{60}{l}\right)\left(-\frac{l^2}{n^2\,\pi^2}\,\sin\,\frac{n\pi x}{l}\right)\right\}_0^l$$

$$=\; \frac{2}{l}\;\left\{-\frac{30\,l}{n\pi}\,(-1)^n\; -\frac{30\,l}{n\pi}\right\}$$

$$b_n\; =\; -\frac{60}{n\pi}\;[(-1)^n + 1]$$

$$u_t\,(x,\,t)\; =\; -\frac{60}{\pi}\;\sum_{1}^{\infty}\;\frac{(-1)^n + 1}{n}\,\sin\,\frac{n\pi x}{l}\;\, e^{-\frac{c^2 n^2 \pi^2 t}{l^2}}$$

$$u_t\,(x,\,t)\; =\; -\frac{60}{\pi}\;\times 2\cdot\;\sum_{1}^{\infty}\;\frac{1}{2n}\,\sin\,\frac{2n\pi x}{l}\;\, e^{-\frac{4\,c^2 n^2 \pi^2 t}{l^2}}$$

$$\therefore\qquad\boxed{u\,(x,\,t)\; =\; 50 - \frac{40\,x}{l}\; -\; \frac{60}{\pi}\,\sum_{1}^{\infty}\,\frac{1}{n}\,\sin\,\frac{2n\pi x}{l}\;\, e^{-\frac{4\,c^2 n^2 \pi^2 t}{l^2}}}$$

Ex. 9 : *Solve* $\dfrac{\partial u}{\partial t}\; =\; c^2\,\dfrac{\partial^2 u}{\partial x^2}\;\;$ *if*

(i)   *u is finite for all t*

(ii)   *u (0, t) = 0,* $\forall t$

(iii) $u(l, t) = 0$, $\forall t$

(iv) $u(x, 0) = u_0$ *for* $0 \leq x \leq l$, *where l being the length of the bar.*   **(May 2008)**

Sol. : (i) The most general solution is

$$u(x, t) = (c_4 \cos mx + c_5 \sin mx) \, e^{-m^2 c^2 t}$$

(ii) $\Rightarrow$ $c_4 = 0$

$$u(x, t) = c_5 \sin mx \, e^{-m^2 c^2 t}$$

(iii) $\Rightarrow$ $0 = c_5 \sin ml \, e^{-m^2 c^2 t}$

$$\sin(ml) = 0, \quad ml = n\pi$$

$$m = \frac{n\pi}{l}, \quad n = 1, 2, \ldots\ldots\ldots\ldots$$

$$u(x, t) = c_5 \sin \frac{n\pi x}{l} \, e^{-\frac{n^2 \pi^2 c^2 t}{l^2}}, \quad n = 1, 2, \ldots\ldots\ldots$$

Or $$u(x, t) = \sum_{n=1}^{\infty} b_n \sin \frac{n\pi x}{l} \, e^{-\frac{n^2 \pi^2 c^2 t}{l^2}} \qquad \ldots \text{(I)}$$

Applying condition (iv),

$$u_0 = \sum_{n=1}^{\infty} b_n \sin \frac{n\pi x}{l}$$

$$b_n = \frac{2}{l} \int_0^l u_0 \sin \frac{n\pi x}{l} \, dx = \frac{2u_0}{l} \left(-\frac{l}{n\pi} \cos \frac{n\pi x}{l} \right)_0^l$$

$$b_n = \frac{2u_0}{\pi} \left(\frac{1 - (-1)^n}{n} \right)$$

$$u(x, t) = \frac{2u_0}{\pi} \sum_{n=1}^{\infty} \left(\frac{1 - (-1)^n}{n} \right) \sin \frac{n\pi x}{l} \, e^{-\frac{n^2 \pi^2 c^2 t}{l^2}}$$

Ex. 10 : *Solve the equation* $\dfrac{\partial u}{\partial t} = a^2 \dfrac{\partial^2 u}{\partial x^2}$ *where* $u(x, t)$ *satisfies the following conditions :*   **(May 2014, Nov. 2015, May 2017)**

(i) $u(0, t) = 0$

(ii) $u(l, t) = 0$ *for all t*

(iii) $u(x, 0) = x$ *in* $0 < x < l$

(iv) $u(x, \infty)$ *is finite.*

Sol. : The most general solution is

$$u(x, t) = (c_4 \cos mx + c_5 \sin mx) \, e^{-a^2 m^2 t}$$

(i) $\Rightarrow$ $c_4 = 0$

$$u(x, t) = c_5 \sin mx \; e^{-a^2 m^2 t}$$

(ii) $\Rightarrow$
$$0 = c_5 \sin ml \; e^{-a^2 m^2 t}$$

$$\sin ml = 0, \qquad ml = n\pi$$

$$m = \frac{n\pi}{l}, \; n = 1, 2, 3, \ldots\ldots$$

$$u(x, t) = c_5 \sin \frac{n\pi x}{l} \; e^{-\frac{a^2 n^2 \pi^2 t}{l^2}}, \; n = 1, 2, \ldots\ldots$$

Combining all these solutions, we get

$$u(x, t) = \sum_{n=1}^{\infty} b_n \sin \frac{n\pi x}{l} \; e^{-\frac{a^2 n^2 \pi^2 t}{l^2}}$$

(iii) $\Rightarrow$
$$x = \sum_{n=1}^{\infty} b_n \sin \frac{n\pi x}{l}, \; 0 < x < l$$

which is nothing but half range sine series for $f(x) = x$ in $(0, l)$.

$\therefore$
$$b_n = \frac{2}{l} \int_0^l x \sin \frac{n\pi x}{l} \, dx$$

$$= \frac{2}{l} \left\{ (x) \left(-\frac{l}{n\pi} \cos \frac{n\pi x}{l} \right) - (1) \left(-\frac{l^2}{n^2\pi^2} \sin \frac{n\pi x}{l} \right) \right\}_0^l$$

$$= \frac{2}{l} \left\{ -\frac{l^2}{n\pi} (-1)^n \right\} = -\frac{2l}{\pi} \left(\frac{(-1)^n}{n} \right)$$

$\therefore$
$$u(x, t) = \frac{2l}{\pi} \sum_{n=1}^{\infty} \frac{(-1)^{n+1}}{n} \sin \frac{n\pi x}{l} \; e^{-\frac{a^2 n^2 \pi^2 t}{l^2}}$$

Ex. 11 : *The temperature at any point of the insulated metal rod of one metre length is governed by the differential equation* $\dfrac{\partial u}{\partial t} = c^2 \dfrac{\partial^2 u}{\partial x^2}$. *Find u(x, t), subject to the following conditions :*   **(May 2015)**

(i) $\quad u(0, t) = 0\,°C$

(ii) $\quad u(l, t) = 0\,°C$

(iii) $\quad u(x, 0) = 50\,°C$ *and hence find the temperature in the middle of the rod at any subsequent time.*

Sol. : The most general solution is

$$u(x, t) = (c_4 \cos mx + c_5 \sin mx) \; e^{-c^2 m^2 t}$$

(i) $\Rightarrow$
$$c_4 = 0$$

$$u\,(x,\,t) = c_5 \,\sin mx \; e^{-\,c^2 m^2 t}$$

(ii) $\Rightarrow$ $0 = c_5 \,\sin m \; e^{-\,c^2 m^2 t}$

$$\sin m = 0 \qquad \therefore \; m = n\pi, \quad n = 1,\,2,\,\ldots\ldots\ldots\ldots$$

$$\therefore \qquad u\,(x,\,t) = c_5 \,\sin n\pi x \; e^{-\,c^2 n^2 \pi^2 t}, \quad n = 1,\,2,\,\ldots\ldots\ldots\ldots$$

Combining all these solutions, we get

$$u\,(x,\,t) = \sum_{n=1}^{\infty} b_n \,\sin n\pi x \; e^{-\,c^2 n^2 \pi^2 t}$$

Applying condition (iii), we get

$$50 = \sum_{n=1}^{\infty} b_n \sin n\pi x, \; 0 < x < 1$$

which is represented by half range Fourier sine series for $f\,(x) = 50$ in $(0,\,1)$

$$\therefore \qquad b_n = 2 \int_0^1 50 \,\sin n\pi x \; dx$$

$$= 100 \left[-\frac{\cos n\pi x}{n\pi} \right]_0^1 \; = \; \frac{100}{\pi} \left(\frac{1 - (-1)^n}{n} \right)$$

$$\therefore \qquad u\,(x,\,t) = \frac{100}{\pi} \sum_{n=1}^{\infty} \frac{1 - (-1)^n}{n} \,\sin n\pi x \; e^{-\,c^2 n^2 \pi^2 t}$$

Now the temperature in the middle of the rod at any subsequent time is

$$u\left(\frac{1}{2},\,0 \right) = \frac{100}{\pi} \sum_{n=1}^{\infty} \frac{1 - (-n)^n}{n} \,\sin \frac{n\pi}{2}$$

$$= 0, \qquad \text{if } n \text{ is even}$$

$$= \frac{200}{\pi} \sum_{n=1}^{\infty} \frac{(-1)^n}{n}, \; \text{if } n \text{ is odd.}$$

EXERCISE 13.2

Solve the one-dimensional heat flow equation $\dfrac{\partial u}{\partial t} = a^2 \dfrac{\partial^2 u}{\partial x^2}$ for function $u(x,\,t)$, subject to following conditions :   **(Nov. 2015)**

1. (i) $u(0, t) = 0$,   (ii) $u(l, t) = 0$, for all t

(iii) $u(x, 0) = x$, $0 < x < l$ (iv) $u(x, \infty)$ is finite.

Hint : $b_n = \dfrac{2l}{n\pi}(-1)^{n-1}$

$$\textbf{Ans. :} \quad u(x, t) = \frac{2l}{\pi} \sum_{n=1}^{\infty} \frac{(-1)^{n-1}}{n} e^{-\frac{n^2 a^2 \pi^2 t}{l^2}} \sin \frac{n\pi x}{l}$$

2. (i) $u(0, t) = 0$,   (ii) $\dfrac{\partial}{\partial x} u(l, t) = 0$, for all t

(iii) $u(x, 0) = x$ (iv) $u(x, \infty)$ is finite

$$\textbf{Ans. :} \quad u(x, t) = \frac{8l}{\pi^2} \sum_{n=1}^{\infty} \frac{(-1)^n}{(2n+1)^2} \sin \frac{(2n+1)\pi x}{2l} e^{-\frac{a^2 (2n+1)^2 \pi^2 t}{4l^2}}$$

3. (i) $u(0, t) = 0$,   (ii) $u(\pi, t) = 0$, for all t

(iii) $u(x, 0) = \pi x - x^2$, $0 < x < \pi$ (iv) $u(x, \infty)$ is finite.

$$\textbf{Ans. :} \quad u(x, t) = \frac{8}{\pi} \sum_{n=1}^{\infty} \frac{\sin(2n-1)x}{(2n-1)^3} e^{-a^2(2n-1)^2 t}$$

4. (i) $\dfrac{\partial}{\partial x} u(0, t) = 0$, and   (ii) $\dfrac{\partial}{\partial x} (l, t) = 0$, for all t

(iii) $u(x, 0) = x^2$, $0 < x < l$ (iv) $u(x, \infty)$ is finite.

$$\textbf{Ans. :} \quad u(x, t) = \frac{l^2}{3} + \frac{4 l^2}{\pi^2} \sum_{n=1}^{\infty} \frac{(-1)^n}{n^2} \cos \frac{n\pi x}{l} e^{-\frac{n^2 a^2 \pi^2 t}{l^2}}$$

5. Solve $\dfrac{\partial u}{\partial t} = \dfrac{\partial^2 u}{\partial x^2}$ if

(i) u is finite, $\forall\, t$ (ii) $u(0, t) = 0$

(iii) $u(\pi, t) = 0$ (iv) $u(x, 0) = \pi x - x^2$, $0 \le x \le \pi$

$$\textbf{Ans. :} \quad u(x, t) = \frac{8}{\pi} \sum_{n=0}^{\infty} \frac{1}{(2n+1)^3} \sin(2n+1)x \; e^{-(2n+1)^2 t}$$

6. Solve $\dfrac{\partial u}{\partial t} = k \dfrac{\partial^2 u}{\partial x^2}$ if

(i) $u(x, t)$ is bounded   (ii) $u(0, t) = 0$

(iii) $u(l, t) = 0$ (iv) $u(x, 0) = \dfrac{u_o\, x}{l}$, $0 \le x \le l$

$$\textbf{Ans. :} \quad u\,(x,\,t) \;=\; \frac{2\,u_o}{\pi} \sum_{n=1}^{\infty} \frac{(-1)^{n+1}}{n}\ \sin\frac{n\pi x}{l}\ e^{-\frac{k\,n^2\,\pi^2\,t}{l^2}}$$

7. The equation for the conduction of heat along a bar of length l is $\dfrac{\partial\theta}{\partial t} = k\,\dfrac{\partial^2\theta}{\partial t^2}$, neglecting radiation. Find an expression for θ if the ends of the bar are maintained at zero temperature and if initially the temperature is T at the centre of the bar and falls uniformly to zero at its ends.

$$\textbf{Hint :}\ \text{(i) }\theta\,(0,\,t)=0,\ \text{(ii) }\theta=(l,\,0)=0,\ \text{(iii) }\theta\,(x,\,0)=\begin{cases}\dfrac{2T}{l}\,x, & 0\le x\le l/2\\[2mm]\dfrac{2T}{l}\,(-x), & l/2\le x\le l\end{cases}$$

$$\textbf{Ans. :}\ \theta\,(x,\,t)\;=\;\frac{8T}{\pi^2}\sum_{1}^{\infty}\frac{1}{n^2}\ \sin\frac{n\pi}{2}\ \sin\frac{n\pi x}{l}\ e^{-\frac{k\,n^2\,\pi^2\,t}{l^2}}$$

8. Solve $\dfrac{\partial u}{\partial t} = c^2\,\dfrac{\partial^2 u}{\partial x^2}$, subject to the following boundary conditions :

(i) $u\,(0,\,t)=0,$ (ii) $u\,(l,\,t)=0,$ (iii) $u\,(x,\,0)=\begin{cases}x, & 0<x\le l/2\\ l-x, & l/2\le x<l\end{cases}$ **(Nov. 16)**

$$\textbf{Ans. :}\quad u\,(x,\,t)\;=\;\frac{4\,l}{\pi^2}\sum_{n=1}^{\infty}\frac{(-1)^n}{(2n-1)^2}\ \sin\frac{(2n-1)\,\pi x}{l}\ e^{-\frac{(2n-1)^2\,\pi^2\,c^2\,t}{l^2}}$$

9. The temperatures at the ends $x = 0$ and $x = 50$ cm in length of a rod are held at 0°C and 50°C respectively until steady-state conditions prevail. The two ends of the rod are suddenly insulated. Find the temperature distribution of the rod assuming that the surface of the rod is impervious to heat.

$$\textbf{Ans. :}\ u\,(x,\,t)\;=\;25\;-\;\frac{200}{\pi^2}\sum_{n=1}^{\infty}\frac{1}{(2n-1)^2}\ \cos\frac{(2n-1)\,\pi x}{50}\ e^{-\frac{(2n-1)^2\,a^2\,\pi^2\,t}{2500}}$$

10. A rod of length l is insulated along its length so that no heat is transformed from its sides, the uniform temperature of the rod is $50°$ C. Suddenly the end $x = 0$ is cooled to $0°$ C and the end $x = l$ heated to $100°$ C and these are maintained afterwards. Find the subsequent temperature distribution of the rod.

$$\textbf{Ans. :}\ u\,(x,\,t)\;=\;\frac{100\,x}{l}\;+\;\frac{100}{\pi}\sum_{n=1}^{\infty}\frac{1}{n}\ \sin\frac{2n\pi x}{l}\ e^{-\frac{4\,n^2\,a^2\,\pi^2\,t}{l^2}}$$

11. A rod of length l has its ends A and B kept at $0°$ C and $75°$ C, until steady-state conditions prevail. If the temperature of A is suddenly raised to $75°$ C and that of B to $175°C$ and maintained thereafter, find the subsequent temperature distribution of the rod.

$$\textbf{Ans. :}\ u(x, t) = 75 + \frac{100\, x}{l} - \frac{300}{\pi} \sum_{n=1}^{\infty} \frac{1}{(2n-1)} \sin \frac{(2n-1)\, \pi x}{l}\ e^{\frac{-(2n-1)^2\, a^2 \pi^2 t}{l^2}}$$

12. A rod of length l has one end kept at $0°$ C and other end B at $100°$ C until steady-state conditions prevail. The temperature of A is suddenly raised to $50°$ C while the end B is insulated. These conditions are maintained thereafter, find the subsequent temperature distribution of the rod.

$$\textbf{Ans. :}\ u(x, t) = 50 + \sum_{n=1}^{\infty} \left[\frac{(-1)^{n-1}\, 800}{(2n-1)^2\, \pi^2} - \frac{200}{(2n-1)\, \pi} \right] \sin \frac{(2n-1)\, \pi x}{2l}\ e^{\frac{-(2n-1)^2\, a^2 \pi^2 t}{4l^2}}$$

13. A rod of length l has its ends A and B maintained at $20°C$ and $40°C$ respectively until steady-state conditions prevail. The temperature at A is suddenly raised to $50°C$ while that at B is lowered to $10°C$ and maintained thereafter. Find the subsequent temperature distribution of the rod.

$$\textbf{Ans. :}\ u\,(x, y) = 50 - \frac{40}{l}\, x - \frac{60}{\pi} \sum_{n=1}^{\infty} \frac{1}{n} \sin \frac{2n\pi x}{l}\ e^{-\frac{4n^2 a^2 \pi^2 t}{l^2}}$$

14. A uniform rod of length l whose surface is thermally insulated, is initially at temperature θ_0. At time $t = 0$, one end is suddenly cooled to temperature $0°C$ and subsequently maintained at this temperature and at the same time, the other end is thermally insulated. Find the temperature at end $x = l$ at any time t.

15. The ends A and B of a insulated rod of length l, have their temperatures at $20°C$ and $80°C$ respectively until steady-state conditions prevail. The temperatures at these ends are changed suddenly to $40°C$ and $60°C$ respectively. Find the temperature distribution of the rod at time t.

$$\textbf{Ans. :}\ u\,(x, t) = \frac{20\, x}{l} + 40 - \frac{40}{\pi} \sum_{1}^{\infty} \frac{1}{n} \sin \frac{2n\pi x}{l}\ e^{-\frac{4c^2 n^2 \pi^2 t}{l^2}}.$$

13.7 MODELING OF TWO-DIMENSIONAL HEAT FLOW

Consider the flow of heat in a metal plate in XOY plane. If the temperature at a point does not depend upon z-coordinate and it depends only on x, y, and t, then the flow is called two-dimensional and the heat flow lies in XOY plane only and is zero along the normal to XOY plane.

Consider a rectangular element of the plate with sides δx and δy and thickness 'h'. As discussed in one-dimensional heat flow along a bar, the quantity of heat that enters the plate per second from the sides AB and AD is given by $- kh\,\delta x\,\left(\dfrac{\partial u}{\partial y}\right)_y$ and $- kh\,\delta y\,\left(\dfrac{\partial u}{\partial x}\right)_x$ respectively.

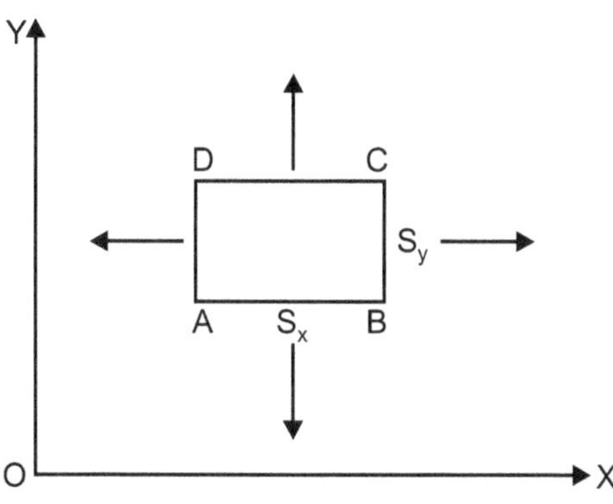

Fig. 13.5

Heat flowing out through sides CD and BC per second is $-kh\,\delta x\,\left(\dfrac{\partial u}{\partial y}\right)_{y+\delta y}$ and $-kh\,\delta y\,\left(\dfrac{\partial u}{\partial x}\right)_{x+\delta x}$ respectively. Therefore, the total gain of heat by rectangular plate ABCD per second

$$= - kh\,\delta x\,\left(\frac{\partial u}{\partial y}\right)_y - kh\,\delta y\,\left(\frac{\partial u}{\partial x}\right)_x + kh\,\delta x\,\left(\frac{\partial u}{\partial y}\right)_{y+\delta y} + kh\,\delta y\,\left(\frac{\partial u}{\partial x}\right)_{x+\delta x}$$

$$= kh\,\delta x\,\delta y\left[\frac{\left(\dfrac{\partial u}{\partial x}\right)_{x+\delta x} - \left(\dfrac{\partial u}{\partial x}\right)_x}{\delta x} + \frac{\left(\dfrac{\partial u}{\partial y}\right)_{y+\delta y} - \left(\dfrac{\partial u}{\partial y}\right)_y}{\delta y}\right] \qquad \ldots (1)$$

The rate of gain of heat by the plate is also given by,

$$S\,\rho h\,\delta x\,\delta y\,\frac{\partial u}{\partial t} \qquad \ldots (2)$$

where, S = specific heat and ρ = density of the metal plate

$\therefore$ Equating equations (1) and (2), we get

$$kh\,\delta x\,\delta y\,.\,\left[\frac{\left(\dfrac{\partial u}{\partial x}\right)_{x+\delta x} - \left(\dfrac{\partial u}{\partial x}\right)_x}{\delta x} + \frac{\left(\dfrac{\partial u}{\partial y}\right)_{y+\delta y} - \left(\dfrac{\partial u}{\partial y}\right)_y}{\delta y}\right] = S\,\rho h\,\delta x\,\delta y\,\frac{\partial u}{\partial t}$$

Dividing by $h\,\delta x\,\delta y$ and taking limit as $\delta x \to 0,\ \delta y \to 0$, we get

$$k\left(\frac{\partial^2 u}{\partial x^2} + \frac{\partial^2 u}{\partial y^2}\right) = S\,\rho\,\frac{\partial u}{\partial t}$$

$$\therefore \qquad \frac{\partial u}{\partial t} = \frac{k}{S\rho}\left(\frac{\partial^2 u}{\partial x^2} + \frac{\partial^2 u}{\partial y^2}\right)$$

Or
$$\frac{\partial u}{\partial t} = c^2 \left(\frac{\partial^2 u}{\partial x^2} + \frac{\partial^2 u}{\partial y^2} \right) \qquad \ldots (3)$$

where
$$\frac{k}{S\rho} = c^2 \text{ is the diffusivity}$$

Equation (3) represents temperature distribution of the plate in the transient state. For steady state when u is independent of t,

$$\frac{\partial u}{\partial t} = 0$$

$\therefore$ Equation (3) reduces to
$$\boxed{\frac{\partial^2 u}{\partial x^2} + \frac{\partial^2 u}{\partial y^2} = 0} \qquad \ldots (4)$$

and is called Laplace's equation in two-dimensions. Equations (3) and (4) can be extended to three-dimensional solids as,

$$\frac{\partial u}{\partial t} = c^2 \left(\frac{\partial^2 u}{\partial x^2} + \frac{\partial^2 u}{\partial y^2} + \frac{\partial^2 u}{\partial z^2} \right) \text{ and } \frac{\partial^2 u}{\partial x^2} + \frac{\partial^2 u}{\partial y^2} + \frac{\partial u^2}{\partial z^2} = 0$$

in a similar way and is called Laplace's equation in three-dimensions.

13.8 SOLUTION OF LAPLACE'S EQUATION IN TWO-DIMENSIONS BY THE METHOD OF SEPARATION OF VARIABLES

Laplace's equation in two-dimensions is $\dfrac{\partial^2 u}{\partial x^2} + \dfrac{\partial^2 u}{\partial y^2} = 0$ $\qquad \ldots (1)$

Let $u = XY$ $\qquad \ldots (2)$

where, X is a function of x alone and Y is a function of y alone, be a solution of equation (1).

Then,
$$\frac{\partial^2 u}{\partial x^2} = X'' Y \quad \text{and} \quad \frac{\partial^2 u}{\partial y^2} = XY''$$

Substituting these values in equation (1), we get
$$X''Y + XY'' = 0$$
$$\therefore \quad \frac{X''}{X} = \frac{-Y''}{Y} \qquad \ldots (3)$$

As L.H.S. is being a function of 'x' alone and R.H.S. being a function of 'y' alone and x and y being independent variables, equation (3) will hold good only if both sides reduce to a constant, say 'k'.

$\therefore$ Equation (3) leads to,
$$\frac{X''}{X} = k \text{ and } \frac{-Y''}{Y} = k$$

Or $X'' - kX = 0$ and $Y'' + kY = 0$

$\therefore$ $(D^2 - k) X = 0$ and $(D^2 + k) Y = 0$ $\qquad \ldots (4)$

Case (i) : Let $k = 0$

$$D^2 X = 0 \implies X = c_1 x + c_2$$

$$D^2 Y = 0 \implies Y = c_3\, y + c_4$$

$\therefore$ Complete solution is

$$\boxed{u\,(x,\,y)\ =\ (c_1\,x + c_2)\ (c_3\,y + c_4)} \qquad \ldots (5)$$

Case (ii) : Let $k > 0$ i.e. $k = m^2$.

From equation (4),

$$(D^2 - m^2)\,X = 0 \implies X = c_1\,e^{mx} + c_2\,e^{-mx}$$

$$(D^2 + m^2)\,Y = 0 \implies Y = c_3\cos my + c_4\sin my$$

$\therefore$ Complete solution is

$$\boxed{u\,(x,\,y)\ =\ (c_1\,e^{mx} + c_2\,e^{-mx})\,(c_3\cos my + c_4\sin my)} \qquad \ldots (6)$$

Case (iii) : Let $k < 0$, i.e. $k = -m^2$.

From equation (4),

$$(D^2 + m^2)\,X = 0 \implies X = c_1\cos mx + c_2\sin mx$$

$$(D^2 - m^2)\,Y = 0 \implies Y = c_3\,e^{my} + c_4\,e^{-my}$$

$\therefore$ Complete solution is

$$\boxed{u\,(x,\,y)\ =\ (c_1\cos mx + c_2\sin mx)\,(c_3\,e^{my} + c_4\,e^{-my})} \qquad \ldots (7)$$

The most benefitting solution will be the one, consistent with the physical nature and the boundary conditions of the problem.

Note : To select the appropriate "most general solution", we will adopt the following procedure :

1. If in a physical problem, the plate subjected to steady temperature extends to infinity in the positive y-direction, we should take the constant $k = -m^2$ to represent each side of equation (3) i.e. if the condition given in a physical problem is $u = 0$ for $y = \infty$ for $\forall\ x$ between $(0,\ l)$ say or $u\,(x,\,\infty) = 0$, $\forall\ x$ in $(0,\ l)$, we always select the most suitable general solution of this nature as

$$\boxed{u\,(x,\,y)\ =\ (c_1\cos mx + c_2\sin mx)\,(c_3\,e^{my} + c_4\,e^{-my})}$$

2. If in a physical problem, the plate subjected to steady temperature extends to infinity in the positive x-direction, we should take the constant $k = m^2$ to represent each side of equation (3) i.e. if the condition given in a physical problem is $u = 0$ for $x = \infty$ for $\forall\ y$ between $(0,\ l)$ (say) or $u\,(\infty,\,y) = 0$, $\forall\ y$ in $(0,\ l)$, we always select the most suitable general solution of this nature as

$$\boxed{u\,(x,\,y)\ =\ (c_1\,e^{mx} + c_2\,e^{-mx})\,(c_3\cos my + c_4\sin my)}$$

3. The constant $k = 0$ is ruled out in physical applications.
4. When the constant $k = m^2$, the solution (6) can be written as

$$\boxed{u\,(x, y)\ =\ (c_1 \cosh mx + c_2 \sinh mx)\,(c_3 \cos my + c_4 \sin my)}$$

5. When the constant $k = -m^2$, the solution (7) can be written as

$$\boxed{u\,(x, y) = (c_1 \cos mx + c_2 \sin mx)\,(c_3 \cosh my + c_4 \sinh my)}$$

ILLUSTRATIONS

Ex. 1 : *Solve the equation* $\dfrac{\partial^2 V}{\partial x^2} + \dfrac{\partial^2 V}{\partial y^2} = 0$ *with conditions*

(i) $V = 0$ *when* $y \to +\infty$ *for all x.*
(ii) $V = 0$ *when* $x = 0$ *for all values of y.*
(iii) $V = 0$ *when* $x = 1$ *for all values of y*
(iv) $V = x\,(1 - x)$ *when* $y = 0$ *for* $0 < x < 1.$ **(May 2006, 2009, 2016; Dec. 2011)**

Sol. : Here in condition (i), $V = 0$ when $y \to \infty$, $\forall\, x$ is given, therefore we will select the most suitable solution as

$$V\,(x, y)\ =\ (c_1 \cos mx + c_2 \sin mx)\,(c_3\, e^{my} + c_4\, e^{-my})$$

Now condition (i) $\Rightarrow$ that $V\,(x, y)$ must remain finite as $y \to \infty$, this is possible only if $\boxed{c_3 = 0}$.

Also applying condition (ii), we must have $\boxed{c_1 = 0}$.

$\therefore$ The most general solution becomes

$$V\,(x, y)\ =\ c_5 . \sin mx . e^{-my}$$

Condition (iii) $\Rightarrow$ $0 = c_5 \sin m\, e^{-my}$, since $c_5 \neq 0$, otherwise $V\,(x, y) = 0$ will become the trivial solution and also, $e^{-my} \neq 0$.

$\therefore$ $\sin m = 0$, $m = n\pi$, $n = 1, 2, 3, \ldots\ldots$
and $V(x, y) = c_5 \sin n\pi x\ e^{-n\pi y}$, $n = 1, 2, \ldots\ldots\ldots$

Combining all these solutions, we get

$$V\,(x, y)\ =\ \sum_{n=1}^{\infty} b_n \sin n\pi x\ e^{-n\pi y}$$

Applying condition (iv), we have

$$x\,(1 - x)\ =\ \sum_{n=1}^{\infty} b_n \sin n\pi x,\ 0 < x < 1$$

which is represented by half range Fourier sine series for $f\,(x) = x\,(1 - x)$ in $(0, 1)$.

$$\therefore\qquad b_n\ =\ 2 \int_0^1 x\,(1 - x) \sin n\pi x\ dx$$

$$= 2\left\{(x - x^2)\left(-\frac{\cos n\pi x}{n\pi}\right) - (1 - 2x)\left(-\frac{\sin n\pi x}{n^2\,\pi^2}\right) + (-2)\left(\frac{\cos n\pi x}{n^3\,\pi^3}\right)\right\}_0^1$$

$$b_n = \frac{4}{\pi^3}\left(\frac{1 - (-1)^n}{n^3}\right)$$

$\therefore$ The complete solution is

$$\boxed{\;V\,(x,\,y) = \frac{4}{\pi^3}\sum_{n=1}^{\infty}\left(\frac{1 - (-1)^n}{n^3}\right)\sin n\pi x \cdot e^{-n\pi y}\;}$$

Ex. 2 : *An infinitely long uniform metal plate is enclosed between lines $y = 0$ and $y = l$ for $x > 0$. The temperature is zero along the edges $y = 0$, $y = l$ and at infinity. If the edge $x = 0$ is kept at a constant temperature u_o, find the temperature distribution $u\,(x,\,y)$.*

(Nov. 2013, Dec. 2014, May 2017)

Sol. : We have to solve the P.D.E.

$$\frac{\partial^2 u}{\partial x^2} + \frac{\partial^2 u}{\partial y^2} = 0$$

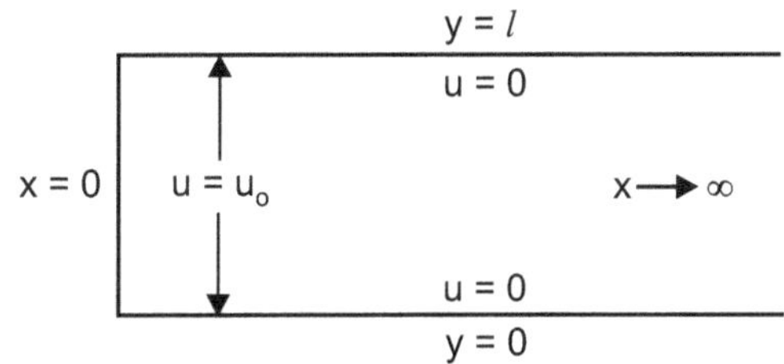

Fig. 13.6

Subject to the boundary conditions :

(i) $u\,(x,\,0) = 0,$ (ii) $u\,(x,\,l) = 0$

(iii) $u\,(\infty,\,y) = 0$ (iv) $u\,(0,\,y) = u_o$

In condition (iii), $u = 0$ when $x \to \infty$ is given; therefore we will select the most general suitable solution as

$$u\,(x,\,y) = (c_1\,e^{mx} + c_2\,e^{-mx})(c_3\cos my + c_4\sin my)$$

Now condition (iii) $\Rightarrow$ $u\,(x,\,y)$ must remain finite as $x \to \infty$, this is possible only if $\boxed{c_1 = 0}$.

Condition (i) $\Rightarrow$ $\boxed{c_3 = 0}$

$\therefore$ $u\,(x,\,y) = c_5\sin my\; e^{-mx}$

Condition (ii) $\Rightarrow$ $0 = c_5\sin ml\; e^{-mx}$

   $c_5 \neq 0$, $e^{-mx} \neq 0,$ $\therefore$ $\sin ml = 0$

$$ml = n\pi \qquad \therefore\; m = \frac{n\pi}{l},\; n = 1,\,2,\,3,\,\ldots\ldots\ldots\ldots$$

$$u(x, y) = c_5 \, \sin \frac{n\pi y}{l} \, e^{-\frac{n\pi x}{l}}, \quad n = 1, 2, \ldots\ldots$$

Combining all these solutions, we have

$$u(x, y) = \sum_{n=1}^{\infty} b_n \, \sin \frac{n\pi y}{l} \, e^{-\frac{n\pi x}{l}}$$

Applying condition (iv), we have

$$u_o = \sum_{n=1}^{\infty} b_n \, \sin \frac{n\pi y}{l}, \quad 0 < y < l$$

which is represented by half range Fourier sine series for $f(y) = u_o$ in $(0, l)$.

$$\therefore \qquad b_n = \frac{2}{l} \int_0^l u_o \, \sin \frac{n\pi y}{l} \, dy = \frac{2 u_o}{l} \left[-\frac{l}{n\pi} \cos \frac{n\pi y}{l} \right]_0^l$$

$$b_n = \frac{2 u_o}{\pi} \left(\frac{1 - (-1)^n}{n} \right)$$

$\therefore$ The complete solution is

$$u(x, y) = \frac{2 u_o}{\pi} \sum_{n=1}^{\infty} \frac{1 - (-1)^n}{n} \, \sin \frac{n\pi y}{l} \, e^{-\frac{n\pi x}{l}}$$

$$u(x, y) = \frac{4 u_o}{\pi} \sum_{n=1}^{\infty} \left(\frac{1}{2n - 1} \right) \, \sin \left(\frac{(2n - 1)\pi y}{l} \right) \cdot e^{\frac{-(2n - 1)\pi x}{l}}$$

Ex. 3 : *A rectangular plate is bounded by $x = 0$, $x = a$, $y = 0$, $y = b$. Its surfaces are insulated and temperature along three edges $x = 0$, $x = a$, $y = 0$ is maintained at $0°C$ while the fourth edge $y = b$ is maintained at constant temperature u_o, until steady state is reached. Find $u(x, y)$.* **(May 2015)**

Sol. : We have to solve the P.D.E. $\dfrac{\partial^2 u}{\partial x^2} + \dfrac{\partial^2 u}{\partial y^2} = 0$, subject to the boundary conditions :

(i) $u(0, y) = 0$

(ii) $u(x, 0) = 0$

(iii) $u(a, y) = 0$

(iv) $u(x, b) = u_o$

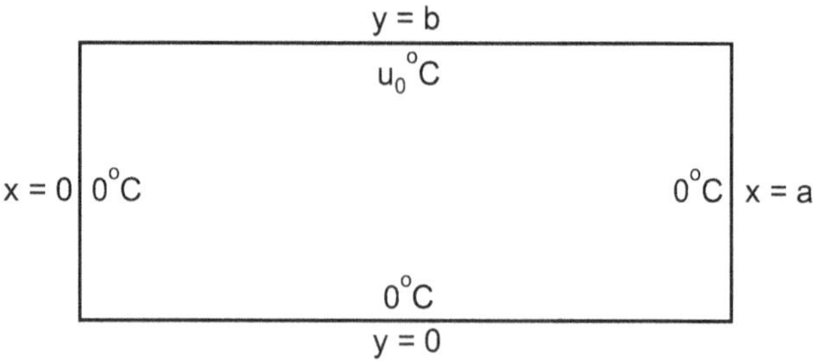

Fig. 13.7

If we consider $u(x, y) = (c_1 \cosh mx + c_2 \sinh mx)(c_3 \cos my + c_4 \sin my)$ then by applying (i), $c_1 = 0$, but then $u(a, y)$ cannot become zero because sinh am cannot be zero, for any non-zero value of m. Hence the possible solution may be given by

$$u(x, y) = (c_1 \cos mx + c_2 \sin mx)(c_3 \cosh my + c_4 \sinh my)$$

(i) $\Rightarrow$ $\qquad c_1 = 0$

(ii) $\Rightarrow$ $\qquad c_3 = 0$

$\therefore$ $\qquad u(x, y) = c_5 \sin mx \sinh my$

(iii) $\Rightarrow$ $\qquad 0 = c_5 \sin ma \sinh my$

$$c_5 \neq 0, \quad \sinh my \neq 0 \quad \therefore \sin ma = 0$$

$$ma = n\pi, \quad m = \frac{n\pi}{a}, \, n = 1, 2, \ldots\ldots\ldots\ldots$$

$\therefore$ $\qquad u(x, y) = c_5 \sin \dfrac{n\pi x}{a} \sinh \dfrac{n\pi y}{a}, \, n = 1, 2, \ldots\ldots\ldots$

Or $\qquad u(x, y) = \displaystyle\sum_{n=1}^{\infty} b_n \sin \dfrac{n\pi x}{a} \sinh \dfrac{n\pi y}{a}$

Applying condition (iv), we get

$$u_o = \sum_{n=1}^{\infty} b_n \sin \frac{n\pi x}{a} \sinh \frac{n\pi b}{a}$$

$\therefore$ $\qquad b_n \sinh \dfrac{n\pi b}{a} = \dfrac{2}{a} \displaystyle\int_0^a u_o \sin \dfrac{n\pi x}{a} \, dx$

$$= \frac{2 u_o}{a} \left[-\frac{a}{n\pi} \cos \frac{n\pi x}{a} \right]_0^a = \frac{2 u_o}{\pi} \left(\frac{1 - (-1)^n}{n} \right)$$

$$b_n = \frac{2 u_o}{\pi \sinh \dfrac{n\pi b}{a}} \left(\frac{1 - (-1)^n}{n} \right)$$

$\therefore$ $\qquad u(x, y) = \dfrac{2 u_o}{\pi} \displaystyle\sum_{n=1}^{\infty} \dfrac{1 - (-1)^n}{n} \cdot \sin \dfrac{n\pi x}{a} \cdot \dfrac{\sinh \dfrac{n\pi y}{a}}{\sinh \dfrac{n\pi b}{a}}$

$$u(x, y) = \frac{4 u_o}{\pi} \sum_{n=1}^{\infty} \frac{1}{2n-1} \cdot \sin \frac{(2n-1)\pi x}{a} \cdot \frac{\sinh \dfrac{(2n-1)\pi y}{a}}{\sinh \dfrac{(2n-1)\pi b}{a}}$$

Ex. 4 : *A rectangular plate with insulated surfaces is 10 cm wide and so long compared to its width that it may be considered infinite in length without introducing an appreciable error. If the temperature along short edge y = 0 is given*

$u(x, 0) = 100 \sin\left(\dfrac{\pi x}{10}\right)$, $0 \le x \le 10$, *while the two long edges x = 0 and x = 10 as well as the other short edge are kept at $0^\circ C$. Find steady-state temperature u(x, y).* **(Dec. 2005)**

Sol. : We have to solve the P.D.E. $\dfrac{\partial^2 u}{\partial x^2} + \dfrac{\partial^2 u}{\partial y^2} = 0$

Subject to the conditions :

(i) $u(x, \infty) = 0$

(ii) $u(0, y) = 0$

(iii) $u(10, y) = 0$

(iv) $u(x, 0) = 100 \sin\left(\dfrac{\pi x}{10}\right)$,

$$0 \le x \le 10.$$

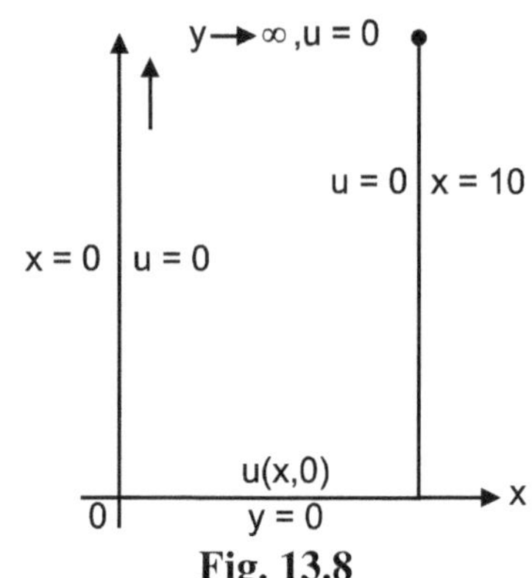

Fig. 13.8

The most general solution is

$$u(x, y) = (c_1 \cos mx + c_2 \sin mx)(c_3 e^{my} + c_4 e^{-my})$$

(i) $\Rightarrow$ $\qquad c_3 = 0$

(ii) $\Rightarrow$ $\qquad c_1 = 0$

$$u(x, y) = c_5 \sin mx \, e^{-my}$$

(iii) $\Rightarrow$ $\qquad 0 = c_5 \sin 10m \, e^{-my}$

$$\sin 10m = 0, \quad 10m = n\pi$$

$\therefore \qquad m = \dfrac{n\pi}{10}, \qquad\qquad\qquad n = 1, 2, 3, \ldots\ldots$

$$u(x, y) = c_5 \sin\dfrac{n\pi x}{10} \, e^{-\frac{n\pi y}{10}}, \qquad\qquad n = 1, 2, \ldots\ldots$$

Or $\qquad \boxed{\; u(x, y) = \sum_{n=1}^{\infty} b_n \sin\dfrac{n\pi x}{10} \, e^{-\frac{n\pi y}{10}} \;}$

Applying condition (iv), we have

$$100 \sin\left(\dfrac{\pi x}{10}\right) = \sum_{n=1}^{\infty} b_n \sin\dfrac{n\pi x}{10}$$

$$100 \sin\left(\dfrac{\pi x}{10}\right) = b_1 \sin\dfrac{\pi x}{10} + b_2 \sin\dfrac{2\pi x}{10} + \ldots\ldots$$

$$b_1 = 100, \; b_2 = 0 = b_3 = b_4 = \ldots\ldots = b_n = \ldots\ldots$$

$\therefore$ The complete solution is

$$u(x, y) = b_1 \sin\dfrac{\pi x}{10} \, e^{-\frac{\pi y}{10}} + b_2 \sin\dfrac{2\pi x}{10} \, e^{-\frac{2\pi y}{10}} + \ldots\ldots$$

$$u\ (x,\ y)\ =\ 100\ \sin\frac{\pi x}{10}\ e^{-\frac{\pi y}{10}}$$

Ex. 5 : *An infinitely long plane uniform plate is bounded by two parallel edges in the y-direction and an end at right angles to them. The breadth of the plate is π. This end is maintained at temperature u_o at all points and other edges at zero temperature. Find the steady-state temperature function u (x, y).*　　**(May 2007, 2011, 2014, Nov. 2015, 2016)**

Sol. : We have to solve the P.D.E. $\dfrac{\partial^2 u}{\partial x^2}\ +\ \dfrac{\partial^2 u}{\partial y^2}\ =\ 0$

Subject to the conditions :

(i)　　$u\ (0,\ y)\ =\ 0$

(ii)　　$u\ (\pi,\ y)\ =\ 0$

(iii)　$u\ (x,\ \infty)\ =\ 0$ for $0 < x < \pi$

(iv)　$u\ (x,\ 0)\ =u_o$ for $0\ <\ x\ <\pi.$

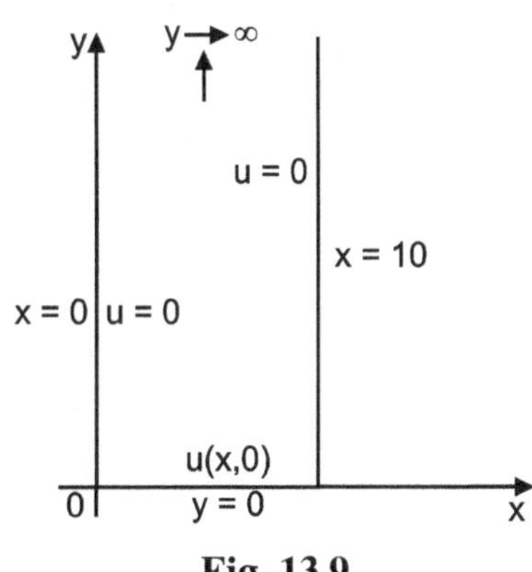

Fig. 13.9

The most general solution is

$$u(x,\ y)\ =\ (c_1 \cos mx + c_2 \sin mx)\ (c_3\ e^{my}\ +\ c_4\ e^{-my})$$

(iii)　$\Rightarrow$　　　　$c_3\ =\ 0$

(i)　　$\Rightarrow$　　　　$c_1\ =\ 0$

　　$\therefore$　　$u\ (x,\ y)\ =\ c_5 \sin mx\ e^{-my}$

(ii)　$\Rightarrow$　　　$0\ =\ c_5 \sin m\pi\ e^{-my}$

　　$c_5\ \neq\ 0,\quad e^{-my}\ \neq\ 0,\quad \sin m\pi\ =0$

　　　　$m\pi\ =\ n\pi,\quad m\ =\ n,\qquad n\ =\ 1, 2, \ldots\ldots$

　$\therefore$　　$u\ (x,\ y)\ =\ c_5 \sin nx\ e^{-ny},\qquad n\ =\ 1, 2, \ldots\ldots$

Or

$$u\ (x,\ y)\ =\ \sum_{n=1}^{\infty}\ b_n\ \sin nx\ e^{-ny}$$

Condition (iv) $\Rightarrow$

$$u_o\ =\ \sum_{1}^{\infty} b_n\ \sin nx,\qquad\qquad 0 < x < \pi$$

$$b_n = \frac{2}{\pi} \int_0^\pi u_o \sin nx \, dx = \frac{2 u_o}{\pi} \left(\frac{-\cos nx}{n} \right)_0^\pi = \frac{2u_o}{\pi} \left(\frac{1-(-1)^n}{n} \right)$$

$$\therefore \qquad u(x, y) = \frac{2 u_o}{\pi} \sum_{n=1}^{\infty} \left(\frac{1-(-1)^n}{n} \right) \sin nx \; e^{-ny}$$

$$u(x, y) = \frac{4 u_o}{\pi} \sum_{n=1}^{\infty} \frac{1}{2n-1} \sin(2n-1) x \; e^{-(2n-1)y}$$

Ex. 6 : *A rectangular plate with insulated surface is 10 cm wide and so long to its width that it may be considered infinite in length without introducing an appreciable error. If the temperature of the short edge $y = 0$ is given by,*

$$u = 20x \qquad ; \; for \; 0 \le x \le 5$$

$$= 20(10-x) ; \; for \; 5 \le x \le 10$$

and the two long edges $x = 0$, $x = 10$ as well as the other short edge are kept at $0^\circ C$, then prove that the temperature u at any point (x, y) is given by,

$$u = \frac{800}{\pi^2} \sum_{1}^{\infty} \frac{(-1)^{n+1}}{(2n-1)^2} \sin \frac{(2n-1)\pi x}{10} \cdot e^{\frac{-(2n-1)\pi y}{10}} \qquad \textbf{(May 08, 12, Dec. 09, 10, 16)}$$

Sol. : The temperature $u(x, y)$ satisfies the equation :

$$\frac{\partial^2 u}{\partial x^2} + \frac{\partial^2 u}{\partial y^2} = 0$$

The boundary conditions being as follows,

(i) $u(0, y) = 0$ for all positive values of y including zero.

(ii) $u(10, y) = 0$ for all $y \ge 0$

(iii) $u(x, \infty) = 0$ for $0 \le x \le 10$ and

(iv) $u(x, 0) = 20x, \;\; 0 \le x \le 5$

          $= 20(10-x), \; 5 \le x \le 10$

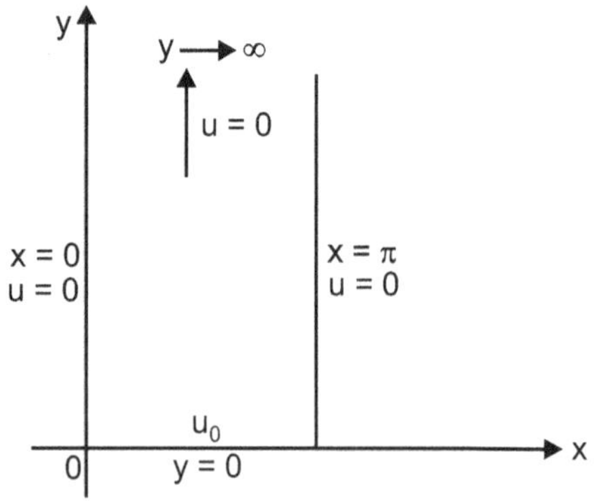

Fig. 13.10

The most suitable solution is

$$u(x, y) = (c_1 \cos mx + c_2 \sin mx)(c_3 e^{my} + c_4 e^{-my})$$

(iii) $\Rightarrow$ $c_3 = 0$

(i) $\Rightarrow$ $c_1 = 0$

$$u(x, y) = c_5 \sin mx \; e^{-my}$$

(ii) $\Rightarrow$ $0 = c_5 \sin 10m \; e^{-my}$

$$c_5 \neq 0, \quad e^{-my} \neq 0, \quad \sin 10m = 0$$

$$10m = n\pi, \quad m = \frac{n\pi}{10}, \quad n = 1, 2, \ldots\ldots$$

$$u(x, y) = c_5 \sin \frac{n\pi x}{10} \; e^{\frac{-n\pi y}{10}}, \quad n = 1, 2, \ldots\ldots$$

Or $$u(x, y) = \sum_{n=1}^{\infty} b_n \sin \frac{n\pi x}{10} \; e^{\frac{-n\pi y}{10}}$$

Applying condition (iv), we get

$$u(x, 0) = \sum_{n=1}^{\infty} b_n \sin \frac{n\pi x}{10}$$

$\therefore$ $$b_n = \frac{2}{10} \left\{ \int_0^5 20x \, \sin \frac{n\pi x}{10} \, dx + \int_5^{10} 20(10-x) \, \sin \frac{n\pi x}{10} \cdot dx \right\}$$

$$= 4 \left\{ \left[(x) \left(-\frac{10}{n\pi} \cos \frac{n\pi x}{10} \right) - (1) \left(-\frac{100}{n^2\pi^2} \sin \frac{n\pi x}{10} \right) \right]_0^5 \right.$$

$$\left. + \left[(10-x) \left(-\frac{10}{n\pi} \cos \frac{n\pi x}{10} \right) - (-1) \left(-\frac{100}{n^2\pi^2} \sin \frac{n\pi x}{10} \right) \right]_5^{10} \right\}$$

$$= 4 \left\{ -\frac{50}{n\pi} \cos \frac{n\pi}{2} + \frac{100}{n^2\pi^2} \sin \frac{n\pi}{2} + \frac{50}{n\pi} \cos \frac{n\pi}{2} + \frac{100}{n^2\pi^2} \sin \frac{n\pi}{2} \right\}$$

$$= \frac{800}{n^2\pi^2} \sin \frac{n\pi}{2}$$

The complete solution is

$$u(x, y) = \frac{800}{\pi^2} \sum_{n=1}^{\infty} \frac{\sin \frac{n\pi}{2}}{n^2} \sin \frac{n\pi x}{10} \; e^{-\frac{n\pi y}{10}}$$

Ex. 7 : *A square metal plate of side a has edges represented by lines x = 0, x = a, y = 0, y = a. The edges x = a and y = a are insulated. The edge x = 0 is kept at 0° C and y = 0 at u_o°C where u_o is a constant. Obtain the temperature distribution u (x, y) under steady-state conditions.*

Sol. : We have to solve the P.D.E. $\dfrac{\partial^2 u}{\partial x^2} + \dfrac{\partial^2 u}{\partial y^2} = 0$

Subject to the boundary conditions :

(i) $u\,(0,\ y) = 0$

(ii) $\left(\dfrac{\partial u}{\partial y}\right)_{y\,=\,a} = 0$

(iii) $\left(\dfrac{\partial u}{\partial x}\right)_{x\,=\,a} = 0$

(iv) $u\,(x,\ 0)\ = u_0\ °C$

If we take solution given by $k = m^2$

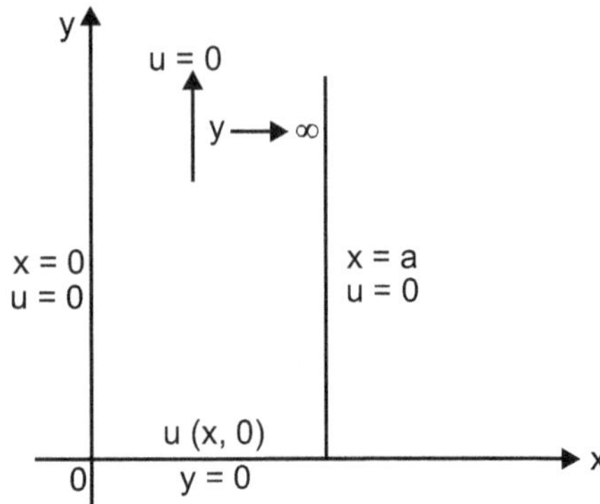

Fig. 13.11

i.e. $u\,(x,\ y) = (c_1 \cosh mx + c_2 \sinh mx)\,(c_3 \cos my + c_4 \sin my)$ then (i) is satisfied if $c_1 = 0$

but then $\dfrac{\partial u}{\partial x}\Big|_{x\,=\,a} = 0$ cannot be satisfied because cosh am can never be zero for any value of m.

Therefore, the most general solution is

$$u\,(x,\ y) = (c_1 \cos mx + c_2 \sin mx)\,(c_3 \cosh my + c_4 \sinh my)$$

(i) $\Rightarrow$ $c_1 = 0$

$\therefore$ $u\,(x,\ y) = \sin mx\,[c_3{}' \cosh my + c_4{}' \sinh my]$

$$\frac{\partial u}{\partial y} = (\sin mx)\ [m\,c_3{}' \sinh my + m\,c_4{}' \cosh my]$$

(ii) $\Rightarrow$ $0 = (\sin mx)\ [m\,c_3{}' \sinh ma + m\,c_4{}' \cosh ma]$

Here $m \neq 0,\quad \sin mx \neq 0$ (otherwise we get trivial solution)

$$c_3{}' \sinh ma + c_4{}' \cosh ma = 0$$

$$c_4{}' = -\frac{c_3{}' \sinh ma}{\cosh ma}$$

$\therefore$ $u\,(x,\ y) = \sin mx \left[c_3{}' \cosh my - \dfrac{c_3{}' \sinh ma}{\cosh ma}\,\sinh my\right]$

$$= \frac{c_3{}' \sin mx}{\cosh ma}\,(\cosh my \cosh ma - \sinh ma \sinh my)$$

$$\frac{\partial u}{\partial x} = \frac{c_3{}'\,m \cos mx}{\cosh ma}\,\cosh\,(a - y)\,m$$

(iii) $\Rightarrow$ $0 = \dfrac{c_3{}'m \cos ma}{\cosh ma}\,\cosh\,(a - y)\,m$

$$\cos ma = 0, \qquad ma = \frac{(2n-1)\pi}{2}$$

$$m = \frac{(2n-1)\pi}{2a}, \quad n = 1, 2, 3, \ldots\ldots\ldots$$

$$\therefore \qquad u(x, y) = \frac{c_3' \, \sin \dfrac{(2n-1)\pi x}{2a} \, \cosh\left(\dfrac{(2n-1)\pi(a-y)}{2a}\right)}{\cosh \dfrac{(2n-1)\pi}{2}}$$

Or

$$u(x, y) = \sum_{n=1}^{\infty} \frac{b_n \, \sin \dfrac{(2n-1)\pi x}{2a}}{\cosh \dfrac{(2n-1)\pi}{2}} \, \cosh\left(\frac{(2n-1)\pi(a-y)}{2a}\right)$$

Applying condition (iv), we get

$$u_o = \sum_{n=1}^{\infty} \frac{b_n \, \sin \dfrac{(2n-1)\pi x}{2a}}{\cosh \dfrac{(2n-1)\pi}{2}} \, \cosh \frac{(2n-1)\pi}{2}$$

$$u_o = \sum_{n=1}^{\infty} b_n \, \sin\left(\frac{(2n-1)\pi x}{2a}\right)$$

$$\therefore \qquad b_n = \frac{2}{a} \int_0^a u_o \sin \frac{(2n-1)\pi x}{2a} \, dx$$

$$= \frac{2 u_o}{a} \left[\frac{-2a}{(2n-1)\pi} \cos \frac{(2n-1)\pi x}{2a} \right]_0^a$$

$$= \frac{-4 u_o}{\pi} \frac{1}{2n-1} [0 - 1] = \frac{4 u_o}{\pi} \frac{1}{2n-1}$$

$$\therefore \qquad u(x, y) = \frac{4 u_o}{\pi} \sum_{n=1}^{\infty} \frac{\dfrac{1}{2n-1} \sin \dfrac{(2n-1)\pi x}{2a}}{\cosh (2n-1)\dfrac{\pi}{2}} \cdot \cosh\left(\frac{(2n-1)\pi(a-y)}{2a}\right)$$

$$\therefore \qquad u(x, y) = \frac{4 u_o}{\pi} \sum_{n=1}^{\infty} \frac{\operatorname{sech}(2n-1)\dfrac{\pi}{2} \sin \dfrac{(2n-1)\pi x}{2a} \cosh \dfrac{(2n-1)\pi(a-y)}{2a}}{\cosh (2n-1)\dfrac{\pi}{2}}$$

EXERCISE 13.3

1. A thin sheet of metal bounded by the x-axis and the lines $x = 0$ and $x = 1$ and stretching to infinity in the y-direction has its upper and lower faces perfectly insulated and its vertical edges and edge at infinity are maintained at the constant

temperature 0°C, while over the base temperature of 100°C is maintained. Find steady-state temperature u (x, y).

$$\textbf{Ans. :}\ u\,(x,\,y)\ =\frac{400}{\pi}\ \sum_{n=1}^{\infty}\ \frac{\sin\,(2n-1)\,\pi x}{2n-1}\ e^{-(2n-1)\,\pi y}$$

2. Work example (1) if the temperature along short edge y = 0 is

$$u\,(x,\,0)\ =\ (x - x^2)\ \text{degrees}$$

$$\textbf{Ans. :}\ \ u\,(x,\,y)\ =\ \frac{4}{\pi^3}\ \sum_{n=1}^{\infty}\ \frac{\sin\,(2n-1)\,nx}{(2n-1)^3}\ e^{-(2n-1)\,\pi y}$$

3. Work example (1) if the temperature along short edge y = 0 is

$$u\,(x,\,0)\ =\ \begin{cases} x & 0 < x \le 0.5 \\[2mm] 1 - x & 0.5 \le x < 1 \end{cases}$$

$$\textbf{Ans. :}\ u\,(x,\,y)\ =\ \frac{4}{\pi^2}\ \sum_{n=1}^{\infty}\ \frac{(-1)^{n-1}\,\sin\,(2n-1)\,\pi x}{(2n-1)^2}\ .\,e^{-(2n-1)\,\pi y}$$

4. The lower side (y = 0) of a rectangular metal plate of length a and width b, with insulated upper and lower surfaces is kept at 100°C while upper side y = b is insulated. If the other two sides are kept at 0°C, find the steady-state temperature distribution of the plate.

$$\textbf{Ans. :}\ u(x,\,y)=\frac{200}{\pi}\ \sum_{n=1}^{\infty}\ \frac{1}{n}\ (1 - \cos\,n\pi)\ \sin\frac{n\pi x}{a}\left(\cosh\frac{n\pi y}{a} - \sinh\frac{n\pi y}{a}\ \tan\frac{n\pi b}{a}\right)$$

5. A square plate has its faces as well as edges x = 0 and x = π (0 < y < π) are insulated. Its edges y = 0 and y = π   are kept at temperature 0°C and f(x) respectively. Show that

$$u\,(x,\,y)\ =\ \frac{a_o}{2}\ +\ \sum_{n=1}^{\infty}\ a_n\ \frac{\sinh\,ny}{\sinh\,nx}\ \cos\,nx$$

where, $a_n\ =\ \dfrac{2}{\pi}\ \displaystyle\int_{0}^{\pi} f\,(x)\,\cos\,nx\ dx,\ \ n = 0, 1, 2, \ldots\ldots$

6. A rectangular plate bounded by lines x = 0, x = a, y = 0 and y = b, has its faces insulated while the edges x = 0, x = a and y = b are kept at zero degree and lower

edge $(y = 0)$ is having temperature distribution. $5 \sin \dfrac{4\pi x}{a} + 3 \sin \dfrac{3\pi x}{a}$. Find the steady-state temperature distribution.

$$\textbf{Ans.:} \quad u\,(x, y) \;=\; 3 \sin \frac{3\pi x}{a} \; \sinh \frac{3\pi\,(b - y)}{a} \; \operatorname{cosech} \frac{3\pi b}{a}$$

$$+ \; 5 \sin \frac{4\pi x}{a} \; \sinh \frac{4\pi\,(b - y)}{a} \; \operatorname{cosech} \frac{4\pi b}{a}\,.$$

7. A square plate has its faces insulated. The edges $x = 0$ and $x = \pi$ are also insulated while the edge $y = \pi$ is kept at $0°$C. The edge $y = 0$ has temperature distribution $u\,(x, 0) = x^2$. Find the steady-state temperature distribution.

$$\textbf{Ans.:} \quad u\,(x, y) \;=\; \frac{\pi^2}{3} + 4 \sum_{n = 1}^{\infty} \frac{(-1)^n \sinh n\,(\pi - y) \cos nx}{n^2 \sinh n\pi}$$

8. A rectangular metal plate is bounded by $x = 0$, $x = a$, $y = 0$, $y = b$. The edges $x = 0$, $x = a$, $y = b$ are insulated and the edge $y = 0$ is kept at temperature $u_o \cos \dfrac{\pi x}{a}$. Find the temperature distribution $u\,(x, y)$ in steady-state conditions.

$$\textbf{Ans.} \quad u(x, y) \;=\; u \cos \frac{\pi x}{a} \cos \frac{\pi}{a}\,(b - y) \sec \frac{\pi b}{a}.$$

13.9 TWO-DIMENSIONAL HEAT FLOW (IN POLAR CO-ORDINATES)

Derivation of Equation :

Consider elementary area ABCD. Mass of this element is $\rho r\, d\theta \; dr\, \alpha$, where α is uniform thickness of the plate whose surfaces are insulated. Heat absorbed by this element will be

$$\rho\, r\, d\theta\, dr\, \alpha \; c \frac{\partial u}{\partial t}$$

The heat that enters through AB is $- k\, \alpha\, \delta r \left(\dfrac{1}{r} \dfrac{\partial u}{\partial \theta} \right)_{\theta}$ and that leaves from edge CD

is $- k\, \alpha\, \delta r \left(\dfrac{1}{r} \dfrac{\partial u}{\partial \theta} \right)_{\theta + \delta\theta}$

Similarly, the heat that enters through edge AD is $- k\alpha\, r\, \delta\theta \left(\dfrac{\partial u}{\partial r} \right)_{r}$

and that leaves from edge BC is $- k\alpha\,(r + \delta r)\, \delta\theta \left(\dfrac{\partial u}{\partial r} \right)_{r + \delta r}$

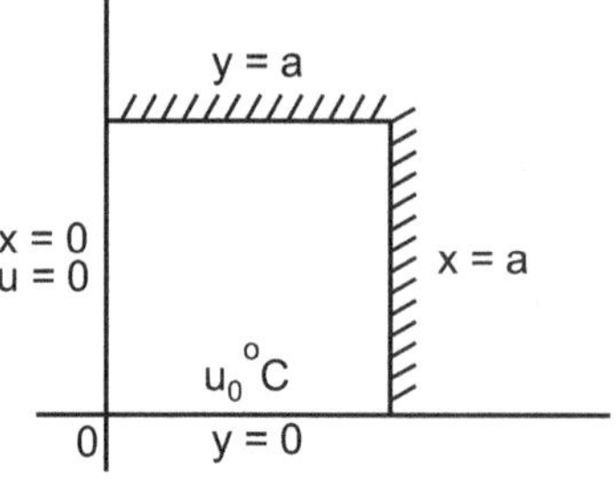

Fig. 13.12

∴ The heat gained by the element is

$$k\,\alpha\,\delta r\left(\frac{1}{r}\frac{\partial u}{\partial t}\right)_{\theta+\delta\theta} - k\,\alpha\,\delta r\left(\frac{1}{r}\frac{\partial u}{\partial t}\right)_{\theta} + r\,k\,\alpha\,\delta\theta\left[\left(\frac{\partial u}{\partial r}\right)_{r+\delta r} - \left(\frac{\partial u}{\partial r}\right)_{r}\right] + k\,\alpha\,\delta r\,\delta\theta\left(\frac{\partial u}{\partial r}\right)_{r+\delta r}$$

$$= \rho\,r\,\delta\theta\,\delta r\,\alpha\,c\,\frac{\partial u}{\partial t}\quad\text{(Heat absorbed by the element)}$$

Dividing by $k\,\alpha\,r\,\delta\theta\,\delta r$, we get

$$\frac{1}{r^2}\left[\frac{\left(\frac{\partial u}{\partial\theta}\right)_{\theta+\delta\theta} - \left(\frac{\partial u}{\partial\theta}\right)}{\delta\theta}\right] + \left[\frac{\left(\frac{\partial u}{\partial r}\right)_{r+\delta r} - \left(\frac{\partial u}{\partial r}\right)_{r}}{\delta r}\right] + \frac{1}{r}\left(\frac{\partial u}{\partial r}\right)_{r+\delta r} - \frac{\rho c}{k}\frac{\partial u}{\partial t}$$

Taking limit as $\delta r \to 0$ and $\delta\theta \to 0$, we get

$$\frac{1}{r^2}\frac{\partial^2 u}{\partial\theta^2} + \frac{\partial^2 u}{\partial r^2} + \frac{1}{r}\frac{\partial u}{\partial r} = \frac{1}{a^2}\frac{\partial u}{\partial t},\quad\text{where }a^2 = \frac{k}{\rho c}$$

Under steady-state condition, $\dfrac{\partial u}{\partial t} = 0$.

$$\therefore\quad \frac{\partial^2 u}{\partial r^2} + \frac{1}{r}\frac{\partial u}{\partial r} + \frac{1}{r^2}\frac{\partial^2 u}{\partial\theta^2} = 0$$

represents the temperature distribution under steady-state conditions in two-dimensional polar co-ordinates.

13.10 SOLUTION OF LAPLACE'S EQUATION IN POLAR CO-ORDINATES

Laplace's equation in polar form is,

$$r^2\frac{\partial^2 u}{\partial r^2} + r\frac{\partial u}{\partial r} + \frac{\partial^2 u}{\partial\theta^2} = 0 \qquad\qquad\qquad \dots(1)$$

Assuming $u = u(r, \theta) = RF$, where 'R' is a function of 'r' alone and 'F' is a function of 'θ' alone, to be the solution of equation (1), we have

$$\frac{\partial u}{\partial r} = R'F, \quad \frac{\partial^2 u}{\partial r^2} = R''F, \quad \frac{\partial u}{\partial \theta} = RF' \text{ and } \frac{\partial^2 u}{\partial \theta^2} = RF''$$

$\therefore$ Equation (1) becomes,

$$r^2 R'' F + rR' F + RF'' = 0$$

Or $\quad (r^2 R'' + rR') F + RF'' = 0$

$\therefore \qquad \dfrac{r^2 R'' + rR'}{R} = \dfrac{-F''}{F}$ ... (2)

As L.H.S. is a function of 'r' alone and R.H.S. is a function of 'θ' alone, equation (2) holds only if both sides reduce to a constant.

$\therefore \qquad \dfrac{r^2 R'' + rR'}{R} = \dfrac{-F''}{F} = k \text{ (say)}$

$\therefore \quad$ we get, $r^2 R'' + rR' - kR = 0$ and $F'' + kF = 0$

Or $\quad r^2 \dfrac{d^2 F}{d\theta^2} + r \dfrac{dR}{dr} - kR = 0$ ... (3)

and $\qquad \dfrac{d^2 F}{d\theta^2} + kF = 0$ ... (4)

Therefore equation (3) is homogeneous.

$\therefore \qquad r = e^z \Rightarrow z = \log r \Rightarrow \dfrac{dz}{dr} = \dfrac{1}{r}$

$\therefore \qquad \dfrac{dR}{dr} = \dfrac{dR}{dz} \dfrac{dz}{dr} \Rightarrow \dfrac{dR}{dr} = \dfrac{1}{r} \dfrac{dR}{dz}$

For $\dfrac{d}{dz} \equiv D$, we get $r \dfrac{dR}{dr} = DR$.

Similarly, $r^2 \dfrac{d^2 R}{dr^2} = D(D-1)R$.

$\therefore$ Equation (3) becomes

$$D(D-1)R + DR - kR = 0 \Rightarrow (D^2 - k)R = 0 \qquad \text{... (5)}$$

Case (i) : $\quad k > 0 \quad$ i.e. $k = m^2$

$\therefore$ From (5), $\quad (D^2 - m^2)R = 0 \Rightarrow$

$$R(r) = c_1 e^{mz} + c_2 e^{-mz}$$

$$R(r) = c_1 r^m + c_2 r^{-m} \qquad\qquad (\because r = e^z)$$

From (4), $\quad (D^2 + m^2) F = 0 \Rightarrow F(\theta) = c_3 \cos m\theta + c_4 \sin m\theta$

∴ Complete solution is

$$\boxed{u\,(r,\,\theta)\;=\;(c_1\,r^m\;+\;c_2\,r^{-m})\;(c_3\,\cos\,m\theta\;+\;c_4\,\sin\,m\theta)}\qquad \ldots\,(6)$$

Case (ii) : Let $k = 0$.

From (5), $D^2\,R = 0 \quad\Rightarrow\quad R(r) = c_1\,z + c_2 = c_1\,\log r + c_2$

From (4), $D^2\,F = 0 \quad\Rightarrow\quad F(\theta) = c_3\,\theta + c_4$

∴ $$\boxed{u\,(r,\,\theta)\;=\;(c_1\,\log r + c_2)\;(c_3\,\theta + c_4)}\qquad \ldots\,(7)$$

Case (iii) : Let $k < 0$ i.e. $k = -m^2$.

From (5), $(D^2 + m^2)\,R = 0$

$$R(r) = c_1\,\cos mz + c_2\,\sin mz$$

$$R(r) = c_1\,\cos (m\,\log r) + c_2\,\sin (m\,\log r)$$

From (4), $(D^2 - m^2)\,F = 0$

$$F(\theta) = c_3\,e^{m\theta} + c_4\,e^{-m\theta}$$

∴ $$\boxed{u\,(r,\,\theta)\;=\;[c_1\,\cos (m\,\log r) + c_2\,\sin (m\,\log r)]\,[c_3\,e^{m\theta} + c_4\,e^{-m\theta}]}\qquad \ldots\,(8)$$

Out of these three solutions (6), (7) and (8), we have to select that which suits the physical nature of the problem and given boundary conditions.

Note : Since u and F must be periodic rather than increasing or decreasing function of θ, it is evident that we must select the solution with $k = m^2$.

i.e. $$u\,(r,\,\theta) = (c_1\,r^m + c_2\,r^{-m})\,(c_3\,\cos m\theta + c_4\,\sin m\theta)$$

ILLUSTRATIONS

Ex. 1 : *In case of a semicircular plate of radius a cm, the bounding diameter is kept at $0^\circ C$ and the circumference at the fixed temperature u_0 until a steady-state condition prevails. Find the temperature distribution in the plate.*

Sol. :   We have to solve Laplace's equation in polar form i.e.

$$r^2\,\frac{\partial^2 u}{\partial r^2} + r\,\frac{\partial u}{\partial r} + \frac{\partial^2 u}{\partial \theta^2} = 0,$$

where $u\,(r,\,\theta)$ is the temperature.

Subject to the following conditions :

(i) $u(r, 0) = 0$

(ii) $u(r, \pi) = 0$

(iii) u is finite as $r \to 0$

(iv) $u(a, \theta) = u_o$, $0 \le \theta \le \pi$

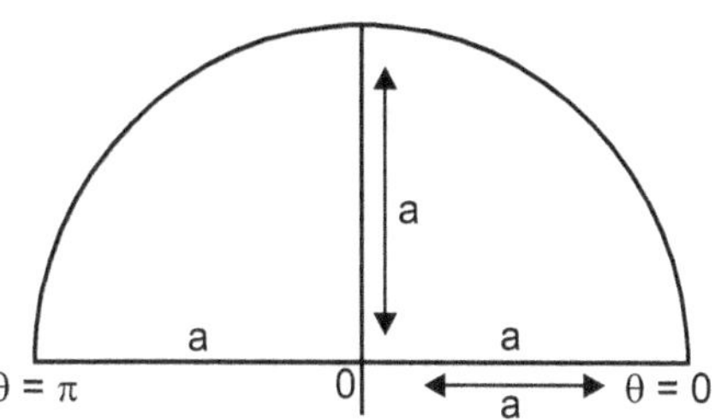

Fig. 13.13

In this case, the most general solution is

$$u(r, \theta) = (c_1 r^m + c_2 r^{-m})(c_3 \cos m\theta + c_4 \sin m\theta)$$

Since $u(r, \theta)$ is to remain finite as $r \to 0$, we must have $\boxed{c_2 = 0}$.

Also, (i) $\Rightarrow$ $\boxed{c_3 = 0}$

$\therefore$ $u(r, \theta) = c_5 \sin m\theta \cdot r^m$

(ii) $\Rightarrow$ $0 = c_5 \sin m\pi \; r^m$

$\qquad c_5 \ne 0, \quad r^m \ne 0, \quad \therefore \; \sin m\pi = 0$

$\qquad m\pi = n\pi, \; m = n, \; n = 1, 2, \ldots\ldots\ldots\ldots$

$\therefore$ $u(r, \theta) = c_5 \sin n\theta \; r^n, \; n = 1, 2, \ldots\ldots\ldots\ldots$

Or $u(r, \theta) = \displaystyle\sum_{n=1}^{\infty} b_n \sin n\theta \; r^n.$

Applying condition (iv), we get

$$u_o = \sum_{n=1}^{\infty} b_n \sin n\theta \; a^n, \; 0 \le \theta \le \pi$$

$\therefore$ $b_n \cdot a^n = \dfrac{2}{\pi} \displaystyle\int_0^{\pi} u_o \sin n\theta \; d\theta = \dfrac{2\,u_o}{\pi} \left(\dfrac{-\cos n\theta}{n}\right)_0^{\pi}$

$$= \dfrac{2\,u_o}{\pi} \left(\dfrac{1 - (-1)^n}{n}\right)$$

$\therefore$ $u(r, \theta) = \dfrac{2\,u_o}{\pi} \displaystyle\sum_{n=1}^{\infty} \left(\dfrac{1 - (-1)^n}{n}\right) \sin n\theta \left(\dfrac{r}{a}\right)^n$

$$u(r, \theta) = \dfrac{4\,u_o}{\pi} \sum_{n=1}^{\infty} \dfrac{1}{2n-1} \sin(2n-1)\theta \left(\dfrac{r}{a}\right)^{2n-1}$$

Ex. 2 : *The bounding diameter of a semicircular plate of radius 10 cm is kept at $0°C$ and the temperature along the semicircular boundary is given by,*

$$u \, (10, \, \theta) = 50 \, \theta \qquad , \qquad 0 < \theta \leq \frac{\pi}{2}$$

$$= 50 \, (\pi - \theta) \, , \qquad \frac{\pi}{2} \leq \theta < \pi.$$

Find the steady-state temperature function $u \, (r, \, \theta)$.

Sol. : The temperature function $u \, (r, \theta)$ in steady state satisfies the Laplace's equation in polar form i.e.

$$r^2 \, \frac{\partial^2 u}{\partial r^2} + r \frac{\partial u}{\partial r} + \frac{\partial^2 u}{\partial \theta^2} = 0$$

Subject to the conditions

(i) $u \, (r, \theta)$ remains finite as $r \to 0$

(ii) $u \, (r, 0) \; = 0$

(iii) $u \, (r, \pi) \; = 0$

(iv) $u \, (10, \theta) = 50 \, \theta, \; 0 < \theta \; \leq \frac{\pi}{2}$

$$= 50 \, (\pi - \theta), \frac{\pi}{2} \leq \theta < \pi$$

The most general solution is

$$u \, (r, \, \theta) = (c_1 \, r^m + c_2 \, r^{-m}) \, (c_3 \cos m\theta + c_4 \sin m\theta)$$

Since $u \, (r, \theta)$ is to remain finite as $r \to 0$, we must have $\boxed{c_2 = 0}$.

(ii) $\Rightarrow$ $\boxed{c_3 = 0}$

$$u \, (r, \, \theta) = c_5 \sin m\theta \; r^m.$$

(iii) $\Rightarrow$ $0 = c_5 \sin m\pi \; r^m$

$$c_5 \neq 0, \; r^m \neq 0, \; \sin (m\pi) = 0$$

$$m\pi = n\pi \qquad \therefore \; m = n, \; \; n = 1, 2, \ldots\ldots$$

$\therefore$ $u \, (r, \theta) = c_5 \; \sin n\theta \; r^n, \; n = 1, 2, \ldots\ldots$

Or $u \, (r, \theta) = \sum_{n=1}^{\infty} b_n \sin n\theta \; r^n$

Applying condition (iv), we get

$$u(10, \theta) = \sum_{n=1}^{\infty} b_n \sin n\theta \, 10^n$$

$$b_n (10)^n = \frac{2}{\pi} \left\{ \int_0^{\pi/2} 50\,\theta \sin n\theta \, d\theta + \int_{\pi/2}^{\pi} 50(\pi - \theta) \sin n\theta \, d\theta \right\}$$

$$= \frac{100}{\pi} \left\{ \left[(\theta) \left(\frac{-\cos n\theta}{n} \right) - (1) \left(\frac{-\sin n\theta}{n^2} \right) \right]_0^{\pi/2} \right.$$

$$\left. + \left[(\pi - \theta) \left(\frac{-\cos n\theta}{n} \right) - (-1) \left(\frac{-\sin n\theta}{n^2} \right) \right]_{\pi/2}^{\pi} \right\}$$

$$= \frac{100}{\pi} \left\{ -\frac{\pi}{2n} \cos \frac{n\pi}{2} + \frac{1}{n^2} \sin \frac{n\pi}{2} + \frac{\pi}{2n} \cos \frac{n\pi}{2} + \frac{1}{n^2} \sin \frac{n\pi}{2} \right\}$$

$$= \frac{200}{\pi} \, \frac{1}{n^2} \sin \frac{n\pi}{2}$$

$$\therefore \quad u(r, \theta) = \frac{200}{\pi} \sum_{n=1}^{\infty} \frac{\sin \dfrac{n\pi}{2}}{n^2} \sin n\theta \left(\frac{r}{10} \right)^n$$

$$u(r, \theta) = \frac{200}{\pi} \sum_{n=1}^{\infty} \frac{(-1)^{n+1}}{(2n-1)^2} \cdot \sin (2n-1)\theta \left(\frac{r}{10} \right)^{2n-1}$$

EXERCISE 13.4

1. The bounding diameter of a semi-circular plate of radius l is kept at $0°C$ and the temperature along semi-circular boundary is given by

$$u(l, \theta) = \begin{cases} \theta, & \text{for } 0 < \theta \le \dfrac{\pi}{2} \\[2mm] \pi - \theta, & \text{for } \dfrac{\pi}{2} \le \theta < \pi \end{cases}$$

Find the steady-state temperature distribution.

$$\textbf{Ans.:} \quad u(r, \theta) = \frac{4}{\pi} \sum_{n=1}^{\infty} \frac{(-1)^{n-1}}{(2n-1)^2} \left(\frac{r}{l} \right)^{2n-1} \sin (2n-1)\theta$$

2. A plate uniform of a circular sector is bounded by the lines $\theta = 0$, $\theta = \dfrac{\pi}{3}$ and $r = a$.

Its surfaces are insulated and the temperature along the boundary are $u(r, 0) = 0$,

$u\left(r, \dfrac{\pi}{3}\right) = 0$, while $u\,(a, \theta) = \lambda\theta\left(\dfrac{\pi}{3} - \theta\right)$, $0 < \theta < \dfrac{\pi}{3}$. Find the steady-state

temperature distribution.

$$\textbf{Ans. :}\ u\,(r, \theta) = \frac{8\lambda}{9\pi} \sum_{n=1}^{\infty} \frac{1}{(2n-1)^3} \left(\frac{r}{a}\right)^{3\,(2n-1)} \sin 3\,(2n-1)$$

3. Find the steady-state temperature in a circular plate of a radius 'a' which has one half of its circumference at 0°C and the other half at 100°C.

13.11 FINITE FOURIER TRANSFORMS

If a function $f(x)$ is defined in the finite interval $0 < x < L$ and satisfies the Dirichlet's conditions, then it can be expressed as half range cosine or sine series. Using these representations, we define finite Fourier sine and cosine transforms for given function $f(x)$.

1. Finite Fourier Cosine Transform : If a function $f(x)$ is defined in the interval $0 \le x \le L$, then half range cosine series for $f(x)$ is given by

$$f(x) = \frac{a_0}{2} + \sum_{n=1}^{\infty} a_n \cos \frac{n\pi x}{L} \qquad \ldots \text{(i)}$$

where, $\qquad a_0 = \dfrac{2}{L} \int_0^L f(x)\, dx \qquad \ldots \text{(ii)}$

and $\qquad a_n = \dfrac{2}{L} \int_0^L f(x) \cos \dfrac{n\pi x}{L}\, dx \qquad \ldots \text{(iii)}$

The **finite Fourier cosine transform** of $f(x)$ is defined as

$$\boxed{\ F_c\,[f(n)] = \int_0^L f(x) \cos \frac{n\pi x}{L}\, dx\ } \qquad \ldots \text{(6)}$$

where, n is an integer.

The function $f(x)$ is then called the **inverse finite Fourier cosine transform** of $F_c\,[f(n)]$ which is given by

$$\boxed{\ f(x) = \frac{1}{L} F_c\,(0) + \frac{2}{L} \sum_{n=1}^{\infty} F_c\,[f(n)] \cos \frac{n\pi x}{L}\ } \qquad \ldots \text{(7)}$$

Note : From (ii) and (iii), we note that

$$a_n = \frac{2}{L} \int_0^L f(x) \cos \frac{n\pi x}{L} \, dx = \frac{2}{L} F_c\,[f(n)] \qquad \ldots \text{(iv)}$$

and
$$a_0 = \frac{2}{L} \int_0^L f(x) \, dx = \frac{2}{L} F_c\,(0) \qquad \therefore \quad \frac{a_0}{2} = \frac{1}{L} F_c\,(0) \qquad \ldots \text{(v)}$$

On substituting (iv) and (v) in (i), we obtained result (15) for inverse finite Fourier transform.

2. Finite Fourier Sine Transform : If a function $f(x)$ is defined in the interval $0 \le x \le L$, then half range sine series is given by

$$f(x) = \sum_{n=1}^{\infty} b_n \sin \frac{n\pi x}{L} \qquad \ldots \text{(i)}$$

where,
$$b_n = \frac{2}{L} \int_0^L f(x) \sin \frac{n\pi x}{L} \, dx \qquad \ldots \text{(ii)}$$

The **finite Fourier Sine Transform** is defined as

$$\boxed{\; \mathbf{F_s\,[f(n)]} = \int_0^L f(x) \sin \frac{n\pi x}{L} \, dx \;} \qquad \ldots \text{(8)}$$

where, n is an integer.

The function $f(x)$ is then called the **inverse finite Fourier sine transform** of $F_s\,[f(n)]$ which is given by

$$\boxed{\; \mathbf{f(x)} = \frac{2}{L} \sum_{n=1}^{\infty} F_s\,[f(n)] \sin \frac{n\pi x}{L} \;} \qquad \ldots \text{(9)}$$

Note : From result (ii), we note that

$$b_n = \frac{2}{L} \int_0^L f(x) \sin \frac{n\pi x}{L} \, dx = \frac{2}{L} F_s\,[f(n)] \qquad \ldots \text{(iii)}$$

On substituting b_n from (iii) in (i), we obtained result (9) for inverse finite Fourier sine transform.

Remark : The finite Fourier cosine and sine transforms can also be denoted by $C(n)$ and $S(n)$ respectively.

ILLUSTRATIONS ON FINITE FOURIER SINE AND COSINE TRANSFORMS

Ex. 1 : *Find the finite Fourier sine and cosine transforms of the following functions :*

(i) $f(x) = 2x$, $0 \le x \le 4$

(ii) $f(x) = lx - x^2$, $0 \le x \le l$

(iii) $f(x) = \begin{cases} kx, & 0 \le x \le \pi/2 \\ k(\pi - x), & \pi/2 \le x \le \pi. \end{cases}$

Sol. :   (i) Finite Fourier Cosine Transform : Using the result (6), we have

$$F_c[f(n)] = \int_0^L f(x) \cos \frac{n\pi x}{L} \, dx = \int_0^4 (2x) \cos \frac{n\pi x}{4} \, dx \quad \left\{ \begin{aligned} &\because L = 4 \\ &\text{and } f(x) = 2x \end{aligned} \right\}$$

$$= \left[2x \left(\frac{4}{n\pi} \sin \frac{n\pi x}{4} \right) - (2) \left(-\frac{16}{n^2 \pi^2} \cos \frac{n\pi x}{4} \right) \right]_0^4$$

$$= 2(4) \left(\frac{4}{n\pi} \sin n\pi \right) + 2 \left(\frac{16}{n^2 \pi^2} \cos n\pi \right) - \frac{32}{n^2 \pi^2} \cos 0$$

$$= \frac{32}{n^2 \pi^2} (\cos n\pi - 1) \,.$$

At $n = 0$, $F_c[f(n)]$ becomes indeterminate, hence we evaluate $F_c(0)$ separately, thus

$$F_c(0) = \int_0^L f(x) \, dx = \int_0^4 2x \, dx = [x^2]_0^4 = 16$$

Hence the finite Fourier cosine transform of $f(x)$ is

$$F_c[f(n)] = \frac{32}{n^2 \pi^2} (\cos n\pi - 1) \quad \text{and} \quad F_c(0) = 16.$$

Finite Fourier Sine Transform : Using the result (8), we have

$$F_s[f(n)] = \int_0^L f(x) \sin \frac{n\pi x}{L} \, dx = \int_0^4 (2x) \sin \frac{n\pi x}{4} \, dx \quad \left\{ \because L = 4 \text{ and } f(x) = 2x \right\}$$

$$= \left[(2x) \left(-\frac{4}{n\pi} \cos \frac{n\pi x}{4} \right) - (2) \left(-\frac{16}{n^2 \pi^2} \sin \frac{n\pi x}{4} \right) \right]_0^4$$

$$= -2(4) \left(\frac{4}{n\pi} \cos n\pi \right) + (2) \left(\frac{16}{n^2 \pi^2 \sin n\pi} \right)$$

$$= -\frac{32}{n\pi} \cos n\pi$$

Hence the finite Fourier sine transform of $f(x)$ is

$$F_s[f(n)] = -\frac{32}{n\pi} \cos n\pi.$$

(ii) Finite Fourier Cosine Transform : From result (6), we have

$$F_c\,[f(n)] \;=\; \int_0^L f(x) \cos\frac{n\pi x}{L}\,dx \;=\; \int_0^l (lx - x^2)\,\cos\frac{n\pi x}{l}\,dx \quad \left\{\begin{array}{l} \because\ L = l \\ \text{and } f(x) = lx - x^2 \end{array}\right\}$$

$$= \left[(lx - x^2)\left(\frac{l}{n\pi}\sin\frac{n\pi x}{l}\right) - (l - 2x)\left(-\frac{l^2}{n^2\pi^2}\cos\frac{n\pi x}{l}\right) + (-2)\left(-\frac{l^3}{n^3\pi^3}\sin\frac{n\pi x}{l}\right) \right]_0^l$$

$$= \; -\frac{l^3}{n^2\pi^2}\cos n\pi - \frac{l^3}{n^2\pi^2} \;=\; -\frac{l^3}{n^2\pi^2}\,(\cos n\pi + 1)$$

At $n = 0$, $F_c\,[f(n)]$ becomes indeterminate, hence we evaluate $F_c(0)$ separately, thus

$$F_c\,(0) \;=\; \int_0^L f(x)\,dx \;=\; \int_0^l (lx - x^2)\,dx$$

$$= \left[l\left(\frac{x^2}{2}\right) - \frac{x^3}{3} \right]_0^l \;=\; \frac{l^3}{2} - \frac{l^3}{3} \;=\; \frac{l^3}{6}$$

Hence finite Fourier cosine transform of $f(x)$ is

$$F_c\,[f(n)] \;=\; -\frac{l^3}{n^2\pi^2}\,(\cos n\pi + 1) \quad \text{and} \quad F_c\,(0) = \frac{l^3}{6}\,.$$

Finite Fourier Sine Transform : From result (8), we have

$$F_s\,[f(x)] \;=\; \int_0^L f(x) \sin\frac{n\pi x}{L}\,dx = \int_0^l (lx - x^2)\sin\frac{n\pi x}{l}\,dx \quad \left\{\begin{array}{l} \because\ L = l \\ \text{and } f(x) = lx - x^2 \end{array}\right.$$

$$= \left[(lx - x^2)\left(-\frac{l}{n\pi}\cos\frac{n\pi x}{l}\right) - (l - 2x)\left(-\frac{l^2}{n^2\pi^2}\sin\frac{n\pi x}{l}\right) + (-2)\left(\frac{l^3}{n^3\pi^3}\cos\frac{n\pi x}{l}\right) \right]_0^l$$

$$= \; -\frac{2l^3}{n^3\pi^3}\cos n\pi + \frac{2l^3}{n^3\pi^3} \;=\; \frac{2l^3}{n^3\pi^3}\,(1 - \cos n\pi)\,.$$

Hence the finite Fourier sine transform of $f(x)$ is

$$F_s\,[f(n)] \;=\; \frac{2l^3}{n^3\pi^3}\,(1 - \cos n\pi).$$

(iii) Finite Fourier Cosine Transform : Using result (6), we have

$$F_c\,[f(n)] \;=\; \int_0^L f(x)\cos\frac{n\pi x}{L}\,dx \;=\; \int_0^\pi f(x)\cos nx\,dx \qquad\qquad [\because\ L = \pi]$$

$$= \int_0^{\pi/2} kx \cos nx\,dx + \int_{\pi/2}^{\pi} k(\pi - x)\cos nx\,dx$$

$$= k\left[x\left(\frac{\sin nx}{n}\right) - (1)\left(-\frac{\cos nx}{n^2}\right)\right]_0^{\pi/2}$$

$$+ k\left[(\pi - x)\left(\frac{\sin nx}{n}\right) - (-1)\left(\frac{\cos nx}{n^2}\right)\right]_{\pi/2}^{\pi}$$

$$= k\left[\left(\frac{\pi}{2}\frac{\sin n\pi/2}{n} + \frac{\cos n\pi/2}{n^2} - \frac{1}{n^2}\right) + \left(-\frac{\cos n\pi}{n^2} - \frac{\pi}{2}\frac{\sin n\pi/2}{n} + \frac{\cos n\pi/2}{n^2}\right)\right]$$

$$= k\left(\frac{2\cos n\pi/2}{n^2} - \frac{\cos n\pi}{n^2} - \frac{1}{n^2}\right)$$

At $n = 0$, $F_c[f(n)]$ becomes indeterminate, hence we evaluate $F_c(0)$ separately, thus

$$F_c(0) = \int_0^L f(x)\,dx = \int_0^{\pi/2} kx\,dx + \int_{\pi/2}^{\pi} k(\pi - x)\,dx$$

$$= k\left[\frac{x^2}{2}\right]_0^{\pi/2} + k\left[\pi x - \frac{x^2}{2}\right]_{\pi/2}^{\pi} = k\left[\frac{\pi^2}{8} + \left(\pi^2 - \frac{\pi^2}{2}\right) - \left(\frac{\pi^2}{2} - \frac{\pi^2}{8}\right)\right]$$

$$= k\left(\frac{\pi^2}{8} + \frac{\pi^2}{8}\right) = \frac{k\pi^2}{4}$$

Hence the finite Fourier cosine transform is

$$F_c[f(n)] = k\left(\frac{2\cos n\pi/2}{n^2} - \frac{\cos n\pi}{n^2} - \frac{1}{n^2}\right) \quad \text{and} \quad F_c(0) = \frac{k\pi^2}{4}.$$

Finite Fourier Sine Transform : Using result (8), we have

$$F_s[f(n)] = \int_0^L f(x)\sin\frac{n\pi x}{L}\,dx = \int_0^{\pi} f(x)\sin nx\,dx \qquad [\because l = \pi]$$

$$= \int_0^{\pi/2} kx\sin nx\,dx + \int_{\pi/2}^{\pi} k(\pi - x)\sin nx\,dx$$

$$= k\left[(x)\left(-\frac{\cos nx}{n}\right) - (1)\left(-\frac{\sin nx}{n^2}\right)\right]_0^{\pi/2}$$

$$+ k\left[(\pi - x)\left(-\frac{\cos nx}{n}\right) - (-1)\left(-\frac{\sin nx}{n^2}\right)\right]_{\pi/2}^{\pi}$$

$$= k \left[\left(-\frac{\pi}{2} \frac{\cos n\pi/2}{n} + \frac{\sin n\pi/2}{n^2} \right) + \left(\frac{\pi}{2} \frac{\cos n\pi/2}{n} + \frac{\sin n\pi/2}{n^2} \right) \right]$$

$$= \frac{2k \sin n\pi/2}{n^2}.$$

Hence the finite Fourier sine transform is

$$F_s\,[f(n)] \;=\; \frac{2k \sin n\pi/2}{n^2}.$$

Ex. 2 : *If $f(x) = \sin kx$, where $0 \le x \le \pi$ and k is an positive integer, then show that*

$$F_s\,[f(n)] \;=\; 0 \ \ if \ \ n \ne k \ \ and \ \ F_s\,[f(n)] \;=\; \frac{\pi}{2} \ \ if \ \ n = k$$

Sol. : Using result (8), we have

$$F_s\,[f(n)] \;=\; \int_0^L f(x) \sin \frac{n\pi x}{L}\, dx \;=\; \int_0^\pi \sin kx \, \sin nx \, dx$$

$$= \frac{1}{2} \int_0^\pi [\cos (n - k)\, x - \cos (n + k)\, x]\, dx$$

$$= \frac{1}{2} \left[\frac{\sin (n - k)\, x}{n - k} - \frac{\sin (n + k)\, x}{n + k} \right]_0^\pi$$

$$= 0 \ \text{as} \ (n - k),\, (n + k) \ \text{are integers but not for} \ n = k.$$

When $n = k$, the first term of the above expression becomes indeterminate, hence we evaluate $F_s\,[f(n)]$ directly by putting $n = k$, thus

$$F_s\,[f(k)] \;=\; \int_0^\pi \sin kx \, \sin kx \, dx = \int_0^\pi \sin^2 kx \, dx$$

$$= \int_0^\pi \left(\frac{1 - \cos 2 kx}{2} \right) dx = \frac{1}{2} \left[x - \frac{\sin 2 kx}{2k} \right]_0^\pi = \frac{\pi}{2}.$$

Ex. 3 : *Find $f(x)$, if*

(i) $\quad F_c\,[f(n)] \;=\; -\dfrac{l^3}{n^2\, \pi^2}\, (1 + \cos n\pi) \quad and \ \ F_c\,(0) = \dfrac{l^3}{6}$, *where $0 \le x \le l$*

(ii) $\quad F_s\,[f(n)] \;=\; \dfrac{2l^3}{n^3\, \pi^3}\, (1 - \cos n\pi)$, *where $0 \le x \le l$*

(iii) $\quad F_c\,[f(n)] \;=\; \dfrac{\cos 2n\pi/3}{(2n + 1)^2}$, *where $0 \le x \le l$*

(iv) $F_s [f(n)] = \dfrac{1 - \cos n\pi}{n^2 \pi^2}$, *where* $0 \leq x \leq \pi$

(v) $F_c [f(n)] = \dfrac{6 (\sin n\pi/2 - \cos n\pi)}{(2n + 1) \pi}$, *for* $n = 1, 2, 3 \dots$ *and* $F_c (0) = -\dfrac{6}{\pi}$,

where $0 \leq x \leq 4$.

Sol. : (i) Since finite Fourier cosine transform is given, we use result (7) to find inverse finite Fourier cosine transform, thus

$$f(x) = \frac{1}{L} F_c (0) + \frac{2}{L} \sum_{n=1}^{\infty} F_c [f(n)] \cos \frac{n\pi x}{L}$$

$$= \frac{1}{l} \left(\frac{l^3}{6} \right) + \frac{2}{l} \sum_{n=1}^{\infty} \left\{ -\frac{l^3}{n^2 \pi^2} (1 + \cos n\pi) \right\} \cos \frac{n\pi x}{l} \qquad \left[\because L = l \right]$$

$$= \frac{l^2}{6} - \frac{2l^2}{\pi^2} \sum_{n=1}^{\infty} \frac{1}{n^2} (1 + \cos n\pi) \cos \frac{n\pi x}{l} .$$

(ii) Since finite Fourier sine transform is given, we use result (9) to find inverse finite Fourier sine transform, thus

$$f(x) = \frac{2}{L} \sum_{n=1}^{\infty} F_s [f(n)] \sin \frac{n\pi x}{L}$$

$$= \frac{2}{l} \sum_{n=1}^{\infty} \frac{2l^3}{n^3 \pi^3} (1 - \cos n\pi) \sin \frac{n\pi x}{l} \qquad [\because L = l]$$

$$= \frac{4l^2}{\pi^3} \sum_{n=1}^{\infty} \frac{1}{n^3} (1 - \cos n\pi) \sin \frac{n\pi x}{l} .$$

(iii) Using result (7), we have

$$f(x) = \frac{1}{L} F_c (0) + \frac{2}{L} \sum_{n=1}^{\infty} F_c [f(n)] \cos \frac{n\pi x}{L}$$

$$= \frac{1}{1} (1) + \frac{2}{1} \sum_{n=1}^{\infty} \frac{\cos 2n \pi/3}{(2n + 1)^2} \cos \frac{n\pi x}{1} \qquad [\because L = 1 \text{ and } F_c (0) = 1]$$

$$= 1 + 2 \sum_{n=1}^{\infty} \frac{\cos 2n \pi/3}{(2n + 1)^2} \cos n\pi x.$$

(iv) Using result (9), we have

$$F(x) = \frac{2}{L} \sum_{n=1}^{\infty} F_s\,[f(x)]\,\sin\frac{n\pi x}{L}$$

$$= \frac{2}{\pi} \sum_{n=1}^{\infty} \left(\frac{1-\cos n\pi}{n^2\,\pi^2}\right)\sin nx \qquad\qquad [\because\ L=\pi]$$

$$= \frac{2}{\pi^3} \sum_{n=1}^{\infty} \frac{1}{n^2}\,(1-\cos n\pi)\,\sin nx.$$

(v) Using result (7), where $l = 4$ and $F_c\,(0) = -\dfrac{6}{\pi}$, we have

$$f(x) = \frac{1}{4}\left(-\frac{6}{\pi}\right) + \frac{2}{4}\sum_{n=1}^{\infty} \frac{6\,(\sin n\pi/2 - \cos n\pi)}{(2n+1)\,\pi} - \cos\frac{n\pi x}{4}.$$

$$= -\frac{3}{2\pi} + \frac{3}{\pi}\sum_{n=1}^{\infty} \frac{(\sin n\pi/2 - \cos n\pi)}{(2n+1)}\cos\frac{n\pi x}{4}.$$

EXERCISE 13.5

1. Find the finite Fourier sine and cosine transform of the following functions :

(i) $f(x) = x^2, \qquad 0 \le x \le 2$

Ans. $F_c\,[f(n)] = \dfrac{16}{n^2\,\pi^2}\,\cos n\pi,\ F_c\,(0) = \dfrac{8}{3}$

$$F_s\,[f(n)] = \frac{8}{n^3\,\pi^3}\,(\cos n\pi - 2) - \frac{8}{n\pi}\,\cos n\pi$$

(ii) $f(x) = x^2, \qquad 0 < x \le \pi$

Ans. $F_c\,[f(n)] = \dfrac{2\pi}{n^2}\,\cos n\pi,\ F_c\,(0) = \dfrac{\pi^3}{3}$

$$F_s\,[f(n)] = \frac{2}{n^3}\,(\cos n\pi - 1) - \frac{\pi^2}{n}\,\cos n\pi$$

(iii) $f(x) = \begin{cases} \pi x, & 0 \le x \le 1 \\ \pi\,(2-x), & 1 \le x \le 2 \end{cases}$

Ans. $F_c\,[f(n)] = \dfrac{4}{n^2\,\pi}\left(2\cos\dfrac{n\pi}{2} - \cos n\pi - 1\right),\ F_c\,(0) = \pi$

$$F_s\,[f(n)] = \frac{8\pi}{n^2\,\pi^2}\,\sin\frac{n\pi}{2}$$

(iv) $f(x) = a\left(1 - \dfrac{x}{l}\right),\ 0 \le x \le l$

Ans. $F_c\,[f(n)] = \dfrac{al}{\pi^2\,n^2}\,(1 - \cos n\pi),\ f(0) = \dfrac{al}{2}$

$$F_s\,[f(n)] = \frac{al}{n\pi}$$

(v) $f(x) = \begin{cases} \pi/3, & 0 \le x \le \pi/3 \\ 0, & \pi/3 \le x \le 2\pi/3 \\ -\pi/3, & 2\pi/3 \le x \le \pi \end{cases}$

$$\textbf{Ans. } F_c\,[f(n)] = \frac{\pi}{3}\,\sin\frac{n\pi}{3}\left(1 + 2\cos\frac{n\pi}{3}\right),\ F_c\,(0) = 0$$

$$F_s\,[f(n)] = -\frac{\pi}{3n}\left(\cos\frac{n\pi}{3} - 1 - \cos n\pi + \cos\frac{2n\pi}{3}\right)$$

2. Find the finite Fourier cosine transforms of the following functions :

(i) $f(x) = \begin{cases} kx, & 0 \le x \le l/2 \\ k\,(l-x), & l/2 \le x \le l \end{cases}$ $\textbf{Ans. } F_c\,[f(n)] = \frac{kl^2}{n^2\,\pi^2}\left(\cos\frac{n\pi}{2} - 1\right),\ F_c\,(0) = \frac{kl^2}{4}$

(ii) $f(x) = \begin{cases} x, & 0 \le x \le \pi/2 \\ \pi-x, & \pi/2 \le x \le \pi \end{cases}$

$$\textbf{Ans. } F_c\,[f(n)] = \frac{1}{n^2}\left(2\cos\frac{n\pi}{2} - \cos n\pi - 1\right),\ F_c\,(0) = \frac{\pi^2}{4}$$

(iii) $f(x) = \sin x,\ 0 \le x \le \pi$ $\textbf{Ans. } F_c\,[f(n)] = -\frac{1}{n^2-1}\,(1 + \cos n\pi),\ F_c\,(0) = 2$

(iv) $f(x) = \left(1 - \dfrac{x}{\pi}\right)^2,\ 0 \le x \le \pi$ $\textbf{Ans. } F_c\,[f(n)] = \frac{2}{\pi n^2}\,;\ F_c\,(0) = \frac{\pi}{3}$

3. Find the finite Fourier sine transforms of the following functions :

(i) $f(x) = \begin{cases} \dfrac{2x}{3}, & 0 \le x \le \dfrac{\pi}{3} \\ \dfrac{\pi-x}{3}, & \dfrac{\pi}{3} \le x \le \pi \end{cases}$ $\textbf{Ans. } F_s\,[f(n)] = \frac{1}{n^2}\,\sin\frac{n\pi}{3}$

(ii) $f(x) = \begin{cases} \dfrac{2k}{l}\,x, & 0 \le x \le l/2 \\ \dfrac{2k}{l}\,(l-x), & l/2 \le x \le l \end{cases}$ $\textbf{Ans. } F_s\,[f(n)] = \frac{4kl}{n^2}\,\sin\frac{n\pi}{2}$

(iii) $f(x) = \cos x,\quad 0 \le x \le \pi$ $\textbf{Ans. } F_s\,[f(n)] = \frac{n}{n^2-1}\,(1 + \cos n\pi)$

(iv) $f(x) = \dfrac{e^{ax} - e^{-ax}}{e^{a\pi} - e^{-a\pi}},\ 0 \le x \le \pi$ $\textbf{Ans. } F_s\,[f(n)] = \frac{-n}{n^2+a^2}\,\cos n\pi$

4. Find f(x), if

(i) $F_c\,[f(n)] = \dfrac{cl}{n\pi}\,\sin\dfrac{n\pi a}{l}$ and $f_c\,(0) = ac$, where $0 \le x \le l$.

$$\textbf{Ans. } f(x) = \frac{ac}{l} + \frac{2c}{\pi}\,\sum_{n=1}^{\infty}\frac{1}{n}\,\sin\frac{n\pi a}{l}\,\cos\frac{n\pi x}{l}$$

(ii) $F_s [f(n)] = \dfrac{2l}{\pi n} \sin^2 \dfrac{n\pi}{4}$, $0 \le x \le l$ **Ans.** $f(x) = \dfrac{4}{\pi} \displaystyle\sum_{n=1}^{\infty} \dfrac{1}{n} \sin^2 \dfrac{n\pi}{4} \sin \dfrac{n\pi x}{l}$

(iii) $F_c [f(n)] = -\dfrac{1}{n^2 - 1} (1 + \cos n\pi)$ and $F_c (0) = 2$, where $0 \le x \le \pi$

$$\textbf{Ans. } f(x) = \frac{2}{\pi} - \frac{2}{\pi} \sum_{n=1}^{\infty} \frac{1}{n^2 - 1} (1 + \cos n\pi) \, \cos nx$$

(iv) $F_s [f(n)] = \dfrac{1}{n^2} \sin \dfrac{n\pi}{3}$, $0 \le x \le \pi$ **Ans.** $f(x) = \dfrac{2}{\pi} \displaystyle\sum_{n=1}^{\infty} \dfrac{1}{n^2} \sin \dfrac{n\pi}{3} \sin nx$

13.12 FOURIER TRANSFORMS OF THE DERIVATIVES OF A FUNCTION

Let $\bar{u} (\lambda, t)$ be the Fourier transform of a function $u(x, t)$ with respect to variable x, i.e.

$$F [u(x, t)] = \bar{u} (\lambda, t) = \int_{-\infty}^{\infty} u(x, t) \, e^{-i\lambda x} \, dx$$

(A) Fourier Transform of $\dfrac{\partial u}{\partial x}$: Suppose $u \to 0$ as $x \to \pm \infty$, then the Fourier transform of $\dfrac{\partial u}{\partial x}$ is given by,

$$F\left[\frac{\partial u}{\partial x}\right] = \int_{-\infty}^{\infty} \frac{\partial u}{\partial x} \, e^{-i\lambda x} \, dx$$

$$= [e^{-i\lambda x} u]_{-\infty}^{\infty} - \int_{-\infty}^{\infty} \{(-i\lambda) e^{-i\lambda x}\} \, u \, dx \quad \text{[Integrating by parts]}$$

$$= 0 + (i\lambda) \int_{-\infty}^{\infty} u(x, t) \, e^{-i\lambda x} \, dx \quad\quad \{\because \, u \to 0 \text{ as } x \to \pm \infty$$

$$= (i\lambda) \, F [u(x, t)] = (i\lambda) \, \bar{u} (\lambda, t)$$

Hence $\boxed{F\left[\dfrac{\partial u}{\partial x}\right] = (i\lambda) \, F[u(x, t)] = (i\lambda) \, \bar{u} (\lambda, t)}$ ... (10)

(B) Fourier Transform of $\dfrac{\partial^2 u}{\partial x^2}$ **:** If u and $\dfrac{\partial u}{\partial x} \to 0$ as $x \to \pm\,\infty$, then the Fourier

transform of $\dfrac{\partial^2 u}{\partial x^2}$ is given by

$$F\left[\frac{\partial^2 u}{\partial x^2}\right] = \int_{-\infty}^{\infty} \frac{\partial^2 u}{\partial x^2}\, e^{-i\lambda x}\, dx = \left[e^{-i\lambda x}\frac{\partial u}{\partial x}\right]_{-\infty}^{\infty} - \int_{-\infty}^{\infty} \{(-\,i\lambda)\, e^{-i\lambda x}\}\, \frac{\partial u}{\partial x}\, dx$$

$$= 0 + (i\lambda) \int_{-\infty}^{\infty} \frac{\partial u}{\partial x}\, e^{-i\lambda x}\, dx \qquad \left\{\because \frac{\partial u}{\partial x} \to 0 \text{ as } x \to \pm\,\infty\right.$$

$$= (i\lambda)\, \{(i\lambda)\, F\,[u(x,\, t)]\} = (i\lambda)^2\, \overline{u}\,(\lambda,\, t) \qquad \text{[By result (10)]}$$

$$= -\,\lambda^2\, F\,[u(x,\, t)] = -\,\lambda^2\, \overline{u}\,(\lambda,\, t)$$

Hence
$$\boxed{\mathbf{F}\left[\frac{\partial^2 \mathbf{u}}{\partial \mathbf{x}^2}\right] = -\,\boldsymbol{\lambda}^2\, \mathbf{F}\,[\mathbf{u(x,\, t)}] = -\,\boldsymbol{\lambda}^2\, \overline{\mathbf{u}}\,(\boldsymbol{\lambda},\, \mathbf{t})} \qquad\qquad \dots\,(11)$$

Remark : In general, we can show that

$$F\left[\frac{\partial^n u}{\partial x^n}\right] = (i\lambda)^n\, F\,[u(x,\, t)] = (i\lambda)^n\, \overline{u}\,(\lambda,\, t)$$

if u, $\dfrac{\partial u}{\partial x}$, $\dfrac{\partial^2 u}{\partial x^2}$, ..., $\dfrac{\partial^n u}{\partial x^n} \to 0$ as $x \to \pm\,\infty$.

(C) Fourier Transform of $\dfrac{\partial u}{\partial t}$ **:** By definition, Fourier transform of $\dfrac{\partial u}{\partial t}$ with

respect to x is given by

$$F\left[\frac{\partial u}{\partial t}\right] = \int_{-\infty}^{\infty} \frac{\partial u}{\partial t}\, e^{-i\lambda x}\, dx = \frac{d}{dt} \int_{-\infty}^{\infty} u(x,\, t)\, e^{-i\lambda x}\, dx$$

$$= \frac{d}{dt}\, F\,[u(x,\, t)] = \frac{d}{dt}\, \overline{u}\,(\lambda,\, t)$$

Hence
$$\boxed{\mathbf{F}\left[\frac{\partial \mathbf{u}}{\partial \mathbf{t}}\right] = \frac{\mathbf{d}}{\mathbf{dt}}\, \mathbf{F}\,[\mathbf{u(x,\, t)}] = \frac{\mathbf{d}}{\mathbf{dt}}\, \overline{\mathbf{u}}\,(\boldsymbol{\lambda},\, \mathbf{t})} \qquad\qquad \dots\,(12)$$

Note : Here we have written the total derivative since F [u(x, t)] depends only on t and not on x.

13.13 FOURIER SINE AND COSINE TRANSFORMS OF $\dfrac{\partial^2 u}{\partial x^2}$

If $\bar{u}_s\,(\lambda,\,t)$ and $\bar{u}_c\,(\lambda,\,t)$ be the Fourier sine and cosine transforms of $u(x,\,t)$ with respect to x, then

$$F_s\,[u(x,\,t)] \;=\; \bar{u}_s\,(\lambda,\,t) = \int_0^\infty u(x,\,t)\,\sin\lambda x\,dx$$

$$F_c\,[u(x,\,t)] \;=\; \bar{u}_c\,(\lambda,\,t) = \int_0^\infty u(x,\,t)\,\cos\lambda x\,dx\;.$$

(A) Fourier Sine Transform of $\dfrac{\partial^2 u}{\partial x^2}$: If u and $\dfrac{\partial u}{\partial x} \to 0$ as $x \to \infty$, then the Fourier sine transform of $\dfrac{\partial^2 u}{\partial x^2}$ is given by,

$$F_s\left[\frac{\partial^2 u}{\partial x^2}\right] \;=\; \int_0^\infty \frac{\partial^2 u}{\partial x^2}\,\sin\lambda x\,dx$$

$$= \left[\sin\lambda x\,\frac{\partial u}{\partial x}\right]_0^\infty - \int_0^\infty (\lambda\cos\lambda x)\,\frac{\partial u}{\partial x}\,dx \qquad \text{[Integrating by parts]}$$

$$= 0 - \lambda\int_0^\infty \frac{\partial u}{\partial x}\,\cos\lambda x\,dx \qquad \left\{\because \frac{\partial u}{\partial x} \to 0 \text{ as } x \to +\infty\right.$$

$$= -\lambda\,[(\cos\lambda x)\,u]_0^\infty + \lambda\int_0^\infty (-\lambda\sin\lambda x)\,u\,dx \quad \text{[Integrating by parts]}$$

$$= \lambda\,[u(x,\,t)]_{x=0} - \lambda^2\int_0^\infty u\,\sin\lambda x\,dx \qquad \left\{\because u \to 0 \text{ as } x \to \infty\right.$$

$$= \lambda\,[u(x,\,t)]_{x=0} - \lambda^2\,F_s\,[u(x,\,t)] \;=\; \lambda\,[u(x,\,t)]_{x=0} - \lambda^2\,\bar{u}_s\,(\lambda,\,t)$$

Hence,

$$\boxed{\;\begin{aligned} F_s\left[\frac{\partial^2 u}{\partial x^2}\right] &= \lambda\,[u(x,\,t)]_{x=0} - \lambda^2\,F_s\,[u(x,\,t)] \\[2mm] &= \lambda\,[u(x,\,t)]_{x=0} - \lambda^2\,\bar{u}_s\,(\lambda,\,t) \end{aligned}\;}$$
$$\qquad \dots (13)$$

(B) Fourier Cosine Transform of $\dfrac{\partial^2 u}{\partial x^2}$: If u and $\dfrac{\partial u}{\partial x} \to 0$ as $x \to \infty$, then the Fourier cosine transform of $\dfrac{\partial^2 u}{\partial x^2}$ is given by,

$$F_c\left[\frac{\partial^2 u}{\partial x^2}\right] = \int_0^\infty \frac{\partial^2 u}{\partial x^2} \cos \lambda x \, dx$$

$$= \left[\cos \lambda x \, \frac{\partial u}{\partial x}\right]_0^\infty - \int_0^\infty (-\lambda \sin \lambda x) \frac{\partial u}{\partial x} \, dx \qquad \text{[Integrating by parts]}$$

$$= -\left[\frac{\partial u}{\partial x}\right]_{x=0} + \lambda \int_0^\infty \frac{\partial u}{\partial x} \sin \lambda x \, dx \qquad \left\{\because \frac{\partial u}{\partial x} \to 0 \text{ as } x \to \infty\right.$$

$$= -\left[\frac{\partial u}{\partial x}\right]_{x=0} + \lambda \left[(\sin \lambda x)\, u\right]_0^\infty - \lambda \int_0^\infty (\lambda \cos \lambda x)\, u \, dx \left[\begin{array}{l}\text{Integrating by}\\ \text{parts}\end{array}\right]$$

$$= -\left[\frac{\partial u}{\partial x}\right]_{x=0} + 0 - \lambda^2 \int_0^\infty u(x, t) \cos \lambda x \, dx \left\{\begin{array}{l}\because u \to 0 \text{ as } x \to \infty\\ \text{and } \sin \lambda u \to 0 \text{ as } x \to 0\end{array}\right.$$

$$= -\left[\frac{\partial u}{\partial x}\right]_{x=0} - \lambda^2 \, F_c\,[u(x, t)] = -\left[\frac{\partial u}{\partial x}\right]_{x=0} - \lambda^2 \, \bar{u}_c\,(\lambda, t)$$

Hence,

$$\boxed{\begin{aligned} F_c\left[\frac{\partial^2 u}{\partial x^2}\right] &= -\left[\frac{\partial u}{\partial x}\right]_{x=0} - \lambda^2 \, F_c\,[u(x, t)]\\[2mm] &= -\left[\frac{\partial u}{\partial x}\right]_{x=0} - \lambda^2 \, \bar{u}_c\,(\lambda, t) \end{aligned}} \qquad \dots (14)$$

Remark 1 : From results (13) and (14), we note that, to find Fourier sine transform of $\dfrac{\partial^2 u}{\partial x^2}$, we require the value of u(x, t) at x = 0 and to find Fourier cosine transform of $\dfrac{\partial^2 u}{\partial x^2}$, we require the value of $\dfrac{\partial u}{\partial x}$ at x = 0.

Remark 2 : In general, Fourier transform of the nth derivative of f(x) is given by

$$F\left[\frac{d^n f}{dx^n}\right] = (i\lambda)^n \, F\,[f(x)] = (i\lambda)^n \, F(\lambda)$$

provided the first (n – 1) derivatives of f(x) will vanish as $x \to \pm \infty$.

For $\quad F\left[\dfrac{d^n f}{dx^n}\right] \; = \; \displaystyle\int_{-\infty}^{\infty} f^n (x)\, e^{-i\lambda x}\, dx$

$$= \left[e^{-i\lambda x} f^{n-1}(x) - (-i\lambda)\, e^{-i\lambda x} f^{n-2}(x) + (-i\lambda)^2 e^{-i\lambda x} f^{n-3}(x) - \ldots \right]_{-\infty}^{\infty}$$

$$+ (-1)^n (-i\lambda)^n \int_{-\infty}^{\infty} e^{-i\lambda x} f(x)\, dx$$

$$= (i\lambda)^n F\,[f(x)] = (i\lambda)^n F(\lambda)$$

By generalised rule of integration by parts and since first $(n - 1)$ derivatives vanish as $x \to \pm\infty$.

13.14 APPLICATIONS OF FOURIER TRANSFORMS TO BOUNDARY VALUE PROBLEMS

Fourier transforms are of great importance in solving boundary value problems and form a basis of powerful method for solution of partial differential equations. For solving boundary value problems, we take Fourier transform of given partial differential equation using given boundary and initial conditions. The required solution is then obtained by taking corresponding inverse transform. The choice of particular transform to be employed for the solution of an equation depends on the boundary conditions of the problem.

We use the following notations for different types of Fourier transform and corresponding inverse transform.

A. **For the interval $-\infty < x < \infty$:** We use infinite Fourier transform

$$F\,[u(x, t)] \; = \; \bar{u}\,(\lambda, t) \; = \; \int_{-\infty}^{\infty} u(x, t)\, e^{-i\lambda x}\, dx \qquad \ldots (15)$$

and corresponding inverse transform is given by

$$u(x, t) \; = \; \frac{1}{2\pi} \int_{-\infty}^{\infty} \bar{u}\,(\lambda, t)\, e^{+i\lambda x}\, d\lambda \qquad \ldots (16)$$

B. **For the interval $0 < x < \infty$:** We use Fourier sine or cosine transforms depending on boundary conditions of the problems.

(i) **Fourier Sine Transform :**

$$F_s\,[u(x, t)] \; = \; \bar{u}_s\,(\lambda, t) = \int_{0}^{\infty} u(x, t)\, \sin \lambda x\, dx \qquad \ldots (17)$$

and the inverse sine transform is

$$u(x, t) \; = \; \frac{2}{\pi} \int_{0}^{\infty} \bar{u}_s\,(\lambda, t)\, \sin \lambda x\, d\lambda \qquad \ldots (18)$$

(ii) **Fourier Cosine Transform :**

$$F_c [u(x, t)] = \bar{u}_c (\lambda, t) = \int_0^\infty u(x, t) \cos \lambda x \, dx \qquad \ldots (19)$$

and the inverse cosine transform is

$$u(x, t) = \frac{2}{\pi} \int_0^\infty \bar{u}_c (\lambda, t) \cos \lambda x \, d\lambda \qquad \ldots (20)$$

C. **For the interval $0 < x < L$:** We use finite Fourier sine or cosine transforms depending on boundary conditions of the problems.

(i) **Finite Fourier Sine Transform :**

$$F_s [u(x, t)] = \bar{u}_s (n, t) = \int_0^L u(x, t) \sin \frac{n\pi x}{L} \, dx \qquad \ldots (21)$$

and the inverse Fourier sine transform is

$$u(x, t) = \frac{2}{L} \sum_{n=1}^\infty \bar{u}_s (n, t) \sin \frac{n\pi x}{L} \qquad \ldots (22)$$

(ii) **Finite Fourier Cosine Transform :**

$$F_c [u(x, t)] = \bar{u}_c (n, t) = \int_0^L u(x, t) \cos \frac{n\pi x}{L} \, dx \qquad \ldots (23)$$

and the inverse finite Fourier cosine transform is

$$u(x, t) = \frac{1}{L} \bar{u}_c (0, t) + \frac{2}{L} \sum_{n=1}^\infty \bar{u}_c (n, t) \cos \frac{n\pi x}{L} \, dx \qquad \ldots (24)$$

13.15 THE CHOICE OF FOURIER TRANSFORMS

Depending on boundary conditions, we select the Fourier transform which is required to be operated on the related partial differential equation for its solution.

A. **If the interval is $-\infty < x < \infty$** and if boundary conditions are

$u \to 0$ as $x \to \pm \infty$ and $\dfrac{\partial u}{\partial x} \to 0$ as $x \to \pm \infty$, we use infinite Fourier transform [result (15)].

B. **If the interval is $0 < x < \infty$** and

(i) If boundary conditions are u and $\dfrac{\partial u}{\partial x} \to 0$ as $x \to \infty$ and $u(x, t) = 0$ or $f(t)$ at $x = 0$ and for all t we use Fourier sine transform [result (17)]

(ii) If boundary conditions are u and $\dfrac{\partial u}{\partial x} \to 0$ as $x \to \infty$ and $\dfrac{\partial u}{\partial x} = 0$ or $f(t)$ at $x = 0$ and for all t we use Fourier cosine transform [result (19)].

Note : For the interval $0 < x < \infty$, we always assume u and $\dfrac{\partial u}{\partial x} \to 0$ as $x \to \infty$, even if it is not given in the problem.

C.   If the interval is $0 < x < L$ and

(i)   If boundary conditions are $u(0, t) = u(L, t) = 0$ for all t, we use finite Fourier sine transform [result (29)].

(ii)   If boundary conditions are $\dfrac{\partial u}{\partial x}(0, t) = \dfrac{\partial u}{\partial x}(L, t) = 0$ for all t, we use finite Fourier cosine transform.

ILLUSTRATIONS ON SOLUTIONS OF BOUNDARY VALUE PROBLEMS USING FOURIER TRANSFORMS

Type 1 : Problems on heat flow in an infinite bar

Ex. 1 : *Use Fourier transform to solve the boundary value problem*

$$\frac{\partial u}{\partial t} = k \frac{\partial^2 u}{\partial x^2} - \infty < x < \infty, \quad t > 0 \qquad \ldots (i)$$

subject to the following conditions :

(a) $u, \dfrac{\partial u}{\partial x} \to 0$ as $x \to \pm \infty$ $\qquad \ldots (ii)$

(b) $u(x, 0) = f(x)$ $\qquad \ldots (iii)$

Sol. : Let $u(x, t)$ be the solution of the given partial differential equation. Since the interval is $-\infty < x < \infty$, we use infinite Fourier transform.

Taking the infinite (general) Fourier transform with respect to x of both sides of the given partial differential equation, we have

$$F\left[\frac{\partial u}{\partial t}\right] = k\, F\left[\frac{\partial^2 u}{\partial x^2}\right] \qquad \ldots (iv)$$

Let $\bar{u}(\lambda, t)$ be the infinite Fourier transform of $u(x, t)$, which is given by [result (15)]

i.e.$\qquad \bar{u}(\lambda, t) = \displaystyle\int_{-\infty}^{\infty} u(x, t)\, e^{-i\lambda x}\, dx \qquad \ldots (v)$

Now$\qquad F\left[\dfrac{\partial u}{\partial t}\right] = \displaystyle\int_{-\infty}^{\infty} \frac{\partial u}{\partial t}\, e^{-i\lambda x}\, dx = \frac{d}{dt} \int_{-\infty}^{\infty} u(x, t)\, e^{-i\lambda x}\, dx$

$\therefore \qquad F\left[\dfrac{\partial u}{\partial t}\right] = \dfrac{d\bar{u}}{dt} \qquad\qquad\qquad$ [refer result (12)] $\ldots (vi)$

Similarly,$\quad F\left[\dfrac{\partial^2 u}{\partial x^2}\right] = \displaystyle\int_{-\infty}^{\infty} \frac{\partial^2 u}{\partial x^2}\, e^{-i\lambda x}\, dx = -\lambda^2\, \bar{u}(\lambda, t)$ [by result (11)] $\quad \ldots (vii)$

Substituting (vi) and (vii) in (iv), we get

$$\frac{d\bar{u}}{dt} = -k\lambda^2\, \bar{u} \qquad \ldots (viii)$$

The solution of this ordinary differential equation (viii) is

$$\bar{u} = \bar{u}(\lambda, t) = A\, e^{-k\lambda^2 t} \qquad \dots \text{(ix)}$$

To find the arbitrary constant A, we take infinite Fourier transform of initial condition (iii), then

$$\bar{u}(\lambda, 0) = \int_{-\infty}^{\infty} u(x, 0)\, e^{-i\lambda x}\, dx = \int_{-\infty}^{\infty} f(x)\, e^{-i\lambda x}\, dx$$

$$= \int_{-\infty}^{\infty} f(u)\, e^{-i\lambda u}\, du$$

$$\therefore \qquad \bar{u}(\lambda, 0) = F(\lambda) \qquad \dots \text{(x)}$$

Now if we put $t = 0$ in (ix) and then using (x), we have

$$\bar{u}(\lambda, 0) = A = F(\lambda) \qquad \dots \text{(xi)}$$

Putting this value of A in (ix), we have

$$\bar{u}(\lambda, t) = F(\lambda)\, e^{-k\lambda^2 t} \qquad \dots \text{(xii)}$$

Taking inverse Fourier transform of (xii), we obtain

$$u(x, t) = \frac{1}{2\pi} \int_{-\infty}^{\infty} F(\lambda)\, e^{-k\lambda^2 t}\, e^{i\lambda x}\, d\lambda \qquad \text{[by result (16)]}$$

$$= \frac{1}{2\pi} \int_{-\infty}^{\infty} \int_{-\infty}^{\infty} f(u)\, e^{-i\lambda u}\, e^{-k\lambda^2 t}\, e^{i\lambda x}\, du\, d\lambda$$

$$= \frac{1}{2\pi} \int_{-\infty}^{\infty} \int_{-\infty}^{\infty} f(u)\, e^{-k\lambda^2 t}\, e^{i\lambda(x-u)}\, du\, d\lambda$$

which is the required solution.

Note : The above solution can be further simplified as

$$u(x, t) = \frac{1}{\pi} \int_{0}^{\infty} \int_{-\infty}^{\infty} f(u)\, e^{-k\lambda^2 t}\, \cos \lambda(x-u)\, du\, d\lambda$$

$$= \frac{1}{\pi} \int_{-\infty}^{\infty} f(u) \int_{0}^{\infty} e^{-k\lambda^2 t}\, \cos \lambda(x-u)\, d\lambda\, du$$

Using result $\int\limits_{0}^{\infty} e^{-a\lambda^2} \cos 2\,b\lambda\, d\lambda = \frac{1}{2}\sqrt{\frac{\pi}{a}}\ e^{-b^2/a}$ with $a = kt$ and $b = \dfrac{x - u}{2}$, we have

$$u(x,\,t)\ =\ \frac{1}{2\sqrt{k\pi t}}\ \int\limits_{-\infty}^{\infty} f(u)\ e^{-(x-u)^2/4kt}\, du$$

$$=\ \frac{1}{\sqrt{\pi}}\ \int\limits_{-\infty}^{\infty} f\left(x + 2\sqrt{kt}\ v\right)\ e^{-v^2}\ dv \qquad \left\{ \begin{array}{l} \text{on putting } v = \dfrac{u - x}{2\sqrt{kt}} \\[2ex] \therefore\ \ dv = \dfrac{du}{2\sqrt{kt}} \end{array} \right.$$

Remark 1 : The conduction of heat along a bar is governed by the one-dimensional heat-flow equation (diffusion equation) $\dfrac{\partial u}{\partial t} = k\,\dfrac{\partial^2 u}{\partial x^2}$.

Remark 2 : Another statement for the Ex. 1 :

Using Fourier transform method, determine the temperature distribution $u(x,\,t)$ in an infinite bar when the initial temperature distribution is $f(x)$ and $-\infty < x < \infty$.

Remark 3 : The condition $\dfrac{\partial u}{\partial x} \to 0$ as $x \to \pm\infty$ represents that temperature $u(x,\,t)$ must be bounded. This condition can also be expressed as $|u(x,\,t)| < M$.

Ex. 2 : *If the initial temperature of an infinite bar is given by*

$$\theta\,(x,\,0)\ =\ \left\{ \begin{array}{ll} \theta_0, & |x| < a \\[2ex] 0, & |x| > a \end{array} \right.$$

determine the temperature at any point x and at any instant t.

Sol. : To determine temperature $\theta(x,\,t)$ at any point at any time, we have to solve one dimensional heat-flow equation.

$$\frac{\partial \theta}{\partial t}\ =\ c^2 \frac{\partial^2 \theta}{\partial x^2} \qquad t > 0 \qquad\qquad \ldots \text{(i)}$$

subject to the initial condition

$$\theta\,(x,\,0)\ =\ \left\{ \begin{array}{ll} \theta_0, & |x| < a \\[2ex] 0, & |x| > a \end{array} \right. \qquad\qquad \ldots \text{(ii)}$$

and the boundary conditions, which we assume are

$$\theta\,(x,\,t)\ \text{ and } \frac{\partial \theta}{\partial x} \to 0 \quad \text{as} \quad x \to \pm\infty \qquad\qquad \ldots \text{(iii)}$$

(since the temperature must be bounded).

Since the interval is $-\infty < x < \infty$, we take infinite Fourier transform [using result (11)] of both sides of partial differential equation (i) i.e.

$$F\left[\frac{\partial \theta}{dt}\right] = c^2 \, F\left[\frac{\partial^2 \theta}{\partial x^2}\right] \qquad \text{... (iv)}$$

Using results (11) and (12), we have

$$\frac{d\,\bar\theta}{dt} = -c^2 \lambda^2 \, \bar\theta \qquad \text{... (v)}$$

Solving the ordinary differential equation (v) for $\bar\theta$, we obtain

$$\bar\theta = \bar\theta\,(\lambda, t) = A\,e^{-c^2\lambda^2 t} \qquad \text{... (vi)}$$

To find arbitrary constant A, we take infinite Fourier transform of initial condition (ii) i.e.

$$\bar\theta\,(\lambda, 0) = \int_{-\infty}^{\infty} \theta\,(x, 0)\,e^{-i\lambda x}\,dx = \int_{-a}^{a} \theta_o\,e^{-i\lambda x}\,dx = \theta_o \left[\frac{e^{-i\lambda x}}{-i\lambda}\right]_{-a}^{a}$$

$$= \theta_o \left[\frac{e^{i\lambda a} - e^{-i\lambda a}}{i\lambda}\right] = \frac{2\theta_o}{\lambda}\,\sin \lambda a \qquad \text{... (vii)}$$

Substituting $t = 0$ in (vi) and using (vii), we have

$$\bar\theta\,(\lambda, 0) = A = \frac{2\theta_o}{\lambda}\,\sin \lambda a \qquad \text{... (viii)}$$

Putting this value of A in (vi), we have

$$\bar\theta\,(\lambda, t) = \frac{2\,\theta_o}{\lambda}\,\sin \lambda a \, e^{-c^2\lambda^2 t} \qquad \text{... (ix)}$$

Taking inverse infinite Fourier transform, we have

$$\theta\,(x, t) = \frac{1}{2\pi} \int_{-\infty}^{\infty} \left(\frac{2\,\theta_o}{\lambda}\,\sin \lambda a \, e^{-c^2\lambda^2 t}\right) e^{i\lambda x}\,d\lambda$$

$$= \frac{\theta_o}{\pi} \int_{-\infty}^{\infty} \frac{\sin \lambda a}{\lambda}\,e^{-c^2\lambda^2 t}\,(\cos \lambda x + i \sin \lambda x)\,d\lambda$$

$$= \frac{2\theta_o}{\pi} \int_{0}^{\infty} \frac{\sin \lambda a}{\lambda}\,e^{-c^2\lambda^2 t}\,\cos \lambda x\,d\lambda \qquad \left\{\begin{array}{l}\text{second integral} \\ \text{vanishes as its} \\ \text{integrand is odd} \\ \text{function}\end{array}\right.$$

$$= \frac{\theta_o}{\pi} \int_{0}^{\infty} e^{-c^2\lambda^2 t} \left[\frac{\sin\,(a + x)\,\lambda + \sin\,(a - x)\,\lambda}{\lambda}\right] d\lambda$$

which is the required solution.

Ex. 3 : *The initial temperature along the length of an infinite bar is given by*

$$u(x, 0) = \begin{cases} 2, & |x| < 1 \\ 0, & |x| > 1 \end{cases} \qquad \ldots (i)$$

If the temperature u(x, t) satisfies the equation

$$\frac{\partial u}{\partial t} = \frac{\partial^2 u}{\partial x^2} \qquad -\infty < x < \infty, \qquad t > 0 \qquad \ldots (ii)$$

find the temperature at any point of the bar at any time t.

Sol. : Let $\bar{u}\,(\lambda, t)$ be the Fourier transform of u(x, t), since the interval is $-\infty < x < \infty$, we take infinite Fourier transform of both sides of given partial differential equation.

$$F\left[\frac{\partial u}{\partial x}\right] = F\left[\frac{\partial^2 u}{\partial x^2}\right]$$

Using results (11) and (12), we have

$$\frac{d\bar{u}}{dt} = -\lambda^2 \bar{u} \qquad \ldots (iii)$$

The solution of this ordinary differential equation is

$$\bar{u}\,(\lambda, t) = A\,e^{-\lambda^2 t} \qquad \ldots (iv)$$

To find arbitrary constant A, we take infinite Fourier transform of (i) i.e.

$$\bar{u}\,(\lambda, 0) = \int_{-\infty}^{\infty} u(x, 0)\,e^{-i\lambda x}\,dx = \int_{-1}^{1} (2)\,e^{-i\lambda x}\,dx$$

$$= 2\left[\frac{e^{-i\lambda x}}{-i\lambda}\right]_{-1}^{1} = \frac{2}{\lambda}\left[\frac{e^{i\lambda} - e^{-i\lambda}}{i}\right]$$

$$= \frac{4}{\lambda}\,\sin\lambda \qquad \ldots (v)$$

Substituting t = 0 in (iv), then we have using (v)

$$\bar{u}\,(\lambda, 0) = A = \frac{4}{\lambda}\,\sin\lambda \qquad \ldots (vi)$$

Putting this value of A in (iv), we have

$$\bar{u}\,(\lambda, t) = \frac{4}{\lambda}\,\sin\lambda\,e^{-\lambda^2 t} \qquad \ldots (vii)$$

Taking inverse infinite Fourier transform, we obtain

$$u\,(x, t) = \frac{1}{2\pi} \int_{-\infty}^{\infty} \frac{4}{\lambda}\,\sin\lambda\,e^{-\lambda^2 t}\,e^{i\lambda x}\,d\lambda$$

$$= \frac{2}{\pi} \int_{-\infty}^{\infty} \frac{\sin\lambda}{\lambda}\,e^{-\lambda^2 t}\,(\cos\lambda x + i\sin\lambda x)\,d\lambda$$

$$= \frac{4}{\pi} \int_0^\infty \frac{e^{-\lambda^2 t}}{\lambda} \sin \lambda \cos \lambda x \, d\lambda \qquad \left\{ \begin{array}{l} \text{second integral} \\ \text{vanishes as its} \\ \text{integrand is odd} \\ \text{function.} \end{array} \right.$$

$$= \frac{2}{\pi} \int_0^\infty e^{-\lambda^2 t} \left[\frac{\sin (1 + x) \lambda + \sin (1 - x) \lambda}{\lambda} \right] d\lambda$$

which is the required solution.

Type 2 : Problems on heat-flow in semi-infinite bar :

Ex. 4 : *Determine the distribution of temperature in the semi-infinite medium $x \geq 0$, when the end $x = 0$ is maintained at zero temperature and the initial distribution of temperature is f(x).*

Sol. : Let u(x, t) be the temperature at any point x at any time t. We have to solve the heat-flow equation

$$\frac{\partial u}{\partial t} = c^2 \frac{\partial^2 u}{\partial x^2}, \qquad 0 < x < \infty, \quad t > 0 \qquad \qquad \text{... (i)}$$

subject to the initial condition

$$u(x, 0) = f(x), \quad x > 0 \qquad \qquad \text{... (ii)}$$

and the boundary condition

$$u(0, t) = 0, \quad t > 0 \qquad \qquad \text{... (iii)}$$

and also the boundary condition

$$u \text{ and } \frac{\partial u}{\partial x} \to 0 \text{ as } x \to \infty \text{ for all } t \qquad \qquad \text{... (iv)}$$

(condition (iv) is always to be assumed)

Since the interval is $0 < x < \infty$ and u (x, t) at x = 0 is given, we use Fourier sine transform given by result (17).

Taking Fourier sine transform with respect to x of both sides of the given partial differential equation, we have

$$F_s\left[\frac{\partial u}{\partial t}\right] = F_s\left[\frac{\partial^2 u}{\partial x^2}\right] \qquad \qquad \text{... (v)}$$

Now, $\qquad F_s\left[\frac{\partial u}{\partial t}\right] = \int_0^\infty \frac{\partial u}{\partial t} \sin \lambda x \, dx = \frac{d}{dt} \int_0^\infty u(x, t) \sin \lambda x \, dx$

$\therefore \qquad F_s\left[\frac{\partial u}{\partial t}\right] = \frac{d \bar{u}_s}{dt} \qquad \qquad \text{... (vi)}$

and $\qquad F_s\left[\frac{\partial^2 \bar{u}}{\partial x^2}\right] = \int_0^\infty \frac{\partial^2 u}{\partial x^2} \sin \lambda x \, dx$

$$= \lambda \, [u(x, t)]_{x = 0} - \lambda^2 \bar{u}_s (\lambda, t) \qquad \qquad \text{[Using result (13)]}$$

$$= - \lambda^2 \bar{u}_s (\lambda, t) \qquad \qquad \text{... (vii)}$$

Substituting (vi) and (vii) in (v), we have $\dfrac{d\overline{u}_s}{dt} = -c^2\lambda^2\overline{u}_s$ ... (viii)

The solution of this equation is $\overline{u}_s(\lambda, t) = A\,e^{-c^2\lambda^2 t}$ ... (ix)

Now, we take Fourier sine transform of initial condition (ii) i.e.

$$F_s[u(x,0)] = \overline{u}_s(\lambda, 0) = \int_0^\infty u(x,0)\sin\lambda x\,dx$$

$$= \int_0^\infty f(x)\sin\lambda x\,dx = \int_0^\infty f(u)\sin\lambda u\,du = F_s(\lambda) \ ... \ (x)$$

Substituting $t = 0$ in (ix) and using (x), we get

$$\overline{u}_s(\lambda, 0) = A = F_s(\lambda) \qquad\qquad ... \ (xi)$$

Putting the value of A from (xi) in (ix), we have

$$\overline{u}_s(\lambda, t) = F_s(\lambda)\,e^{-c^2\lambda^2 t} \qquad\qquad ... \ (xii)$$

Taking inverse Fourier sine transform of (xii), we obtain

$$u(x,t) = \frac{2}{\pi}\int_0^\infty F_s(\lambda)\,e^{-c^2\lambda^2 t}\sin\lambda x\,d\lambda \qquad\qquad \text{[By result (26)]}$$

$$= \frac{2}{\pi}\int_0^\infty\int_0^\infty f(u)\,e^{-c^2\lambda^2 t}\sin\lambda u\,\sin\lambda x\,du\,d\lambda \qquad\qquad \text{[from (x)]}$$

which is the required solution.

Note : Using result $\sin\lambda x\,\sin\lambda u = \dfrac{1}{2}[\cos\lambda(u-x) - \cos\lambda(u+x)]$ and integral result $\displaystyle\int_0^\infty$

$e^{-a\lambda^2}\cos\ b\lambda\ d\lambda = \dfrac{1}{2}\sqrt{\dfrac{\pi}{a}}\,e^{-b^2/4a}$, we can write the above solution

(on substituting $\dfrac{u-x}{2c\sqrt{t}} = v$ in the first integral and $\dfrac{u+x}{2c\sqrt{t}} = v$ in the second integral)

as

$$u(x,t) = \frac{1}{\sqrt{\pi}}\left[\int_{-x/2c\sqrt{t}}^\infty e^{-v^2}f\left(x + 2c\sqrt{t}\,v\right)dv - \int_{x/2c\sqrt{t}}^\infty e^{-v^2}f\left(2c\sqrt{t}\,v - x\right)dv\right]$$

If we let initial temperature $f(x) = u_o$ (constant), then

$$u(x,t) = \frac{2u_o}{\sqrt{\pi}}\left[\int_0^{x/2c\sqrt{t}} e^{-v^2}\,dv\right] = u_o\,\mathrm{erf}\left(\frac{x}{2c\sqrt{t}}\right).$$

Ex. 5 : *Use Fourier transform to solve the equation*   **(Dec. 09, 14, May 14, 15, 16)**

$$\frac{\partial u}{\partial t} = \frac{\partial^2 u}{\partial x^2} \qquad 0 < x < \infty, \; t > 0 \qquad \qquad \text{... (i)}$$

subject to the following conditions :

(a) $u(0, t) = 0 \quad t > 0$ $\qquad\qquad$ ... (ii)

(b) $u(x, 0) = \begin{cases} 1, & 0 < x < 1 \\ 0, & x > 1 \end{cases}$ $\qquad\qquad$ ... (iii)

(c) $u(x, t)$ *is bounded.* $\qquad\qquad$ ... (iv)

Sol. : Since the interval is $0 < x < \infty$ and $[u(x, t)]$ at $x = 0$ is given, taking Fourier sine transform of both sides of the given equation, we get

$$F_s\left[\frac{\partial u}{\partial t}\right] = F_s\left[\frac{\partial^2 u}{\partial x^2}\right]$$

Using results (12) and (13), we get

$$\frac{d\,\overline{u}_s}{dt} = \lambda\,[u(x, t)]_{x=0} - \lambda^2 \overline{u}_s\,(\lambda, t)$$

or $\qquad\qquad \dfrac{d\,\overline{u}_s}{dt} = -\lambda^2 \overline{u}_s$ $\qquad\qquad$ [By (ii)]

or $\qquad\qquad \dfrac{d\,\overline{u}_s}{dt} + \lambda^2 \overline{u}_s = 0$ $\qquad\qquad$ ... (v)

Solution of the equation (v) is given by

$$\overline{u}_s\,(\lambda, t) = A\,e^{-\lambda^2 t}, \; \text{where, A is the arbitrary constant.} \qquad \text{... (vi)}$$

To find arbitrary constant A, we take Fourier sine transform of initial condition (iii), i.e.

$$\overline{u}_s\,(\lambda, 0) = \int_0^\infty u(x, 0) \sin \lambda x \, dx = \int_0^1 (1) \sin \lambda x \, dx + \int_1^\infty (0) \, \sin \lambda x \, dx$$

$$= \left[\frac{-\cos \lambda x}{\lambda}\right]_0^1 = \frac{1 - \cos \lambda}{\lambda} \qquad \qquad \text{... (vii)}$$

Substituting $t = 0$ in (vi) and using (vii), we get

$$\overline{u}_s\,(\lambda, 0) = A = \frac{1 - \cos \lambda}{\lambda} \qquad\qquad \text{... (viii)}$$

Putting the value of A from (viii) in (vi), we have

$$\overline{u}_s\,(\lambda, t) = \frac{1 - \cos \lambda}{\lambda} \, e^{-\lambda^2 t} \qquad\qquad \text{... (ix)}$$

Taking inverse Fourier sine transform of (ix), we obtain

$$u(x, t) = \frac{2}{\pi} \int_0^\infty \frac{1 - \cos \lambda}{\lambda} \, e^{-\lambda^2 t} \, \sin \lambda x \, d\lambda$$

which is the required solution.

Ex. 6 : *Using Fourier sine transform, solve the partial differential equation*

$$\frac{\partial u}{\partial t} = 2 \frac{\partial^2 u}{\partial x^2} \qquad 0 < x < \infty, \ t > 0 \qquad \text{... (i)}$$

subject to the following conditions :   **(Dec. 10, Nov. 15)**

(a) $u(0, t) = 0$ $t > 0$ *... (ii)*

(b) $u(x, 0) = e^{-x}$ $x > 0$ *... (iii)*

(c) u *and* $\dfrac{\partial u}{\partial x} \to 0$ *as* $x \to \infty$ *... (iv)*

Sol. : Since the interval is $0 < x < \infty$ and boundary condition $u(0, t) = 0$ for all t is given, taking Fourier sine transform of both sides of the given equation, we get

$$F_s \left[\frac{\partial u}{\partial t} \right] = 2 F_s \left[\frac{\partial^2 u}{\partial x^2} \right]$$

Using results (12) and (13), we get

$$\frac{d \bar{u}_s}{d t} = 2 \left\{ \lambda \, [u(x, t)]_{x = 0} - \lambda^2 \bar{u}_s (\lambda, t) \right\}$$

$$\frac{d \bar{u}_s}{d t} = 2 \left\{ 0 - \lambda^2 \bar{u}_s (\lambda, t) \right\} \qquad \text{[By (ii)]}$$

$$\therefore \qquad \frac{d \bar{u}_s}{d t} = - 2 \lambda^2 \bar{u}_s \qquad \text{... (v)}$$

Solution of this ordinary differential equation is

$$\bar{u}_s (\lambda, t) = A (\lambda) \, e^{-2 \lambda^2 t} \qquad \text{... (vi)}$$

To determine constant A, we take Fourier sine transform of initial condition (iii), i.e.

$$\bar{u}_s (\lambda, 0) = \int_0^\infty u(x, 0) \sin \lambda x \, dx = \int_0^\infty e^{-x} \sin \lambda x \, dx$$

$$= \left[\frac{e^{-x}}{1 + \lambda^2} (- \sin \lambda x - \lambda \cos \lambda x) \right]_0^\infty$$

$$= \frac{\lambda}{1 + \lambda^2} \qquad \text{... (vii)}$$

Substituting $t = 0$ in (vi) and using (vii), we get

$$\bar{u}_s (\lambda, 0) = A = \frac{\lambda}{1 + \lambda^2} \qquad \text{... (viii)}$$

Putting the value of A from (viii) in (vi), we have

$$\bar{u}_s (\lambda, t) = \frac{\lambda}{1 + \lambda^2} \, e^{-2\lambda^2 t} \qquad \text{... (ix)}$$

Hence taking inverse Fourier sine transform of (ix), we obtain

$$u(x, t) \; = \; \frac{2}{\pi} \int_0^\infty \overline{u}\,(\lambda, t) \; \sin \lambda x \; d\lambda$$

$$= \; \frac{2}{\pi} \int_0^\infty \frac{\lambda}{1 + \lambda^2} \; e^{-2\lambda^2 t} \; \sin \lambda x \; d\lambda$$

which is the required solution.

Ex. 7 : *Solve the equation*

$$\frac{\partial u}{\partial t} \; = \; k \, \frac{\partial^2 u}{\partial x^2} \qquad 0 < x < \infty, \;\; t > 0 \qquad\qquad \text{... (i)}$$

subject to the boundary condition

$$u(0, t) \; = \; f(t), \quad t > 0 \qquad\qquad \text{... (ii)}$$

and the initial condition

$$u(x, 0) \; = \; 0, \quad x > 0. \qquad\qquad \text{... (iii)}$$

Sol. : Here the boundary and initial conditions are

(a) $u \to 0$ as $x \to \infty$ $t > 0$

(b) $\dfrac{\partial u}{\partial x} \to 0$ as $x \to \infty$ $t > 0$ $\qquad\qquad \text{... (iv)}$

(c) $u(0, t) = f(t)$ $t > 0$

(d) $u(x, 0) = 0$ $x > 0$

[**Note :** Conditions (a) and (b) are always to be assumed when $0 < x < \infty$.]

Since the interval is $0 < x < \infty$ and $u(0, t)$ is given, we take Fourier sine transform of both sides of equation (i), i.e.

$$F_s \left[\frac{\partial u}{\partial t} \right] \; = \; k \, F_s \left[\frac{\partial^2 u}{\partial x^2} \right]$$

Using results (12) and (13), we get

$$\frac{d \overline{u}_s}{d t} \; = \; k \left\{ \lambda \, [u(x, t)]_{x=0} - \lambda^2 \overline{u}_s \, (\lambda, t) \right\}$$

$$= \; k \left\{ \lambda \, u(0, t) - \lambda^2 \overline{u}_s \, (\lambda, t) \right\}$$

$$= \; k \lambda \, f(t) - k \, \lambda^2 \overline{u}_s \, (\lambda, t)$$

$$\text{or} \qquad \frac{d \overline{u}_s}{d t} + k\lambda^2 \overline{u}_s \; = \; k\lambda \; f(t) \qquad\qquad \text{... (v)}$$

Solving Linear differential equation (v) in $\bar{u}$ and t, we get

$$\bar{u}_s \, e^{k\lambda^2 t} = \int_0^t k\lambda \, f(t) \, e^{k\lambda^2 t} \, dt + A \qquad \begin{cases} \text{G.S. of } \dfrac{dy}{dx} + Py = Q \text{ is} \\[2mm] y \cdot \text{I. F.} = \int Q \cdot \text{I.F.} \, dx + A \\[2mm] \text{where I.F.} = e^{\int P dx} \end{cases}$$

or
$$\bar{u}_s (\lambda, t) = e^{-k\lambda^2 t} \int_0^t k\lambda \, f(t) \, e^{k\lambda^2 t} \, dt + A \, e^{-k\lambda^2 t}$$

$$= e^{-k\lambda^2 t} \int_0^t k\lambda \, f(z) \, e^{k\lambda^2 z} \, dz + A \, e^{-k\lambda^2 t}$$

[replacing t by z in the integral]

$$= \int_0^t k\lambda \, f(z) \, e^{k\lambda^2 (z-t)} \, dz + A \, e^{-k\lambda^2 t} \qquad \dots \text{(vi)}$$

Now to determine arbitrary constant A, we take Fourier sine transform of the initial condition (iii), which is

$$F_s [u(x, 0)] = \bar{u}_s (\lambda, 0) = \int_0^\infty u(x, 0) \sin \lambda x = 0 \qquad \dots \text{(vii)}$$

Substituting t = 0 in (vi) and using (vii), we get

$$\bar{u} (\lambda, 0) = A = 0 \qquad \dots \text{(viii)}$$

Putting this value of A from (viii) in (vi), we get

$$\bar{u}_s (\lambda, t) = \int_0^t k\lambda \, f(z) \, e^{k\lambda^2 (z-t)} \, dz \qquad \dots \text{(ix)}$$

Taking inverse of Fourier transform (ix), we obtain

$$u(x, t) = \frac{2}{\pi} \int_0^\infty \bar{u}_s (\lambda, t) \sin \lambda x \, d\lambda$$

$$= \frac{2}{\pi} \int_0^\infty \int_0^\infty k\lambda \, f(z) \, e^{k\lambda^2 (z-t)} \sin \lambda x \, dz \, d\lambda$$

$$= \frac{2k}{\pi} \int_{\lambda=0}^\infty \int_{z=0}^k \lambda \, f(z) \, e^{k\lambda^2 (z-t)} \sin \lambda x \, dz \, d\lambda$$

which is the required solution.

Ex. 8 : Use Fourier transform to solve   **(Dec. 2009, Nov. 2013, May 2017)**

$$\frac{\partial u}{\partial t} = \frac{\partial^2 u}{d\, x^2} \qquad 0 < x < \infty,\ t > 0 \qquad \qquad \dots \text{(i)}$$

where, $u(x, t)$ satisfies the conditions :

(a) $\left(\dfrac{\partial u}{\partial x}\right)_{x=0} = 0 \qquad t > 0 \qquad \qquad \dots \text{(ii)}$

(b) $u(x, 0) = \begin{cases} x, & 0 < x < 1 \\ 0, & x > 1 \end{cases} \qquad \qquad \dots \text{(iii)}$

(c) $|u(x, t)| < M \qquad \qquad \dots \text{(iv)}$

Sol. : Since the interval is $0 < x < \infty$ and $u_x\,(0, t)$ is given, taking Fourier cosine transform of both sides of the given equation, we get

$$F_c\left[\frac{\partial u}{\partial t}\right] = F_c\left[\frac{\partial^2 u}{\partial x^2}\right]$$

Using results (12) and (14), we have

$$\int_0^\infty \frac{\partial u}{\partial t}\ \cos \lambda x\ dx = \int_0^\infty \frac{\partial^2 u}{\partial x^2}\ \cos \lambda x\ dx$$

$$\frac{d\,\bar{u}_c}{d\,t} = -\left[\frac{\partial u}{\partial x}\right]_{x=0} - \lambda^2 \bar{u}_c\,(\lambda, t)$$

or $\qquad \dfrac{d\,\bar{u}_c}{d\,t} = -\lambda^2 \bar{u}_c \quad$ (variable separable form) $\qquad \qquad \dots \text{(v)}$

Solving this ordinary differential equation, we get

$$\bar{u}_c\,(\lambda, t) = A\, e^{-\lambda^2 t} \qquad \qquad \dots \text{(vi)}$$

To determine arbitrary constant A, we take Fourier cosine transform of initial condition (iii), i.e.

$$\bar{u}_c\,(\lambda, 0) = F_c\,[u(x, 0)] = \int_0^\infty u(x, 0)\, \cos \lambda x\ dx$$

$$= \int_0^1 x \cos \lambda x\ dx + \int_1^\infty (0)\, \cos \lambda x\ dx$$

$$= \left[x\left(\frac{\sin \lambda x}{\lambda}\right) - (1)\left(-\frac{\cos \lambda x}{\lambda^2}\right)\right]_0^1$$

$$= \frac{\sin \lambda}{\lambda} + \frac{\cos \lambda - 1}{\lambda^2} = \frac{\lambda \sin \lambda + \cos \lambda - 1}{\lambda^2} \qquad \qquad \dots \text{(vii)}$$

Substituting t = 0 in (vi) and using (vii), we get

$$\bar{u}_c(\lambda, 0) = A = \frac{\lambda \sin \lambda + \cos \lambda - 1}{\lambda^2} \qquad \ldots \text{(viii)}$$

Putting this value of A in (vi), we get

$$\bar{u}_c(\lambda, t) = \frac{\lambda \sin \lambda + \cos \lambda - 1}{\lambda^2} \, e^{-\lambda^2 t} \qquad \ldots \text{(ix)}$$

Taking inverse Fourier cosine transform of (ix), we obtain

$$u(x, t) = \frac{2}{\pi} \int_0^\infty \frac{\lambda \sin \lambda + \cos \lambda - 1}{\lambda^2} \, e^{-\lambda^2 t} \, \cos \lambda x \, d\lambda$$

which is the required solution.

Type 3 : Problems on finite Fourier transforms :

Ex. 9 : *Use finite Fourier transform to solve*

$$\frac{\partial u}{\partial t} = k \frac{\partial^2 u}{\partial x^2} \qquad 0 < x < 4, \quad t > 0 \qquad \ldots (i)$$

subject to the conditions :

(a) u(x, 0) = 2x, 0 < x < 4   *... (ii)*

(b) u(0, t) = u(4, t) = 0, 0 < x < 4, t > 0   *... (iii)*

Sol. : Since the boundary conditions are   u(0, t) = u(4, t) = 0,

we use finite Fourier sine transform.

$$\text{Let } \bar{u}_s(n, t) = F_s[u(x, t)] = \int_0^4 u(x, t) \sin \frac{n\pi x}{4} \, dx \qquad \text{[by result (29)] } \ldots \text{(iv)}$$

Taking finite Fourier sine transform of the given equation, we get

$$F_s\left[\frac{\partial u}{\partial t}\right] = k \, F_s\left[\frac{\partial^2 u}{\partial x^2}\right]$$

$$\therefore \int_0^4 \frac{\partial u}{\partial t} \sin \frac{n\pi x}{4} \, dx = k \int_0^4 \frac{\partial^2 u}{\partial x^2} \sin \frac{n\pi x}{4} \, dx \qquad [\because L = 4] \qquad \ldots \text{(v)}$$

$$\text{Now, } \int_0^4 \frac{\partial u}{\partial t} \sin \frac{n\pi x}{4} \, dx = \frac{d}{dt} \int_0^4 u(x, t) \sin \frac{n\pi x}{4} \, dx = \frac{d\bar{u}_s}{dt} \qquad \ldots \text{(vi)}$$

$$\text{and } \int_0^4 \frac{\partial^2 u}{\partial x^2} \sin \frac{n\pi x}{4} \, dx = \left[\left(\frac{\partial u}{\partial x} \sin \frac{n\pi x}{4}\right)_0^4 - \int_0^4 \frac{\partial u}{\partial x} \frac{n\pi}{4} \cos \frac{n\pi x}{4} \, dx\right], \text{[integrating by parts]}$$

$$= 0 - \frac{n\pi}{4} \int_0^4 \frac{\partial u}{\partial x} \cos \frac{n\pi x}{4} \, dx$$

$$= -\frac{n\pi}{4}\left[\left(u\cos\frac{n\pi x}{4}\right)_0^4 - \int_0^4 u\left(-\frac{n\pi}{4}\sin\frac{n\pi x}{4}\right)dx\right]$$

$$= -\frac{n^2\pi^2}{16}\int_0^4 u(x,\,t)\sin\frac{n\pi x}{4}\,dx \qquad\qquad \text{[By (iii)]}$$

$$= 0 - \frac{n^2\pi^2}{16}\,\overline{u}_s \qquad\qquad \text{[By (iv)] ... (vii)}$$

Thus from (v), (vi) and (vii), we have

$$\frac{d\,\overline{u}_s}{d\,t} = -\frac{k\,n^2\pi^2}{16}\,\overline{u}_s \qquad\qquad\qquad \text{... (viii)}$$

The solution of this ordinary differential equation is

$$\overline{u}_s(n,\,t) = A\,e^{-\frac{k\,n^2\pi^2}{16}t} \qquad\qquad\qquad \text{... (ix)}$$

To determine A, we take finite Fourier sine transform of initial condition (ii), i.e.

$$\overline{u}_s(n,\,0) = \int_0^4 u(x,\,0)\sin\frac{n\pi x}{4}\,dx = \int_0^4 2x\sin\frac{n\pi x}{4}\,dx$$

$$= 2\left[x\left(-\frac{4}{n\pi}\cos\frac{n\pi x}{4}\right) - (1)\left(-\frac{16}{n^2\pi^2}\sin\frac{n\pi x}{4}\right)\right]_0^4$$

$$= 2\left[-\frac{16}{n\pi}\cos n\pi\right] = -\frac{32}{n\pi}\cos n\pi \qquad\qquad \text{... (x)}$$

Substituting $t = 0$ in (ix) and using (x), we have

$$\overline{u}_s(n,\,0) = A = -\frac{32}{n\pi}\cos n\pi \qquad\qquad \text{[from (x)] ... (xi)}$$

Putting the value of A from (xi) in (ix), we get

$$\overline{u}_s(n,\,t) = -\frac{32}{n\pi}\cos n\pi\,e^{-\frac{k\,n^2\pi^2 t}{16}} \qquad\qquad \text{... (xii)}$$

Taking inverse finite sine transform of (xii) [by result (30)], we obtain

$$u(x,\,t) = \frac{2}{L}\sum_{n=1}^{\infty}\overline{u}_s(n,\,t)\sin\frac{n\pi x}{L},\quad (L=4)$$

$$= \frac{2}{4}\sum_{n=1}^{\infty}-\frac{32}{n\pi}\cos n\pi\,e^{-\frac{k\,n^2\pi^2 t}{16}}\sin\frac{n\pi x}{4}$$

$$= \frac{16}{\pi}\sum_{n=1}^{\infty}\frac{(-1)^{n+1}}{n}\,e^{-\frac{k\,n^2\pi^2 t}{16}}\sin\frac{n\pi x}{4}$$

which is the required solution.

Ex. 10 : *Solve the equation* $\dfrac{\partial u}{\partial t} = \dfrac{\partial^2 u}{\partial x^2}$ $0 < x < \pi,\ t > 0$ ... (i)

subject to the conditions :

(a) $u(x, 0) = 1$ $0 < x < \pi$ ... (ii)

(b) $u(0, t) = u(\pi, t) = 0$ $0 < x < \pi,\ t > 0$ ... (iii)

using appropriate transform.

Sol. : Since the boundary conditions are $u(0, t) = u(\pi, t) = 0$, we take finite Fourier sine transform of both sides of given equation i.e.

$$F_s\left[\frac{\partial u}{\partial t}\right] = F_s\left[\frac{\partial^2 u}{\partial x^2}\right] \qquad \text{... (iv)}$$

Let $\qquad \bar{u}_s(n, t) = F_s[u(x, t)] = \displaystyle\int_0^\pi u(x, t)\ \sin nx\ dx \qquad [\because\ L = \pi] \quad \text{... (v)}$

$$\therefore \quad \int_0^\pi \frac{\partial u}{\partial t}\ \sin nx\ dx = \int_0^\pi \frac{\partial^2 u}{\partial x^2}\ \sin nx\ dx$$

$$\frac{d}{dt}\int_0^\pi u\ \sin nx\ dx = \left[\left(\frac{\partial u}{\partial x}\ \sin nx\right) - n\int_0^\pi \frac{\partial u}{\partial x}\ \cos nx\ dx\right] \quad \text{[integrating by parts]}$$

$$\frac{d\,\bar{u}_s(n, t)}{dt} = 0 - n\left[\{u(x, t)\cos nx\}\Big|_0^\pi + n\int_0^\pi u(x, t)\ \sin nx\ dx\right]$$

$$= -n\left[0 + n\int_0^\pi u(x, t)\ \sin nx\ dx\right] = -n^2\bar{u}_s(n, t) \quad \text{[By (iii)]}$$

$$\therefore \qquad\qquad \frac{d\,\bar{u}_s}{dt} = -n^2\bar{u}_s \qquad\qquad \text{... (vi)}$$

The solution of this ordinary differential equation is

$$\bar{u}_s(n, t) = A(n)\ e^{-n^2 t} \qquad\qquad \text{... (vii)}$$

Now to determine $A(n)$, we take finite Fourier sine transform of initial condition (ii), i.e.

$$\bar{u}_s(n, 0) = \int_0^\pi u(x, 0)\ \sin nx\ dx = \int_0^\pi (1)\ \sin nx\ dx$$

$$= \left[-\frac{\cos nx}{n}\right]_0^\pi = \frac{1 - \cos n\pi}{n} \qquad\qquad \text{... (viii)}$$

Substituting $t = 0$ in (viii), we get

$$\bar{u}_s(n, 0) = A(n) = \frac{1 - \cos n\pi}{n} \qquad \ldots (ix)$$

Putting this value of $A(n)$ from (ix) in (viii), we get

$$\bar{u}_s(n, t) = \frac{1 - \cos n\pi}{n} \, e^{-n^2 t} \qquad \ldots (x)$$

Taking inverse finite Fourier sine transform of (x) [by result (30)], we get

$$u(x, t) = \frac{2}{L} \sum_{n=1}^{\infty} \bar{u}_s(n, t) \sin nx$$

$$= \frac{2}{\pi} \sum_{n=1}^{\infty} \frac{1 - \cos n\pi}{n} \, e^{-n^2 t} \sin nx$$

which is the required result.

Ex. 11 : *Using finite Fourier transform, solve* $\dfrac{\partial u}{\partial t} = \dfrac{\partial^2 u}{\partial x^2}$ $\qquad \ldots (i)$

subject to the following conditions :
(a) $u_x(0, t) = u_x(6, t) = 0, \quad 0 < x < 6, \quad t > 0$ $\qquad \ldots (ii)$
(b) $u(x, 0) = x(6 - x), \quad 0 < x < 6$ $\qquad \ldots (iii)$

Sol. : Since the boundary conditions are $u_x(0, t) = u_x(6, t) = 0$, we take finite Fourier cosine transform of both sides of given equation i.e.

$$F_c\left[\frac{\partial u}{\partial t}\right] = F_c\left[\frac{\partial^2 u}{\partial x^2}\right] \qquad \ldots (iv)$$

Let $\bar{u}_c(n, t) = F_c[u(x, t)] = \displaystyle\int_0^6 u(x, t) \cos \frac{n\pi x}{6} \, dx \quad [\because L = 6] \qquad \ldots (v)$

$$\therefore \quad \int_0^6 \frac{\partial u}{\partial t} \cos \frac{n\pi x}{6} \, dx = \int_0^6 \frac{\partial^2 u}{\partial x^2} \cos \frac{n\pi x}{6} \, dx$$

$$\frac{d}{dt} \int_0^6 u(x, t) \cos \frac{n\pi x}{6} \, dx = \left[\left(\frac{\partial u}{\partial x} \cos \frac{n\pi x}{6}\right)_0^6 - \int_0^6 \frac{\partial u}{\partial x}\left(-\frac{n\pi}{6} \sin \frac{n\pi x}{6}\right) dx\right]$$

$$\frac{d\, \bar{u}_c(n, t)}{dt} = 0 + \frac{n\pi}{6} \int_0^6 \frac{\partial u}{\partial x} \sin \frac{n\pi x}{6} \, dx \qquad \text{[by (ii)]}$$

$$= \frac{n\pi}{6}\left[\left(u \sin \frac{n\pi x}{6}\right)_0^6 - \int_0^6 u\left(\frac{n\pi}{6} - \cos \frac{n\pi x}{6}\right) dx\right]$$

$$= \frac{n\pi}{6}\left[0 - \frac{n\pi}{6} \int_0^6 u \cos \frac{n\pi x}{6} \, dx\right] = -\frac{n^2 \pi^2}{36} \bar{u}_c(n, t)$$

$$\therefore \qquad \frac{d\,\bar{u}_c}{d\,t} = -\frac{n^2\,\pi^2}{36}\,\bar{u}_c \qquad \qquad \dots \text{(vi)}$$

The solution of (vi) is given by

$$\bar{u}_c(n,\,t) = A(n)\,e^{-\frac{n^2\,\pi^2\,t}{36}} \qquad \qquad \dots \text{(vii)}$$

To determine A(n), we take finite Fourier cosine transform of initial condition (iii), i.e.

$$\bar{u}_c(n,\,0) = \int_0^6 u(x,\,0)\,\sin\frac{n\pi x}{6}\,dx = \int_0^6 x\,(6-x)\,\sin\frac{n\pi x}{6}\,dx$$

$$= \left[(6x-x^2)\left(\frac{6}{n\pi}\sin\frac{n\pi x}{6}\right) - (6-2x)\left(-\frac{36}{n^2\,\pi^2}\cos\frac{n\pi x}{6}\right) + (-2)\left(-\frac{216}{n^2\,\pi^2}\sin\frac{n\pi x}{6}\right)\right]_0^6$$

[by generalised rule of integration by parts]

$$= -\frac{216}{n^2\,\pi^2}\,(1+\cos n\pi) \qquad \qquad \dots \text{(viii)}$$

Substituting $t=0$ in (vii) and using (viii), we get

$$\bar{u}_c(n,\,0) = A(n) = -\frac{216}{n^2\,\pi^2}\,(1+\cos n\pi) \qquad \qquad \dots \text{(ix)}$$

Putting the value of A(n) from (ix) in (vii), we have

$$\bar{u}_c(n,\,t) = -\frac{216}{n^2\,\pi^2}\,(1+\cos n\pi)\,e^{-\frac{n^2\,\pi^2\,t}{36}} \qquad \qquad \dots \text{(x)}$$

When $n=0$ in (ix), A(n) becomes indeterminate, hence we evaluate A(n), for $n=0$, separately. Thus

$$\left[\bar{u}_c(n,\,0)\right]_{n=0} = \int_0^6 u(x,\,0)\,\cos(0)\,x\,dx = \int_0^6 x\,(6-x)\,dx$$

i.e. $\qquad \bar{u}_c(0,\,0) = \left[3x^2 - \frac{x^3}{3}\right]_0^6 = 36 \qquad \qquad \dots \text{(xi)}$

Hence from (vii) and using (xi), we have

$$\bar{u}_c(0,\,0) = A(0) = 36 \qquad \qquad \dots \text{(xii)}$$

Thus from result (vii), when $n=0$

$$\bar{u}_c(0,\,t) = 36 \qquad \qquad \dots \text{(xiii)}$$

Taking inverse Fourier cosine transform of $\bar{u}_c$ (n, t), using (ix) and (xii), we obtain

$$u(x, t) = \frac{1}{L}\bar{u}_c(0, t) + \frac{2}{L}\sum_{n=1}^{\infty}\bar{u}_c(n, t)\cos\frac{n\pi x}{L} \qquad [\because L = 6]$$

$$= \frac{1}{6}(36) - \frac{2}{6}\sum_{n=1}^{\infty}\frac{216}{n^2\pi^2}(1 + \cos n\pi)\, e^{\frac{-n^2\pi^2 t}{36}}\cos\frac{n\pi x}{6}$$

$$= 6 - \frac{72}{\pi^2}\sum_{n=1}^{\infty}\frac{1}{n^2}(1 + \cos n\pi)\, e^{-\frac{n^2\pi^2 t}{36}}\cos\frac{n\pi x}{6}$$

which is the required result.

Ex. 12 : *Using finite Fourier transform, find the solution of the wave equation*

$$\frac{\partial^2 y}{\partial t^2} = c^2\frac{\partial^2 y}{\partial x^2} \qquad \ldots (i)$$

subject to the conditions :

(a) $\quad y(0, t) = y(\pi, t) = 0$ $\qquad \ldots (ii)$

(b) $\quad y(x, 0) = f(x)$ $\qquad \ldots (iii)$

(c) $\quad \left(\dfrac{\partial y}{\partial t}\right)_{t=0} = g(x)$ $\qquad \ldots (iv)$

Sol. : Since the boundary conditions are $y(0, t) = y(\pi, t) = 0$, we take finite Fourier sine transform with respect to x of both sides of equation (i).

$$F_s\left[\frac{\partial^2 y}{\partial t^2}\right] = F_s\left[\frac{\partial^2 y}{\partial x^2}\right] \qquad \ldots (v)$$

Let $\qquad \bar{y}_s(n, t) = \int_0^L y(x, t)\sin\frac{n\pi x}{L}\, dx \qquad \ldots (vi)$

$$\therefore \qquad \int_0^\pi \frac{\partial^2 y}{\partial t^2}\sin nx\, dx = c^2\int_0^\pi \frac{\partial^2 y}{\partial x^2}\sin nx\, dx$$

or $\quad \dfrac{d^2}{d t^2}\displaystyle\int_0^\pi y(x, t)\,\sin nx\, dx = c^2\left[\left(\dfrac{\partial y}{\partial x}\sin nx\right)_0^\pi - n\int_0^\pi \dfrac{\partial y}{\partial u}\cos nx\, dx\right]$

or $\qquad \dfrac{d^2\bar{y}_s}{d t^2} = c^2\left[0 - n\left\{(y\cos nx)_0^\pi + n\int_0^\pi y\sin nx\, dx\right\}\right]$

or $\qquad \dfrac{d^2\bar{y}_s}{d t^2} = -c^2 n^2\bar{y}_s \qquad \ldots (vii)$

Solution of the differential equation (vii) is

$$\bar{y}_s(n, t) = A(n)\cos cnt + B(n)\sin cnt \qquad \ldots (viii)$$

Now taking the finite Fourier sine transforms of conditions (iii) and (iv), we get

$$\bar{y}_s(n, 0) = \int_0^\pi f(x) \sin nx \, dx = F_s[f(n)] \qquad \ldots \text{(ix)}$$

$$\left(\frac{d\bar{y}_s}{dt}\right)_{t=0} = \int_0^\pi g(x) \sin nx \, dx = F_s[g(n)] \qquad \ldots \text{(x)}$$

From (viii), we have

$$\frac{d\bar{y}_s}{dt}(n, t) = A(n)(-cn \sin cnt) + B(n)(cn \cos cnt) \qquad \ldots \text{(xi)}$$

Putting $t = 0$ in (viii) and (xi) and using (ix) and (x), we have

$$\bar{y}_s(n, 0) = A(n) = F_s[f(n)] \qquad \ldots \text{(xii)}$$

$$\frac{d\bar{y}_s}{dt}(n, 0) = cn\, B(n) = F_s[g(n)] \qquad \ldots \text{(xiii)}$$

Hence on substituting $A(n)$ and $B(n)$ from (xii) and (xiii) in (viii), we get

$$\bar{y}_s(n, t) = F_s[f(n)] \cos cnt + \frac{1}{cn} F_s[g(n)] \sin cnt \qquad \ldots \text{(xiv)}$$

Taking inverse Fourier transform, we have

$$y(x, t) = \frac{2}{\pi} \sum_{n=1}^\infty \left[F_s[f(n)] \cos cnt + \frac{1}{cn} F_s[g(n)] \sin cnt \right] \sin nx$$

Using results (ix) and (x), we get

$$y(x, t) = \frac{2}{\pi} \sum_{n=1}^\infty \left[\left\{ \int_0^\pi f(u) \sin nu \, du \right\} \cos cnt + \frac{1}{cn} \left\{ \int_0^\pi g(u) \sin nu \, du \right\} \sin cnt \right] \sin x$$

which is the required solution.

Type 4 : Solution of Laplace's equation :

Ex. 13 : *Show that solution of Laplace's equation $\nabla^2 V = 0$, for V inside the semi-infinite strip $x > 0$, $0 < y < b$ such that $V = f(x)$ when $y = 0$, $0 < x < \infty$; $V = 0$ when $y = b$, $0 < x < \infty$ and $V = 0$ when $x = 0$, $0 < y < b$, is given by*

$$V(x, y) = \frac{2}{\pi} \int_0^\infty \int_0^\infty f(u) \frac{\sinh(b-y)\lambda}{\sinh b\lambda} \sin \lambda x \sin \lambda u \, du \, d\lambda.$$

Sol. : Here we have to solve two-dimensional Laplace's equation

$$\nabla^2 V = \frac{\partial^2 V}{\partial x^2} + \frac{\partial^2 V}{\partial y^2} = 0 \quad, \qquad x > 0 \quad 0 < y < b \qquad \ldots \text{(i)}$$

subject to the conditions :

(a) $V(x, 0) = f(x)$, $x > 0$ $\qquad\qquad\qquad\qquad$ ... (ii)

(b) $V(x, b) = 0$, $x > 0$ $\qquad\qquad\qquad\qquad$ ... (iii)

(c) $V(0, y) = 0$, $0 < y < b$. $\qquad\qquad\qquad$ ... (iv)

Taking Fourier sine transform with respect to x of both sides of the given equation, we have

$$F_s\left[\frac{\partial^2 V}{\partial x^2}\right] + F_s\left[\frac{\partial^2 V}{\partial y^2}\right] = 0 \qquad \ldots \text{(v)}$$

Let

$$V_s(\lambda, y) = F_s[V(x, y)] = \int_0^\infty V(x, y)\sin \lambda x\, dx$$

$$\therefore \quad F_s\left[\frac{\partial^2 V}{\partial y^2}\right] = \int_0^\infty \frac{\partial^2 V}{\partial y^2}\sin \lambda x\, dx = \frac{d^2 V_s(\lambda, y)}{d y^2} \qquad \ldots \text{(vi)}$$

and

$$F_s\left[\frac{\partial^2 V}{\partial x^2}\right] = \int_0^\infty \frac{\partial^2 V}{\partial x^2}\sin \lambda x\, dx = \left[\left(\frac{\partial V}{\partial x}\sin \lambda x\right)_0^\infty - \int_0^\infty \lambda \cos \lambda x\, \frac{\partial V}{\partial x}\, dx\right]$$

$$= 0 - \lambda\left[(V(x, y)\cos \lambda x)_0^\infty \int\, - \lambda \sin \lambda x\, V(x, y)\, dx\right]$$

$$= -\lambda^2 \int_0^\infty V(x, y)\sin \lambda x\, dx = -\lambda^2 V_s(\lambda, y) \qquad \ldots \text{(vii)}$$

From (v), (vi) and (vii), we get

$$\frac{d^2 V_s}{d y^2}(\lambda, y) - \lambda^2 V_s(\lambda, y) = 0 \qquad \ldots \text{(viii)}$$

or

$$(D^2 - \lambda^2)\, V_s(\lambda, y) = 0 \qquad \ldots \text{(ix)}$$

General solution of this equation is

$$V_s(\lambda, y) = c_1 \cosh \lambda y + c_2 \sinh \lambda y \qquad \ldots \text{(x)}$$

Now to find c_1 and c_2, we take Fourier sine transform of given conditions (ii) and (iii),

when $y = 0$,

$$V_s(\lambda, 0) = \int_0^\infty V(x, 0)\sin \lambda u\, du = \int_0^\infty f(x)\sin \lambda u\, du \qquad \ldots \text{(xi)}$$

and when $y = b$,

$$V_s(\lambda, b) = \int_0^\infty V(x, b)\sin \lambda u\, du = 0 \qquad \ldots \text{(xii)}$$

From (x), on putting $y = 0$ and using (xi), we have

$$c_1 \cosh 0 + 0 = V_s(\lambda, 0) = \int_0^\infty f(u)\sin \lambda x\, du$$

$$\therefore \qquad c_1 = \int_0^\infty f(u)\sin \lambda u\, du \qquad \ldots \text{(xiii)}$$

Similarly, on putting $y = b$ in (x) and using (xii), we have

$$c_1 \cosh \lambda b + c_2 \sinh \lambda b = V_s(\lambda, b) = 0$$

$$\therefore \qquad c_2 = -c_1 \frac{\cosh \lambda b}{\sinh \lambda b} = -\frac{\cosh \lambda b}{\sinh \lambda b} \int_0^\infty f(u) \sin \lambda u \, du \qquad \ldots \text{(xiv)}$$

Substituting the values of c_1 and c_2 from (xiii) and (xiv) in (x), we get

$$V_s(\lambda, y) = \cosh \lambda y \int_0^\infty f(u) \sin \lambda u \, du - \frac{\cosh \lambda b}{\sinh \lambda b} \sinh \lambda y \int_0^\infty f(u) \sin \lambda u \, du$$

$$= \left(\cosh \lambda y - \frac{\cosh \lambda b}{\sinh \lambda b} \sinh \lambda y \right) \int_0^\infty f(u) \sin \lambda u \, du$$

$$= \frac{\sinh (b - y) \lambda}{\sinh \lambda b} \int_0^\infty f(u) \sin \lambda u \, du$$

$$\therefore \qquad V_s(\lambda, y) = \int_0^\infty f(u) \sin \lambda u \, \frac{\sinh (b - y) \lambda}{\sinh \lambda b} \, du \qquad \ldots \text{(xv)}$$

Taking inverse Fourier sine transform of (xv), we obtain

$$V(x, y) = \frac{2}{\pi} \int_0^\infty V_s(\lambda, y) \sin \lambda x \, d\lambda$$

$$= \frac{2}{\pi} \int_0^\infty \int_0^\infty f(u) \sin \lambda u \, \frac{\sinh (b - y) \lambda}{\sinh \lambda b} \sin \lambda x \, du \, d\lambda$$

which is the required result.

Ex. 14 : *Find the bounded harmonic function $V(x, y)$ in the semi-infinite strip $x > 0$, $0 < y < 1$ that satisfies the boundary conditions $V_x(0, y) = 0$, $V_y(x, 0) = 0$ and $V(x, 1) = f(x)$,*

where (i) $f(x) = \begin{cases} 1 & , \quad 0 < x < 1 \\ 0 & , \quad \quad x > 1 \end{cases}$ (ii) $f(x) = e^{-x} \quad x > 0$

Sol. : Here we have to solve the two-dimensional Laplace's equation (two-dimensional heat-flow equation)

$$\frac{\partial^2 V}{\partial x^2} + \frac{\partial^2 V}{\partial y^2} = 0 \quad x > 0, \qquad 0 < y < 1 \qquad \ldots \text{(i)}$$

subject to the conditions :

(a) $\dfrac{\partial V}{\partial x} = 0$ for $x = 0$, for all y $\qquad \ldots \text{(ii)}$

(b) $\dfrac{\partial V}{\partial y} = 0$ for $y = 0$, for all x $\qquad \ldots \text{(iii)}$

(c) $V(x, 1) = f(x)$ $\qquad \ldots \text{(iv)}$

Using method of separation of variables, solution of the given partial differential equation can be written as

$$V(x, y) = (c_1 \cos \lambda x + c_2 \sin \lambda x)(c_3 \cosh \lambda y + c_4 \sinh \lambda y) \qquad \ldots (v)$$

$$\therefore \quad \frac{\partial V}{\partial x} = (-c_1 \lambda \sin \lambda x + c_2 \lambda \cos \lambda x)(c_3 \cosh \lambda y + c_4 \sinh \lambda y)$$

$$\text{and} \quad \frac{\partial V}{\partial y} = (c_1 \cos \lambda x + c_2 \sin \lambda x)(c_3 \lambda \sinh \lambda y + c_4 \cosh \lambda y)$$

Imposing conditions [from (ii) and (iii)],

$$\frac{\partial V}{\partial x} = 0 \quad \text{at } x = 0 \quad : \quad \text{we get } c_2 = 0$$

$$\text{and} \quad \frac{\partial V}{\partial y} = 0 \quad \text{at } y = 0 \quad : \quad \text{we get } c_4 = 0$$

Hence from equation (v), we have

$$V(x, y) = c_1 c_3 \cosh \lambda y \, \cos \lambda x$$

or $\qquad V(x, y) = A \cosh \lambda y \cos \lambda x,$ $\qquad\qquad$ where, $A = c_1 c_3 \ \ldots (vi)$

Since the bar is semi-infinite and there is no restriction on λ, we can replace A by $A(\lambda)$ and integrate over λ to obtain (i.e. to write (vi) in terms of integral)

$$V(x, y) = \int_0^\infty A(\lambda) \cosh \lambda y \cos \lambda x \, d\lambda \qquad \ldots (vii)$$

To find $A(\lambda)$, we substitute $y = 1$ in (vii) and using boundary condition (iv), we have

$$V(x, 1) = \int_0^\infty A(\lambda) \cosh \lambda \cos \lambda x \, d\lambda = f(x) \qquad \ldots (viii)$$

Here $A(\lambda) \cosh \lambda$ is the cosine transform of $V(x, t) = f(x)$

$$\therefore \quad A(\lambda) \cosh \lambda = \frac{2}{\pi} \int_0^\infty f(x) \cos \lambda x \, dx \qquad \ldots (ix)$$

Case I : When $f(x) = \begin{cases} 1 & , \quad 0 < x < 1 \\ 0 & , \quad\quad x > 1 \end{cases}$

$$A(\lambda) \cosh \lambda = \frac{2}{\pi} \left[\int_0^1 f(x) \cos \lambda x \, dx + \int_0^\infty f(x) \cos \lambda x \, dx \right]$$

$$= \frac{2}{\pi} \int_0^1 (1) \, \cos \lambda x \, dx = \frac{2}{\pi} \left[\frac{\sin \lambda x}{\lambda} \right]_0^1 = \frac{2}{\pi \lambda} \, \sin \lambda$$

$$\therefore \quad A(\lambda) = \frac{2}{\pi} \left[\frac{\sin \lambda x}{\lambda \cosh \lambda} \right] \qquad \ldots (x)$$

Substituting this value of $A(\lambda)$ in (vii), we obtain

$$V(x, y) = \frac{2}{\pi} \int_0^\infty \frac{\sin \lambda}{\lambda \cosh \lambda} \cosh \lambda y \cos \lambda x \, d\lambda \qquad \ldots \text{(xi)}$$

Case II : When $f(x) = e^{-x}, \quad x > 0$

$$A(\lambda) \cosh \lambda = \frac{2}{\pi} \int_0^\infty e^{-x} \cos \lambda x \, dx$$

$$= \frac{2}{\pi} \left[\frac{e^{-x}}{1 + \lambda^2} (- \cos \lambda x + \lambda \sin \lambda x) \right]_0^\infty$$

$$= \frac{2}{\pi} \left(\frac{1}{1 + \lambda^2} \right)$$

$$\therefore \qquad A(\lambda) = \frac{2}{\pi} \left[\frac{1}{(1 + \lambda^2) \cosh \lambda} \right] \qquad \ldots \text{(xii)}$$

Substituting this value of $A(\lambda)$ in (vii), we obtain

$$V(x, y) = \frac{2}{\pi} \int_0^\infty \frac{1}{(1 + \lambda^2) \cosh \lambda} \cosh \lambda y \cos \lambda x \, d\lambda$$

which is the required solution.

Ex. 15 : *Find the bounded harmonic function $V(x, y)$ in the semi-infinite strip $y > 0$, $0 < x < 1$, which satisfies the conditions*

$V_y(x, 0) = 0, \quad V(0, y) = e^{-y}$ *and* $V(1, y) = 0.$

Sol. : Here we have to solve the two-dimensional Laplace's equation

$$\frac{\partial^2 V}{\partial x^2} + \frac{\partial^2 V}{\partial y^2} = 0, \quad y > 0, \; 0 < x < 1 \qquad \ldots \text{(i)}$$

subject to conditions :

(a) $\quad \dfrac{\partial V}{\partial y} = 0$ at $y = 0$ and for all x $\qquad \ldots \text{(ii)}$

(b) $\quad V(0, y) = e^{-y}$ $\qquad \ldots \text{(iii)}$

(c) $\quad V(1, y) = 0$ $\qquad \ldots \text{(iv)}$

Using variables separable form, solution of the given partial differential equation can be written as

$$V(x, y) = (c_1 \cosh \lambda x + c_2 \sinh \lambda x)(c_3 \cos \lambda y + c_4 \sin \lambda y) \qquad \ldots \text{(v)}$$

$$\therefore \qquad \frac{\partial V}{\partial y} = (c_1 \cosh \lambda x + c_2 \sinh \lambda x)(- c_3 \lambda \sin \lambda y + c_4 \lambda \cos \lambda y) \qquad \ldots \text{(vi)}$$

Imposing conditions [from (ii) and (iv)],

$$\frac{\partial V}{\partial y} = 0 \quad \text{at } y = 0, \text{ we get } c_4 = 0.$$

Hence from equation (v), we have

$$V(x, y) = (c_1 \cosh \lambda x + c_2 \sinh \lambda x) \, c_3 \cos \lambda y \qquad \dots \text{(vii)}$$

Also $\qquad V(1, y) = 0 \Rightarrow 0 = c_1 \cosh \lambda + c_2 \sinh \lambda \qquad \dots \text{(by } x = 1 \text{ in (vii))}$

$$\therefore \qquad c_2 = -c_1 \frac{\cosh \lambda}{\sinh \lambda}$$

Substituting the value of c_2 in (vii), we get

$$V(x, y) = \left[c_1 \cosh \lambda x - c_1 \frac{\cosh \lambda}{\sinh \lambda} \sinh \lambda x \right] c_3 \cos \lambda y$$

$$= c_1 c_3 \left[\frac{\sinh \lambda \cosh \lambda x - \cosh \lambda \sinh \lambda x}{\sinh \lambda} \right] \cos \lambda y$$

$$= A \frac{\sinh \lambda \, (1 - x)}{\sinh \lambda} \cos \lambda y, \quad \text{where } A = c_1 c_3 \qquad \dots \text{(viii)}$$

Since the strip is semi-infinite and on replacing A by $A(\lambda)$, the most general solution is

$$V(x, y) = \int_0^\infty A(\lambda) \frac{\sinh \lambda \, (1 - x)}{\sinh \lambda} \cos \lambda y \, d\lambda \qquad \dots \text{(ix)}$$

Also at $x = 0$, $\quad V(0, y) = e^{-y}$ (given)

$$\therefore \qquad V(0, y) = \int_0^\infty A(\lambda) \cos \lambda y \, d\lambda = e^{-y} \qquad \dots \text{(x)}$$

Here $A(\lambda)$ is the cosine transform of e^{-y}

$$\therefore \qquad A(\lambda) = \frac{2}{\pi} \int_0^\infty e^{-y} \cos \lambda y \, dy \qquad \dots \text{(xi)}$$

$$= \frac{2}{\pi} \left[\frac{e^{-y}}{1 + \lambda^2} (- \cos \lambda y + \lambda \sin \lambda y) \right]_0^\infty$$

$$= \frac{2}{\pi} \frac{1}{1 + \lambda^2} \qquad \dots \text{(xii)}$$

Substituting this value of $A(\lambda)$ in (ix), we obtain

$$V(x, y) = \frac{2}{\pi} \int_0^\infty \frac{1}{1 + \lambda^2} \frac{\sinh \lambda \, (1 - x)}{\sinh \lambda} \cos \lambda y \, d\lambda$$

which is the required solution.

Note : To solve Laplace's equation using variables separable form, let $V = XY$, where X depends only on x and Y depends only on y. Then on separating the variables, we have $\dfrac{X''}{X} = -\dfrac{Y''}{Y} = k.$

When $k = \lambda^2$, we get the solution of the form

$$V(x, y) \;=\; (c_1 \cosh \lambda x + c_2 \sinh \lambda x)(c_3 \cos \lambda y + c_4 \sin \lambda y) \qquad \dots \text{(i)}$$

and when $k = -\lambda^2$, we get the solution of the form

$$V(x, y) \;=\; (c_1 \cos \lambda x + c_2 \sin \lambda x)(c_3 \cosh \lambda y + c_4 \sinh \lambda y) \qquad \dots \text{(ii)}$$

Then if $x > 0$ and $0 < y < a$, we consider the solution of the form (ii)

and if $y > 0$ and $0 < x < b$, we consider the solution of the form (i).

EXERCISE 13.6

1. Solve the equation

$$\frac{\partial \theta}{\partial t} \;=\; c^2 \frac{\partial^2 \theta}{\partial x^2} \quad -\infty < x < \infty, \quad t > 0$$

subject to the condition $\theta(x, 0) = f(x)$, where $f(x) = \begin{cases} \theta_0, & |x| < 1 \\[2mm] 0, & |x| > 1 \end{cases}$

Ans. $\theta(x, t) = \dfrac{1}{2\pi} \displaystyle\int\limits_{-\infty}^{\infty} \int\limits_{-\infty}^{\infty} f(u)\, e^{-c^2 \lambda^2 t}\, e^{i\lambda(x-u)}\, du\, d\lambda$

2. Solve the following equation

$$\frac{\partial u}{\partial t} \;=\; c^2 \frac{\partial^2 u}{\partial x^2} \quad 0 < x < \infty, \; t > 0$$

subject to the conditions :

(i) $u(0, t) = 0$ (ii) $u(x, 0) = f(x)$, where $f(x) = \begin{cases} 1, & a < x < b, \; a > 0 \\[2mm] 0, & \text{otherwise} \end{cases}$

Ans. $u(x, t) = \dfrac{2}{\pi} \displaystyle\int\limits_{0}^{\infty} e^{-c^2 \lambda^2 t} \sin \lambda u \, \sin \lambda x \, du \, d\lambda$

3. Using Fourier sine transform, solve the equation

$$\frac{\partial V}{\partial t} \;=\; k \frac{\partial^2 V}{\partial x^2} \quad x > 0, \quad t > 0$$

subject to the conditions : $V = V_0$ when $x = 0$, $t > 0$ and $V = 0$ when $t = 0$, $x > 0$

Ans. $V(x, t) = V_0 \left[1 - \dfrac{2}{\pi} \displaystyle\int\limits_{0}^{\infty} \dfrac{e^{-k\lambda^2 t}}{\lambda} \sin \lambda x \, d\lambda \right]$

4. The initial temperature distribution in a semi-infinite bar perfectly insulated is given by

$$f(x) \;=\; \begin{cases} 1 - x^2, & 0 \le x < 1 \\[4pt] 0, & x \ge 1 \end{cases} \qquad \textbf{(May 2012)}$$

Find the temperature at any point of the bar at any time t if the temperature gradient at one end of the bar is zero. **Ans.** $u(x, t) = \dfrac{2}{\pi} \displaystyle\int_0^\infty -\dfrac{2}{\lambda^3} (\sin \lambda + \lambda \cos \lambda)\, e^{-\lambda^2 t} \cos \lambda x\, d\lambda$

5. The temperature θ in the semi-infinite strip $0 \le x \le \infty$ is determined by the differential equation

$$\frac{\partial \theta}{\partial t} \;=\; k^2 \frac{\partial^2 \theta}{\partial t^2}$$

subject to the conditions : (i) $\theta (x, 0) = 0$, (ii) $\left(\dfrac{\partial \theta}{\partial x}\right)_{x = 0} = -\mu$ (a constant) for all $t > 0$.

$$\textbf{Ans. } \theta (x, t) = \frac{2\mu}{\pi} \int_0^\infty \frac{\cos \lambda x}{\lambda^2} (1 - e^{-k \lambda^2 t})\, d\lambda$$

6. The semi-infinite plate $0 < x < \infty,\; -\infty < y < \infty$ is insulated along the edge $x = 0$ and the temperature satisfies the equation

$$\frac{\partial^2 \theta}{\partial x^2} \;=\; \frac{1}{k} \frac{\partial \theta}{\partial t}$$

If at $t = 0$, $\theta = ce^{-x}$, prove by Fourier transform method that

$$\theta(x, t) \;=\; \frac{2c}{\pi} \int_0^\infty \frac{1}{1 + \lambda^2}\, e^{-k \lambda^2 t} \cos \lambda x\, d\lambda$$

Hint : Since the plate is insulated at $x = 0$, take $\dfrac{\partial \theta}{\partial x} = 0$ at $x = 0$. Assume that θ and $\dfrac{\partial \theta}{\partial t} \to 0$ as $x \to \infty$. Hence use Fourier cosine transform to obtain the required solution.

7. Solve by using finite Fourier transform,

$$\frac{\partial V}{\partial t} \;=\; \frac{\partial^2 V}{\partial x^2}, \quad 0 \le x \le 6, \;\; t > 0$$

subject to the conditions : $V(0, t) = V(6, t) = 0$, $V(x, 0) = \begin{cases} 1, & 0 \le x \le 3 \\[4pt] 3, & 3 \le x \le 6 \end{cases}$

$$\textbf{Ans. } V(x, t) = \frac{2}{\pi} \sum_{n = 1}^\infty \left(1 - \cos \frac{n\pi}{2}\right) e^{-\frac{n^2 \pi^2 t}{36}} \sin \frac{n\pi x}{6}$$

8. Use finite Fourier transform to solve

$$\frac{\partial V}{\partial t} = \frac{\partial^2 V}{\partial x^2}, \quad 0 \le x \le 6, \quad t > 0$$

subject to the conditions : $V_x(0, t) = 0, \quad V_x(6, t) = 0, \quad V(x, 0) = 2x$

$$\textbf{Ans. } V(x, t) = 6 + \frac{24}{\pi^2} \sum_{n=1}^{\infty} \frac{\cos n\pi - 1}{n^2} e^{-\frac{n^2 \pi^2 t}{36}} \cos \frac{n\pi x}{6}$$

9. Solve the equation

$$\frac{\partial u}{\partial t} = k \frac{\partial^2 u}{\partial x^2}$$

subject to the conditions :

(i) u is not infinite when $t \to \infty$

(ii) $\dfrac{\partial u}{\partial x} = 0$ for $x = 0$ and $x = l$

(iii) $u = lx - x^2$ for $t = 0$ between $x = 0$ and $x = l$.

Using finite transform, show that the solution of the equation is

$$u(x, t) = \frac{l^2}{6} - \frac{l^2}{\pi^2} \sum_{n=1}^{\infty} \frac{1}{n^2} \cos \frac{2n\pi x}{l} e^{-\frac{4n^2 \pi^2 t}{l^2}}$$

10. Using finite Fourier transform, find the solution of the wave equation

$$\frac{\partial^2 u}{\partial t^2} = a^2 \frac{\partial^2 u}{\partial x^2}$$

subject to the conditions

$$u(0, t) = u(\pi, t) = 0, \quad u(x, 0) = 3 \sin x + 4 \sin 4x$$

and $u_t(x, 0) = 0$ for $0 \le x \le \pi, \ t > 0$

$$\textbf{Ans. } u(x, t) = 3 \cos at \sin x + 4 \cos 4 \, at \sin 4x$$

11. Solve by using finite transform

$$\frac{\partial^2 u}{\partial t^2} = 9 \frac{\partial^2 u}{\partial x^2} \quad 0 \le x \le 2$$

subject to the conditions $u(0, t) = u(2, t) = 0, \quad u(x, 0) = x(2 - x)$ and $u_t(x, 0) = 0$

$$\textbf{Ans. } u(x, t) = \frac{16}{\pi^2} \sum_{n=1}^{\infty} \frac{1 - \cos n\pi}{n^2} \cos \frac{3n\pi t}{2} \sin \frac{n\pi x}{2}$$

12. If $y(x, t)$ satisfies the equation

$$\frac{\partial^2 y}{\partial t^2} = c^2 \frac{\partial^2 y}{\partial x^2}$$

using finite transform, find the solution, where $y(x, t)$ satisfies the conditions

$$y(0, t) = y(l, t) = 0, \quad \frac{\partial y}{\partial t}(x, 0) = 0, \quad y(x, 0) = lx - x^2, \ 0 \le x \le l.$$

$$\textbf{Ans. } y(x, t) = \frac{8l^2}{\pi^3} \sum_{n=0}^{\infty} \frac{1}{(2n+1)^3} \sin \frac{(2n+1)\pi x}{l} \cos \frac{(2n+1)\pi \, at}{l}$$

13. Using finite Fourier transform, find the solution of the wave equation $\dfrac{\partial^2 u}{\partial t^2} = 4 \dfrac{\partial^2 u}{\partial x^2}$

subject to the conditions $u(0, t) = u(\pi, t) = 0$, $u(x, 0) = (0.1) \sin x + (0.01) \sin 4x$ and $u_t (x, 0) = 0$ for $a < x < \pi, t > 0$.

Ans. $u(x, t) = (0.1) \cos 2 t \sin x + (0.01) \cos 8 t \sin 4x$

14. Find the bounded harmonic function $V(x, y)$ in the semi-infinite strip $y > 0, 0 < x < 1$ which satisfies the conditions,

$V_y (x, 0) = 0$, $V(0, y) = 0$ and $V_x (1, y) = f(y)$

$$\textbf{Ans. } V(x, y) = \frac{2}{\pi} \int_0^\infty \int_0^\infty \frac{f(u) \cos \lambda u}{\lambda \cos h\lambda} \sinh \lambda x \cos \lambda y \, du \, d\lambda$$

Time : 1 Hrs.   **(ONLINE PHASE-I AND PHASE-II)**   **Max. Marks : 50**

Unit I : Linear Differential Equations :

1. The solution of differential equation $\frac{d^3y}{dx^3} - 7\frac{dy}{dx} - 6y = 0$ is   (2)

    (A) $c_1e^x + c_2e^{2x} + c_3e^{3x}$ (B) $c_1e^{-x} + c_2e^{-2x} + c_3e^{6x}$

    (C) $c_1e^{-x} + c_2e^{2x} + c_3e^x$ (D) $c_1e^{-x} + c_2e^{-2x} + c_3e^{3x}$

2. Particular Integral $\frac{1}{D+1}\left(\frac{1}{1+e^x}\right)$ where $D \equiv \frac{d}{dx}$ is   (2)

    (A) $e^{-x}\log(1 + e^x)$ (B) $\log(1 + e^x)$

    (C) $e^x\log(1 + e^x)$ (D) $e^x\log(1 - e^x)$

3. Particular Integral of differential equation $(D^4 + D^2 + 1)y = 53x^2 + 17$ is   (2)

    (A) $53x^2 + 17$ (B) $53x^2 - 89$

    (C) $53x^2 + 113$ (D) $3x^2 - 17$

4. For the differential equation $x^2\frac{d^2y}{dx^2} - x\frac{dy}{dx} + 4y = \cos(\log x) + x\sin(\log x)$, complimentary function is given by   (2)

    (A) $\left[c_1\cos\sqrt{3}(\log x) + c_2\sin\sqrt{3}(\log x)\right]$

    (B) $x\left[c_1\cos\sqrt{2}(\log x) + c_2\sin\sqrt{2}(\log x)\right]$

    (C) $x\left[c_1\cos\sqrt{3}(\log x) + c_2\sin\sqrt{3}(\log x)\right]$

    (D) $x\left[c_1\cos(\log x) + c_2\sin(\log x)\right]$

5. For the simultaneous Linear DE $\frac{dx}{dt} + 5x - 2y = t$, $\frac{dy}{dt} + 2x + y = 0$, solution of y using $D \equiv \frac{d}{dt}$ is obtain from   (2)

    (A) $(D^2 + 6D + 9)y = 2t$ (B) $(D^2 + 6D + 9)x = 1 + t$

    (C) $(D^2 + 6D + 1)y = 1$ (D) $(D^2 - 6D + 1)y = t$

6. The solution of differential equation $\frac{d^3y}{dx^3} - 3\frac{dy}{dx} - 2y = 0$ is   (2)

    (A) $c_1e^x + c_2e^{2x} + c_3e^{3x}$ (B) $c_1e^{-x} + c_2e^{-2x} + c_3e^{-3x}$

    (C) $c_1e^x + c_2e^{-x} + c_3e^{2x}$ (D) $(c_1x + c_2)e^{-x} + c_3e^{2x}$

(P.1)

7. Particular Integral $\dfrac{1}{\phi(D^2)} \sin(ax + b)$, where $D \equiv \dfrac{d}{dx}$ and $\phi(-a^2) \neq 0$ is　(1)

   (A) $\dfrac{1}{\phi(-a^2)} \cos(ax + b)$　　　　(B) $\dfrac{1}{\phi(-a^2)} \sin(ax + b)$

   (C) $x\,\dfrac{1}{\phi(-a^2)} \sin(ax + b)$　　　(D) $\dfrac{1}{\phi(a^2)} \sin(ax + b)$

8. To reduce the differential equation $(x + 2)^2 \dfrac{d^2y}{dx^2} - (x + 2)\dfrac{dy}{dx} + y = 4x + 7$ to Linear differential equation with constant coefficient, substitution is　(1)

   (A) $x + 2 = e^z$　　　　　　　　(B) $x = z + 1$

   (C) $x + 2 = e^z$　　　　　　　　(D) $x + 2 = \log z$

9. $L\,[t \cos 2t]$ is equal to　(2)

   (A) $\dfrac{4 + s^2}{(s^2 - 4)^2}$　　　　　　　(B) $\dfrac{s^2 - 4}{(s^2 + 4)^2}$

   (C) $\dfrac{s^2 - 4}{(s^2 + 4)}$　　　　　　　(D) $\dfrac{4 - s^2}{(s^2 + 4)}$

10. $L^{-1}\left[\log \dfrac{s + b}{s + a}\right]$ is equal to　(2)

    (A) $t\,(e^{-at} - e^{bt})$　　　　　　(B) $\left(\dfrac{e^{at} - e^{bt}}{t}\right)$

    (C) $\left(\dfrac{e^{-bt} + e^{-at}}{t}\right)$　　　　(D) $\left(\dfrac{e^{-at} - e^{-bt}}{t}\right)$

11. By using Laplace transform the solution of differential equation $\dfrac{dy}{dt} + y(t) = e^{-t}$, given $y(0) = 0$ is　(2)

    (A) $y(t) = t\,e^t$　　　　　　　(B) $y(t) = \sin t$

    (C) $y(t) = t\,e^{-t}$　　　　　　(D) $y(t) = \dfrac{t^2}{2}\,e^{-t}$

12. The Fourier transform $F(\lambda)$ of $f(x) = \begin{cases} 1, & x > 0 \\ 0, & x < 0 \end{cases}$ is　(2)

    (A) $\dfrac{1}{i\lambda}$　　　　　　　　　(B) $i\lambda$

    (C) $\dfrac{1}{\lambda}$　　　　　　　　　(D) λ

13. If $f(x) = \begin{cases} x^2 , & 0 < x < 1 \\ 0 , & x > 1 \end{cases}$ then Fourier sine transform $F_s(\lambda)$ of $f(x)$ is given by   (2)

(A) $\dfrac{\lambda^2 \cos \lambda - 2\lambda \sin \lambda + 2 (\cos \lambda - 1)}{\lambda^3}$

(B) $\dfrac{\lambda^2 \cos \lambda + 2\lambda \sin \lambda + 2 (\cos \lambda - 1)}{\lambda^3}$

(C) $\dfrac{-\lambda^2 \cos \lambda + 2\lambda \sin \lambda + 2 (\cos \lambda - 1)}{\lambda^3}$

(D) $\dfrac{\lambda^2 \cos \lambda - 2\lambda \sin \lambda - 2 (\cos \lambda - 1)}{\lambda^3}$

14. If $f(t) = t^n$, $n > -1$ then $L[t^n]$ is equal to   (1)

(A) $\dfrac{1}{s^{n+1}}$, $s > 0$

(B) $\dfrac{\overline{|n+1}}{s^{n+1}}$, $s > 0$

(C) $\dfrac{s^2}{s^2 + a^2}$, $s > 0$

(D) $\dfrac{\overline{|n}}{s^{n+1}}$, $s > 0$

15. The fourier integral representation of $f(x)$ defined in the interval $-\infty < x < \infty$ is   (1)

(A) $\dfrac{1}{2\pi} \displaystyle\int_{-\infty}^{\infty} \int_{-\infty}^{\infty} f(u)\, e^{-i\lambda(u-x)}\, du\, d\lambda$

(B) $\displaystyle\int_{-\infty}^{\infty} \int_{-\infty}^{\infty} f(u)\, e^{-i\lambda(u-x)}\, du\, d\lambda$

(C) $\dfrac{1}{2\pi} \displaystyle\int_{-\infty}^{\infty} \int_{-\infty}^{\infty} f(u)\, e^{i\lambda u}\, du\, d\lambda$

(C) $\dfrac{1}{2\pi} \displaystyle\int_{-\infty}^{\infty} \int_{-\infty}^{\infty} f(u)\, e^{-\lambda(u-x)}\, du\, d\lambda$

16. The standard deviation and arithmetic mean of aggregate marks obtained three group of students x, y, z are as follow :

	Arithmetic mean	Standard deviation
x	532	11
y	831	9
z	650	10

The more variable group is   (2)

(A) y and z

(B) z

(C) y

(D) x

17. If $\sum xy = 90$, $\bar{x} = 4$, $\bar{y} = 4$, $n = 10$, $\sigma_x = 1.732$, $\sigma_y = 2$ then correlation coefficient $r(x, y)$ is equal to   (2)

(A) 0.8342

(B) 0.91287

(C) 0.7548

(D) 0.5324

18. Line of regression y on x is $8x - 10y + 66 = 0$. Line of regression x on y is $40x - 18y - 214 = 0$. The value of variance of x is 9. The standard deviation of y is equal to   (2)

(A) 2   (B) 5

(C) 6   (D) 4

19. 20% of bolts produced by machine are defective. The probability that out of three bolts chosen at random 1 is defective is   (2)

(A) 0.384   (B) 0.9728

(C) 0.5069   (D) 0.6325

20. X is normally distributed. The mean of X is 30 and variance 25. The probability $p(26 \le x \le 40)$ is   (2)

(Given : Area corresponding to $z = 0.8$ is 0.2881 and Area corresponding to $z = 2$ is 0.4772)

(A) 0.8562   (B) 0.6574

(C) 0.7653   (d) 0.3745

21. Coefficient of kurtosis β_2 is given by   (1)

(A) $\dfrac{\mu_4}{\mu_2^{\,2}}$ (B) $\dfrac{\mu_4}{\mu_2}$

(C) $\dfrac{\mu_3}{\mu_2^{\,2}}$ (D) $\dfrac{\mu_4}{\mu_2^{\,3}}$

22. Standard deviation of binomial probability distribution is   (1)

(A) $\sqrt{pq}$ (B) $\sqrt{npq}$

(C) $\sqrt{np}$ (D) np

Unit IV : Vector Differential Calculus :

23. If $\bar{r}(t) = t^2\,\bar{i} + t\,\bar{j} - 2t^3\,\bar{k}$ then the value of $\bar{r} \times \dfrac{d^2\bar{r}}{dt^2}$ is   (2)

(A) $12t^2\,\bar{i} + 8t^3\,\bar{j} + 2t\,\bar{k}$ (B) $-12t^2\,\bar{i} + 8t^3\,\bar{j}$

(C) $-12t^2\,\bar{i} + 16t^3\,\bar{j} + (t^2 - 2t)\,\bar{k}$ (D) $-12t^2\,\bar{i} + 8t^3\,\bar{j} - 2t\,\bar{k}$

24. If $\phi = mx^2 + y + z$, $\bar{b} = 2\bar{i} - 3\bar{j} + \bar{k}$ and $\nabla\phi$ at the point $(1, 0, 1)$ is perpendicular to $\bar{b}$ then m is equal to   (2)

(A) 0   (B) $\dfrac{3}{2}$

(C) $\dfrac{1}{2}$ (D) $-\dfrac{5}{2}$

25. The directional derivative of $\phi = xy^2 + yz^3$ at the point $(1, -1, 1)$ in the direction of vector $\bar{u} = 2\bar{i} + 4\bar{j} + 4\bar{k}$ is   (2)

(A) $\dfrac{7}{3}$ (B) $-\dfrac{7}{3}$

(C) -7 (D) $-\dfrac{7}{6}$

26. $\nabla \cdot [(\log r)\,\bar{r}]$ is equal to   (2)

(A) $3 \log r + \dfrac{1}{r}$ (B) $3 \log r + \dfrac{1}{r^2}\bar{r}$

(C) $5 + 6 \log r$ (D) $1 + 3 \log 4$

27. If $\bar{F}$ is a solenoidal vector field and curl curl $\bar{F} = -\nabla^2\bar{F}$ then curl curl curl curl $\bar{F}$ is   (2)

(A) $\nabla^2\bar{F}$ (B) $-\nabla^4\bar{F}$

(C) $\nabla^4\bar{F}$ (D) $\bar{0}$

28. Vector field $\bar{F}$ is solenoidal if   (1)

(A) $\nabla \cdot \bar{F} = 0$ (B) $\nabla \times \bar{F} = 0$

(C) $\nabla^2\bar{F} = 0$ (D) $\bar{F} \cdot \nabla = 0$

29. For scalar function ϕ and vector function $\bar{u}$, $\nabla \times (\phi\bar{u})$ is equal to   (1)

(A) $\phi(\nabla \times \bar{u}) + \bar{u} \times \nabla\phi$ (B) $\phi(\nabla \cdot \bar{u}) - \nabla\phi \cdot \bar{u}$

(C) $\phi(\nabla \times \bar{u}) + \nabla\phi \times \bar{u}$ (D) $\phi(\nabla \cdot \bar{u}) + \nabla\phi \cdot \bar{u}$

30. $\nabla^2 f(r)$ is equal to   (1)

(A) $\dfrac{f'(r)}{r}\bar{r}$ (B) $\dfrac{d^2f}{dr^2} + \dfrac{df}{dr}$

(C) $\dfrac{d^2f}{dr^2} - \dfrac{2}{r}\dfrac{df}{dr}$ (D) $\dfrac{d^2f}{dr^2} + \dfrac{2}{r}\dfrac{df}{dr}$

Answers

1. (D)	2. (A)	3. (B)	4. (C)	5. (A)	6. (D)	7. (B)	8. (C)
9. (B)	10. (D)	11. (C)	12. (A)	13. (C)	14. (B)	15. (A)	16. (D)
17. (B)	18. (D)	19. (A)	20. (C)	21. (A)	22. (B)	23. (D)	24. (C)
25. (B)	26. (D)	27. (C)	28. (A)	29. (C)	30. (D)		

Time : 2 Hrs.   **(THEORY EXAM.)**   Max. Marks : 50

1. (a) **Solve any two :** (8)

(i) $\dfrac{d^2y}{dx^2} + 4y = x \sin x$

(ii) $\dfrac{d^2y}{dx^2} + y = \operatorname{cosec} x$ [use method of variation of parameters]

(iii) $x^3 \dfrac{d^2y}{dx^2} + 3x^2 \dfrac{dy}{dx} + xy = \sin(\log x)$.

(b) Find the Fourier integral representation of the function $f(x) = \begin{cases} 1 \,, & |x| < 1 \\ 0 \,, & |x| > 1 \end{cases}$ and

hence evaluate $\displaystyle\int_0^\infty \dfrac{\sin \lambda \cos \lambda x}{\lambda}\, d\lambda$ (4)

OR

2. (a) A weight of 3 kgs stretches a spring 15 cms. If the weight is pulled 10 cms below the equilibrium position and released, find the position of weight at time t. Find the amplitude and frequency of motion. (4)

(b) Solve any one : (4)

(i) $L\left\{ \dfrac{\cos at - \cos bt}{t} \right\}$

(ii) $L^{-1}\left\{ \dfrac{2s + 1}{(s^2 + s + 1)^2} \right\}$

(c) Using Laplace transform method, solve the equation $\dfrac{d^2y}{dt^2} + 2\dfrac{dy}{dt} + 5y = e^{-t} \sin t$

subject to the conditions, $y(0) = 0$, $y'(0) = 1$. (4)

3. (a) The first four moments of a distribution about the value 5 are 2, 20, 40 and 50. Calculate the first four central moments. (4)

(b) A manufacturer of cotter pins known that 2% of his product is defective. If he sells cotter pins in boxes of 100 pins and guarantees that not more than 5 pins will be defective in a box, find the probability that a box will fail to meet the guaranteed quality. (4)

(c) Find the directional derivative of $\phi = xy^2 + z^3$ at $(1, -2, 1)$ along a line equally inclined with co-ordinate axes. (4)

(S.1)

OR

4. (a) Find the regression line of y on x for the following data :   (4)

x	10	14	19	26	30	34	39
y	12	16	18	26	29	35	38

(b) Establish any one of the following :   (4)

(i) $\quad \nabla^2\left[\nabla \cdot \left(\dfrac{\overline{r}}{r^2}\right)\right] = \dfrac{2}{r^4}$

(ii) $\quad \nabla \times \left(\dfrac{\overline{a} \times \overline{r}}{r^3}\right) = \dfrac{-\overline{a}}{r^3} + \dfrac{3\,(\overline{a} \cdot \overline{r})}{r^5}\,\overline{r}$

(c) Show that $\overline{F} = f(r)\,\overline{r}$ is always irrotational and find $f(r)$ such that $\overline{F}$ is solenoidal also.   (4)

5. (a) A vector field is given by $\overline{F} = \sin y\,\overline{i} + x\,(1 + \cos y)\,\overline{j}$, evaluate the integral $\int_C \overline{F} \cdot d\overline{r}$,

where 'c' is the arc of the ellipse $\dfrac{x^2}{a^2} + \dfrac{y^2}{b^2} = 1$, $z = 0$.   (4)

(b) Use the divergence theorem to evaluate $\iint_S (y^2 z^2\,\overline{i} + z^2 x^2\,\overline{j} + x^2 y^2\,\overline{k}) \cdot d\overline{s}$, where s is

the upper part of the sphere $x^2 + y^2 + z^2 = 9$ above the xoy plane.   (5)

(c) Verify stokes theorem for $\overline{F} = x^2\,\overline{i} + xy\,\overline{j}$ for the surface of a square lamina bounded by $x = 0$, $y = 0$, $x = 2$, $y = 2$.   (4)

OR

6. (a) Evaluate $\int_C \overline{F} \cdot d\overline{r}$ for $\overline{F} = (2y + 3)\,\overline{i} + xz\,\overline{j} + (yz - x)\,\overline{k}$ along the path $x^2 = 2t^2$, $y = t$,

$z = t^3$ from $t = 0$ to $t = 1$.   (4)

(b) Evaluate $\iint_S \dfrac{x\overline{i} + y\overline{j} + z\overline{k}}{r^2} \cdot d\overline{s}$ where s is the surface of the sphere $x^2 + y^2 + z^2 = a^2$.   (5)

(c) Apply stokes theorem to evaluate $\int_C 4y\,dx + 2z\,dy + 6y\,dz$.   (4)

7. (a) An elastic string of length 'l' is tightly stretched between two fixed points $x = 0$ and $x = l$. Initially it is displaced to occupy the shape $y = y_0 \sin^3 \dfrac{\pi x}{l}$ and then released from rest. Find the subsequent motion of the string. (7)

$$\left[\text{Governing equation } \frac{\partial^2 y}{\partial t^2} = c^2 \frac{\partial^2 y}{\partial x^2} \right].$$

(b) Solve the Laplace equation $\dfrac{\partial^2 u}{\partial x^2} + \dfrac{\partial^2 u}{\partial y} = 0$. (6)

Subject to the condition $u(x, 0) = 0$, $u(x, l) = 0$, $u(\infty, y) = 0$, $u(0, y) = a_0$.

OR

8. (a) Use Fourier transform to solve the boundary value problem $\dfrac{\partial u}{\partial t} = k \dfrac{\partial^2 u}{\partial x^2}$, $-\infty < x < \infty$, $t > 0$. (7)

Subject to the conditions :

(a) $u, \dfrac{\partial u}{\partial x} \to 0$ as $x \to \pm \infty$

(b) $u(x, 0) = f(x)$.

(b) Solve the equation : (6)

$\dfrac{\partial^2 y}{\partial t^2} = c^2 \dfrac{\partial^2 y}{\partial x^2}$ subject to the conditions :

(i) $y(0, t) = 0$, (ii) $y(l, t) = 0$, (iii) $\left. \dfrac{\partial y}{\partial t} \right|_{t=0} = 0$, (iv) $y(x, 0) = k(lx - x^2)$.

Time : 2 Hours   **Max. Marks : 50**

---

1. (a) Solve any two of the following :   **(8)**

     (i) $\dfrac{d^2 y}{dx^2} - 3 \dfrac{dy}{dx} + 2y = x^2 + \sin x$

     (ii) $\dfrac{d^3 y}{dx^3} - 7 \dfrac{dy}{dx} - 6y = e^{2x} (1 + x)$

     (iii) $\dfrac{d^2 y}{dx^2} + \dfrac{1}{x} \dfrac{dy}{dx} = A + B \log x$

   (b) Find the Fourier transform of $f(x) = e^{-|x|}$ **(4)**

OR

2. (a) A body of weight W = 3 N stretches a spring to 15 cm. If the weight is pulled down 10 cm below the equilibrium position and then given a downward velocity 60 cm/sec. Find the subsequent motion of the weight.   **(5)**

   (b) Find : (i) $L^{-1}\left\{\dfrac{1}{s^3 (s^2 + 1)}\right\}$ OR   (ii) $L^{-1}\left\{\dfrac{1}{(s + 1)(s^2 + 1)}\right\}$ **(3)**

   (c) Using Laplace transform method, solve the differential equaiton   **(4)**

$$\dfrac{d^2 y}{dt^2} - 3 \dfrac{dy}{dt} + 2y = 12\, e^{-2t} \text{ with conditions } y(0) = 2,\ y'(0) = 6.$$

3. (a) Find the coefficient of correlation between x and y from the table   **(4)**

x	1	3	4	6	8	9	11	14
y	1	2	4	4	5	7	8	9

   (b) Prove that (any one) :

     (i) $\nabla^4 e^r = e^r + \dfrac{4}{r} e^r$ (ii) $\nabla \cdot \left[r\nabla \dfrac{1}{r^n}\right] = \dfrac{n(n-2)}{r^{n+1}}$ **(4)**

   (c) Show that the vector field $\overline{F} = (y^2 \cos x + z^2)\, i + 2y \sin x\, j + 2xz k$ is irrotational and find scalar potential ϕ such that $\overline{F} = \nabla\phi$.   **(4)**

OR

---

4. (a) If the probability that an individual suffers a bad reaction from a certain injection is 0.001, determine the probability that out of 2000 individual, more than 2 individuals will suffer a bad reaction. **(4)**

(b) Find the directional derivative of div $(x^5 i + y^5 j + z^5 k)$ at (1, 2, 3) in the direction of outward normal to the surface $x^2 + y^2 + z^2 = 9$ at (1, 2, 3). **(4)**

(c) Calculate the first four moments about mean for the following data : **(4)**

x	1	2	3	4	5	6	7	8	9
f	1	6	13	25	30	22	9	5	2

5. (a) Evaluate $\int_c \overline{F} \cdot d\overline{r}$, where 'c' is any square with sides of length 5 and

$$\overline{F} = (2x^2 - y)\,\overline{i} + (\tan y - e^y + 4x)\,\overline{j}$$ **(4)**

(b) Evaluate $\iint_S (z^2 - x)\,dy\,dz - xy\,dx\,dz + 3z\,dx\,dy$

where 's' is the surface of closed region bounded by $z = 4 - y^2$ and planes $x = 0$, $x = 3$, $z = 0$. **(5)**

(c) Evaluate $\iint_S (\nabla \times \overline{F}) \cdot d\overline{s}$ for $\overline{F} = y\,\overline{i} + z\overline{j} + x\,\overline{k}$ over the surface

$x^2 + y^2 = 1 - z,\ z \geq 0$. **(4)**

OR

6. (a) Evaluate $\int_c \overline{F} \cdot d\overline{r}$, where $\overline{F} = y\overline{i} + xz^3\overline{j} - zy^2\overline{k}$ and 'c' is the circle $x^2 + y^2 = 4$, $z = 1$. **(4)**

(b) Evaluate $\int_c \overline{F} \cdot d\overline{r}$, by using Stokes theorem for $\overline{F} = 4y\overline{i} - 4x\overline{j} + 3\overline{k}$, where 's' is a disk of radius 1 laying on the plane $z = 1$ and 'c' is its boundary. **(5)**

(c) If $\overline{n}$ is the unit outward drawn normal to any closed surface 's' of area then evaluate

$$\iiint_v \nabla \cdot \overline{n}\ dv$$ **(5)**

7. (a) If a string of length 4 cm is initially at rest in its equilibrium position and each of its point is given a velocity v (x) such that $v\,(x) = \begin{cases} 3x, & 0 \leq x \leq 2 \\ 3(4 - x), & 2 \leq x \leq 4 \end{cases}$. Obtain the displacement y (x, t) at any time t. **(7)**

(b) Solve : $\dfrac{\partial u}{\partial t} = \dfrac{\partial^2 u}{\partial x^2}$ if

   (i)   u is finite for all t,

   (ii) u (0, t) = 0

   (iii) u = (l, t) = 0

   (iv) u (x, 0) = $\dfrac{3x}{l}$, $0 \le x \le l$ **(6)**

OR

8. (a) Use Fourier transform to solve   **(6)**

$$\frac{\partial u}{\partial t} = \frac{\partial^2 u}{\partial x^2}, 0 < x < \infty , t > 0$$

where u (x, t) satisfies the conditions :

   (i) $\left(\dfrac{\partial u}{\partial t}\right)_{x = 0} = 0$, $t > 0$

   (ii) u (x, 0) = $\begin{cases} x, 0 < x < 1 \\ 0, x > 1 \end{cases}$

   (iii) |u (x, t)| < M

(b) An infinitely long uniform metal plate is enclosed between lines y = 0 and y = l for x > 0. The temperature is zero along the edges y = 0, y = l and at infinity. If the edge x = 0 is kept at a constant temperature u_0, find the temperature distribution u (x, y).

   (6)

Time : 2 Hours   **Max. Marks : 50**

1. (a) Solve any two of the following :   **(8)**

      (i) $(D^2 + D + 1) y = x \sin x$

      (ii) $(D^2 - 4D + 4) y = e^{2x} \cos^2 x$

      (iii) $(3x + 2)^2 \dfrac{d^2y}{dx^2} + 3 (3x + 2) \dfrac{dy}{dx} - 36y = 3x^2 + 4x + 1$

  (b) find the Fourier Transform of   **(4)**

$$f(x) = \begin{cases} 1, & |x| \le a \\ 0, & |x| > a \end{cases}$$

OR

2. (a) A body weighting W = 20N is hung from the spring. A pull of 40N will stretch the spring to 10 cm. The body is pulled down to 20 cm bellow the static equilibrium position and then released. Find the displacement of the body from its equilibrium position in time 't' seconds. Also find the maximum velocity and Period of oscillation.   **(4)**

  (b) Solve any one of the following :   **(4)**

      (i) Find the Laplace Transform of : $f(t) = te^{3t} \sin 2t$

      (ii) Find inverse Laplace Transform of :

$$F(s) = \frac{1}{(S - 2)^4 (S + 3)}$$

  (c) Solve the following Differential equation by Laplace Transform method.   **(4)**

$$\frac{d^2y}{dt^2} + 2 \frac{dy}{dt} + 5y = e^{-t} \sin t$$

  Given that : $y(0) = 0,\ y'(0) = 1$

3. (a) Following are the values of import of raw material and export of finished product in suitable units   **(4)**

Export	10	11	14	14	20	22	16	12	15	13
Import	12	14	15	16	21	26	21	15	16	14

  Calculate the coefficient of correlation between the import and export values.

  (b) Find curl curl $\bar{F}$ at the point (1, 1, 2) where $\bar{F} = x^2y\,\bar{i} + xyz\,\bar{j} + z^2y\,\bar{k}$ **(4)**

  (c) Prove the following (any one)   **(4)**

(i) $\nabla \cdot \left(\dfrac{\overline{a} \times \overline{r}}{r} \right) = 0$

(ii) $\overline{a} \cdot \nabla \left[\overline{b} \cdot \nabla \left(\dfrac{1}{r} \right) \right] = \dfrac{3 \, (\overline{a} \cdot \overline{r}) \, (\overline{b} \cdot \overline{r})}{r^5} - \dfrac{(\overline{a} \cdot \overline{b})}{r^3}$

OR

4. (a) In a distribution, exactly normal, 7% of the items are under 35 and 89% are under 63. Find the mean and standard deviation of the distribution. **(4)**

$[A_1 = 0.43, z_1 = 1.48, A_2 = 0.39, z_2 = 1.23]$

(b) Number of road accidents on a highway during a month follows a Poisson distribution with mean 5, Find the probability that in a certain month, number of accidents on the highway will be **(4)**

   (i) Less than 3

   (ii) Between 3 and 5

(c) Find the constant a and b, so that the surface $ax^2 - byz = (a + 2) \, x$ will be orthogonal to the surface $4x^2y + z^3 = 4$ at the point $(1, -1, 2)$. **(4)**

5. (a) Find the work done in moving a particle along the path $x = 2 \, t^2$, $y = t$, $z = t^3$, from $t = 0$ to $t = 1$ in a force field $\overline{F} = (2y + 3) \, \overline{i} + xz\overline{j} + (yz - x) \, \overline{k}$ **(4)**

(b) Evaluate : $\iint\limits_{S} (x\overline{i} + y\overline{j} + z^2\overline{k}) \cdot d\overline{S}$, where s is curved surface of cylinder $x^2 + y^2 = 4$ bounded by the planes $z = 0$ and $z = 2$. **(5)**

(c) Apply Stokes's theorem to calculate $\int\limits_{c} (y \, dx + z \, dy + x \, dz)$, C being intersection of

$x^2 + y^2 + z^2 = a^2$, $x + z = a$. **(4)**

OR

6. (a) (i) Using Green's lemma evaluate

$\oint\limits_{C} x^2 \, dx + xy \, dy$, where C is the boundary of region R which is enclosed by

$y = x^2$ and $y = x$ **(4)**

(b) Evaluate $\iint\limits_{S} (\nabla \times \overline{F}) \cdot \hat{n} \, dS$ where S is the curved surface of the paraboloid

$x^2 + y^2 = 2z$ bounded by the plane $z = 2$ and $\overline{F} = 3 \, (x - y) \, \overline{i} + 2xz \, \overline{j} + xy\overline{k}$. **(4)**

(c)   Prove that

$$\iint\limits_{S} (\phi\nabla\psi - \psi\nabla\phi) \cdot d\bar{S} = \iiint\limits_{V} (\phi\nabla^2\psi - \psi\nabla^2\phi)\, dv \;,\; \text{where S is closed surface enclosing}$$

volume V.   **(4)**

7. (a)   A string of length L is stretched and fastened to two ends. Motion is started by displacing the string in the form $u\,(x) = a\,\sin\left(\dfrac{\pi x}{l}\right)$ from which it is released at t = 0.

Find the displacement 'u' at any time 't', if it satisfies the equation $\dfrac{\partial^2 y}{\partial t^2} = c^2 \dfrac{\partial^2 y}{\partial x^2}.$ **(7)**

(b)   Solve $\dfrac{\partial u}{\partial t} = a^2 \dfrac{\partial^2 u}{\partial x^2}$ if   **(6)**

  (i)   u (x, ∞) is finite   (ii)   u (0, t) = 0

  (iii)   u (*l*, t) = 0   (iv)   u (x, 0) = x, 0 < x < *l*

OR

8. (a)   An infinitely long plane uniform plate is bounded by two parallel edges in the y direction and an end at right angles to them. The breadth of the plate is π. This end is maintained at temperature u_0 at all points other edges at zero temperature. Find steady state temperature u (x, y). If it satisfies $\dfrac{\partial^2 u}{\partial x^2} + \dfrac{\partial^2 u}{\partial y^2} = 0.$ **(7)**

(b)   Use Fourier Transform to solve $\dfrac{\partial u}{\partial t} = \dfrac{\partial^2 u}{\partial x^2}$; 0 < x < ∞, t > 0, where u (x , t) satisfies the conditions :   **(6)**

  (i)   u (x, t) < M

  (ii) $\left(\dfrac{\partial u}{\partial t}\right)_{x\,=\,0} = 0$ at t > 0

  (iii)   u (x, 0)   = x,   0 < x < 1

              = 0,   x > 1

Time : 2 Hours   **Max. Marks : 50**

1. (a) Solve any one of the following :   (8)

   (i) $(D^2 - 4D + 4)y = e^x \cdot \cos^2 x$

   (ii) $(D^2 + 5D + 6)y = e^{-2x} \cdot \sec^2 x\,(1 + 2\tan x)$

   (iii) $\dfrac{d^2 y}{dx^2} + y = \operatorname{cosec} x$, by variation of parameters.

   (b) Find the Fourier transform of   (4)

$$f(x) = 1, \quad |x| \le a$$
$$= 0, \quad |x| > a$$

OR

2. (a) Weight of 1 N, stretches a spring 5 cms. A weight of 3 N is attached to the spring and weight W is pulled 10 cm below the equilibrium position and released. Determine the position and the velocity as a function of time.   (4)

   (b) Solve any one of the following :   (4)

   (i) Find the Laplace Transform of : $f(t) = \dfrac{(e^{-at} - e^{-bt})}{t}$

   (ii) Find Inverse Laplace Transform of the function : $F(s) = \dfrac{3s + 1}{(s - 1)(s^2 + 1)}$

   (c) Solve the following equation using Laplace transform method :   (4)

$$y''(t) - 3y'(t) + 2 \cdot y(t) = 12.\ e^{-2t}\,;\ y(0) = 2,\ y'(0) = 6$$

3. (a) If the directional derivative of :   (4)

$$\phi = axy + byz + cxz \text{ at } (1, 1, 1)$$

has maximum magnitude 4 in a direction parallel to x axis, find the values of a, b, c.

   (b) Show that the vector field : $\overline{F} = (2xz^3 + 6y)\,i + (6x - 2yz)\,j + (3x^2 z^2 - y^2)\,k$ (4)

is irrotational and find scalar function ϕ such that $\overline{F} = \nabla\phi$.

   (c) Find the coefficient of correlation for the following data :   (4)

x	y
10	18
14	12
18	24
22	6
26	30
30	36

OR

4. (a) Prove the following (any one) : **(4)**

(i) $\nabla^4 e^r = e^r + \dfrac{4}{r} e^r$

(ii) $\nabla \cdot \left[r \nabla \left(\dfrac{1}{r^n} \right) \right] = \dfrac{n\,(n-2)}{r^{n+1}}$

(b) Between 2 p.m. and 3 p.m. the average number of phone calls per minute coming into company are 2. Find the probability that during one particular minute there will be 2 or less calls. **(4)**

(c) Calculate the first four moments about the mean of the given distribution. Also find β_1 and β_2. **(4)**

x	f
2	5
2.5	38
3	65
3.5	92
4	70
4.5	40
5	10

5. (a) Evaluate $\displaystyle\int_C \overline{F} \cdot d\overline{r}$ for :

$\overline{F} = 3x^2\,\overline{i} + (2xz - y)\,\overline{j} + z\overline{k}$

along the straight line joining (1, 2, 1) and (2, 1, 3). **(4)**

(b) Evaluate : $\displaystyle\iint_S \overline{F} \cdot d\overline{S}$ where $\overline{F} = (x + y^2)\,\overline{i} - 2x\overline{j} + 2yz\,\overline{k}$

and S is the surface of the tetrahedron bounded by the co-ordinate planes and the plane : **(5)**

$$2x + y + 2z = 6$$

(c) Evaluate : $\displaystyle\int_c (xy\,dx + xy^2\,dy)$ by Stoke's theorem, where C is the square x-y plane

with vertices (0, 0), (1, 0), (1, 1), (0, 1) **(4)**

OR

6. (a) (i) Using Green's theorem, show that the area bounded by a simple closed curve C is given by :

$$\frac{1}{2}\int xdy - y\,dx$$

Hence find the area of circle x = a cos θ, y = a sin θ. **(4)**

(b) Evaluate : $\iint\limits_{S} (x^3\,\overline{i} + y^3\,\overline{j} + z^3\overline{k}) \cdot d\overline{S}$ **(5)**

where S is the surface of the sphere : $x^2 + y^2 + z^2 = a^2$

(c) Evaluate :

$\iint\limits_{S} (\nabla \times \overline{F}) \cdot \hat{n}\ dS$ where $\overline{F} = (x - y)\,\overline{i} + (x^2 + yz)\,\overline{j} - 3xy^2\overline{k}$ and S is the surface of the

cone : $z = 4 - \sqrt{x^2 + y^2}$ above xoy plane.   **(4)**

7. (a) If $\dfrac{\partial^2 y}{\partial t^2} = c^2 \dfrac{\partial^2 y}{\partial x^2}$ represents the vibrations of a string of length l fixed at both ends,

find solution with conditions :   **(7)**

(i) $y\,(0, t) = 0$

(ii) $y(l, t) = 0$

(iii) $\left(\dfrac{\partial y}{\partial t}\right)_{t=0} = 0$

(iv) $y\,(x, 0) = k\,(lx - x^2),\ 0 \le x \le l$

(b) A homogeneous rod of conducting material of length 100 cm has ends kept at zero
temperature and the temperature initially is :   **(6)**

$$u\,(x, 0) = x, \qquad 0 \le x \le 50$$
$$= 100 - x, \quad 50 \le x \le 100$$

Find the temperature u (x, t) at any time t.

OR

8. (a) An infinitely long plane uniform plate is enclosed between lines $y = 0$ and $y = l$ for
$x > 0$. The temperature is zero along the edges :   **(7)**

$$y = 0,\ y = 1$$

and at infinity. If the edge $x = 0$ is kept at a constant temperature u_0. Find the
temperature distribution u (x, y).

(b) Use Fourier transform to solve :   **(6)**

$$\frac{\partial u}{\partial t} = \frac{\partial^2 u}{\partial x^2}, 0 < x < \infty, t > 0$$

subject to the following conditions :

(i) $u\,(0, t) = 0,\ t > 0$

(ii) $u\,(x, 0) = 1,\ 0 < x < 1$

$$= 0,\ x > 1$$

(iii) u (x, t) is bounded.

Time : 2 Hours   **Max. Marks : 50**

1. (a) Solve any one of the following :   **(8)**

     (i) $(D^2 + 9)\, y = x \cdot \sin 2x$

     (ii) $(D^2 - 6D + 13)\, y = e^{3x} \cdot \sin 4x + 3^x$

     (iii) $(D^2 + 4)\, y = \dfrac{1}{1 + \sin 2x}$

     (using method of variation of parameters.)

   (b) Using Fourier cosine integral of e^{-mx} ($m > 0$ show that :   **(4)**

$$\int_0^\infty \frac{m \cos \lambda x \, d\lambda}{m^2 + \lambda^2} = \frac{\pi}{2} \cdot e^{-mx}, \ (m > 0, x > 0)$$

OR

2. (a) A body of weight "W = 20N" is hung from a spring. a pull of "40N" will stretch the spring to 10 cm. The body is pulled down to 20 cm below the static equilibrium position and then released. Find the displacement of the body from its equilibrium position in time 't' seconds.   **(4)**

   (b) Solve any one of the following :   **(4)**

     (i) Find the Laplace Transform of : $f(t) = \displaystyle\int_0^t \frac{\sin t}{t}\, dt$

     (ii) Find the inverse Laplace Transform of $F(s) = \log\left(\dfrac{s + 4}{s + 8}\right)$

   (c) Solve the following differential equation by using Laplace transform method :   **(4)**

$$y''(t) + 9y(t) = 18t \text{ given that : } y(0) = 0,\ y\left(\frac{\pi}{2}\right) = 1$$

3. (a) Calculate the first four moments about the mean of the given distribution :   **(4)**

x	f
2.0	4
2.5	36
3.0	60
3.5	90
4.0	70
4.5	40
5	10

   (b) Between 2 p.,m. and 3 p.m. the average number of phone calls per minute coming into company are 3. Find the probability that during one particular minute there will be 2 or less calls.   **(4)**

(c)　Find the directional derivative of

$$\phi = xy^2 + yz^3 \qquad \textbf{(4)}$$

at $(1, -1, 1)$ in the direction of tangent to the curve $x = \sin t$, $y = \cos t$, $z = t$ at $t = \dfrac{\pi}{4}$.

OR

4.　(a)　Find the coefficient of correlation data :　　　　**(4)**

x	y
10	18
14	12
18	24
22	06
26	30
30	36

(b)　Prove that (any one) :　　　　**(4)**

(i)　$\nabla\left(\dfrac{\bar{a}\cdot\bar{r}}{r^n}\right) = \dfrac{\bar{a}}{r^n} - \dfrac{n\,(\bar{a}\cdot\bar{r})}{r^{n+2}}\,\bar{r}$

(ii)　$\nabla^4 (r^2 \log r) = \dfrac{6}{r^2}$

(c)　Show that :　　　　**(4)**

$\bar{F} = (6xy + z^3)\,i + (3x^2 - z)\,j + (3xz^2 - y)\,k$ is irrotational. Find the scalar ϕ such that :

$\bar{F} = \nabla\phi.$

5.　(a)　Evaluate : $\displaystyle\int_C \bar{F}\cdot d\bar{r}$ for :　　$\bar{F} = 3x^2 i + (2xz - y)\,\bar{j} + z\bar{k}$　　　　**(4)**

along the curve : $x = 2t^2$, $y = t$, $z = 4t^2 - t$ from $t = 0$ to $t = 1$.

(b)　Evaluate : $\displaystyle\iint_S \bar{F}\cdot d\bar{s}$ where $\bar{F} = 4xz\bar{i} + xyz^2\bar{j} + 3z\bar{k}$　　　　**(5)**

and S is the surface of the cone : $z^2 = x^2 + y^2$ bounded by $z = 4$.

(c)　Apply Stoke's theorem to caluculate : $\displaystyle\int_C 4y\,dx + 2z\,dy + 6y\,dz$　　　　**(4)**

where C is the curve of intersection of $x^2 + y^2 + z^2 = 6z$ and $z = x + 3$.

OR

6. (a) Evaluate : $\int_C \overline{F} \cdot d\overline{r}$ for $\overline{F} = x^2\overline{i} + 2xy\overline{j} + z\overline{k}$ and C is the straight line joining

(1, 0, 2), (3, 1, 1). **(4)**

(b) Show that : $\iint_S \dfrac{\overline{r}}{r^3} \cdot \hat{n}\, ds = 0$ **(4)**

(c) Evaluate using Stoke's theorem : $\int_C (y\, dx + z\, dy + x dz)$ **(5)**

C being intersection of $x^2 + y^2 + z^2 = a^2$, $x + z = a$

7. (a) A string is stretched and fastened to two points l apart. Motion is started by displacing the string into the form $y = k\,(lx - x^2)$ from which it is released at time $t = 0$. Find the displacement of any point on the string at a distance of x from one end at time t. Using differential equation : **(7)**

$$\frac{\partial^2 y}{\partial t^2} = C^2 \frac{\partial^2 y}{\partial x^2}$$

(b) The temperature at any point of the insulated metal rod of one metre length is governed by the differential equation : $\dfrac{\partial u}{\partial t^2} = C^2 \dfrac{\partial^2 u}{\partial t^2}$ **(6)**

Find u (x, t) subject to the following :
(i) u (0, t) = 0°C
(ii) u (1, t) = 0°C
(iii) u (x, 0) = 50°C

OR

8. (a) Solve the partial differential equation : $\dfrac{\partial^2 u}{\partial x^2} + \dfrac{\partial^2 u}{\partial y^2} = 0$ **(7)**

Subject to boundary conditions :
(i)   u(0, y) = 0
(ii)   u (x, 0) = 0
(iii) u (a, y) = 0
(iv) u (x, b) = 40

(b) Use Fourier transform to solve the equation : $\dfrac{\partial u}{\partial t} = \dfrac{\partial^2 u}{\partial x^2}$, $0 < x < \infty$, $t > 0$

subject to the following conditions : **(6)**
(i)   u (0, t) = 0, t > 0

(ii) u (x, 0) = $\begin{cases} 1 & 0 < x < 1 \\ 0 & x > 1 \end{cases}$

(iii) u (x, t) is bounded.

November 2015

Time : 2 Hours   **Max. Marks : 50**

1. (a) Solve any two of the following :   **[8]**

(i) $(D^2 + 4D + 4) y = \dfrac{e^{-2x}}{x^2}$.

(ii) $(D^2 + 1) y = \operatorname{cosec} x$ (using method of variation of parameters)

(iii) $(x^2 D^2 - xD + 1) y = x \log x$.

(b) Using Fourier Integral representation, show that :   **[4]**

$$\int_0^\infty \frac{\cos\dfrac{\pi\lambda}{2} \cdot \cos\lambda x}{1 - \lambda^2} \cdot d\lambda = \begin{cases} \dfrac{\pi}{2}\cos x, & |x| \le \dfrac{\pi}{2} \\[2mm] 0, & |x| > \dfrac{\pi}{2} \end{cases}$$

OR

2. (a) The weight of '1N', stretches a spring by 5 cm. A weight of '3N' is attached to the spring and weight 'W' is pulled '10 cm' below the equilibrium position and released. Determine the position and velocity as function of time.   **[4]**

(b) Solve any one of the following :   **[4]**

(i) Find the Laplace transform of $f(t) = \left\{\dfrac{e^{-at} - e^{-bt}}{t}\right\}$.

(ii) Find the inverse Laplace transform of : $F(s) = \left\{\dfrac{3s + 1}{(s - 1)(s^2 + 1)}\right\}$

(c) Solve the following differential equation by using Laplace transform method : $y''(t) - 3y'(t) + 2y(t) = 12 \cdot e^{-2t}$. Given that : $y(0) = 2, y'(0) = 6.$ **[4]**

3. (a) Find the lines of regression for the following data :   **[4]**

x	y
2	2
3	5
5	8
7	10
9	12
10	14
12	15
15	16

(b) A random sample of 200 screws is drawn from a population which represent size of screws. If a sample is distributed normally with a mean 3.15 cm and standard deviation 0.025 cm, find the expected number of screws whose size fall between 3.12 cm and 3.2 cm.

Area corresponding to 1.2 → 0.3849

Area corresponding to 2.0 → 0.4772   **[4]**

(c) Find the directional derivative of the function $\phi = e^{2x-y-z}$ at (1, 1, 1) in the direction of normal to the surface $x^2 + y^2 + z^2 = 9$ at (1, 2, 2).   **[4]**

OR

4. (a) Calculate the correlation coefficient for the following data :   **[4]**

x	y
6	9
2	11
10	5
4	8
8	7

(b) Attempt any one :   **[4]**

(i) For a solenoidal vector field $\bar{\varepsilon}$, show that curl curl culr curl $\bar{\varepsilon} = \nabla^4\bar{\varepsilon}$.

(ii) Prove that : $\bar{b} \times \nabla [\bar{a} \cdot \nabla \log r] = \dfrac{\bar{b} \times \bar{a}}{r^2} - \dfrac{2 (\bar{a} \cdot \bar{r})}{r^4} (\bar{b} \times \bar{r})$

(c) Show that the vector field given by :   **[4]**

$$\bar{F} = (y^2 \cos x + z^2) \, i + (2y \sin x) \, j + 2xzk$$

is irrotation. Find the scalar field ϕ such the $\bar{F} = \nabla\phi$.

5. (a) Evaluate $\int_C \bar{F} \cdot d\bar{r}$ for $\bar{F} = (2x + y) \, \bar{i} + (3y - x) \, \bar{j}$ and 'c' is the straight line joining the points (0, 0) and (3, 2).   **[4]**

(b) Evaluate $\iint_S \bar{F} \cdot d\bar{s}$ where $\bar{F} = yz\bar{i} + zx\bar{j} + xy\bar{k}$ and s is the part of the surface of the sphere $x^2 + y^2 + z^2 = 1$ which lies in the first octant.   **[4]**

(c) Evaluate $\iint_S \text{curl} \, \bar{F} \cdot \hat{n}ds$ for the surface of the hemisphere $x^2 + y^2 + z^2 = a^2$ above the xy plane, where : $\bar{F} = (x^2 + y - 4) \, \bar{i} + 3xy\bar{j} + (2xz + z^2) \, \bar{k}$.   **[5]**

OR

6. (a) Verify Green's theorem for the field $\bar{F} = x^2\bar{i} + xy\bar{j}$ over the region R enclosed by $y = x^2$ and the line $y = x$. **[5]**

(b) Show that : $\iiint\limits_{V} \dfrac{dv}{r^2} = \iint\limits_{S} \dfrac{\bar{r} \cdot \hat{n}}{r^2}\, dS.$ **[4]**

(c) Evaluate $\iint\limits_{S} (\nabla \times \bar{F}) \cdot \hat{n}\, dS$ for $\bar{F} = x^2\bar{i} + y^2z\bar{j} + xy\bar{k}$ for the plane surface S bounded by $x = 0,\ y = 0,\ x = 2,\ y = 2,\ z = 0.$ **[4]**

7. (a) A tightly stretched string with fixed end points $x = 0$ and $x = l$, is initially in a position given by $y\,(x,\,0) = y_0 \sin^3 \dfrac{\pi x}{l}$. If it is released from this position, find the displacement y at any distance x from one end at any time t with the differential equation : $\dfrac{\partial^2 y}{\partial t^2} = c^2 \dfrac{\partial^2 y}{\partial x^2}.$ **[7]**

(b) Solve the equation $\dfrac{\partial u}{\partial t} = a^2 \dfrac{\partial^2 u}{\partial x^2}$ where u(x, t) satisfies the following conditions : **[6]**

(i) $u\,(0,\,t) = 0$

(ii) $u\,(l,\,t) = 0$ for all t

(iii) $u\,(x,\,0) = x$ in $0 < x < l$.

OR

8. (a) An infinitely long plane uniform plate is bounded by two parallel edges in the y-direction and an end at right angles to them. The breadth of the plate is π. This end is maintained at temperature 40 at all points and other edges at zero temperature. Find the steady-state temperature function u (x, y). **[7]**

(b) Using Fourier sine transform solve the partial differential equation : **[6]**

$$\frac{\partial u}{\partial t} = 2\frac{\partial^2 u}{\partial x^2},\ 0 < x < \infty,\ t > 0$$

subject to the following conditions :

(i) $u\,(0,\,t) = 0,\ t > 0$

(ii) $u\,(x,\,0) = e^{-x},\ x > 0$

(iii) u and $\dfrac{\partial u}{\partial x} \to 0$ as $x \to \infty$

❏❏❏

May 2016

Time : 2 Hours　　　　　　　　　　　　　　　　　　　**Max. Marks : 50**

1. (a)　Solve any two:　　　　　　　　　　　　　　　　　　**[8]**

(i)　$\dfrac{d^3y}{dx^3} + \dfrac{dy}{dx} = \cos x.$

(ii)　$(D^2 - 4D + 4)y = e^{2x}\sec^2 x$ (by variation of parameter method)

(iii)　$(1 + x)^2\,\dfrac{d^2y}{dx^2} + (1 + x)\,\dfrac{dy}{dx} + y = 2\sin[\log(1 + x)].$

(b)　Find Fourier cosine transform of :　　　　　　　　　　**[4]**

$$f(x) = \cos x \quad\quad 0 < x < a$$
$$= 0 \quad\quad\quad x > a.$$

OR

2. (a)　A body of weight 2 N is suspended from a spring stretches it 4 cm. If the weight is pulled down 8 cm below the equilibrium position and then released, find amplitude and period of motion.　　**[4]**

(b)　Solve any one :　　　　　　　　　　　　　　　　　　**[4]**

(i)　Find Laplace transform of $e^{4t}(t + 2)^2.$

(ii)　Find inverse Laplace transform of :　$F(s) = \dfrac{s}{(s - 1)(s - 2)(s - 3)}$

(c)　Solve by Laplace transform method : $y'' - 3y' + 2y = 4e^{2t},\ y(0) = -3,\ y'(0) = 5.$　　**[4]**

3. (a)　The first four moments of a distribution about the value 4 are −1.5, 17, − 30 and 108. Find the first four moments about the mean and coefficient of skewness and kurtosis.　　**[4]**

(b)　Assuming that the diameter of 1000 brass plugs taken consecutively from machine form normal a distribution with mean 0.7515 cm and standard deviation 0.0020 cm. How many plugs are likely to approved if acceptable diameter is 0.752 ± 0.004 cm ? (Given : A (z = 2.25) = 0.4878, A(z = 1.75) = 0.4599)　　**[4]**

(c)　Find the directional derivative of : $\phi = 5x^2y - 5y^2z + 2z^2x,$　　**[4]**

at (1, 1, 1) in the direction of the line : $\dfrac{x - 1}{2} = \dfrac{y - 3}{-2} = \dfrac{z}{1}.$

OR

4. (a)　Obtain the regression lines for the following data :　　**[4]**

x	y
2	2
3	5
5	8
7	10
9	12
10	14

(b) Prove the following (any one) :   **[4]**

    (i) $\nabla \times (\bar{a} \times \bar{r}) = 2\bar{a}$

    (ii) $\bar{a} \cdot \nabla \left[\bar{b} \cdot \nabla \left(\dfrac{1}{r} \right) \right] = \dfrac{3\,(\bar{a} \cdot \bar{r})\,(\bar{b} \cdot \bar{r})}{r^5} - \dfrac{\bar{a} \cdot \bar{b}}{r^3}.$

(c) Show that the vector field :   **[4]**

$$\bar{F} = (6xy + z^3)\,\hat{i} + (3x^2 - z)\,\hat{j} + (3xz^2 - y)\,\hat{k}$$

is irrotational. Find scalar ϕ such that $\bar{F} = \nabla\phi$.

5. (a) Evaluate : $\displaystyle\int_C \dfrac{(x\,dx + y\,dy)}{(x^2 + y^2)^{3/2}}$ along : $\bar{r} = e^t \cos t\, i + e^t \sin t\, j$ joining $(1, 0)$ to $(e^{2\pi}, 0)$.   **[4]**

    (b) Evaluate : $\displaystyle\iint_S (x^3 i + y^3 j + z^3 k) \cdot \bar{ds}$ over the surface of $\dfrac{x^2}{a^2} + \dfrac{y^2}{b^2} + \dfrac{z^2}{c^2} = 1.$ **[5]**

    (c) Evaluate : $\displaystyle\int_C [\sin z\, dx - \cos x\, dy + \sin y\, dz]$ where 'C' is the boundary of rectangle

    $0 \le x \le \pi,\ 0 \le y \le 1,\ z = 3.$ **[4]**

OR

6. (a) Apply Green's theorem to evaluate : $\displaystyle\int_C (3y\, dx + 2x\, dy)$ where 'C' is boundary of

    $0 \le x \le \pi,\ \ 0 \le y \le \sin x.$ **[4]**

    (b) Evaluate : $\displaystyle\iint_S (\nabla \times \bar{F}) \cdot \bar{ds}$ where : $\bar{F} = (x + 2y)\, i - 3zj + xk$ and 'S' is the surface of the

    plane $2x + y + 2z = 6$ bounded by the co-ordinate planes $x = 0,\ y = 0$ and $z = 0.$ **[5]**

    (c) Using Gauss divergence theorem, show that : $\displaystyle\iint_C \dfrac{\bar{r}}{r^2} \cdot \hat{n}\, dS = \iiint_V \dfrac{1}{r^2}\, dV.$ **[4]**

7. (a) If $\dfrac{\partial^2 u}{\partial t^2} = c^2 \dfrac{\partial^2 u}{\partial x^2}$ represents the vibrations of a string of length l fixed at both ends,

    find the solution with boundary conditions :

    (i) $u\,(0, t) = 0$

    (ii) $u\,(l, t) = 0$, and initial conditions,

    (iii) $\left(\dfrac{\partial u}{\partial t} \right)_{t = 0} = 0$

    (iv) $u\,(x, 0) = lx - x^2,\ 0 \le x \le l$ **[7]**

(b)　Solve $\dfrac{\partial u}{\partial t} = \dfrac{\partial^2 u}{\partial x^2}$ if :

　　(i)　u (0, t) = 0　　　　　　　(ii)　u(*l*, t) = 0 for all t

　　(iii)　u(x, 0) = 20x, 0 < x < *l*　　(iv)　u (x, ∞) is finite.　　　　**[6]**

OR

8.　(a)　Solve the equation : $\dfrac{\partial^2 u}{\partial x^2} + \dfrac{\partial^2 u}{\partial y^2} = 0$ with conditions :

　　(i)　u = 0 when y → ∞ for all x

　　(ii)　u = 0 when x = 0 for all values of y

　　(iii)　u = 0 when x = 10 for all values of y

　　(iv)　u = k (1 – x) when y = 0 for 0 < x < 10.　　　　**[6]**

　(b)　Use Fourier transform to solve the equation :

$$\frac{\partial u}{\partial t} = 5\frac{\partial^2 u}{\partial x^2}, \ 0 < x < \infty, \ t > 0$$

　　Subject to the condition :

　　(i)　u (0, t) = 0 , t > 0

　　(ii)　u (x, 0) = $\begin{cases} 1, & 0 < x < 1 \\ 0, & x > 1 \end{cases}$

　　(iii)　u(x, t) is bounded.　　　　**[7]**

November 2016

Time : 2 Hours   **Max. Marks : 50**

1. (a) Solve any two :   **[8]**

   (i) $(D^3 - 7D - 6) y = e^{2x} (1 + x)$

   (ii) $(D^2 + 1) y = 3x - 8 \cot x$ (by variation of parameter method).

   (iii) $(2x + 1)^2 \dfrac{d^2 y}{dx^2} - 2 \ (2x + 1) \dfrac{dy}{dx} - 12 \ y = 12 \ x.$

   (b) Find the Fourier cosine transform of $f(x) = e^{-x} + e^{-2x}, \ x > 0$ **[4]**

2. (a) A body weighing W = 20 N is hung from a spring. A pull of 40 N will strech the spring to 10 cm. The body is pulled down to 20 cm below the static equilibrium position and then released. Find the displacement of the body from its equilibrium position in time t seconds, the maximum velocity and period of oscillation.   **[4]**

   (b) Solve any one :   **[4]**

   (i) Find Laplace transform of $te^{-2t} (2 \cosh 3t - 4 \sinh 2t)$

   (ii) Find inverse Laplace transform of $F(s) = \dfrac{s^2 - 2s + 3}{(s - 1)^2 \, (s + 1)}$

   (c) Using Laplace transform, solve the differential equation :   **[4]**

   $$\frac{dy}{dt} + 2y(t) + \int_0^t y(t) \, dt = \sin t \quad \text{given} \quad y(0) = 1$$

3. (a) The first four moments of a distribution about the value 2 are –2, 12,–20 and 100. Find the first four central moments and B_1, B_2.   **[4]**

   (b) Number of absent student in a class follow Poisson distribution with mean 5. Find the probability that in a certain month number of absent student in a class will be **[4]**

   (i) More than 3

   (ii) Between 3 and 5

   (c) Find the directional derivative of $\phi = x^2 yz^3$ at (2, 1, –1) along the vector

   $-4\bar{i} - 4\bar{j} + 12\bar{k}.$ **[4]**

OR

4. (a) Find coefficient of correlation for the following data :   **[4]**

x	y
6	9
2	11
10	5
4	8
8	7

(b) Show that vector field $\overline{F} = (x^2 - yz)\,\overline{i} + (y^2 - zx)\,\overline{j} + (z^2 - xy)\,\overline{k}$ is irrotational. Hence find scalar potential ϕ such that $\overline{F} = \nabla\phi$. **[4]**

(c) Prove the following (any one) : **[4]**

   (i) $\nabla^4(r^2 \log r) = \dfrac{6}{r^2}$

   (ii) $\overline{a} \cdot \nabla\left[\overline{b} \cdot \nabla\left(\dfrac{1}{r}\right)\right] = \dfrac{3\,(\overline{a} \cdot \overline{r})\,(\overline{b} \cdot \overline{r})}{r^5} - \dfrac{(\overline{a} \cdot \overline{b})}{r^3}$

5. (a) Evaluate : $\displaystyle\int_c \overline{F} \cdot d\overline{r}$ where $\overline{F} = x^2\overline{i} + xy\overline{j}$ and 'c' is the arc of parabola joining $(0, 0)$ and $(1, 1)$. Equation of parabola is $y = x^2$. **[4]**

(b) Show that : $\displaystyle\iint_s \dfrac{\overline{r}}{r^3} \cdot \hat{n}\ ds = 0$

(c) Verify Stoke's theorem for $\overline{F} = xy^2\overline{i} + y\overline{j} + z^2x\overline{k}$ for the surface of a rectangular lamina, bounded by $x = 0$, $y = 0$, $x = 1$, $y = 2$, $z = 0$ **[5]**

OR

6. (a) Evaluate $\displaystyle\oint_c \overline{F} \cdot d\overline{r}$ where $\overline{F} = (2x - y)\,\overline{i} + (x - 2y)\,\overline{j} + z\overline{k}$ and c is the arc of the ellipse $\dfrac{x^2}{9} + \dfrac{y^2}{4} = 1$, $z = 0$. **[4]**

(b) Evaluate : $\displaystyle\iint_s (x\overline{i} + y\overline{j} + z\overline{k}) \cdot d\overline{s}$ over the surface of a sphere $x^2 + y^2 + z^2 = 1$. **[4]**

(c) Evaluate : $\displaystyle\iint_s \operatorname{curl} \overline{F} \cdot \hat{n}\,ds$ for the surface of the paraboloid $z = 9 - (x^2 + y^2)$ and

   $\overline{F} = (x^2 + y - 4)\,\overline{i} + 3xy\,\overline{j} + (2xz + z^2)\,\overline{k}.$ **[5]**

7. Attempt Any Two :

(a) Solve the equation : $\dfrac{\partial u}{\partial t} = a^2\dfrac{\partial^2 u}{\partial x^2}$

   where u (x, t) satisfies the following conditions : **[6]**

   (i) $u\,(0, t) = 0$

   (ii) $u\,(L, t) = 0$

   (iii) $u\,(x, 0) = x, \qquad 0 \le x \le \dfrac{L}{2}$

         $= L - x, \quad \dfrac{1}{2} \le x \le L$

   (iv) $u\,(x, \infty)$ is finite.

(b) If $\dfrac{\partial^2 y}{\partial t^2} = c^2 \dfrac{\partial^2 y}{\partial x^2}$ represents the vibrations of a string of Length L fixed at both ends, find the solution with boundary conditions : **[7]**

   (i) $y(0, t) = 0$

   (ii) $y(L, t) = 0$

   (iii) $\left(\dfrac{\partial y}{\partial t}\right)_{t=0} = 0$

   (iv) $y(x, 0) = k(Lx - x^2),\ 0 \le x \le L$

(c) An infinitely long plane uniform plate is bounded by two parallel edges $x = 0$ and $x = \pi$ and an end at right angles to them. The breadth of the plate is π. This edge is maintained at temperature u_0 at all points and other edges at zero temperature. Find the steady state temperature function $u(x, y)$. Also use $y \to \infty,\ u = 0$. **[6]**

OR

8. Attempt any two :

(a) Solve : $\dfrac{\partial u}{\partial t} = \dfrac{\partial^2 u}{\partial x^2}$ **[6]**

   if

   (i) u is finite for all t

   (ii) $u(0, t) = 0$

   (iii) $u(\pi, t) = 0$

   (iv) $u(x, 0) = \pi x - x^2,\ 0 \le x \le \pi$

(b) A string stretched and fastened to two points 'L' apart. Motion is started by displacing the string in the form $y = a \sin \dfrac{\pi x}{L}$ from which it is released at time $t = 0$. Find displacement $y(x, t)$ from one end. **[7]**

(c) A rectangular plate with insulated surface is 10 cm wide and so long to its width that it may be considered infinite in length without introducing an appreciable error. It the temperature of short edge $y = 0$ is given by : **[6]**

$$u \quad = 20x, \qquad\qquad 0 \le x \le 5$$
$$= 20(10 - x) \qquad 5 \le x \le 10$$

and two edges $x = 0$ and $x = 10$ as well as other short edge are kept 0°C , then find $u(x, y)$.

May 2017

Time : 3 Hours **Max. Marks : 50**

1. (a) Solve any two of the following : **[8]**

    (i) $(D^2 + 13D + 36)y = e^{-4x} + \sinh x$

    (ii) $(D^2 - 2D + 2)\, y = e^x \tan x$

       (using method of variation of parameter)

    (iii) $x^2 \dfrac{d^2y}{dx^2} - 4x \dfrac{dy}{dx} + 6y = x^5$

  (b) Using Fourier integral representation show that : **[4]**

$$\int_0^\infty \frac{\lambda^3 \sin \lambda x}{\lambda^4 + 4}\, d\lambda = \frac{\pi}{2} e^{-x} \cos x, \; x > 0$$

2. (a) A body of weight 9.8 N is suspended from a spring having constant 4 N/m. Prove that the motion is one of the resonance if a force 16 sin 2t is applied and damping force is negligible. Assume that initially the weight is at rest in the equilibrium position. **[4]**

  (b) Solve any one : **[4]**

    (i) Find the Laplace transform of $\cosh t \displaystyle\int_0^t e^t \cosh(t)\, dt$

    (ii) Find the Inverse Laplace Transform of $\cot^{-1}\left(\dfrac{s-2}{3}\right)$.

  (c) Using Laplace transform solve the D.E. $y'' + 2y' + y = te^{-t}$, $y(0) =1$, $y'(0) = -2$ **[4]**

3. (a) If $\quad \Sigma f = 27, \Sigma fx = 91, \Sigma fx^2 = 359,$

        $\Sigma fx^3 = 1567, \Sigma fx^4 = 7343$

    Find the first four moments about origin. Also find μ_2, μ_3, μ_4.

  (b) An unbiased coin is thrown 10 times. Find the probability of getting exactly 6 heads and at least 6 heads using binomial distribution. **[4]**

  (c) Find the directional derivative of $xy^2 + yz^3$ at $(2, -1, 1)$ along the line

    $2(x - 2) = y + 1 = z - 1.$ **[4]**

OR

4. (a) Obtain regression lines for the following data : **[4]**

x	y
6	9
2	11
10	5
4	8
8	7

(b) Prove the following (any one) : **[4]**

(i) $\nabla^2 f(r) = f''(r) + \dfrac{2}{r} f'(r)$

(ii) $\nabla \cdot \left[r \nabla \left(\dfrac{1}{r^3} \right) \right] = \dfrac{3}{r^4}$

(c) Show that the vector field $\overline{F} = (x + 2y + 4z)\,\overline{i} + (2x - 3y - z)\,\overline{j} + (4x - y + 2z)\,\overline{k}$

is irrotational and hence find scalar function ϕ such that $\overline{F} = \nabla \phi$. **[4]**

5. (a) Evaluate : $\displaystyle\int_C \overline{F} \cdot d\overline{r}$ where $\overline{F} = x^2 \overline{i} + xy \overline{j}$

and C is the straight line $y = x$, joining $(0, 0)$ and $(1, 1)$. **[4]**

(b) Prove that : $\displaystyle\iint_S (\phi \nabla \psi - \psi \nabla \phi) \cdot d\overline{s} \iiint_V (\phi \nabla^2 \psi - \psi \nabla^2 \phi)\, dV$ **[4]**

(c) Use Stoke's theorem to evaluate $\displaystyle\int_C (4y\overline{i} + 2z\overline{j} + 6y\overline{k}) \cdot d\overline{r}$ where C is the curve of

intersection of $x^2 + y^2 + z^2 = 2z$ and $x = z - 1$ **[5]**

OR

6. (a) Evaluate : $\displaystyle\int_C \overline{F} \cdot d\overline{r}$ where $\overline{F} = xy^2 \overline{i} + y \overline{j}$ and C is curve $x = t,\ y = t^2$, joining $t = 0$

and $t = 1$. **[4]**

(b) Evaluate : $\displaystyle\iint_S \overline{F} \cdot d\overline{s}$ where $\overline{F} = yz\overline{i} + zx\overline{j} + xy\overline{k}$ and S the upper part of the sphere
$x^2 + y^2 + z^2 = 1$ above xoy plane. **[4]**

(c) Evaluate : $\displaystyle\iint_S (\nabla \times \overline{F}) \cdot \hat{n}\, ds$ where $\overline{F} = xy^2 \overline{i} + y \overline{j} + z^2 x \overline{k}$ and S is the surface of a

rectangular lamina bounded by $x = 0,\ y = 0,\ x = 1,\ y = 2,\ z = 0$ **[4]**

7. (a) Solve the wave equation $\dfrac{\partial^2 u}{\partial t^2} = c^2 \dfrac{\partial^2 u}{\partial x^2}$ **[7]**

with boundary conditions :

(i) $u(0, t) = 0,\ \forall t$

(ii) $u(l, t) = 0,\ \forall t$

(iii) $\left(\dfrac{\partial u}{\partial t} \right)_{t=0} = 0$

(iv) $u(x, 0) = a \sin \dfrac{\pi x}{l}$

(b) Solve the heat equation $\dfrac{\partial u}{\partial t} = a^2 \dfrac{\partial^2 u}{\partial x^2}$ for the function $u\,(x,\ t)$, subject to the following conditions :

(i) $u\,(0,\ t) = 0$

(ii) $u\,(l,\ t) = 0,\ \forall t$

(iii) $u(x,\ 0) = x,\ 0 \le x < l$

(iv) $u(x,\ \infty)$ is finite.   **[6]**

OR

8. (a) Solve the Laplace equation   **[6]**

$$\frac{\partial^2 u}{\partial x^2} + \frac{\partial^2 u}{\partial y^2} = 0$$

Subject to condition :

(i) $u\,(x,\ 0) = 0$

(ii) $u\,(x,\ l) = 0$

(iii) $u\,(\infty,\ y) = 0$

(iv) $u\,(0,\ y) = \alpha_0$

(b) Use Fourier transform to solve $\dfrac{\partial u}{\partial t} = \dfrac{\partial^2 u}{\partial x^2}$, $0 < x < \infty$, $t > 0$ where $u\,(x,\ t)$ satisties the conditions :

(i) $\left(\dfrac{\partial u}{\partial x}\right)_{x=0} = 0,\ t > 0$

(ii) $u\,(x,\ 0) = \begin{cases} x & 0 < x < 1 \\ 0 & x > \end{cases}$

(iii) $|u\,(x,\ t)| < m$ **[7]**